Good**BEER**Guide
GERMANY

STEVE THOMAS

BOOKS

Published by the Campaign for Real Ale
230 Hatfield Road
St Albans
Hertfordshire AL1 4LW

www.camra.org.uk/books

ISBN 10: 1-85249-219-8
ISBN 13: 978-1-85249-219-9

A CIP catalogue record for this book is available from
the British Library

Printed and bound in the United Kingdom at
the University Press, Cambridge

Head of Publications: Joanna Copestick
Project Editor: Sylvia Goulding
Project Coordinator: Debbie Williams
Copy Editor: Mike Goulding
Editorial Assistance: Emma Lloyd
Design/typography: Dale Tomlinson/FFUnit
Picture Research: Sarah Airey, Nadine Bazar
Maps: John Macklin
Additional articles/research: Sigi Fenske,
    Sylvia Goulding, Angelika Ilies, Rafael Pauley
Marketing Manager: Georgina Rudman

PHOTO CREDITS
All photographs taken by the author except for the following:
Simon Brazel 65, 85, 364, 428
CAMRA archive 28
Corbis/Franz Marc Frei 34
Corbis/zefa/Uli Wiesmeier 23
Mike-Gerlach.com 352, 442
Thomas Gerlach 26
Gettyimages/Jorg Greuel (Frankfurt) 456
Hafen Hamburg/Hettchen 280, 460, 463
David Icke 21, 295, 318, 394, 490
Dave Jackson 4
Howard Jolley 192, 262, 276, 397
Photolibrary.com/Jon Arnold Images/Alan Copson 492
Photolibrary.com/M Romanko Karen (Glasses) 32/33
Rex Features/Action Press 367
Superstock/age footstock 275, 298, 370
Superstock/Prisma 37
Superstock/Steve Vidler 38
Rick Zaple 304, 311, 327, 387, 388, 468, 502

Contents

Introduction

Like many of the best things in life, this book came about accidentally. As a fan of Germany and its beers, I had been visiting the country several times a year for a decade or so along with a number of friends when, one day in early 2001, I decided to do a bit of research. Until then our only sources of brewery information had been John Conen's *Good Beer in Bamberg and Franconia*, Graham Lees' *Good Beer Guide to Munich and Bavaria*, Michael Jackson's *Pocket Beer Book* and Stefan Mack's *Die neue Fränkische Brauereikarte*. Now, although these excellent publications together covered more than 500 breweries, we were starting to run out of new places to visit that were easily reached by public transport. We'd heard there were supposed to be around 1,300 breweries in total, so I thought it would be easy enough to find a bit of information about a few more. At the time my only intention was to find some new places for us to explore on our next trip. What I found amazed me.

Within a few weeks I'd amassed a list of more than 1,700 breweries, many in towns and cities visited previously but missed, as their existence had been unknown to us – frustrating to say the least. Evidently around a quarter of these had stopped brewing, some (as I was to discover) decades previously. Many of these were easily eliminated but others were far more difficult – it's common for breweries in Germany to stay in business long after actual brewing has ceased. Some simply act as wholesalers for others but many either re-badge beers as their own or have their former brands contract-brewed. So began the laborious process of eliminating those that no longer brewed themselves.

It soon dawned on me that the information I was gathering would make a useful little book which may be of interest to a few others.

Initially, I thought that a list of breweries, together with addresses and phone numbers, would provide sufficient material for a 60-page book. A little later I decided that the inclusion of brewery taps would be helpful – before long I was also including all the beers I'd discovered. As the year wore on I decided to contact each brewery in order to get as much up-to-date and accurate information as possible – at this stage I still envisaged publishing 500 copies of the book myself the following year (2002).

Needless to say, my self-imposed deadline came and went, as did countless others. As time went by, the amount of data I was amassing continued to increase inexorably, and it was proving increasingly difficult to keep it all up-to-date. The more detail I had on each brewery, the more I needed on all the others – and so it went on. I still envisaged publishing a few hundred copies myself, always in six months' time. However, for much of 2003 I lost interest and little work was done. Writing resumed with renewed vigour in the autumn of that year following a chance meeting on a train...

You meet the strangest people...

On 25 September 2003, I found myself waiting for a train at Marktredwitz – as you do – together with the usual suspects. One of our party, Rick Zaple, a CAMRA stalwart, had got to the platform first and found someone to talk to. Nothing unusual there, we thought. Once on the train he rejoined us and said there was someone I should meet. "Really?" I said. "Yes", said Rick, "he writes books about beer and is thinking of starting a publishing company."

Well, I was going to publish the Guide myself the following March, but thought it couldn't do any harm to meet him. That man turned out to be Tim Webb, co-founder of CAMRA Books and author of numerous Belgian beer guides. For reasons that will probably always remain unexplained, Tim was on his way from Prague to Munich to catch a flight. I showed him what little of the book I had with me, and he asked numerous questions. I was impressed by his extensive knowledge of both the brewing and publishing trades, and even more by his ability not to bat an eyelid at the strange goings-on among some of the members of our party. To my great surprise he said it was a shame I was close to finishing the book as he hoped to have his company up and running the following summer and was interested in publishing it himself. We exchanged addresses and, probably to his great relief, left him at Regensburg.

Eighteen months later I contacted Tim out of the blue and asked if he'd still like to publish the book. He said he would, but thought CAMRA might also be interested and would try to arrange a meeting with their Head of Publications, Joanna Copestick. I still can't quite believe they said yes.

Cheers, then…

…to the following people, without whom none of this would have happened: Dave Icke and Dave Jackson, and their livers, for fearlessly going where the Guide hasn't been and telling all; to the Brazel brothers, David, Sean and Simon, for their unstinting dedication to good beer, and in Sean's case, showing us disbelievers that it is possible to eat two *Schweinshaxes* in one sitting; to Howie, Gary and Mike for their company and wise counsel. Thanks to Rick for introducing me to Tim… thanks to Tim for introducing me to Jo… thanks to Jo and all at CAMRA books for showing remarkable faith in a complete unknown. Special mention is also due to my editor, Sylvia Goulding, and Debbie Williams at CAMRA, who had the unenviable task of co-ordinating production. I'd also like to thank my family, particularly my wife Lyn, whose patience has been extraordinary as I spent day after day sweating over a hot keyboard, or yet another weekend in Germany 'researching'. If I've missed anyone out, I'm sorry, but you know how it is.

I'd especially like to thank all those breweries that have responded to my requests for information. Quite what they made of the unsolicited, faxed questionnaires, and the phone calls in broken German I'll never know, but they've helped make this book a far more accurate reflection of the current German brewing scene than would have otherwise been the case.

STEVE THOMAS
Cardiff, April 2006

How to use the Guide

A few words of warning...

First and foremost, this is a guide to German breweries. As there are currently 1,257 of those (we think), producing more than 7,750 beers, that doesn't leave a lot of room for much else. We know some of you would like detailed descriptions of each brewery and tap, tasting notes on all the beers, etc., but we just can't do that. It's taken five years to produce this much, we can only guess at how many more years would be required for Good Beer Guide levels of completeness. Decades. And you'd need a new bookcase. In the meantime, please accept our apologies for the paucity of information. However, we intend to increase our coverage, so your findings are more than welcome at GermanBreweries@aol.com.

Breweries

In the time it's taken to write the Guide, around 150 new breweries have opened in Germany. The vast majority are brewpubs that supply their own pub and no one else. At the same time a similar number have closed, many being small, family-run breweries supplying just a few pubs.

We've tried to include every brewery that's currently operating in Germany. We define an operating brewery as one that brews its own beer on its own premises. This is not as straightforward as one might expect. A number of former breweries continue to have their beers brewed elsewhere, the contracted beer being known as *Lohnbier*. Many are quite open about this but others are not. Indeed, some go to extraordinary lengths to conceal from you the fact that they no longer brew. Short of actually going to each one and watching them brew, there's little we can do except take them at their word. Where we know, or at least think we know, the actual brewer of a former brewery's beer, we tell you. There is a section for beers of unknown origin on page 511.

For each brewery entry we have tried to list contact details, the founding year and the owner, the annual output and the number of pubs where the beers can be found regularly, all the beers they brew and details of the brewery tap. We also ramble on for a few lines, occasionally breaking into a coherent description of the brewery with the odd useless fact thrown in.

One thing we have also tried to do is list each brewery under its actual location. This is not as simple as it may sound. In Germany post codes (*Postleitzahl* or *PLZ*) are allotted to cities, towns and some villages. Those places that don't have their own postcode are treated as though they don't exist by the Post Office and their addresses come under the name of the nearest post-coded place. This can cause no end of confusion for the unwary beer nut, as the brewery you seek may be a number of miles from the town it is coded under. The most extreme example of this we came across is the small town of Bad Staffelstein, which, if you believe the Post Office, has nine breweries. In fact, there are no longer any breweries in the town, the nine mentioned all being in surrounding villages. To cap this off, two of the breweries have the same name. In this Guide all are listed under their respective villages, Bad Staffelstein appearing in brackets after the actual village name.

Brewery taps 🍺

In an ideal world each brewery would have a cosy little pub next door selling the full range of beers. Happily, this is in fact often the case. However, many breweries have their tap away from the brewery. It may be across the street, in a different part of town, or, occasionally, 20 miles away. Wherever it is, we've tried to include it.

A significant number of breweries (around 140) said they had no tap at all. In most cases these are larger breweries that have a number of pubs in the vicinity of the brewery. Unfortunately, some are much smaller and finding their beers can be something of a challenge. If no pub is listed, try contacting the brewery and asking them to recommend one.

For each tap we have listed the contact details, opening hours and the distance to the nearest railway station. If we know that accommodation is available we have noted this, but the absence of a mention does not necessarily mean they don't do it – phone or email to check.

Opening hours

Two simple little words but one big headache for the Guide. We have tried our best, we really have, but regular opening hours are not high on the average German publican's list of priorities. Although a pub may say it is going to open or close at a particular time, this is often not the case. If it's busy, they may stay open late. If it's quiet they may close early. If they expect it to be quiet they may open late, or not at all. Many have one or more closing days (*Ruhetag*) during the week and these can and do change. It's also common for a pub to shut for a couple of weeks while the owners go on holiday. In short, treat all opening times as a rough guide only and phone in advance to avoid disappointment.

Public holidays

Public holidays are a further complication for the beer tourist, especially as not all are observed by every single state. Many pubs vary their hours on these days, often opening as per their Sunday times. If a public holiday falls on a *Ruhetag* it may open but then close the following day. Then again, it may not. Public holidays in 2006/2007 are:

New Year's Day (1 January)
Epiphany* (6 January)
Good Friday (6 April 07)
Easter Monday (9 April 07)
Labour Day (1 May)
Ascension Day (25 May 06, 17 May 07)
Whit Monday (5 June 06, 28 May 07)
Corpus Christi* (15 June 06, 7 June 07)
Ascension of the Virgin Mary* (15 August)
Day of Unity (3 October)
Day of Reformation* (31 October)
All Saints Day* (1 November)
Repentance Day* (22 Nov 06, 21 Nov 07)
Christmas Day (25 December)
Boxing Day (26 December)

*not observed in all states

In addition there are regional and local holidays which affect pub opening hours. In Köln and surroundings, for example, pubs stay open virtually around the clock for Carnival.

Spellings

Beers are listed as their names appear on the bottles or by the names the breweries have supplied. However, there are lots of variations, and even the breweries' own websites may list three versions of Hefe Weizen, Hefeweizen and Hefe-Weizen. In addition there are regional variations for the brewery taps – variously known as Braustube, Bräustüble or similar. Finally, the German language has a bizarre letter, ß, which exists in lower case only. Thus street will be correctly spelled Straße in lower case but STRASSE in capitals. Adding confusion to oddity, the continually evolving German Rechtschreibungsreform (spelling reform), which has removed some but not all occurrences of ß, has been adopted by some but not all breweries/pubs/councils/states, and so you will find both Schlossbrauerei and Schloßbrauerei…

The listings

We use the following transport symbols to avoid repeating the names each time:

🚌 bus
🚊 tram
Ⓤ U-Bahn
Ⓢ S-Bahn
🄳🄱 railway

The symbols mirror those you are likely to see in the streets.

Other abbreviations:

SW = Stammwürze
T telephone
F fax
E email

Maps

Each town with a brewery appears on the relevant state map. Due to constraints of space, these towns are numbered rather than named (from 1 through to 1005), the number after a town's name in the brewery section corresponding to the number on the map. Similarly, each city guide has a map, although the numbers on each of these are not unique – take care to ensure you're looking at the correct city map.

Getting there

IT'S NEVER BEEN EASIER, cheaper or quicker to get from Britain to Germany. How you travel is obviously a matter of personal preference, but your choice is likely to be influenced by where you live, where you're heading and how long you've got to get there.

BY AIR

The quickest way to reach Germany from Britain is by air. Nine airlines currently operate direct scheduled flights or fly from smaller regional airports via other towns. Fares vary considerably.

The airlines
The following airlines currently fly direct from Britain to Germany, but the list of destinations is extremely changeable, especially among the low-cost lines, with routes constantly being added or removed. Check the airlines' websites or that of your destination airport.

Air Berlin (AB) www.air-berlin.de
British Airways (BA) www.ba.com
Cirrus (C9) www.cirrus-world.de
Easyjet (EZY) www.easyjet.com
German Wings (4U) www.germanwings.de
Hapag Lloyd Express (HLX) www.hlx.de
Lufthansa (LH) www.lufthansa.com
OLT (OL) www.olt.de
Ryanair (FR) www.ryanair.com

The airports
Although the airports won't change, new ones may be added to the list as low-cost flyers open new routes, often to former US army airfields. Distances given are to the relevant city centre unless otherwise stated.

Altenburg-Nobitz (AOC, www.flughafen-altenburg.de) 5km; connecting bus to Leipzig

Berlin-Schönefeld (SXF, www.berlin-airport.de) 20km
Berlin-Tegel (TXL, www.berlin-airport.de) 8km
Bremen (BRE, www.airport-bremen.de) 5km
Dortmund (DTM, www.flughafen-dortmund.de) 12km; buses to Holzwickede and Unna
Düsseldorf (DUS, www.duesseldorf-international.de) 8km
Frankfurt/Main-International (FRA, www.frankfurt-airport.de) 12km
Friedrichshafen (FDH, www.fly-away.de) 4km
Hahn (HHN, www.hahn-airport.de) Trier 70km, Koblenz 75km, Bullay 23km, Kirn 35km, Frankfurt 145km – Ryanair advertise the airport as Frankfurt (Hahn)!
Hamburg (HAM, www.airport.de) 12km; Ohlsdorf 4km
Hannover (HAJ, www.flughafen-hannover.de) 12km
Karlsruhe–Baden-Baden (FKB, www.baden-airpark.de) Baden-Baden 16km, Karlsruhe 35km
Köln-Bonn (CGN, www.airport-bremen.de) Köln 15km, Bonn 25km
Leipzig-Halle (LEJ, www.leipzig-halle-airport.de) Leipzig 20km, Halle 20km
Lübeck-Blankensee (LBC, www.flughafen-luebeck.de) Lübeck 9km, Hamburg 60km
München (MUC, www.munich-airport.de) 35km
Münster-Osnabrück (FMO, www.fmo.de) Greven 8km, Münster 22km, Osnabrück 30km
Nürnberg (NUE, www.airport-nuernberg.de) 6km
Paderborn-Lippstadt (PAD, www.flughafen-paderborn-lippstadt.de) Salzkotten 9km, Paderborn 17km, Lippstadt 25km
Stuttgart (STR, www.stuttgart-airport.com) 14km
Weeze (NRN, www.airport-weeze.de) Weeze 5km, Kevelaer 10km, Krefeld 50km, Düsseldorf 75km – advertised by Ryanair as Düsseldorf (Weeze)!

BY RAIL

www.bahn.co.uk

Since the advent of the Channel Tunnel and Eurostar, rail travel to Germany has become much easier. The fastest journey time from London (Waterloo) to Köln is currently just over five hours. With further changes it's possible to reach much of Germany within a day, typical journey times to Berlin and München being around ten hours. If your destination is in south-western Germany, it may be quicker to travel via Paris.

Tickets

Sadly, Eurostar (www.eurostar.com) seem to be of the opinion that no one who uses their services would want to travel to Germany and so doesn't offer any through-fares to anywhere other than Aachen and Köln. Rail Europe (www.raileurope.co.uk) is not much better, seemingly only quoting the highest fares on their website. For onward travel in Germany we recommend one of the many rover tickets available (see 'Getting around').

BY ROAD

Given the lack of tarmac across the English Channel you'll have to put your car or van on a ferry or the tunnel shuttle train. From Calais or Boulogne it's around 300km to the German border at Aachen, and roughly 900km to Berlin or München.

The obvious advantages of driving are the convenience of having your own vehicle, which allows you to get to out-of-the-way villages, and the ability to bring back a lot of beer (for your own consumption, of course). The disadvantages include long, tedious motorway journeys and the fact that somebody has to drive. NB: the alcohol limit for drivers is lower in Germany than in the UK, 0.5 rather than 0.8mg.

BY SEA

There are currently no direct ferry services from Britain to Germany, but there are, of course, plenty of routes across the English Channel and North Sea to ports in France, Belgium and Holland. The Speedferries (www.speedferries. com) Dover–Boulogne service is usually one of the cheapest. Be warned that not all routes accept foot passengers and rail services from some ports are surprisingly poor.

Getting around

GERMANY has one of the finest rail networks in the world and is also blessed with excellent bus, tram and underground systems. To help you choose the best way of reaching a pub or brewery, each entry throughout the Guide includes the nearest railway station and the distance to it in metres or kilometres. Where a tram or underground stop is closer, that has been listed too. Buses are usually only mentioned when the nearest station is more than 2km away.

For journey planning www.bahn.co.uk can't be beaten. Although it is the website of the national rail operator, all modes of land transport are covered. Just enter your starting point, destination and date of travel and it should provide you with a journey plan. If you're going to a village without railway station enter the name of the town or village as listed in the brewery's address (i.e. Stegaurach-Debring for Debring).

BUS (Bus)

Buses in Germany are modern, clean and, above all, reliable. Most large towns and cities have a central bus station (Zentral-Omnibus-Bahnhof, usually shortened to ZOB), often near the main railway station. Bus and tram stops are indicated by a yellow circle with a green 'H' in the middle. Tickets are available from ticket machines (*Fahrkartenautomat*) at many stops, or alternatively, can be bought from the driver on most buses. Don't forget to validate your ticket when you board – failure to do so may result in a fine.

TAXI (Taxi)

Generally a little more costly than their British counterparts, at least outside London, taxis are usually plentiful in towns and cities, but may be hard to get and expensive in rural areas. All are beige and, almost without exception, Mercedes.

In some parts of the country where there are no buses, or the bus service finishes early, community taxis operate. These ASTs (*Anruf-Sammel-Taxi* = call-collect-taxi) run to a timetable and always have to be booked in advance by phone, generally at least 20–60 minutes before departure.

TRAIN (Zug)

Deutsche Bahn (DB, www.bahn.co.uk) operate the largest railway network in Europe. Trains generally run at regular intervals, and even the smallest stations are usually served by at least one train an hour. In recent years many local lines have been privatised. While this won't affect you if you've bought a simple single or return ticket, you may find rover tickets are not valid on these routes. Check before you buy.

The timetable for the entire network is so large it comes in eight sections, housed in a box. A practical proposition is Thomas Cook's *Continental Timetable*, available from Thomas Cook shops in the UK. You can also pick up free pocket timetables from stations in Germany.

Stations

Most stations display good maps of the locality either in the station building or on the forecourt. Automatic ticket machines can be found at all stations, many with an English-language option. Some allow you to look up and print out itineraries and other useful information. Timetables are prominently displayed, departures (*Abfahrt*) being printed on yellow pages, arrivals (*Ankunft*) on white. Trains are listed in chronological order rather than by destination. Symbols and letters next to each train signify which days they run on.

Tickets

The fare structure in Germany is generally much simpler than that in the UK. Fares are based on distance travelled and work out at roughly €15 for every 100km travelled (all prices quoted are for second class). Supplements are payable for express and overnight trains. These cost more if bought on board. For details of special offers and season tickets check www.bahn.co.uk.

Euro Domino – Valid on all DB services for between 3 and 8 days within a month, and including all IC, EC and ICE supplements. Prices start at £103 for youths (under 26) and £140 for adults (26+). Each additional day costs £11–£15. DB (but not Rail Europe) also quote a separate fare for the over-60s.

InterRail – No longer the preserve of under-26s. Based on groups of countries, the German zone also includes Austria and Switzerland. The current cost for one zone only is £145 for a youth ticket and £215 for an adult (26+). Tickets are valid for 16 days but may not be used on some private lines, and supplements are payable on express and overnight trains.

Länder Tickets – The German states (*Länder*) all offer day tickets on which up to five people can travel. Prices start at €21 and are cheaper to buy from a machine than a booking office. They are valid on all IRE, RE, RB and S-Bahn services, together with most bus, tram and U-Bahn systems in any given area. All are valid from 09.00 until 03.00 the next day, some start at midnight on the weekend and bank holidays. Each ticket is covered in detail at www.bahn.co.uk.

Schönes-Wochenende-Ticket – The *Happy Weekend Ticket*, only sold on Saturdays and Sundays and valid from 00.01 until 03.00 the following day. It can be used on all IRE, RE, RB and S-Bahn trains throughout Germany, as well as on many buses, trams and underground trains. As with *Länder Tickets*, up to five people can travel on one ticket. The current cost is €30 from a machine or €32 from a booking office.

Types of train

Trains are classified according to speed and comfort, and prices vary accordingly. Below is a list of the types of train you can expect to encounter.

ICE (*Inter City Express*) – The German high speed train, the equivalent of the French TGV. ICEs operate over much of Germany on a mixture of new high-speed lines and traditional routes. A special supplement is payable based on time saved compared to conventional trains.

EC *(Euro-City)* – European network of express trains. Supplement payable.

IC *(Inter-City)* – The domestic express train network. Supplement payable.

EN *(Euro-Nacht)* – European network of overnight trains that feature sleeping cars, couchettes and (usually) reclining seats. Reservation compulsory/supplement payable.

CNL *(City-Night-Line)* – Overnight trains that run on a few cross-border routes. Similar facilities and restrictions to *EN* trains.

NZ *(Nachtzug)* – Domestic overnight train, usually with sleeping cars, couchettes and ordinary seating. Reservation compulsory, supplement payable.

IR *(Inter-Regio)* – A network of fast, inter-regional trains that is gradually being phased out. Supplement payable if travelling under 50km.

D *(Schnellzug)* – An almost extinct classification used for express trains with no buffet car. Supplement payable if travelling under 50km.

IRE *(Inter-Regio-Express)* – Introduced on routes where IR services have been withdrawn, IREs are closer to *RE* trains in terms of speed and stopping pattern.

RE *(Regional-Express)* – Semi-fast trains.

RB *(Regional-Bahn)* – Stopping trains, likely to call at every station en-route.

S-Bahn *(Schnell-Bahn)* – Suburban railway networks found only around the major cities.

Straßenbahn

Trams never went out of fashion in Germany, and they still operate in more than 50 towns and cities. Tickets can't be bought from the driver so you'll have to buy one from a machine, either at the stop or on board the tram. As on the buses, tickets must generally be validated.

U-Bahn

A number of major cities have underground networks. Most consist of trams that run underground in the city centre but then take to the streets in the suburbs. Berlin, Hamburg, München and Nürnberg have the only true underground systems. We have listed them all as U-Bahns as this is how they perceive themselves. Tickets must be bought before boarding and validated using the machines at the entrance to each platform or on the trains.

German beer styles

ASK MOST BRITISH people what they know about German beer and the reply is likely to run along the lines of, 'Well it's all lager, isn't it?' I, too, initially dismissed it all as 'fizzy rubbish' (those may not have been my exact words...), back in my days as a real ale militant who would refuse to buy a pint of lager, even for someone in the same round! Thankfully, I saw sense. My conversion started with the discovery that Kulmbacher Reichelbräu brewed a beer that tasted not dissimilar to Hop Back Summer Lightning. A few days later I first tasted Spezial Rauchbier Lager, and I've never looked back.

In fact, although Pilsener accounts for the majority of German beer production, around 40 other styles are regularly produced. What follows is a comprehensive list of beer styles brewed today, together with a brief description. Please note that it is notoriously difficult to categorise some German beers, many styles having much in common with others, while some are hybrids of two or more styles.

To add further to the confusion, some breweries describe their beers differently depending on where they are served, or seemingly, on a whim. It is, for example, not all that unusual to find the same beer described as Lagerbier when in a bottle, Helles when on draught and Kellerbier when served in a beer garden.

The Guide endeavours to cut a swathe through all this fug but it is inevitable that we'll have missed some beers because we thought they were re-badged, while including others that really are. We hope you forgive us when we get it wrong.

Alkoholfrei
Alcohol-free beer, defined as having an alcohol content of less than 0.5%. Most large breweries produce an Alkoholfrei Pilsener – far and away the most common alcohol-free style. Not considered 'beer' for the purposes of this book, so not listed.

Altbier
Literally 'old beer' in reference to the method of brewing, which predates more recent bottom-fermented beer. Often compared to British bitter in style. Reddish-brown in colour, Altbier is top-fermented and then cold-conditioned. Synonymous with Düsseldorf, surprisingly only around three per cent of Altbier, or Alt, is actually brewed in the city. Although widely available throughout the country, without question the best place to drink the stuff is in the taps and pubs around Düsseldorf's old town, where it is usually served in a squat 0.25l glass known as a *Becher* (beaker). Altbier, almost always containing 4.8% alcohol, is usually fairly fruity with a dry, bitter finish.

Berliner Weisse (or Weiße)
Top-fermented, sour wheat beer with – for Germany – an unusually low alcoholic content of around 3%. When ordering you'll probably be asked *"rot oder grün?"* (red or green), as most Berliners drink it with a dash of either raspberry syrup (*rot – Schuss Himbeer*) or woodruff syrup (*grün – Schuss Waldmeister*) to mask the sourness of the beer. Politely

decline this offer and ask for it *ohne Schuss* (without a dash) – it's far better drunk in its natural state. Only three breweries still produce the stuff – Berliner Bürgerbräu, Kindl and Schultheiss. Sadly, at the time of writing Kindl was due to close early in 2006, with production likely to move to Schultheiss. Berliner Bürgerbräu only produces Berliner Weisse canned, with the syrup already added. Only available in its pure form bottled, Berliner Weisse is a refreshing, tart beer that is unlike anything else brewed in Germany.

Bock

Strong, bottom-fermented beer. Originally brewed in the northern town of Einbeck, the brewing capital of Germany in medieval times. In the 14th century, there were more than 700 brewers in the town, each using a communal brewing kettle that was wheeled from house to house. Beer for export had a high alcohol content to help it withstand the frequently long journeys from Einbeck, and the style proved so popular that it was copied by brewers all over Germany and beyond. The term Bock is thought to be a corruption of the -beck in Einbeck. Bock also happens to be the German for billy-goat, and consequently many bottle labels feature the animal.

Typically with an alcohol content of at least 6%, Bocks vary in colour from pale gold to black. They can be exceptionally easy to drink, many people being unaware of its potency

until they try to stand up and their legs no longer work properly. Some Bocks are available all year but most are seasonal, appearing in spring (see Maibock) or late autumn. Stronger versions are also produced (see Doppelbock and Eisbock). Further variations include those made with wheat (see Weizenbocks), most of which are brewed in Bayern.

Braunbier

Braunbier is regularly produced by just a few breweries. Said to have originated in Bayreuth, it is made with dark malts and is usually bottom-fermented. The style is undergoing something of a revival and often brewed seasonally in a number of modern brewpubs. As you would expect, most are a rich brown colour.

Dampfbier

Literally 'steam beer', although opinion is divided as to the origin of the term. Some say the name derives from the warm, often violent top fermentation which causes carbon dioxide bubbles to explode, giving the impression that the beer is steaming. Others say it stems from the introduction of steam-driven machinery in pioneering breweries in the 19th century. We prefer the former explanation, so that is what we believe. A style revived in recent years by a handful of Bavarian breweries and occasionally brewed as a seasonal elsewhere. Expect a dry, fruity, amber beer with little carbonation.

Diät Pils

Not the 'diet beer' that many suppose, but a Pilsener with reduced carbohydrate that was originally intended for diabetics. Produced by comparatively few breweries, Diät Pils tends to be a little 'thin' when compared to standard versions.

Dinkelbier

Top-fermented beer made with a proportion of spelt malt (*Dinkel*) and usually including both malted barley and wheat. A style of beer that had died out by the 1930s, it was re-introduced in the 1990s. Today it is produced by several breweries all year round, and it's also gaining popularity as a seasonal beer in some brewpubs. Usually a golden-orange colour and cloudy, with a clean, fruity flavour.

Doppelbock

A speciality of Bavarian brewers but also found elsewhere, Doppelbock is a stronger version of Bock (literally 'double-bock'). Typically, Doppel-bocks are dark and have an alcohol content at least 7%. Many have names that end in -ator, a homage to Paulaner Salvator, the Munich beer which is widely acknowledged as the original Doppelbock. Very few are produced all year round, most appearing during the Starkbierzeit (strong beer time) around Lent.

Dortmunder Export

Pale, bottom-fermented style that became associated with Dortmund in the late 19th century. Stronger but less hoppy than Pilsener, typically with around 5.2% alcohol, its popularity has declined in recent years, partly because of its perceived blue-collar image. Following the merger of Dortmund's large brewers in the late 1980s and early 1990s, only two breweries remain that produce true Dortmunder Export, although half a dozen brands survive. This is likely to be further reduced in 2006 with the planned closure of Brauerei Brinkhoff. Although beers of a similar style are brewed in other parts of the country and beyond, you will find these beers described as 'Dortmunder' only outside Germany. Expect a golden, malty beer with a dryish finish.

Dunkel (Dunkles)

Dark beer. In Germany, Dunkel describes beers that are anything from pale brown to black, but typically towards the darker end of the scale. Until the mid-19th century, most beer was dark but since the advent of golden lagers, dark beers have become less common. In modern Germany the main areas of production are Bavaria, Saxony and Thuringia. In southern Bavaria Dunkel is often brewed in the Munich style (Münchner Art), featuring roasted malt and caramel flavours. Further north Dunkel beers tend to be drier and have a more pronounced hop character. In the southern states of the former east they are usually much darker and frequently described as Schwarzbier (black beer)

Dark beers brewed elsewhere in Germany are usually of the München type, although Schwarzbier is finding increasing favour. Modern brewpubs tend to serve their examples unfiltered.

Dunkel (Dunkles, if used as an adjective) is also often used to describe the colour of various different styles, i.e. Bockbier Dunkel (dark bock) or Dunkles Hefeweizen (dark wheat beer).

Eisbock

Essentially, Eisbock (ice bock) is Bockbier that has been lagered at sub-zero temperatures. Some of the water in the beer forms ice crystals that are removed, thereby increasing the alcohol content. Typically slightly stronger than Doppelbocks, Eisbocks are not commonly produced but are well worth seeking out. Even rarer is the wheat version, currently brewed by just two breweries. Both styles should be treated with respect!

Export

Typically a golden, bottom-fermented beer, somewhere between Dortmunder Export and Münchner Helles in style, although dark versions are by no means rare. The alcohol content normally weighs in at around 5.2%. Many breweries describe beers in this style as Premium or Original. Often a brewery's flagship product, Export beers are sometimes named after the founder or to commemorate an event or anniversary. Generally maltier, slightly sweeter and not as dry as a Pilsener.

Festbier

Any beer brewed for a festival. Some breweries produce several such beers over the course of the year, often named after the festival concerned. As a rough guide Festbiers average 5.5% alcohol by volume but can vary considerably in strength. Most are brewed in either Export or Märzen style but again, variation is considerable. We estimate that several hundred may be missing from the Guide as breweries do not always list their one-off beers when questioned. If you find any beer you think we should know about, don't hesitate to contact us at GermanBreweries@aol.com.

Gose

Top-fermented, sour wheat beer, with coriander and salt among the ingredients. Originally brewed in Goslar (hence the name), it became synonymous with Leipzig during the 19th century. The style disappeared in the 1960s when the last Gose brewery closed, but was revived on a small scale in the late 1980s by the owner of local pub Ohne Bedenken. Today three breweries regularly brew Gose, and it is once again comparatively widely available in Leipzig. Like Berliner Weisse, Gose is often served with a dash of syrup to mask its acidity, but as with the former it tastes considerably better *"ohne Schuss"*.

Haferbier

Haferbier, another recent revival, is made with oats. A far as we're aware, there are currently just three breweries producing Haferbier seasonally, and just one that brews it all year.

Hanfbier

Brewed with hemp blossom rather than hops, Hanfbier was re-introduced in 1996 by Kronen-brauerei Wahl in Gundelfingen (Cannabia) and Bier-Company in Berlin (Turn). Neither of those breweries survives, although Cannabia and Turn are still around, having been contracted to brewers outside Germany. Within Germany we know of just two brewpubs that brew Hanfbier seasonally, both in Saxony.

Hefeweizen/Hefeweißbier

Unfiltered wheat beer. Hefe is German for yeast, and indicates that some yeast has been left in the bottle or barrel. Sometimes, particularly in modern brewpubs, wheat beer is advertised simply as 'Hefe'. See also Weißbier.

Hell (Helles)

Nothing diabolical here but simply a pale *(helles)* beer. Often used indiscriminately to describe any beer of pale appearance, if you order a Helles you could end up with anything from a Lagerbier to an Export. When specifically used to describe a type of beer you will usually find something in the style of a Lagerbier or Vollbier, with between 4.7% and 5% ABV. Expect a light, slightly malty beer with some hoppiness, but don't be surprised to find something more full-bodied or dry. Most modern brewpubs serve their Hell unfiltered or *naturtrüb*, often describing it as just that. Hell (or Helles) is also used in the same manner as Dunkel to desribe the colour of other, unrelated styles of beer.

Kellerbier

Unfiltered and generally very dry and hoppy, Kellerbier is commonly produced in the area around Bamberg, although interpretations of this style appear all over the country. Often copper-coloured, Kellerbier is usually lightly carbonated compared to most German beers due to the bleeding-off of carbon-dioxide during conditioning. Traditionally sold in earthenware mugs (a *Krug*) so that the drinker is not offended by the haziness of the beer.

Kölsch

Related to Altbier, although you'd be hard-pushed to tell. Since the Kölsch Convention of 1985, a beer may only be described as Kölsch if it is brewed in the metropolitan area of Cologne, although a few established producers outside the city have retained the right to brew the style. The convention also decrees that Kölsch must be sold in a *Stange*, a narrow, straight-sided glass, 0.2l or 0.3l in volume. In traditional pubs these *Stangen* are carried on circular trays called *Kranz* (wreath) where each glass sits in its own hole. Today around 15 breweries produce approximately 30 varieties of Kölsch, the vast majority with the same ABV – 4.8%. All are pale-gold in colour, variety coming from the flavour which is generally clean, light and fruity.

Kräusen

Unfiltered beer that has had a small amount of wort added during conditioning to increase carbonation. Only produced by a dozen or so breweries. Those we've tried have had a bit of bite to them.

Kristallweizen

Filtered wheat beer. Always pale and only available bottled. Has the high carbonation of an unfiltered wheat beer but without the character-istic cloudiness. Kristallweizen is usually a brewery's standard Weißbier that has simply been filtered, and therefore usually has the same ABV. A refreshing style, although often lacking the body of its cloudy brother. Worryingly, the Guide has noticed a growing trend for Kristall-weizen to be served with a slice of lemon.

Lagerbier

Although many British people may believe that all German beer is Lager, only in Franconia will you commonly find it described as such. Before modern cooling methods were introduced, beer was stored *(gelagert)* in cool caves and cellars during summer months to prevent it from going off. Eventually, beer was deliberately condition-

Lüttje Lage

A speciality of Hannover, Lüttje Lage (little round) is a dark, top-fermented Schankbier of 2.8% that's traditionally drunk simultaneously with a light schnapps (32%) – the beer in a 0.1 litre glass, the spirit in a 15cl measure. The trick is to hold both in one hand and drink them without spilling a drop. Holding the beer glass between thumb and index finger and the schnapps glass between middle and ring finger, you allow the schnapps to drain into the beer and both together into your mouth! Some practice may be necessary...

Maibock

Brewed to celebrate spring and usually available from mid-April until late May (*Mai*), Maibocks are typically stronger than standard Bocks, often at a strength associated with Doppelbock. However, unlike most Doppelbocks, Maibocks tend to be pale in colour.

Malzbier

Non-alcoholic, extremely malty and usually very dark. Produced by a couple of dozen of the breweries listed in this guide, as well as five Maltbeer-only breweries that I haven't included. We do not consider Malzbier to be beer. Particularly not since we tried the bloody stuff!

Märzen

In the days before refrigeration, when successful summer brewing was difficult, beer was brewed in large quantities in March (*März*) and stored in caves and cellars for drinking over the summer months. This beer tended to be slightly stronger than average to help it last the six months or so until brewing resumed, and the style became known as Märzen. Usually copper-coloured or darker, and full-bodied, with an ABV of 5.3–5.8%. Some breweries now brew Märzen all year round, while many modern brewpubs sell Märzen only in March.

ed this way and became known as Lager. Often used by breweries to describe their standard product, Lagerbier is bottom-fermented but can be almost any colour, hoppy or malty, even smoky. Just as likely to be called Vollbier (which encompasses an equally broad range of colours and flavours).

Landbier

Country beer, and as you may expect, brewed almost exclusively by rural breweries. Low in carbonation, it shares many characteristics with Kellerbier, Ungespundet and Zwickelbier, but unlike these, Landbiers are often filtered. Typically amber in colour, they can also be anything from gold through to dark brown. One of many German styles that's very difficult to define!

Leicht

Low-alcohol beer, usually with between 2.5 and 3% alcohol by volume. The English Light is frequently used in place of Leicht. Many breweries produce low-alcohol Pilseners or Hefeweizen but other styles are rare. Those we've tried understandably lack the flavour and body of full-strength versions, but they are a compromise if you're driving.

Münchner Dunkel

A dark, bottom-fermented beer of around 5%. The style originated in Munich in the 19th century and became much copied. Generally dark brown, with a pronounced roasted malt flavour and only lightly hopped. Beers of this style are commonly found throughout much of Germany but only in München will you find them called Münchner Dunkel.

Münchner Hell

Paler than many German beers, Münchner Hell is generally a little stronger than an ordinary Helles, but does share many of the characteristics of that style. Usually fairly malty with little or no bitterness. As with Münchner Dunkel, you will not find beer described as Münchner Hell outside Munich, however true to the style it may be.

Pilsener

This ubiquitous brew accounts for more than 60 per cent of all beer brewed and drunk in Germany – many of the country's largest breweries produce nothing else. In the north, Pilseners tend to be straw-gold, dry and hoppy. In the southern states they are often a little darker and maltier. Sadly, a great deal of what is brewed, particularly by the larger producers, is pretty bland. There are, however, some fantastic examples out there. You've just got to know where to look.

Rauchbier

Smoke beer. Rauchbier is produced using malt that has been smoked over beechwood, once a common method of malting barley in central Europe. Now brewed mainly in Bamberg and surroundings, about ten breweries produce Rauchbier all year round, although a number of modern brewpubs do brew it seasonally. There's nothing to stop any sort of beer being made from smoked malt, although the only styles we've encountered are Lager, Kellerbier, Märzen, Weizen and Bock. The degree of smokiness depends entirely on the brewer and varies considerably.

Roggen

Top-fermented beer made with malted rye (*Roggen*). Similar in appearance to Hefeweizen Dunkel but sweeter, Roggen usually includes both malted barley and wheat as well as rye.

Currently brewed all year round by just four breweries, it also appears seasonally at a few brewpubs.

Schankbier

Beer with a lower-than-usual alcohol content of between 3 and 4.5%, often in the style of a Helles. Very few breweries produce any beers in this range and fewer still call the end result Schankbier.

Schwarzbier

Literally 'black beer', Schwarzbier is, not surprisingly, very dark in appearance. Particularly associated with Saxony and Thuringia, although not uncommon in northern Bavaria. The style has grown in popularity in recent years as it is now brewed by increasing numbers of breweries. Expect strong roasted malt flavours but little bitterness.

Spezial

Largely confined to southern Bayern, Spezial is a more-powerful-than-average premium beer, somewhere between Export and Bock in strength. Always pale, this bitter-sweet style is usually lightly hopped and full-bodied. Notable examples are Augustiner Edelstoff and Tegernseer Spezial.

Steinbier

A method of brewing in which red-hot (1,200°C) rocks (*Stein* meaning stone) are lowered into the beer to caramelise the malt. Revived in the 1980s by Werner-Bräu at Neustadt near Coburg, production moved to Altenmünster Kronenbrauerei in 1993. Sadly, brewing there ceased in 2003 following the take-over of the parent company (Sailer-Bräu) by Allgäuer Brauhaus. A style that is currently extinct, but we live in hope that someone may revive it.

Ungespundet

A *Spund* is the bung in the top of a barrel which prevents carbon dioxide from escaping. In the days before steel fermenting vessels, beer was lagered in large wooden barrels and the Spund was loosened to prevent the build-up of carbon dioxide causing the barrel to explode. Ungespundet (unbunged) beer is not lagered under pressure and therefore has relatively little carbonation compared to most German beers.

Closely related to Kellerbier, Ungespundet is usually unfiltered, dry and hoppy. Only made by a handful of breweries within a 30km radius of Bamberg.

Vollbier

'Full beer', typically copper-coloured but frequently lighter or darker. Like Lagerbier, you'll only normally find beer described as Vollbier in Franconia, despite it being an official German beer classification. Usually a little more full-bodied than Lagerbier, although the line between the two styles is blurred, to say the least. The term is often used indiscriminately to describe the standard house beer.

Weißbier/Weizenbier

Top-fermented beer, typically made with equal parts wheat and barley malt, and usually served in distinctive, tall, flared glasses. Generally known as Weizenbier (wheat beer) in the south and Weißbier (white beer) elsewhere, wheat beer has gone through something of a revival since the 1970s and is now quite a fashionable drink, particularly among younger Germans and in summer. Today, the majority of German breweries brew at least one wheat beer, and around 20 produce nothing else. Most Weißbiers are termed pale *(hell)*, although they are usually darker than bottom-fermented Helles. A number of breweries also brew dark wheat beers, but although pale wheats are regularly found on draught, the darker versions are almost always bottled. The norm is for it to be served in its natural, cloudy state with yeast still in the beer *(hefetrüb)*, but many breweries also filter their standard wheat beer to produce Kristallweizen. Bock and Doppelbock varieties are also produced, mainly by southern Bavarian breweries. Flavours vary enormously, but expect a generally fruity beer with high carbonation. Don't be surprised if you can taste or smell bananas!

Zoigl

Perhaps the most eccentric of all German brewing traditions, Zoigl is a beer brewed in communal breweries in Oberpfalz (the Upper Palatinate), the north-eastern region of Bavaria. The practice originated in medieval times when people were given the right to brew in the communal brewhouse and then sell the beer from their houses. This right was handed down through the generations, and the practice still survives in five towns. After brewing, the wort is taken to the brewer's house where it is lagered for a few weeks and then sold. Generally, each Zoigl house opens on roughly 10 weekends a year – there will usually be only one open at a time. The exception to the rule is Windischeschenbach where three pubs sell Zoigl on an almost daily basis. If you visit at the weekend, you could find Zoigl on sale in five places. Zoigl is also brewed by around a dozen commercial breweries, although purists would argue that this is not the real McCoy. There are also four communal breweries in the Franken (Franconia) region where local residents brew in a similar manner, but these do not produce Zoigl, and only one (in Neuhaus) follows the Oberpfalz tradition of rotating opening days. Further information and details of opening days can be found at www.zoigl.de which has English pages.

Zwickel

Unfiltered, bottom-fermented beer, so-named because of the Zwickel (tap) used to draw the beer from the conditioning tank. Often, Zwickel is simply one of a brewery's other beers that has been left unfiltered. Much more common in the south than in other parts of the country.

Beer gardens in Munich and elsewhere

THERE ARE 100 BEER GARDENS in and around Munich. The smallest can accommodate only a few dozen people; the largest (Hirschgarten) caters for 8,000, the equivalent of a small town. Whatever their size, 'beer gardens' are a traditional part of summer life in Munich. The city's continental climate can push the thermometer as high as 35°C for several days at a time, driving many people who live in flats to find a cool spot outdoors. In the evenings, office workers wind down here after work and many companies have a *Stammtisch* (regulars' table) reserved for their employees. At weekends, whole families join in the ritual of heading to the beer gardens for a picnic.

Some are situated right in the heart of the city, for example the Augustiner-Keller or the one on Viktualienmarkt. Others are next to lakes, in attractive green parks or a short way outside the town limits, in beautiful countryside yet easily reached on a cycling tour, perhaps after a dip in one of the lakes.

The beer garden season is weather dependant. Some large gardens, such as the one near Chinesischer Turm in Englischer Garten, open in March if the weather is mild enough, and a warm autumn can keep the beer gardens busy until early November. Opening hours are also dictated by the weather. In residential areas, some close at 10pm, though others may continue to serve until midnight if the weather is warm.

A traditional beer garden consists of long benches beneath horse chestnut trees. Sometimes there's a children's playground; occasionally there is a brass or a jazz band playing; the Hirschgarten even has a deer enclosure. But beer and food are the two constant features. Sometimes, beer gardens are attached to pubs, though the largest and most popular are oases in parks where people can take their own picnics.

The Bavarian beer garden idea developed in the days before the industrial revolution. A Bavarian law of 1539 stipulated that brewers could only brew their beers between two saints' days: St Michael (29 September) and St George (23 April). In the summer months, the brewing process was too dangerous – the brew kettles could cause fires and were therefore sealed. Thus brewers had to brew ahead of themselves (which is how the strong, hoppy and longer-lived Märzen or March beers originated).

Throughout the summer, brewers had to store (or 'lager') their beers in cool places, both to help it mature and stop it going sour. Caves were cut into hillsides and storage cellars dug into the ground for this purpose – the first underground *Bierkellers*. The high ground-water level, prevented them making the cellars as deep as they wanted, and so they sawed ice blocks out of the frozen lakes nearby to keep the cellars cool. On the ground above, they planted horse chestnut trees, trees that gave the maximum shade with their large leaves. Some brewers began to open a couple of barrels on site in spring or early summer, and word rapidly spread that their beer tasted much fresher than the warm, flat and sometime sour stuff that had been stored elsewhere.

Eventually, the brewers decided to exploit this growing trend by providing comfortable facilities for their new customers. Food sales followed later, though it became enshrined in law that customers were also entitled to take their own food along if they wished. Today you can see the entire range – some will buy the beer garden's *Schweinshaxe, Würstchen, Brezen* or other Bavarian specialities, others will bring elaborate outdoor food of their own. They'll place tablecloths and candelabra, and enjoy a full silver-service with their friends, each one contributing. One, Mangostin, offers more

adventurous fare such as Thai and Japanese food. Beers may be bought at the bar or served by a strong waitress who can hold up to ten 1-litre mugs in her two hands – not an easy feat!

Bavarian beers, especially wheat beer which has become a popular summer drink, have conquered the rest of Germany, and you are just as likely to see them being drunk in Berlin, Hamburg or Cologne as you are in Bavaria. A few Bavarian breweries have also set up in other towns, notably Paulaner, Löwenbräu and Andechser. And as with Bavarian beer and beer

culture, the beer gardens have taken hold in the north. Many towns already had their own open-air culture, with pubs and restaurants setting up tables and chairs outdoors, especially near rivers and lakes – Berlin on the lakes in the south-east, Hamburg along the Alster, Cologne on the Rhine – but 'proper' Bavarian beer garden with long tables and benches and shade from chestnut trees are a more recent advent.

Based on Graham Lees' article for the *Good Beer Guide to Munich and Bavaria* (CAMRA Books).

The typical German

GERMANS ENJOY a reputation for accuracy, precision and efficiency – words often used to describe their excellent cars – although an equally enduring image is that of *Lederhosen*-clad Bavarians hoisting beer steins at the Oktoberfest. Neither of these stereotypes reflects the diversity of Germany's towns and cities – from romantic Heidelberg to the medieval Nuremberg of Dürer, from the Weimar of Goethe and Schiller to the lively port cities of Hamburg and Bremen, from the beerhalls of Munich to the carnival celebrations in Cologne, from the financial powerhouse of Frankfurt to the revitalised cities of the former east such as Halle, Leipzig and Dresden. Overshadowing them all is lively and cosmopolitan Berlin, where politicians and bureaucrats of the new/old capital rub shoulders with artists and techno clubbers.

Travelling between Bavaria in the south and Lower Saxony in the north, the Rhineland in the west and Saxony in the east, you will come across vastly different traditions that manifest themselves in regional foods – and beers – as much as in the dialects and general attitudes. Southern and western Germany for instance, predominantly rural and Catholic, feed the tourist stereotype of fairytale castles and timber-framed houses in quaint old towns. The north and the east of the country, on the other hand, are more industrialised, urbanised and mainly Protestant. To understand why this is so it is worth taking a very brief look at German history.

Germany has, in fact, rarely been united. For most of the two millennia that German-speaking peoples have inhabited central Europe between the North Sea and the Alps, the area was a patchwork of hundreds of duchies, principalities, fiefdoms, free cities, bishoprics and archbishoprics. Not even the Romans managed to unite the country under one government; they occupied only its southern and western areas. Around AD800, the emperor Charlemagne established an empire, but this fell apart a generation later, when it had to be divided among his three sons.

Medieval Germany was characterised by endless fragmentation. While France and England slowly evolved into united nation-states, Germany was racked by ceaseless wars between its many local rulers. The Habsburg Dynasty's long monopoly of the crown of the Holy Roman Empire provided only the semblance of German unity as German princes continued to fight each other. The Protestant Reformation deprived Germany of even its religious unity, leaving its south and west predominantly Roman Catholic and its north and east predominantly Lutheran. These religious divisions added ferocity to the Thirty Years' War (1618–48), during which Germany was ravaged to a degree not seen again until World War II.

The Peace of Westphalia in 1648 left Germany divided into a multitude of states – 1,789 independent territories including some 50 free city states at one count. During the next 200 years, the two largest states – Prussia and Austria – jockeyed for dominance while the smaller ones allied themselves at various times with one or another. From the mid-1790s until 1813, when Napoleon was defeated in the Battle of Leipzig, much of the country was occupied by French troops. Napoleon's officials abolished numerous microstates, and after the Congress of Vienna in 1815 Germany counted a mere 35 states and 4 free cities.

In the following decades, pressure for German unification grew. Nationalist and liberal academics, politicians and businessmen agitated for a united Germany driven by a desire and need for uniform laws, a single currency and democracy. The so-called bourgeois revolution of 1848 seemed at first likely to realize this dream of unity and freedom, but King Friedrich

Wilhelm IV of Prussia, who was offered the crown of a united Germany, rejected it. Like the other rulers of Germany's states, he saw German unity as a threat to his own power base.

German unification finally happened in 1871, as a result of the Franco-Prussian war. It was, however, not brought about by revolutionary or liberal forces, but by a conservative Prussian aristocrat, Otto von Bismarck. Sensing the power of nationalism, Bismarck sought to use it for his own aims: the preservation of a feudal social order and the triumph of his own country, Prussia, over Austria. By a series of masterful diplomatic manoeuvres and three brief yet dazzlingly successful military campaigns, Bismarck created a united 'small' Germany,

consisting of Prussia and the remaining German states but excluding Austria.

The country then remained united – and was considerably enlarged under Hitler through invasion and annexation of neighbouring states – until the end of World War II. After a period of occupation by US, British, French and Russian troops, Germany was officially divided into two states in 1949 – the Federal Republic of Germany (west) and the German Democratic Republic (east). This division lasted for 40 years, until a 'velvet revolution' led to reunification on 3 October 1989.

Today Germany is a confederation of 16 states, including the city-states of Berlin, Hamburg and Bremen. Each of the states or

Bundesländer (federal states) has its own capital and regional government, responsible for its own laws, budget and education system, although these must conform to the Federal Republic's. The Länder are governed by a cabinet led by a Ministerpräsident (Minister-President), together with a unicameral legislative body known as the Landtag ('State Diet'). The cities are governed slightly differently from the other states – the executive branch consisting of a Senate with duties equivalent to those of the ministers in the larger Länder. Decentralisation has also led to a greater importance for regional cities (such as Frankfurt, Hamburg or Munich) than you would find in other European countries like France or England.

Each Bundesland has autonomy over their police force, education and culture, among other things. This manifests itself, for example, in the fact that the German spelling reform that has been underway for the last decade or so was accepted in some states but not others – so a *Schloss* (castle) in one state may still be a *Schloß* in another. Regional dialects are, in fact, so strong that people up and down the country often cannot understand the dialects from another state. Regional theatre companies may have their plays shown on television – with High German subtitles.

The dialects do not just differ in the way the words are pronounced; often entirely different words are used to describe the same thing. A bread roll, for example, is a *Brötchen* in High German and in western areas, a *Semmel* in Bavaria and the south, a *Rundstück* in Hamburg and a *Schrippe* in Berlin; a hamburger will be known as *Frikadelle* in Köln, *Fleischpflanzerl* in München, *Bulette* in Berlin and as *Fleischklops* in other areas. This linguistic variety may even lead to great surprise – and disappointment – when a *Halver Hahn* ordered in a restaurant in Köln turns out to be a bread roll with cheese rather than half a roast chicken which the very similar sounding *Halber Hahn* might have led you to expect.

Germany's regional cuisine varies considerably as you would notice on a tour of the country. Coastal states like Niedersachsen or Mecklenburg-Vorpommern are obviously influenced by the produce available from the sea, while the more mountainous southern states often feature game on their menus. Neighbouring countries too have added their own culinary traditions – the Saar has an equivalent to quiche, eastern states enjoy roast geese from Poland and Bavarians share their Austrian neighbours' predilection for all things sweet.

Celebrations are also strongly local and regional, in some cases because of prevalent religions, but in others just as a result of their separate histories. Epiphany, Corpus Christi and Assumption, for example, are only holidays in regions or districts with a predominantly Catholic population, while Reformation Day and the Day of Prayer and Repentance are celebrated today just in the largely Protestant former east.

Most cities and villages will have their own festivities, often accompanied by funfairs and processions, sometimes linked to local saints' days. Fathers' Day is worth mentioning in a beer guide – where it is celebrated (on Ascension Day), large groups of men can be seen to 'enjoy' themselves together, usually with the help of copious quantities of beer and often ending in a brawl. Regional festivities, such as Carnival or the Oktoberfest, meanwhile, have spread well beyond their origins, and international celebrations like Valentine's Day or Halloween have made inroads in gift and card shops.

In addition there are many other celebrations, some quite unusual like 'Dance into May' and a witches' festival on 30 April, known in the Harz Mountains as Walpurgisnacht. There's Peace Day in Augsburg on 8 August; the release of new-season cider in Frankfurt, new wine in the wine-growing areas, new beers in brewery towns and villages, and not forgetting the official start of carnival on 11 November. Many celebrations are accompanied by song and dance as well as the consumption of copious amounts of beer (or wine) and most will affect shop, restaurant and pub opening times.

Whenever and wherever something is being celebrated, however, you will be invited to join in, and you are likely to find it very easy to get to know the locals. You'll probably find yourself speaking their local dialect, even if your knowledge of German as such is nil. Enjoy!

Cologne carnival

"Drink doch eene met / stell dich nit esu ahn / du steihst he de janze Zick eröm. / Häs de och kei Jeld / dat is janz ejal / drink doch eene met / un kümmer dich net dröm."

("Have a drink on me / don't be shy / you're just hanging around here. / If you have no money / it doesn't really matter / just have a drink on me / and don't worry about it.")

Bläckfööß (Barefeet)

So GOES ONE OF THE BEST-KNOWN carnival songs, and drinking certainly plays an important role during carnival! Many German breweries even produce a special carnival beer, variously known as Faschingsbier, Fasnetbier, Fasnets-Fläschle, Fasnetsbier, Carnevale... (Fastnacht and Fasching are alternative regional names for the event).

So what exactly is it? The word carnival comes from the Latin meaning 'meat farewell', and is derived from the Christian pre-Lent fast. Carnival is celebrated over large parts of Germany, but is particularly associated with the Rhineland, especially Mainz, Aachen, Düsseldorf and Köln, the epicentre of all things carnevalistic. In the latter city, street carnival spans the six-day period preceding Lent. The official start date, however, and the beginning of indoor *Sitzungen* (sessions or shows) is on Remembrance Day of all days: the 11th of the 11th (November) at 11.11 am – and at this time you will see costumed, painted and masqueraded people queuing around the block to get into the most popular pubs.

The carnival proper commences with *Weiberfastnacht* (women's carnival), the Thursday before Lent when at 11.11am the women of Köln are ceremoniously handed the town keys by the mayor and rule the city for the day. This entails every good-looking bloke,

especially policemen, getting kissed by heavily lipsticked girls, and having his tie ritually cut short – so don't wear one! Shops may be open, but the service you'll get will not be quite up to scratch. Much better to spend the day in one of the pubs, where hordes of be-costumed people will be enjoying the proper start to the 'Fifth Season'. You'll see clowns, of course, lots of furry animals, fantasy costumes teamed with colourful wigs and groups of people in themed outfits, all on a pub crawl, possibly accompanied by a giant ear-shattering drum.

The Friday is quiet apart from the numerous indoor or private events, but things rev up again on the Saturday night with the ghost procession. This was first introduced in 1992 when all other official events were cancelled because of the first Iraq War. It has since become a regular alternative night-time procession of ghosts, ghouls, witches and vampires, all with a hefty dose of politics. On Sunday, in the daytime, you can watch the large city-centre procession of schools and districts with their home-made floats which will also be part of numerous smaller processions in the districts on Tuesday.

The main event is on Rose Monday when all shops are (or should be) shut. A procession some 7km in length snakes its way along a 6km route for six hours or longer, watched by between 1 and 2 million costumed, singing and drinking carousers, often in sub-zero temperatures. The procession comprises around 10,000 participants, including 125 marching bands, plus about 500 horses and 100 floats, often with a political theme. Walkers and people atop the floats throw some 150 tons of sweets, 700,000 bars and 220,000 boxes of chocolate, 300,000 flower bouquets plus assorted other gifts such as dolls or CDs for the spectators to catch and enjoy.

Carnival 2006: Prinz Rico I (Prince Carnival, with three long feathers) and Bauer Rüdiger (Peasant, with white fur hat) on stage at one of the indoor sessions, surrounded by members of various guards.

Also taking part in the procession are Guards in their traditional officers' costumes of red-and-white, blue-and-white, yellow-and-green and various other combinations. Each guard has a Mariechen, an attractive young girl wearing a very short skirt who has studied a series of dance steps and gets thrown in the air or balanced on the hand of one of the less portly officers. Towards the end of the procession comes one float carrying Peasant and Virgin (a man) and another float with the Prince of Carnival. Together they make up the Dreigestirn, the big three elected afresh each year, a highly coveted position in the various carnival associations, not usually open to the average man on the street. Procedures vary slightly in other towns; Düsseldorf, for example, has a Prince and a Princess instead.

In the evenings and throughout the nights there's high life in the pubs, full to bursting wherever you go. Tables will have been removed to provide more standing room, yet the waiters will still ply you with supplies of fresh Kölsch – although this time you'll have to pay on the spot and some pubs institute a coupon system. There's singing and dancing and even if you speak no German you'll be soon be fluent in the Kölsch dialect and friends with everyone.

All the fun is over at midnight on Tuesday – Ash Wednesday is the start of Lent. In some pubs, the *Nubbel*, a Guy-Fawkes-like cloth doll, is burnt at midnight and ritually mourned by those who've lasted the course. Now everyone goes home to nurse their hangovers and wait for November!

The Oktoberfest

UNDERSTANDABLY RENOWNED as the world's biggest piss-up, Munich's famous Oktoberfest first took place in 1810 to celebrate the wedding of the future (Bavarian) King Ludwig I and Princess Theresa. Those not fortunate enough to be invited held their own celebrations in a meadow at the edge of the city, later renamed *Theresenwiese* (Theresa's meadow), which has since given its name to the fest: *die Wies'n*. Ironically, the first event didn't feature beer, just horse racing and a fair. Beer soon played a part, but for many decades it remained primarily an agricultural show and racing meet.

Nowadays, the name is a little misleading. Although the event originally took place in October, over the years it's been brought forward into September, mainly to ensure a greater likelihood of good weather for outdoor carousing. Dates vary from year to year but the festival almost always ends on the first Sunday in October (it may run into the Monday if that happens to be a bank holiday), and starts on the Saturday two weeks earlier. In 2007 the festival will run from 22 Sep–7 Oct; in 2008 the dates will be 20 Sep–5 Oct.

With the exception of 1854 & 1873, when outbreaks of cholera led to its cancellation, and during wars, the Oktoberfest has been held every year since. During the mid-19th century it evolved into more of a festival of Bavarian identity, due in large part to the Bavarian state's desire to assert its independence from Prussian efforts to create a German nation. Today the festival is an international event, with Australian, American and British accents being prominent. It does, however, retain a fiercely loyal Bavarian following and many local firms give their employees a half-day off to visit. Like other Bavarian institutions, such as wheat beer and the beer garden, the Oktoberfest has also continued its march across the rest of Germany, becoming an annual event in many northern and foreign pubs.

On the first morning of the festival a parade of brewery drays, each drawn by liveried horses and accompanied by brass bands and Schäfflertänzer (the local equivalent of morris dancers – though not so bad), wends its way through the city to the Wies'n. At the stroke of midday the Lord Mayor dons his ceremonial beer apron and hammers a brass tap into the first wooden barrel. "O'zapft is", he loudly proclaims (the beer is tapped), before handing the first *Maß* to the guest of honour. Over the next fortnight another 7 million or so will follow (around 13 million pints), equivalent to the annual output of a medium-sized brewery. It's not just the beer consumption that's impressive – each year around 95 oxen, 380,000 sausages, 500,000 roasted chickens and 56,000 pork knuckles will find their way into the mouths of the visitors.

The festival site is covered by a large fairground and 14 cavernous beer halls, perhaps not entirely appropriately known as tents, most seating around 6,000. The 'tents' all have their own special character: there's the trendy Hippodrom which also serves sparkling wine, the Cross-Bow Shooting Tent, the world-famous Hofbräu Festhalle, the rock'n'roll Hacker tent, the Schotenhamel where the Lord Mayor starts the fest, the Winzerer Fähndl serving Paulaner, the Schützenfestzelt where you can get a delicious roast suckling pig, the gourmet restaurant Käfer's Wies'n-Schänke, the Wine Tent with 15 different wines for non-beer drinkers, the Löwenbräu-Festhalle with its roaring lion, the Bräurosl serving Pschorr to the sounds of its own yodeller, the friendly Augustiner-Festhalle, the Ox Roasting Tent and the Fischer Vroni's tent where you can get a traditional skewered fish meal.

Only breweries from within the city limits are allowed to supply the festival. In a bid to get round this rule Prince Luitpold of Kaltenberg fame opened a brewpub in the Luitpold Park. However, the council simply changed the rules to bar any brewery established after 1970. Whether other brewers in the area plan to challenge the cartel remains to be seen. Each of Munich's five large breweries brews a special Oktoberfestbier (Paulaner/Hacker-Pschorr brews one under each name). Most are golden, malty beers, far removed from the dark Märzen that was originally sold at the event; Hacker-Pschorr's is closest in style to the original beers. Perhaps bizarrely, each brewery also offers an alcohol-free version.

If you plan to visit the festival, the Guide recommends you either book your accommodation very early or stay outside the city. Munich's hotels and guesthouses get booked up months in advance and many mercilessly exploit the demand for rooms, hiking prices to exorbitant levels. We also recommend you book a table in one of the tents (this can be done through the local tourist board) – they get extremely busy, particularly from early evening and those without a booking may face a very long wait. Service is by waitress only and there's no standing.

The tents generally open at 11.00 but are busiest from late afternoon, although it must be said they're not exactly quiet earlier on. Each has a brass band on a raised stage in the centre. Most are closed by 23.00 but you may find one or two smaller ones that stay open until midnight. Beer is sold in 1-litre measures only and currently costs around €7.00 a glass. Do not attempt to smuggle a glass out – there are plenty of people employed to stop you doing this. And don't stand on the tables either – as the evening wears on it's commonplace to find people standing on the benches but the tables are out of bounds. In the Guide's experience it's also worth ensuring you have a spare pair of trousers at your hotel – the floors, tables and benches are usually awash with beer by the end of the night.

Most of all, enjoy yourself. The Oktoberfest may be touristy but it's definitely worth a visit at least once, the atmosphere being infectious, particularly after a *Maß* or five. It's one of the great levellers, with Germans of all age and class mixing, drinking, singing and, eventually, getting drunk together. Some of the sights at the end of the night have to be seen to be believed…

Five favourite...

BREWERIES

Anywhere that is too large to be called a brewpub.

Augustiner, München – Proof that not all large breweries brew bland beers. Each of their beers is an excellent example of the style.

Göller, Zeil – Brews one of the largest and best ranges of beers in Franconia. We're particularly glad their Rauchbier has returned to the fold.

Mahr's Bräu, Bamberg – Recently voted the best brewery in the world by an American magazine, it's hard to find too many faults with Mahr's beers.

Pinkus Müller, Münster – Best known for their Alt (sometimes served with fresh fruit syrup), Pinkus Müller brew several other worthy beers.

St. Georgen, Buttenheim – Renowned for their Kellerbier, St. Georgen also brew some other styles particularly well.

BREWPUBS (old)

These date from before 1984 and may supply a few other outlets.

Krug, Geisfeld – An excellent example of a traditional Franconian village brewpub. It's just a shame there are no buses to the village.

Schlössle, Neu-Ulm – Impressive looking brewpub that brews an excellent Zwickel. They have a very pleasant beer garden.

Schrüfer, Priesendorf – Well worth the potentially awkward journey, nothing much seems to have changed here for decades.

Spezial, Bamberg – Half-timbered inn that has been brewing Rauchbier longer than anyone else. Outstanding beer and good-value food.

Uerigen, Düsseldorf – It's a tough choice but we reckon this is the pick of Düsseldorf's traditional brewpubs. Whatever you do, don't ask for Kölsch...

BREWPUBS (new)

The post-1984 boom in brewpubs is one of the few positives in the current brewing scene.

Altes Brauhaus, Fallersleben – Characterful pub under the largest roof we've ever seen. Proof that new brewpubs aren't all copper and pine.

Bayerischer Bahnhof, Leipzig – If only more new breweries would revive local beer styles and not just be content to brew Hell, Dunkel and Weizen!

Griesbräu, Murnau – We were seriously impressed when a roasted pig appeared on the narrow-gauge railway that runs through the pub.

Kössel-Bräu, Speiden – They've achieved that rare thing for a new brewpub – become the focal point for village life.

Rathausbräu, Michelstadt – Full of antique furnishings, this attractive brewpub is in the historic centre of Michelstadt.

TAPS

The main outlet for a brewery. It may or may not be next door.

Früh am Dom, Köln – The archetypal Kölsch house that seemingly has the same dimensions as the tardis.

Hacklberger Bräustüberl, Passau – Atmospheric, vaulted pub, opposite one of the most attractive breweries anywhere.

Kneitinger, Regensburg – Sometimes boisterous tap in front of the brewery, home to one of the world's finest dark beers.

Mahr's-Bräu, Bamberg – Wonderful pub next to one of Germany's finest breweries. The evening is the best time to visit.

Pinkus Müller, Münster – Unspoilt pub with outstanding beer and food. Some tables have seemingly been carved on by generations of patrons.

PUBS

These don't brew themselves and cannot be described as taps.

Augustiner Keller, München – Large pub close to the Hauptbahnhof with one of the nicest (and largest) beer gardens you could hope to find.

Hütt'n, Nürnberg – One of the few genuine freehouses we've found, an excellent place to try a range of local beers, both draught and bottled.

Ohne Bedenken, Leipzig – Classic east German city pub whose owner was single-handedly responsible for reviving Gose.

Pelikan, Bamberg – If you ever get fed up with drinking in Bamberg's many taps, try this bustling Kneipe, a few minutes walk from Schlenkerla.

Schlampazius, Stuttgart – Some people will hate this pub but we absolutely love it. A must for all lovers of classic rock and nicotine-stained walls.

BOCK BEERS

Generally seasonal but always worth a try.

Andechser Doppelbock Dunkel, Andechs – Dark chestnut-coloured beer with a very full body. Rich, roasted malt and toffee flavours with a spicy fruitiness.

Kneitinger Bock, Regensburg – Easy drinking, stronger version of Kneitinger Dunkel. We recommend you try it draught from the wood.

Kronenbrauerei Natureis-Bock Hell, Ulm – One of the most dangerously drinkable beers we've encountered. Kicks like a horse.

Mahr's Bräu Bock-Bier, Bamberg – Golden, fruity, bitter bock. Full-bodied and fantastic. It's just a shame it's seasonal.

Weltenburger Kloster Asam Bock, Weltenburg – One of the few Weltenburger beers still brewed at the abbey, this deep ruby-coloured beer is very rich and malty but extremely drinkable.

DARK BEERS

Covers everything from mid-brown to black.

Altstadthof Schwarze, Nürnberg – An excellent example of the style – the best dark beer from a new-wave brewery we've tasted.

Augustiner-Bräu Dunkel, München – Classic Münchner Dunkel. Dark chestnut colour, roasted malt and caramel flavours with a little bitterness in the finish.

Klosterbräu Schwärzla, Bamberg – Almost as black as they come, roasted malt dominates but there's some fruit and liquorice.

Kneitinger Dunkel, Regensburg – Very smooth, surprisingly soft dark beer. A good one to use if you want to convince a Dunkel sceptic. Try it in Regensburg – it doesn't travel as well as some.

Krug Lagerbier, Geisfeld – Too dark to be classified Hell but much paler than the above four, this is a lovely dry, hoppy beer, typical of the Oberfranken region.

PALE BEERS

A huge number to choose from, these are a few we could drink and drink...

Andechser Hell, Andechs – Lovely light, refreshing Helles that you could seemingly drink all day.

Augustiner-Bräu Lagerbier Hell, München – Often overshadowed by its stronger stablemate, Edelstoff. Slightly sweet but with some bitter hop flavours. Very smooth.

Pinkus Müller Special, Münster – Pale, well-balanced, unfiltered, organic beer. Happily, it can sometimes be found in wholefood shops in Britain.

Schlössle Zwickel, Neu-Ulm – Only available at the tap in Neu-Ulm, this is a cracking example of a Zwickel – dry but fruity.

Zehendner Lagerbier, Mönchsambach – Unfiltered lager, typical of the Franconian style. Full of flavour with a lovely bitter finish.

PILSENERS

Much maligned style, sometimes deservedly so. These Pilseners may help change a few minds.

Eutin St. Michaelis Bräu Pils, Eutin – One of Germany's most northerly breweries, Brauhaus Eutin produces this unfiltered, refreshingly hoppy beer, a favourite of at least one Guide contributor.

Hofer-Bräu Pils, Furth im Wald – Not surprisingly for a beer produced on the Czech border, this is a rich, heavily-hopped, Bohemian-style Pilsener.

Forschungs-Pilsissimus, München – Wonderful, rich, hoppy beer. The antithesis of all bland, mass-produced Pilseners.

Pyraser Hopfenpflücker Pils, Pyras – Unfiltered, refreshing beer with citrus flavours and a crisp, dry finish. Unfortunately, it's only available seasonally.

St. Georgen Pils, Buttenheim – Best known for their Kellerbier, St. Georgen produce several other memorable beers, the pick of which is this cracking Pils.

SPECIALITY BEERS

You may spot a regional bias here. There's a reason for that...

Heller Aecht Schlenkerla Urbock, Bamberg – Very dark, full-bodied Rauchbier, perhaps more approachable than their Märzen. Some people will loathe it, poor souls.

Löwen-Bräu Ungespundetes, Buttenheim – Sometimes described as a Kellerbier, this is a fruity, hoppy beer with an exceptionally dry finish.

Mahr's-Bräu Ungespundet, Bamberg – Known locally as 'U' (pronounced 'Oooh'), this dry, fruity beer is available bottled but we reckon the only way to drink it is direct from the barrel.

Spezial Rauchbier Lager, Bamberg – This beer is at least partly responsible for the appearance of this Guide, having bewitched the author back in April 1991. We still love it.

St. Georgen Bräu Keller Bier, Buttenheim – Possibly the perfect beer to convert a bitter drinker to German 'lager'. Chestnut brown, fruity, hoppy, wonderful.

WHEAT BEERS

Bananas, bubblegum, lemon... don't be surprised to find any of these flavours here.

Andechser Weißbier Hell, Andechs – We reckon this is the classic pale wheat beer, though others are sure to disagree. Expect lots of fruit, with banana dominating.

Heller Schlenkerla Rauchweizen, Bamberg – A superb blend of two styles – think spicy wheat beer with some smoked bacon thrown in. A beer to polarise opinions.

Karg Dunkles Hefe-Weißbier, Murnau – If the bottle's been standing for a while this can be incredibly claggy, with great lumps of yeast floating in the highly carbonated beer. Lots of citrus and banana flavours.

Schneider Aventinus, Kelheim – The classic strong wheat beer, Aventinus is dark, very fruity and alcoholic. Available all year, this is best drunk in the warm on freezing cold night.

Schneider Weisse Original, Kelheim – One of the largest wheat beer producers, Schneider confound the 'small is beautiful' rule by producing some of the best Weizens around, not least this, their standard-bearer.

31

The Reinheitsgebot

IN GERMANY, beer is a serious business. No surprise then that in 1516 a beer purity law was introduced in Bavaria. Known as the Reinheitsgebot, it was introduced in part to protect the public from the growing number of unsavoury and often unsafe ingredients that were used in the brewing process. It was obviously needed, since an early medieval survey found poisonous plants such as fly agaric mushrooms and ivy, pitch, chalk, soot, snake juice and ox-liver fluid as adjuncts used regularly in the brewing process.

Only three ingredients were initially specified by the Reinheitsgebot for inclusion in beer – barley malt, hops and water. This was later amended to include yeast, the exact workings of which had not been entirely understood when the law was first introduced. The restriction of the grain used for brewing to barley only, was designed to prevent price competition with bakers for wheat, ensuring that sufficient amounts of affordable bread were available. The use of wheat in the brewing process was only permitted from the seventeenth century onwards, but was restricted to brewers of the nobility.

As a condition of joining the new German republic in 1918, Bavaria insisted on the countrywide adoption of the Reinheitsgebot, a condition also offering the added bonus of protecting Bavarian brewers from outside competition. Although its principles were not adopted throughout western Germany until the early 1950s, the end result was the extinction of several long-standing local brewing traditions and beer styles that were not Reinheitsgebot compliant, such as North German spiced beer for example.

The German market became dominated by Pilsener style beers, though some regional styles like Düsseldorfer Altbier did manage to survive.

The Reinheitsgebot is no longer part of German law. In 1952 it was replaced by the Provisional German Beer Law (Vorläufiges deutsches Biergesetz), which allowed other ingredients previously prohibited by the Reinheitsgebot, including wheat malt and cane sugar, to be used.

Thirty-five years later, after claims that the German authorities had contravened European Community free-market rules by banning the import of beers into Germany because they were not brewed according to the Reinheitsgebot/Biergesetz, the European Court of Justice ruled that the Biergesetz should be lifted. Under current law, anything allowed in other foods is also allowed in beer, although beers brewed according to the Reinheitsgebot still receive special treatment as a protected, 'traditional' food. Despite this, by far the majority of breweries brewing in Germany today claim that they still abide by the Reinheitsgebot.

So was it only the existence of the beer purity laws that made Germany the great beer-producing nation that it is today? From the early 19th century, until it was superseded by the change in EU law, the Reinheitsgebot was also enforced in Greece due to a law by the first Greek king, Otto who was originally a Bavarian prince. Greece is hardly known for its high quality beer brewing though, so perhaps not.

Although the German beer-drinking public firmly believes that the Reinheitsgebot is a good thing, the law does restrict the range of beer styles it's possible to produce and thus severely limits experimentation. There are a couple of dozen breweries, virtually all of them modern brewpubs, that now openly brew their own non-Reinheitsgebot beers. The law may also restrict the revival of some traditional and long-forgotten beers, although there are some obscure exemptions which allowed Gose, for example, to be brewed with salt and coriander yet still be classified as a beer. These same laws, however, prevented the *Neuzeller Kloster Brewery*, a former monastery brewery in East Germany, from marketing its traditional black beer, a product possibly older than the *Reinheitsgebot* itself, as beer, since it contained sugar syrup. This decision has recently been reversed, but only after a ten-year legal battle.

It seems that the Reinheitsgebot has led to some confusion as to why German beer is generally of such high quality. The idea that German beer is pure is quite erroneous, since it is perfectly permissible to treat both the grain and the water used in brewing with chemicals. In fact, the Reinheitsgebot has nothing to say about poor tasting beer, or that which leaves the brewery in an unfit state to be drunk. The simple insistence that all German beer is good because it is pure has been an excellent marketing tool for German breweries, but it doesn't mean that all of them are providing a top-quality product. The overall high quality of German beers probably has more to do with the care lavished by their highly skilled and well trained brewers than by any adherence to a beer purity law.

Like many things, then, although the law was intended to protect the consumer – a good thing – it may now be used to protect large-scale brewing interests and to stop smaller, more adventurous businesses – not so good. Seek out the experimenters and draw your own conclusions!

The Breweries

A bit about the breweries

It's often said that every town in Germany has a brewery; in Bavaria nearly every village claims to have one. Although these statements may not have been too wide off the mark 125 years ago, nowadays they're a long way from the truth.

The golden age of German brewing was in the late 19th century. In 1880 some 19,000 breweries were in existence – 15 times today's total. New production methods, World War I and subsequent hyperinflation saw a rapid decline in numbers, to approximately 4,000 at the start of the 1930s. Even 30 years ago, Germany still counted nearly 1,800 breweries in the west and east combined (compared to 130 in Britain). Unfortunately, more than half of these have since closed. Brewery numbers have never fallen much below 1,250 since the early 1990s, but this figure has been distorted by the emergence of new brewpubs. As in previous decades, an average of 30 long-established breweries still close each year – some because of the owner's retirement; some due to financial problems; some simply stop brewing as they can buy in beer more cheaply than making it themselves. Others fall victim to take-overs, their beers either disappearing altogether or moving to the predator's brewery. A new, more sinister threat today is globalisation. Only 20 years ago every German brewery was German-owned. These days there are a few familiar faces on the scene, such as Carlsberg, Heineken and InBev. Together, these three brewing conglomerates are now responsible for almost 30 per cent of German beer production.

One further factor is the overall decline in beer consumption. In 1992 Germans drank more than 120 million hectolitres of beer. Twelve years later the total was barely 106 million hl. The average German is now more health-conscious and less likely to drink beer than before, while younger Germans are less likely to drink any alcohol at all. In a desperate attempt to win over the latter, many breweries, who should know better, now produce *Biermischgetränke* (beer mixers) – not just the traditional shandy, but vile cocktails containing anything from Schwarzbier and cola to wheat beer and banana syrup. We wish them ill (which is probably what you'd be if you tried one).

It's not all bad news though. Around 550 new breweries have opened since 1984, with roughly 80 per cent of them surviving to this day. Many produce excellent beers. A few have revived previously extinct styles or have experimented with ingredients not used in German brewing since the nationwide adoption of the Reinheitsgebot. It would have been impossible, for example, to drink Gose 20 years ago, or a beer made from oats and rye. Honey or fruit as additives would have been unthinkable. While not commonplace, these beers can now be found if you know where to look.

The bulk of this book is devoted to the breweries themselves, listing each one that we know about, their beers and other details. Where known, their tap is included beneath. We would love to have included tasting notes for each beer but this was simply impossible – there are more than 7,750 on these pages, many only available in one pub in the world, often for just a few weeks a year. What we have done is list a few beers of various styles which we've drunk regularly and particularly like. Future editions may expand upon this. We've also attempted to include the output (in hectolitres) of each brewery. For reference: one hectolitre equals 176 pints or 0.61 barrels. To give you a comparison, these are the approximate annual outputs of three well-known British breweries – Cotleigh 11,000hl; Harveys 60,000hl; Fuller's 300,000hl. We haven't distinguished between what some may term national and independent brewers as we feel it's probably more helpful to group breweries regionally rather than by ownership, certainly in this first edition. There is, however, a short section towards the rear which identifies the major brewing groups and which breweries each owns.

Every one of the 1,257 breweries in this Guide was contacted between July 2005 and January 2006, starting with Baden-Württemberg and finishing with Thüringen. Most were contacted by fax, some by post, a few by phone. By no means all replied but we're confident that the vast majority of entries are accurate. Earlier entries are naturally more likely to be out of date than those towards the rear of the book. At the current rate, assuming the Guide to have been 100 per cent accurate when it went to press (which, sadly, is almost impossible), five breweries will have opened and five will have closed before it appears in print. Please bear this in mind when visiting Germany. We will attempt to keep you up to date at www.german-breweries.com.

A FEW USELESS FACTS

Well, we say facts. A few educated guesses is probably more accurate...

The oldest brewery – Weihenstephan, Freising (1040)

The youngest brewery – Stiftscheuer, Kirchheim unter Teck (Easter 2006)

The largest brewery – Krombacher, Krombach (we think – 5,000,000hl)

The smallest brewery – Weizenbierglas-museum, Nürnberg (5hl)

The highest brewery – Rothaus, Rothaus (1000m)

The lowest brewery – Klüvers, Neustadt in Holstein (2m)

Baden-Württemberg

THIS BUNDESLAND in the south-west was created in 1952 when Baden, Hohenzollern and Württemberg were combined to form one large state. Largely forested and lacking much of the heavy industry found in other parts of the country, Baden-Württemberg is one of Germany's most popular tourist destinations. Among the attractions are the Black Forest (Schwarzwald), Lake Constance (Bodensee) and the up-market spa town of Baden-Baden. There are many well-preserved medieval towns, Schwäbisch Hall, Tübingen and Heidelberg boasting more than their fair share of half-timbered buildings. Two of Europe's great rivers flow through the state – the Danube (Donau) has its source in the palace grounds at Donaueschingen, and the Rhine (Rhein) marks the border with France and Switzerland.

Baden-Württemberg has been at the forefront of the brewpub revolution, around half of the 169 breweries in the state having been founded in the last 20 years. There are also many long-established brewers as well as some very large producers, although few are well known ouside Germany.

Transport: www.bahn.co.uk
A regional railway ticket covering the state costs €17 for one person and €25 for two to five people. Valid Mon–Fri 09.00–03.00 the following day and all day at the weekend, it covers many private lines and municipal bus, tram and underground services but not express trains (IR, IC, ICE, etc.).

Left: Young woman in traditional attire, Black Forest Germany.

AALEN   1

Aalener Löwenbrauerei

Aalener Löwenbrauerei Gebr. Barth KG
Galgenbergstraße 8–10, 73431 Aalen
T 07361 325 97   **F** 07361 325 77
www.bestesbier.de
Owners: the Barth family   Founded: 1668
Output: 4,500hl
REGULAR BEERS:
Aalener Löwenpils (4.5%)
Aalener Zwickelpils (4.5%)
Aalener Spezial (5.3%)
SEASONAL BEERS:
Aalener Märzen
Aalener Eberhards-Bock

Three of Aalen's four breweries are huddled near each other behind the station. Aalener Löwenbrauerei is the only one with a direct tap. (Not to be confused with Löwenbrauerei Wasseralfingen.)

🍺 **Löwenbräukeller**
Galgenbergstraße 8, 73431 Aalen
T 07361 325 90   **F** 07361 35 01 04
Closed Thu; Fri–Wed 11.00–14.00 & from 17.00
DB Aalen 450m

Grünbaum

Grünbaum-Brauerei Christian Schmid e.K.
Ziegelstraße 9–17, 73431 Aalen
T 07361 323 30   **F** 07361 356 02
Owner: Christian Schmid   Founded: 1686
Output: 2,500hl
REGULAR BEERS:
Grünbaum Pils (4.7%)
Grünbaum Hefe-Pils (4.7%)
Grünbaum Weizen Hell (4.7%)
Grünbaum Weizen Dunkel (4.7%)
Grünbaum Export (5%)

The small Bräustüble is opposite a church on a pleasant street at the edge of the town centre. Wilhelmshöhe is a pub with a large beer garden on the southern side of town.

Grünbaum Bräustüble

An der Stadtkirche 3, 73430 Aalen
T 07361 624 06
Mon–Sat 11.00–14.00 & 17.00–24.00,
Sun 12.00–14.00 & 17.00–24.00
[DB] Aalen 600m

Wilhelmshöhe

Stuttgarter Straße 55, 73430 Aalen
T 07361 648 15
Daily from 18.00
[DB] Aalen 1km

Köpf

Köpf Brauerei GmbH & Co.
Hirschbachstraße 6, 73431 Aalen
T 07361 930 60   **F** 07361 93 06 70
www.kellerberg-biere.de
Owner: Ursula Schepp   Founded: 1680
Output: 40,000hl
REGULAR BEERS:
Kellerberg Lager
Kellerberg Premium Pils
Kellerberg Hefeweizen
Kellerberg Hefeweizen Dunkel
Kellerberg Kristallweizen
Kellerberg Privat
SEASONAL BEER:
Kellerberg Schwarzer Bock
FOR RÖTTER, GEROLFINGEN:
Gerolfinger Rötter Privat

The former Brauerei zum Ochsen. The tap, tucked away down a lane in the old town, was the original site of the brewery.

Roter Ochse

Radgasse 9, 73430 Aalen
T 07361 625 17   **F** 07361 694 13
Closed Sun; Mon–Sat 11.00–14.00 & 17.30–24.00
[DB] Aalen 600m

Löwenbrauerei Wasseralfingen

Löwenbrauerei Anton Ebert GmbH & Co. KG
Wilhelmstraße 162, 73433 Aalen-Wasseralfingen
T 07361 572 00   **F** 07361 57 20 57
www.wasseralfinger.de
Founded: 1864   Output: 60,000hl

REGULAR BEERS:
Wasseralfinger Pils (4.8%)
Wasseralfinger Spezial (5.2%)
SEASONAL BEERS:
Wasseralfinger Festbier, Wasseralfinger Bock

On the main road, half-way between Aalen and Wasseralfingen stations, stands the second of Aalen's lion breweries. Wasseralfingen was a separate town but is now a suburb of Aalen.

Löwenbräustüble

Wilhelmstraße 162, 73433 Aalen-Wasseralfingen
T 07361 618 68
Closed Sat; Sun–Fri from 10.00
[DB] Aalen 1.2km, Wasseralfingen 1.2km

ALPIRSBACH   2

Alpirsbacher Klosterbräu

Alpirsbacher Klosterbräu Glauner GmbH & Co KG
Marktplatz 1, 72275 Alpirsbach
T 07444 670   **F** 07444 15 10
www.alpirsbacher.de
Owner: Carl W. Glauner   Founded: 1880
Output: 225,000hl   Availability: c. 2,500 pubs
REGULAR BEERS:
Alpirsbacher Klosterbräu Pils (4.9%)
Alpirsbacher Klosterbräu Schwarzes Pils (4.9%)
Alpirsbacher Klosterbräu Kleiner Mönch (5.2%)
Alpirsbacher Klosterbräu Naturtrüb (5.2%)
Alpirsbacher Klosterbräu Spezial (5.2%)
Alpirsbacher Klosterbräu Weizen-Hell (5.2%)
Alpirsbacher Klosterbräu Weizen-Dunkel (5.2%)
Alpirsbacher Klosterbräu Kristallweizen (5.2%)
SEASONAL BEERS:
Alpirsbacher Maximilian Ritter Urtyp (5.2%),
Alpirsbacher Kloster Weihnachtsbier (5.6%),
Alpirsbacher Klosterbräu Martini-Bock (7%)

Large brewery and museum. The beers are widely available throughout the Black Forest. The tap housed the original brewery.

Löwen-Post

Marktplatz 12, 72275 Alpirsbach
T 07444 955 95   **F** 07444 95 59 44
Apr–Sep: Tue 11.00–14.30, Wed–Mon 11.00–24.00
Oct–Mar: closed Tue; Sat & Sun 10.00–23.30,
Mon & Wed–Fri 11.00–14.30 & 17.00–23.30;
food 11.30–14.00 & 18.00–21.30; rooms available
[DB] Alpirsbach 250m

BAD RAPPENAU 3

Häffner

Häffner Bräu GmbH
Salinenstraße 24, 74906 Bad Rappenau
T 07264 80 50 **F** 07264 80 51 19
www.haeffner-braeu.de
Owners: Hannelore & Willi Häffner
Founded: 1881 Output: 1,500hl
REGULAR BEERS:
Häffner Bräu Kur-Pils (4.5%)
Häffner Bräu Export (4.9%)
Häffner Bräu Schwärzberg Gold (5.1%)
Rabans-Bräu Kellertrüb
SEASONAL BEER:
Häffner Bräu Weihnachtsbier

Long-established brewpub in a surprisingly
modern-looking building. Annual holiday from
Christmas until late January.

 Häffner-Bräu
Salinenstraße 24, 74906 Bad Rappenau
Closed Fri; Sat–Thu 09.30–23.00; rooms
available
DB Bad Rappenau 500m

BAD SCHUSSENRIED 4

Schussenrieder

Brauerei Ott GmbH & Co. KG
Wilhelm-Schussen-Straße 12,
88427 Bad Schussenried
T 07583 40 40 **F** 07583 404 10
www.schussenrieder.de
Owner: Jürgen Josef Ott Founded: 1834
Output: 95,000hl Availability: c. 650 pubs
REGULAR BEERS:
Schussenrieder Leichte Weisse (2.7%)
Schussenrieder Urtyp Lager (4.7%)
Schussenrieder Naturtrüb Original No. 1 (4.7%)
Schussenrieder Pils (4.9%)
Schussenrieder Bergkristall (4.9%)
Schussenrieder Vollmond-Bier (5%)
Schussenrieder Weisse (5.1%)
Schussenrieder Schwarze Weisse (5.1%)
Schussenrieder Schwarzbier (5.3%)
Schussenrieder Original Spezial (5.3%)
SEASONAL BEER:
Schussenrieder Josefsbock (7.2%)

Family-owned brewery with its own *Bierkrug*
museum (Tue–Sun 10.00–17.00). The brewery
tap has a large beer garden.

 Schussenrieder Erlebnisbrauerei
Wilhelm-Schussen-Straße 12,
88427 Bad Schussenried
T 07583 404 11 **F** 07583 404 12
Closed Mon; Tue–Sun from 10.00; rooms
available
DB Bad Schussenried 1.5km

BAD WALDSEE 5

Steinacher Hausbräu

Steinacherstraße 135, 88339 Bad Waldsee
T/F 07524 99 67 54
Owner: Rainer Heckenberger Founded: 2004
Output: 300hl Availability: 2 pubs
REGULAR BEER:
Steinacher Hausbräu Halbe Märzen (5%)
SEASONAL BEERS:
Steinacher Hausbräu Hefe Weißbier (5%),
Steinacher Hausbräu Dunkles Export (5%)

Small brewery in the eastern suburb of
Steinach. The Mühlbergstüble is around the
corner. Bus No. 30 runs from the station.

 Mühlbergstüble
Reutestraße 102, 88339 Bad Waldsee
T 07524 62 77
Closed Wed; Thu & Fri 10.00–24.00,
Sat 10.00–22.00, Sun–Tue 10.00–24.00
DB Bad Waldsee 1.4km

BAISINGEN (Rottenburg) 6

Baisinger Löwenbrauerei

Baisinger Löwenbrauerei Teufel GmbH
Ergenzinger Straße 13,
72108 Rottenburg-Baisingen
T 07457 943 00 **F** 07457 94 30 30
www.baisinger.de
Owners: the Teufel family Founded: 1775
Output: 30,000hl
REGULAR BEERS:
Baisinger Leichte
Baisinger Luxus Pils (4.8%)
Baisinger Keller-Teufel
Baisinger Spezial (5.2%)

Baisinger Teufels Weisse-Hell (5.2%)
Baisinger Teufels Weisse-Dunkel (5.2%)
Baisinger Teufels Weisse-Kristall (5.2%)
SEASONAL BEERS:
Baisinger Weihnachtsbier,
Baisinger Teufelsbock (7%)

Owned by the Teufel family since it was founded and now in the hands of the ninth generation. There is a limited bus service on several routes from both Ergenzingen and Eutingen.

Baisinger Braustuben
Ergenzinger Str. 17, 72108 Rottenburg-Baisingen
T 07457 88 48
Closed Thu; Fri–Wed 10.00–24.00
DB Ergenzingen 3km, Eutingen 3km

BALLENBERG (Ravenstein) 7

Spall

Brauerei Albert Spall
Georg-Metzler-Straße 21,
74747 Ravenstein-Ballenberg
T 06297 219 **E** brauerei-spall@arcor.de
Owner: Jürgen Spall   Founded: 1883
Output: 5,000hl
REGULAR BEERS:
Spall Pils
Spall Kellerpils
SEASONAL BEER:
Spall Weihnachtsbock

Small brewery in northern Baden-Württemberg, supplying Zum Ochsen and a few other outlets. Bus No. 844 from Osterburken station.

Zum Ochsen
Georg-Metzler-Straße 21,
74747 Ravenstein-Ballenberg
Closed Mon; Tue–Thu from 16.00,
Fri–Sun from 10.00
DB Osterburken 11km

BERG (Ehingen) 8

Berg

Berg Brauerei Ulrich Zimmermann GmbH & Co. KG
Brauhausstraße 2, 89584 Ehingen-Berg
T 07391 771 70   **F** 07391 77 17 50
www.bergbier.de

Owner: Uli Zimmerman   Founded: 1466
Output: 31,000hl Availability: c. 100 pubs
REGULAR BEERS:
Berg Leichtes Hefeweizen (2.7%)
Berg Braumeister Pils (4.5%)
Berg Original (4.8%)
Berg Kristallweizen (4.8%)
Berg Ulrichsbier (5%)
Berg Dunkles Hefeweizen (5%)
Berg Hefe-Weizen (5.1%)
SEASONAL BEERS:
Berg Schläfleshimmel (5.6%),
Berg Weihnachtsbier (5.6%),
Berg Märzen (6.1%),
Berg 23.04 Das Jahrgangsbier (6.5%),
Berg Sankt Ulrichs-Bock (7.1%).

Often listed as based in Ehingen, 3km to the north, the Berg brewery has been in the hands of the Zimmermann family since 1757.

Bergbier Brauereiwirtschaft
Graf-Konrad-Straße 21, 89584 Ehingen-Berg
T 07391 63 09   **F** 07391 75 21 99
Closed Tue; Wed–Mon 12.00–14.00 & from 17.00
DB Ehingen (Donau) 3km

BERG (Kressbronn) 9

Max & Moritz

Gasthaus-Brauerei Max & Moritz GmbH
Weinbichl 6, 88079 Kressbronn-Berg
T 07543 65 08   **F** 07543 57 42
www.maxmoritz-bier.de
Founded: 1994   Output: 1,000hl
REGULAR BEERS:
Max & Moritz Kellerpils
Max & Moritz Hefeweizen
Max & Moritz Spezial
SEASONAL BEERS:
Max & Moritz Nikolausbock,
Max & Moritz Maibock,
Max & Moritz Maximator

Modern brewpub to the north of Kressbronn with scenic views of Lake Constance and the Swiss alps. We don't think there are any buses to the pub.

Max & Moritz
Weinbichl 6, 88079 Kressbronn-Berg
Daily 11.00–24.00
DB Kressbronn 2.5km

BERNHAUSEN (Filderstadt) 10

Schwanen-Bräu

Bernhauser Hauptstraße 36,
70794 Filderstadt-Bernhausen
T 0711 70 69 54   F 0711 70 51 56
www.schwanen-braeu.de
Owner: Rene Wiedenhöfer   Founded: 1987
Output: 1,500hl
REGULAR BEERS:
Schwanen-Bräu Pils-Naturtrüb
Schwanen-Bräu Weißbier
SEASONAL BEERS:
Schwanen-Bräu Dunkles Pils,
Schwanen-Bräu Dunkles Hefeweizen,
Schwanen-Bräu Herbstbier,
Schwanen-Bräu Maibock

Known as Stadlerbräu until 2004, this brewpub
is in Bernhausen's pedestrianised main street,
close to the new Filderstadt S-Bahn station.

🍺 **Schwanen-Bräu**
Bernhauser Hauptstraße 36,
70794 Filderstadt-Bernhausen
Daily 10.00–24.00
DB Filderstadt 300m

BIBERACH (Heilbronn) 11

Kronenbrauerei Halter

Bonfelder Straße 24–26,
74078 Heilbronn-Biberach
T 07066 72 82   F 07066 44 76
www.kronenbrauerei-halter.de
Owners: Christine & Harald Halter
Founded: 1894   Output: 5,000hl
Availability: c. 50 pubs
REGULAR BEERS:
Kronen-Bräu Pils (4.8%)
Kronen-Bräu Pilsener Naturtrüb (4.8%)
Kronen-Weisse (5.1%)
Kronen-Bräu Export (5.2%)
Kronen-Bräu Export-Dunkel (5.2%)
SEASONAL BEER:
Kronen-Bräu Festbier (5.6%, Oct–Dec)

Small, family-run brewery near Heilbronn.
From Heilbronn Hbf Biberach can be reached by
bus No. 683, which stops in Bonfelder Straße.

🍺 **Krone**
Bonfelder Straße 23, 74078 Heilbronn-Biberach
T 07066 90 29 74
Closed Mon; Tue–Sun 11.30–24.00
DB Bad Wimpfen 4km, Heilbronn Hbf 10km

BIBERACH (Riß) 12

Grüner Baum

Brauerei Grüner Baum Theodor Schanz OHG
Schulstraße 9/1, 88400 Biberach
T 07351 150 10   F 07351 15 01 44
www.gruener-baum-bc.de
Owners: Theodor Schanz senior & junior
Founded: 1622
Output: 2,500hl   Availability: 10 pubs
REGULAR BEERS:
Grüner Baum Pilsener (4.7%)
Grüner Baum Goldweizen (4.9%)
Grüner Baum Hefe-Weizen Hell (4.9%)
Grüner Baum Hefe-Weizen Dunkel (4.9%)
Grüner Baum Spezial (5.3%)
SEASONAL BEER:
Grüner Baum Festbier (5.5%)

The small brewery is behind the pub, on the
edge of the town centre. It supplies a handful of
other outlets.

🍺 **Grüner Baum**
Schulstraße 5–9, 88400 Biberach
T 07351 80 20 40   F 07351 802 04 44
Daily 11.00–14.30 & 17.30–24.00; rooms
available
DB Biberach 700m

BÖBLINGEN 13

Schönbuch

W. Dinkelaker Schönbuch-Bräu KG
Postplatz 6–8, 71032 Böblingen
T 07031 217 30   F 07031 21 73 15
www.schoenbuchbraeu.de
Owner: Werner Dinkelaker   Founded: 1823
Output: 35,000hl   Availability: 60 pubs
REGULAR BEERS:
Schönbuch Lightlife Leichtes Weizen (3.6%)
Schönbuch Horst Hell (4.8%)
Schönbuch Ur-Edel (4.8%)
Schönbuch Pilsner (4.9%)

Schönbuch Forstmeister Pils (4.9%)
Schönbuch Naturtrüb
Schönbuch Hefeweizen Hell (5.1%)
Schönbuch Hefeweizen Dunkel (5.1%)
Schönbuch Kristallweizen (5.1%)
Schönbuch Polar Weizen (5.1%)
SEASONAL BEERS:
Schönbuch Weihnachtsbier (Christmas),
Schönbuch Bock-Bier (6.8%)

Brewery in the centre of Böblingen. The modern Brauhaus is behind the brewery on Lange Straße, the more traditional Braustuben next door, on Postplatz.

🍺 **Schönbuch-Bräu Brauhaus**
Lange Straße 20, 71032 Böblingen
T 07031 68 13 23
Daily 11.00–24.00
DB Böblingen 1.1km

🍺 **Schönbuch-Bräu Braustuben**
Postplatz 5, 71032 Böblingen
T 07031 22 03 43
Closed Tues; Sun 10.30–13.00,
Mon & Wed–Sat 10.30–13.00 & from 17.00
DB Böblingen 950m

BÖHRINGEN (Römerstein) 14

Hirschbrauerei Schilling

Aglishardter Straße 37,
72587 Römerstein-Böhringen
T 07382 938 80   **F** 07382 93 88 33
www.boehringer-biere.de
Owner: Marianne Spitzer   Founded: c. 1798
Output: 6,000hl   Availability: 20 pubs
REGULAR BEERS:
Römerstein Pils
Römerstein Pilsner
Römerstein Kellerpils
Römerstein Johannes-Dunkel
Römerstein Urtyp
Römerstein Märzen
SEASONAL BEERS:
Römerstein Festbier (6%),
Römerstein Goldner-Hirsch Bockbier (6.5%)

The brewery is on the southern edge of the town, the tap close to the centre. Böhringen is easily reached from Bad Urach by bus No. 7646.

🍺 **Zum Hirsch**
Albstraße 9, 72587 Römerstein-Böhringen

T 07382 939 70   **F** 07382 93 97 93
Closed Mon & Tues; Wed–Sun 11.30–21.00
DB Bad Urach 10km

BRÄUNLINGEN 15

Löwenbrauerei

Bräunlinger Löwenbrauerei Friedrich Kalb KG
Friedhofstraße 2–4, 78199 Bräunlingen
T 0771 611 21   **F** 0771 644 12
Owner: Friedrich Kalb   Founded: 1783
Output: 5,000hl
REGULAR BEERS:
Bräunlinger Löwenbräu Kellerpils (4.9%)
Bräunlinger Löwenbräu Pils (5%)
Bräunlinger Löwenbräu Weisser Leo (5%)
Bräunlinger Löwenbräu Export (5%)

Small brewery on the edge of the Black Forest. A few years ago the railway to the town re-opened, making it much more accessible.

🍺 **Zum Löwen**
Friedhofstraße 4, 78199 Bräunlingen
T 0771 158 85 20
Closed Tue; Sat & Sun 11.15–24.00,
Mon & Wed–Fri 10.00–11.00
DB Bräunlingen Bahnhof 1km

BRETTEN 16

Michaeli Bräu

Melanchtonstraße 68, 75015 Bretten
T 07252 97 34 01   **F** 07252 97 34 02
www.michaelibraeu.de
Owner: Michael Kuhn   Founded: 2000
Availability: 1 pub
REGULAR BEERS:
Michaeli Bräu Pils
Michaeli Bräu Weizen

Street-corner brewpub, not far from the station. Two regular beers plus various seasonals.

🍺 **Zum Hirsch**
Melanchtonstraße 68, 75015 Bretten
Closed Sun; Mon–Fri 16.00–01.00,
Sat 10.00–01.00; rooms available
DB Bretten 300m

BRIELHOF (Hechingen) 17

Domänen Bräu

Brielhof 1, 72379 Hechingen-Brielhof
T 07471 91 06 46   F 07471 91 06 48
www.hofgut-domaene.de
Owner: Thomas Lacher   Founded: 1999
Output: 1,500hl   Availability: 1 pub
REGULAR BEERS:
Domänen-Bräu Keller Pils (3.8%)
Domänen-Bräu Hefeweizen
SEASONAL BEER:
Domänen-Bräu Winter-Starkbier (8.2%)

Half-timbered brewpub just off the B27 outside Hechingen, with an unusually weak session beer. The petting zoo should keep the kids occupied.

🍺 Hofgut Domäne
Brielhof 1, 72379 Hechingen-Brielhof
Closed Mon; Tue–Sun 11.00–01.00
DB Hechingen 3km

BRUCHSAL 18

Wallhall

Brauhaus Wallhall Hotel & Restaurant
Am Kübelmarkt 8, 76646 Bruchsal
T 07251 72 1 30   F 07251 72 13 99
www.brauhaus-wallhall-bruchsal.de
Owner: Christian Hochhaus   Founded: 1995
Output: 1,000hl   Availability: 4 pubs
REGULAR BEERS:
Wallhall Pils (5%)
Wallhall Schwarzbier (5%)
Wallhall Weizen (5%)
SEASONAL BEERS:
Wallhall Dreikorn (4.7%, Feb), **Wallhall Vierkorn**, **Wallhall Märzen** (5.2%, Mar), **Wallhall Rauchbier** (5.2%, Apr), **Wallhall Roggenbier** (5.2%, Aug), **Wallhall Amber** (5.2%, Sep), **Wallhall Oktoberfestbier** (5.2%, Oct), **Wallhall Weihnachtsbier** (5.2%, Nov & Dec), **Wallhall Maibock** (7.5%, May), **Wallhall Winterbock** (7.5%, Jan)

Modern brewpub and hotel in the centre of Bruchsal. The seasonal beers are more adventurous than in most brewpubs.

🍺 Wallhall
Am Kübelmarkt 8, 76646 Bruchsal
Daily 11.00–24.00, rooms available
DB Bruchsal 600m

CRAILSHEIM 19

Engel

Crailsheimer Engel-Bräu G. Fach GmbH & Co.
Haller Straße 29, 74564 Crailsheim
T 07951 919 30   F 07951 91 93 30
www.engelbier.de
Owner: Wilhelm Fach   Founded: 1877
Output: 44,000hl   Availability: 85 pubs
REGULAR BEERS:
Engel Landbier-Hell (4.8%)
Engel Premium (4.9%)
Engel Kellerpils (4.9%)
Engel Export (5.1%)
Engel Gold Original (5.2%)
Engel Kellerbier Hell (5.2%)
Engel Kellerbier Dunkel (5.2%)
Engel Crailsheimer Dunkel (5.2%)
Engel Spezial (5.2%)
Engel Helles Hefe-Weizen (5.5%)
Engel Dunkles Hefe-Weizen (5.5%)
Engel Kristall-Weizen (5.5%)
Engel First Lady (5.9%)
Engel 2000 (6.1%)
Engel Bock Hell (7%)
Engel Bock Dunkel (7%)
SEASONAL BEERS:
Engel Volksfestbier (5.4%), **Weihnachts-Engel** (5.4%), **Oster-Engel** (5.4%), **Engel Frühlingsbock** (7%), **Engel Winterbock** (7%)

This regional brewery, on the opposite side of the railway to the town centre, has a larger than average range of regular beers. They also brew some beer for Pyraser but we're not certain which beers or how much.

🍺 Engelkeller
Haller Straße 29, 74564 Crailsheim
T 07951 225 60
Daily 11.00–24.00; rooms available
DB Crailsheim 500m

DELLMENSINGEN (Erbach) 20

Adlerbrauerei

Adlergasse 2, 89155 Erbach-Dellmensingen
T 07305 93 11 90   F 07305 931 19 59
www.adler-dellmensingen.de
Owner: Alfons Brehm   Founded: 1349
Output: 1,000hl   Availability: 1 pub

REGULAR BEERS:
Dellmensinger Pils (4.7%)
Brehm's Edelbitter (4.8%)
Brehm's Urbier-Hell (4.8%)
Brehm's Haferbier (4.9%)
Dellmensinger Hefeweizen (4.9%)
Brehm's Urbier-Dunkel (5.2%)

One of Germany's older brewpubs. If you wish to try their beers you have to come here. Bus No. 239 runs from Erbach to Dellmensingen on weekdays.

🍎 **Adler**
Adlergasse 2, 89155 Erbach-Dellmensingen
Closed Mon; Tue–Sun 08.00–24.00; rooms
available   DB Erbach (Württemberg) 3km

DIETMANNSWEILER
(Tettnang)   **21**

Schörebräu

Dietmannsweiler 2,
88069 Tettnang-Dietmannsweiler
T 07528 23 17 **F** 07528 25 87 **www.schoere.de**
Owner: Georg Bentele   Founded: 1996
Output: 1,000hl   Availability: 1 pub
REGULAR BEERS:
Schörebräu Lager Dunkel (4.7%)
Schörebräu Lager Hell (5%)
SEASONAL BEER:
Dunkler Schöre-Bock (7.5%, Lent)

One of the few modern yet truly traditional brewpubs. Home-grown hops are used in the beer, and the meat on the menu comes from the owner's farm. Bus No. 7545 from Wangen is the only direct connection to the rail network.

🍎 Schöre
Dietmannsweiler 2,
88069 Tettnang-Dietmannsweiler
Closed Mon; Sat, Sun & hols from 10.00, Tue–Fri
from 16.00 (from 10.00 in summer)
DB Wangen 14km, Friedrichshafen 15km

DISTELHAUSEN
(Tauberbischofsheim)   **22**

Distelhäuser

Distelhäuser Brauerei Ernst Bauer GmbH & Co.
Grünsfelder Straße 3, 97941
Tauberbischofsheim-Distelhausen

T 09341 80 50   **F** 09341 805 27
www.distelhaeuser.de
Owner: Stefan Bauer   Founded: 1876
Output: 208,000hl
REGULAR BEERS:
Distelhäuser Leichtes (2.9%)
Distelhäuser Premium Pils (4.9%)
Distelhäuser Landbier (5.1%)
Distelhäuser Export (5.2%)
Distelhäuser Hefe-Weissbier (5.4%)
Distelhäuser Dunkles Weissbier (5.4%)
Distelhäuser Kristall-Weizenbier (5.4%)
Distelhäuser Märzen (5.4%)
SEASONAL BEERS:
Distelhäuser Festbier (5.4%),
Distelhäuser Winterbock (6.8%)

Large regional brewery whose beers are widely available throughout the area. The brewery tap is a recent addition.

🍎 Brauhaus
Grünsfelder Straße 3, 97941
Tauberbischofsheim-Distelhausen
T 09341 80 58 20
Daily 11.00–22.00
DB Distelhausen 700m

DITZINGEN   **23**

Wichtel

Ditzinger Wichtel Hausbrauerei
Korntaler Straße 4, 71254 Ditzingen
T 07156 51 54   **F** 07156 395 10
www.wichtel.de
Owner: Jens Täuber   Founded: 1989
Output: 1,800hl   Availability: 1 pub
REGULAR BEERS:
Wichtel Pils (SW 12.7%)
Wichtel Dunkles Hefeweizen (SW 12.8%)
SEASONAL BEERS:
Wichtel Märzen (SW 13.8%), **Wichtel
Sommerbier** (SW 15%), **Wichtel Schwarzbier**
(SW 15.2%), **Wichtel Maibock** (SW 16.5%),
Wichtel Winterbock (SW 16.5%)

Brewpub that unusually produces a Hefeweizen Dunkel in preference to the usual pale version. A second branch opened in Stuttgart in 2002.

🍎 Wichtel
Korntaler Straße 4, 71254 Ditzingen
DB Ditzingen 800m
Fri & Sat 11.00–01.00, Sun–Thu 11.00–24.00

DONAUESCHINGEN 24

Fürstenberg

Fürstlich Fürstenbergische Brauerei GmbH & Co.
Postplatz 1–4, 78166 Donaueschingen
T 0771 860 **F** 0771 863 98
www.fuerstenberg.de
Owner: Brau Holding International, München
Founded: 1283
Output: 700,000hl Availability: 6,000 pubs
REGULAR BEERS:
Fürstenberg Light (2.8%)
Fürstenberg Premium Pilsener (4.8%)
Fürstenberg Gold (4.9%)
Fürstenberg Premium Lager (5.1%)
Fürstenberg Export (5.3%)
Fürstenberg Festbier (5.3%)
Fürstenberg Weizen Hefe Hell (5.4%)
Fürstenberg Weizen Hefe Dunkel (5.4%)
Fürstenberg Weizen Kristallklar (5.4%)
SEASONAL BEER:
Fürstenberg Fasnetbier (5.1%).
FOR BÄRENBRAUEREI, SCHWENNINGEN:
Bären Pilsner
FOR RIEGELER, RIEGEL:
Riegeler Felsen-Pils (4.9%),
Riegeler Altbadisch Bock (6.9%)

Owned by the Princes of Fürstenberg from 1283
until 2004 when it came under the control of
Brau Holding International. The beers are widely
available throughout the state and beyond.

📍 Fürstenberg Bräustüble
Postplatz 1–4, 78166 Donaueschingen
T 0771 36 69 **F** 0771 863 98
Closed Wed; Thu–Tue 11.00–24.00
DB Donaueschingen 800m

DUNSTELKINGEN
(Dischingen) 25

Härtsfelder

Härtsfelder Familienbrauerei Hald
Hofener Str.19, 89561 Dischingen-Dunstelkingen
T 07327 922 90 **F** 07327 92 29 29
Owner: Christoph Hald Founded: 1664
Output: 20,000hl Availability: 70 pubs
REGULAR BEERS:
Härtsfelder Helles (4.5%)
Härtsfelder Meister Pils (4.7%)

Härtsfelder Land-Bier (4.7%)
Härtsfelder Öko-Krone Export (5%)
Härtsfelder Gold-Engel (5.2%)
Härtsfelder Klosterbraunbier
Härtsfelder Ursprung Export
Härtsfelder Engel-Weisse
Härtsfelder Land-Weizen
Härtsfelder Engel-Weizen
SEASONAL BEERS:
Härtsfelder Fest-Engel,
Härtsfelder Maximilian's Starkbier,
Härtsfelder Christopherus Doppelbock

Getting to Dunstelkingen and back in the same
day by public transport is a bit of a challenge.
Best combined with an overnight stay, or
driving there.

📍 Härtsfelder
Brunnenstraße 10,
89561 Dischingen-Dunstelkingen
T 07327 92 29 90 **F** 07327 92 29 91
Closed Mon & Tues; Wed–Fri 10.00–14.00 &
17.00–23.00, Sat & Sun 10.00–23.00
DB Heidenheim 25km

DÜRREN (Kißlegg) 26

Edelweissbrauerei

Hofgut Dürren 1, 88353 Kißlegg-Dürren
T 07522 978 80 **F** 07522 97 88 10
www.farny.de
Owner: Oskar Farny Founded: 1833
Output: 100,000hl Availability: c. 500 pubs
REGULAR BEERS:
Farny Hefe-Weizen Leicht (3.2%)
Farny Kristall-Weizen Leicht (3.2%)
Oskar Farny Premium-Pils
Farny Humpis Original
Farny Alte Dürrener Weiße (5.1%)
Farny Hofgutsbier (5.2%)
Farny Kristall-Weizen (5.3%)
Farny Edelweiss (5.3%)
Farny Schambrinus Edel-Weizenbier

Family-owned brewery that specialises in
wheat beers. Bus No. 7550 runs (infrequently)
between Wangen and Kißlegg.

📍 Farny
Hofgut Dürren 1, 88353 Kißlegg-Dürren
T 07522 61 73
Closed Fri; Sat–Thu 11.30–20.00
DB Wangen 7km, Kißlegg 8km

EHINGEN (Donau)   27

Rößle

Brauerei Rößle Friedrich Buckenmaier
Hauptstraße 171, 89584 Ehingen
T 07391 534 65   **F** 07391 75 86 84
Owner: Friedrich Buckenmaier   Founded: 1663
Output: 3,000hl   Availability: 10 pubs
REGULAR BEERS:
Rößle Dunkel-Extra (5%)
Rößle Spezial-Hell (5.2%)
Rößle Edel-Ross (5.2%)
SEASONAL BEER:
Rößle Weihnachtsbock (7%, Christmas)

This small brewery on the edge of the town
centre, in the same family since 1663, supplies
the tap and a few other pubs.

🍺 **Rößle**
Hauptstraße 171, 89584 Ehingen
Daily 09.00–24.00
DB Ehingen (Donau) 700m

Schwanenbrauerei

Herrengasse 7, 89584 Ehingen
T 07391 534 20   **F** 07391 736 45
Owner: Karl Miller   Founded: 1697
Output: 500hl   Availability: 1 pub
REGULAR BEERS:
Schwanenbräu Zwickel
Schwanenbräu Dunkel
Schwanenbräu Export
Schwanenbräu Spezial

Small, family-run brewpub in the centre of town.
The brewery can be seen from inside the pub.

🍺 **Schwanen**
Herrengasse 7, 89584 Ehingen
Closed Sun; Mon–Sat 10.00–14.00 & 17.00–24.00
DB Ehingen (Donau) 400m

Zum Schwert

Viehmarkt 9, 89584 Ehingen
T 07391 12 88   **F** 07391 512 81
Owner: Siegfried Einsiedler   Founded: 1802
Output: 2,500hl
REGULAR BEERS:
Schwert Lager Hell
Schwert Dunkel
Schwert Pils

Schwert Weizen Hell
Schwert Weizen Dunkel
SEASONAL BEER:
Schwert Weizen Bock

Brewery and tap close to the station.
Very reasonably priced rooms.

🍺 **Zum Schwert**
Viehmarkt 9, 89584 Ehingen
Closed Sat; Sun–Fri 07.00–24.00; rooms
available
DB Ehingen (Donau) 300m

ELLWANGEN   28

Rotochsen

Alte Steige 4, 73479 Ellwangen
T 07961 20 39   **F** 07961 555 23
www.roter-ochsen-ellwangen.de
Owner: Hermann Veit   Founded: 1680
REGULAR BEERS:
Rotochsen Leicht
Rotochsen Stiftsherren Pils (4.7%)
Rotochsen Edel-Export
Rotochsen Hefe-Weizen Hell (5.2%)
Rotochsen Hefe-Weizen Dunkel (5.2%)
Rotochsen Kristall-Weizen (5.2%)
SEASONAL BEERS:
**Rotochsen Weihnachtsbier, Rotochsen
Traditionsbock**

The brewery is on the eastern edge of Ellwangen,
the tap and hotel are in the centre just south of
the station.

🍺 **Roter Ochsen**
Schmiedstraße 16, 73479 Ellwangen
T 07961 40 71   **F** 07961 536 13
Closed Mon; Tue–Sat 07.00–24.00,
Sun 07.00–15.00; rooms available
DB Ellwangen 250m

ELZACH   29

Löwenbrauerei

Löwenbrauerei Otto Dold
Neunlindenstraße 6, 79215 Elzach
T 07682 352   **F** 07682 674 53
Owner: Johannes Dold   Founded: 1856
Output: 5,000hl

REGULAR BEERS:
Elzacher Löwenbräu Löwen-Pils
Elzacher Löwenbräu Krausen-Pils
Elzacher Löwenbräu Löwen Export
Elzacher Löwenbräu Der Weiße Löwe

Brewery in the small town of Elzach, on the edge of the Black Forest. The tap is on the main road.

🍺 **Löwen**
Hauptstraße 54, 79215 Elzach
T 07682 92 40 05
Closed Mon; Tue 17.00–24.00,
Wed–Sun 11.00–24.00
[DB] Elzach 400m

EPPINGEN   30

Palmbräu

Palmbräu Zorn Söhne GmbH & Co. KG
Brettener Straße 12, 75031 Eppingen
T 07262 6020   **F** 07262 60250
www.palmbraeu.de
Founded: 1835   Output: 70,000hl
Availability: 500 pubs
REGULAR BEERS:
Palmbräu Kraichgau Pilsner (4.8%)
Palmbräu Rezent Weizen Kristall (4.9%)
Palmbräu Rezent Weizen Hefe-Hell (4.9%)
Palmbräu Unser Bestes Premium Pils (5%)
Palmbräu Export Classic (5.1%)
Palmbräu Rezent Weizen Hefe-Dunkel (5.2%)
SEASONAL BEERS:
Palmbräu Weihnachtsbier (5.2%, Oct–Dec),
Palmbräu Ur-Märzen (5.5%),
Palmbräu Zornickel (7%, Apr & May),
Palmbräu Schwarzer Zornickel (8%, Oct–Apr)

Large brewery near the centre of Eppingen. The tap is close by and easily found from the station.

🍺 **Palmbräuhaus**
Rappenauer Straße 5, 75031 Eppingen
T 07262 84 22
Closed Tues; Wed–Sun 11.30–14.30 &
18.00–24.00, Mon 11.30–14.30
[DB] Eppingen Bf 500m

ERGENZINGEN (Rottenburg)   31

Hirschbrauerei Grammer

Stuttgarter Straße 7,
72108 Rottenburg-Ergenzingen
T 07457 13 58   **F** 07457 50 49
Owner: Wilhelm Grammer
Founded: 1866
Output: 4,000hl
REGULAR BEERS:
Hirsch'le Naturtrüb
Hirschbräu Hell
Hirschbräu Dunkel
Hirsch Weisse-Hell
Hirsch Weisse-Dunkel
Hirsch Weisse-Kristall

Small brewery and pub. Also has a drinks market on Mercedesstraße which is often quoted as the brewery address. Sometimes listed under Rottenburg which is, in fact, 12km away.

🍺 **Hirsch**
Stuttgarter Straße 7,
72108 Rottenburg-Ergenzingen
T 07457 93 09 02
Closed Mon; Tue–Sun 11.00–14.00 & 17.00–02.00;
rooms available
[DB] Ergenzingen 1km

Ochsen

Albrecht-Wirt-Straße 5,
72108 Rottenburg-Ergenzingen
T 07457 12 63   **F** 07457 692 52
Owner: Franz Digeser
Founded: 1824
Output: 2,000hl
REGULAR BEERS:
Ochsenbräu Pilsener
Ochsenbräu Kellerbier
Ochsenbräu Export
SEASONAL BEER:
Ochsenbräu Bock

Like the Hirschbrauerei, often confusingly listed under Rottenburg. No brewery tap. Given its small size, finding the beers may prove a bit of a challenge.
[DB] Ergenzingen 800m

ESSLINGEN (Neckar) 32

Zum Schwanen

Franziskanergasse 3, 73728 Esslingen
T 0711 319 78 30   **F** 0711 319 78 47
www.brauhaus-zum-schwanen.de
Owner: Andreas M. Langheck   Founded: 1987
Output: 250hl   Availability: 1 pub
REGULAR BEER: **Schwanenbräu Naturtrüb** (4.8%)
SEASONAL BEERS: **Schwanenbräu Pilsner** (4.8%),
Schwanenbräu Märzen (4.9%), **Schwanenbräu**
Helles Hefe-Weizen (5.1%), **Schwanenbräu**
Dunkles Bock (6.4%)

Brewpub in the centre of Esslingen. Parts of the
building date back to 1444.

Zum Schwanen
Franziskanergasse 3, 73728 Esslingen
T 0711 35 32 53   **F** 0711 350 84 65
Daily 11.30–14.00 & 18.00–24.00
DB Esslingen (Neckar) 1km

ETTLINGEN 33

Vogel

Vogel Hausbräu GmbH & Co. KG
Rheinstraße 4, 76275 Ettlingen
T 07243 137 39   **F** 07243 385 83
www.vogelbraeu.de
Owner: Rudi Vogel   Founded: 1988
Output: 4,000hl
REGULAR BEER: **Vogelbräu Pils** (5%)
SEASONAL BEERS: **Vogelbräu Sonnenwendbier**
(4.7%, Jun), **Vogelbräu Rauchbier** (4.8%, Feb),
Vogelbräu Altbier (4.8%, Oct), **Vogelbräu**
Schwarzbier (5%, Jan), **Vogelbräu Hefe-Weizen**
Hell (5.1%, Jun), **Vogelbräu Hefe-Weizen Dunkel**
(5.1%, Jul), **Vogelbräu Märzen** (5.3%, Mar),
Vogelbräu Erntebier (5.3%, Sep), **Vogelbräu**
Festbier (5.3%, Oct), **Vogelbräu Nikolaus-**
Festbier (5.3%, Dec), **Vogelbräu Braunbier**
(Feb), **Vogelbräu Geheimbier** (Apr), **Vogelbräu**
Halloweenbier (Oct), **Vogelbräu Winterbier** (5.6%,
Dec), **Vogelbräu Maibock** (6%, May), **Vogelbräu**
Weizen-Doppelbock (6%, Sep), **Vogelbräu**
Porter (6%, Nov), **Vogelbräu Doppelbock** (7.8%,
Mar), **Vogelbräu Vogellennium** (9.2%, Dec)

Brewpub located in an old cinema. Rudi Vogel
has two other brewpubs in Karlsruhe and also
owns Brauhaus Watzke in Dresden.

Vogel
Rheinstraße 4, 76275 Ettlingen
Fri & Sat 10.00–01.00, Sun–Thu 10.00–24.00
DB Ettlingen Stadt 500m, Ettlingen West 1.3km

FLEIN 34

Reiners Rosine

Reiners Rosine Restaurant-Vinothek-Brauerei
Bildstraße 6, 74223 Flein
T 07131 309 09   **F** 07131 203 71 64
www.reiners-rosine.de
Owner: Gerd Reiner   Founded: 1997
Output: 20hl   Availability: 1 pub
REGULAR BEERS:
Reiners Spezial-Bräu (5.4%)
Reiners Hefeweißbier (5.5%)
SEASONAL BEERS:
Reiners Frühjahrsbier (4.6%), **Reiners**
Weihnachtsbier (5.9%), **Reiners Maibock Hell**
(6.9%), **Reiners Dunkler Doppelbock** (7.5%)

Quality restaurant with a tiny brewery in the
cellar. Brews the equivalent of ten pints a day!
Bus No. 61 runs at least half-hourly from
Heilbronn Hbf and takes 20 minutes.

Reiners Rosine
Bildstraße 6, 74223 Flein
Closed Mon & 1st Sat & Sun of month; Sun 12.00–
14.00 & 18.00–22.00, Tue–Sat 18.00–23.30
DB Heilbronn Hbf 5km

FLÖZLINGEN (Zimmern) 35

Hirschbrauerei

Eschachstraße 15, 78658 Zimmern-Flözlingen
T 07403 489   **F** 07403 75 44
www.hirsch-braeu.de
Owner: Rolf Schittenhelm   Founded: 1793
Output: 350hl
REGULAR BEERS:
Flözlinger Hirschbräu Spezial
Flözlinger Hirschbräu Halbdunkel
SEASONAL BEER:
Flözlinger Hirschbräu Weihnachtsbock (6.5%)

Traditional brewpub and distillery east of
Rottweil. Buses stop outside but you may have
to change en route.

Zum Hirsch
Eschachstraße 15, 78658 Zimmern-Flözlingen
Closed Mon & Tue; Sat, Sun & hols from 10.00,
Wed–Fri from 11.00 DB Rottweil 7km

FRAUENALB (Marxzell)   36

König von Preußen

Klosterstraße 10, 76359 Marxzell-Frauenalb
T 07248 16 17   F 07248 41 30
www.koenig-von-preussen.de.vu
Founded: 2004   Output: 200hl
Availability: 1 pub
REGULAR BEERS:
Rathsbräu Pils
Rathsbräu Dunkel
SEASONAL BEERS:
Rathsbräu Maibock, Rathsbräu Eisbock

Smart brewpub in the picturesque village of
Frauenalb. The accommodation looks to be
very good value for money.

König von Preußen
Klosterstraße 10, 76359 Marxzell-Frauenalb
Daily 11.00–22.00; rooms available
DB Frauenalb-Schielberg 300m

FREIBURG (Breisgau)   37

Ganter

Brauerei Ganter GmbH & Co. KG
Schwarzwaldstraße 43, 79117 Freiburg-Wiehre
T 0761 218 50   F 0761 38 21 16
www.ganter.com
Founded: 1852
Output: 250,000hl   Availability: 1,200 pubs
REGULAR BEERS:
Ganter Leichtes Pilsner (2.5%)
Ganter Urtrunk (4.5%)
Ganter Pilsner (4.9%)
Ganter Spezial (5.2%)
Ganter Badisch Weizen-Hell (5.4%)
Ganter Badisch Weizen-Dunkel (5.4%)
Ganter Badisch Weizen-Kristall (5.4%)
SEASONAL BEERS:
Ganter Festbier (5.5%), **Ganter Maibock**
(6.8%), **Ganter Wodan** (7.5%)
OTHER BEER:
Freiburger Pilsener

Large brewery on the eastern edge of Freiburg.
The main brewery tap is in the city centre,
opposite the cathedral. There's a second tap and
beer garden built into the walls of the brewery.

Ganter Brauereiausschank
Münsterplatz 18–20, 79098 Freiburg-Altstadt
T 0761 343 67   F 0761 211 95 82
Daily 10.00–01.00
Tram Bertoldsbrunnen 250m
DB Freiburg Hbf 900m

Ganter Hausbiergarten/Wodanhalle
Leo-Wohleb-Straße 4, 79117 Freiburg-Wiehre
T 0761 707 04 44
Daily 17.00–24.00
Tram No. 1 Ganter Bräu 100m
DB Freiburg Hbf 1.8km

Feierling

Gerberau 46, 79098 Freiburg-Altstadt
T 0761 24 34 80   F 0761 256 88
www.feierling.de
Owner: M. Feierling-Rombach & W. Rombach
Founded: 1989   Availability: 1 pub
REGULAR BEER: **Feierling Inselhopf**
SEASONAL BEERS: **Feierling Dunkel, Feierling**
Insel Weisse Dunkel, Feierling Festmärzen,
Feierling Doppelbock

Brewpub built on the site of the former Insel-
Brauerei Feierling and owned by the same family.

Feierling
Gerberau 46, 79098 Freiburg-Altstadt
Fri & Sat 11.00–01.00, Sun–Thu 11.00–24.00
Tram No. 1 Oberlinden 180m
DB Freiburg Hbf 1km

Kleines Freiburger Brauhaus

Moltkestraße 27, 79098 Freiburg-Altstadt
T 0761 366 11
Owner: Robert Schweigmann   Founded: 1992
Availability: 1 pub
REGULAR BEERS:
Freiburger Helles
Freiburger Roggen

Small brewpub near the main station that –
unusually – brews a rye beer all year round.

Kleines Freiburger Brauhaus
Moltkestraße 27, 79098 Freiburg-Altstadt
Closed Sun; Mon–Sat 17.00–01.00
DB Freiburg Hbf 300m

Martin's-Bräu

Martinsgässle 1, 79098 Freiburg-Altstadt
T 0761 387 00 18   **F** 0761 336 27
www.freiburger-markthalle.de
Founded: 1988   Output: 1,200hl
Availability: 1 pub
REGULAR BEER:
Martins-Bräu Pils

Brewpub near the Martinstor, a medieval tower.
The one regular beer is supplemented by
seasonal brews.

🍴 Martin's-Bräu
Martinsgässle 1, 79098 Freiburg-Altstadt
Daily 11.00–01.00
🚋 Bertoldsbrunnen 150m
🚆 Freiburg Hbf 900m

FREUDENSTADT   38

Turm-Bräu

Freudenstädter Brauhaus am Markt Turm-Bräu
Marktplatz 64, 72250 Freudenstadt
T 07441 90 51 21   **F** 07441 90 51 22
www.turmbraeu.de
Owners: Matthias & Oliver Grohe, Peter Herre
Founded: 1999
Output: 1,600hl   Availability: 1 pub
REGULAR BEERS:
Turm-Bräu Pils (5%)
Turm-Bräu Weizen (5%)

Modern brewpub decorated in rustic style.
Despite the address, it's actually on Stuttgarter
Straße, in the centre of the market square.

🍴 Turm-Bräu
Marktplatz 64, 72250 Freudenstadt
Fri & Sat 10.30–03.00, Sun–Thu 10.30–01.00;
food 11.00–23.00
🚆 Freudenstadt Stadt 400m, Hbf 1.3km

GAGGENAU   39

Christoph-Bräu

Alois-Degler-Straße 3, 76571 Gaggenau
T 07225 703 93   **F** 07225 34 79
www.christophbraeu.de
Owners: Christoph & Michael Werner
Founded: 1995

Output: 1,000hl   Availability: 2 pubs
REGULAR BEER:
Christoph-Bräu Pils (5%)
SEASONAL BEERS:
Christoph-Bräu Rauchbier (5%, Jan),
Christoph-Bräu Schwarzbier (5%, Lent),
Christoph-Bräu Weizen (5%, Jun),
Christoph-Bräu Kastanienbier (5%, Nov),
Christoph-Bräu Holunderblütenbier (Easter),
Christoph-Bräu Maibock (6.5%, May),
Christoph-Bräu Weizenbock (6.5%, Oct),
Christoph-Bräu Nicolator (7.5%, Dec)

On the other side of the river from the town
centre and station. Also has a beer garden in
Bad Rotenfels at the Kurpark.

🍴 Christoph-Bräu
Alois-Degler-Straße 3, 76571 Gaggenau
Sat, Sun & hols 11.00–01.00, Mon–Fri 16.00–
01.00, food 17.00–23.00 (Fri & Sat until 24.00)
🚆 Gaggenau 500m

GAILDORF   40

Häberlen

Brauerei Eugen Häberlen
Karlstraße 66, 74405 Gaildorf
T 07971 62 50   **F** 07971 214 71
Owner: Christina Manske   Founded: 1865
REGULAR BEERS:
Gaildorfer Edel-Pils
Gaildorfer Spezial
Gaildorfer Spezial-Dunkel

Small brewery that is currently without a tap – the
old one next door closed a few years ago. Bus No.
43 runs into town from the main bus station.
🚆 Gaildorf-West 2km

GEISLINGEN (Steige)   41

Adlerbrauerei Götz

Adlerbrauerei Karl Götz GmbH & Co. KG
Stuttgarterstraße 214, 73312 Geislingen
T 07331 30 49 30   **F** 07331 30 49 37
www.adler-brauerei.de
Owner: Karl Götz   Founded: 1672
REGULAR BEERS:
Adler Filstal-Pils
Adler Zwickel Pils

Adler Exquisit
Adler Gutshof Weizen
Adler Bartelsteiner Weisse
Adler Gutshof Weizen Kristall
SEASONAL BEERS:
Adler Oha Bräu, Adler Weihnachtsbier
FOR MASH, STUTTGART:
Mash Silver (4.8%)

Medium-sized brewery in Geislingen-Altenstadt. Much closer to Geislingen-West than the main station.

🍺 Brauereigaststätte
Stuttgarterstraße 214, 73312 Geislingen
T 07331 612 04　**F** 07331 68 06 32
Closed Mon; Tue–Sun 10.00–14.00 & from 17.00
DB Geislingen-West 500m,
Geislingen (Steige) 2km

Kaiser

Kaiser Brauerei W. Kumpf GmbH & Co.
Schubartstraße 24–26,
73312 Geislingen (Steige)
T 07331 937 20　**F** 07331 93 72 48
www.kaiser-brauerei.de
Founded: 1881
REGULAR BEERS:
Kaiser Junker Leicht & Frisch
Kaiser Weizen Leichtes Hefe
Kaiser Keller-Pils
Kaiser Edel-Pils
Kaiser Grüß de Gott Alois
Kaiser Kult
Kaiser Original
Kaiser Schubart-Dunkel
Kaiser Weizen Hefe Natur
Kaiser Weizen Schwarzes Hefe
Kaiser Weizen Kristall Klar
SEASONAL BEERS:
Kaiser Frühlings-Märzen, Kaiser Carnevale
FOR STAUFEN, GÖPPINGEN:
Staufen Edel, Staufen Maientags-Bier

Town-centre brewery that also brews beers for Staufen Bräu of Göppingen.

🍺 Braustüble
Schubartstraße 26, 73312 Geislingen (Steige)
T 07331 414 62
Closed Tue; Wed–Mon 11.00–24.00
DB Geislingen (Steige) 600m

GIENGEN (Brenz)　42

Schlüsselbräu

Schlüsselbräu Privatbrauerei Helmut Bosch
Oggenhauser Straße 34, 89537 Giengen (Brenz)
T 07322 965 70　**F** 07322 96 57 10
www.schluesselbraeu.de
Owner: Helmut Bosch　Founded: 1838
Output: 10,000hl
REGULAR BEERS:
Giengener Leicht (2.9%)
Giengener Kristall-Weizen (4.5%)
Giengener Hefe-Weizen (4.8%)
Giengener Premium Pils (4.9%)
Giengener Spezial (5%)
Giengener Schlüssele Kellerbier (5%)
SEASONAL BEER:
Giengener Festbier (5.3%)

Small brewery with two taps. The Schlüsselkeller is next to the brewery; the Brauerei-Gasthof is in the town centre and was the original home of the brewery. Both offer accommodation.

🍺 Schlüsselkeller
Oggenhauser Straße 34, 89537 Giengen (Brenz)
T 07322 32 43
Sun 11.00–15.00 & from 18.00, Mon from 18.00,
Tue–Sat 11.00–14.00 & from 18.00; rooms available
DB Giengen (Brenz) 1km

🍺 Schlüssel
Marktstraße 68, 89537 Giengen
T 07322 53 34　**F** 07322 93 18 47
Sun 10.00–14.00, Mon 18.00–22.00, Tue–Sat
10.00–14.00 & 18.00–22.00; rooms available
DB Giengen (Brenz) 900m

GRABEN-NEUDORF　43

Oasen-Bräu

Benzstraße 11, 76676 Graben-Neudorf
T 07255 768 99 99　**F** 07255 768 99 98
www.oasenbraeu.com
Founded: 2004
Output: 1,300hl　Availability: 1 pub
REGULAR BEERS:
Oasen-Bräu Pils (4.9%)
Oasen-Bräu Weizen (5.2%)

Large, recently opened brewpub near the station. Currently brews two regular beers.

🍺 Oasen-Bräu
Benzstraße 11, 76676 Graben-Neudorf
Sun & hols 10.00–24.00, Mon–Sat 11.00–24.00
DB Graben-Neudorf 200m

GRUIBINGEN 44

Lammbrauerei Hilsenbeck
Hauptstraße 37, 73344 Gruibingen
T 07335 964 40   **F** 07335 96 44 10
www.lammbrauerei-hilsenbeck.de
Owner: Hans-Dieter Hilsenbeck   Founded: 1728
Output: 6,000hl   Availability: 20 pubs
REGULAR BEERS:
Hilsenbeck's Stiefel Pils (4.8%)
Hilsenbeck's Dorfbräu Export (5.1%)
Hilsenbeck's Brunnenbier Naturtrüb (5.1%)
SEASONAL BEER:
Gruibinger Meister-Bock (7.1%, Dec)

Small brewery that's been owned by the
Hilsenbeck family for over 275 years. The
brewery tap is currently closed. If using public
transport, bus No. 31 from Göppingen offers the
best connection.

🍺 Brauereigaststätte
Hauptstraße 37, 73344 Gruibingen
Currently closed
DB Göppingen 14km

HAILTINGEN (Dürmentingen) 45

Adlerbrauerei
Betzenweiler Straße 15,
88525 Dürmentingen-Hailtingen
T/F 07371 86 58
Owner: Anna Rupf   Founded: 1760
Output: 800hl
REGULAR BEERS:
Adlerbräu Bussen Kindle Pilsner
Adlerbräu Spezialbier

Traditional brewpub. Bus No. 312 runs regularly
between Riedlingen and Biberach Monday to
Friday, but there's no Sunday service.

🍺 Bräuhaus Hailtingen
Betzenweiler Straße 15,
88525 Dürmentingen-Hailtingen
Closed Sat; Sun–Fri 08.00–24.00
DB Riedlingen 5km

HEIDELBERG 46

Heidelberger
Heidelberger Brauerei GmbH
Kurpfalzring 112, 69123 Heidelberg-Pfaffengrund
T 06221 901 40   **F** 06221 90 14 55
www.heidelberger-brauerei.de
Owner: Michael Mack   Founded: 1750
Output: 50,000hl
REGULAR BEERS:
Heidelberger Original Hell (4.7%)
Heidelberger Pils (4.7%)
Heidelberger Hefeweizen-Hell (5%)
Heidelberger Hefeweizen-Dunkel (5%)
Heidelberger Kristallweizen (5%)
Heidelberger Original Dunkel (5.1%)
Heidelberger 1603 Premium Pilsener (5.4%)
Heidelberger Export (5.4%)
SEASONAL BEERS:
Heidelberger Osterbier (5.4%), **Heidelberger
Weihnachtsbier** (5.4%)

Modernised brewery in an industrial part of the
city, known as Heidelberger Schloßquellbrauerei
until 1998. No brewery tap, but the beer is easy
to find in Heidelberg.
Tram No. 2 Kranichweg 300m
DB Heidelberg Hbf 3km

Kulturbrauerei
Kulturbrauerei Heidelberg AG
Leyergasse 6, 69117 Heidelberg-Altstadt
T 06221 50 29 80   **F** 06221 502 98 79
www.heidelberger-kulturbrauerei.de
Owner: Jürgen Merz   Founded: 2000
Output: 1,200hl   Availability: 2 pubs
REGULAR BEERS:
Scheffel's Kräusen (5%)
Scheffel's Kellerbier (5.6%)
SEASONAL BEERS:
Scheffel's Hefeweizen Hell (5.2%), **Scheffel's
Hefeweizen Dunkel** (5.4%), **Scheffel's Porter** (6%),
Scheffel's Weihnachtsbock (6.8%), **Scheffel's
Maibock** (7%), **Scheffel's Weizenbock** (7.2%)

Brewpub and hotel in the old town, between the
castle and the Neckar River. The building has
housed a brewery in the past. Other seasonal
beers may be brewed from time to time.

🍺 Kulturbrauerei
Leyergasse 6, 69117 Heidelberg-Altstadt
T 06221 502 98 37   **F** 06221 502 98 79

Daily 11.30–01.00; rooms available
DB Heidelberg-Karlstor 400m

Vetter

Vetter's Alt Heidelberger Brauhaus GmbH
Steingasse 9, 69117 Heidelberg-Altstadt
T 06221 16 58 50   **F** 06221 16 58 57
www.brauhaus-vetter.de
Owner: Klaus Peter Vetter   Founded: 1987
Output: 1,800hl   Availability: 1 pub
REGULAR BEERS:
Vetter Helles (4.5%)
Vetter 33 (11.5%)
SEASONAL BEERS:
Vetter Dunkel (4.5%), **Vetter Weizen-Dunkel**
(4.5%), **Vetter Märzen** (5.2%), **Vetter Maibock**
(6.2%), **Vetter Weihnachtsbock** (6.2%)

This brewpub made it into the *Guinness Book of
Records* – Vetter 33 was once recognised as the
strongest beer in the world! Vetter's second
brewpub in Heidelberg-Neuenheim shut in 2005.

🍺 **Alt-Heidelberger Brauhaus**
Steingasse 9, 69117 Heidelberg-Altstadt
Fri & Sat 11.30–02.00, Sun–Thu 11.30–24.00
(may not open until 16.30 on winter weekdays)
DB Heidelberg-Karlstor 700m

HEILBRONN   47

Barfüßer

Barfüßer Das Kleine Brauhaus GmbH
Allee 35, 74072 Heilbronn
T 07131 96 34 41   **F** 07131 96 35 74
www.barfuesser-brauhaus.de
Founded: 1995
Output: 1,500hl   Availability: 1 pub
REGULAR BEERS:
Barfüßer Blonde (4.9%)
Barfüßer Schwarze (4.9%)
Barfüßer Weiße (4.9%)

One of a chain of four brewpubs (the others are
in Neu-Ulm, Nürnberg & Ulm). If you come from
Karlsruhe by S-Bahn, stay on the tram/train and
get off at Heilbronn-Harmonie.

🍺 **Barfüßer**
Allee 35, 74072 Heilbronn
Sat 10.00–01.00, Sun–Fri 11.00–01.00
Tram S4 Heilbronn-Harmonie 200m
DB Heilbronn Hbf 1.2km

HERBSTHAUSEN
(Bad Mergentheim)   48

Herbsthäuser

Herbsthäuser Brauerei Wunderlich KG
Alte Kaiserstraße 28, 97980 Bad Mergentheim-
Herbsthausen
T 07932 910 00   **F** 07932 91 00 80
www.herbsthaeuser.de
Owner: Klaus Wunderlich   Founded: 1581
Output: 50,000hl
REGULAR BEERS:
Herbsthäuser Leichtes (2.9%)
Herbsthäuser Lager (4.6%)
Herbsthäuser Edel-Pils (4.9%)
Herbsthäuser Hefe-Weizen Hell (5.2%)
Herbsthäuser Hefe-Weizen Dunkel (5.2%)
Herbsthäuser Kristall-Weizen (5.2%)
Herbsthäuser Alt-Fränkisch (5.5%)
Herbsthäuser Gold-Märzen (5.5%)
SEASONAL BEERS:
Herbsthäuser Weihnachtsbier (5.8%),
Herbsthäuser Heller Bock (6.8%),
Herbsthäuser Schwarzer Schwan (6.8%)

Large village brewery. Bus No. 955 runs from
Bad Mergentheim station to Herbsthausen.

🍺 **Herbsthäuser**
Alte Kaiserstraße 28,
97980 Bad Mergentheim-Herbsthausen
T 07932 286   **F** 07932 75 72
Closed Tue; Wed–Fri & Mon 11.00–14.00 &
17.00–23.00, Sat & Sun 11.00–23.00
DB Bad Mergentheim 12km

HERRENZIMMERN (Bösingen) 49

Sonne

Bösingerstraße 1, 78662 Bösingen-Herrenzimmern
T 07404 24 44   **F** 07404 914 21 34
E familie.mauch@t-online.de   Founded: 2002
REGULAR BEERS:
Sonne Spezial
Sonne Weizen

The Sun started brewing again in 2002, 97 years
after the original brewery had closed. Bus No. 20
runs from Rottweil, Monday to Saturday.

🍺 **Sonne**
Bösingerstraße 1, 78662 Bösingen-Herrenzimmern

Closed Mon; Tue & Wed from 16.30, Thu from 14.00, Fri & Sat from 15.00, Sun from 09.30
DB Rottweil 7km

HEUBACH 50

Heubacher

Hirschbrauerei Heubach L. Mayer
Hauptstraße 99, 73540 Heubach
T 07173 180 00   F 07173 18 00 29
www.heubacher.de
Owners: Doris Caliz & Gabriele Mayer
Founded: 1725   Output: 60,000hl
REGULAR BEERS:
Heubacher Hopfen Leicht
Heubacher Albfels Pilsener (4.5%)
Heubacher Hefe-Weißbier (4.7%)
Heubacher Dunkle Weiße (4.7%)
Heubacher Weizen (4.7%)
Heubacher Uralb-Spezial (4.8%)
Heubacher Altes Sudhaus Dunkel

Another brewery with two taps, and this time they're next door to each other. Bus No. 267 from Böbingen is the quickest option, but bus No. 1 from Schwäbisch Gmünd has a more frequent service.

🍺 **Altes Sudhaus**
Hauptstraße 86a, 73540 Heubach
T 07173 57 22
Fri 12.00–01.00, Sat & Sun 16.00–01.00,
Mon–Thu 11.30–13.30 & 17.00–01.00
DB Böbingen 4km

🍺 **Goldener Hirsch**
Hauptstraße 86, 73540 Heubach
T 07173 87 03   F 07173 92 01 52
Closed Mon; Tue–Sun 11.00–14.00 &
17.00–22.00
DB Böbingen 4km

HOCHDORF (Nagold) 51

Hochdorfer Kronenbrauerei

Hochdorfer Kronenbrauerei Otto Haizmann KG
Rottweiler Straße 16–20, 72202 Nagold-Hochdorf
T 07459 929 20   F 07459 92 92 99
www.hochdorfer.de
Owner: Eberhard Haizmann   Founded: 1654
Output: 75,000hl   Availability: c. 300 pubs

REGULAR BEERS:
Hochdorfer Hopfen-Leicht (2.7%)
Hochdorfer s'kleine Weizen Hefe Hell (3.7%)
Hochdorfer Pils-Krone (4.7%)
Hochdorfer Pilsener (4.7%)
Hochdorfer Gold (5.1%)
Hochdorfer Weizen Hefe Hell (5.1%)
Hochdorfer Weizen Hefe Dunkel (5.1%)
Hochdorfer Weizen Kristall (5.1%)
Hochdorfer Kult Bier
SEASONAL BEERS:
Hochdorfer Fasnets-Fläschle, Hochdorfer Festbier
(Oct–Dec), **Hochdorfer Maibock** (7%, Mar–Jun),
Hochdorfer Barbara-Bock (7.5%, Oct–Feb)

Reasonably large brewery on the edge of the Black Forest. The tap is in the centre of the village, the brewery on the road to the station.

🍺 **Krone**
Böblinger Straße 1, 72202 Nagold-Hochdorf
T 07459 933 00
Closed Mon; Tue–Sat 11.30–14.00 & 16.30–24.00,
Sun 10.30–24.00; rooms available
DB Hochdorf (bei Horb) 1.6km

HOCKENHEIM 52

Zum Stadtpark

Parkstraße 1b, 68766 Hockenheim
T 06205 28 36 88   F 06205 28 36 89
www.brauereizumstadtpark.de
Founded: 14.12.2002
REGULAR BEER:
Stadtparkbräu Helles (3.8%)
SEASONAL BEERS:
Stadtparkbräu Märzen (4.5%, Feb & Oct–Nov),
Stadtparkbräu Weizen Dunkel (4.8%, Apr–Jun),
Stadtparkbräu Weizen Hell (4.8%, Jun–Sep),
Stadtparkbräu Hoggemer Original (5%, Jan),
Stadtparkbräu Schwarzbier (5.5%, Mar–Apr),
Stadtparkbräu Weizenbock (6.8%, Sep),
Stadtparkbräu Nachtgrabb (7%, Dec)

Brewpub in the centre of Hockenheim, a mile or so from the famous Grand Prix circuit. There should be a seasonal beer available at all times.

🍺 **Zum Stadtpark**
Parkstraße 1b, 68766 Hockenheim
Fri 16.30–01.00, Sat 11.00–01.00,
Sun & hols 11.00–24.00, Mon–Thu 16.30–24.00
DB Hockenheim 1.2km

HORNBERG 53

Ketterer

Privatbrauerei M. Ketterer GmbH & Co. KG
Frombachstraße 27, 78132 Hornberg
T 07833 939 60   **F** 07833 93 96 20
www.kettererbier.de
Owners: Bärbel & Michael Ketterer
Founded: 1877
REGULAR BEERS:
Ketterer Pils (4.8%)
Ketterer Zwickel-Pils (4.8%)
Ketterer Ur-Weisse (5%)
Ketterer Ur-Weisse Dunkel (5%)
Ketterer Ur-Weisse Kristall (5%)
Ketterer Edel-Export (5.2%)
SEASONAL BEERS:
Ketterer Weihnachtsbier (5.2%),
Ketterer Schützen-Bock (7.5%)

Hornberg is a small town in the middle of the
Black Forest. Ketterer doesn't have a tap, but
you'll find the beer easily enough somewhere in
town.
DB Hornberg 700m

HÖRVELSINGEN (Langenau) 54

Pflugbrauerei Georg Gnann

Wirtsgasse 7, 89129 Langenau-Hörvelsingen
T 07348 62 37   **F** 07348 62 44
Owner: Fritz Gnann   Founded: 1681
Output: 5,000hl
REGULAR BEERS:
Pflug Spezial
Pflug Dunkel
Pflug Pils
Pflug Weizen
SEASONAL BEER:
Pflug Bock

One of the last two breweries in Germany to use
ice as a method of cooling the beer. Buses Nos.
58 from Ulm or 582 from Langenau are the
easiest options for those without a car.

🍺 **Brauereigaststätte**
Wirtsgasse 7, 89129 Langenau-Hörvelsingen
Closed Wed; Thu–Tue from 10.00
DB Langenau (Württemberg) 7km, Ulm Hbf 10km

HUNDERSINGEN
(Herbertingen) 55

Adlerbrauerei

Ortsstraße 1, 88518 Herbertingen-Hundersingen
T 07586 378   **F** 07586 53 60
www.adlerbrauerei.com
Owner: Anton Bischofsberger   Founded: 1885
Output: 800hl
REGULAR BEERS:
Adler Pils (4.8%)
Adler Zwicklbier (4.9%)
Adler Spezial (5.1%)

For those who can't face the walk, bus No. 19
runs – infrequently – from Herbertingen station.
Annual holiday for two weeks after Christmas.

🍺 **Adler**
Ortsstraße 1, 88518 Herbertingen-Hundersingen
Closed Sat; Sun–Fri from 07.00; rooms available
DB Herbertingen 2.3km

ISNY 56

Stolz

Brauerei Stolz Gmbh & Co. KG
Rotenbacher Weg 2, 88316 Isny
T 07562 97 11 30   **F** 07562 97 11 55
www.brauerei-stolz.de
Founded: 1752   Output: 18,000hl
REGULAR BEERS:
Stolz Leichtes Hefe-Weizen (2.8%)
Stolz Blaubändele (4.6%)
Stolz Pils (4.7%)
Stolz Isnyer Hopfen-Perle (4.8%)
Stolz Hefe-Weizen (4.8%)
Stolz Weizenstolz (4.8%)
Stolz Export (5.1%)

Family-run brewery close to the Bavarian border.
Bus No. 50 from Kempten Hbf is the easiest and
quickest service if you are using public transport.

🍺 **Zum Engel**
Bahnhofstraße 36, 88316 Isny
T 07562 24 36
Closed Tue; Wed–Mon 11.00–14.00 &
from 17.00
DB Wangen 18km, Kempten Hbf 28km

KARLSRUHE 57

Badisch Brauhaus

Stephanienstraße 38-40,
76133 Karlsruhe/Innenstadt-West
T 0721 14 47 00   F 0721 14 44 41
www.badisch-brauhaus.de
Owners: the Weber family   Founded: 2000
Availability: 1 pub
REGULAR BEERS:
Badisch Hell (5.2%)
Badisch Dunkel (5.2%)
SEASONAL BEERS:
Badisch Weizen,
Badisch Oktoberfestbier,
Badisch Maibock

Brewpub in a hotel and leisure complex.
Probably the only one in the world where you
can get from one floor to another by slide!

🍺 Badisch Brauhaus
Stephanienstraße 38–40,
76133 Karlsruhe/Innenstadt-West
Daily 11.30–01.00; rooms available
Tram Europaplatz 300m
DB Karlsruhe Hbf 2.2km

Hoepfner

Privatbrauerei Hoepfner GmbH & Co. KG
Haid-und-Neu-Str. 18, 76131 Karlsruhe-Oststadt
T 0721 618 30   F 0721 618 31 17
www.hoepfner.de
Owner: Brau Holding International, München
Founded: 1798   Output: 200,000hl
Availability: c. 1,000 pubs
REGULAR BEERS:
Hoepfner Leicht (2.9%)
Hoepfner Pilsner (4.7%)
Hoepfner Hefe-Weizen (4.9%),
Hoepfner Keller-Weizen (4.9%)
Hoepfner Edel-Weizen (4.9%)
Hoepfner Kräusen (5.1%)
Hoepfner Export (5.2%)
Hoepfner Goldköpfle (5.5%)
Hoepfner Porter (5.8%)
SEASONAL BEERS:
Hoepfner Jubelbier (5.5%, Oct–Feb),
Hoepfner Maibock (6.6%, Apr–May)

Karlsruhe's largest brewery. Came under the
control of Brau Holding International in 2004.

🍺 Hoepfner Burghof
Haid-und-Neu-Str. 18, 76131 Karlsruhe-Oststadt
T 0721 618 34 00   F 0721 618 34 03
Daily from 11.00; rooms available
Tram Nos. 4 & 5 Karl-Wilhelm-Platz 250m
DB Karlsruhe Hbf 3km

Kühler Krug

Wilhelm-Baur-Str. 3a, 76135 Karlsruhe-Weststadt
T 0721 831 64 16   F 0721 831 64 18
www.brauhaus-kuehler-krug.com
Owner: Barbara Fraß   Founded: 2001
Output: 2,000hl   Availability: 1 pub
REGULAR BEERS:
Kühler Krug Zwickel Pils
Kühler Krug Dunkel
Kühler Krug Weizen

Brewpub in a park on the western side of
Karlsruhe. The accommodation offers excellent
value. A seasonal beer is usually available.

🍺 Kühler Krug
Wilhelm-Baur-Str. 3a, 76135 Karlsruhe-Weststadt
Fri & Sat 11.00–01.00, Sun 10.00–23.00,
Mon–Thu 11.00–24.00; rooms available
Tram Kühler Krug 150m
DB Karlsruhe West 700m, Hbf 3km

Moninger

Brauerei Moninger AG, Durmersheimer Straße 59,
76185 Karlsruhe-Grünwinkel
T 0721 570 20   F 0721 570 23 29
www.moninger.de
Founded: 1856   Output: 200,000hl
REGULAR BEERS:
Moninger Zwickel (4.9%)
Moninger Pilsener (4.9%)
Moninger Pilsener Extra Dry (4.9%)
Moninger Hefe-Weizen (5%)
Moninger Dunkles Weizen (5%)
Moninger Kristall-Weizen (5%)
Moninger Alt-Badisch Dunkel
Moninger Urtrübes Helles (5.2%)
Moninger Export (5.2%)
SEASONAL BEERS:
Moninger Maien Festbier (5.6%, May),
Moninger Oktober Festbier (5.6%, Oct),
Moninger Festbier (5.6%, Nov–Dec),
Moninger Bertold Bock (6.7%, Oct–Dec)

Large brewery on the western side of the city.
The brewery tap is alongside on Zeppelinstraße.

🍺 Moninger

Zeppelinstraße 17, 76185 Karlsruhe-Grünwinkel
T 0721 921 22 13
Sat & Sun 10.00–24.00, Mon–Fri 11.00–24.00
🚋 Nos. 2 & S2, Eckenerstraße 500m
DB Karlsruhe West 500m, Hbf 4km

Vogelbräu

Erste Karlsruhe Lokalitätenbrauerei Vogelbräu
Kapellenstr. 50, 76131 Karlsruhe/Innenstadt-Ost
T 0721 37 75 71   **F** 0721 37 09 02
www.vogelbraeu.de
Owner: Rudi Vogel   Founded: 1985
Output: 2,500hl
REGULAR BEER: **Vogelbräu Pils** (5%)
SEASONAL BEERS: **Vogelbräu Sonnenwendbier**
(4.7%, Jun), **Vogelbräu Rauchbier** (4.8%, Feb),
Vogelbräu Altbier (4.8%, Oct), **Vogelbräu
Schwarzbier** (5%, Jan), **Vogelbräu Hefe-Weizen
Hell** (5.1%, Jul), **Vogelbräu Hefe-Weizen Dunkel**
(5.1%, Jul), **Vogelbräu Märzen** (5.3%, Mar),
Vogelbräu Erntebier (5.3%, Sep), **Vogelbräu
Festbier** (5.3%, Oct), **Vogelbräu Nikolaus-Festbier**
(5.3%, Dec), **Vogelbräu Braunbier** (Feb), **Vogelbräu
Geheimbier** (Apr), **Vogelbräu
Halloweenbier** (Oct), **Vogelbräu Winterbier**
(5.6%, Dec), **Vogelbräu Maibock** (6%, May),
Vogelbräu Weizen-Doppelbock (6%, Sep),
Vogelbräu Porter (6%, Nov), **Vogelbräu
Doppelbock** (7.8%, Mar), **Vogelbräu
Vogellennium** (9.2%, Dec)

The original Vogel brewpub. There are now
others in Karlsruhe-Durlach and Ettlingen,
and Rudi Vogel also owns Brauhaus Watzke in
Dresden. All three Vogel pubs brew the same
range of seaonal beers.

🍺 Der Vogelbräu

Kapellenstraße 46–50,
76131 Karlsruhe/Innenstadt-Ost
Daily 10.00–01.00
🚋 Durlacher Tor 250m,
   No. 3 Mendelssohnplatz 300m
DB Karlsruhe Hbf 2.3km

Vogel Hausbräu

Amalienbadstraße 16, 76227 Karlsruhe-Durlach
T 0721 81 96 80   **F** 0721 819 68 22
www.vogelbraeu.de
Owner: Rudi Vogel   Founded: 2004
Output: 2,000hl   Availability: 1 pub

REGULAR BEER: **Vogelbräu Pils** (5%)
SEASONAL BEERS: **Vogelbräu Sonnenwendbier**
(4.7%, Jun), **Vogelbräu Rauchbier** (4.8%, Feb),
Vogelbräu Altbier (4.8%, Oct), **Vogelbräu
Schwarzbier** (5%, Jan), **Vogelbräu Hefe-Weizen
Hell** (5.1%, Jun), **Vogelbräu Hefe-Weizen Dunkel**
(5.1%, Jul), **Vogelbräu Märzen** (5.3%, Mar),
Vogelbräu Erntebier (5.3%, Sep), **Vogelbräu
Festbier** (5.3%, Oct), **Vogelbräu Nikolaus-Festbier**
(5.3%, Dec), **Vogelbräu Braunbier** (Feb), **Vogel-
bräu Geheimbier** (Apr), **Vogelbräu Halloweenbier**
(Oct), **Vogelbräu Winterbier** (5.6%, Dec),
Vogelbräu Maibock (6%, May), **Vogelbräu
Weizen-Doppelbock** (6%, Sep), **Vogelbräu Porter**
(6%, Nov), **Vogelbräu Doppelbock** (7.8%, Mar),
Vogelbräu Vogellennium (9.2%, Dec)

Rudi Vogels latest, located in the Blaue Reiter
Hotel. Like the other two, just one regular beer
and 19 seasonals.

🍺 Vogel Hausbräu

Amalienbadstraße 16, 76227 Karlsruhe-Durlach
Fri & Sat 10.00–01.00, Sun–Thu 10.00–24.00
🚋 Nos. 1 & 8 Friedrichschule 300m
DB Karlsruhe-Durlach 600m

Wolf

Brauerei Max Wolf GmbH
Marienstraße 38, 76137 Karlsruhe-Südstadt
T 0721 93 28 10   **F** 0721 932 81 99
www.wolfbraeu.de
Founded: 1885   Output: 15,000hl
REGULAR BEERS:
Wolf Pils (4.9%)
Wolf Wölfle Pils (4.9%)
Wolf Kräusen Pils (4.9%)
Wolf Wolfsblut (4.9%)
Wolf Schwarz (5%)
Wolf Export (5%)
Wolf Hefe-Weizen (5%)
Wolf Hefeweizen Dunkel (5%)
SEASONAL BEER:
Wolf Indianer Bock (6.7%)

Brewery and pub on the south-western side of the
city. Not suprisingly, wolves feature heavily in the
brewery's advertising – check out the website.

🍺 Wirtshaus Wolfbräu

Werderstraße 51, 76137 Karlsruhe-Südstadt
T 0721 354 57 70
Daily 11.00–01.00
🚋 No. 3 Werderstraße 200m
DB Karlsruhe Hbf 1.3km

KENZINGEN   58

Hirschen

Hirschengasse 4, 79341 Kenzingen
T 07644 238   **F** 07644 91 32 38
Owner: Norbert Weber   Founded: 1649
Output: 1,000hl   Availability: 4 pubs
REGULAR BEERS:
Kenzinger Hirschen Hell
Kenzinger Hirschen Dunkel
Kenzinger Hirschen Pils
SEASONAL BEER:
Kenzinger Hirschen Bockbier

The brewery has been owned by the Weber
family since 1649. The beer is available in the
tap and just three other pubs.

🍺 **Hirschen**
Hauptstraße 7, 79341 Kenzingen
T 07644 61 71
Closed Mon; Tue–Sun 09.00–24.00; rooms
available
DB Kenzingen 1km

KIRCHHEIM unter Teck   59

Stiftsscheuer

Erste Kirchheimer Gasthausbrauerei
Widerholtstraße 6–8, 73230 Kirchheim-Teck
www.stiftsscheuer.de
Founded: 2006
Output: 200hl   Availability: 1 pub
REGULAR BEERS:
Stiftsscheuer Weizen (4.4%)
Stiftsscheuer Pils (4.9%)
SEASONAL BEERS:
Stiftsscheuer Erntebier (4%),
Stiftsscheuer Bock (5.7%)

Small brewpub in the historic centre of Kirchheim
that hadn't opened as we closed for press but
was due to do so before Easter 2006. We don't
have telephone or fax numbers as yet but these
should appear on the website in due course.

🍺 **Stiftsscheuer**
Widerholtstraße 6–8, 73230 Kirchheim-Teck
Closed Wed; Thu–Tue 11.30–14.00 & 17.00–24.00
DB Kirchheim (Teck) 1km

KÖNIGSEGGWALD   60

Königsegger Walderbräu

Hauptstraße 6, 88376 Königseggwald
T 07587 950 40   **F** 07587 95 04 20
www.koenigsegger.de
Founded: 1874
Output: 12,000hl   Availability: 130 pubs
REGULAR BEERS:
Königsegger Lager (4.9%)
Flattermann Lager (4.9%)
Königsegger Edelpils (4.9%)
Walder Dunkel (4.9%)
Königsegger Hefeweizen (5%)
Walderbräu Keller-Pils (5%)
Königsegger Spezial (5.4%)
Walderbräu Naturtrüb Hell (5.5%)
SEASONAL BEERS:
Königsegger Festbier (5.6%, Nov–Dec),
Walder Böckle (6.6%, Nov–Mar)

Small brewery whose beers nevertheless make it
as far away as Stuttgart and Ludwigshafen. The
Golden Lion is their only pub in Königseggwald.
Bus No. 7567 from Bad Saulgau takes you there.

🍺 **Goldener Löwen**
Hauptstraße 18, 88376 Königseggwald
T 07587 15 08   **F** 07587 920 93
Closed Thu; Fri–Wed 11.00–13.30 & 16.00–24.00
DB Bad Saulgau 14km

KONSTANZ   61

Johann Albrecht

Konradigasse 2, 78462 Konstanz-Altstadt
T 07531 250 45   **F** 07531 278 86
www.brauhaus-joh-albrecht.de/kon.html
Founded: 1993
Output: 800hl   Availability: 1 pub
REGULAR BEERS:
Johann Albrecht Messing Hell
Johann Albrecht Kupfer Dunkel
Johann Albrecht Weizen

One of a chain of six brewpubs across the country.
All brew Messing (brass) and Kupfer (copper),
but this is the only one to produce a wheat beer.

🍺 **Johann Albrecht**
Konradigasse 2, 78462 Konstanz-Altstadt
Daily 11.30–01.00
DB Konstanz 700m

Ruppaner

Ruppaner Brauerei Gebrüder Ruppaner
Hoheneggstraße 41–51, 78464 Konstanz-Staad
T 07531 937 30   **F** 07531 93 73 99
www.ruppaner.de
Owners: K. B. Ruppaner & Andrea Scheidtweiler
Founded: 1795   Output: 50,000hl
REGULAR BEERS:
Ruppaner Hell (4.8%)
Ruppaner Edel-Pils (5%)
Ruppaner Schimmele Hefe-Pilsner (5%)
Ruppaner Hefe-Weizen (5.1%)
Ruppaner Hefeweizen-Dunkel (5.1%)
Ruppaner Kristall-Weizen (5.1%)
Ruppaner Spezial-Export (5.2%)

Brewery and tap at the western end of the
Bodensee (Lake Constance). Bus No. 1 runs
from Konstanz station to the Staad–Meersdorf
ferry terminal. The stop before the end may be
your best bet.

🍺 **Brauereiausschank Hohenegg**
Hoheneggstraße 45, 78464 Konstanz-Staad
T 07531 335 30   **F** 07531 319 36
Closed Thu; Fri from 16.00, Sat–Wed from 11.00
DB Konstanz 4km

LAUPHEIM　62

Kronenbrauerei

Kirchberg 5, 88471 Laupheim
T 07392 83 45   **F** 07392 170 03
Owner: Paul Eble   Founded: 1753
REGULAR BEERS:
Laupheimer Kronen Pils
Laupheimer Kronen Dunkel
Laupheimer Kronen Spezial
SEASONAL BEERS:
Laupheimer Kronen Festbier,
Laupheimer Kronen Equator

Small brewery with its own maltings. Owned by
the Eble family since 1874. No brewery tap.
DB Laupheim-Stadt 700m

LEIMEN　63

Bergbrauerei

Bergbrauerei Leimen GmbH & Co. KG
Heltenstraße 2–4, 69181 Leimen

T 06224 970 30   **F** 06224 765 89
www.leimener-bergbraeu.de
Founded: 1862
Output: 25,000hl   Availability: 140 pubs
REGULAR BEERS:
Leimener Pilsener (4.9%)
Leimener Kellermeister (5.1%)
Leimener Export (5.2%)

Street-corner brewery in a 1950s building in
Boris Becker's home town. From St. Ilgen, take
bus No.758. Tram No.3 runs there from Heidelberg.

🍺 **Bergbrauerei**
Nusslocher Straße 1, 69181 Leimen
T 06224 725 19   **F** 06224 725 21
Closed Wed; Thu–Sat & Mon–Tue 17.00–24.00,
Sun & hols 11.00–14.00 & 17.00–24.00
DB St. Ilgen 2.3km, Heidelberg Hbf 7km

LENZKIRCH　64

Rogg

Privatbrauerei Rogg
Bonndorfer Straße 61, 79853 Lenzkirch
T 07653 700   **F** 07653 66 23
www.brauerei-rogg.de
Owners: A. & J. Rogg   Founded: 1846
Output: 6,000hl   Availability: 30 pubs
REGULAR BEERS:
Lenzkircher Pils (4.9%)
Lenzkircher Helles (5%)
Lenzkircher Spezial Dunkel (5%)
Lenzkircher Zwickel (5%)
Lenzkircher Rogg Zipfel (5.1%)
Lenzkircher Hefe-Weizen Hell (5.2%)
Lenzkircher Dunkles Hefe-Weizen (5.2%)

At 850m, this small Black Forest brewery is one
of Germany's most elevated. Take bus No. 7257
from Titisee or No. 7258 from Neustadt.

🍺 **Rogg**
Bonndorfer Straße 61, 79853 Lenzkirch
T 07653 758   Daily from 10.00
DB Titisee 7km, Neustadt (Schwarzwald) 8km

LEONBERG　65

Sacher

Hertichstraße 56, 71229 Leonberg
T 07152 33 95 16

www.brauhaus-sacher.de
Owner: Dominik Sacher   Founded: 02.04.2004
Availability: 8 pubs
REGULAR BEERS:
Sacher Pils (5.1%)
Sacher Weizen (5.5%)

Recently opened brewpub on the southern edge of town. Monthly seasonal beers are brewed in addition to the regulars.

🍴 **Sacher**
Hertichstraße 56, 71229 Leonberg
Closed Sun & hol; Mon–Thu 15.00–23.00,
Fri 13.00–23.00, Sat 11.00–23.00
DB Leonberg 2km

LEOPOLDSHAFEN
(Eggenstein) 66

Andreasbräu

Donauring 71, 76344 Eggenstein-Leopoldshafen
T 07247 96 32 00   F 07247 96 32 02
www.andreasbraeu.de
Owners: Andreas Philip & Andreas Bogner
Founded: 1996   Output: 1,700hl
Availability: 1 pub
REGULAR BEER:
Andreasbräu Pils (5.2%)
SEASONAL BEERS:
Andreasbräu Schwarzbier (5.3%),
Andreasbräu Roggenbier (5.3%),
Andreasbräu Märzen (5.3%),
Andreasbräu Weizen (5.4%),
Andreasbräu Rauchweizen (5.4%),
Andreasbräu Rauchbier (5.5%),
Andreasbräu Festbier (5.5%),
Andreasbräu Weihnachtsbier (5.6%),
Andreasbräu Maibock (7%),
Andreasbräu Doppelbock (7.5%)

Brewpub named after the two owners. The train is actually a tram that runs both on the mainline and through the streets of Karlsruhe.

🍴 **Andreasbräu**
Donauring 71, 76344 Eggenstein-Leopoldshafen
Daily 10.00–24.00
Ⓢ S1 & S11 Viermorgen 500m

LEUTKIRCH (Allgäu) 67

Härle

Brauerei Clemens Härle
Am Hopfengarten 5, 88299 Leutkirch (Allgäu)
T 07561 98 28 22   F 07561 98 28 50
www.haerle.de
Founded: 1897
Output: 27,000hl   Availability: 220 pubs
REGULAR BEERS:
Härle Hopfenleicht (3%)
Härle-Pilsener (4.6%)
Härle Gold (5%)
Härle's Feine Weisse (5.1%)
Härle's Dunkle Weisse (5.1%)
Härle Clemens-Spezial (5.2%)
SEASONAL BEER:
Härle's Böckle (6.2%)

Fairly small regional brewery whose beers are available throughout the Allgäu region.

🍴 **Zum Mohren**
Wangener Straße 1, 88299 Leutkirch (Allgäu)
T 07561 987 50   F 07561 98 57 27
Closed Thu; Fri–Wed 09.00–14.00 & from 18.00; rooms available
DB Leutkirch 650m

LÖRRACH 68

Kulturbrauhaus

Marie-Curie-Straße 9, 79539 Lörrach
T 07621 422 58 90   F 07621 4225 89 20
www.kulturbrauhaus.de
Founded: 2000
REGULAR BEERS:
Kantine Weizen (4.8%)
Kantine Pilsener (5%)
Kantine Dunkles Export (5%)
SEASONAL BEERS:
Kantine Maibock (7%),
Kantine Weihnachtsbock (7%)

Until 2004 this brewpub was known as Kantine Brauhaus Lörrach. The beer names remain unchanged.

🍴 **Kulturbrauhaus**
Marie-Curie-Straße 9, 79539 Lörrach
Thu–Sat 11.00–01.00, Sun–Wed 11.00–24.00
DB Lörrach 500m

Lasser

Brauerei Lasser GmbH
Belchenstraße 5, 79539 Lörrach
T 07621 402 00   **F** 07621 40 20 46
www.lasser.de
Owner: Dorothee Walter   Founded: 1850
Output: 80,000hl   Availability: c. 500 pubs
REGULAR BEERS:
Lasser Premium Pils (5%)
Lasser Dunkel (5.2%)
Lasser Export (5.2%)
Lasser 1850 Jubiläumsbier (5.2%)
SEASONAL BEERS:
Lasser Urbock (6.8%), **Lasser Urtrunk** (6.8%)

Tucked away in the far south-western corner of
Baden-Württemberg, Lasser beers can be found
all over this part of the state. Lasser also brew
Ueli beers for Brauerei Fischerstube in Basel/
Switzerland.

🍺 Lasser
Wallbrunnstraße 31, 79539 Lörrach
T 07621 24 44
Closed Sun; Mon–Sat 10.00–24.00
DB Lörrach 500m

LUDWIGSBURG   69

Rossknecht

Brauerei zum Rossknecht Rothacker GmbH
Reithausplatz 21, 71634 Ludwigsburg
T 07141 90 25 51   **F** 07141 90 25 04
www.rossknecht.net
Owner: Andreas Rothacker   Founded: 1988
Output: 2,000hl   Availability: 4 pubs
REGULAR BEERS:
Rossknecht Urhell (4.9%)
Rossknecht Weizen (4.9%)
SEASONAL BEERS:
**Rossknecht Fachingsbier, Rossknecht Rotbier,
Rossknecht Altböhmisches Schwarzbier,
Rossknecht Rauchbier, Rossknecht Rolhbock**
(6.9%), **Rossknecht Maibock, Rossknecht St.
Martins Bock**

An old pub on the edge of the town centre that
looks as though it's been brewing for centuries,
until you see the gleaming coppers at one end.
There's some dispute over the spelling of
'Rolhbock', but we swear this is how it was
written when we visited.

🍺 Rossknecht
Reithausplatz 21, 71634 Ludwigsburg
Fri & Sat 10.00–01.00, Sun–Thu 10.00–24.00
DB Ludwigsburg 850m

Sudhaus

Sudhaus Brauerei und Gaststätte GmbH
Bahnhofstraße 17, 71638 Ludwigsburg
T 07141 90 17 67   **F** 07141 90 29 61
www.sudhaus-lb.de
Owner: Anne Knecht   Founded: 1989
Availability: 1 pub
REGULAR BEERS:
Sudhaus Hausbräu (4.7%)
Sudhaus Weizen (5.2%)
SEASONAL BEERS:
Sudhaus Rauchbier (autumn), **Sudhaus Festbier,
Sudhaus Weizenbock** (spring & Christmas),
Sudhaus Maibock (May), **Sudhaus Doppelbock**
(spring & autumn)

Brewpub, tucked away behind a bank opposite
the station. Two regular beers and a seasonal
are usually available.

🍺 Sudhaus
Bahnhofstraße 17, 71638 Ludwigsburg
Fri & Sat 11.00–02.00, Sun 10.00–24.00,
Mon–Thu 11.00–01.00
DB Ludwigsburg 50m

MALSCH   70

Alter Bahnhof

Bahnhofstraße 2, 76316 Malsch
T 07246 30 59 44   **F** 07246 30 59 45
www.alterbahnhofmalsch.de
Owner: Hardy Schröder   Founded: 2001
Output: 750hl   Availability: 1 pub
REGULAR BEERS:
Alter Bahnhof Pils (SW 11.5%)
Alter Bahnhof Hell (SW 11.7%)
Alter Bahnhof Weizen (SW 12.5%)
SEASONAL BEERS:
Alter Bahnhof Dunkel (SW 11.7%), **Alter
Bahnhof Alt** (SW 12%), **Alter Bahnhof Rauchbier**
(SW 13.5%), **Alter Bahnhof Märzen** (SW 13.5%),
Alter Bahnhof Oktober Festbier (SW 13.5%),
Alter Bahnhof Maibock (SW 16%), **Alter Bahnhof
Weizenbock** (SW 16%), **Alter Bahnhof
Weihnachtsbock** (SW 17%)

Brewpub in the old station building at Malsch, between Karlsruhe and Rastatt (beware – there are two routes!). You shouldn't have too many problems finding this place from the platform – but will you find the train later on?!

🍺 Alter Bahnhof

Bahnhofstraße 2, 76316 Malsch
Sat 10.00–24.00, Sun 10.00–23.00,
Mon 11.00–23.00, Tue–Fri 11.00–24.00
DB Malsch 0m

MANNHEIM 71

Eichbaum

Eichbaum-Brauereien AG
Käfertaler Straße 170,
68167 Mannheim-Wohlgelegen
T 0621 337 00   F 0621 337 02 11
www.eichbaum.de
Founded: 1679   Owner: Actris AG
Output: 1,800,000hl   Availability: 1,800 pubs
REGULAR BEERS:
Eichbaum Leichter Typ (2.2%)
Eichbaum Ureich Premium Pils (4.8%)
Eichbaum Kellerbier (4.8%)
Eichbaum Pilsener (4.9%)
Eichbaum Schwarzbier (4.9%)
Eichbaum Apostel-Bräu (5%)
Eichbaum Hefe-Weizen (5%)
Eichbaum Dunkles Weizen (5%)
Eichbaum Kristall Weizen (5%)
Eichbaum Export (5.5%)
SEASONAL BEERS:
Eichbaum Festbier (5.8%), **Eichbaum Weihnachtsbier** (5.8%), **Eichbaum Apostulator** (7.6%, winter), **Habereckl Feuerio Tropfen** (9.5%, Lent)

Very large brewery north-east of the city centre, close to the university hospital. The beers are widely available throughout Baden-Württemberg, Rheinland-Pfalz and Hessen. The Actris group is based here.

🍺 Eichbaum Brauhaus

Käfertaler Straße 168,
68167 Mannheim-Wohlgelegen
T 0621 353 85   F 0621 397 41 84
Daily 10.00–24.00
Tram No. 7 Bibienastraße 100m
DB Mannheim Hbf 2.5km

MARBACH 72

Salzscheuer

Mittlere Holdergasse 12, 71672 Marbach
T 07144 88 97 54   F 07144 88 97 55
Owners: Dieter & Kathrein Baader
Founded: 24.06.2000   Output: 25hl
REGULAR BEERS:
Salzscheuer Bräu Lager (4.5%)
Salzscheuer Bräu Gassewoize Weizen (4.5%)

Tiny brewery within the medieval town wall (dating from 1409). The last remnants of the earlier town wall form part of the brewery. There's a tap room which opens by appointment.
DB Marbach (Neckar) 600m

MECKESHEIM 73

Mall

Bierbrauerei Fridolin Mall
Eschelbronnerstraße 23, 74909 Meckesheim
T 06226 93 90 40   F 06226 603 31
Owner: Fridolin Mall   Founded: 1670
REGULAR BEERS:
Mall-Bräu Pils
Mall-Bräu Alt Meckesheimer Dunkel
Mall-Bräu Privat-Export
Mall-Bräu Meckesheimer Ur-Weizen
Mall-Bräu Hugo's Spezial
SEASONAL BEER:
Mall-Bräu Jahrtausend Bock (Nov–Dec)

Small brewery whose beers may prove difficult to find. We believe their only outlet in Meckesheim is the pizzeria below.

🍺 Pizzeria Roma

Friedrichstraße 27, 74909 Meckesheim
T 06226 99 34 30
Daily 10.30–14.00 & 17.00–24.00
DB Meckesheim 500m

MICHELBACH (Wallhausen) 74

Adlerbrauerei Schmetzer

Reubacherstr. 3, 74599 Wallhausen-Michelbach
T 07955 22 34
Owner: Irma Schmetzer   Founded: 1716
Output: 5,000hl

REGULAR BEERS:
Schmetzer Pils
Schmetzer Export
Schmetzer Export-Dunkel
SEASONAL BEER:
Schmetzer Bock

Small village brewery a few hundred metres from the Franconian border. No brewery tap. If you want to reach Michelbach by public transport, bus No. 817 from Rothenburg is the only realistic option.
DB Rot am See 8km, Rothenburg 20km

MÖGGLINGEN 75

Adlerbrauerei

Hauptstraße 22, 73563 Mögglingen
T 07174 306   **F** 07174 67 24
Owner: Hans Dodell   Founded: 1494
Output: 3,000hl
REGULAR BEERS:
Mögglinger Meister Pils
Mögglinger Premium
Mögglinger Spezial
Mögglinger Märzen
SEASONAL BEERS:
Mögglinger Bock Hell, Mögglinger Bock Dunkel

Small brewery and tap on the high street. The beers are available here and in a few other pubs.

🍺 **Reichsadler**
Hauptstraße 22, 73563 Mögglingen
T 07174 53 89   Closed Sat; Sun 10.00–23.00, Mon–Fri 10.00–14.00 & 16.00–23.00
DB Mögglingen (bei Gmünd) 400m

MOOSBEUREN (Oberstadion) 76

Kreuz

Biberacher Straße 39,
89613 Oberstadion-Moosbeuren
T 07357 13 31   **F** 07357 92 13 95
Owner: Rainer Heckenberger   Founded: 2001
REGULAR BEER:
Kreuz Hell

Brewing at the Cross started in 2001, the year before brewing ceased down the road at the Adler. Bus No. 317 runs from Biberach but is of limited use due to the late opening time of the pub.

🍺 **Kreuz**
Biberacher Straße 39,
89613 Oberstadion-Moosbeuren
Closed Mon & Tue; Wed–Sun from 18.00
DB Biberach (Riß) 10km

MOSBACH 77

Mosbacher Brauhaus

Eisenbahnstraße 18, 74821 Mosbach
T 06261 369 69   **F** 06261 385 95
www.mosbacher-brauhaus.de
Owner: Hans-Georg Thielecke   Founded: 1997
Output: 900hl   Availability: 2 pubs
REGULAR BEERS:
Mosbacher Hell (5.2%)
Mosbacher Dunkel (5.2%)
Mosbacher Weizen (5.2%)
SEASONAL BEERS:
Mosbacher Bockbier (6.8%),
Mosbacher Maibock (7.5%),
Mosbacher Weihnachtsbock (7.5%)

Brewpub in a former roasting house close to Mosbach station. The town itself is on the Elz river, close to its confluence with the Neckar.

🍺 **Mosbacher Brauhaus**
Eisenbahnstraße 18, 74821 Mosbach
Daily 11.00–01.00
DB Mosbach (Baden) 200m

MÖSSINGEN 78

Fischer's Brauhaus

Auf der Lehr 30, 72116 Mössingen
T 07473 954 40   **F** 07473 95 44 95
www.brauhaus-moessingen.de
Owner: Heinrich Fischer   Founded: 1882
Availability: 40 pubs
REGULAR BEERS:
Fischer's Heinerle (4.9%)
Fischer's Pilsner (4.9%)
Fischer's Dreifürsten-Pils (4.9%)
Fischer's Kellerbier (5%)
Fischer's Hefeweizen (5.2%)
Fischer's Dunkles Weizen (5.2%)
Fischer's Fischer's Kristallweizen (5.2%)
SEASONAL BEERS:
Fischer's Feschtbier, Fischer's Böckle (5.7%)

Medium-sized brewery that also owns Brauhaus Neckarmüller in Tübingen. Fischer's own the hotel next door to the tap with 30 rooms.

🍺 Zur Krone
Auf der Lehr 32, 72116 Mössingen
T 07473 76 27
Closed Tue; Wed–Mon 12.00–14.00 &
17.00–23.00; rooms available
DB Mössingen Bahnhof 1.5km

NAGOLD 79

Anker

Anker-Brauerei Nagold GmbH
Freudenstädter Straße 14, 72202 Nagold
T 07452 24 31 **F** 07452 699 86
www.anker-brauerei.de
Owners: Eugen & Hans-Martin Walz
Founded: 1880 Output: 5,000hl
REGULAR BEERS:
Nagolder Herren Pils
Nagolder Hefeweizen
Nagolder Kristallweizen
Nagolder Urtyp-Export
SEASONAL BEERS:
Nagolder Osterhäsle (Easter), **Nagolder Weih-nachtsbier** (Christmas), **Nagolder Martinator**

In a wooded valley on the northern edge of the Black Forest, the Anchor is the last brewery in a small town that once boasted seventeen.

🍺 Anker
Freudenstädter Straße 14, 72202 Nagold
T 07452 919 18 88
Sat 11.00–01.00, Sun–Fri 16.00–01.00
DB Nagold 800m

NATTHEIM 80

Nattheimer

Privatbrauerei Gebrüder Schlumberger
Heidenheimer Straße 7, 89564 Nattheim
T 07321 979 80 **F** 07321 729 16
www.nattheimer.de
Owner: Heinz Schlumberger Founded: 1847
Output: 40,000hl Availability: c. 50 pubs
REGULAR BEERS:
Nattheimer Bierchen (3%)
Nattheimer Pilsner (4.8%)

Nattheimer Edel-Pils (4.8%)
Nattheimer Dinkel (5%)
Nattheimer Weißbier Hell (5.2%)
Nattheimer Weißbier Dunkel (5.2%)
Nattheimer Kristallweizen (5.2%)
Nattheimer Schwarzer Ochs (5.3%
Nattheimer Spezial (5.4%)
SEASONAL BEERS:
Nattheimer Festbier (5.6%),
Nattheimer Doppelbock (7.5%)

Brewery that started out as Brauerei zum Ochsen in the present tap but moved to its current location in 1966. Buses Nos. 50 and 68 run from Heidenheim (poor weekend service).

🍺 Zum Ochsen
Hauptstraße 14, 89564 Nattheim
T 07321 79 29
Closed Mon; Tue–Sat from 17.00,
Sun & hols 11.00–14.30 & from 17.00
DB Heidenheim (Brenz) 7km

NECKARSULM 81

Neckarsulmer Brauhaus

Felix-Wankel-Straße 9, 74172 Neckarsulm
T 07132 34 35 11 **F** 07132 34 35 12
www.neckarsulmer-brauhaus.de
Founded: 2001 Availability: 1 pub
REGULAR BEERS:
Neckarsulmer Pils
Neckarsulmer Weizen
Neckarsulmer Dunkles Märzen
SEASONAL BEERS:
Neckarsulmer Bayrisch Hell, Neckarsulmer Roter Flitzer, Neckarsulmer Irish Ale, Neckarsulmer Dunkles Weizen, Neckarsulmer Wintertraum, Neckarsulmer Weihnachtsbier, Neckarsulmer Hopfenbock, Neckarsulmer Maibock

Modern brewpub and hotel on the northern edge of the town centre, opposite the Ballei Leisure Centre.

🍺 Neckarsulmer Brauhaus
Felix-Wankel-Straße 9, 74172 Neckarsulm
Sat 17.00–01.00, Sun–Fri 11.00–24.00; rooms available
DB Neckarsulm 750m

NEULER 82

Ladenburger

Brauerei Ladenburger GmbH
Hauptstraße 16, 73491 Neuler
T 07961 911 40   **F** 07961 91 14 50
www.brauerei-ladenburger.de
Owner: Karl Ladenburger   Founded: 1789
Output: 40,000hl
REGULAR BEERS:
Ladenburger Exclusiv-Pils (4.9%)
Ladenburger Alt-Schwäbisch Dunkel
Ladenburger Premium Export (5.1%)
Ladenburger Hefe Weizen (5.1%)
Ladenburger Hefe Weizen Dunkel (5.1%)
Ladenburger Kristallweizen (5.1%)
SEASONAL BEER:
Ladenburger Winterbock

Known as Adlerbrauerei until 1967. Ladenburger's tap is in Espachweiler, 2km north-west of Neuler. Bus No. 350 runs from Ellwangen to Neuler via Schrezheim and Espachweiler.

🍺 **Seegasthof Espachweiler**
Bussardweg 1, 73479 Ellwangen-Espachweiler
T 07961 77 60   **F** 07961 538 46
Closed Fri; Sat–Thu 11.00–23.00; rooms available
DB Schrezheim 2.5km, Ellwangen 4.5km

NÜRTINGEN 83

Schlachthof

Schlachthof Bräu Gastronomie GmbH
Mühlstraße 15, 72622 Nürtingen
T 07022 93 95 71   **F** 07022 93 95 72
www.schlachthofbraeu.de
Owners: Steffen Reikel, J. & R. Buxbaum
Founded: 1999   Output: 1,000hl
Availability: 1 pub
REGULAR BEERS:
Schlachthof Pilsener (4.9%)
Schlachthof Hefeweizen (5.1%)
SEASONAL BEERS:
Schlachthof Woiza Light (2.7%),
Schlachthof Lager (4.8%),
Schlachthof Dunkel (5.1%),
Schlachthof Festbier (5.5%),
Schlachthof Bock (6.5%)

Brewpub in a former abbatoir just north of the town centre. The interior retains many features from its previous incarnation (sorry!).

🍺 **Schlachthof**
Mühlstraße 15, 72622 Nürtingen
Sun & hols 10.00–24.00, Mon–Sat 11.00–01.00
DB Nürtingen 700m

OBERDORF (Bopfingen) 84

Schwind

Altbachweg 3, 73441 Bopfingen-Oberdorf
T 07362 72 77
Owner: Conrad Schwind   Founded: 1780
Output: 700hl
REGULAR BEERS:
Deutschhof Schwarzes
Deutschhof Export
Deutschhof Weizen
SEASONAL BEER:
Deutschhof Bock

Brewpub in a village on the edge of Bopfingen. The Guide believes the beers are only available from the brewery shop and tap.

🍺 **Zum Deutschen Hof**
Altbachweg 3, 73441 Bopfingen-Oberdorf
Closed Tue; Wed–Mon 08.00–24.00
DB Bopfingen 1.6km

ÖDENWALDSTETTEN (Hohenstein) 85

Speidel's Brauerei'le

Im Dorf 5, 72531 Hohenstein-Ödenwaldstetten
T 07387 989 00   **F** 07387 13 80
www.speidels-brauereile.de   Founded: 2001
REGULAR BEERS:
Speidel's Hell
Speidel's Weißbier

Small brewery, based in Hotel & Gasthof Lamm. Bus No. 7607 runs direct from Reutlingen twice a day Monday to Friday (and once the other way). At other times at least one change is necessary.

🍺 **Lamm**
Im Dorf 5, 72531 Hohenstein-Ödenwaldstetten
Closed Tue; Wed–Mon 11.00–14.00 & from 17.30
DB Reutlingen Hbf 25km

OFFENBURG 86

Kronenbrauerei

Kronenbrauerei Offenburg GmbH
Zeller Straße 46, 77654 Offenburg
T 0781 938 00   **F** 0781 361 42
www.kronen-brauhaus.de
Founded: 1847   Output: 100,000hl
REGULAR BEERS:
Kronen Krönle (2.7%)
Kronen Pilsner (4.7%)
Kronen Exquisit (4.9%)
Kronen Dunkel (5.1%)
Kronen Export (5.4%)
Kronen Wintertraum (5.6%)
FOR JEHLE, BIBERACH (Baden):
Jehle Privatpilsner (4.7%), **Jehle Landbier** (5.1%)
FOR WAGNER, OFFENBURG:
Wagner Pilsener (4.7%), **Wagner Privat** (4.9%),
Wagner Hefe-Weisse (5.2%), **Wagner Dunkle-
Weisse** (5.2%), **Wagner Kristall-Weizen** (5.2%)

Large brewery on the other side of the railway
from the city centre. Jehle beers are only
available on draught.

🍺 **Brandeck**
Zeller Straße 44, 77654 Offenburg
T 0781 303 52
Daily 11.00–14.00 & 17.00–24.00
DB Offenburg Hbf 900m

OGGENHAUSEN
(Heidenheim) 87

Königsbräu Majer

Hauptstraße 1, 89522 Heidenheim-Oggenhausen
T 07321 979 70   **F** 07321 97 97 11
www.koenigsbraeu.de
Owner: the Majer family   Founded: 1827
Output: 50,000hl
REGULAR BEERS:
Königsbräu Leichtes
Königsbräu Leichtes Weißbier
Königsbräu Edel-Pils
Königsbräu Pilsner
Königsbräu Dunkel
Königsbräu Weisse
Königsbräu Weißbier Dunkel
Königsbräu Weizen
Königsbräu Spezial

SEASONAL BEERS:
Königsbräu Festbier, Königsbräu Heller Bock
'KING' BEERS:
King 2000, King Hefe

Oggenhausen is due east of Heidenheim.
Bus No. 68 runs between the two Mon–Sat and
stops outside the brewery.

🍺 **Zum König**
Hauptstraße 6, 89522 Heidenheim-Oggenhausen
T 07321 714 14
Closed Mon; Tue–Sun 11.00–22.00
DB Heidenheim (Brenz) 7km

PFORZHEIM 88

Bayerisches Brauhaus Pforzheim

St-Georgen-Stiege 12, 75175 Pforzheim
T 07231 600 80   **F** 07231 60 08 99
www.brauhaus-pforzheim.de
Owners: the Ruppaner & Scheidtweiler families
Founded: 1889   Output: 30,000hl
REGULAR BEERS:
Brauhaus Goldstadt Premium Leicht (2.2%)
Brauhaus Pforzheim Flößer Hell (4.7%)
Brauhaus Pforzheim Goldstadt Pilsner (4.9%)
Brauhaus Pforzheim Ratskeller Pils (4.9%)
Brauhaus Pforzheim Jubiläums Dunkel (5%)
Brauhaus Pforzheim Goldstadt Export (5%)
Brauhaus Pforzheim Goldstadt Weizen (5.1%)
Brauhaus Pforzheim Goldstadt Hefeweizen (5.1%)
SEASONAL BEER:
Brauhaus Pforzheim St. Georgen Bock (6.3%)

Brewery on a hill out of the town, with its tap in
the centre on the market square. Pforzheim is
know as the 'Golden Town', a fact reflected in the
Goldstadt beer names.

🍺 **Ratskeller**
Marktplatz 1, 75175 Pforzheim
T 07231 10 12 22
Daily 11.00–24.00
DB Pforzheim Hbf 450m

Hopfenschlingel

Hausbrauerei Hopfenschlingel GmbH
Weiherstraße 13, 75173 Pforzheim
T 07231 244 77   **F** 07231 47 16 01
www.hopfenschlingel-bier.de
Owners: Helga & Wolfgang Wühr
Founded: 1988

REGULAR BEER:
Hopfenschlingel Pils

Brewpub just south of the town centre. Only one regular beer but there's usually a seasonal brew on tap. A second Hopfenschlingel opened in Rastatt in 1997.

Hopfenschlingel
Weiherstraße 13, 75173 Pforzheim
Sat from 11.00, Sun from 17.00, Mon–Fri from 15.30 (in summer from 11.00)
DB Pforzheim Hbf 750m

Ketterer

Privatbrauerei Wilhelm Ketterer KG
Jahnstraße 10-22, 75173 Pforzheim
T 07231 921 10   **F** 07231 92 11 29
www.brauerei-ketterer.de
Founded: 1888   Output: 40,000hl
REGULAR BEERS:
Ketterer Pilsener (5.1%)
Ketterer Edel-Pils (5.2%)
Ketterer Gold Privat Export (5.3%)
Ketterer Sebastian Hefe-Weissbier (5.4%)
Ketterer Sebastian Dunkel Hefeweizen (5.4%)
SEASONAL BEERS:
Ketterer Weihnachtsbier (5.4%),
Ketterer Maibock (7.1%),
Ketterer Heller Bock (7.1%),
Ketterer Trumpf Doppelbock Dunkel (7.6%)

Medium-sized brewery one street down from Hopfenschlingel. The brewery tap will shortly celebrate its centenary.

Ketterer's Braustüble
Jahnstraße 10, 75173 Pforzheim
T 07231 217 32
Closed Mon; Tue–Sun 10.00–23.00
DB Pforzheim Hbf 950m

PLANKSTADT   89

Welde-Bräu

Brauereistraße 1, 68723 Plankstadt
T 06202 930 00   **F** 06202 93 00 90
www.welde.de
Founded: 1752   Output: 100,000hl
REGULAR BEERS:
Welde No. 1 Light (2.9%)
Welde No. 1 (4.8%)

Welde Schwarze Wonne (4.8%)
Welde Silber (5%)
Welde Weizen Wonne (5%)
Welde Weizen Lust (5%)
Welde Kristall Weizen (5%)
Welde Jubiläum Ex (5.3%)
SEASONAL BEER:
Welde Kraftprotz

The brewery is on the outskirts of Plankstadt. The tap, in nearby Schwetzingen, was the original home of the brewery. There's also a beer garden that opens on Sundays in summer only.

Weldelust-Garten
Brauereistraße 1, 68723 Plankstadt
T 06202 27 13 33
Closed Oct–Apr; closed Mon–Sat;
Sun in fine weather only
DB Schwetzingen 2.5km

Welde Stammhaus
Mannheimerstraße 2a, 68723 Schwetzingen
T 06202 48 30
Daily 10.00–24.00
DB Schwetzingen 400m

POPPELTAL (Enzklösterle)   90

Poppel-Mühle

Mühleweg 11, 75337 Enzklösterle-Poppeltal
T 07085 78 70   **F** 07085 16 97
www.poppel-muehle.de
Owners: the Wedenig family   Founded: 2003
Output: 200hl   Availability: 2 pubs
REGULAR BEERS:
Poppelbräu Hell (4.8%)
Poppelbräu Dunkel (4.8%)
Poppelbräu Weizen (5.2%)

Small brewery in a country museum. The beers are available in a pub on the site that is only open from May to October. Catch buses Nos. 780 or F17 from either Bad Wildbad or Freudenstadt.

Mühlenschänke
Mühleweg 11, 75337 Enzklösterle-Poppeltal
Closed mid-Oct–Apr.
May–mid-Oct in fine weather: closed Mon & Tue;
Wed–Sun 11.00–18.00
DB Bad Wildbad 17km, Freudenstadt 20km

RASTATT 91

Franz

Brauerei C. Franz GmbH
Rauentaler Straße 4, 76437 Rastatt
T 07222 973 70   **F** 07222 97 37 55
Founded: 1842   Output: 15,000hl
REGULAR BEERS:
Franz Uhl-Pils (4.9%)
Franz Kellerbier
Franz Freiheitsbier Dunkel (5.3%)
Franz Schloss-Favorit-Export (5.3%)
SEASONAL BEERS:
Franz Festbier, Franz Türkenlouis Bock

The brewery is located between the station and town-centre but doesn't have a tap. The beers are, however, widely available in the town.
DB Rastatt 600m

Hofbräuhaus Hatz

Kapellenstraße 36, 76437 Rastatt
T 07222 76 50   **F** 07222 765 10
www.hatz.de
Owner: Dr. Thomas Hatz   Founded: 1863
Output: 100,000hl   Availability: c. 350 pubs
REGULAR BEERS:
Hatz Pils (4.9%)
Hatz Export (5.2%)
Hatz Privat (5.2%)
Hatz Weizen Hefetrüb (5.2%)
Hatz Weizen Dunkel (5.2%)
Hatz Weizen Kristallklar (5.2%)

Large brewery, a couple of hundred metres from Franz. The tap is nearby on the edge of the pedestrianised town centre.

🍺 **Bräustüb'l**
Poststraße 12, 76437 Rastatt
T 07222 78 81 80   **F** 07222 78 81 75
Sun 11.00–23.00, Mon–Sat 11.00–14.00 & 17.00–23 00
DB Rastatt 800m

Hopfenschlingel

Hausbrauerei Hopfenschlingel GmbH
Owners: Helga & Wolfgang Wühr
Militärstraße 2, 76437 Rastatt
T 07222 300 99   **F** 07222 93 81 65
www.hopfenschlingel-bier.de
Founded: 1997

REGULAR BEER:
Hopfenschlingel Pils

Sister brewpub of the Pforzheim Hopfenschlingel. This pub is about a mile south of the centre, close to the main railway line.

🍺 **Hopfenschlingel**
Militärstraße 2, 76437 Rastatt
Sun 11.00–24.00, Mon–Sat 16.00–01.00
DB Rastatt 1.8km

RAVENSBURG 92

Leibinger

Brauerei Max Leibinger GmbH
Friedhofstraße 20-36, 88212 Ravensburg
T 0751 369 90   **F** 0751 36 99 90
www.leibinger.de
Owner: Michael Leibinger   Founded: 1894
Output: 105,000hl   Availability: c. 300 pubs
REGULAR BEERS:
Leibinger Hefe-Weizen Leicht
Leibinger Zwickel
Leibinger Hefe-Weizen (5%)
Leibinger Dunkles Weizen (5%)
Leibinger Kristall Weizen (5%)
Leibinger Edel-Spezial (5.2%)
Leibinger Edel-Pils (5.2%)
Leibinger Max Fünf Komma 2 (5.2%)
Leibinger Schwarzer Veri

On the far end of town centre from the station, this large brewery's tap nestles among the brewery buildings.

🍺 **Leibinger Bräustüble**
Friedhofstraße 26, 88212 Ravensburg
T 0751 36 99 45
Closed Sun; Mon–Sat from 15.00
DB Ravensburg 1.3km

REMMINGSHEIM (Neustetten) 93

Kronenbrauerei Schimpf

Kronenbrauerei Alfred Schimpf GmbH
Hauptstr. 1, 72149 Neustetten-Remmingsheim
T 0472 989 40   **F** 07472 98 94 15
www.brauerei-schimpf.de
Owner: Alfred Schimpf   Founded: 1870
Output: 10,000hl   Availability: 30 pubs

REGULAR BEERS:
Schimpf Krone-Pils (4.8%)
Schimpf Trend
Schimpf Urtrüb
Schimpf Hefeweizen (5%)
Schimpf Hefeweizen Dunkel (5%)
Schimpf Kristallweizen (5%)
Schimpf Spezial (5.2%)
SEASONAL BEERS:
Schimpf Fasnetsbier,
Schimpf Weihnachtsbier,
Schimpf Bockbier (May & Christmas)

The brewery is in the centre of Remmingsheim. Unusually, the tap has moved away from the brewery and is now a few streets along on the southern edge of town. Bus No. 7633 runs from Rottenburg to Ergenzingen Monday to Saturday.

🍺 Zur Krone
Hohenstauferstraße 28,
72149 Neustetten-Remmingsheim
T 07472 248 07
Closed Mon & Wed; Tue & Thu–Sun 10.00–14.00
& from 16.00
DB Rottenburg 5km, Ergenzingen 7km

RIEDBACH (Schrozberg)   94

Franken Bräu

Franken Bräu Riedbach Krauß GmbH
Heuchlinger Weg 4, 74575 Schrozberg-Riedbach
T 07936 261   **F** 07936 786
www.franken-braeu.de
Owner: Dieter Krauß   Founded: 1807
Output: 20,000hl
REGULAR BEERS:
Franken Bräu Unser Leichtes (2.7%)
Franken Bräu Pils (4.7%)
Franken Bräu Pardus Dunkel (5.1%)
Franken Bräu Kellerbier (5.1%)
Franken Bräu Spezial (5.1%)
Franken Bräu Hefeweizen (5.4%)
SEASONAL BEERS:
Franken Bräu Festbier (5.3%, Christmas),
Franken Bräu Heller Bock (7.8%), **Franken Bräu Florinator** (7.8%)

The brewery, its architecture reminiscent of a school, stands at the southern end of the village. The tap is on the main road. Bus No. 104 runs from Schrozberg Monday to Friday only.

🍺 Brauereigaststätte
Kaiserstraße 11, 74575 Schrozberg-Riedbach
T 07936 286
Closed Wed; Thu from 15.00, Fri–Tue from 10.30
DB Schrozberg 5km

RIEGEL   95

Elchbräu

Silbergasse 7, 79359 Riegel
T 0160 9414 44 67   **F** 07642 93 00 27
www.elchbraeu.de.tf
Founded: 2004
REGULAR BEERS:
Elchbräu Pils
Elchbräu Weizen

Elchbräu occupies part of the former Riegeler Brewery (whose two remaining beers are now brewed by Fürstenberger). There's currently no brewery tap but the beers are available for sale Fri 17.30–20.00 and Sat 09.00–16.00.
DB Riegel-Ort 400m, Riegel 2km

RISSTISSEN (Ehingen)   96

Adler

Adler Brauerei und Brennerei Gebhard Föhr
Rißstraße 2, 89584 Ehingen-Rißtissen
T 07392 21 38   **F** 07392 59 70
Owner: Gebhard Fohr   Founded: 1785
Output: 2,500hl
REGULAR BEERS:
Adler Pils
Adler Edel-Pils
Adler Hefeweizen
SEASONAL BEER:
Adler Bock

Small village brewery with its tap down the street. Buses Nos. 21 and 225 run between Ehingen and Laupheim, via Rißtissen, Monday to Friday only.

🍺 Zur Traube
Rißstraße 32, 89584 Ehingen-Rißtissen
T 07392 164 03
Closed Mon; Tue–Sat 11.00–14.00 & from 17.00,
Sun from 11.00
DB Laupheim Stadt 8km, Ehingen 9km

ROSENFELD 97

Lehner

Brauerei Günther-Lehner-Stiftung GmbH
Balinger Straße 7, 72348 Rosenfeld
T 07428 94 51 60   F 07428 24 13
www.lehner-wein.de
Founded: 1931
Output: 8,000hl   Availability: 40 pubs
REGULAR BEERS:
Lehner Landbier Kellertrüb (4.8%)
Lehner Pilsner (4.8%)
Lehner Premium Pils (4.9%)
Lehner Export Spezial (5.1%)
Lehner Hefe-Weizen (5.1%)
Lehner Hefe-Weizen Dunkel (5.1%)
Lehner Kristallweizen (5.1%)
Lehner Premium Hefe-Weizen (5.1%)
SEASONAL BEERS:
Lehner Festtagsbier (5.1%, Nov–Dec), **Lehner Maibock** (6.8%, Mar–May), **Lehner Winterbock** (6.8%, Oct–Feb)

Vineyard and brewery. Bus No. 7430 runs from both Balingen and Oberndorf Monday to Friday, the former offering the better service. No brewery tap.
DB Oberndorf 11km, Balingen 12km

ROTHAUS (Grafenhausen) 98

Rothaus

Badische Staatsbrauerei Rothaus AG
Rothaus 1, 79865 Grafenhausen-Rothaus
T 07748 52 20   F 07748 522 79
www.rothaus.de
Owner: Baden-Württemberg state
Founded: 1791   Output: 915,000hl
Availability: c. 1200 pubs
REGULAR BEERS:
Rothaus Pils/Pils-Tannenzäpfle (5.1%)
Rothaus Hefeweizen/Hefeweizen Zäpfle (5.4%)
Rothaus Märzen Export/Eiszäpfle (5.6%)

Very large brewery owned by the State of Baden-Württemberg. The three beers are marketed as 'Zäpfle' when in 0.33l bottles, but the recipes remain the same. Bus No. 7342 runs from Seebrugg.

🛏 **Schwarzwaldhotel** Rothaus
Rothaus 2, 79865 Grafenhausen-Rothaus

T 07748 920 90   F 07748 920 91 99
Daily 10.00–23.00, food 12.00–21.00; rooms available
DB Seebrugg 4km

SCHILLINGSTADT (Ahorn) 99

Dörzbacher

Privat-Brauerei Dörzbacher
Lange Straße 53, 74744 Ahorn-Schillingstadt
T 07930 374   F 07930 87 19
www.doerzbacher-brauerei.de
Owner: Ludwig Dörzbacher   Founded: 1760
Output: 5,000hl   Availability: 20 pubs
REGULAR BEERS:
Dörzbacher Zwickel (4.9%)
Dörzbacher Edel Pils (4.9%)
Dörzbacher Export (5.2%)
SEASONAL BEER:
Dörzbacher Festbier (5.5%)

Small village brewery, no tap. The closest railway stations (Boxberg-Wölchingen and Eubigheim, both 7km away) are only very poorly served by trains. There are one or two direct buses from Bad Mergentheim and Osterburken.
DB Osterburken 14km

SCHMIEHEIM (Kippenheim) 100

Schlossbrauerei

Schlossbrauerei zu Schmieheim
Schlossstraße 64, 77971 Kippenheim-Schmieheim
T 07825 96 69   F 07825 76 77
www.hieronymus-bier.info
Owner: Jörg Lusch   Founded: 1843
Output: 8,000hl   Availability: c. 70 pubs
REGULAR BEERS:
Schlossbrauerei Schmieheim Pils (4.6%)
Schlossbrauerei Schmieheim Hieronymus (4.9%)
Schlossbrauerei Schmieheim Lager (4.9%)
Schlossbrauerei Schmieheim Geroldsecker (5.7%)
SEASONAL BEER:
Schlossbrauerei Schmieheim Bock (6.5%)
FOR ALTE SCHMIEDE, KARLSRUHE:
Türmberg Bräu Pilsener Naturtrüb (4.8%)

The brewery is on the southern side of the village, close to the castle. The tap is in the centre. To reach Schmieheim you'll need to change buses. Bock is brewed for the Kippenheim Bockbierfest which takes place every year on the first weekend of July.

Hieronymus
Dorfstraße 25, 77971 Kippenheim-Schmieheim
T 07825 86 97 86
Closed Tue; Wed–Fri & Mon 16.00–24.00,
Sat & Sun 11.00–24.00
DB Orschweier 7km, Lahr 9km

SCHORNDORF 101

Kesselhaus
Arnoldstraße 3, 73614 Schorndorf
T 07181 48 49 33   F 07181 48 49 35
www.brauerei-kesselhaus.de
Owner: GHB Die Bierspezialisten AG
Founded: 2000   Output: 1,900hl
Availability: 1 pub
REGULAR BEERS:
Kesselhaus Pils (4.7%)
Kesselhaus Weißbier (5%)

Modern brewpub near the railway. Seasonal beers are brewed in addition to the regular two but we have no details of these.

Kesselhaus
Arnoldstraße 3, 73614 Schorndorf
Thu 09.00–02.00, Fri & Sat 09.00–03.00,
Sun–Wed 09.00–01.00
DB Schorndorf 250m

SCHWÄBISCH HALL 102

Haller Löwenbräu
Löwenbrauerei Hall Fr. Ebhard GmbH & Co. KG
Ritterstraße 6, 74523 Schwäbisch Hall
T 0791 50 90   F 0791 50 93 54
www.haller-loewenbraeu.de
Founded: 1724   Output: 100,000hl
REGULAR BEERS:
Haller Löwenbräu Pilsner (4.7%)
Haller Löwenbräu Edel-Pils (4.9%)
Haller Löwenbräu Schwarzer Löwe (4.9%)
Haller Löwenbräu Meistergold (4.9%)
Löwenbräu Haalgeist Hefe Weiße (4.9%)
Löwenbräu Haalgeist Dunkle Weiße (4.9%)
Löwenbräu Haalgeist Kristall Weizen (4.9%)
Haller Löwenbräu Mohrenköpfle Landbier (5.4%)
Haller Löwenbräu Mohrenköpfle Weizen (5.4%)

SEASONAL BEERS:
Haller Löwenbräu Weihnachtsbier (5.5%),
Haller Löwenbräu Böckle

Large, modern brewery above the station. The brewery tap is down the hill from the station, close to the original brewery (now Sudhaus).

Zum Alten Brauhaus
Mauerstraße 17, 74523 Schwäbisch Hall
T 0791 717 59   F 0791 978 26 73
Closed Tue; Wed–Mon 11.30–14.30 & 16.30–23.00
DB Schwäbisch Hall 500m

Sudhaus
Sudhaus an der Kunsthalle Würth
Lange Straße 35/1, 74523 Schwäbisch Hall
T 0791 946 72 70   F 0791 946 72 75
www.sudhaus-sha.de
Owner: Panorama Hotel & Service GmbH
Founded: 22.05.2004   Output: 1,500hl
Availability: 4 pubs
REGULAR BEERS:
Sudhaus Hell (4.5%)
Sudhaus Dunkel (4.5%)
SEASONAL BEERS:
Sudhaus Hefeweizen (5%), **Sudhaus Maibock** (8%), **Sudhaus Winterbock** (8%)

Brewpub in the former brewhouse of Haller Löwenbräu (the brewery moved in 1987). In the same complex, you'll find four different restaurants and an art gallery.

Sudhaus
Lange Straße 35/1, 74523 Schwäbisch Hall
Daily 10.00–24.00   DB Schwäbisch Hall 400m

SCHWETZINGEN 103

Zum Ritter
Schwetzinger Brauhaus zum Ritter GmbH & Co.
Schloßplatz 1, 68723 Schwetzingen
T 06202 92 49 50   F 06202 92 49 51
www.brauhaus-zum-ritter.de
Founded: 1998   Output: 3,000hl
REGULAR BEERS:
Ritter Hell (5%)
Ritter Schwarz (5%)
Ritter Weissbier (5%)

Large, attractive brewpub at the edge of the castle gardens. Seasonal beers are brewed in addition to the three regulars.

🍺 **Zum Ritter**
Schloßplatz 1, 68723 Schwetzingen
Daily 10.00–01.00; food 11.00–24.00
DB Schwetzingen 600m

SIGMARINGEN   104

Zoller-Hof

Brauerei Zoller-Hof Graf und Fleischhut GmbH
Leopoldstraße 40, 72488 Sigmaringen
T 07571 72 10   **F** 07571 721 30
www.zoller-hof.de
Owner: Claudia Sieben
Founded: 1845
REGULAR BEERS:
Zoller-Hof Hefe-Weizen Leicht
Zoller-Hof Fürsten-Pils
Zoller-Hof Brenzkofer-Dunkel
Zoller-Hof Spezial-Export
Zoller-Hof Hefeweizen
Zoller-Hof Fidelis-Weizen
Zoller-Hof Fürsten-Weizen
SEASONAL BEER:
Zoller-Hof Dunkles Böckle

Regional brewery on the outskirts of town. The
brewery tap is next door, and the beer is widely
available in the centre if you don't fancy the walk.

🍺 **Zoller-Hof**
Leopoldstraße 42, 72488 Sigmaringen
T 07571 129 35
Closed Sat; Sun–Fri 10.00–24.00
DB Sigmaringen 1.3km

SIMMOZHEIM   105

Mönchwasen

Im Mönchsgraben 30, 75397 Simmozheim
T 07033 80 90 30   **F** 07033 80 90 31
www.moenchwasen.com
Founded: 2000
REGULAR BEERS:
Mönchwasen Naturtrüb
Mönchwasen Weizen
SEASONAL BEER:
Mönchwasen Weizenbock

Brewpub on the southern edge of town. Bus No.
670 runs between Calw and Weil via Simmozheim.

🍺 **Mönchwasen**
Im Mönchsgraben 30, 75397 Simmozheim
Sat 16.00–01.00, Sun & hols 11.00–23.00,
Mon–Fri 17.00–01.00
DB Weil der Stadt 5km, Calw 8km

SÖHNSTETTEN (Steinheim)   106

Hirsch

Heidenheimerstraße 27,
89555 Steinheim-Söhnstetten
T 07323 65 58   **F** 07323 35 50
Owner: Klaus-Dieter Schmitt   Founded: 1896
Output: 5,000hl
REGULAR BEERS:
Söhnstetter Zwickel Pils (4.8%)
Söhnstetter Hirsch Pils (4.8%)
Söhnstetter Weißbier (5%)
Söhnstetter Weißbier Dunkel (5%)
Söhnstetter Bier (5.3%)
SEASONAL BEER:
Söhnstetter Weizenbock (7%)

Brewery and tap in a village on the Schwäbische
Albstraße (Swabian alpine road). Bus No. 7688
from Heidenheim stops outside the pub.

🍺 **Zum Hirsch**
Heidenheimerstraße 27,
89555 Steinheim-Söhnstetten
Closed Thu; Fri & Mon–Wed 10.00–21.00, Sat &
Sun 10.00–14.00 & 17.00–21.00
DB Heidenheim 13km

SPIELBACH (Schrozberg)   107

Gold Ochsen

Spielbach 19, 74575 Schrozberg-Spielbach
T 07939 461
Owner: Fritz Unbehauen   Founded: 1880
Output: 2,000hl
REGULAR BEER:
Gold Ochsen Spezial
SEASONAL BEER:
Gold Ochsen Festbock

Close to the Franconian border, between
Schrozberg and Rothenburg. The owner's own
farm supplies the meat for the pub. Bus No. 104
runs from Schrozberg on weekdays.

🍺 **Gold Ochsen**
Spielbach 19, 74575 Schrozberg-Spielbach
Mon–Sat 18.00–22.30, Sun 11.00–22.30
DB Schrozberg 10km

ST. GEORGEN 108

Klimperkasten Kellerbräu

Bahnhofstraße 70, 78112 St. Georgen
T 07724 56 43   **F** 07724 912 33
Founded: 2001
REGULAR BEER:
Kellerbräu Pils

Brewpub in the centre of town. After its foundation in 2001, brewing ceased for a while, but today one beer is once again being produced.

🍺 **Klimperkasten**
Bahnhofstraße 70, 78112 St. Georgen
Mon–Sat 11.00–02.00, Sun 14.00–02.00
DB St. Georgen (Schwarzwald) 850m

STEINACH (Baden) 109

Mellert

Brauerei und Getränkehandel Hubert Mellert e.K.
Hauptstraße 62–66, 77790 Steinach (Baden)
T 07832 28 08   **E** mellert_hubert@baden-mail.de
Owner: Hubert Mellert   Founded: 1863
Output: 2,000hl
REGULAR BEERS:
Mellert-Bräu Pils
Mellert-Bräu Export
Mellert-Bräu Weizen

This small brewery, on the main street, also has a distillery. The brewery tap across the road was closed at the time of writing.

🍺 **Mellert**
Hauptstraße 55–57, 77790 Steinach (Baden)
Currently closed   DB Steinbach (Baden) 750m

STEINSFURT (Sinsheim) 110

Jupiter

Brauhaus Jupiter zu Steinsfurt
Keltergasse 21, 74889 Sinsheim-Steinsfurt
T 07261 97 55 37   **F** 07261 97 55 39

www.brauhausjupiter.de
Owner: Ulrike Doll   Founded: 2000
Output: 550hl   Availability: 1 pub
REGULAR BEERS:
Jupiter Hell (5.2%)
Jupiter Dunkel (5.2%)
SEASONAL BEERS:
Jupiter Weizenbier (4.9%, summer), **Jupiter Märzenbier** (5.3%, Mar), **Jupiter Jupiator Doppelbock** (6.5%, Dec), **Jupiter Maibock** (6.6%, May)

Modern brewpub close to the Sinsheim Auto und Technik Museum (www.museum-sinsheim.de). The two regular beers are occasionally joined by a seasonal brew.

🍺 **Jupiter**
Keltergasse 21, 74889 Sinsheim-Steinsfurt
Daily 11.00–24.00
DB Steinsfurt 650m

STUTTGART 111

Calwer-Eck-Bräu

Calwer-Eck-Bräu – 1. Stuttgarter Lokalbrauerei
Calwer Straße 31, 70173 Stuttgart-Mitte
T 0711 2224 94 40   **F** 0711 2224 944 22
www.calwereck.de
Owners: the Breitmayer family   Founded: 1987
Output: 2,000hl   Availability: 2 pubs
REGULAR BEERS:
Calwer Eck Helles Hefeweizen (4.9%)
Calwer Eck Naturtrübes Pils (5%)
Calwer Eck Braumeisterbier (5.5%)
SEASONAL BEERS:
Calwer Eck Sommerbier (3.3%), **Calwer Eck Dunkles Pils** (5%), **Calwer Eck Schwarzbier** (5.%), **Calwer Eck Landherrenbier** (5.5%), **Calwer Eck Volksfestbier** (5.8%), **Calwer Eck Weihnachtsbier** (5.8%), **Calwer Eck Jubiläums-Maibock** (6.9%)

The vanguard of Stuttgart's now numerous modern brewpubs, Calwer-Eck-Bräu is based on the first floor of a building on the corner of Lange Straße.

🍺 **Calwer-Eck-Bräu**
Calwer Straße 31, 70173 Stuttgart-Mitte
Fri 09.00–02.00, Sat 10.00–02.00, Sun 10.00–01.00, hols 17.00–01.00, Mon–Thu 09.00–01.00
U Rotebühlplatz 100m
S Stadtmitte 150m   DB Stuttgart Hbf 1.2km

Dinkelacker-Schwaben

Dinkelacker-Schwaben Bräu AG
Tübinger Straße 46, 70178 Stuttgart-Süd
T 0711 648 10   **F** 0711 648 12 00
www.ds-ag.de
Owner: InBev   Founded: 1809
Output: 1,200,000hl
CLUSS BEERS, HEILBRONN:
Cluss Kellerpils (5%), **Cluss Export** (5.2%)
DINKELACKER BEERS:
Dinkelacker Diät Pilsener (4.5%), **Dinkelacker
CD Pils** (4.9%), **Dinkelacker Privat** (5.1%),
Dinkelacker Märzen (5.4%)
SEASONAL DINKELACKER BEERS:
Dinkelacker Volksfestbier (5.5%), **Dinkelacker
Weihnachtsfestbier** (5.5%)
SANWALD BEERS:
Sanwald Hefeweizen Leicht (2.8%), **Sanwald
Hefeweizen** (4.9%), **Sanwald Weizen Dunkel**
(4.9%), **Sanwald Kristallweizen** (4.9%)
SCHWABEN BRÄU BEERS:
Schwaben Bräu Meister-Pils (4.9%), **Schwaben
Bräu Pilsener** (4.9%), **Schwaben-Bräu Das
Schwarze** (4.9%), **Schwaben Bräu Das Helle** (5%),
Schwaben Bräu Das Weizen (5%), **Schwaben
Bräu Das Echte Märzen** (5.5%), **Schwaben Bräu
Urtyp Export** (5.1%)
SEASONAL SCHWABEN BRÄU BEERS:
Schwaben Bräu Volksfestbier (5.5%),
Schwaben Bräu Weihnachtsbier (5.5%)

Dinkelacker & Schwaben Bräu merged in 1996 to
form what is now Baden-Württemberg's second
largest brewery, owned by InBev since 2004.
Cluss and Sanwald were two breweries taken
over by Dinkelacker. All beer is now brewed at
the original Dinkelacker brewery.

🍺 **Dinkelacker**
Tübinger Straße 48, 70178 Stuttgart-Süd
T 0711 60 37 97
Closed Sun & hols; Mon–Sat 11.30–24.00
U U1 & U14 Österreicher Platz 400m
DB Stuttgart Hbf 2km

Mash

Forststraße 7, 70174 Stuttgart-Mitte
T 0711 120 93 30   **F** 0711 1209 33 22
www.mash-stuttgart.de
Founded: 2001   Availability: 1 pub
REGULAR BEERS:
Mash One (5.1%)
Mash Hefe (5.1%)

Trendy, open-plan bar and brewery in the
Bosch-Areal centre. A third beer, Mash Silver, is
brewed by Adlerbrauerei Götz in Geislingen.

🍺 **Mash**
Forststraße 7, 70174 Stuttgart-Mitte
Fri 11.30–04.00, Sat 17.00–03.00,
Sun–Thu 11.30–01.00
U Berliner Platz 250m
DB Stuttgart Hbf 1.5km

Schloßturm

SI-Erlebnis-Centrum, Plieninger Straße 100,
70567 Stuttgart-Möhringen
T 0711 721 20 06   **F** 0711 721 29 50
Founded: 1998
REGULAR BEER:
Schloßturm Pils
SEASONAL BEERS:
Schloßturm Märzen, Schloßturm Bock

Brewpub in the SI-Centrum, a complex of
restaurants, bars, theatres and hotels on the
southern side of the city.

🍺 **Schloßturm**
SI-Erlebnis-Centrum, Plieninger Straße 100,
70567 Stuttgart-Möhringen
Sat 12.00–02.00, Sun 11.00–24.00, Mon & Wed
16.00–24.00, Tue, Thu & Fri 16.00–01.00
U U3 Sälzacker (SI-Centrum) 250m
DB Stuttgart Hbf 8km

Sophie's

Marienstraße 28, 70178 Stuttgart-Mitte
T 0711 61 09 62   **F** 0711 61 18 75
www.sophies-brauhaus.de
Owner: Roland Janke   Founded: 1993
Output: 800hl   Availability: 1 pub
REGULAR BEERS:
Sophie's Hausbräu
Sophie's Schwarz
Sophie's Hefeweissbier

First-floor brewpub. The entrance is actually off
Sophienstraße, the street from which the pub
takes its name. Occasional seasonal beers.

🍺 **Sophie's**
Marienstraße 28, 70178 Stuttgart-Mitte
Sun 10.30–24.00, Mon–Sat 16.00–01.00
(Sep–May from 11.00)
U Rotebühlplatz 200m
DB Stadtmitte 300m, Stuttgart Hbf 1.4km

Stuttgarter Hofbräu

Böblinger Straße 104–132, 70199 Stuttgart-Süd
T 0711 648 80   **F** 0711 648 82 04
www.stuttgarter-hofbraeu.de
Owner: Oetker Gruppe AG
Founded: 1872
Output: 900,000hl
Availability: c. 4,000 pubs
REGULAR BEERS:
Stuttgarter Hofbräu Herrenpils (4.6%)
Stuttgarter Hofbräu Pilsner (4.9%)
Stuttgarter Hofbräu Bügel Premium (5.3%)
MALTESER WEISSBIER:
Malteser Weissbier Hefe Hell (5%), **Malteser Weissbier Hefe Dunkel** (5%), **Malteser Weissbier Kristall** (5%)
SEASONAL BEERS:
Stuttgarter Hofbräu Frühlingsbier (5.4%),
Stuttgarter Hofbräu Volksfestbier (5.4%),
Stuttgarter Hofbräu Weihnachtsbier (5.7%)

Beyond Dinkelacker-Schwaben lies this very large brewery. The Malteser wheat beers are brewed under licence from the former Malteser brewery in Amberg. No brewery tap.
U U1 & U14 Schreiberstraße 200m
DB Stuttgart Hbf 3.3km

Tü 8

Der Bräu im Tü 8
Tübinger Straße 8, 70178 Stuttgart-Süd
T 0711 29 59 49   **F** 0711 29 38 14
www.tue8.de
Owner: Domino Gastronomie GmbH
Founded: 1988
Availabilty: 3 pubs
REGULAR BEERS:
Tü 8 Pils
Tü 8 Hefeweizen

Tü8 is a group of three restaurants on the same site: Hacienda, s'Mäxle and Spaghettisssimo. The brewery itself is located inside Hacienda. If you're in the area before Hacienda opens, and fancy a beer, the latter two establishments open at 11.30 and 11.00, respectively.

🍺 Hacienda
Tübinger Straße 8, 70178 Stuttgart-Süd
Daily 17.00–03.00
U Rotebühlplatz 250m
DB Stadtmitte 400m, Stuttgart Hbf 1.4km

Wichtel

Stuttgarter Straße 21, 70469 Stuttgart-Feuerbach
T 0711 82 05 16 90   **F** 0711 820 51 69 14
www.wichtel.de
Owner: Jens Täuber   Founded: 2002
Availability: 1 pub
REGULAR BEERS:
Wichtel Pils (SW 12.7%)
Wichtel Dunkles Hefeweizen (SW 12.8%)
SEASONAL BEERS:
Wichtel Märzen (SW 13.8%), **Wichtel Sommerbier** (SW 15%), **Wichtel Schwarzbier** (SW 15.2%), **Wichtel Dunkles Pils** (5.8%), **Wichtel Maibock** (SW 16.5%), **Wichtel Winterbock** (SW 16.5%)

The second Wichtel brewpub is in the northern suburb of Feuerbach. The same range of beers is brewed as in original pub in Ditzingen.

🍺 Wichtel
Stuttgarter Straße 21, 70469 Stuttgart-Feuerbach
Fri & Sat 11.00–01.00, Sun–Thu 11.00–24.00
DB Stuttgart-Feuerbach 400m

TETTNANG   112

Krone

Brauerei und Gasthof Krone F. Tauscher GmbH
Bärenplatz 7, 88069 Tettnang
T 07542 74 52   **F** 07542 69 72
www.krone-tettnang.de
Owners: Franz, Fritz & Roman Tauscher
Founded: 1847   Ouput: 6,000hl
REGULAR BEERS:
Tettnanger Keller-Pils (4.9%)
Tettnanger Kronen-Bier (4.9%)
Tettnanger Kronen-Pils (4.9%)
Tettnanger See-Weizen (5.2%)
SEASONAL BEERS:
Tettnanger Jehu-Pils (4.9%), **Tettnanger Frühlingsmärzen** (5%), **Tettnanger 23.04 – Das Jahrgangsbier** (Jul), **Tettnanger Coronator Hell** (7.2%, Christmas), **Tettnanger Coronator Dunkel** (7.2%, Lent)

Traditional brewery and pub on the main square. Buses Nos. 28 and 38 run from Meckenbeuren on weekdays, bus No. 7586 runs all week from the Friedrichshafen railway stations and airport.

🍺 Krone
Bärenplatz 7, 88069 Tettnang

Closed Mon; Tue–Sun 10.00–14.00 & 17.00–24.00;
rooms available
DB Meckenbeuren 4km, Friedrichshafen Stadt/
Hafen 12km

TROCHTELFINGEN
(Hohenzollern) 113

Albquell Bräuhaus

Lindenplatz 6, 72818 Trochtelfingen
T 07124 733   F 07124 24 22
www.albquell-brauhaus.de
Owner: Lambert Schmid   Founded: 1851
Output: 6,000hl
REGULAR BEERS:
Albquell Bräuhaus Pilsener (4.9%)
Albquell Bräuhaus Edelbier (5%)
Albquell Bräuhaus Urtrunk (5.1%)
Albquell Bräuhaus Weizenbier
Albquell Bräuhaus Bräu Josef (5.4%).
SEASONAL BEER:
Albquell Bräuhaus Festbier (5.3%)

Small brewery and pub with its own Bierkrug
museum. Bus No. 400 runs from Gammertingen,
and there are occasional weekend tourist trains.

🍺 **Albquell Bräuhaus**
Lindenplatz 6, 72818 Trochtelfingen
Closed Sun; Mon–Sat 09.00–24.00; rooms
available
DB Gammertingen 10km

TÜBINGEN 114

Neckarmüller

Gartenstraße 4, 72074 Tübingen
T 07071 278 48   F 07071 276 20
www.neckarmueller.de
Owner: Heinrich Fischer   Founded: 1992
REGULAR BEERS:
Neckarmüller Weiße Hell (4.9%)
Neckarmüller Weiße Dunkel (4.9%)
SEASONAL BEERS:
Neckarmüller Maibock (5.8%),
Neckarmüller Weihnachtsbock (5.8%)

Modern brewpub next to the river Neckar. Owned
by Fischer's Brauhaus in Mössingen, their beers
are available alongside the house-brewed wheat
beers. Annual holiday Christmas to New Year.

🍺 **Neckarmüller**
Gartenstraße 4, 72074 Tübingen
Daily 10.00–01.00
DB Tübingen 500m

UHINGEN 115

Gerber Bräu

Gerber Bräu Gastronomie GmbH
Kanalstraße 47, 73066 Uhingen
T 07161 94 69 70   F 07161 946 97 19
www.gerberbraeu.de
Owner: Andreas Schlosser
Founded: 2003
Output: 1,500hl
Availability: 1 pub
REGULAR BEERS:
Gerber-Bräu Pilsner (4.7%)
Gerber-Bräu Edel (4.7%)
Gerber-Bräu Hefeweizen (5%)
SEASONAL BEERS:
Gerber-Bräu Schwarzbier (4.7%), **Gerber-Bräu
Sommerweizen** (4.8%), **Gerber-Bräu Festbier**
(5.5%), **Gerber-Bräu Maibock** (6.6%), **Gerber-
Bräu Heller Weihnachtsbock** (6.6%)

Large, modern brewpub that occcupies a former
tannery (*Gerberei*). Large outdoor drinking area.

🍺 **Gerber Bräu**
Kanalstraße 47, 73066 Uhingen
Sat 16.00–02.00, Sun & hols 11.00–24.00,
Mon–Thu 16.00–01.00, Fri 16.00–02.00
DB Uhingen 650m

ULM (Donau) 116

Barfüßer

Barfüßer Das Kleine Brauhaus GmbH
Lautenberg 1, 89073 Ulm-Mitte
T 0731 602 11 10   F 0731 151 56 16
www.barfuesser-brauhaus.de
Founded: 1994   Output: 2,000hl
REGULAR BEERS:
Barfüßer Blonde (4.9%)
Barfüßer Schwarze (4.9%)
Barfüßer Weiße (4.9%)

Just around the corner from the cathedral, this
first-floor pub is one of four Barfüßers (the others
are in Heilbronn, Neu-Ulm & Nürnberg).

🍺 Barfüßer

Lautenberg 1, 89073 Ulm-Mitte
Thu & Fri 11.00–02.00, Sat 10.00–02.00,
Sun–Wed 11.00–01.00
DB Ulm Hbf 550m

Gold Ochsen

Brauerei Gold Ochsen GmbH
Veitsbrunnenweg 3–8, 89073 Ulm-Mitte
T 0731 16 40   F 0731 16 42 00
www.goldochsen.de
Founded: 1597   Output: 300,000hl
REGULAR BEERS:
Gold Ochsen Original Leicht (2.8%)
Gold Ochsen Weisse-Leicht
Gold Ochsen Premium Pils (5.1%)
Gold Ochsen Original (5.1%)
Gold Ochsen Gold Weisse-Kristall (5.4%)
Gold Ochsen Gold Weisse (5.5%)
Gold Ochsen Gold Weisse Dunkel (5.5%)
Gold Ochsen Special (5.5%)
SEASONAL BEER:
Gold Ochsen Weihnachtsbier (5.6%)
OXX BEERS:
OXX Lager (4.8%), **OXX White**

Ulm's last remaining large brewery following
the closure of Ulmer-Münster (whose beers are
now brewed by Memminger). No brewery tap,
but the beers won't prove difficult to find
around the city.
DB Ulm Ost 500m, Ulm Hbf 1.4km

Kronenbrauerei Söflingen

Schlossergasse 31, 89077 Ulm-Söflingen
T 0731 38 83 20   F 0731 388 65 74
www.soeflinger-kronenbier.de
Owners: Artur & Thomas Russ   Founded: 1887
Output: 2,500hl
REGULAR BEERS:
Kronen Bier Natureis Lager
Kronen Bier Kellerpils (4.8%)
Kronen Bier Spezial-Hell (5.1%)
Kronen Bier Kloster Urtrunk Dunkel (5.1%)
Kronen Bier Kloster Weisse Hell
Kronen Bier Kloster Weisse Dunkel
Kronen Bier Natureis-Bock Hell (7.2%)
Kronen Bier Natureis-Bock Dunkel (7.2%)
SEASONAL BEERS:
Kronen Bier Weihnachtsbier,
Kronen Bier Maibock

This small brewery and pub stands next to the
western terminus of Ulm's last remaining tram
route. One of only few to brew an Eisbock.

🍺 Zur Krone

Uhrenmachergasse 10, 89077 Ulm-Söflingen
T 0731 38 46 35
Closed Sun & Mon; Tue–Sat 10.00–24.00
Tram No. 1 Söflingen 50m   DB Ulm Hbf 2.5km

ULM (Renchen) 117

Bauhöfer

Familienbrauerei Bauhöfer GmbH & Co. KG
Ullenburgstraße 12, 77871 Renchen-Ulm
T 07843 947 40   F 07843 94 74 74
www.ulmer-bier.de
Founded: 1852   Output: 45,000hl
REGULAR BEERS:
Ulmer Pilsener (5%)
Ulmer Hefeweizen-Hell (5.1%)
Ulmer Hefeweizen-Dunkel (5.1%)
Ulmer Kristallweizen (5.1%)
Ulmer Vollmond-Bier (5.2%)
Ulmer Export (5.4%)
SEASONAL BEERS:
Ulmer Hexensud (4.8%), **Ulmer Maibock** (7.2%),
Ulmer Winterbock (7.4%)

Brewery with an imposing tap in the centre of
the village. Bus No. 7124 runs from Achern on
weekdays. If you don't mind the walk or have a
bike, Renchen station is closer.

🍺 Bauhöfer's Bräustüb'l

Ullenburgstraße 16, 77871 Renchen-Ulm
T 07843 695   F 07843 970 17
Closed Thu; Fri–Wed from 10.00
DB Renchen 4km, Achern 8km

UMMENDORF 118

Ummendorf

Bräuhaus Ummendorf GmbH
Bachstraße 10, 88444 Ummendorf
T 07351 444 30   F 07351 44 43 10
www.braeuhaus.de
Owner: Stefan Dobler   Founded: 1870
Output: 4,000hl   Availability: 10 pubs
REGULAR BEERS:
Bräuhaus Ummendorf 's Angele Pils (4.7%)

Bräuhaus Ummendorf Keller-Bier (5%)
Bräuhaus Ummendorf Placidus Cobaldus
    Dunkel (5%)
Bräuhaus Ummendorf Spezial 's Blaue (5.2%)
SEASONAL BEER:
Bräuhaus Ummendorf Bock 's Rote (7%)

Village brewery, distillery, hotel and pub.
Several bus routes run here from Biberach.

📍 **Bräuhaus Ummendorf**
Bachstraße 10, 88444 Ummendorf
Closed Wed; Thu–Tue 09.00–24.00; rooms
available
DB Biberach (Riß) 6km

UNTERGRÖNINGEN
(Abstgmünd)   119

Lammbrauerei

Haller Str. 2, 73453 Abstgmünd-Untergröningen
T 07975 284   F 07975 53 78
www.lammbrauerei.de
Owner: Andreas Kunz   Founded: 1830
Output: 4,000hl   Availability: 15 pubs
REGULAR BEERS:
Lamm Bräu Bierappel Naturtrüb (4.8%)
Lamm Bräu Kocherreiter Pils Hell (4.8%)
Lamm Bräu Kocherreiter Pils Dunkel (4.8%)
Lamm Bräu Kristall-Pilsener (4.8%)
Lamm Bräu Qualitätsbier (5.4%)
SEASONAL BEERS:
Lamm Bräu Hexenbier,
Lamm Bräu Weihnachtsbock

Brewery and pub in the centre of the village.
There's no longer a rail service but bus No. 45 will
take you here from Gaildorf West on weekdays.

📍 **Lamm**
Haller Str. 2, 73453 Abstgmünd-Untergröningen
Daily 07.00–24.00; rooms available
DB Gaildorf West 17km

UNTERGROMBACH
(Bruchsal)   120

Bundschuh-Bräu

Weingartener Straße 3,
76646 Bruchsal-Untergrombach
T 07257 47 75
www.bundschuh-braeu.de

Owner: Mathias Hochadel   Founded: 2003
REGULAR BEERS:
Bundschuh-Bräu Hell
Bundschuh-Bräu Dunkel
Bundschuh-Bräu Weizen

Recently opened brewpub which currently brews
three regular beers but no seaonals.

📍 **Der Bundschuh**
Weingartener Straße 3,
76646 Bruchsal-Untergrombach
Fri & Sat 18.00–02.00, Sun 18.00–24.00,
Mon–Thu 18.00–01.00
DB Untergrombach 700m

UNTERSCHEFFLENZ
(Schefflenz)   121

Egolf

Hintere Klinge 1–3,
74850 Schefflenz-Unterschefflenz
T 06293 488   F 06293 92 99 40
www.brauerei-egolf.de
Owner: Günther Egolf   Founded: 1987
Output: 200hl   Availability: 5 pubs
REGULAR BEERS:
Schefflenzer Pils
Schefflenzer Weißbier

Small brewery with a brewery tap on site that
opens only by arrangement. The beer is regularly
available in four other pubs listed on the website.
DB Oberschefflenz 3km

UTTENWEILER   122

Sauter

August Sauter Bierbrauerei
Hauptstraße 27, 88524 Uttenweiler
T 07374 921 10   F 07374 92 11 22
www.uttenweilerbier.de
Owner: Richard Sauter   Founded: 1555
REGULAR BEERS:
Uttenweiler Hell (4.6%)
Uttenweiler Pilsener (4.9%)
Uttenweiler Kellerbier (5.2%)
Uttenweiler Spezial (5.2%)
SEASONAL BEERS:
Uttenweiler Festbier (5.2%),
Uttenweiler Bock (7%)

Brewery in the small town of Uttenweiler with the tap next door. Bus No. 380 shuttles between Riedlingen and Biberach from Monday to Friday.

Zum Rössle

Hauptstraße 28, 88524 Uttenweiler
T 07374 21 92
Closed Mon; Tue–Fri 11.00–14.00 & 18.00–01.00, Sat, Sun & hols 17.00–24.00
DB Riedlingen 11km, Biberach (Riß) 18km

WAIBSTADT 123

Adler

Adler-Brauerei Waibstadt
Hauptstraße 38, 74915 Waibstadt
T 07263 58 52   **F** 07263 40 88 23
www.baubier.de
Owner: Wolfgang Haag   Founded: 1768
Output: 1,500hl   Availability: 15 pubs
REGULAR BEERS:
Adler Zwicklbier (5.3%)
Adler Export (5.3%)
SEASONAL BEER:
Adler Festbier (5.6%)

Small brewery in the centre of Waibstadt. The Zwicklbier, available on draught only, is sold in the brewery tap and just one other pub.

Zum Adler

Hauptstraße 38, 74915 Waibstadt
T 07263 51 21
Closed Sat; Sun–Fri 11.00–01.00
DB Waibstadt 400m

WALDBRONN 124

Lindenbräu

Stuttgarter Straße 43, 76337 Waldbronn
T 07234 65 28 81   **F** 07234 65 28 82
www.lindenbraeu-waldbronn.de
Founded: 2000   Output: 1,000hl
REGULAR BEERS:
Lindenbräu Pils (4.8%)
Lindenbräu Waldbronner Original
SEASONAL BEERS:
Lindenbräu Altbier, Lindenbräu Weizen-Hell (5.4%), **Lindenbräu Weizen-Dunkel** (5.4%), **Lindenbräu Waldbronner Festbier, Lindenbräu Weizenbock** (7%), **Lindenbräu Maxxximator**

Modern brewpub in an attractive small town south-east of Karlsruhe. Regular seasonal beers supplement the standard ones.

Lindenbräu

Stuttgarter Straße 43, 76337 Waldbronn
Sat, Sun & hols 10.00–01.00,
Mon–Fri 16.00–01.00
DB Reichenbach (bei Ettlingen) 800m

WALDHAUS (Weilheim) 125

Waldhaus

Privatbrauerei Waldhaus Joh. Schmid GmbH
Waldhaus 1, 79809 Weilheim-Waldhaus
T 07755 922 20   **F** 07755 92 22 99
www.privatbrauerei-waldhaus.de
Founded: 1846   Availability: 100 pubs
REGULAR BEERS:
Waldhaus Light Line (2.9%)
Waldhaus Diplom Pils (4.9%)
Waldhaus Spezial Bier (5.6%)
Waldhaus Schwarzwald Weisse (5.6%)
Waldhaus Ohne Filter (5.6%)
Waldhaus Fun Hefeweizen (5.7%)
SEASONAL BEER:
Waldhaus Doppel-Bock (8.5%)

You may struggle to find Waldhaus on a map – it's situated at the southern end of the Black Forest, on the B500, just north of Bannholz. Bus No. 7322 runs from Waldshut seven days a week.

Waldhaus

Waldhaus 1, 79809 Weilheim-Waldhaus
T 07755 16 00   **F** 07755 82 44
Closed Mon; Tue–Sun 09.00–23.00
DB Walshut 10km

WALDKIRCH 126

Hirschenbrauerei

Hirschenbrauerei Waldkirch GmbH & Co. KG
Goethestraße 21, 79183 Waldkirch
T 07681 408 10   **F** 07681 40 81 20
www.hirschenbrauerei.de   Founded: 1868
REGULAR BEERS:
Hirschen-Bräu Pils (4.9%)
Hirschen-Bräu Kellerbier (4.9%)
Hirschen-Bräu Dunkel (5.2%)
Hirschen-Bräu Export (5.2%)

SEASONAL BEERS:
Hirschen-Bräu Festbier (5.5%),
Hirschen-Bräu Bock (6.1%)

Attractive brewery on the southern edge of this Black Forest town. The brewery tap stands alongside.

🍺 **Zum Stadtrainsee**
Goethestraße 21, 79183 Waldkirch
T 07681 227 78   Daily 11.00–24.00
DB Waldkirch 1.2km

WEILHEIM
(Rietheim-Weilheim)   127

Lammbrauerei

Schillerstraße 3, 78604 Rietheim-Weilheim/
Weilheim   **T** 07461 738 22   **F** 07461 155 66
www.lammbrauerei-weilheim.de
Owner: Horst Storz   Founded: 1887
Output: 8,000hl
REGULAR BEERS:
Weilheimer Germanentrunk (4.8%)
Weilheimer Premium-Pils (5%)
Weilheimer Schwarzes Wäldle (5.1%)
Weilheimer Export (5.2%)
SEASONAL BEERS:
Weilheimer Bockbier-Hell (9%),
Weilheimer Bockbier-Dunkel (9%)

Village in a wooded valley north of Tuttlingen. The brewery and tap are a few dozen metres from each other.

🍺 **Lamm**
Untere Hauptstraße 11,
78604 Rietheim-Weilheim/Weilheim
T 07461 738 00
Closed Tue & Fri; Wed, Thu & Sat–Mon from 16.30
DB Weilheim (Württemberg) 200m

WEINHEIM   128

Woinemer

Woinemer Hausbrauerei Hardt & Andreas OHG
Friedrichstraße 23, 69469 Weinheim
T 06201 120 01   **F** 06201 158 70
www.woinemer-hausbrauerei.de
Owners: Hochen Hardt & Christiane Andreas
Founded: 1986   Output: 3,000hl
Availability: 5 pubs

REGULAR BEERS:
Woinemer Hell (4.9%)
Woinemer Dunkel (5%)
Woinemer Weizen (5%)
SEASONAL BEERS:
**Woinemer Irish Black, Woinemer Sommerbier,
Woinemer Kupfer, Woinemer Märzen** (5.2%),
Woinemer Maibock (5.6%), **Woinemer
Weihnachtsbock** (5.6%), **Woinemer
Weizenbock** (5.6%), **Woinemer Herbstbock,
Woinemer Tillator** (6.3%)

Rustic brewpub and distillery close to the town centre. Supplies several other pubs in the area.

🍺 **Woinemer**
Friedrichstraße 23, 69469 Weinheim
Sat 10.00–01.00, Sun–Fri 10.00–24.00
DB Weinheim (Bergstrasse) 600m

WIERNSHEIM   129

Adler

Bei der Linde 5, 75446 Wiernsheim
T 07044 92 07 78   **F** 07044 92 07 80
www.adlerbraeu.de
Owners: Ramona Jentzsch-Volk & Robert Volk
Founded: 1865   Output: 2,000hl
Availability: 9 pubs
REGULAR BEERS:
Adler-Bräu Leopils (5.1%)
Adler-Bräu Werschemer-Woiza (5.1%)
Adler-Bräu Export (5.5%)
SEASONAL BEERS:
Adler-Bräu Lindenquell (4.3%), **Adler-Bräu
Dunkel** (5.7%, Easter & Christmas), **Adler-Bräu
Conrad Märzen** (5.8%), **Adler-Bräu Conrator** (8.5%)

Traditional brewery that still uses wooden barrels for its draught beer. From Mühlacker, take bus No. 713, from Pforzheim bus No. 739.

🍺 **Adler**
Marktplatz 28, 75446 Wiernsheim
T 07044 75 75   Closed Wed; Thu–Tue from 12.00
DB Mühlacker 8km, Pforzheim Hbf 13km

WIESENSTEIG   130

Zum Lamm

Bierbrauerei zum Lamm Karl Ege GmbH & Co.
Westerheimer Straße 4, 73349 Wiesensteig
T 07335 64 63   **F** 07335 64 84

Owner: Karl Ege   Founded: 1682
Output: 5,000hl
REGULAR BEERS:
Wiesensteiger Pils (4.8%)
Wiesensteiger Keller-Pils Naturtrüb (4.8%)
Wiesensteiger Spezial (5%)
Wiesensteiger Dunkel (5%)
Wiesensteiger Weissbier (5.2%)
SEASONAL BEER:
Wiesensteiger Goissbock (7%)

Small brewery with a tap that only opens on Sunday mornings. Bus No. 56 offers a direct service from Geislingen (including Sunday mornings).

🍺 **Zum Lamm**
Westerheimer Straße 4, 73349 Wiesensteig
Closed Mon–Sat; Sun 10.00–14.00
DB Geislingen 20km

WOLFENWEILER (Schallstadt)   131

Mooswald-Heimbräu

Gewerberstraße 27, 79227 Schallstadt-Wolfenweiler
T 07664 60 03 35   **F** 07664 61 81 50
Owner: Manfred Schulz   Founded: 1991
Output: 500hl
REGULAR BEER:
Mooswald Hell

A house brewery in the truest sense: this tiny brewpub is actually inside Manfred Schulz's home. The one regular beer is sometimes joined by a seasonal.

🍺 **Mooswald-Heimbräu**
Gewerberstraße 27, 79227 Schallstadt-Wolfenweiler
Closed Sat; Fri & Sun from 17.00, Mon–Thu from 16.30
DB Ebringen 700m

WURMLINGEN   132

Hirschbrauerei

Hirschbrauerei Honer GmbH & Co. KG
Friedrichstraße 34, 78573 Wurmlingen
T 07461 94 20   **F** 07461 94 21 50
www.hirschbrauerei.de
Founded: 1782   Output: 90,000hl
REGULAR BEERS:
Hirsch Sport Weisse (3.3%)
Hirsch Pils (5%)

Hirsch Zwickl/Hirsch Zwuckl (5%)
Hirsch Gold (5.2%)
Hirsch 1782 (5.2%)
Hirsch Hefe Weisse (5.4%)
Hirsch Dunkle Hefe Weisse (5.4%)
Hirsch Kristall Weisse (5.4%)
SEASONAL BEER:
Hirsch 16-Ender Dunkler Bock (7%)

Large regional brewery. The beers are widely available in the southern part of the Black Forest.

🍺 **Hirsch**
Obere Hauptstraße 13, 78573 Wurmlingen
T 07461 121 96   **F** 07461 756 13
Closed Sat; Sun 16.00–23.00, Mon 15.30–01.00, Tue–Thu 11.00–13.00 & 15.30–01.00, Fri 11.00–02.00
DB Wurmlingen 750m

ZUZENHAUSEN   133

Adler

Adlerbräu Herbert Werner GmbH & Co.KG
Hoffenheimer Straße 1, 74939 Zuzenhausen
T 06226 93 90 20   **F** 06226 939 02 22
www.dachsenfranz.de
Owner: Wilhelm Werner   Founded: 1832
REGULAR BEERS:
Dachsenfranz Dunkel (4.8%)
Adler Pils (4.9%)
Dachsenfranz Kellerbier Naturtrüb (5.2%)
Adler Export (5.1%)
Dachsenfranz Waize (5.3%)
SEASONAL BEERS:
Dachsenfranz Weihnachtsbier (5.3%), **Dachsenfranz Märzen** (5.4%), **Dachsenfranz Jahrgangsbier** 23.04 (5.8%)

Brewery and tap in a small town near Sinsheim. Dachsenfranz (Badger Francis) was an Italian, on the run after having fought alongside Garibaldi. He lived in harmony with nature in the nearby forests during the late 19th and early 20th centuries, before disappearing without trace in 1915.

🍺 **Adler zum Dachsenfranz**
Hoffenheimer Straße 1, 74939 Zuzenhausen
T 06226 920 70   **F** 06226 92 07 40
Closed Tue; Wed–Fri & Sun 11.00–14.00 & 17.30–24.00, Sat 17.30–24.00; rooms available
DB Zuzenhausen 250m

ZWIEFALTEN 134

Zwiefalter Klosterbräu

Hauptstraße 24, 88529 Zwiefalten
T 07373 20 00   **F** 07373 200 30
www.zwiefalter.de
Founded: 1521   Output: 90,000hl
REGULAR BEERS:
Zwiefalter Kloster Weizen Hefeleicht (2.6%)
Zwiefalter Kloster Pils (4.7%)
Zwiefalter Klosterbräu Pilsner Edeltyp (5%)
Zwiefalter Exclusiv (5.2%)
Zwiefalter Kloster Weizen-Hefetrüb (5.2%)
Zwiefalter Kloster Weizen-Hefedunkel (5.2%)
Zwiefalter Kloster Weizen-Kristallklar (5.2%)
Zwiefalter Klosterbräu Spezial Export (5.3%)
SEASONAL BEERS:
Zwiefalter Schwarzer Kieler (5.3%, Oct-Mar),
Zwiefalter Festbier (5.5%, Christmas)

Like at most abbey breweries, the beer here is
no longer brewed by monks – the brewery has
been in private hands since 1803. Served by
several different bus routes from Riedlingen,
although not regularly.

🍺 **Klosterbräu**
Hauptstraße 24, 88529 Zwiefalten
T 07373 912 12   **F** 07373 912 13
Daily 10.00–24.00   DB Riedlingen 13km

ZWIEFALTENDORF
(Riedlingen) 135

Blank

Von-Speth-Straße 19,
88499 Riedlingen-Zwiefaltendorf
T 07373 643   **F** 07373 25 33
www.brauerei-blank.de
Owner: Thomas Blank
Founded: 1878
Output: 900hl
REGULAR BEERS:
Blank's Edelbier (4.9%)
Blank's Spezial-Dunkel (5%)
Blank's Naturtrübes (5%)
Blank's Weisse (5%)

One of only two breweries in Germany we're
aware of that produces its own cider, it also has
a small distillery. Bus No. 320 runs from
Riedlingen Monday to Friday only.

🍺 **Blank's Brauereigasthof**
Von-Speth-Straße 19,
88499 Riedlingen-Zwiefaltendorf
Closed Sun; Mon–Sat 11.30–24.00; rooms
available
DB Riedlingen 11km

Bayern (Bavaria)

GERMANY'S LARGEST state and probably the one that's most influenced stereotypes of Germany abroad. Divided into seven districts (Niederbayern, Mittelfranken, Oberbayern, Oberfranken, Oberpfalz, Schwaben and Unterfranken), the 'Free State' of Bavaria almost feels like a country in its own right, and that's certainly how many locals perceive it.

Bayern possesses many of the most popular tourist attractions in Germany as well as superb scenery, from the Alps in the south to Bamberg in the north, you could spend months here and barely scratch the surface. Most tourists start in München (*Munich*), and many go nowhere else. Other popular destinations include Nürnberg (*Nuremberg*), Rothenburg ob der Tauber and 'Mad' King Ludwig's castle Schloss Neuschwanstein. All are worth a visit, just don't expect to be the only one there...

For beer lovers Bavaria is the undisputed capital of the brewing world. There are still 618 breweries in the state – one for every 19,500 inhabitants. To put that into perspective: Britain would need an additional 2,500 breweries to achieve such a ratio. In Oberfranken there are even more: about 1:1,000. Impressive as these statistics undoubtedly are, spare a thought for the 150 or so Bavarian breweries that have stopped brewing in the last 15 years. At the current rate the state may not remain the beer paradise it undoubtedly is for more than a few decades.

If you're planning to fly in there are two international airports: München and Nürnberg. The former is actually a few miles south of Freising (home of the world's oldest brewery). Also worth considering are Frankfurt International, Friedrichshafen and Stuttgart, all within 50 miles of the border.

Transport: Although largely rural, Bavaria is fairly well served by the railway with several main lines criss-crossing the state and numerous secondary lines filling many of the gaps. Bus services are generally good but some rural areas see few services during the week, never mind the weekend. A Bayern-Ticket will set one person back €17 and costs €24 for up to five people travelling together. Valid 09.00–03.00 on weekdays and all day at the weekend, it can be used on S, RB, RE and IRE services within the state as well as many buses, underground and tram services and some private railway lines. Check for details.

ABENSBERG 136

Hofbräu

Stadionstraße 3-9, 93326 Abensberg
T 09443 90 56 66 **F** 094443 90 56 68
Owner: Josef Neumayer   Founded: 1879
Output: 6,000hl
REGULAR BEERS:
Hofbräu Hell
Hofbräu Pils
Hofbräu Millennium Pils
Hofbräu Weiss Blau
Hofbräu Dunkles Hefeweizen
Hofbräu Jubiläumsbier Dunkel
SEASONAL BEERS:
Hofbräu Märzen-Spezial, Hofbräu Bock

This small brewery shares its name (meaning Court Brewery) with 13 other German breweries. The tap is on the town square, just up from Zum Kuchlbauer.

Hofbräu Stuben

Stadtplatz 13, 93326 Abensberg
T 09443 91 83 78
Closed Mon; Tue–Sat 10.00–01.00,
Sun 10.00–24.00

Kuchlbauer

Brauerei zum Kuchlbauer GmbH & Co. KG
Römerstraße 5–9, 93326 Abensberg
T 09443 910 10   T 09443 75 53
www.kuchlbauer.de
Founded: 1300   Output: 100,000hl
REGULAR BEERS:
Kuchlbauer Helles Bier (4.9%)
Kuchlbauer Weisse (5.2%)
Kuchlbauer Alte Liebe (Dunkle Weisse) (5.2%)
SEASONAL BEERS:
Kuchlbauer Roggen, Kuchlbauer Märzen,
Kuchlbauer Aloysius Weißbierbock (7.2%)

The oldest, and by far the largest of Abensberg's
three breweries. The large brewery tap
dominates the town square.

Zum Kuchlbauer

Stadtplatz 2, 93326 Abensberg
T 09443 14 84   F 09443 90 31 88
Closed Tue; Wed–Mon 09.00–24.00
DB Abensberg 550m

Ottenbräu

Brewery: Ulrichstraße 15, 93326 Abensberg
Office: Schulhausplatz 2a, 93326 Abensberg
T 09443 13 48   F 09443 90 34 48
DB Abensberg 400m
Owner: Robert Neumaier   Founded: 1609
Output: 3,000hl   Availability: 4 pubs
REGULAR BEERS:
Ottenbräu Pils (4.8%)
Ottenbräu Dunkles Lagerbier (4.9%)
Ottenbräu Hefe-Weizen (5.2%)
Ottenbräu Märzen (5.2%)
SEASONAL BEERS:
Ottenbräu Gillamoosbier (5.5%), Ottenbräu
Bock (7%), Ottenbräu Doppelbock (8%)

Abensberg's smallest brewery stands behind
the brewery tap on Ulrichstraße. We're not sure
if the beer is sold outside the town.

Ottenbräu

Ulrichstraße 15, 93326 Abensberg
T 09443 62 42
Daily 09.00–24.00
DB Abensberg 600m

ADLDORF (Eichendorf)   137

Graf Arco

Gräfliche Brauerei Arco-Valley GmbH
Hauptstraße 14, 94428 Eichendorf-Adldorf
T 09952 28 11   F 09952 28 27
www.graf-arco.de
Owner: Monica Gräfin von Arco auf Valley
Founded: 1630   Output: 125,000hl
Availability: 600 pubs
REGULAR BEERS:
Graf Arco Light (3.2%)
Graf Arco Weißbier Leicht (3.3%)
Graf Arco Pils (4.7%)
Graf Arco Grafen Hell (4.8%)
Graf Arco Kellerbier
Graf Arco Weißbier Dunkel (5.2%)
Graf Arco Export Hell (5.4%)
Graf Arco Weißbier Hell (5.5%)
Graf Arco Grafentrunk Festbier (5.7%)
SEASONAL BEER:
Graf Arco Arcolator (7.8%)
FOR GRAF ARCO, VALLEY:
Valley Gold (4.3%), Valley Lager (4.3%)

Owned by the Countess of Arco-Valley who also
owns the Graf Arco brewery in Bad Birnbach.
Bus No. 6235 runs from Landau Monday to
Friday and once on Saturday. The tap may stay
open all day at the weekend.

Arco-Quelle

Hauptstraße 17, 94428 Eichendorf-Adldorf
T 09952 373   F 09952 90 59 18
Closed Mon; Tue–Sun 11.00–14.00 & 17.00–24.00
DB Landau (Isar) 14km

ADLERSBERG (Pettendorf)   138

Prößlbräu

Dominikanerstraße 2–3,
93186 Pettendorf-Adlersberg
T 09404 18 22   F 09404 52 33
Owner: Heinrich Prößl   Founded: 1838
Output: 7,000hl
REGULAR BEERS:
Prößlbräu Adlersberger Hell (4.8%)
Prößlbräu Jubiläums Dunkel (5%)
Prößlbräu Adlersberger Pils (5%)
SEASONAL BEER:
Prößlbräu Palmator (7%)

This former monastery became a brewery in 1838. Bus No. 12 runs from Regensburg to Adlersberg-Kreuzung (not Sun), and from there it's roughly 1km to the pub. If you don't mind a longer walk, Ettershausen station is 4km away.

Prößlbräu
Dominikanerstraße 2–3,
93186 Pettendorf-Adlersberg
Closed Mon; Tue–Sun 07.00–24.00;
rooms available
DB Regensburg Hbf 10km

AFFECKING (Kelheim) 139

Frischeisen

Regensburger Straße 69,
93309 Kelheim-Affecking
T 09441 504 90 F 09441 36 98
www.brauerei-frischeisen.de
Owner: Cornelia Auer Founded: 1851
Output: 7,000hl Availability: 10 pubs
REGULAR BEERS:
Frischeisen Urtyp Hell (4.9%)
Frischeisen Pils (4.9%)
Frischeisen Dunkel (5.1%)
Frischeisen Märzen (5.3%)

Often quoted as being in Kelheim, Frischeisen is actually in the large village of Affecking, between Saal and Kelheim. Buses Nos. 6009 and 6022 run from Saal station.

Frischeisen
Regensburger Straße 69,
93309 Kelheim-Affecking
Closed Fri; Sat–Thu 09.00–24.00;
rooms available
DB Saal (Donau) 3km

AHORNBERG (Konradsreuth) 140

Ahornberger

Ahornberger Landbrauerei Strössner Bräu KG
Brauereiweg 7, 95176 Konradsreuth-Ahornberg
T 09292 959 80 F 09292 10 91
www.ahornberger.de
Owners: the Schödel and Strössner families
Founded: 1739 Output: 70,000hl
Availability: 11 pubs

REGULAR BEERS:
Ahornberger Landbier Würzig (4.9%)
Ahornberger Landbier Hopfig (4.9%)
Ahornberger Landbier Premium (5.2%)
Ahornberger Landbier Dunkel (5.3%)
Ahornberger Weissbier Hell (5.3%)
Ahornberger Weissbier Dunkel (5.3%)
Ahornberger Landbier Märzen (5.4%)
SEASONAL BEERS:
Ahornberger Festbier,
Ahornberger Maibock (6.2%)

Ahornberger has comparatively few pubs given its large output. No brewery tap but bus No. 8943 runs from Münchberg Mon–Fri only.
DB Münchberg 6km

AIDENBACH 141

Aidenbach

Brauhaus Aidenbach Woerlein KG
Marktplatz 49, 94501 Aidenbach
T 08543 13 40 F 08543 91 85 10
E woerlein@vilstal.net
Owner: Heinrich Woerlein Founded: 1897
REGULAR BEERS:
Brauhaus Aidenbach Kellerbier (4.7%)
Brauhaus Aidenbach Braumeister-Pils (4.8%)
Brauhaus Aidenbach Urtyp-Hell
Brauhaus Aidenbach Edel-Weizen (5.1%)
SEASONAL BEERS:
Brauhaus Aidenbach Märzen,
Brauhaus Aidenbach Weizen-Bock (6.4%)

Small brewery and pub on the market square. Bus No. 6111 runs from Vilshofen Monday to Friday and once on Saturday.

Zum Weißbräu
Marktplatz 49, 94501 Aidenbach
Tue, Thu & Sat 09.00–22.00,
Wed, Fri & Sun/Mon 09.00–18.00
DB Vilshofen (Niederbayern) 13km

AISCH (Adelsdorf) 142

Rittmayer

Hauptstraße 5, 91325 Adelsdorf-Aisch
T 09195 72 22 F 09195 92 83 43
Owner: Alois Rittmayer Founded: before 1600
Output: 1,600hl Availability: 1 pub

REGULAR BEERS:
Rittmayer Hausbräubier (4.3%)
Aischer Hausbier (4.8%)
SEASONAL BEER:
Rittmayer Kerwabier (5%, 1st week in Aug)

Brewpub in the centre of the village. Bus No. 205 runs from Erlangen on weekdays. The Hausbräubier (we think) is sold as Zoigl by the pub of the same name at Ludwigstraße 47 in Kaufbeuren, open on the first Saturday of each month 13.00–02.00.

🍎 **Rittmayer**
Hauptstraße 5, 91325 Adelsdorf-Aisch
Closed Mon; Tue–Sun 09.00–14.30 & 17.00–23.00
DB Erlangen 23km

ALDERSBACH 143

Aldersbach
Freiherr-von-Aretin-Platz 1, 94501 Aldersbach
T 08543 9 60 40 **F** 08543 96 04 44
www.aldersbacher.de
Owners: Georg Adam Freiherr von Aretin
Founded: 1268 Output: 100,000hl
Availability: c. 500 pubs
REGULAR BEERS:
Aldersbacher Leicht (3%)
Aldersbacher Kloster Weisse Leicht (3.1%)
Aldersbacher Kloster Dunkel (5%)
Aldersbacher Klosterhell (5.1%)
Aldersbacher Urhell (5.1%)
Aldersbacher Freiherrn Pils (5.1%)
Aldersbacher Kloster Weisse Hell (5.1%)
Aldersbacher Kloster Weisse Dunkel (5.1%)
Aldersbacher Ursprung Export (5.6%)
SEASONAL BEERS:
Aldersbacher Kloster Weisse Spezial (5.2%),
Aldersbacher Festbier (6%)

Brewery in a former monastery owned by Baron von Aretin. There's a small brewery museum on site. Bus No. 6111 runs from Vilshofen Monday to Friday and once on Saturday.

🍎 **Bräustüberl Aldersbach**
Freiherr-von-Aretin-Platz 1, 94501 Aldersbach
T 08543 17 75 **F** 08543 96 04 44
Closed Sun; Mon–Sat from 14.00
DB Vilshofen (Niederbayern) 10km

ALTDROSSENFELD
(Neudrossenfeld) 144

Schnupp
Brauerei-Gasthof Schnupp GmbH
Hauptstraße 8, 95512 Neudrossenfeld-Altdrossenfeld
T 09203 99 20 **F** 09203 992 50
www.brauereigasthof-schnupp.de
Owners: the Schnupp family Founded: 1726
Output: 3,000hl Availability: 5 pubs
REGULAR BEERS:
Schnupp Storchen Leichte
Schnupp Vollbier-Hell
Schnupp Edelpilsener (5.1%)
Schnupp Altfränkisch Dunkel (5.3%)
SEASONAL BEERS:
Schnupp Märzen-Festbier,
Schnupp Doppelbock (8%)

This small brewery has been in the hands of the Schupp family since 1726. It is served by bus No. 8354 from Bayreuth on weekdays.

🍎 **Schnupp**
Hauptstraße 8, 95512 Neudrossenfeld-Altdrossenfeld
Closed Fri; Sat–Thu 09.00–23.00;
rooms available
DB Bayreuth Hbf 12km

ALTENKUNSTADT 145

Leikeim
Brauerei Leikeim GmbH & Co. KG
Langheimer Straße 14, 96264 Altenkunstadt
T 09572 750 50 **F** 09572 75 05 31
www.leikeim.info
Owner: Christine Leikeim Founded: 1887
Output: 70,000hl
REGULAR BEERS:
Leikeim Premium (4.9%)
Leikeim Premium-Dry (4.9%)
Leikeim Schwarzbier (4.9%)
Leikeim Premium-Weisse (5.1%)
Leikeim White (5.2%)
Leikeim Schwarze Weiße (5.3%)
Leikeim Landbier Hell (5.4%)
SEASONAL BEER:
Leikeim Wintertraum (5.4%)

Large brewery without a tap but the beers are easily found throughout much of northern Franconia. If you want to try them locally and don't fancy the walk, bus No. 1 runs from Burgkunstadt station Mon–Fri. Also owns Brauerei Altenburg in Thüringen.

DB Burgkunstadt 1.7km

ALTOMÜNSTER 146

Kapplerbräu

Kapplerbräu Hans Wiedemann GmbH & Co. KG
Am Vogelgarten 2, 85250 Altomünster
T 08254 12 22   F 08254 92 34
www.kapplerbraeu.de
Founded: 1561   Output: 7,000hl
REGULAR BEERS:
Kapplerbräu Leichte Weisse (2.9%)
Kapplerbräu Pater Simon Pils (5%)
Kapplerbräu Pater Simon Piccolo Weizen (5.2%)
Kapplerbräu Echt Altomünsterer Weisse (5.4%)
Kapplerbräu Export Hell (5.5%)
Kapplerbräu Probst Sutor Märzen (5.5%)

Small brewery on the edge of the town centre. Brewing used to take place in the tap which dates from 1561. Has its own brewery museum.

Der Kapplerbräu
Nerbstraße 8, 85250 Altomünster
T 08254 777
Closed Mon; Tue–Sun 10.00–01.00; rooms available
DB Altomünster 450m

Maierbräu

Marktplatz 2, 85250 Altomünster
T 08254 998 70   F 08254 99 87 20
www.maierbraeu.de
Owners: Christoph & Jakob Maier
Founded: 1886   Output: 30,000hl
Availability: 150 pubs
REGULAR BEERS:
Maierbräu Mensch Maier (4.9%)
Maierbräu Alto-Dunkel (4.9%)
Maierbräu Jacobi Pils (4.9%)
Maierbräu Export Hell (4.9%)
Maierbräu Landler Weisse (5%)
Maierbräu Landler Dunkel Weisse (5%)
SEASONAL BEER:
Maierbräu Jahrtausend Sud Spezialbier Hell

Brewery and pub on the market square. Larger than its near-neighbour, Maierbräu beers can also be found in München.

Maierbräu
Marktplatz 2, 85250 Altomünster
T 08254 12 79   F 08254 99 87 66
Closed Tue; Wed–Mon 09.00–24.00; rooms available
DB Altomünster 300m

ALTÖTTING 147

Altöttinger Hell-Bräu

Herrenmühlstraße 15, 84503 Altötting
T 08671 981 50   F 08671 98 15 99
www.altoettinger-hellbraeu.de
Founded: 1890   Output: 20,000hl
REGULAR BEERS:
Altöttinger Pils (4.8%)
Altöttinger Fein-Herb (5%)
Altöttinger Weissbier (5%)
Altöttinger Weissbier Dunkel (5%)
Altöttinger Bayrisch Dunkel (5.2%)
Altöttinger Dult-Märzen (5.8%)
SEASONAL BEER:
Altöttinger Doppel-Bock (7.5%, Lent)

Hell-Bräu's brewery tap closed a few years ago, but you should still be able to find the beers fairly easily in this small market town.
DB Altötting 1.1km

ALZENAU 148

Brezel-Bräu

Wasserloser Straße 1, 63755 Alzenau
T 06023 13 50   F 06023 317 44
www.brezelbraeu.de
Founded: 2004   Output: 30hl
REGULAR BEERS:
Brezel-Bräu Märzen (5.5%)
Brezel-Bräu Weizenbier (5.5%)
SEASONAL BEER:
Brezel-Bräu Doppelbock-Dunkel (7.5%)

Pub and hotel on the southern side of town; began brewing in March 2004. Alzenau is on the KVG private line from Kahl to Schöllkrippen.

Zur Brezel
Wasserloser Straße 1, 63755 Alzenau

Closed Sun; Mon–Sat from 17.00; rooms available
DB Alzenau-Burg 700m, Alzenau 1.1km

AMBERG 149

Bruckmüller

Braurei Bruckmüller GmbH
Vilsstraße 2–6, 92224 Amberg
T 09621 488 00   **F** 09621 48 80 48
www.bruckmueller.de
Owners: the Bruckmüller family
Founded: 1490   Output: 30,000hl
REGULAR BEERS:
Bruckmüller Hell (4.7%)
Bruckmüller Pils-03 (4.7%)
Bruckmüller Hefeweizen (5.1%)
Bruckmüller Knappentrunk Dunkel (5.2%)
Bruckmüller Kellerbier (5.3%)
Bruckmüller Märzen (5.3%)
SEASONAL BEER:
Bruckmüller Superator

Amberg's largest brewery, Bruckmüller is close to the old town wall on the far side of the old town from the station. It was formerly a monastery.

🍺 Bruckmüller
Vilsstraße 2, 92224 Amberg
Closed Mon; Tue–Sun 09.00–23.00
DB Amberg 850m

Kummert

Brauerei Kummert GmbH & Co. KG
Raigeringer Straße 11–15, 92224 Amberg
T 09621 132 32   **F** 09621 132 10
Founded: 1927   Output: 20,000hl
REGULAR BEERS:
Kummert Bräu Leichtes Pils
Kummert Leichtes Vilstaler Weizen (2.9%)
Kummert Bräu Bayrisch Hell (4.7%)
Kummert Bräu 27er Urtyp (4.8%)
Kummert Bräu Export Pils (4.9%)
Kummert Bräu Altbayrisch Weizen (4.9%)
Kummert Bräu Kurpfalz Hefe-Weizen (4.9%)
Kummert Bräu Kristall Weizen (4.9%)
SEASONAL BEER:
Kummert Bräu Festbier
FOR BRAUHAUS AMBERG, AMBERG:
Brauhaus Amberg Vollbier (4.7%), **Brauhaus Amberg Pils** (4.9%), **Brauhaus Amberg Export** (5.3%)

Kummert's brewery and pub lie outside the walls on the eastern side of the town. Brews beers for Brauhaus Amberg which stopped in 1990.

🍺 Zum Kummert-Bräu
Raigeringer Straße 11, 92224 Amberg
T 09621 152 59   Daily 09.00–24.00
DB Amberg 1.2km

Schloderer

Schloderer Bräu OHG
Rathausstraße 4, 92224 Amberg
T 09621 42 07 07   **F** 09621 42 06 94
www.schlodererbraeu.de
Owners: Gerhard Schmidkonz & Wolf Trautner
Founded: 1998   Output: 1,000hl
Availability: 1 pub
REGULAR BEERS:
Schloderer Hell (4.9%)
Schloderer Weizen (5.1%)
Schloderer Dunkel (5.2%)
SEASONAL BEERS:
Schloderer Festbier (5.5%), **Schloderer Hexenstoff** (6.5%), **Schloderer Schlodator** (8.2%)

Brewpub in the centre of the old town, in a small courtyard off Rathausstraße. Opens very early, for those who can't do without a beer before breakfast.

🍺 Schloderer
Rathausstraße 4, 92224 Amberg
Sun 10.00–01.00, Mon–Sat 07.30–01.00
DB Amberg 400m

Sudhang

Hausbrauerei Am Sudhang
Sudhang 7, 92224 Amberg
T 09621 254 13
http://sudhang.de/sudhang-braeu
Owner: Arno Diener   Founded: 1985
Output: 100hl   Availability: 2 pubs
REGULAR BEERS:
Sudhang-Bräu Hell (4.8%)
Sudhang-Bräu Vollbier (5%)
Sudhang-Bräu Dunkel (5.5%)
SEASONAL BEERS:
Sudhang-Bräu Märzen (5.5%), **Sudhang-Bräu Weizen** (5.5%), **Sudhang-Bräu Fünfzehn Plus** (6.2%), **Sudhang-Bräu Bock** (7%)

Essentially a hobby brewery, Sudhang has been included as it supplies some local outlets. It's

found on the north-eastern edge of town.
DB Amberg 1.7km

Winkler

Brauerei Winkler GmbH & Co.KG
Schanzgäßchen 6, 92224 Amberg
T 09621 78 48 80   **F** 09621 784 88 22
www.brauerei-winkler.de
Owner: Josef Winkler   Founded: 1617
Output: 15,000hl
REGULAR BEERS:
Winkler Amberger Leichtes Helles
Winkler Amberger Leichtes Weizen
Winkler Premium Lager 1617 (4.5%)
Winkler Alt Amberger Urhell (4.8%)
Winkler Amberger Premium Pils (4.9%)
Winkler Alt Amberger Hefe-Weizen (5.1%)
SEASONAL BEER:
Winkler Alt Amberger Doppelbock (7.5%)
FOR SCHLIESSL, AMBERG:
Schliessl Standard Hell (4.8%), **Schliessl Silber Pils** (4.9%)

Small brewery just inside the old town walls on
Schanzgäßchen. Brews beers for Brauerei
Schliessl which can still be found in their pub at
Untere Nabburger Straße 8, just down the road
from the Winkler tap.

🍺 **Winkler**
Untere Nabburger Straße 34, 92224 Amberg
T 09621 232 39
Closed Tue; Wed–Mon 09.00–24.00
DB Amberg 450m

AMMERNDORF   150

Dorn-Bräu

Marktplatz 1–2, 90614 Ammerndorf
T 09127 575 44   **F** 09127 71 68
Owner: Helmut Murmann   Founded: 1730
Output: 10,000hl   Availability: 10 pubs
REGULAR BEERS:
Ammerndorfer Leicht
Ammerndorfer Hell (4.6%)
Ammerndorfer Pils (4.9%)
Ammerndorfer Lager-Urtyp (4.9%)
Ammerndorfer Spezial (5.2%)
Ammerndorfer Hefe-Weisse (5.2%)
Ammerndorfer Märzen
Ammerndorfer Landbier-Dunkel (5.6%)

SEASONAL BEERS:
Ammerndorfer Jubiläumstrunk,
Ammerndorfer Bockbier

Small brewery on the market square, with the
brewery tap close by. Possibly the easiest way to
reach Ammerndorf by public transport is on bus
No. 113 from Nürnberg (Rothenburger Straße).

🍺 **Zur Sonne**
Marktplatz 5, 90614 Ammerndorf
T 09127 86 33
Closed Tue; Wed–Mon 10.00–24.00
DB Roßtal 4km, Nürnberg Hbf 19km

AMPFERBACH (Burgebrach)   151

Herrmann

Brückenstraße 3, 96138 Burgebrach-Ampferbach
T 09546 372   **F** 09546 59 21 37
Owner: Georg Herrmann   Founded: 1754
Output: 800hl   Availability: 1 pub
REGULAR BEERS:
Herrmann Vollbier (5%)
Herrmann Lagerbier (5.5%)
Herrmann Hefe-Weißbier (5.5%)
SEASONAL BEER:
Herrmann Bock (6.5%)

Brewpub on the edge of the Steigerwald. Max-
Bräu, the other brewery in the village (open Tue,
Fri & Sat evenings only), has its beer brewed by
Zehendner in Mönchsambach. Bus No. 8244
runs direct from Bamberg on weekdays only.

🍺 **Herrmann**
Brückenstraße 3, 96138 Burgebrach-Ampferbach
Closed Tue; Wed–Mon from 9.00
DB Bamberg 20km

ANDECHS   152

Klosterbrauerei Andechs

Bergstraße 2, 82346 Andechs
T 08152 37 60   **F** 08152 37 62 67
www.andechs.de
Owners: Abtei St. Bonifaz München & Andechs
Founded: 1455   Output: 90,000hl
REGULAR BEERS:
Andechser Dunkel (4.7%)
Andechser Hell (4.8%)
Andechser Weißbier Hell (5.5%)

Andechser Weißbier Dunkel (5.5%)
Andechser Spezial Hell (5.8%)
Andechser Dunkel Naturtrüb (5.9%)
Andechser Bergbock Hell (6.9%)
Andechser Doppelbock Dunkel (7.1%)

Famous brewery that's still owned by Andechs Monastery. Although there are buses from Herrsching we recommend you try the walk up through the woods instead.

🍺 **Bräustüberl**
Bergstraße 2, 82346 Andechs
T 08152 37 62 61
Daily 10.00–20.00
DB Herrsching 4km

🍺 **Klostergasthof Andechs**
Bergstraße 9, 82346 Andechs
T 08152 930 90   **F** 08152 93 09 11
Daily 10.00–23.00

APPENDORF (Lauter)   153

Fößel-Mazour

Baunacher Straße 28, 96169 Lauter-Appendorf
T 09544 203 90
Founded: before 1871
Output: 500hl   Availability: 1 pub
REGULAR BEER:
Fößel-Mazour Kellerbier

Small brewpub which recently changed its name from Fößel-Batz. The beer is only available on draught. Bus 9110 runs a few times a day from Bamberg and Baunach, Monday to Friday only.

🍺 **Fößel-Mazour**
Baunacher Straße 28, 96169 Lauter-Appendorf
Closed Tue; Mon–Thu 09.00–23.00, Fri 09.00–13.00 & 17.00–23.00, Sat/Sun 09.00–23.00
DB Baunach 5km, Bamberg 13km

ARNHAUSEN (Bad Kissingen)   154

Wittelsbacher Turm-Bräu

Am Wittelsbacher Turm, Scheinberg, 97688
Bad Kissingen-Arnhausen
T 0971 785 88 20   **F** 0971 785 88 30
www.wittelsbacher-turm.de
Founded: 2002
Output: 1,000hl   Availability: 1 pub

REGULAR BEERS:
Turm-Bräu Vollbier
Turm-Bräu Hefeweizen
SEASONAL BEER:
Turm-Bräu Bock

Brewpub next to the Wittelsbacher tower on the Scheinberg, south-west of Arnshausen. No public transport – the nearest you can get by bus is Arnhausen village or Wilmsthal, both around 3km walk. Closes for the last three weeks in January.

🍺 **Wittelsbacher Turm**
Am Wittelsbacher Turm, Scheinberg, 97688
Bad Kissingen-Arnhausen
Apr–Oct: Mon/Tue & Wed 11.00–23.00, Thu–Sat 11.00–24.00, Sun & hols 10.00–23.00
Nov–Mar: closed Mon; Tue & Wed 11.00–22.00, Thu–Sat 11.00–24.00, Sun & hols 10.00–22.00
DB Oerlenbach 5km, Bad Kissingen 9km

ARNSCHWANG   155

Mühlbauer

Further Straße 10, 93473 Arnschwang
T 09977 221   **F** 09977 90 20 14
www.brauerei-muehlbauer.de
Owner: Peter Mühlbauer   Founded: 1150
Output: 12,000hl
REGULAR BEERS:
Mühlbauer Der Leichte Bär (2.7%)
Arnschwanger Pils (4.8%)
Mühlbauer Edel-Hell (5%)
Arnschwanger Bärenweisse (5%)
FOR SPÄTH-BRÄU, FURTH IM WALD:
Späth-Bräu Further Drachenweisse (4.5%),
Späth-Bräu Drachenblut (5.5%)

Small brewery in the Bavarian Forest, less than 10km from the Czech border. Brews beer for Späth-Bräu of Furth im Wald following that brewery's closure in 2001. No brewery tap.
DB Arnschwang 750m

ARNSTEIN   156

Arnsteiner

Arnsteiner Brauerei Max Bender GmbH & Co. KG
Schweinfurter Straße 9, 97450 Arnstein
T 09363 909 10   **F** 09363 90 91 11

www.arnsteiner-brauerei.de
Owners: Günther & Dr. Susan Schubert
Founded: 1885   Output: 30,000hl
REGULAR BEERS:
Arnsteiner Pils (4.9%)
Arnsteiner Ernte Hell (4.9%)
Arnsteiner Weissbier (5.2%)
Arnsteiner Ur-Weisse (5.4%)
Arnsteiner Dunkel Spezial (5.4%)
SEASONAL BEER:
Arnsteiner Festbier (5.4%)
FOR BURGBRAUEREI, THÜNGEN:
Herzog der Schwarze (5%),
Herzog Weisse (5.2%),
Herzog Ur-Weisse (5.4%), **Herzog Bock** (7.2%)

Arnsteiner also own Michelsbräu in
Babenhausen and Burgbrauerei in Thüngen.
The Guide believes most of the latter's beers
are brewed in Arnstein and the brewery did not
dispute this when contacted. Bus No. 8134 runs
from Waigolshausen on weekdays and bus No.
8114 runs from Würzburg Monday to Saturday.

🍺 Arnsteiner Bräustüberl
Schweinfurter Straße 9, 97450 Arnstein
T 09363 99 79 44
Closed Mon & Tue; Wed–Sat from 17.00,
Sun 11.00–22.00
[DB] Waigolshausen 13km, Würzburg 27km

ARNSTORF   157

Schloßbrauerei

Graf von Deym'sche Schloßbrauerei Arnstorf
Oberes Schloß 3, 94424 Arnstorf
T 08723 515   **F** 08723 430
Owner: Joseph Graf von Deym   Founded: 1618
Output: 3,000hl   Availability: 20 pubs
REGULAR BEERS:
Schloßbrauerei Arnstorf Pils
Schloßbrauerei Arnstorf Plinganser Bier
Schloßbrauerei Arnstorf Weißbier
Schloßbrauerei Arnstorf Export
SEASONAL BEER:
Schloßbrauerei Arnstorf Festbier

The brewery is in the castle grounds near the
town centre and the tap close by. Bus No. 6213
from Pfarrkirchen has the best service (only
one bus Sat, none Sun), but there are a couple
of direct buses from Landau and Osterhofen.

🍺 Oberwirt
Oberer Markt 5, 94424 Arnstorf
T 08723 16 11   **F** 08723 16 13
Daily 10.00–23.00; rooms available
[DB] Pfarrkirchen 18km

ASCHAFFENBURG   158

Schwindbräu

Schweinheimer Straße 119, 63743
Aschaffenburg-Schweinheim
T 06021 93 00 92   **F** 06021 96 00 06
Founded: 1761   Output: 15,000hl
REGULAR BEERS:
Schwind Bräu Pilsner Exclusiv (4.8%)
Schwind Bräu Edelquell Export (5.1%)
Schwind Bräu Alt Schwoihier Dunkel (5.2%)
SEASONAL BEERS:
Schwind Bräu Volksfestbier,
Schwind Bräu Josefator (6.8%)

Brewery in the suburb of Schwindheim. The tap
is built in a former brewhouse. Buses Nos. 5 and
10 run from the Hauptbahnhof to Schwindheim

🍺 Altes Sudhaus
Schweinheimer Straße 117, 63743
Aschaffenburg-Schweinheim
T 06021 96 06 09   **F** 06021 97 01 03
Closed Sat; Sun–Fri from 16.00;
rooms available
[DB] Aschaffenburg Süd 1.2km, Hbf 2.7km

ASCHAU am Inn   159

Ametsbichler

Hauptstraße 13, 84544 Aschau
T 08638 32 04   **F** 08638 95 41 99
www.ametsbichler.de
Owner: Georg Ametsbichler   Founded: 1876
Output: 1,500hl   Availability: 25 pubs
REGULAR BEERS:
Aschauer Hell (5%)
Aschauer Dunkel (5%)
Aschauer Spezial Pils (5%)

Small, family-run brewery in the Inn Valley with
a 100% organic production. Has recently
stopped brewing the Prima Weisse range. Take
bus No. 30 from Waldkraiburg on weekdays.

🍺 **Bräustüberl**

Hauptstraße 13, 84544 Aschau
Closed Tue; Wed–Mon 15.00–24.00
DB Waldkraiburg 4km

AU (Hallertau)   160

Schlossbrauerei

Schlossbrauerei Au/Hellertau Willibald
Freiherr Beck von Peccoz GmbH & Co. KG
Schlossbräugasse 2, 84072 Au
T 08752 8 63 20   F 08752 86 32 30
www.auer-bier.de
Owner: Freiherr Beck von Peccoz   Founded: 1590
Output: 75,000hl
REGULAR BEERS:
Schlossbrauerei Auer Light (2.9%)
Schlossbrauerei Holledauer Light (3.3%)
Schlossbrauerei Auer Hell (4.7%)
Schlossbrauerei Auer Pils (4.7%)
Schlossbrauerei Ecco Pilsner (4.9%)
Schlossbrauerei Holledauer Dunkles (5.3%)
Schlossbrauerei Hopfengold (5%)
Schlossbrauerei Auer Dunkel (5.2%)
Schlossbrauerei Holledauer Weisses (5.3%)
SEASONAL BEER:
Schlossbrauerei Peccator (7.9%)

One of Germany's many castle breweries (there
are 38 Schlossbrauereien, most of them in
Bayern), this is larger than most. Bus No. 610
runs from Freising daily.

🍺 **Schlossbräu Keller**

Schlossbräugasse 2, 84072 Au
T 08752 98 22   F 08752 86 90 22
Closed Mon; Tue–Thu 17.00–01.00, Fri–Sun
11.00–01.00   DB Freising 20km

AU am Inn   161

Kloster-Bräu

Kloster-Bräu Au am Inn
Klosterhof 3, 83546 Au am Inn
T 08073 12 09   F 08073 22 58
www.kloster-braeu.de
Owner: Hubert Gaßner   Founded: 1635
Output: 4,000hl   Availability: 10 pubs
REGULAR BEERS:
Kloster Au Chorherrn-Pils (5.3%)

Kloster Au Hell (5.3%)
Kloster Au Dunkel (5.3%)
Kloster Au Klostergold (5.8%)
SEASONAL BEER:
Kloster Au Ambrosiator (7.7%)

Brewery at Au's Franciscan monastery, though we
don't believe the monks have anything to do with
the brewing these days. There's only one bus a
day when the pub is open, No. 31 to/from Gars,
so if you don't have a car you might need to take
a taxi – or stay until the next bus comes along…

🍺 **Bräustüberl**

Klosterhof 4, 83546 Au am Inn
Sat, Sun & hols 10.00–24.00,
Mon–Fri 12.00–24.00   DB Gars (Inn) 7km

AUFKIRCH (Kaltental)   162

Kaltentaler Brauhaus

Blonhofener Straße 12, 87662 Kaltental-Aufkirch
T 08345 15 65   F 08345 92 57 38
www.kaltentaler-brauhaus.de   Founded: 2005
Output: 500hl   Availability: 3 pubs
REGULAR BEERS:
Kaltentaler Brauhaus Zwickl (5%)
Kaltentaler Brauhaus Weisse (5%)
SEASONAL BEERS:
Kaltentaler Brauhaus Schwarze (5.3%),
Kaltentaler Brauhaus Bock (February)

Brewing started next door to Gasthaus zur
Traube in June 2005, in a restored former
brewery, and already they supply three outlets.
Bus No. 58 runs from Kaufbeuren on weekdays
and there's an AST service at other times.

🍺 **Kaltentaler Brauhaus**

Blonhofener Straße 12, 87662 Kaltental-Aufkirch
Closed Wed; Thu–Tue 16.00–23.30
DB Kaufbeuren 13km

AUFSESS   163

Rothenbach

Brauerei Frank Rothenbach GmbH
Im Tal 70b, 91347 Aufseß
T 09198 82 82   F 09198 737
www.aufsesser.de
Owner: Frank Rothenbach   Founded: 1886
Output: 15,000hl   Availability: 30 pubs

REGULAR BEERS:
Aufsesser Dunkel (4.7%)
Aufsesser Pils (4.9%)
Aufsesser Weizen (5.1%)
SEASONAL BEERS:
Aufsesser Festbier (5.1%), **Aufsesser Bock** (6.5%)

Small brewery in the area known as Fränkische Schweiz (Franconian Switzerland). Bus No. 8235 runs a couple of times a day from Ebermannstadt and once from Bamberg, Mon–Fri only.

🍺 Sonnenhof
Im Tal 70, 91347 Aufseß
T 09198 929 20   **F** 09198 9 29 22 90
Closed Tue; Wed–Mon 08.00–23.00; rooms available
DB Ebermannstadt 15km, Bamberg 25km

AUGSBURG   164

Augusta
Lauterlech 10–14, 86152 Augsburg-Innenstadt
T 0821 34 67 80   **F** 0821 15 73 61
www.augusta-brauerei.de
Owners: the Engelsmann family
Founded: 1488   Output: 12,000hl
Availability: c. 60 pubs
REGULAR BEERS:
Augusta Leicht (2.8%)
Augusta Urhell (4.8%)
Augusta Pils (4.8%)
Augusta Kellerbier (4.8%)
Augusta Schwarzbier (5.1%)
Augusta Hefe-Weizen (5.1%)
Augusta Privat (5.2%)
Augusta Edelquell Märzen (5.6%)
Augusta Hunnen-Bock (8%)
SEASONAL BEERS:
Augusta Jakober Kirchweih Festbier (5.6%),
Augusta Weihnachtsbier (5.6%)

Town-centre brewery that was damaged during World War II. The brewery tap is behind the Fuggerei.

🍺 Drei Königinnen
Meister-Veits-Gäßchen 32,
86152 Augsburg-Innenstadt
T 0821 15 84 05
Closed Mon; Tue–Sun 18.00–01.00
Tram No. 1 Jakobsplatz 250m
DB Augsburg Hbf 1.6km

Charly Bräu
Ulmer Straße 43, 86154 Augsburg-Oberhausen
T 0821 42 63 46   **F** 0821 42 63 43
www.charly-braeu.de
Owner: Dieter Held   Founded: 1992
Output: 700hl   Availability: 1 pub
REGULAR BEERS:
Charly Bräu Kellerbier
Charly Weisse
Charly Bräu Oberhauser-Dunkel
SEASONAL BEER:
Charly Bräu Primus

Street-corner brewpub on the square outside Oberhausen station. Formerly owned by Hofbräuhaus Traunstein.

🍺 Charly Bräu
Ulmer Straße 43, 86154 Augsburg-Oberhausen
Fri & Sat 11.00–01.00, Sun–Thu 11.00–24.00
Tram No. 2 Oberhausen Bahnhof 20m
DB Augsburg-Oberhausen 150m

Hasen-Bräu
Brewery: Konrad-Adenauer-Allee 33,
86150 Augsburg-Innenstadt
Office: Unterer Talweg 87,
86179 Augsburg-Haunstetten
T 0821 329 90   **F** 0821 329 91 11
www.hasen-braeu.de
Owner: Oetker Gruppe AG   Founded: 1464
Output: 180,000hl
REGULAR BEERS:
Hasen-Bräu Leichte
Hasen-Bräu Leichte Weiße
Hasen-Bräu Urhell (5%)
Hasen-Bräu Pilsener (5%)
Hasen-Bräu 33 Dry (5%)
Hasen-Bräu Weißer Hase (5.2%)
Hasen-Bräu Extra (5.3%)
SEASONAL BEER:
Hasen-Bräu Oster-Festbier (6%)
FOR BÜRGERBRÄU, AUGSBURG:
Burgerbräu Hell, Burgerbräu Hefe-Weizen Hell, Burgerbräu Alte Weiße
FOR GOLDENE GANS, AUGSBURG:
Goldene Gans Leichte Weisse, Goldene Gans 1346 Urhell, Goldene Gans Karolinen Weisse
FOR KLOSTERBRAUEREI, SCHEYERN:
Scheyern Kloster Gold (5.4%), **Scheyern Kloster Export-Dunkel** (5.4%), **Scheyern Kloster Dunkles Weizen, Scheyern Kloster Doppelbock Dunkel**

Large brewery, now owned by the Oetker Group. The tap is in the old town, not far from the main square. Hasen continue to brew around 15,000hl of beer a year for Klosterbrauerei Scheyern, despite the latter re-opening in late 2005.

Zum Weißen Hasen
Annastraße/Unter dem Bogen 4,
86150 Augsburg-Innenstadt
T 0821 51 85 08
Daily 10.00–22.00
Nos. 1 & 2 Rathausplatz 150m
DB Augsburg Hbf 1km

König von Flandern

Karolinenstraße 12, 86150 Augsburg-Innenstadt
T 0821 15 80 50   **F** 0821 31 42 87
www.koenigvonflandern.de
Founded: 1988
Output: 1,300hl   Availability: 1 pub
REGULAR BEERS:
Drei-Heller-Bier Hell (4.9%)
Drei-Heller-Bier Dunkel (5.1%)
Alligator (7.2%)

The King of Flanders is a brewpub in the cellar of the old Augsburg bath houses, just up the street from the town hall.

König von Flandern
Karolinenstraße 12, 86150 Augsburg-Innenstadt
Sun & hols 17.00–01.00, Mon–Sat 11.00–01.00
Nos. 1 & 2 Rathausplatz 100m
DB Augsburg Hbf 1.2km

Riegele

Brauhaus Sebastian Riegele
Frölichstraße 26, 86150 Augsburg-Innenstadt
T 0821 320 90   **F** 0821 32 09 80
www.riegele.de
Owner: Dr. Sebastian Priller-Riegele & family
Founded: 1884   Output: 200,000hl
Availability: c. 400 pubs
REGULAR BEERS:
Riegele Leichte Weisse (2.9%)
Riegele Feines Urhell (4.7%)
Riegele Augsburger Herren Pils (4.7%)
Riegele Aechtes Dunkel (4.9%)
Sebastian Riegele's Weisse (5%)
Riegele Alte Weisse (5%)
Riegele Würziges Export (5.1%)
Commerzienrat Riegele Privat (5.2%)

SEASONAL BEERS:
Riegele Augsburger Christkindl Bier (5.2%),
Riegele Speziator Doppelbock (7.5%)

Augsburg's largest brewery is next to the railway, just north of the main station. The upmarket tap is a couple of hundred metres away, directly opposite the station.

Hotel Riegele
Viktoriastraße 4, 86150 Augsburg-Innenstadt
T 0821 50 90 00   **F** 0821 51 77 46
Sun 11.00–14.00, Mon–Sat 11.00–14.00 &
17.00–22.00; rooms available
DB Augsburg Hbf 130m

Thorbräu

Wertachbrucker-Tor-Straße 9,
86152 Augsburg-Zentrum
T 0821 365 61   **F** 0821 15 88 27
www.thorbraeu.de
Founded: 1582
Output: 15,000hl
Availability: c. 50 pubs
REGULAR BEERS:
Thorbräu Leichte Weisse (2.7%)
Thorbräu Hell (4.8%)
Thorbräu Pils (4.8%)
Thorbräu Export (5%)
Thorbräu Hefe-Weizen (5%)
Thorbräu Augsburger Altstadt Weiße (5%)
Thorbräu Celtic Bier (5%)
Thorbräu Maximilian's Premium (5.5%)
Thorbräu Maximilian's Kellerbier (5.5%)
Thorbräu Dunkel (5.5%)
Thorbräu Dunkel Unfiltriert (5.5%)
SEASONAL BEER:
Thorbräu Portator (7.5%)

Brewery and tap on the northern edge of the city centre, opposite the Wertacher tower.

Zum Thorbräu
Wertachbrucker-Tor-Straße 9,
86152 Augsburg-Zentrum
T 0821 346 35 57
Closed Mon; Tue–Fri 11.00–14.00 & 18.00–24.00,
Sat 18.00–24.00, Sun 11.00–14.00 & 18.00–24.00
No. 2 Senkelbach 170m
DB Augsburg Hbf 1.5km

AUTENRIED (Ichenhausen) 165

Schlossbrauerei

Schlossbrauerei Autenried GmbH
Bräuhausstraße 2, 89335 Ichenhausen-Autenried
T 08223 968 40   **F** 08223 96 84 20
www.autenrieder.de
Owners: Leonhard & Rudolf Feuchtmayr
Founded: 1650   Output: 60,000hl
Availability: 180 pubs
REGULAR BEERS:
Autenrieder Schlossbräu Leicht (3%)
Autenrieder Ernte Weizen (3%)
Autenrieder Urtyp Hell (5%)
Autenrieder Pilsner (5%)
Autenrieder Urytp Dunkel (5.3%)
Autenrieder Weizenbier (5.3%)
Autenrieder Dunkles Weizen (5.3%)
Autenrieder Weizen Bock (7.2%)
Autenrieder Leonhardi Bock (7.8%)
SEASONAL BEER:
Autenrieder Festbier (5.6%)

Fairly large village brewery and tap with some
rooms available. Space 2000, Anno 1650 Zwickel
and Schwarzer Baron have all recently been
dropped from the range. Bus No. 870 will take
you there from Ichenhausen (no Sun service).

🍴 **Brauereigasthof**
Bräuhausstraße 2, 89335 Ichenhausen-Autenried
T 08223 96 84 40
Closed Sat; Sun–Thu 09.00–23.00, Fri 09.00–
14.00; food 11.00–23.00 (14.00 on Friday);
rooms available
DB Ichenhausen 4.5km

AYING 166

Aying

Zornedinger Straße 1, 85653 Aying
T 08095 880   **F** 08095 88 50
www.ayinger-bier.de
Owner: Franz Inselkammer   Founded: 1878
Output: 140,000hl
REGULAR BEERS:
Ayinger Leichte Bräu-Weisse (3.2%)
Ayinger Bräu-Hell (4.9%)
Ayinger Liebhard's Kellerbier (4.9%)
Ayinger Premium Pils (5%)
Ayinger Altbairisch Dunkel (5%)

Ayinger Bräu-Weisse (5.1%)
Ayinger Jahrhundertbier (5.5%)
Ayinger Ur-Weisse (5.8%)
Ayinger Celebrator Doppelbock (6.7%)
SEASONAL BEERS:
Ayinger Frühlingsbier (5.5%, spring), **Ayinger
Kirta-Halbe** (5.8%), **Ayinger Oktober Fest-Märzen**
(5.8%), **Ayinger Winter-Bock** (6.7%, Nov–Jan),
Ayinger Mai Bock (6.8%)

Ayinger beers will be familiar to many British
readers as some are brewed under licence by
Samuel Smith. The brewery is no longer at
Zornedinger Straße 1, having moved to new
premises on the outskirts of town in 1999.

🍴 **Aying**
Zornedinger Straße 2, 85653 Aying
T 08095 906 50   **F** 08095 90 65 66
Daily 11.30–14.30 & from 18.00; rooms available
DB Aying 1km

BAD BIRNBACH 167

Graf Arco

Gräfliche Brauerei Arco-Valley
Graf-Arco-Straße 1, 84364 Bad Birnbach
T 08563 964 90   **F** 08563 96 49 49
www.graf-arco.de
Owner: Monica Gräfin von Arco auf Valley
Founded: 1673
REGULAR BEER:
Graf Arco Birnbacher Schwarzbier (4.8%)

Graf Arco's second brewery, which these days
brews nothing but Schwarzbier. There's no
brewery tap in Bad Birnbach, Arco-Quelle in
Adldorf serving as the tap for both breweries.
DB Bad Birnbach 2.7km

BAD NEUSTADT (Saale) 168

Karmeliter-Bräu

Schweinfurter Straße 105–107,
97616 Bad Neustadt
T 09771 13 23   **F** 09771 983 99
www.karmeliter-braeu.de
Founded: 1352
Output: 18,000hl   Availability: 50 pubs
REGULAR BEERS:
Karmeliter Lager (4.8%)

Karmeliter Edel-Pils (4.8%)
Karmeliter Rhöner Dunkel (5.2%)
Karmeliter Export (5.2%)
Karmeliter Weissbier (5.2%)
Karmeliter Märzen (5.2%)

Long-established brewery in a walled town in northern Franconia. The brewery tap is in the old town, close to the wall.

🍺 Rathschenke
Roßmarktstraße 36, 97616 Bad Neustadt
T 09771 26 92
Closed Mon; Tue–Sun 11.00–24.00
DB Bad Neustadt (Saale) 1.2km

BAD REICHENHALL 169

Bürgerbräu

Bürgerbräu Bad Reichenhall August Röhm & Söhne KG
Waaggasse 1–3, 83435 Bad Reichenhall
T 08651 60 80   **F** 08651 60 86 29
www.buergerbraeu.com
Founded: 1633
REGULAR BEERS:
Unser Bürgerbräu Leichte Weiße (3%)
Unser Bürgerbräu Edel-Pilsner (4.8%)
Unser Bürgerbräu Ruperti-Dunkel (4.9%)
Unser Bürgerbräu Kur-Pils (4.9%)
Unser Bürgerbräu Pils-Superior (4.9%)
Unser Bürgerbräu Hefe-Weizen (5.2%)
Unser Bürgerbräu Hefe-Weizen Dunkel (5.2%)
Unser Bürgerbräu Export (5.4%)
Unser Bürgerbräu Braumeister-Bier (5.4%)
SEASONAL BEERS:
Unser Bürgerbräu Rupertus (7%),
Unser Bürgerbräu Hallgrafen-Bock (7.2%),
Unser Bürgerbräu Suffikator (7.3%)

Brewery and tap at the southern end of the town centre. If you're coming by train, the small Bad Reichenhall-Kirchberg station is much closer to the brewery than Bad Reichenhall itself.

🍺 Bürgerbräu
Waaggasse 1, 83435 Bad Reichenhall
T 08651 60 89   **F** 08651 60 85 04
Daily 10.00–24.00
DB Bad Reichenhall-Kirchberg 450m

BAD WINDSHEIM 170

Bürgerbräu

Bad Windsheimer Bürgerbräu Strauß KG
Metzgergasse 8–18, 91438 Bad Windsheim
T 09841 666 20   **F** 09841 66 62 99
Founded: 1923   Output: 35,000hl
Availability: 100 pubs
REGULAR BEERS:
Windsheimer Hell (4.8%)
Windsheimer Primus Pils (4.9%)
Alt Windsheimer Kiliani Dunkel
Windsheimer Meister-Gold
Windsheimer Weisse
Windsheimer Schwarze
SEASONAL BEER:
Windsheimer Festbier

The largest of Bad Windsheim's three breweries, Bürgerbräu also runs its smallest, the Fränkisches Freilandmuseum's brewery. It is believed Bürgerbräu stopped brewing in 2001. We think it's now brewing again – we may be wrong!

🍺 Bürgerbräu-Stuben
An der Alten Weed 10, 91438 Bad Windsheim
T 09841 15 44   **F** 09841 32 52
Closed Mon; Tue–Sun 10.00–15.00 & 17.00–01.00
DB Bad Windsheim 500m

Döbler

Kornmarkt 6, 91438 Bad Windsheim
T 09841 20 02   **T** 09841 797 77
www.brauhaus-doebler.de
Owner: Wilhelm Döbler   Founded: 1867
Output: 5,000hl   Availability: 10 pubs
REGULAR BEERS:
Döbler Leichtes Pils (2.9%)
Döbler Altstadt Hell (4.8%)
Döbler Pils (4.9%)
Döbler Windsheimer Reichsstadtbier (5%)
Döbler Land Märzen (5.4%)
Döbler Hefeweizen (5.6%)
SEASONAL BEERS:
Döbler Fränkisches Festtagsbier (5.8%),
Döbler Weihnachts-Festbier (5.8%),
Döbler Doppelbock (8.1%)

Small brewery on the old Corn Market. Döbler Museums Löschauer Dunkel is brewed in the Freilandmuseum, then lagered and bottled by Döbler. Note the complicated opening hours.

🍺 Döbler

Kornmarkt 6, 91438 Bad Windsheim
Closed Sun & hols; Mon, Wed & Fri 09.00–23.00,
Tue 09.00–13.00, Thu 09.00–19.00, Sat 09.00–
17.00
DB Bad Windsheim 700m

Fränkisches Freilandmuseum

Eisweiherweg 1, 91438 Bad Windsheim
T 09841 668 00   **F** 09841 66 80 99
www.freilandmuseum.de
Founded: 1996   Output: 500hl
REGULAR BEERS:
Freilandmuseum Zwickel-Pils (4.6%)
Freilandmuseum Pils (4.8%)
Freilandmuseum Dunkel (5%)
Döbler Museums Löschauer Dunkel (5.3%)

Country museum with two breweries moved
here for preservation, Hofbrauhaus Kraisdorf
and Kommunbrauhaus Schlüsselfeld. The former
only brews once a year on 23rd April, the latter
brews most Wednesdays from late spring.

🍺 Wirtschaft am Brauhaus

Haus 32, Eisweiherweg 1,
91438 Bad Windsheim
T 09841 65 09 50   **F** 09841 65 10 60
Mon 09.00–15.00, Tue–Sun 09.00–22.00
DB Bad Windsheim 1.5km

BAD WÖRISHOFEN   171

Löwenbräu

Bad Wörishofer Löwenbräu
Hermann-Aust-Straße 2, 86825 Bad Wörishofen
T 08247 968 40   **F** 08247 320 51
www.loewenbraeu-bad-woerishofen.de
Owner: Roland Forster   Founded: 1905
REGULAR BEERS:
Bad Wörishofer Löwenbräu Kur-Pils (4.7%)
Bad Wörishofer Löwen-Urtrunk (4.9%)
Bad Wörishofer Löwenbräu Helles (4.9%)
Bad Wörishofer Dunkel (5%)
Bad Wörishofer Weißbier (5.2%)
Bad Wörishofer Löwen-Krone (5.3%)
SEASONAL BEER:
Bad Wörishofer Löwenbräu Leusator (7.5%)

Large brewpub and hotel in this northern
Allgäu spa town. The spa itself is nearby.

🍺 Löwenbräu

Hermann-Aust-Straße 2, 86825 Bad Wörishofen
Closed Mon; Tue–Sun 07.00–24.00; rooms
available   DB Bad Wörishofen 800m

BAMBERG   172

Ambräusianum

Dominikanerstraße 10, 96049 Bamberg
T 0951 509 02 62   **F** 0951 29 71 96 99
www.ambraeusianum.de
Owner: Ambros Michael Mahr
Founded: 04.08.2004
REGULAR BEERS:
Ambräusianum Hell
Ambräusianum Dunkel
Ambräusianum Weizen

Ambräusianum, a couple of doors along from
Brauerei Heller's famous tap, opened August
2004, the first brewpub to do so in Bamberg
since 1887.

🍺 Ambräusianum

Dominikanerstraße 10, 96049 Bamberg
Daily 11.00–24.00
DB Bamberg 1.6km

Fässla

Brauerei Fässla oHG
Obere Königstraße 19–21, 96052 Bamberg
T 0951 265 16   **F** 0951 20 19 89
www.faessla.de
Owner: Roland Kalb   Founded: 1649
Output: 13,000hl
REGULAR BEERS:
Fässla Weizla-Hell (5%)
Fässla Weizla-Dunkel (5%)
Fässla Lagerbier (5.5%)
Fässla Gold-Pils (5.5%)
Fässla Zwergla (6%)
SEASONAL BEER:
Fässla Bambergator (8.5%)

Brewery and tap in the new town. The rooms
above the pub are good value and some overlook
the brewery at the back.

🍺 Fässla

Obere Königstraße 19–21, 96052 Bamberg
Sun 08.30–13.00, Mon–Sat 08.30–23.00;
rooms available   DB Bamberg 700m

Greifenklau

Privater Brauereigasthof Greifenklau
Laurenziplatz 20, 96049 Bamberg
T 0951 532 19   **F** 0951 595 99
www.greifenklau.de
Owner: Sigmund Brockard   Founded: 1719
Output: 1,300hl
REGULAR BEERS:
Greifenklau Lagerbier (4.8%)
Greifenklau Pils (4.9%)
Greifenklau Weizen (5.2%)
SEASONAL BEERS:
Greifenklau Festbier (5.5%),
Greifenklau Bockbier (7%)

The smallest of Bamberg's established breweries,
Greifenklau stands above the old town on the
Kaulberg. The beer range has expanded in recent
years to include a Pils and a Weizen.

🍺 **Greifenklau**
Laurenziplatz 20, 96049 Bamberg
Closed Mon; Tue–Sat 09.00–23.30,
Sun & hols 09.30–14.00
DB Bamberg 2.6km

Heller

Heller-Bräu Trum KG
Brewery: Oberer Stephansberg 27–31,
96049 Bamberg
Office: Dominikanerstraße 6, 96049 Bamberg
T 0951 560 60   **F** 0951 540 19
www.smokebeer.com
Owners: the Trum family   Founded: 1678
Output: 12,000hl
REGULAR BEERS:
Schlenkerla Lagerbier (4.3%)
Aecht Schlenkerla Rauchbier-Märzen (5.1%)
Schlenkerla Rauchweizen (5.1%)
SEASONAL BEERS:
Aecht Schlenkerla Fastenbier (5.5%, Lent),
Aecht Schlenkerla Rauchbier-Urbock (6.5%)

Commonly known as Schlenkerla, which is
actually the name of its famous brewery tap,
the brewery moved to its current location on the
Stephansberg in 1936.

🍺 **Schlenkerla**
Dominikanerstraße 6, 96049 Bamberg
T 0951 560 60   **F** 0951 540 19
Closed Tue; Wed–Mon 09.30–13.30
DB Bamberg 1.6km

Kaiserdom

Kaiserdom Privatbrauerei Wörner GmbH & Co.
Breitäckerstraße 9, 96049 Bamberg-Gaustadt
T 0951 604 50   **F** 0951 60 45 60
www.kaiserdom.de   Owner: Georg Wörner
Founded: 1718   Output: 200,000hl
REGULAR BEERS:
Kaiserdom Pilsener (4.8%)
Kaiserdom Meranier Schwarzbier (4.8%)
Kaiserdom Export (5.2%)
Weizenland Weissbier Hefetrüb (5.3%)
Weizenland Weissbier Dunkel (5.3%)
Weizenland Weissbier Kristallklar (5.3%)
FOR RÖCKELEINS KELLER, BAMBERG:
Röckeleins Kellerbier

Known as Bürgerbräu until 1983, Kaiserdom is
Bamberg's largest brewery by far. It brewed
Röckeleins Kellerbier for the Röckeleins Keller
which closed in 2003, but the beer was still
available in summer 2005.

🍺 **Kaiserdom**
Gaustadter Hauptstraße 26, 96049
Bamberg-Gaustadt
T 0951 96 51 40   **F** 0951 965 14 44
Mon 18.00–22.00, Tue–Sun 11.00–14.00 &
17.00–22.00; rooms available
DB Bamberg 3.8km

Keesmann

Wunderburg 5, 96050 Bamberg
T 0951 98 19 80   **F** 0951 981 98 14
www.keesmann-braeu.de
Owner: Elisabeth Keesmann   Founded: 1867
Output: 15,000hl
REGULAR BEERS:
Keesmann Hell (4.5%)
Keesmann Bamberger Herren-Pils (4.6%)
Keesmann Weissbier (4.8%)
Keesmann Sternla (5%)
SEASONAL BEER:
Keesmann Josephi Bock (6.2%, Mar–Apr),
Keesmann Bock (6.4%, Oct–Dec)

This small brewery and tap is located in the
village of Wunderburg, now a suburb in south-
east Bamberg. Brauerei Mahr is opposite.

🍺 **Keesmann**
Wunderburg 5, 96050 Bamberg
T 0951 981 98 10
Closed Sun; Mon–Fri 09.00–23.00,
Sat 09.00–15.00   DB Bamberg 1.6km

Klosterbräu

Obere Mühlbrücke 1–3, 96049 Bamberg
T 0951 577 22   **F** 0951 592 94
www.klosterbraeu.de
Owner: Anne-Rose Schröder-Braun
Founded: 1533   Output: 4,000hl
REGULAR BEERS:
Klosterbräu Schwärzla (4.9%)
Klosterbräu Braun's Weisse (4.9%)
Klosterbräu Bamberger Gold (5%)
Klosterbräu Braunbier (5.7%)
SEASONAL BEERS:
Klosterbräu Maibock (7%), **Klosterbräu Bock** (7%),
Klosterbräu Schwärzla Bock (7%)

Bamberg's oldest brewery sits at the foot of the
Stephansberg, close to the river Regnitz.
There's a Braunbierfest each August.

🍺 **Klosterbräu**

Obere Mühlbrücke 1–3, 96049 Bamberg
T 0951 522 65   **F** 0951 50 02 74
Sat, Sun & hols 10.00–23.00, Mon–Fri 10.30–23.00;
food 11.00–14.30 & 17.00–22.00
DB Bamberg 1.8km

Mahr's Bräu

Wunderburg 10, 96050 Bamberg
T 0951 91 51 70   **F** 0951 915 17 30
www.mahrs.de
Owner: Ingmar Michel   Founded: 1670
Output: 25,000hl   Availability: c. 30 pubs
REGULAR BEERS:
Mahr's-Bräu Leicht (2.8%)
Mahr's-Bräu Lager (4.8%)
Mahr's-Bräu Hell (4.9%)
Mahr's-Bräu Pilsner (4.9%)
Mahr's Weisse (4.9%)
Mahr's-Bräu Ungespundet (5.2%)
SEASONAL BEERS:
Mahr's-Bräu Jubelfestbier (4.9%), **Mahr's Gig**
(5.2%), **Mahr's KLGB Bier** (5.2%), **Mahr's Kaiser
Heinrich** (5.2%), **Mahr's Festtags-Weisse** (5.5%),
Mahr's-Bräu Bock-Bier (6.5%), **Mahr's Weisse-
Bock** (7.2%)

Just across the street from Keesmann, Mahr's
brewery sits alongside the tap and beer garden.
Recently voted 'best brewery in the world' by an
American magazine.

🍺 **Mahr's-Bräu**

Wunderburg 10, 96050 Bamberg
Daily 09.00–23.00   DB Bamberg 1.6km

Maisel

Maisel Bräu Bamberg Privatbrauerei GmbH & Co
Moosstraße 46, 96050 Bamberg
T 0951 91 82 70   **F** 0951 169 63
www.maisel-braeu-bamberg.de
Owner: Udo Zoebelein   Founded: 1894
Output: 80,000hl   Availability: 200 pubs
REGULAR BEERS:
Maisel Bamberger Leichtes (2.6%)
Maisel Bamberger Hell (4.6%)
Maisel Pils (4.7%)
Maisel Domreiter Pils (4.7%)
Maisel Premium Lager (4.9%)
Maisel Kellerbier (4.9%)
Maisel Eine Bamberger Weisse (5.2%)
Maisel Eine Bamberger Weisse-Dunkel (5.2%)
SEASONAL BEERS:
Maisel Festbier (5.2%),
Maisel Heller Bock Premium (6.7%),
Maisel Dunkler Bock Premium (6.7%)
ST. MICHAELSBERG BEERS:
St. Michaelsberg Dunkel (4.4%),
St. Michaelsberg Feinherb (4.6%),
St. Michaelsberg Urtyp (4.6%)

Bamberg's second largest brewery is to the east
of the railway, about a mile south of the station.
The brewery tap close-by is the only one in
Bamberg to stay open past midnight. The
Michaelsberg beers were formerly brewed by
Brauerei Michaelsberg, now the Franconian
Brewery Museum, which closed in 1969.

🍺 **Maisel-Keller**

Moosstraße 32, 96050 Bamberg
T 0951 149 75
Sat 10.00–02.00, Sun–Fri 10.00–01.00
DB Bamberg 1.6km

Robesbierre

Oberer Stephansberg 49, 96049 Bamberg
E brauhaus-robesbierre@web.de
Owner: Robert Pawelczak   Founded: 2000
Output: 15hl
REGULAR BEERS:
Robesbierre Pils (5%)
Robesbierre Ungespundet (5%)
Robesbierre Stephansberger Urtyp (5.8%)
SEASONAL BEERS:
Robesbierre Festbier (6%),
Robesbierre Bock (7.5%)

Tiny brewery under the Wilde Rose Keller in the
former lagerhaus of the Wilde Rose brewery.

More a hobby than a commercial enterprise, Robert Pawelczak only brews around six times a year. The beers are very rare, but they do occasionally appear in the Stöhrenkeller.

🍺 Stöhrenkeller
Obere Stephansberg 11, 96049 Bamberg
T 0951 302 07 88
Closed Sun; Mon–Sat 19.00–01.00
DB Bamberg 2.5km

Spezial

Obere Königstraße 10, 96052 Bamberg
T 0951 243 04   **F** 0951 263 30
www.brauerei-spezial.de
Owner: Christian Merz   Founded: 1536
Output: 6,000hl   Availability: 3 pubs
REGULAR BEERS:
Spezial Rauchbier Lager (4.7%)
Spezial Ungespundet (4.9%)
Spezial Rauchbier Weissbier (5.2%)
Spezial Rauchbier Märzen (5.3%)
SEASONAL BEER:
Spezial Rauchbier Bock (6.5%)

The world's oldest producer of Rauchbier (smoke beer), Spezial is directly opposite Fässla. The small brewery and maltings are behind the pub. Annual holiday first week in September.

🍺 Spezial
Obere Königstraße 10, 96052 Bamberg
Sat 09.00–14.00, Sun–Fri 09.00–23.00; rooms available
DB Bamberg 700m

BARTHELMESAURACH
(Kammerstein)   **173**

Gundel

Brauerei Gundel GmbH
Nördlinger Straße 15,
91126 Kammerstein-Barthelmesaurach
T 09178 15 04   **F** 09178 57 93
www.brauerei-gundel.de
Owner: the Gundel family   Founded: 1602
Output: 3,000hl   Availability: 10 pubs
REGULAR BEERS:
Gundel Urhell (4.9%)
Gundel Pils (5%)
Gundel Dunkles Gold (5.2%)
Gundel Export (5.2%)

SEASONAL BEERS:
Gundel Festbier (5.4%, Christmas),
Gundel Bock (6.5%, Christmas)

Small brewery that's been owned by the Gundel family since 1908. There's a very poor bus service from Schwabach (No. 607) that is only of any use on weekday mornings. The tap specialises in Greek food.

🍺 Bräustüberl
Nördlinger Straße 14,
91126 Kammerstein-Barthelmesaurach
T 09178 15 03
Closed Mon; Tue–Sun 11.00–14.00 & 17.00–01.00
DB Schwabach 10km

BAUMBURG (Altenmarkt)   **174**

Klosterbrauerei Dietl

Brauerei Dietl, Klosterbrauerei Baumburg
Baumburg 20, 83352 Altenmarkt-Baumburg
T 08621 982 60   **F** 08621 98 26 24
www.baumburger.de
Owner: Ludwig Dietl   Founded: 1612
Output: 4,000hl   Availability: 20 pubs
REGULAR BEERS:
Baumburger Kloster-Hell (4.8%)
Baumburger Kloster-Hell Zwickelbier (4.8%)
Baumburger Pils (4.8%)
Baumburger Kloster-Weiße (4.8%)
Baumburger Export Hell (5.3%)
Baumburger Dunkle Weiße (5.3%)
SEASONAL BEER:
Baumburger Festbier (5.6%),
Baumburger Chorherren Bock (6.9%)

Small brewery close to the monastery in the village of Baumburg, near Altenmarkt. The beer range has expanded in recent years.

🍺 Bräustübl Baumburg
Baumburg 12, 83352 Altenmarkt-Baumburg
T/F 08621 51 55
Daily 11.00–24.00   DB Altenmarkt (Alz) 600m

BAUNACH   **175**

Sippel

Burgstraße 20, 96148 Baunach
T 09544 24 88   Owner: Johann Baptist Fößel
Founded: 1600

Output: 400hl   Availability: 1 pub
REGULAR BEER:
Sippel Vollbier-Dunkel

Small brewpub across the river from the station. The beer is only available at the pub, and only on draught.

🍺 **Sippel**
Burgstraße 20, 96148 Baunach
Closed Wed; Thu–Tue 09.00–24.00; rooms available   DB Baunach 350m

BAYREUTH   176

Becher-Bräu
St. Nikolausstraße 25, 95445 Bayreuth-Altstadt
T 0921 689 93   **F** 0921 51 35 11
Owner: Anna Hacker   Founded: 1781
Output: 2,000hl   Availability: 3 pubs
REGULAR BEERS:
Becher Hell (4.7%)
Becher Pils (4.7%)
Becher Dunkel (4.7%)
Becher Kräusenpils
SEASONAL BEERS:
Becher Festbier (5.5%), **Becher Bockbier** (winter)

Bayreuth's smallest brewery is tucked away on the western side of the city. Bus No. 5 from the station to Geseeser Weg is probably the best bet if you don't mind the long walk.

🍺 **Becher-Bräu**
St. Nikolausstraße 25, 95445 Bayreuth-Altstadt
Closed Tue; Wed–Mon 09.00–24.00
DB Bayreuth Hbf 2.6km

Bürgerbräu
(formerly '**Brauhaus Schinner**')
Bindlacher Straße 10,
95448 Bayreuth-Industriegebiet
T 0921 797 80   **F** 0921 79 78 20
www.buergerbraeu-bth.de
Founded: 1860   Output: 50,000hl
BÜRGERBRÄU BEERS:
Bürgerbräu Edel-Pils (4.9%)
Bürgerbräu Edel-Weisse (4.9%)
Bürgerbräu Premium Schwarzbier (5%)
Bürgerbräu Export Hell (5%)
SCHINNER BEERS:
Schinner Premium Edel-Pils (4.9%), **Schinner Altfranken Urstoff** (4.9%), **Schinner Premium**

Edel-Weisse (4.9%), **Schinner Premium Kellerbier** (4.9%), **Schinner Altfranken Braunbier** (5%), **Schinner's Altfranken Markator** (7.2%)

The brewery changed its name in the late 1990s but remains in an industrial part of north-eastern Bayreuth. The brewery tap is east of the city centre, a few doors down from the Richard-Wagner-Museum. As we closed for press there were unconfirmed reports that brewing had ceased.

🍺 **Schinner Braustuben**
Richard-Wagner-Straße 38, 95444 Bayreuth-City
T 0921 676 73   **F** 0921 516 60 55
Daily 10.00–14.00 & from 17.00
DB Bayreuth Hbf 1.1km

Glenk
Exportbierbrauerei Richard Glenk OHG
Eichelweg 9–14, 95445 Bayreuth-Altstadt
T 0921 75 71 90   **F** 0921 51 16 26
www.glenk-braeu.de
Owners: Heinrich & Pauline Glenk
Founded: 1852   Output: 10,000hl
REGULAR BEERS:
Glenk Leicht
Glenk Hell
Glenk Pils (4.8%)
SEASONAL BEER:
Glenk Festbier (Christmas)

Around the corner from Becher-Bräu. The brewery tap is a beer garden and hall that only opens during spring and summer in fine weather.

🍺 **Glenk's-Biergarten**
Eichelweg 12, 95445 Bayreuth-Altstadt
T 0921 630 60
Oct–Apr closed. May–Sep in fine weather:
Sun & hols from 10.00, Mon–Sat from 16.00
DB Bayreuth Hbf 2.5km

Maisel
Brauerei Gebrüder Maisel KG
Hindenburgstraße 9, 95444 Bayreuth-City
T 0921 40 10   **F** 0921 40 12 06
www.maisel.com
Founded: 1887   Output: 400,000hl
REGULAR BEERS:
Maisel's Weisse Light (3.2%)
Maisel's Edelhopfen Diät-Pilsner (4.9%)
Maisel's Dampfbier (4.9%)

Maisel's Weisse Hell (5.2%)
Maisel's Weisse Kristall (5.2%)
Maisel's Weisse Original (5.4%)
Maisel's Weisse Dunkel (5.4%)
FOR BAYREUTHER BIERBRAUEREI:
Aktien Hell (4.8%), Aktien Pilsner (4.9%),
Aktien Dunkel (4.9%), Aktien Original (4.9%),
Aktien Zwick'l Kellerbier (5.5%)

One of the largest wheat beer producers, Maisel
has also been brewing Bayreuther Bierbrauerei
beers for several years. There is a large museum
in the old Maisel brewery, at Kulmbacher
Straße 40. The Golden Lion is the Maisel tap,
while the Bayreuther Bierbrauerei's is
Brauereischänke am Markt.

🍺 Goldener Löwe
Kulmbacher Straße 30, 95445 Bayreuth-Kreuz
T 0921 410 46
Mon from 17.00, Tue–Sat 11.00–14.30 & from
17.00, Sun 11.00–14.30; rooms available
DB Bayreuth Hbf 1.3km

🍺 Brauereischänke am Markt
Maximilianstraße 56, 95444 Bayreuth-City
T 0921 649 19
Closed Sun; Mon–Sat 09.00–23.00
DB Bayreuth Hbf 850m

BEILNGRIES   177

Schattenhofer Bräu
Hauptstraße 44, 92339 Beilngries
T 08461 641 30   **F** 08461 64 13 89
www.schattenhofer.com
Owners: Anita & Elisabeth Schattenhofer
Founded: 1363   Output: 2,000hl
Availability: 10 pubs
REGULAR BEERS:
Schattenhofer Urhell (4.8%)
Schattenhofer Pils (5%)
Schattenhofer Wotans Trunk (5%)
Schattenhofer Export (5.1%)

Brewery, pub and hotel in the centre of the
Altmühl valley market town of Beilngries.
Bus No. 515 runs from Neumarkt via Berching.

🍺 Goldener Hahn
Hauptstraße 44, 92339 Beilngries
Daily 07.00–24.00; rooms available
DB Neumarkt (Opf) 28km

BERCHING   178

Schuller
Brauerei Franz Schuller
St. Lorenzstraße 14, 92334 Berching
T 08462 302   Owner: Franz Schuller
Founded: 1725   Output: 1,800hl
REGULAR BEERS:
Schuller Helles
Schuller Dunkel
Schuller Pils
Schuller Export
Schuller Weizen
SEASONAL BEERS:
Schuller Festbier, Schuller Bockbier

Small brewery and tap, formerly known as
Brauerei Zur Krone. We think the beers are only
available here. Bus No. 515 runs from Neumarkt.

🍺 Zur Krone
St. Lorenzstraße 14, 92334 Berching
Daily from 09.00; rooms available
DB Neumarkt (Opf) 23km

Winkler
Privatbrauerei Winkler
Reichenauplatz 22, 92334 Berching
T 08462 273 31   **F** 08462 271 28
www.brauereigasthof-winkler.de
Owner: Josef Winkler   Founded: 1826
Output: 4,300hl
REGULAR BEERS:
Winkler Berchinger Leichtes Weissbier
Winkler Berchinger Premium-Pils (4.6%)
Winkler Berchinger Lagerbier (4.8%)
Winkler Alt-Berchinger Dunkel (5%)
Winkler Berchinger Weissbier (5.2%)
Winkler Bärentrunk (5.4%)
SEASONAL BEERS:
Winkler Berchinger Festbier (5.4%), Winkler
Josefi-Bock (March), Winkler Weizenbock
(Christmas)

Brewery and tap close to the Main–Donau Canal
in this attractive walled town. Bus No. 515 runs
from Neumarkt.

🍺 Winkler
Reichenauplatz 22, 92334 Berching
T 08462 13 27
Sun 09.00–13.00, Mon–Sat 10.00–24.00;
rooms available   DB Neumarkt (Opf) 23km

BERCHTESGADEN 179

Hofbrauhaus

Bräuhausstraße 13–15, 83471 Berchtesgaden
T 08652 966 40   F 08652 96 64 16
www.berchtesgadener-bier.de
Owner: InBev   Founded: 1645
Output: 50,000hl
REGULAR BEERS:
Hofbrauhaus Berchtesgaden Hell (4.5%)
Hofbrauhaus Berchtesgaden Pils (4.5%)
Hofbrauhaus Berchtesgaden Kellerbier
Hofbrauhaus Jahrhundert Jubiläumsbier (5.1%)
Hofbrauhaus Ludwig-Thoma Dunkel (5.2%)
Hofbrauhaus Berchtesgaden Bockbier (6.7%)

Now under the control of Spaten–Franziskaner who are themselves owned by InBev. It was formerly part of the Thurn & Taxis empire.

🍺 **Bräustüberl**
Bräuhausstraße 13, 83471 Berchtesgaden
T 08652 97 67 24
Daily 10.00–24.00
DB Berchtesgaden 900m

BIBERACH (Roggenburg) 180

Schmid

Weißenhorner Straße 24,
89297 Roggenburg-Biberach
T 07300 303   F 07300 203
www.brauerei-biberach.de
Owner: Richard Schmid   Founded: 1844
Output: 1,000hl   Availability: 1 pub
REGULAR BEERS:
Biberacher Ur-Dunkel
Biberacher Landbier
Biberacher Märzen

Village brewpub with limited opening hours. If you're travelling from Vöhringen, take bus No. 812 from Krumbach to Weißenhorn and change there.

🍺 **Zum Wolf**
Weißenhorner Straße 24,
89297 Roggenburg-Biberach
Closed Mon–Wed & Fri; Thu from 17.00,
Sat from 15.00, Sun & hols from 09.30
DB Vöhringen 13km, Krumbach 15km

BIESWANG (Pappenheim) 181

Wurm

Hirschbräu Friedrich Wurm KG
Hutgasse 2, 91788 Pappenheim-Bieswang
T 09143 83 79 50   F 09143 18 51
Founded: 1612   Output: 15,000hl
REGULAR BEERS:
Wurm Leicht
Wurm Hefe-Weizen Leicht
Wurm Vollbier-Hell
Wurm Vollbier-Dunkel
Wurm Pils-Export
Wurm Hefe-Weizen Hell
Wurm Hefe-Weizen Dunkel
Wurm Märzen
SEASONAL BEERS:
Wurm Festbier (summer), **Wurm Bock-Hell** (spring), **Wurm Bock-Dunkel** (winter)

The brewery tap closed in the late 1990s and we don't believe there's a pub in the village that sells Wurm beers. The family also own a maltings in nearby Pappenheim. If you want to try your luck in Bieswang, bus No. 698.1 runs from Pappenheim, on weekdays only.
DB Pappenheim 7km

BIRKACH am Forst (Untersiemau) 182

Eller

Brunnenstraße 10, 96253 Untersiemau-Birkach
T 09565 10 33   F 09565 61 55 73
Owner: Christian Eller   Founded: 1822
Output: 1,200hl   Availability: 4 pubs
REGULAR BEERS:
Eller Lagerbier (4.8%)
Eller Landpils (4.8%)

Village brewery and tap. Public transport is virtually non-existent, bus No. 8319 running occasionally through the area but only once a day on weekdays through Birkach itself.

🍺 **Eller**
Brunnenstraße 10, 96253 Untersiemau-Birkach
Closed Wed; Thu–Tue 09.00–24.00; rooms available
DB Creidlitz 8km, Lichtenfels 9km

BISCHBERG 183

Zur Sonne

Hausbrauerei zur Sonne
Regnitzstraße 2, 96120 Bischberg
T/F 0951 625 71
Owners: Christian & Dieter Schuhmann
Founded: 1587   Output: 2,500hl
REGULAR BEERS:
Sonne Urtyp Hell (4.8%)
Sonne Sonnen-Pils (5%)
Sonne Sonnen-Weisse (5.2%)
Sonne Landbier (5.3%)
Sonne Zunft-Trunk (5.3%)
SEASONAL BEER:
Sonne Sonnen-Bock (6.5%)

Brewpub in the centre of Bischberg, a large village just outside Bamberg, a mile or so beyond the Kaiserdom brewery and tap, served by bus No. 6 from Bamberg bus station.

Zur Sonne
Regnitzstraße 2, 96120 Bischberg
Closed Tue; Thu–Mon 09.00–01.00
DB Bamberg 6km

BODENMAIS 184

Adam-Bräu

Bahnhofstraße 51–53, 94249 Bodenmais
T 09924 940 00   **F** 09924 940 01 00
www.adam-braeu.de
Owner: Josef Adam   Founded: 1990
Output: 1,000hl
REGULAR BEERS:
Adam-Bräu Hefe-Weisse (5.1%)
Adam-Bräu Waidler-Hell (5.2%)
Adam-Bräu Bodenmaiser Dunkel (5.2%)
SEASONAL BEERS:
Adam-Bräu Weihnachtsbock (5.8%),
Adam-Bräu Adamator (6.8%)

Brewpub, guesthouse and hotel deep in the Bavarian Forest. The area is popular for winter sports.

Adam-Bräu-Keller
Bahnhofstraße 51–53, 94249 Bodenmais
Closed Wed; Thu–Tue 07.00–01.00; rooms available
DB Bodenmais 200m

BODENWÖHR 185

Jacob

Familienbrauerei Jacob
Ludwigsheide 2, 92439 Bodenwöhr
T 09434 941 00   **F** 09434 94 10 66
www.brauerei-jacob.de
Owners: the Jacob family   Founded: 1758
Availability: c. 30 pubs
REGULAR BEERS:
Jacob Bodenwöhrer Leichte Dunkle Weisse (2.7%)
Jacob Altbayerisch Hell (4.7%)
Jacob Edel-Pils (4.9%)
Jacob Hammer Pils (4.9%)
Jacob Bodenwöhrer Weissbier (5.2%)
Jacob Bodenwöhrer Weissbier Dunkel (5.2%)
Jacob Bodenwöhrer Winter Weisse (5.2%)
Jacob Spezial Export (5.3%)
Jacob Jacobator (6.5%)

Family-run brewery, pub and hotel on the banks of the Hammersee. Buses Nos. 43 and 106 run from Bodenwöhr Nord station but don't always connect well with trains.

Jacob
Ludwigsheide 2, 92439 Bodenwöhr
Daily 09.00–23.00; rooms available
DB Bodenwöhr Nord 2.5km

BREITENGÜSSBACH 186

Hümmer

Bambergerstraße 22, 96149 Breitengüßbach
T 09544 203 44   **F** 09544 27 44
www.brauerei-huemmer.com
Owner: Georg Hümmer   Founded: 1642
Output: 2,000hl
REGULAR BEERS:
Hümmer Güßbacher Urtyp (5%)
Hümmer Lager (5%)
Hümmer Pils (5%)
Hümmer Altfränkisches Dunkel (5.2%)
Hümmer Weisse (5.2%)
SEASONAL BEER:
Hümmer Bock (6.8%, Nov–Feb)

Brewery and pub in the centre of the village. They also sell their own range of soft drinks.

Hümmer
Bambergerstraße 22, 96149 Breitengüßbach

Closed Mon; Tue–Fri & Sun from 09.00,
Sat 09.00–13.00   DB Breitengüßbach 300m

BREITENLESAU
(Waischenfeld)   **187**

Krug-Bräu

Breitenlesau 1, 91344 Waischenfeld-Breitenlesau
T 09202 535   **F** 09202 17 21
www.krug-braeu.de
Owner: Konrad Krug   Founded: 1834
Output: 20,000hl   Availability: 60 pubs
REGULAR BEERS:
Krug-Bräu Pilsner (4.7%)
Krug-Bräu Dunkles Lagerbier (5%)
Krug-Bräu Festbier (5.5%)
SEASONAL BEERS:
Krug-Bräu Bockbier (May & Christmas, 6.8%)

Country brewery between Forchheim and
Bayreuth. As far as we can tell there is no public
transport to Breitenlesau.

🍺 Krug
Breitenlesau 1, 91344 Waischenfeld-Breitenlesau
T 09202 535
Closed Mon; Tue–Sun 08.00–24.00; rooms
available
DB Ebermannstadt 15km, Bayreuth 25km

BRUCKBERG (Landshut)   **188**

Wimmer

Bräuberg 1, 84079 Bruckberg
T 08765 206   **F** 08765 12 67
www.brauerei-wimmer.de
Owner: Albert Kellerer   Founded: 1875
Output: 8,000hl   Availability: 30 pubs
REGULAR BEERS:
Bruckberger Hell
Bruckberger Export-Hell
Bruckberger Export-Dunkel
Bruckberger Weiße
SEASONAL BEER:
Bruckberger Festbier

Small brewery is in the centre of the village,
currently without tap, but we think the beers
are easily found locally.
DB Bruckberg 1.1km

BRUCKBERG (Mittelfranken)   **189**

Dietz

Der Hausbrauer Dietz
Feuerbachstraße 1, 91590 Bruckberg
T 09824 222   **F** 09824 82 12
www.hausbrauer-dietz.de
Owner: Helmut Dietz   Founded: 1616
Output: 2,000hl   Availability: 5 pubs
REGULAR BEERS:
Dietz Hell
Dietz Dunkel
Dietz Brauer-Weisse
Dietz Mehrkornbier

Small brewery and tap in the southern part of the
village. Bus No. 716 runs from Ansbach daily
except Sunday.

🍺 Bräustüberl
Feuerbachstraße 1, 91590 Bruckberg
Closed Mon; Tue–Thu from 17.00,
Fri–Sun from 10.00   DB Ansbach 11km

Dorn-Bräu

Markgrafenstraße 3, 91590 Bruckberg
T 09824 326   **F** 09824 13 87
Owners: Georg & Karl Dorn   Founded: 1766
Output: 3,000hl   Availability: 10 pubs
REGULAR BEERS:
Bruckberger Dorn-Bräu Hell (5%)
Bruckberger Dorn-Bräu Pils (5%)
Bruckberger Dorn-Bräu Gambrinus-Weiße
Bruckberger Dorn-Bräu Dunkel-Export (5.5%)
SEASONAL BEER:
Bruckberger Dorn-Bräu Doppelbock (winter)

Slightly larger than Dietz, Bruckberg's second
brewery is in the centre of the village.

🍺 Dorn-Bräu
Markgrafenstraße 3, 91590 Bruckberg
Closed Wed and last Sun of month;
Thu–Mon 09.00–24.00, Tue 09.00–14.00
DB Ansbach 11km

BÜCHENBACH (Pegnitz)   **190**

Herold

Marktstraße 29, 91257 Pegnitz-Büchenbach
T/F 09241 33 11   www.beckn-bier.de
Owner: Johann Herold   Founded: 1568

Output: 1,500hl Availability: 3 pubs
REGULAR BEER:
Beck'n Bier (4.6%)
SEASONAL BEER:
Beck'n Bockbier (7.1%, May & Christmas)

The Herold family have apparently owned the brewery for the last 400 years. We don't believe there is any public transport to Büchenbach.

🍺 Herold
Marktstraße 29, 91257 Pegnitz-Büchenbach
Closed Tue; Wed–Mon 09.00–23.00; rooms available DB Pegnitz 6km

BURGEBRACH   191

Schwanenbräu
Hauptstraße 16, 96138 Burgebrach
T 09546 306 **F** 09546 592 01 95
www.schwanawirt.de
Owners: Ingeborg & Konrad Lechner
Founded: 1394 Output: 1,200hl
Availability: 2 pubs
REGULAR BEERS:
Schwanenbräu Helles (4.6%)
Schwanenbräu Dunkel
Schwanenbräu Lager Bier (4.9%)
Schwanenbräu Pils (4.9%)
Schwanenbräu Weizen
SEASONAL BEERS:
Schwanenbräu Festbier,
Schwanenbräu Alexator Doppelbock

Brewpub in the centre of Burgebrach. The brewery's Keller opens daily in fine weather from May to September. Bus No. 8223 runs from Bamberg station (not Sundays).

🍺 Schwan
Hauptstraße 16, 96138 Burgebrach
Closed Tue; Wed–Fri & Mon from 15.30, Sat from 11.00, Sun from 09.00; rooms available
DB Bamberg 16km

BURGKUNSTADT   192

Gick-Bräu
Lichtenfelser Staße 17, 96224 Burgkunstadt
T 09572 20 04 **F** 09572 43 52
Owners: Adelbert & Erwin Gick Founded: 1814
Output: 4,000hl

REGULAR BEERS:
Gick-Bräu Weiße (4.9%)
Gick-Bräu Ritter Kuno Trunk (5%)
Gick-Bräu Pils (5%)
Gick-Bräu Schuster-Öl (5%)
SEASONAL BEER:
Gick-Bräu Bock (7%)

Family-run brewery on the edge of the town centre. The brewery tap is opposite the Günther-Bräu Gaststätte, just below Brauerei Hellmuth.

🍺 Gick-Bräu
Kulmbacher Straße 39, 96224 Burgkunstadt
T 09572 65 15
Daily from 17.00
DB Burgkunstadt 900m

Günther-Bräu
Kulmbacher Straße 36, 96224 Burgkunstadt
T 09572 92 61 **F** 09572 57 29
www.guenther-braeu.de
Owner: Rudolf Günther Founded: 1840
Output: 6,000hl
REGULAR BEERS:
Günther-Bräu Lagerbier (4.9%)
Günther-Bräu Premium-Pilsener (4.9%)
Günther-Bräu Weißbier (4.9%)
Günther-Bräu Schwarzbier (5.2%)
SEASONAL BEER:
Günther-Bräu Bockbier (6.8%)

The largest of Burgkunstadt's three breweries, Günther's tap is opposite Gick-Bräu's. We have heard rumours the brewery may now be at In der Au 27. Any reports are welcome.

🍺 Günther-Bräu
Kulmbacher Straße 36, 96224 Burgkunstadt
T 09572 92 61 **F** 09572 57 29
Daily 12.00–22.00
DB Burgkunstadt 900m

Hellmuth
Lend 9, 96224 Burgkunstadt
T 09572 15 75
Owner: Rita Deuerling Founded: c. 1900
Output: 900hl Availability: 1 pub
REGULAR BEERS:
Hellmuth Dunkel (5%)
Hellmuth Export Hell (5.5%)

Small brewpub on the edge of the upper town. The beers are only available here.

🍺 **Hellmuth**

Lend 9, 96224 Burgkunstadt
Daily 09.00–13.00 & from 16.00
DB Burgkunstadt 800m

BURGLENGENFELD   193

Birkenseer

Brauerei Josef Birkenseer
Friedhofstraße 8, 93133 Burglengenfeld
T 09471 12 27   F 09471 803 45
Founded: 1860   Availability: 30 pubs
REGULAR BEERS:
Burglengenfelder Hell (4.8%)
Burglengenfelder Pils (4.9%)
Burglengenfelder Weißbier (5.1%)
SEASONAL BEERS:
Burglengenfelder Festbier (5.5%),
Burglengenfelder Bock

Brewery and pub close to the old station, on the opposite side of the river to the main part of town. Bus No. 41 runs between Regensburg and Schwandorf via Maxhütte-Haidhof.

🍺 **Birkenseer**

Friedhofstraße 8, 93133 Burglengenfeld
Daily 08.00–13.00 & from 16.00
DB Maxhütte-Haidhof 6km

BUTTENHEIM   194

Löwenbräu

Marktstraße 8, 96155 Buttenheim
T 09545 332   F 09545 707 89
www.loewenbraeu-buttenheim.de
Owner: Johann Modschiedler   Founded: 1880
Output: 15,000hl   Availability: c. 50 pubs
REGULAR BEERS:
Löwen-Bräu Keller Leicht (2.5%)
Löwen-Bräu Ungespundetes Lagerbier (4.8%)
Löwen-Bräu Vollbier Hell (5%)
SEASONAL BEERS:
Löwen-Bräu Anna-Festbier (5%), **Löwen-Bräu Weihnachtsbier** (5%), **Löwen-Bräu Bockbier** (6.3%)

The smaller of Buttenheim's two breweries, Löwenbräu is opposite the church, next door to its larger neighbour. The brewery tap closes for two weeks in September. Be warned that Buttenheim station is actually in the village of Altendorf.

🍺 **Löwenbräu**

Marktstraße 8, 96155 Buttenheim
Closed Mon; Tue–Sun 09.00–24.00; rooms
available   DB Buttenheim 1.5km

St. Georgen Bräu

Marktstraße 12, 96155 Buttenheim
T 09545 44 60   F 09545 446 46
www.kellerbier.de
Owner: Familie Modscheidler   Founded: 1624
Output: 100,000hl   Availability: c. 200 pubs
REGULAR BEERS:
St. Georgen Bräu Helles (4.6%)
St. Georgen Bräu Weiß-Bier (4.6%)
St. Georgen Bräu Pilsener (4.9%)
St. Georgen Bräu Keller Bier (4.9%)
St. Georgen Bräu Land-Bier (4.9%)
SEASONAL BEERS:
St. Georgen Bräu Gold-Märzen (5.6%), **St. Georgen Bräu Anna-Festbier** (5.6%), **St. Georgen Bräu Schwarz-Bock** (7.3%)
FOR WAGNER-BRÄU, POTTENSTEIN:
Pottensteiner Höhlentrunk

One of the largest independent breweries in the region, St. Georgen's beers can be found over a wide area. The accommodation is in a house across the street.

🍺 **St. Georgen Bräustübla**

Marktstraße 12, 96155 Buttenheim
T 09545 95 01 60
Closed Thu; Fri–Wed 09.00–24.00; rooms
available
DB Buttenheim 1.5km

CHAMMÜNSTER *(Cham)*   195

Hintereder

Chammünster 48, 93413 Cham-Chammünster
T 09971 36 25
Owner: Alfons Hintereder   Founded: 1522
Output: 3,000hl   Availability: 10 pubs
REGULAR BEERS:
Hintereder Münster Hell (4.8%)
Hintereder Münster Märzen (5.3%)
SEASONAL BEER:
Hintereder Münster Festbier (5.1%)

Small village brewery, the oldest in the region. There are occasional buses from Cham Mon–Fri (Nos. 610 & 620).

Hintereder
Chammünster 48, 93413 Cham-Chammünster
Closed Sun; Mon–Sat 10.00–23.00
DB Cham (Oberpfalz) 4km

DEBRING (Stegaurach) 196

Müller

Würzburger Straße 1, 96135 Stegaurach-Debring
T 0951 291 91   F 0951 992 11 31
Owner: Franz Müller
Founded: 1872
Output: 700hl
Availability: 1 pub
REGULAR BEERS:
Müller Debringer Stöffla
Müller Debringer Vollbier-Dunkel
Müller Debringer Pils
SEASONAL BEER:
Müller Debringer Bockbier

Brewery and tap on the main road through the village. Buses Nos. 12 & 8223 run from Bamberg.

Müller
Würzburger Straße 1, 96135 Stegaurach-Debring
Closed Mon; Tue–Sun 11.00–24.00
DB Bamberg 7km

DEISENHOFEN 197

Weißbräu

Hubertusplatz 5, 82041 Deisenhofen
T 089 613 16 17   F 089 625 22 05
www.hotel-weissbraeu.de
Owner: Bartholomäus Gmeineder
Founded: 1899
Output: 600hl
Availability: 1 pub
REGULAR BEER:
Deisenhofener Weißbräu (4.9%)

Hotel, pub and brewery in this small commuter town south of München. The beer is only sold at the tap.

Weißbräu
Hubertusplatz 5, 82041 Deisenhofen
Closed Thu; Fri–Wed 10.00–24.00; rooms available
DB Deisenhofen 700m

DENTLEIN am Forst 198

Hauf-Bräu

Dinkesbühler Straße 5, 91599 Dentlein am Forst
T 09855 95 20   F 09855 95 21
www.dentleiner.de
Owners: Hannes, Marga & Hans Hauf
Founded: 1680   Output: 10,000hl
Availability: 25 pubs
REGULAR BEERS:
Dentleiner Lager (4.7%)
Dentleiner Landbier (4.7%)
Dentleiner Original (4.9%)
Dentleiner Forst Pils (4.9%)
Dentleiner Lebens-Art (5%)
Dentleiner Hefeweizen (5%)
Dentleiner Klosterhof Dunkel (5.3%)
SEASONAL BEER:
Dentleiner Erntebier (4.9%), **Dentleiner Festbier** (4.9%), **Dentleiner Doppelbock** (winter)

Hauf-Bräu have no brewery tap and if you want to try your luck in Dentlein by public transport, the bus service from Ansbach (No. 802) is very poor.
DB Ansbach 27km

DEUERLING 199

Goss

Regensburger Straße 16, 93180 Deuerling
T 09498 15 12   E brauerei.goss@t-online.de
Owner: Josef Goss   Founded: 1878
Output: 3,000hl   Availability: 8 pubs
REGULAR BEERS:
Goss-Bräu Leichtes Weizen (2.8%)
Goss-Bräu Hell (4.9%)
Goss-Bräu Pils (5%)
Goss-Bräu Weizen (5%)
Goss-Bräu Märzen (5.5%)
SEASONAL BEERS:
Goss-Bräu Heller Bock (6.8%)

Brewery and tap in the centre of the village, near the river. The beers are available in a few other pubs locally.

Goss
Regensburger Straße 16, 93180 Deuerling
Closed Tue; Wed–Mon 09.00–23.00; rooms available
DB Deuerling 1.4km

DIETZHOF (Leutenbach)　200

Alt

Dietzhof 8, 91359 Leutenbach-Dietzhof
T 09199 267　**E** brauerei.alt@walberla.de
Owner: Reimund Alt　Founded: 1851
Output: 2,000hl
REGULAR BEER:
Alt Vollbier-Hell (4.5%)

Brewpub in the small village of Dietzhof.
Bus No. 223 runs from Forchheim station via
Wiesenthau Mon–Fri only.

🍺 Alt
Dietzhof 8, 91359 Leutenbach-Dietzhof
Closed Mon; Tue–Fri 17.00–23.00,
Sat 16.00–23.00, Sun 11.30–23.30
DB Wiesenthau 3km, Forchheim 9km

DINGOLFING　201

Wasserburger

Brauerei Xaver Wasserburger
Bräuhausgasse 10–12, 84130 Dingolfing
T 08731 500 08　**F** 08731 500 10
www.brauerei-wasserburger.de
Owner: Xaver Wasserburger　Founded: 1859
Output: 10,000hl
REGULAR BEERS:
Wasserburger Leichtes Weizen (2.8%)
Wasserburger Urtyp Hell (4.8%)
Wasserburger Pils (5.1%)
Wasserburger Hefe Weißbier (5.1%)
Wasserburger Hefe Weißbier Dunkel (5.1%)
Wasserburger Der Jubilar (5.1%)
Wasserburger Schwarzer 5er (5.1%)
Wasserburger Felsentrunk (5.6%)
Wasserburger Prinzensud (5.6%)
SEASONAL BEERS:
Wasserburger Festbier (5.6%),
Wasserburger Tassilator (7.7%)

Owned by the family for nearly 150 years, the
brewery and tap are on the south side of the river
Isar. Dingolfing is home to a large BMW factory.

🍺 Hofbräuhaus
Bräuhausgasse 12, 84130 Dingolfing
T 08731 39 73 66
Closed Tue; Wed–Mon 10.00–24.00
DB Dingolfing 2km

DINKELSBÜHL　202

Hauf

Brauerei Hauf GmbH
Brewery: Feuchtwanger Straße,
91550 Dinkelsbühl
Office: Heininger Straße 28,
91550 Dinkelsbühl
T 09851 575 20　**F** 09851 57 52 22
www.hauf-bier.de
Founded: 1901
Output: 25,000hl　Availability: c. 100 pubs
REGULAR BEERS:
Hauf Pils (4.8%)
Hauf Edel-Hell (5%)
Friedrich Hauf 1901 Bayerisch Dunkel (5%)
Hauf Export (5.1%)
Hauf Hefe-Weißbier (5.3%)
Hauf Dunkle Weisse (5.3%)
SEASONAL BEERS:
Hauf Festbier (5.4%, May–Aug),
Hauf Weihnachtsbier Spezial (5.4%),
Hauf Dinkelator (6.9%, Nov–Feb)

Small regional brewery on the outskirts of town.
Zum Wilden Mann (The Wild Man) was the
original home of the brewery. There are various
means of getting to Dinkelsbühl by bus,
although Crailsheim and Dombühl are probably
the best starting points.

🍺 Zum Wilden Mann
Wörnitsstraße 1, 91550 Dinkelsbühl
T 09851 55 25 25　**F** 09851 55 25 26
Daily 10.00–01.00
DB Crailsheim 23km, Dombühl 23km

Weib's Brauhaus

Untere Schmiedgasse 13, 91550 Dinkelsbühl
T 09851 57 94 90　**F** 09851 579 49 49
www.weibsbrauhaus.de
Owner: Melanie Gehring　Founded: 1999
Output: 350hl　Availability: 1 pub
REGULAR BEERS:
Weib's Helles (4.8%)
Weib's Weißbier (5%)

Brewpub in the centre of this walled town.
Steam-hauled passenger trains run on the
normally freight only line to Dinkelsbühl on
several weekends during the year, offering an
alternative to the bus.

🍺 Weib's Brauhaus
Untere Schmiedgasse 13, 91550 Dinkelsbühl
Closed Tue; Wed 18.00– 01.00,
Thu–Mon 11.00–0100; rooms available
DB Crailsheim 23km, Dombühl 23km

DIRLEWANG   203

Hirschbräu

Brauerei zum Hirsch
Mühlsbachstraße 14, 87742 Dirlewang
T 08267 232
Owner: Hans Lederle   Founded: 1806
Output: 1,500hl
REGULAR BEERS:
Hirschbräu Hell
Hirschbräu Export
SEASONAL BEER:
Hirschbräu Weihnachtsfestbier

Small brewery and tap a few miles south of
Mindelheim. Buses Nos. 913 and 914 run
irregularly from Mindelheim.

🍺 Zum Hirsch
Mühlsbachstraße 14, 87742 Dirlewang
Closed Sun; Mon–Sat 09.00–23.00
DB Mindelheim 5km

DORFEN   204

Bachmayer

Josef Bachmayer's Nachfolger GmbH & Co. KG
Marienplatz 1, 84405 Dorfen
T 08081 27 53   F 08081 46 32
Owner: Josef Hörmann   Founded: 1847
REGULAR BEERS:
Bachmayer Hell (4.7%)
Bachmayer Classic Pils (4.9%)
Bachmayer Dunkel (5%)
SEASONAL BEERS:
Bachmayer Festbier,
Bachmayer Josefator

Small brewery in the centre of town. The old tap
has been turned into a trendy bar, so we've listed
the nearby Dorfener Stube as an alternative.

🍺 Dorfener Stube
Johannisplatz 2, 84405 Dorfen
T 08081 13 99   F 08081 956 78 28

Closed Mon; Tue 17.00–23.00, Wed–Sun
10.00–14.00 & 18.00–23.00
DB Dorfen Bahnhof 1.2km

DÖRFLEINS (Hallstadt)   205

Eichhorn

Brauerei Schwarzer Adler
Dörfleinser Straße 43, 96103 Hallstadt-Dörfleins
T 0951 756 60   F 0951 971 04 07
www.brauerei-eichhorn.de
Owner: Alfons Eichhorn   Founded: before 1870
Output: 2,500hl
REGULAR BEERS:
Eichhorn Kellerbier Naturtrüb (5%)
Eichhorn Export (5%)
Eichhorn Weisse
SEASONAL BEER:
Eichhorn Bock Naturtrüb

Village brewery a few miles north of Bamberg.
Bus No. 4 runs from Bamberg bus station,
No. 8229 from Bamberg railway station.

🍺 Schwarzer Adler
Dörfleinser Straße 43, 96103 Hallstadt-Dörfleins
Closed Mon; Tue, Wed, Fri & Sun 09.00–23.00,
Thu 09.00–19.00, Sat 09.00–20.00
DB Hallstadt (Bamberg) 2.2km, Bamberg 5km

DRACHSELRIED   206

Falterbräu

Hofmark 5, 94256 Drachselried
T 09945 94 32 30   F 09945 94 32 33
Owners: Eduard & Michael Falter
Founded: 1890   Output: 5,000hl
REGULAR BEERS:
Falterbräu Arber Hell
Falterbräu Arber Pils
Falterbräu Arber Export

Small brewery and tap close to Drachselried's
other brewery, Schlossbräu. Buses Nos. 6093
and 6196 run from Bodenmais, the latter going
through to Kötzting.

🍺 Falter
Hofmark 5, 94256 Drachselried
Closed Mon; Tue–Sun 09.00–22.30
DB Bodenmais 9km, Kötzting 14km

Drachselrieder Schlossbräu

Schlossbrauerei Drachselried R. Bruckmayer
Hofmark 1, 94256 Drachselried
T 09945 940 70   **F** 09945 94 07 45
www.schlossbraeu.de
Owner: Richard Bruckmayer   Founded: 1650
Output: 30,000hl   Availability: c.150 pubs
REGULAR BEERS:
Drachselrieder Schlossbräu Aegidi Leichte (2.8%)
Drachselrieder Schlossbräu Zellertal Lager (4.8%)
Drachselrieder Schlossbräu Nobles Pils (4.9%)
Drachselrieder Schlossbräu Respekt (5.2%)
Drachselrieder Schlossbräu Dunkles Kini (5.4%)
Drachselrieder Schlossbräu Waidler Gold (5.4%)
Drachselrieder Schlossbräu Aegidi Weisse (5.4%)
SEASONAL BEERS:
Drachselrieder Schlossbräu Weihnachtsfestbier
(5.2%), **Drachselrieder Schlossbräu Respektator**
(6.5%), **Drachselrieder Schlossbräu Aegidius**
Weizenbock (7.5%)

Much the larger of the town's two breweries,
Schlossbräu's beers can be found over much of
the Bayerischer Wald. The tap also has a hotel.

🍺 Zum Schloßbräu
Hofmark 1, 94256 Drachselried
T 09945 10 38
Closed Thu; Fri–Wed 09.00–22.00; rooms
available
DB Bodenmais 9km, Kötzting 14km

DREUSCHENDORF
(Buttenheim)   207

Meusel-Bräu

Dreuschendorf 27, 96155 Buttenheim-
Dreuschendorf
T 09545 74 24   **F** 09545 7 09 32
Owner: Ottmar Meusel   Founded: 1500
Output: 15,000hl
REGULAR BEERS:
Meusel-Bräu Fein & Leicht (2.9%)
Meusel-Bräu Hell (4.6%)
Meusel-Bräu Kellertrunk (4.8%)
Meusel-Bräu Pilsener (4.8%)
Meusel-Bräu Edel Gold Diät Pilsener (4.9%)
Meusel-Bräu Spezial Märzen (5.4%)
SEASONAL BEERS:
Meusel-Bräu Festbier (5.5%), **Meusel-Bräu**
Weizenbock (6.3%), **Meusel-Bräu Heller Bock** (7%)

Small regional brewery, a couple of kilometres
east of Buttenheim. There's currently no brewery
tap and the two daily buses from Buttenheim
only run when the brewery is closed.
DB Buttenheim 4km

DROSENDORF (Memmelsdorf) 208

Göller

Scheßlitzer Straße 7,
96117 Memmelsdorf-Drosendorf
T 09505 17 45   **E** brauerei.goeller@t-online.de
Owners: Georg Göller junior & senior
Founded: 1865   Output: 1,000hl
Availability: 1 pub
REGULAR BEERS:
Göller Pils (5%)
Göller Lagerbier (5.2%)

Brewpub on the main road through the village.
Owned by the same family as Brauerei Göller in
Zeil. Buses Nos. 7 and 8224 run from Bamberg.

🍺 Göller
Scheßlitzer Straße 7,
96117 Memmelsdorf-Drosendorf
Closed Mon; Tue–Sun from 09.00
DB Bamberg 9km

DRÜGENDORF (Eggolsheim) 209

Goldener Löwe

Drügendorf 26, 91330 Eggolsheim-Drügendorf
T 09545 85 83   **F** 09545 44 13 21
www.brauerei-foerst.de
Owner: Gerhard Först   Founded: 1525
Output: 4,000hl   Availability: 1 pub
REGULAR BEERS:
Goldener Löwe Vollbier-Premium (4.6%)
Goldener Löwe Altfränkisches Lager (4.9%)
Goldener Löwe Edel-Pils (4.9%)
Goldener Löwe Export (5.3%)

Brewery and tap in the edge of Fränkische
Schweiz (Franconian Switzerland). Bus No. 220
runs between Eggolsheim and Ebermannstadt
via Drügendorf Mon–Fri.

🍺 Goldener Löwe
Drügendorf 26, 91330 Eggolsheim-Drügendorf
Closed Thu; Fri–Wed 09.00–23.00
DB Ebermannstadt 8km, Eggolsheim 8km

EBENSFELD 210

Ebensfelder Brauhaus

Brauerei Engelhardt – Schwanen-Bräu
Oberer Kehlbachdamm 7, 96250 Ebensfeld
T 09573 885
Owner: Hans Karl Engelhardt   Founded: 1752
Output: 6,000hl
REGULAR BEERS:
Schwanen-Bräu Fränkisches Landbier
Schwanen-Bräu Pilsener
Schwanen-Bräu Schwanen Weisse
Schwanen-Bräu Adam Riese Urtrunk
SEASONAL BEERS:
Schwanen-Bräu Festbier, Schwanen-Bräu Bock,
Schwanen-Bräu Schwanador

Village brewery known by at least three names.
The tap is on the main road, with the brewery
off a lane behind. Annual holiday last week in
August/first week in September.

🍺 **Zum Schwan**
Hauptstraße 46, 96250 Ebensfeld
T 09573 57 71   **F** 09573 95 08 30
Closed Mon, (Tue after hol); Tue–Sun 10.00–23.00
DB Ebensfeld 500m

EBERMANNSTADT 211

Schwanenbräu

Marktplatz 2, 91320 Ebermannstadt
T 09194 76 71 90   **F** 09194 58 36
www.schwanenbraeu.de
Owner: Helga Dotterweich   Founded: 1812
Output: 1,500hl   Availability: 1 pub
REGULAR BEERS:
Schwanenbräu Lager (5%)
Schwanenbräu Pils (5%)
Schwanenbräu Export (5.5%)
SEASONAL BEER:
Schwanenbräu Bock (Nov–Dec)

The brewery tap is in one corner of the market
square. The brewery is listed as being at the
same address but we believe it may actually be
next door to the Bierkeller, at Ramsertalstraße 1.

🍺 **Schwanenbräu**
Marktplatz 2, 91320 Ebermannstadt
Sun 09.00–15.00, Mon–Sat 09.00–24.00;
rooms available   DB Ebermannstadt 550m

Sonnenbräu

Brauerei-Gasthof-Hotel Sonne
Hauptstraße 29, 91320 Ebermannstadt
T 09194 90 93   **F** 09194 767 48 80
Owner: Josef Herbst
Founded: 1803
Output: 2,500hl
Availability: 3 pubs
REGULAR BEERS:
Sonnenbräu Schluck-Specht (4.9%)
Sonnenbräu Premium Pils (4.9%)
Sonnenbräu Eber-Weisse (5%)
Sonnenbräu Kellerbier (5%)
Sonnenbräu Sonnengold (5%)
SEASONAL BEER:
Sonnenbräu Festbier (5.3%)

Town-centre brewery, distillery, pub and hotel,
opposite Schwanenbräu. The beers are available
in a couple of other local pubs.

🍺 **Sonne**
Hauptstraße 29, 91320 Ebermannstadt
T 09194 76 74 80
Wed 16.00–24.00, Thu–Tue 07.00–24.00;
rooms available
DB Ebermannstadt 530m

EBING (Rattelsdorf) 212

Schwanen-Bräu

Marktplatz 11, 96179 Rattelsdorf-Ebing
T 09547 481   **F** 09547 76 36
www.schwanen-braeu-ebing.de
Owner: Barbara Hübner
Founded: 1859
Output: 1,500hl
Availability: 1 pub
REGULAR BEERS:
Schwanen-Bräu Vollbier-Dunkel
Schwanen-Bräu Zwickelbier-Hell
SEASONAL BEER:
Schwanen-Bräu Maibock (May)

Brewpub in the centre of the village that also has
its own distillery. Owned by the same family for
almost 150 years.

🍺 **Schwanen**
Marktplatz 11, 96179 Rattelsdorf-Ebing
Closed Thu; Fri–Wed from 09.00; rooms available
DB Ebing 1.1km

ECK (Böbrach) 213

Ecker Bräu

Eck 1, 94255 Böbrach-Eck
T 09923 840 50 **F** 09923 84 05 55
www.brauerei-eck.de
Owner: Lydia Schönberger Founded: 1462
Output: 3,000hl
REGULAR BEERS:
Ecker Bräu Vollbier Hell
Ecker Bräu Böbracher Pils
Ecker Bräu Wilderer Dunkel
SEASONAL BEERS:
Ecker Bräu Festbier, Ecker Bräu Maibock

Brewery, pub and hotel in the small hamlet of Eck
which is on the main road (St2139), a few hundred
metres south-west of Böbrach. Bus No. 23 runs
here from Bodenmais.

Eck
Eck 1, 94255 Böbrach-Eck
Closed Mon; Tue–Sat 07.00–23.00,
Sun 07.00–20.00; rooms available
DB Bodenmais 5km

EDELSFELD 214

Heldrich

Sulzbacher Straße 3, 92265 Edelsfeld
T 09665 441 **F** 09665 83 87
Owner: Michael Heldrich Founded: 1877
Output: 2,500hl
REGULAR BEERS:
Heldrich Vollbier (4.9%)
Heldrich Pils (5.2%)
Heldrich Blaustöpsel (5.7%)
SEASONAL BEER:
Heldrich Festbier

Brewery in the centre of the village, with the tap
and three-star hotel next door. Bus No. 6310
runs from Luitpoldplatz in Sulzbach-Rosenberg
Mon–Fri.

Goldener Greif
Sulzbacher Straße 5, 92265 Edelsfeld
T 09665 914 90 **F** 09665 914 91 00
Closed Tue; Wed–Mon 09.00–14.00 & 18.00–
22.00; rooms available
DB Neukirchen (b. Sulzbach) 9km, Sulzbach-
Rosenberg 11km

EGGOLSHEIM 215

Schwarzes Kreuz

Hauptstraße 33, 91330 Eggolsheim
T 09545 88 43
E schulz.wolfgang@planet-interkom.de
Owner: Wolfgang Schulz Founded: 1524
Output: 500hl
REGULAR BEER:
Schwarzes Kreuz Vollbier (4.5%)

Brewpub in the centre of town. The railway
station is in the village of Neuses an der Pegnitz
on the opposite side of the A73.

Schwarzes Kreuz
Hauptstraße 33, 91330 Eggolsheim
Closed Wed; Thu–Tue 09.00–23.00
DB Eggolsheim 1.7km

EICHHOFEN (Nittendorf) 216

Schlossbrauerei

Von-Rosenbusch-Straße 8,
93152 Nittendorf-Eichhofen
T 09404 954 50 **F** 09404 95 45 16
www.eichhofener.de
Owner: Michael A.Schönharting Founded: 1692
Output: 20,000hl
REGULAR BEERS:
Eichhofener Helles Leicht (2.8%)
Eichhofener Hefeweizen Leicht (2.8%)
Eichhofener Helles (5%)
Eichhofener Premium Pils (5%)
Eichhofener Hefeweizen (5.2%)
Eichhofener Spezial Dunkel (5.5%)
SEASONAL BEERS:
Eichhofener Festbier (5.5%), **Eichhofener
Eichator Doppelbock** (8%, winter)

Brewery and tap in the small village of Eichhofen
in the Laaber valley. It's thought the brewery
may date back as far as 1300.

Brauereigasthof Eichhofen
Von-Rosenbusch-Straße 8,
93152 Nittendorf-Eichhofen
T/F 09404 16 62
Wed 16.00–23.00, Thu–Tue 10.30–23.00
DB Undorf 2.2km

EICHSTÄTT 217

Hofmühl

Privatbrauerei Hofmühl GmbH
Hofmühlstraße 10, 85072 Eichstätt
T 08421 980 80   **F** 08421 98 08 40
www.hofmuehl.de
Owner: Benno Emslander   Founded: 1492
REGULAR BEERS:
Hofmühl Weissbier Leicht (2.9%)
Hofmühl Hell (4.9%)
Hofmühl Dunkel (4.9%)
Hofmühl Kellergold (4.9%)
Hofmühl Privat Pils (4.9%)
Hofmühl Willibaldi-Sud (5.4%)
Hofmühl Weissbier (5.4%)
Hofmühl Ur-Weisse Dunkel (5.4%)
Hofmühl Alligator (7.5%)
SEASONAL BEERS:
Hofmühl Volksfestbier (5.4%), **Hofmühl
Weihnachtsbier** (5.4%)

The brewery is alongside the railway at Rebdorf-
Hofmühle station, the tap is in the centre of town.

🍺 **Trompete**
Ostenstraße 3, 85072 Eichstätt
T 08421 981 70   **F** 08421 981 73 90
Daily 07.00–02.00; rooms available
DB Eichstätt Stadt 600m

EITTING 218

Eittinger Fischerbräu

St. Georg Straße 8, 85462 Eitting
T 08122 429 02   **F** 08122 861 84
www.eittinger-fischerbraeu.de
Owner: Christoph Vincenti   Founded: 1932
Output: 6,000hl   Availability: 20 pubs
REGULAR BEERS:
Eittinger Hell (4.9%)
Eittinger Fischer Weisse (5.2%)
Eittinger Urtyp-Dunkel (5.4%)
Eittinger Spezial (5.8%)
SEASONAL BEERS:
**Eittinger Fest-Weisse, Eittinger Weihnachtsbier,
Eittinger St. Georg Doppelbock** (7.1%)

Brewery and tap in a village east of München
Airport. Public transport is very poor but there
are a couple of buses from Erding on weekdays.

🍺 **Braustüberl Eitting**
St. Georg Straße 8, 85462 Eitting
Closed Wed; Thu–Sat 10.00–24.00, Sun 10.00–
14.00, Mon 10.00–22.00, Tue 10.00–18.00
DB Erding 8km

ELLINGEN 219

Fürstliches Brauhaus

Brewery: Schloßstraße 8-10, 91792 Ellingen
Office: Schloßstraße 19, 91792 Ellingen
T 09141 978 60   **F** 09141 978 58
www.fuerst-carl.de
Owner: Carl Friedrich Fürst von Wrede
Founded: 1690   Output: 18,000hl
Availability: c.30 pubs
REGULAR BEERS:
Fürst Carl Urhell (4.9%)
Fürst Carl Dunkel (4.9%)
Fürst Carl Premium Pils (4.9%)
Fürst Carl Schlossgold (5.4%)
SEASONAL BEERS:
Fürst Carl Josephi-Bock (7%),
Fürst Carl Weihnachtsbock (7.5%)

Brewery owned by Prince Carl Friedrich von
Wrede, with the tap next door.

🍺 **Schloßbräustüberl**
Schloßstraße 6, 91792 Ellingen
T 09141 703 40   **F** 09141 92 31 38
Closed Mon; Tue–Sun 10.00–23.00
DB Ellingen (Bay) 1.1km

ELSENDORF (Schlüsselfeld) 220

Sternbräu

Braugasse 2, 96132 Schlüsselfeld-Elsendorf
T 09552 310   **F** 09552 62 57
www.landgasthof-sternbraeu.de
Owner: Gerhard Lindner   Founded: 1709
Output: 2,000hl   Availability: 6 pubs
REGULAR BEERS:
Sternbräu Hell (4.4%)
Sternbräu Pilsner (4.6%)
Sternbräu Kellerbier-Dunkel (5%)
Sternbräu Zwicklbier (5%)
SEASONAL BEERS:
Sternbräu Festbier (Dec),
Sternbräu Maibock (May)

Village brewery and pub with extensive accommodation and its own distillery. Bus No. 8227 runs a few times a day from Bamberg via Hirschaid.

🏠 Sternbräu

Braugasse 2, 96132 Schlüsselfeld-Elsendorf
Closed Tue; Wed–Mon 11.30–01.00; rooms available   DB Hirschaid 25km

ENZENREUTH (Schnaittach) 221

Enzensteiner

Enzenreuth 8, 91220 Schnaittach-Enzenreuth
T 09153 92 47 33   **F** 09153 92 47 34
www.enzensteiner.de
Owners: Martin Kreß   Founded: 1998
Output: 100hl
REGULAR BEERS:
Enzensteiner Landbier
Enzensteiner Pilsener
Original Enzensteiner
Enzensteiner Helles Weizen
Enzensteiner Dunkles Weizen
SEASONAL BEERS:
Enzensteiner Hafer-Bier,
Enzensteiner Vetus Millena

Tiny, wood-fired brewery on a farm in the hamlet of Enzenreuth. Vetus Millena is brewed to a thousand-year-old recipe. There's no public transport so if you don't have your own, it's a walk from Schnaittach to work up a thirst. The tap only opens in fine weather.

🏠 Enzensteiner Biergarten

Enzenreuth 8, 91220 Schnaittach-Enzenreuth
Oct–Apr: closed. May–Sep: closed Mon–Thu;
Fri 18.00–22.00, Sat, Sun & hols 11.00–22.00
DB Schnaittach-Markt 3km

ERDING 222

Erdinger Weißbräu

Erdinger Weißbräu Werner Brombach GmbH
Brewery: Franz-Brombach-Straße 1–20, 85435 Erding
Office: Lange Zeile 1–3, 85435 Erding
T 08122 40 90   **F** 08122 40 91 15
www.erdinger.de
Owner: Werner Brombach   Founded: 1886
Output: 1,500,000hl

REGULAR BEERS:
Erdinger Weißbier Leicht (2.9%)
Erdinger Champ (4.7%)
Erdinger Weißbier (5.3%)
Erdinger Weißbier Kristallklar (5.3%)
Erdinger Weißbier Dunkel (5.6%)
Erdinger Pikantus Weizenbock (7.3%)
SEASONAL BEER:
Erdinger Schneeweiße (5.6%)

Situated on the western edge of town, Erdinger Weißbräu is the largest wheat beer producer in the world and one of Germany's largest independent breweries. The tap and offices are in the town centre, at the former brewery site.

🏠 Erdinger Weißbräu

Lange Zeile 1, 85435 Erding
T 08122 122 08   **F** 08122 140 14
Daily 09.00–01.00
DB Erding 600m

ERHARTING 223

Erharting

Brauerei Erharting Jakob Röhrl oHG
Hauptstraße 6, 84513 Erharting
T 08631 994 66   **F** 08631 996 10
www.erhartinger-bier.de
Owners: Amelie & Marlis Röhrl
Founded: 1872
Output: 20,000hl
REGULAR BEERS:
Erharting Leicht (1.8%)
Erharting Leichte Weisse (2.9%)
Erharting Pils (5%)
Erharting Dunkel (5.2%)
Erharting Dunkle Ritter-Weisse (5.2%)
Erharting Export Hell (5.4%)
Erharting Hefe-Weisse (5.6%)
SEASONAL BEERS:
Erharting Festbier (5.6%),
Erharting Doppel Ritter (7%)

Export Hell is sold in 0.33l bottles as Ritter Zwerg (Dwarf Knight). The former tap is now the brewery office. If you want to look for the beers in Erharting, bus No. 11 runs from Mühldorf via Töging.
DB Töging (Inn) 3km, Mühldorf (Oberbayern) 6km

ERLANGEN 224

Kitzmann

Kitzmann-Bräu KG
Südliche Stadtmauerstraße 25, 91054 Erlangen
T 09131 810 80 **F** 09131 81 08 43
www.kitzmann.de
Founded: 1733 Output: 130,000hl
Availability: c. 180 pubs
REGULAR BEERS:
Kitzmann Leichtes Weißbier (2.9%)
Kitzmann Zwickl (4.8%)
Kitzmann Helles (4.9%)
Kitzmann Edelpils (5%)
Kitzmann Hefe-Weizen (5.6%)
Kitzmann Jubiläums-Erlanger Dunkel (5.7%)
Kitzmann Weißbier Bock (7%)
SEASONAL BEERS:
Kitzmann Erlanger Wintergold (5.9%, winter),
Kitzmann Bergkirchweihbier (5.9%, Apr),
Kitzmann Erlanger Urbock (7.1%, winter)

Large brewery in the centre of Erlangen. There's
no official brewery tap but the beers can be found
in more than 70 pubs and restaurants in town.
DB Erlangen 600m

Steinbach Bräu

Vierzigmannstraße 4, 91054 Erlangen
T 09131 89 59 12 **F** 09131 89 59 22
www.steinbach-braeu.de
Owner: Christoph Gewalt Founded: 1995
Output: 1,000hl Availability: 2 pubs
REGULAR BEER:
Steinbach Bräu Storchenbier (5.2%)
SEASONAL BEERS:
**Steinbach Bräu Goldblondchen-Weizen,
Steinbach Bräu Dunkles-Goldblondchen,
Steinbach Bräu Braunbier, Steinbach Bräu
Alterlanger Dunkel, Steinbach Bräu Scotty,
Steinbach Bräu Bergkirchweihbier, Steinbach
Bräu Faschingsbier, Steinbach Bräu Froscher
Bock, Steinbach Bräu Ladykiller Weizenbock**

Brewpub to the north of the town centre that
takes its name from a former local brewery.
The Storchenbier is named after the storks that
nest here, captured on a webcam.

🍺 **Steinbach Bräu**
Vierzigmannstraße 4, 91054 Erlangen
Daily from 17.00
DB Erlangen 850m

ESCHENBACH (Eltmann) 225

Eschenbacher Wagner-Bräu

Eschenbacher Privatbrauerei GmbH
Eltmanner Straße 12, 97483 Eltmann-Eschenbach
T 09522 288 **F** 09522 287
www.eschenbacher.de
Owner: Karl Werner Wagner Founded: 1750
Output: 90,000hl
REGULAR BEERS:
Eschenbacher Hausbräu (4.6%)
Eschenbacher Urtyp (4.6%)
Eschenbacher Zwickl (4.6%)
Eschenbacher Dunkel
Eschenbacher Pilsener (4.9%)
Eschenbacher Weißbier
Eschenbacher Export (5.2%)
Eschenbacher Edel-Märzen (5.5%)
WALLBURG BEERS:
Wallburg Hell (4.6%),
Wallburg Pilsner (4.9%),
Wallburg Export (5%)

Large brewery in a small village. We have no
idea who they brew the beers for but we think
Wallburg is a hill near Eltmann. Buses Nos. 8180
and 8229 serve Ebelsbach but you may find it
more convenient to catch the bus from Bamberg
rather than Ebelsbach-Eltmann.

🍺 **Eschenbacher Bräustübla**
Eltmanner Straße 12, 97483 Eltmann-Eschenbach
Closed Mon; Tue–Sun 17.00–22.00
DB Ebelsbach-Eltmann 4km

ESLARN 226

Bauriedl

Privatbrauerei Bauriedl
Ludwig-Müller-Straße 21, 92693 Eslarn
T 09653 274 **F** 09653 273
Owner: Josef Bauriedl Founded: 1874
Output: 3,500hl
REGULAR BEERS:
Bauriedl Eslarner Helles (4.9%)
Bauriedl Eslarner Edel-Pils (4.9%)
Bauriedl Geistertrunk Schwarzbier (4.9%)
Bauriedl Eslarner Hefeweizen (4.9%)
Bauriedl Eslarner Urtrunk 1874 (5.2%)
SEASONAL BEER:
Bauriedl Eslarner Festbier (5.4%)

Small family-run brewery on the southern edge of town. About as far as it's possible to get from a railway station in Germany, bus services to Eslarn are sparse, to say the least. Good luck!

🍺 Bauriedl

Ludwig-Müller-Straße 21, 92693 Eslarn
T 09653 16 11
Closed Tue; Wed–Mon 10.00–23.00
DB Weiden (Oberpfalz) 35km, Nabburg 38km

Kommunbrauerei

Brennerstraße 30, 92693 Eslarn
T 09653 920 70   **F** 09653 92 07 50
www.eslarn.de
Owner: Mark Eslarn   Founded: 1522
Output: 1,000hl   Availability: 2 pubs
REGULAR BEERS:
Eslarner Rebhuhn-Zoigl (5%)
Eslarner Kommunbier (5%)

Communal brewery in the next street to Bauriedl. The only pub that is currently supplied is Beim Ströhern, which opens every three or four weeks. See the website for details.

🍺 Beim Ströhern

Tillystraße 4, 92693 Eslarn
T 09653 13 55   **F** 09653 92 98 40
Closed Mon–Thu; once a month Fri–Sat 14.00–24.00
DB Weiden (Oberpfalz) 35km, Nabburg 38km

ESSING 227

Kleines Brauhaus im Altmühltal

Altmühlgasse 10, 93343 Essing
T 09447 918 00   **F** 09447 91 80 20
www.brauereigasthof-schneider.de
Owner: Josef Schneider   Founded: 1640
Output: 1,500hl   Availability: 3 pubs
REGULAR BEERS:
Josef Schneider's Hell (4.8%)
Josef Schneider's Kleines Blondes (4.9%)
Josef Schneider's Dunkel (4.9%)
Josef Schneider's Weizenbier (5.3%)
Josef Schneider's Privat (5.5%)
SEASONAL BEERS:
**Josef Schneider's Weihnachtsfestbier,
Josef Schneider's Maibock** (7%)

Blessed with a particularly attractive location between cliffs and the river, Josef Schneider's

brewery and pub can be reached by bus No. 6022 from Saal station.

🍺 Schneider

Altmühlgasse 10, 93343 Essing
Nov–Easter: closed Mon & Tue;
Wed–Sun 09.00–24.00
Easter–Oct: daily 09.00–24.00; rooms available
DB Saal (Donau) 12km

ETTAL 228

Klosterbrauerei

Kaiser-Ludwig-Platz 1, 82488 Ettal
T 08822 744 50   **F** 08822 744 12
www.kloster-ettal.de   Founded: 1609
Owner: Benedikter Abtei Ettal (Kloster Ettal)
Output: 12,000hl   Availability: 55 pubs
REGULAR BEERS:
Ettaler Kloster Pils (5%)
Ettaler Weißbier Hell (5%)
Ettaler Weißbier Dunkel (5%)
Ettaler Kloster Edel-Hell (5.2%)
Ettaler Kloster Dunkel (5.5%)
Ettaler Curator (7%)

The village is dominated by the Benedictine abbey which owns and houses the brewery. They also have a renowned distillery. Bus No. 9606 runs from Oberau station.

🍺 Ludwig der Bayer

Kaiser-Ludwig-Platz 10–12, 82488 Ettal
T 08822 91 50   **F** 08822 91 54 20
Daily 11.00– 24.00; rooms available
DB Oberau 5km

ETTENSBERG (Blaichach) 229

Klier Bräu

Reuteweg 23a, 87544 Blaichach-Ettensberg
T 08321 60 86 57   **F** 08321 60 86 58
www.klier-bier.de
Owner: Markus Klier   Founded: 1997
REGULAR BEERS:
Ettensberger Spezial (5%)
Ettensberger Weizenbier Dunkel (5.5%)
SEASONAL BEERS:
Ettensberger Dinkelbier, Ettensberger Dunkles Pils, Ettensberger Weizenbier Hell, Ettensberger Maibock, St. Martinus Weizen-Doppelbock (7.8%)

Small brewery which started as a hobby but appears to be developing into something more significant. No brewery tap as yet.

DB Blaichach (Allgäu) 1km

ETZELWANG 230

Pürner

Hauptstraße 3, 92268 Etzelwang
T 09663 12 09 **F** 09663 20 08 94
Owner: Stefan Pürner Founded: 1859
Output: 1,000hl Availability: 5 pubs
REGULAR BEERS:
Etzelwanger Vollbier Hell (4.4%)
Etzelwanger Pils (4.5%)
Etzelwanger Hefe Weissbier (5%)
Etzelwanger Festbier (5.6%)
Etzelwanger Märzen (5.6%)
SEASONAL BEER:
Etzelwanger Bockbier (6.4%)

Small brewery next to the station. The brewery tap is on the opposite side of the railway, at the edge of a forest. We're not certain if it opens when it's raining.

Etzelwanger Felsenkeller
92268 Etzelwang (off Bahnhofstraße)
T 09663 555 Nov–Easter closed.
Ester–Oct: closed Mon–Thu;
Fri from 16.00, Sat, Sun & hols from 10.00
DB Etzelwang 300m

FALKENBERG 231

Kommunbrauauerei

Kommunbrauerei Markt Falkenberg
In der Schwaige 1, 95685 Falkenberg
T 09637 382 **F** 09637 25 11
www.markt-falkenberg.de
Owner: Falkenberg council Founded: 1878
Output: 600hl Availability: 1 pub
REGULAR BEER:
Falkenberger Zoigl

Communal brewery in the castle town of Falkenberg. The sole public outlet for the beer only opens every third weekend. Getting there when it's open may be a problem as the buses from Wiesau run Mon–Fri until 18.00 and not at all at the weekend!

Beim Kramer
Tirschenreuther Straße 4, 95685 Falkenberg
T 09637 328
Closed Mon–Thu; opens every third weekend
Fri–Sun, phone for details or check the website.
DB Wiesau (Oberpfalz) 6km

FATTIGAU (Oberkotzau) 232

Schloßbrauerei

Schloßbrauerei Christian Stelzer, Fattigau
Hauptstraße 3, 95145 Oberkotzau-Fattigau
T 09286 62 60 **F** 09286 83 90
www.schlossbrauerei-stelzer.de
Owner: Theodor Stelzer
Founded: 1353
Output: 13,000hl
REGULAR BEERS:
Schloßbrauerei Fattigau Urtyp Hell (4.3%)
Schloßbrauerei Fattigau Bio-Gold (4.7%)
Schloßbrauerei Fattigau Schloß Pils (5%)
Schloßbrauerei Fattigau Zwicklpils (5%)
Schloßbrauerei Doppel-Hopfen Pils (5%)
Schloßbrauerei Schloß-Export (5.2%)
Schloßbrauerei Fattigau Ritter Trunk (5.3%)
SEASONAL BEER:
Schloßbrauerei Schloß Bock (6.5%, Oct–Apr)

Brewery and tap in the middle of the village. If you don't fancy the walk from the station, bus No. 6341 runs from Hof via the centre of Oberkotzau.

Braukeller
Hauptstraße 9, 95145 Oberkotzau-Fattigau
T 09286 950 20
Jan–Feb: daily 11.00–14.00 & 16.30–24.00
Mar–Dec: daily 11.00–24.00; rooms available
DB Oberkotzau 2.8km

FELDKIRCHEN 233

Fliegerbräu

Die Gastro Fliegerbräu GmbH & Co. KG
Sonnenstraße 2, 85622 Feldkirchen
T 089 903 60 32 **F** 089 903 96 00
www.fliegerbraeu.de
Founded: 1991
Output: 1,000hl
Availability: 1 pub

REGULAR BEER:
Flieger-Schwarze
Flieger-Weiße (5.4%)

Brewpub in an old distillery. They used to be owned by Hofbräuhaus Traunstein but don't advertise if that's still the case.

📍 **Fliegerbräu**
Sonnenstraße 2, 85622 Feldkirchen
Daily 11.00–01.00
DB Feldkirchen 500m

FLADUNGEN 234

Freilandmuseum

Fränkisches Freilandmuseum Fladungen
Bahnhofstraße 19, 97650 Fladungen
T 09778 912 30   F 09778 91 23 45
www.freilandmuseum-fladungen.de
Founded: 1990   Output: 30hl
SEASONAL BEER:
Freilandmuseum Märzen (5.5%)

Reconstructed brewery that was originally in Alsleben. It brews just once a year and the beer is only available on the fourth Sunday in June and the last weekend in August. Bus No. 8153 runs from Mellrichstadt Mon–Fri and there are occasional tourist trains at the weekend from May to October (see the website).
DB Mellrichstadt 18km

FLUGHAFEN-MÜNCHEN 235

Airbräu

München Airport Center, Terminalstraße Mitte 18, 85356 München-Flughafen
T 089 9759 31 01   F 089 9759 31 06
www.airbraeu.de
Owner: Allresto Flughafen München Hotel und Gaststätten GmbH   Founded: 1999
Output: 2,500hl   Availability: 2 pubs
REGULAR BEERS:
Airbräu Flieger-Quell (5.2%)
Airbräu Kumulus Weißbier (5.4%)
SEASONAL BEERS:
Airbräu Krampus (5.3%, Christmas),
Airbräu Mayday Dunkles-Weizen (5.6%, May),
Airbräu Jet A-1 (5.8%),
Airbräu Aviator (7.8%, winter)

Brewpub in the heart of München airport, above the S-Bahn terminus. They have a second outlet airside in Terminal 2.

📍 **Airbräu**
Terminalstraße Mitte 18,
85356 Flughafen-München
Daily 10.00–01.00
DB Flughafen München Terminal 50m

FORCHHEIM 236

Eichhorn

Brauerei Eichhorn e.K.
Bamberger Straße 9, 91301 Forchheim
T 09191 23 79   www.brauereieichhorn.de
Owner: Konrad Greif   Founded: 1835
Output: 2,000hl   Availability: 5 pubs
REGULAR BEERS:
Eichhorn Erstes Forchheimer Leicht (2.9%)
Eichhorn Vollbier (4.9%)
Eichhorn Vollbier-Dunkel (4.9%)
Eichhorn Edel-Pils (5.4%)
Eichhorn Märzen (5.7%)
SEASONAL BEER:
Eichhorn Fest-Bier (5.7%)

The smallest of Forchheim's breweries, Eichhorn is just north of the pedestrianised town centre.

📍 **Eichhorn**
Bamberger Straße 9, 91301 Forchheim
T/F 09191 647 68
Closed Tue & Wed; Thu–Mon 10.00–23.00
DB Forchheim (Oberfranken) 950m

Greif

Brauerei Josef Greif
Serlbacher Straße 10, 91301 Forchheim
T 09191 72 79 20   F 09191 72 79 22
www.brauerei-greif.de
Owner: Christian Schuster   Founded: 1848
Output: 10,000hl
REGULAR BEERS:
Greif-Bräu Leicht (2.5%)
Greif-Bräu Weisse Leicht (3.2%)
Greif-Bräu Lager (4.7%)
Greif-Bräu Hell (4.9%)
Greif-Bräu Edel-Pils (5.1%)
Greif-Bräu Jubel-Export (5.2%)
Greif-Bräu Weisse (5.4%)
Greif-Bräu Dunkle Weisse (5.4%)

SEASONAL BEERS:
Greif-Bräu Capitulare Jubiläumsbier (5.5%),
Greif-Bräu Anna-Festbier (5.5%, July),
Greif-Bräu Weihnachtsfestbier (5.5%, Dec)

Don't be fooled by the pub at Sattlertorstraße 18 – this was the original location of Brauerei Greif but brewing ceased here in 1953. The brewery is now just off the ring road, on the northern edge of town, with the tap next door.

🍺 Greif

Serlbacher Straße 10, 91301 Forchheim
Sat 09.30–14.00, Sun 09.00–13.00, Fri, Mon & Wed 08.30–22.00, Tue & Thu 08.30–14.00
DB Forchheim (Oberfranken) 1.3km

Hebendanz

Sattlertorstraße 14, 91301 Forchheim
T 09191 12 22   **F** 09191 674 62
Owners: D. Harrer & Fritz Hebendanz
Founded: 1579   Output: 10,000hl
Availability: 5 pubs
REGULAR BEERS:
Hebendanz Bächla-Leicht (2.8%)
Hebendanz Export-Hell (5%)
Hebendanz Bayerisch Edel-Pils (5.1%)
Hebendanz Erstes Forchheimer Weizen (5.1%)
Hebendanz Märzen-Gold (5.2%)
SEASONAL BEERS:
Hebendanz Jubiläums-Festbier (5.3%),
Hebendanz Starker Fritz Festbier (5.3%)

Half-timbered brewery and tap opposite the old town hall, owned by the family since 1579. Its future was in some doubt as we closed for press, following a serious fire in mid-December 2005.

🍺 Hebendanz

Sattlertorstraße 14, 91301 Forchheim
Thu 08.30–12.00, Fri 08.30–23.00, Sat, Mon, Tue & Wed 08.30–20.00, Sun 13.00–20.00
DB Forchheim (Oberfranken) 950m

Neder

Brauerei Neder GmbH
Sattlertorstaße 10, 91301 Forchheim
T 09191 24 00   **F** 09191 24 24
Owner: Betty Neder   Founded: 1554
Output: 6,000hl   Availability: 10 pubs
REGULAR BEERS:
Neder Klassik 1554 (4.9%)
Neder Pils (4.9%)

Neder Erstes Forchheimer Braunbier (4.9%)
Neder Anna Weisse (5%)
Neder Schwarze Anna (5.2%)
Neder Kellerbier (5.2%)
Neder Export (5.2%)
SEASONAL BEERS:
Neder Anna-Festbier (5.2%, Jul),
Neder Weihnachts-Festbier (5.2%, Christmas)

Brewery and tap a couple of doors along from Hebendanz at the northern end of the pedestrianised part of town.

🍺 Neder

Sattlertorstaße 10, 91301 Forchheim
Closed Tue; Wed–Mon 09.00–19.00
DB Forchheim (Oberfranken) 950m

FORSTING (Pfaffing)   237

Gut Forsting

Privat-Brauerei Gut Forsting e.G.
Münchner Straße 23, 83539 Pfaffing-Forsting
T 08094 10 11   **F** 08094 81 78
E brauerei-gut-forsting@t-online.de
Founded: 1871
Output: 15,000hl   Availability: 41 pubs
REGULAR BEERS:
Gut Forsting Xamax (4.7%)
Gut Forsting Weissbier (5%)
Gut Forsting Export Hell (5.2%)
Gut Forsting Export Dunkel (5.4%)

The brewery is in the centre of the village with the tap next door. Brews what is likely to be the only beer to start and finish with an 'X'.

🍺 Forsting

Münchner Straße 21, 83539 Pfaffing-Forsting
T 08094 909 70   **F** 08094 90 97 40
Closed Wed; Thu–Tue 07.00–01.00; rooms available   DB Forsting 150m

FRAMMERSBACH   238

Waldschloss-Bräu

Waldschloss-Brauerei GmbH
Orber Straße 103, 97833 Frammersbach
T 09355 973 40   **F** 09355 97 34 13
www.waldschloss-brauerei.de
Owners: Jens & Sylvia Reinhart   Founded: 1886
Output: 15,000hl

REGULAR BEERS:
Waldschloss-Bräu Pilsner (4.7%)
Waldschloss-Bräu Kellerbier
Waldschloss-Bräu Dunkel (5%)
Waldschloss-Bräu Export (5.1%)
Frammersbacher Fuhrmann's Weisse (5.2%)
Frammersbacher Fuhrmann's Weisse-Dunkel (5.2%)
SEASONAL BEER:
Waldschloss-Bräu Doppelbock (7%)

The brewery and tap are located on the northern edge of town. From Partenstein station take bus No. 8045 to Waldschloßstraße (no weekend service).

🍺 **Waldschloss-Bräustübl**
Orber Straße 103, 97833 Frammersbach
Daily 10.30–12.00 & 15.00–20.00
DB Partenstein 6km

FRAUENDORF
(Bad Staffelstein)   239

Hetzel

Brauerei Hetzel OHG
Frauendorf 11, 96231 Bad Staffelstein-Frauendorf
T 09573 64 35   **F** 09573 31 09 65
Owner: Anton Hetzel
Founded: 1820
Output: 4,000hl
REGULAR BEERS:
Hetzel Frauendorfer Vollbier (4.9%)
Hetzel Frauendorfer Landbier (4.7%)
Hetzel Frauendorfer Pils (5.3%)
SEASONAL BEERS:
Hetzel Frauendorfer Weihnachtsfestbier,
Hetzel Frauendorfer Bock (Christmas)

Small brewery on the main road through the village. The brewery tap (The Peacock) only opens on Sundays, buses from Bad Staffelstein run daily and are provided by a local operator.

🍺 **Zum Pfau**
Frauendorf 11, 96231 Bad Staffelstein-Frauendorf
Closed Mon–Sat; Sun 10.00–12.00 & from 14.30
DB Bad Staffelstein 7km

FREILASSING   240

Weißbräu

Weißbräu Freilassing
Bräuhausstraße 5, 83395 Freilassing
T 08654 97 25   **F** 08654 29 61
E weissbraeu@t-online.de
Owners: Familie Kuhn   Founded: 1910
Output: 500hl   Availability: 2 pubs
REGULAR BEERS:
Freilassinger Edelweizen (5.3%)
Freilassinger Edelweizen Dunkel (5.7%)
SEASONAL BEER:
Renator Weizendoppelbock-Dunkel (7.8%)

Small family-run brewpub and hotel in the centre of Freilassing. The beers are only available at one other pub.

🍺 **Weißbräu**
Bräuhausstraße 5, 83395 Freilassing
Closed Mon; Tue–Sun 09.00–23.00; rooms available
DB Freilassing 700m

FREISING   241

Bräuhaus Freising

Bräuhaus in Lerchenfeld – Erste Freisinger Gasthaus-Brauerei
Am Lohmühlbach 8, 85356 Freising-Lerchenfeld
T 08161 818 98   **F** 08161 823 56
www.brauhaus-freising.de
Owners: the Gritz family   Founded: 1991
Output: 1,000hl   Availability: 1 pub
REGULAR BEERS:
Freisinger Bräuhaus Hell (4.6%)
Freisinger Bräuhaus Weißbier (4.6%)
Freisinger Bräuhaus Schwarzbier (4.8%)
SEASONAL BEERS:
Freisinger Bräuhaus Kellerbier,
Freisinger Bräuhaus Gogolori,
Freisinger Bräuhaus Erntedankbier,
Freisinger Bräuhaus Nikolausbier,
Freisinger Bräuhaus Weihnachtsbier,
Freisinger Bräuhaus Maibock,
Freisinger Bräuhaus Doppelbock

Brewpub in the south-western suburb of Lerchenfeld. Buses Nos. 511 and 622 run from the station to Güte Anger, a short walk from the pub.

🍺 Bräuhaus Freising

Am Lohmühlbach 8, 85356 Freising-Lerchenfeld
Closed Mon; Tue–Thu 10.00–01.00, Fri & Sat
10.00–02.00, Sun 10.00–24.00
DB Freising 2.3km

Hofbrauhaus

Gräfliches Hofbrauhaus Freising GmbH
Mainburger Straße 26, 85356 Freising
T 08161 60 10   **F** 08161 683 09
www.hofbrauhaus-freising.de
Owner: Graf zu Törring-Jettenbach
Founded: 1160   Output: 250,000hl
REGULAR BEERS:
Hofbrauhaus Freisinger Leicht (2.9%)
Hofbrauhaus Freising Dunkel (4.8%)
Hofbrauhaus Freising Urhell (4.9%)
Hofbrauhaus Freising Jägerbier (5.3%)
SEASONAL BEER:
Hofbrauhaus Freising Festbier (5.8%)
GRAF IGNAZ BEERS:
Graf Ignaz Lager (4.9%),
Graf Ignaz Premium Pilsner (4.9%)
HUBER WEISSES BEERS:
Huber Weisses Leicht (2.9%), **Huber Weisses
Fresh** (5.2%), **Huber Weisses Original** (5.4%),
Huber Weisses Dunkel (5.4%), **Huber Weisses
Kristall** (5.4%)
*FOR BRAUHAUS JETTENBACH &
BRAUHAUS PÖRNBACH:*
Graf Toerring Original Urhell (4.8%),
Graf Toerring Hell (4.9%), **Graf Toerring
Schwarzbier** (5.2%), **Graf Toerring Edeltrunk**
(5.2%), **Graf Toerring Original Urhell Export**
(5.2%), **Graf Toerring Bock** (6.5%)

Large brewery just north of the town centre with
the brewery tap in the next street. Also brews
the beers for the company's former breweries in
Jettenbach and Pörnbach.

🍺 Hofbrauhauskeller

Lankesbergstraße 5, 85356 Freising
T 08161 93 88 00   f 08161 93 88 01
Daily 10.00–24.00   DB Freising 1.5km

Weihenstephan

Bayerische Staatsbrauerei Weihenstephan
Alte Akademie 2, 85354 Freising-Weihenstephan
T 08161 53 60   **F** 08161 53 62 00
www.weihenstephaner.de
Owner: Freistaat Bayern   Founded: 1040
Output: 225,000hl

REGULAR BEERS:
Weihenstephaner Hefeweissbier Leicht (3.2%)
Weihenstephaner Original (5.1%)
Weihenstephaner Pilsner (5.1%)
Weihenstephaner Tradition Dunkel (5.2%)
Weihenstephaner Hefeweissbier Dunkel (5.3%)
Weihenstephaner Hefe-Weissbier (5.4%)
Weihenstephaner Kristall-Weissbier (5.4%)
Weihenstephaner Xan Hefe Weiße (5.4%)
SEASONAL BEERS:
Weihenstephaner Festbier (5.8%),
Weihenstephaner Korbinian (7.4%)

The world's oldest brewery sits on a hill west of
the town centre. The first brewing licence was
granted in 1040 and they've been brewing (on
and off) ever since. Weihenstephan is also home
to the famous brewing school, a department of
the Technical University of Munich.

🍺 Bräustüberl

Weihenstephaner Berg 10,
85354 Freising-Weihenstephan
T 08161 130 04   **F** 08161 410 66
Daily 10.00–24.00
DB Freising 1.4km

FREUDENBERG   242

Märkl

Brauerei Alwin Märkl
Hauptstraße 11, 92272 Freudenberg
T 09627 912 40   **F** 09627 912 41
Owner: Alwin Märkl
Founded: 1466
Output: 4,000hl
REGULAR BEERS:
Freudenberger Leichtes Vollbier (2.7%)
Freudenberger Leichtes-Weizen (2.7%)
Freudenberger Hell (4.9%)
Freudenberger Dunkel (4.9%)
Freudenberger Pils (5.1%)
Freudenberger Hefe-Weizen (5.2%)
SEASONAL BEERS:
Freudenberger Festbier,
Freudenberger Märkator

Small brewery with no tap of its own. If you'd
like to try and find the beers in Freudenberg,
bus No. 6312 runs from Amberg Mon–Sat.
DB Amberg 12km

FREUDENECK (Rattelsdorf) 243

Fischer

Freudeneck 2, 96179 Rattelsdorf-Freudeneck
T 09547 488   **F** 09547 870 98 91
Owner: Jürgen Fischer
Founded: c. 1900
Output: 600hl
Availability: 1 pub
REGULAR BEER:
Fischer Vollbier Hell (4.8%)
SEASONAL BEER:
Fischer Bock (Oct–Dec)

Brewpub in a hamlet north of Rattelsdorf. Bus
No. 8219 runs on weekdays only from Bamberg
via Ebing station.

📍 **Fischer**
Freudeneck 2, 96179 Rattelsdorf-Freudeneck
Closed Mon; Tue–Sun 09.00–23.00
DB Ebing 5km

FREYUNG 244

Lang-Bräu

Lang-Bräu Nepomuk Lang
Langgasse 2, 94078 Freyung
T 08551 577 60   **F** 08551 57 76 26
www.lang-braeu-freyung.de
Owner: Erika Lang   Founded: 1856
Output: 30,000hl   Availability: 150 pubs
REGULAR BEERS:
Lang-Bräu Leicht (2.8%)
Lang-Bräu Leichtes Weizen (2.9%)
Lang-Bräu Hell (4.8%)
Lang-Bräu Pils (4.9%)
Lang-Bräu Hefeweizen-Hell (5.3%)
Lang-Bräu Hefeweizen-Dunkel (5.3%)
Lang-Bräu Export Dunkel (5.5%)
SEASONAL BEERS:
Lang-Bräu Märzen,
Lang-Bräu Festbier (Christmas),
Lang-Bräu Josefi Bock (6%, Lent)

Small regional brewery in the Bayrischer Wald.
The tap is around the corner on the main road
through town. There's talk of the railway to
Freyung re-opening but until it does, buses No.
6117 from Grafenau and No. 6110 from Passau
are the only options for those without transport.

📍 **Lang-Bräu**
Stadtplatz 3, 94078 Freyung
T 08551 59 90   **F** 08551 91 08 05
Closed Wed; Thu–Tue 10.00–14.00 & 17.00–24.00
DB Grafenau 16km, Passau Hbf 37km

FRIEDBERG 245

Herzog Ludwig

Brauhaus Herzog Ludwig
Jungbräustraße 8, 86316 Friedberg
T 0821 267 92 17   **F** 0821 60 71 26
www.herzog-ludwig.de
Owners: Christa & Wolfgang Faig
Founded: 1995   Output: 200hl
REGULAR BEER:
Herzog Ludwig Hell

Brewpub in the centre of Friedberg that also has
a sister pub at the rear, on Bauernbräustraße.
The latter opens one hour earlier and also at
Sunday lunchtime 11.00–14.00.

📍 **Herzog Ludwig**
Jungbräustraße 8, 86316 Friedberg
Closed Mon & Tue; Wed–Sun 19.00–24.00
DB Friedberg (bei Augsburg) 450m

FRIEDENFELS 246

Schloßbrauerei

Schloßbrauerei Friedenfels GmbH & Co. KG
Gemmingenstraße 33, 95688 Friedenfels
T 09683 910   **F** 09683 485
www.schlossbrauerei-friedenfels.de
Owner: Eberhard Freiherr von Gemmingen-
Hornberg   Founded: 1885
Output: 60,000hl   Availability: 250+ pubs
REGULAR BEERS:
Friedenfelser Weizen Leicht (2.7%)
Friedenfelser Leichtes Pils (2.8%)
Friedenfelser Urtyp Hell (4.8%)
Friedenfelser Zwick'l (5%)
Friedenfelser Pils (5%)
Friedenfelser Hefeweizen (5.2%)
Friedenfelser Dunkles Weizen (5.2%)
Friedenfelser Edel (5.5%)
SEASONAL BEERS:
Friedenfelser Karpfentrunk (5%),
Friedenfelser Wintertrunk (5.2%)

Regional brewery owned by Baron Gemmingen-Hornberg. The Schwarzer Ritter Zoigl is brewed by Scheuerer in Moosbach. Several bus routes that stop outside the brewery run Mon–Fri from both Reuth and Wiesau.

🍺 Schloßschänke

Gemmingenstraße 31, 95688 Friedenfels
T 09683 92 97 88   **F** 09683 92 98 18
Closed Mon; Tue–Sun from 10.00
DB Reuth (bei Erbendorf) 6km, Wiesau 8km

FRONTENHAUSEN 247

Postbrauerei Renkl

Postgasse 3, 84160 Frontenhausen
T 08732 12 12   **E** postbier@t-online.de
Owner: Markus Renkl
Founded: 1700
Output: 4,000hl
Availability: 10 pubs
REGULAR BEERS:
Postbräu Kellerbier (4.9%)
Postbräu Hell (5%)
Postbräu Vilslaus Dunkel (5%)
Postbräu Weissbier (5%)
SEASONAL BEER:
Postbräu Manna Doppelbock Dunkel (7%)

Small brewery in the centre of town that is rumoured to have stopped brewing. The brewery tap is on the main road. Public transport to Frontenhausen is appalling, with just two buses a day from Landshut and on weekdays only. If you catch the earlier one you have eight minutes in Frontenhausen before the last bus of the day out!

🍺 Postbräu

Bahnhofstraße 2, 84160 Frontenhausen
T/F 08732 93 94 84
Daily 09.00–23.00
DB Dingolfing 12km, Landshut 35km

Röhrl Bräu

Marienplatz 16, 84160 Frontenhausen
T 08732 919 80   **F** 08732 91 98 29
www.roehrlbraeu.de
Owner: Brauerei Röhrl, Straubing
Founded: 1836   Output: 15,000hl
REGULAR BEERS:
Röhrl's Export Hell (5.2%)
Röhrl Weisse (5.3%)

As with Postbräu, there's talk that Röhrl Bräu no longer brews. However, the parent brewery in Straubing specifically mentions the above beers as being brewed in Frontenhausen.

🍺 Röhrl Bräu

Marienplatz 16, 84160 Frontenhausen
T 08732 14 40
Closed Tue; Wed–Mon 10.00–23.00
DB Dingolfing 12km, Landshut 35km

FUCHSBERG (Teunz) 248

Schloßbrauerei

Schloßbrauerei Fuchsberg GmbH & Co. KG
Bierbrunnen 1, 92552 Teunz–Fuchsberg
T 09671 15 18   **F** 09671 35 15
www.fuchsberger-bier.de
Founded: 1663
Output: 15,000hl   Availability: 30 pubs
REGULAR BEERS:
Fuchsberger Urhell (4.8%)
Fuchsberger Pils (4.8%)
Fuchsberger Pilsener Premium (4.8%)
Fuchsberger Weisse (5.4%)

Situated in a small village a couple of kilometres from Teunz, Schloßbrauerei Fuchsberg has no brewery tap. There's also no public transport to Fuchsberg but there are several buses from Nabburg to Teunz on weekdays (No. 6273).
DB Nabburg 20km

FUCHSSTADT (Reichenberg) 249

Wolf

Privat Brauerei Georg Wolf KG
Brauereistraße 2, 97234 Reichenberg-Fuchsstadt
T 09333 971 20   **F** 09333 97 12 99
www.wolf-bier.de
Owner: Harald Wolf   Founded: 1739
Output: 20,000hl   Availability: 64 pubs
REGULAR BEERS:
Fuchsstadter Leichte Schankbier (2.6%)
Fuchsstadter Leichtes Weissbier (2.8%)
Fuchsstadter Wolf Pils (4.9%)
Fuchsstadter Keller Pils Naturtrüb (4.9%)
Wolf Spirit Pils (4.9%)
Fuchsstadter Weissbier (5.2%)
Fuchsstadter Dunkles Weissbier (5.2%)

SEASONAL BEER:
Fuchsstadter Bock (7.2%, autumn & winter)

The brewery has been in the same family since it was founded. Bus No. 42 runs occasionally from Geroldshausen but the best service is from Würzburg.

🍺 **Bräustube Fuchsstadt**
Dorfstraße 6, 97234 Reichenberg-Fuchsstadt
T/F 09333 14 94
Closed Mon; Tue–Sun 11.00–01.00
DB Würzburg Hbf 13km

FÜRNHEIM (Wassertüdingen) 250

Forstquell

Forstquell Brauerei von Friedrich Höhenberger
Fürnheim 35, 91717 Wassertüdingen-Fürnheim
T 09832 96 57   **F** 09832 96 72
www.forstquell.de
Owner: Oettinger Gruppe   Founded: 1997
Output: 400hl   Availability: 1 pub
REGULAR BEERS:
Forstquell Gold
Forstquell Kupfer
Forstquell Weiße
SEASONAL BEERS:
Forstquell Vierkornbier (Oct),
Forstquell Bock (Lent)

Brewpub that was home to Brauerei Höhenberger until 1958. Owned by Oettinger who also use it for brewing research and teaching. Getting there by bus is possible but a challenge.

🍺 **Höhenberger**
Fürnheim 35, 91717 Wassertüdingen-Fürnheim
Daily 11.00–24.00; rooms available
DB Gunzenhausen 23km, Nördlingen 28km

FÜRSTENFELDBRUCK 251

Schloßbrauerei Kaltenberg

König Ludwig GmbH & Co. KG Schloßbrauerei Kaltenberg
Augsburger Straße 41, 82256 Fürstenfeldbruck
T 08141 24 30   **F** 08141 24 31 38
www.koenig-ludwig.com
Owner: Luitpold Prinz von Bayern
Founded: 1870   Output: 750,000hl
KALTENBERG BEERS:

Kaltenberg Leicht (2.9%)
Kaltenberg 3,8 (3.8%)
Kaltenberg Pils (4.8%)
Kaltenberg Hell (4.9%)
Kaltenberg Diät Pils (4.9%)
Kaltenberg Schloss-Keller Naturtrüb (5.1%)
Kaltenberg Spezial (5.6%)
Kaltenberg Ritterbock (9.5%)
SEASONAL BEER:
Kaltenberg Königliches Festtags-Bier (5.6%)
PRINZREGENT LUITPOLD BEERS:
Prinzregent Luitpold Weissbier Leicht (2.9%),
Prinzregent Luitpold Weissbier Hell (5.5%),
Prinzregent Luitpold Weissbier Dunkel (5.5%),
Prinzregent Luitpold Weissbier Kristall (5.5%)

By far the largest of the two Kaltenberg breweries. The other one is at the castle in Kaltenberg, near Geltendorf. They took over Bärenbräu Nesselwang and Brauhaus Füssen in 2002, and we think brew at least one beer for the latter. They also own Postbräu in Thannhausen who brew some Prinzregent Luitpold wheat beer.

🍺 **Brauhaus Bruck**
Augsburger Straße 41, 82256 Fürstenfeldbruck
T 08141 254 90   **F** 08141 35 31 75
Daily 10.00–23.00   DB Fürstenfeldbrück 1.5km

FÜRTH 252

Tucher

Tucher Bräu GmbH & Co. KG
Schwabacher Straße 106, 90763 Fürth
T 0911 977 60   **F** 0971 977 63 70
Owner: Oetker Gruppe AG   Founded: 1600
REGULAR BEERS:
Tucher Light (2.9%)
Tucher Leichtes Hefe Weizen (2.9%)
Tucher Original Urbräu (4.8%)
Tucher Pilsener (4.9%)
Tucher Diät Pils (4.9%)
Tucher Urfränkisch Dunkel (5.2%)
Tucher Helles Hefe Weizen (5.3%)
Tucher Dunkles Hefe Weizen (5.3%)
Tucher Kristall Weizen (5.3%)
Tucher Übersee Export (5.3%)
SEASONAL BEERS:
Tucher Sebaldus Festbier (5.9%), **Tucher Christkindlmarkt Bier** (6%, Dec), **Tucher Lorenzi Bock Hell** (7.2%, Lent), **Tucher Bajuvator** (7.2%)

HUMBSER BEERS:
Humbser Pils (4.9%), Humbser Export (5.4%)
LEDERER BEERS:
**Lederer Premium Leicht (2.9%),
Lederer Premium Pils (5.1%),
Kroko Spezial Kellerbier (5.4%)**
PATRIZIER BEERS:
**Patrizier Bräu Urbräu Hell (4.9%), Patrizier
Bräu Albrecht Dürer Pils (4.9%), Patrizier Bräu
Weißbier (5.3%), Patrizier Bräu Königstrunk
Export Hell (5.5%)**

The former Humbser brewery, latterly owned by
Patrizier and now by Tucher. We're not 100 per
cent certain which beers are actually brewed
here as Tucher still have their original brewery
in Nürnberg, but we think all Humbser, Lederer
and Patrizier beers are brewed here.

🍺 **Tucher-Bräu am Opernhaus**
Am Kartäusertor 1, 90402 Nürnberg-Lorenz
T 0911 20 46 49   **F** 0911 20 32 22
Daily 11.00–24.00
Ⓤ U2 & U21 Opernhaus 30m
DB Nürnberg Hbf 500m

FURTH im Wald 253

Dimpfl

Dimpfl Bräu Strauß KG
Bräuhausstraße 34, 93437 Furth im Wald
T 09973 38 16   **F** 09973 29 69
www.dimpfl-bier.de   Owner: Matthias Strauß
Founded: 1600   Output: 12,000hl
REGULAR BEERS:
**Dimpfl Bräu Urbräu (4.6%)
Dimpfl Bräu Dimpfl (5%)
Dimpfl Bräu Pilsener (5%)
Dimpfl Bräu Further Ritterschaft (5.5%)**
SEASONAL BEER:
Dimpfl Bräu Cave Gladium

Brewery in the southern part of town. They have
no brewery tap but the beers are available in a
dozen or so pubs locally.
DB Furth im Wald 700m

Hofer

Hofer Biere & Getränke
Waldschmidtstraße 20, 93437 Furth im Wald
T 09973 13 27   **F** 09973 46 23
www.hotel-hofer.de

Owner: Christa Hofer   Founded: 1909
Output: 10,000hl   Availability: c. 45 pubs
REGULAR BEERS:
**Hofer-Bräu Hell (4.7%)
Hofer-Bräu Pils (4.9%)
Hofer-Bräu Schwirza vom Landl Dunkel (4.9%)
Hofer-Bräu Weisse (5%)
Hofer-Bräu Drei-Wappen-Weiße (5%)
Hofer-Bräu Export (5.3%)**
SEASONAL BEER:
Hofer-Bräu Grenzfähnlein Festbier (5.9%)

Brewery, tap and hotel between the station and
town centre. Schwirza vom Landl Dunkel is
named after a local smuggler.

🍺 **Hofer**
Waldschmidtstraße 20, 93437 Furth im Wald
T 09973 841 10
Closed Sat; Sun 10.00–14.30 & 17.30–01.00,
Mon & Fri 10.00–01.00, Tue–Thu 16.00–01.00;
rooms available
DB Furth im Wald 350m

GARITZ (Bad Kissingen) 254

Stärker

Hausbrauerei Stärker
Nepomukgasse 1, 97688 Bad Kissingen-Garitz
T 0971 617 73   **F** 0971 78 54 85 15
www.staerkerbraeu.de
Owner: Hubert Stärker
Founded: 09.12.2000
Output: 100hl
Availability: 1 pub
REGULAR BEERS:
**Stärker's Hausbräu Hell
Stärker's Hausbräu Dunkel-Kellerbier
Stärker's Hausbräu Hefe-Weizen Hell**
SEASONAL BEER:
Stärker's Hausbräu Starkator (Lent)

Small brewpub in a suburb of Bad Kissingen. We
believe the local council operates a bus service
to Garitz but information is hard to come by.

🍺 **Museums-Brauhaus Jägersruh**
Baptist-Hoffmann-Straße 61, 97688 Bad
Kissingen-Garitz
T/F 0971 668 99
Closed Mon & Tue; Wed–Sun 18.00–24.00
DB Bad Kissingen 2.5km

GARS am Inn   255

Baumer

Marktplatz 1, 83536 Gars am Inn
T 08073 12 19
Owner: Christine Mürkens   Founded: 1890
REGULAR BEERS:
Baumer Hell
Baumer Dunkel
Baumer Weizen
Baumer Märzen

Small brewery and tap in the centre of town,
on the opposite side of the river to the station.
We're not sure if they supply any other pubs but
suspect they do not.

🍺 **Baumer**
Marktplatz 1, 83536 Gars am Inn
Closed Sat; Sun 08.00–13.00, Mon–Fri from 08.00
DB Gars (Inn) 1.7km

GEISELHÖRING   256

Erl

Brauerei Ludwig Erl
Straubinger Straße 10, 94333 Geiselhöring
T 09423 941 70   **F** 09423 94 17 25
www.brauerei-erl.de
Owner: Ludwig Erl   Founded: 1871
Output: 35,000hl
REGULAR BEERS:
Leichtes Erl (2.8%)
Erlkönig Pilsener (4.9%)
Erl-Hell (5%)
Erl-Weisse (5.1%)
Erl-Weisse Dunkel (5.1%)
Erlkönig Bügel-Weisse (5.1%)
Erl-Dunkel (5.3%)
Erlkönig Extra Hell (5.5%)
SEASONAL BEERS:
Erl Fest-Bier, Erl-Bock (7.2%)

The official brewery tap is Brauereigasthof
Erl-Bräu at Stadtplatz 17 but there is a pub at the
brewery that opens earlier and has a different
rest day. The Erlkönig is a mythical figure in a
well-known Goethe poem.

🍺 **Bräustüberl**
Straubinger Straße 10, 94333 Geiselhöring
T 09423 24 45

Closed Wed; Thu–Tue from 10.00
DB Geiselhöring 750m

🍺 **Erl-Bräu**
Stadtplatz 17, 94333 Geiselhöring
T 09423 90 20 87   **F** 09423 90 20 88
Closed Mon; Tue–Sun 11.00–23.00; rooms
available
DB Geiselhöring 600m

GEISFELD (Strullendorf)   257

Griess

Brauerei-Gasthof Griess
Magdalenenstraße 6, 96129 Strullendorf-Geisfeld
T 09505 16 24
www.brauerei-griess.de
Owners: Peter & Petra Griess   Founded: 1872
Output: 1,300hl   Availability: 2 pubs
REGULAR BEERS:
Griess Pilsner (5.5%)
Griess Kellerbier (5.5%)
SEASONAL BEERS:
Griess Racherla Rauchbier (5.5%, Aug),
Griess Doppelbock (7.5%, Christmas)

Brewpub that also operates a Bierkeller on the
south-western edge of the village in summer.
These are the only two places where the beer is
sold.

🍺 **Griess**
Magdalenenstraße 6, 96129 Strullendorf-Geisfeld
Closed Wed; Thu, Fri, Mon & Tue 15.00–22.00,
Sat & Sun 10.00–22.00
DB Strullendorf 7km, Bamberg 10km

Krug

Alte Dorfstraße 11, 96129 Strullendorf-Geisfeld
T 09505 484   **F** 09505 80 44 37
www.brauerei-krug.de
Owner: Stefan Krug   Founded: 1820
Output: 750hl   Availability: 1 pub
REGULAR BEER:
Krug Lagerbier (SW 12%)
SEASONAL BEERS:
Krug Das Helle (SW 12%), **Krug Das Elefant**
(SW 12%), **Krug Das Schwarze Schaf** (SW 12%)

Geisfeld's other brewpub has recently
expanded its beer range to include three
seasonals. Unfortunately, there is no public

transport to Geisfeld so it's either a long walk, a taxi or your own transport if you want to visit.

🍺 Krug
Alte Dorfstraße 11, 96129 Strullendorf-Geisfeld
Closed Tue; Wed–Fri from 16.00, Sat from
14.00, Sun & hols from 10.15, Mon from 16.00
DB Strullendorf 7km, Bamberg 10km

GESSERTSHAUSEN   258

Schimpfle
Hauptstraße 16, 86459 Gessertshausen
T 08238 9 63 70   **F** 08238 70 36
www.brauerei-schimpfle.de
Owners: Alfons & Josef Schimpfle
Founded: 1870
REGULAR BEERS:
Lösch-Zwerg Herb (5%)
Lösch-Zwerg Weizen (5%)
Lösch-Zwerg Würzig (5.2%)
SEASONAL BEER:
Lösch-Zwerg Bombastic (7.8%)

The brewery is in the middle of Gessertshausen but the tap is in the nearby village of Deubach. Lösch-Zwerg translates as dwarf fireman, the symbol of the brewery.

🍺 Zech Stuben
Sankt Gallus Straße 33,
86459 Gessertshausen-Deubach
T 08238 96 50 07
Closed Tue; Wed–Fri 11.00–14.00 & 17.00–23.00,
Sat & Sun 11.00–23.00, Mon 11.00–14.00 &
17.00–23.00
DB Gessertshausen 1.4km

GNODSTADT (Marktbreit)   259

Düll
Hausbrauerei Düll
Pfarrer-Geyer-Straße 1,
97340 Marktbreit-Gnodstadt
T 09332 86 63   **F** 09332 50 00 63
www.duell-gnodstadt.de
Owners: Christa & Sebastian Rank
Founded: 1840   Output: 1,500hl
Availability: 1 pub
REGULAR BEER:
Düll Pils (4.8%)

SEASONAL BEER:
Düll Bock (6.8%)

There are occasional buses on weekdays from Marktbreit but they're not much use for visiting the pub. Closed late August/early September.

🍺 Schwarzer Adler
Pfarrer-Geyer-Straße 1,
97340 Marktbreit-Gnodstadt
Closed Wed; Thu & Fri 11.30–14.00 & 17.00–22.00,
Sat, Sun & hols 11.30–22.00, Mon & Tue 11.30–
14.00 & 17.00–22.00
DB Marktbreit 4km, Ochsenfurt 6km

GOTTSMANNSGRÜN (Berg)   260

Gottsmannsgrüner
v. Koch'sche Familien-Brauerei GmbH & Co. KG
von-Koch-Straße 2, 95180 Berg-Gottsmannsgrün
T 09293 93 30 10   **F** 09293 81 80
www.gottsmannsgruener.de
Owner: Freiherr von Waldenfels-Künsberg
Founded: 1535   Output: 15,000hl
Availability: c.150 pubs
REGULAR BEERS:
Gottsmannsgrüner Lager (4.6%)
Gottsmannsgrüner Pils (4.8%)
Gottsmannsgrüner Das Schwarze (4.8%)
Gottsmannsgrüner Export (5%)
Gottsmannsgrüner Hefe Weisse (5.4%)
SEASONAL BEERS:
Gottsmannsgrüner Festbier (5.3%),
Gottsmannsgrüner Doppelbock (7.8%)

Bright yellow brewery, owned by the Baron von Waldenfels-Künsberg. Bus No. 6364 runs from Naila to Gottsmannsgrün, Mon–Fri only.

🍺 Bräustübl
Roßbergstraße 1, 95180 Berg-Gottsmannsgrün
T 09293 93 37 73
Closed Mon & Tue; Wed–Sun from 17.00
DB Naila 12km

GRABENSTÄTT   261

Chiemseebräu
Gasthausbrauerei Chiemseebräu
Gewerbestraße 1a, 83355 Grabenstätt
T 08661 92 99 22   **F** 08661 92 99 25
www.chiemseebraeu.de

Owner: Oliver Lange   Founded: 1994
Output: 180hl   Availability: 1 pub
REGULAR BEERS:
Chiemseebräu Zwickelbier
Chiemseebräu Weißbier
SEASONAL BEERS:
Chiemseebräu Braunbier, Chiemseebräu Bock

Brewpub close to the lake from which it takes its name. Bus No. 9509 runs from both Traunstein and Übersee but offers only a limited service at the weekend.

🍺 Chiemseebräu
Gewerbestraße 1a, 83355 Grabenstätt
Closed Tue; Wed–Fri & Mon 17.00–01.00, Sat & Sun 11.00–02.00
DB Übersee 7km, Traunstein 9km

GRAFENAU   262

Bucher Bräu
Bucher Bräu Grafenau GmbH & Co. KG
Elsenthaler Straße 5–7, 94481 Grafenau
T 08552 408 70   **F** 08552 40 87 27
www.bucher-braeu.de
Founded: 1843
Output: 25,000hl
Availability: 40 pubs
REGULAR BEERS:
Bucher Bräu Leichte (2.8%)
Bucher Bräu Leichtes Weizen (2.8%)
Bucher Bräu Helles (4.9%)
Bucher Bräu Pils (5.1%)
Bucher Bräu Alt-Bayrisch Dunkel (5.2%)
Bucher Bräu Hefe Weizen (5.2%)
Bucher Bräu Dunkles Weizen (5.3%)
Bucher Bräu Premium Edel-Hell (5.4%)
Bucher Bräu XXL Doppelbock
SEASONAL BEER:
Bucher Bräu Grafenauer Säumer-Festbier

Previously at Freyungstraße 7, the brewery moved to its current site near the station in 1982. They now have a tap alongside.

🍺 Bucher Bräustüberl
Elsenthaler Straße 5, 94481 Grafenau
T 08552 92 10 02
Closed Sun; Mon–Sat from 15.00
DB Grafenau 300m

GRÄFENBERG   263

Friedmann
Jägersberg 16, 91322 Gräfenberg
T 09192 318   **F** 09192 308
www.brauerei-friedmann.de
Owner: Siglinde Friedmann   Founded: 1875
Output: 5,000hl   Availability: 15 pubs
REGULAR BEERS:
Friedmann Fränkisches Landbier (4.7%)
Friedmann Pils (5%)
Friedmann Hefe-Weizen (5%)
Friedmann Ritter-Wirnt Trunk (5.1%)
SEASONAL BEERS:
Friedmann Sigi's Lager (4.9%),
Friedmann Festbier

From the station take Friedhofgäßchen to the top of the hill. The tap is on the left, the brewery a couple of hundred metres to the left. The Ritter Wirnt Trunk is named after Gräfenberg's most famous son, a 12th-century knight and minnesinger.

🍺 Friedmann's Bräustüberl
Bayreuther Straße 14, 91322 Gräfenberg
T 09192 99 74 35
Closed Mon; Tue–Sat 11.30–14.30 & 17.00–24.00, Sun & hols 11.30–24.00
DB Gräfenberg 500m

Lindenbräu
Brauerei-Gasthof Lindenbräu e.K.
Am Bach 2, 91322 Gräfenberg
T 09192 348   **F** 09192 99 78 37
www.lindenbraeu.de
Owner: Irene Brehmer-Stockum   Founded: 1932
Output: 3,500hl   Availability: 15 pubs
REGULAR BEERS:
Lindenbräu Leichtbier (2.8%)
Lindenbräu Vollbier Dunkel (4.8%)
Lindenbräu Pilsner (4.8%)
Lindenbräu Weizen (5%)
SEASONAL BEERS:
Lindenbräu Gräfenberger Festbier (5.4%),
Lindenbräu Gräfenberger Bock (6.5%)

Slightly smaller than the town's other brewery, Lindenbräu also has a distillery. If you plan to travel by train from Nürnberg, be warned that the line is isolated from the rest of the railway network and you need to catch the U-Bahn to Nordostbahnof.

🍺 **Lindenbräu**
Am Bach 3, 91322 Gräfenberg
Closed Fri; Sat–Thu 11.00–22.00
DB Gräfenberg 800m

GRAFING   264

Wildbräu-Grandauer

Wildbräu Grafing GmbH
Rotter Straße 15, 85567 Grafing
T 08092 700 90   **F** 08092 70 09 11
www.wildbraeu.de
Owners: Max Josef Schlederer   Founded: 1616
Output: 20,000hl
GRANDAUER BEERS:
Grandauer Leichte Weisse (2.9%)
Grandauer Schwarzbier (5.2%)
Grandauer Urstoff Export (5.2%)
Grandauer Ur-Hefe Weisse (5.4%)
Grandauer Dunkle Weisse (5.4%)
WILDBRÄU BEERS:
Wildbräu Leichte Weisse (2.9%)
Wildbräu Landpils (5%)
Wildbräu Weissbier Pils (5%)
Wildbräu Bayrisch Hell (5.2%)
Wildbräu Jagahalbe (5.2%)
Wildbräu Hefe Weisse (5.4%)
Wildbräu Dunkle Weisse (5.4%)
Wildbräu Meistersud (5.6%)
SEASONAL BEERS:
Wildbräu Weihnachtsbier (5.6%),
Wildbräu Festbier (5.8%)

The Schlederer family, owners of Wildbräu,
bought Grandauer in 1993. Today both beer
ranges are brewed under one roof. Jagahalbe is
listed on the website as a Grandauer beer but
the brewery tell us it's Wildbräu.

🍺 **Heckerbräu**
Marktplatz 26, 85567 Grafing
T 08092 86 31 35   **F** 08092 86 31 36
Daily 10.00–23.00   DB Grafing Stadt 450m

GRAMING (Altötting)   265

Graminger Weissbräu

Graming 79, 84503 Altötting-Graming
T 08671 961 40   **F** 08671 96 14 44
www.graminger-weissbraeu.de

Owner: Karlmann Detter   Founded: 1900
Output: 2,500hl   Availability: 20 pubs
REGULAR BEERS:
Graminger Leichtere Weisse (3.8%)
Graminger Pils (4.9%)
Graminger Weissbier (5.3%)
Graminger Kirta Dunkles Weissbier (5.4%)
Graminger Märzen (5.4%)
SEASONAL BEER:
Graminger Berggeist Weizenbock (6.8%)

Brewery and tap just south of Altötting on the
outskirts of the hamlet of Graming. There's no
bus but it's no great distance to walk from the
railway station in Altötting.

🍺 **Weisse Bräuhaus**
Graming 79, 84503 Altötting-Graming
Closed Thu; Fri–Wed 08.00–01.00; rooms
available
DB Altötting 1.6km

GRASMANNSDORF
(Burgebrach)   266

Kaiser

Grasmannsdorf 9,
96138 Burgebrach-Grasmannsdorf
T 09546 390   **F** 09546 59 33 14
www.brauerei-kaiser.de
Owner: Johann Kaiser   Founded: 1783
Output: 3,000hl   Availability: 1 pub
REGULAR BEERS:
Kaiser Pils (4.9%)
Kaiser Weißbier (4.9%)
SEASONAL BEERS:
Kaiser Festbier (5%, Dec),
Kaiser Starkbier (7%, Mar),
Kaiser Bockbier (7.5%, Nov)

Brewpub in a small village. Bus No. 8223 runs
from Bamberg to Ebrach, with some buses going
via Grasmannsdorf during the week. It's a 2-km
walk from either Burgebrach or Oberharnsbach,
if you catch a bus that doesn't call.

🍺 **Kaiser**
Grasmannsdorf 9,
96138 Burgebrach-Grasmannsdorf
Closed Mon; Tue–Fri 09.00–23.00, Sat 09.00–
18.00, Sun 09.00–12.00 & 14.00–23.00
DB Bamberg 15km

GREUTH (Höchstadt)   267

Fischer

Brauerei Norbert Fischer
Greuth 11, 91315 Höchstadt-Greuth
T 09502 545   **F** 09502 49 01 33
Owner: Norbert Fischer   Founded: 1702
Output: 1,500hl
REGULAR BEER:
Fischer Lagerbier (4.9%)
Fischer Rauchbier (4.9%)
Fischer Kellerbier (5%)
Fischer Weissbier (5%)
SEASONAL BEER:
Fischer Bockbier (7%, Christmas)

Small brewery whose tap now only opens at
lunchtime on summer Sundays. They do also
have a Bierkeller on the outskirts of the hamlet
that opens more frequently but, again, only in
summer. It is possible to get to Greuth by bus
but only Mon–Fri.

🏠 **Fischer**
Greuth 11, 91315 Höchstadt-Greuth
Closed Mon-Sat; Sun 11.00–14.00 (summer only)
DB Hirschaid 11km

🏠 **Fischer Bierkeller**
91315 Höchstadt-Greuth
Oct–Apr: closed. May–Sep: closed Mon & Tue;
Sun & hols from 10.00 in fine weather only,
Mon–Sat from 16.00 in fine weather only
DB Hirschaid 11km

GROSSHESSELOHE (Pullach)   268

Isarbräu

Di Gastro Isarbräu GmbH & Co. KG
Kreuzeckstraße 23, 82049 Pullach-Großhesselohe
T 089 79 89 61   **F** 089 791 47 23
www.isarbraeu.de   Founded: 1988
Output: 2,000hl   Availability: 1 pub
REGULAR BEER:
Isartaler Stationsweizen (5.4%)

Brewpub in the former station buildings at
Großhesselohe Isartalbahnhof. Like Fliegerbräu
in Feldkirchen, it certainly used to be owned by
Hofbräuhaus Traunstein but whether it still is
we're not entirely sure. S-Bahn S7 stops at the
platforms opposite.

🏠 **Isarbräu**
Kreuzeckstraße 23, 82049 Pullach-Großhesselohe
Sun & hols 10.00–24.00, Mon–Sat 10.00–01.00
Ⓢ S7 Großhesselohe Isartalbahnhof 0m

GROSSKÖLLNBACH (Pilsting)   269

Egerer

Privatbrauerei & Mineralbrunnenbetrieb H. Egerer
Dachingerstraße 27, 94431 Pilsting-Großköllnbach
T 09953 30 10   **F** 09953 301 30
www.egerer.de
Owner: Heinrich Egerer   Founded: 1919
Output: 50,000hl
REGULAR BEERS:
Egerer Bierkutscher Hell Urtyp (4.7%)
Egerer Bierkutscher Edel Pils (4.7%)
Egerer König Wilhelm Helles (4.9%)
Egerer Weizen Hell (4.9%)
Egerer Weizen Dunkel (4.9%)
Egerer Bierkutscher Original Export (5%)
Egerer Bierkutscher Altbayerisch Dunkel (5.2%)
Egerer Bierkutscher Gold Märzen (5.5%)
SEASONAL BEER:
Egerer Bierkutscher Festbier (5.5%)

Regional brewery that produces a greater volume
of soft drinks than beer. Bus No. 6150 runs from
Landau, on weekdays only.

🏠 **Egerer**
Dachingerstraße 27, 94431 Pilsting-Großköllnbach
T 09953 16 99
Sun 17.00–22.00, Mon, Tue, Thu–Sat 10.30–22.00,
Wed 10.30–14.00; rooms available
DB Landau (Isar) 10km

GROSSOSTHEIM   270

Eder & Heylands

Eder & Heylands Brauerei GmbH & Co. KG
Aschaffenburger Straße 3–5, 63762 Großostheim
T 06026 50 90   **F** 06026 50 91 30
www.eder-heylands.de
Founded: 1872   Output: 300,000hl
BAVARIA BEERS:
Bavaria Hefe Weizen (5.3%), **Bavaria Dunkles
Hefe Weizen** (5.3%), **Bavaria Kristall Weizen**
(5.3%), **Bavaria Dunkles Starkbier** (7.5%)

EDER BEERS:
Eder's Pilsener (4.9%), **Eder's Export** (5.5%)
HEYLANDS BEERS:
Heyland's Premium Pilsener (4.8%),
Heyland's Anno 1792 (5.2%),
Heyland's Edel Export (5.5%)
FOR SCHLAPPESEPPEL, ASCHAFFENBURG:
Schlappeseppel Pils (4.8%),
Das Schlappeseppel (5.2%),
Schlappeseppel Urbräu Dunkel (5.2%),
Schlappeseppel Kellerbier (5.5%),
Schlappeseppel Export (5.5%)
SEASONAL BEER:
Schlappeseppel Winterbock (7.5%)

Large brewery in the centre of town. Eder merged
with Heylands in 1998, having previously taken
over Bavaria of Aschaffenburg in 1983. We think
they've been brewing Schlappeseppel beers
since around 1980. Bus No. 54 runs from
Aschaffenburg if you want to visit the Eder tap.

🍺 Eder Keller
Aschaffenburger Straße 4, 63762 Großostheim
T 06026 48 07
Closed Mon; Tue–Sun 11.00–14.00 & 16.00–24.00
DB Aschaffenburg Hbf 9km

🍺 Schlappeseppel
Schloßgasse 28, 63739 Aschaffenburg
T 06021 92 92 06   Daily from 11.00
DB Aschaffenburg Hbf 800m

GRÜNBACH (Bockhorn)   271

Schloßbrauerei
Schloßbrauerei Grünbach bei Erding GmbH
Kellerberg 2, 85461 Bockhorn-Grünbach
T 08122 410 07   **F** 08122 410 09
www.schlossbrauerei-gruenbach.de
Founded: 1810   Output: 20,000hl
REGULAR BEERS:
Grünbacher Schloßtaler Weisse (2.8%)
Grünbacher Altweizen Gold (5.3%)
Grünbacher Altweizen Dunkel (5.3%)
Grünbacher Benno Scharl Weizen (5.3%)
SEASONAL BEER:
Grünbacher Prinzenbock

Wheat beer brewery in a village east of Erding.
The only transport to Grünbach when the pub is
open is an AST taxi service that must be booked
at least 20 minutes in advance.

🍺 Bräustüberl Grünbach
Kellerberg 2, 85461 Bockhorn-Grünbach
T 08122 472 37
Closed Mon–Wed; Thu & Fri from 17.30,
Sat & Sun from 11.00
DB Erding 9km

GUNDELFINGEN   272

Bucher
Spezialbierbrauerei & Mineralbrunnen Bucher
Untere Vorstadt 15–19, 89423 Gundelfingen
T 09073 959 80   **F** 09073 95 98 20
www.brauerei-bucher.de
Owner: Alois Bucher   Founded: 1644
Output: 25,000hl
REGULAR BEERS:
Bucher Leichte Helle
Bucher Fit-Weisse
Bucher Lager
Bucher Gundelfinger Sud-Hell
Bucher Pils Juwel
Bucher Urdeutsch Dunkel
Bucher Hefe Weizen
Bucher Dunkle Weisse
Bucher Spezial
Bucher Feines Export
SEASONAL BEER:
Bucher Bockbier

Although it's in the centre of Gundelfingen,
Brauerei Bucher doesn't have a tap. Despite
this, you shouldn't have too much difficulty
finding the beers around the town.
DB Gundelfingen (Donau) 800m

GÜNZBURG   273

Radbrauerei Bucher
Radbrauerei Gebrüder Bucher KG
Peter-Henlein-Straße 6, 89312 Günzburg
T 08221 20 77 20   **F** 08221 2 0772 30
www.guenzburger-weizen.de
Owners: Georg & Hans Bucher   Founded: 1590
REGULAR BEERS:
Günzburger Leichtes Weizen (2.9%)
Günzburger Radbier Hell (5.1%)
Günzburger Hefe-Weizen (5.1%)
Günzburger Ur-Weizen Dunkel (5.1%)
Günzburger Radbier Märzen Spezial (5.5%)

SEASONAL BEER:
Günzburger Weizenbock (6.6%)

The brewery moved from its former location to a new site north of the town in 1997. The tap remains in the centre on the market square. Close to Zum Rad is the former tap of Brauerei Münz whose beers are now brewed by Postbräu in Thannhausen.

🍺 **Zum Rad**
Marktplatz 40, 89312 Günzburg
T 08221 367 36 77
Closed Mon; Tue–Fri 10.00–14.00 & 17.00–24.00, Sat & Sun 10.00–24.00   DB Günzburg 750m

GUNZENDORF (Buttenheim) 274

Sauer

Brauerei Andreas Sauer GmbH & Co. KG
Jurastraße 30, 96155 Buttenheim-Gunzendorf
T 09545 215   **F** 09545 78 67   Founded: 1612
Owners: Marianne Sauer & Susanne Boeser
Output: 5,000hl   Availability: 6 pubs
REGULAR BEERS:
Gunzendorfer Lagerbier (4.9%)
Gunzendorfer Vollbier (4.9%)
Gunzendorfer Edelpils (4.9%)
Gunzendorfer Weiße (5.2%)
Gunzendorfer Schlückla Rauchbier (5.6%)
SEASONAL BEERS:
Gunzendorfer Festbier (5.6%, Christmas),
Gunzendorfer Andreasbock (7.2%)

Although it's possible to get to Gunzendorf by bus from Buttenheim when the pub is open, you can't get back by the same means unless you have a very quick drink.

🍺 **Sauer**
Jurastraße 30, 96155 Buttenheim-Gunzendorf
T 09545 15 98
Closed Tue; Wed–Fri & Mon 16.30–23.00, Sat, Sun & hols 10.00–23.00
DB Buttenheim 5km

GUNZENHAUSEN 275

Leuchtturm

Gasthaus-Brauerei Leuchtturm KG
Ansbacher Straße 9, 91710 Gunzenhausen
T 09831 675 60   **F** 09831 67 56 75

www.leuchtturm-gun.de
Owner: Michael Probach   Founded: 1997
Output: 1,500hl   Availability: 1 pub
REGULAR BEERS:
Leuchtturm Helles (4.7%)
Leuchtturm Märzen (5.2%)
SEASONAL BEERS:
Leuchtturm Weizen (5.1%), **Leuchtturm Weihnachtsbock** (6.5%, Dec)

Brewpub on the opposite side of the railway to the town centre. Just look for the lighthouse – a navigation device for thirsty visitors, not ships.

🍺 **Leuchtturm**
Ansbacher Straße 9, 91710 Gunzenhausen
Oct–Apr: closed Mon; Tue–Sun 10.00–01.00
May–Sep: daily 10.00–01.00
DB Gunzenhausen 300m

GUTENSTETTEN 276

Windsheimer

Brauerei Windsheimer GmbH
Hauptstraße 13, 91468 Gutenstetten
T 09161 22 93   **F** 09161 66 47 85
Owner: Hans Windsheimer   Founded: 1767
Output: 7,000hl   Availability: 5 pubs
REGULAR BEERS:
Aischgründer Vollbier (4.7%)
Aischgründer Lagerbier (4.7%)
Aischgründer Dunkel (4.9%)
Aischgründer Pils (4.9%)
Aischgründer Märzen (5.5%)
SEASONAL BEERS:
Aischgründer Festbier, Aischgründer Bock

Small brewery and tap in a village just north of Neustadt. Rather than the tap in Gutenstetten, the brewery recommended Günthner Brennereistuben in Wilhelmsdorf as the place to try their beers. Walkable from Emskirchen, they have their own distillery.

🍺 **Windsheimer**
Hauptstraße 13, 91468 Gutenstetten
Closed Mon; Tue–Sun from 18.00
DB Neustadt (Aisch) 7km

🍺 **Günthner Brennereistuben**
Bergstraße 21, 91489 Wilhelmsdorf
T 09104 21 41   **F** 09104 21 48
Closed Mon; Tue–Sun 09.00–24.00; rooms available   DB Emskirchen 2.2km

HAAG (Oberbayern) 277

Unertl

Unertl Weißbier GmbH
Lerchenberger Straße 6, 83527 Haag
T 08072 82 97   **F** 08072 24 88   www.unertl.de
Owner: Alois Unertl III   Founded: 1900
Output: 25,000hl   Availability: 250 pubs
REGULAR BEERS:
Unertl Leichte-Weisse (2.6%)
Unertl Weissbier (4.8%)
Unertl Ursud (5.8%)
SEASONAL BEER:
Unertl Weissbier Bock (6.7%)

Family-run wheat beer brewery on the western
side of town. Bus No. 9411 runs from Soyen but
the timetable's not great if you want to return
the same day.

🍺 **Unertl**
Lerchenberger Straße 2, 83527 Haag
T 08072 29 65   **F** 08072 95 80 96
Closed Mon; Tue–Thu 16.00–24, Fri 15.00–24.00,
Sat, Sun & hols 10.00–24.00; rooms available
DB Soyen 8km

HAIMHAUSEN 278

Schloßbrauerei

Haniel von Haimhausen'sche Schloßbrauerei
Hauptstraße 3a, 85778 Haimhausen
T 08133 918 30   **F** 08133 81 35
www.schlossbrauerei-haimhausen.de
Owner: Günter Haniel von Haimhausen
Founded: 1608   Output: 6,000hl
Availability: 14 pubs
REGULAR BEERS:
Haimhauser Schloß-Hell (4.5%)
Haimhauser Schloß-Pils (4.5%)
Haimhauser Kellerbier Dunkel (4.8%)
Haimhauser Schloß-Weisse (4.8%)
Haimhauser Schloß-Weisse Dunkel (4.8%)

Small brewery and tap on the main road through
Haimhausen. Bus No. 693 runs from Lohhof
station on weekdays.

🍺 **Schloßklause**
Hauptstraße 3, 85778 Haimhausen
T 08133 62 69   Daily from 11.30
DB Lohhof 4km

HALLERNDORF 279

Lieberth

Forchheimer Straße 2, 91352 Hallerndorf
T 09545 85 58   **F** 09545 44 27 37
E brauerei.lieberth@t-online.de
Owners: Alfred & Maria Volkmuth
Founded: 1679   Output: 2,000hl
REGULAR BEERS:
Lieberth Pilsner (4.8%)
Lieberth Lagerbier (5%)
SEASONAL BEER:
Lieberth Festbier

Small brewery that supplies its own pub plus two
Bierkellers on the outskirts of town. Bus No. 265
runs from both Eggolsheim and Forchheim Mon–
Fri, but provides limited opportunities to return
from Hallerndorf when the breweries are open.

🍺 **Lieberth**
Forchheimer Straße 2, 91352 Hallerndorf
Closed Mon; Tue–Sun 16.00–24.00
DB Eggolsheim 5km, Forchheim 11km

Rittmayer

Brauerei Rittmayer Hallerndorf OHG
An der Mark 1, 91352 Hallerndorf
T 09545 502 92   **F** 09545 502 91
www.rittmayer.de   Founded: 1422
Owners: Franz & Georg Rittmayer
Output: 10,000hl   Availability: 5 pubs
REGULAR BEERS:
Rittmayer Hallerndorfer Landbier Hell (4.9%)
Rittmayer Hallerndorfer Kellerbier (5%)
Rittmayer Hallerndorfer Raiterla Rauchbier (5%)
Rittmayer Hallerndorfer Hefeweißbier (5%)
SEASONAL BEERS:
Rittmayer Hallerndorfer Winter Weizen (5.2%),
Rittmayer Hallerndorfer Bockbier (6.8%)

The larger of Hallerndorf's two breweries,
Rittmayer's beers can occasionally be found as
far away as Cardiff! The tap is in the centre of the
village, close to Lieberth, the brewery is on the
other side of the river. Like Lieberth's, its beers
are sold in two Kellers outside the town.

🍺 **Rittmayer**
Trailsdorfer Straße 4, 91352 Hallerndorf
T 09545 50 92 14
Closed Tue; Wed–Mon from 16.00
DB Eggolsheim 5km, Forchheim 11km

HAUSHAM 280

Hausham

Brauhaus Hausham
Schlierseer Straße 8, 83734 Hausham
T 08026 92 12 21   **F** 08026 386 02
www.brauhaus-hausham.de
Owner: Peter Auer
Founded: 1935
Output: 500hl
REGULAR BEERS:
Brauhaus Hausham Bayrisch Hell (5.2%)
Brauhaus Hausham Weißbier (5.3%)
Brauhaus Hausham Urtyp Märzen (5.6%)

Traditional brewpub across the road from Hausham station. We don't think the beers are available anywhere else.

🍺 Hausham
Schlierseer Straße 8, 83734 Hausham
T 08026 82 03
Closed Tue; Wed, Thu & Mon 10.00–14.00 & 16.30–24.00, Fri–Sun 10.00–23.00
DB Hausham 50m

HECKENHOF (Aufseß) 281

Kathi-Bräu

Heckenhof 1, 91347 Aufseß-Heckenhof
T 09198 277   **F** 09198 12 73
Owner: Josef Schmitt
Founded: 1498
Output: 700hl
Availability: 1 pub
REGULAR BEERS:
Kathi-Bräu Leichtes Dunkel
Kathi-Bräu Dunkles Lagerbier
SEASONAL BEER:
Kathi-Bräu Bock (March)

Brewpub much favoured by bikers in the heart of the Fränkische Schweiz region (Franconian Switzerland). There are a couple of buses from Ebermannstadt on weekdays but you'll have to walk to Aufseß to catch one back.

🍺 Kathi-Bräu
Heckenhof 1, 91347 Aufseß-Heckenhof
Daily 09.00–23.00
DB Ebermannstadt 16km

HEILGERSDORF (Seßlach) 282

Scharpf

Brauerei und Gastwirtschaft Scharpf
Hauptstraße 16, 96145 Seßlach-Heilgersdorf
T/F 09569 12 32   www.scharpf-heilgersdorf.de
Owner: Werner Scharpf   Founded: c. 1800
Output: 800hl   Availability: 1 pub
REGULAR BEER:
Scharpf Märzenbier

The White Horse is a brewpub in the centre of the village that produces beer for the tap and nowhere else. Heilgersdorf can be reached by bus No. 8301 from Coburg on weekdays.

🍺 Weißes Roß
Hauptstraße 16, 96145 Seßlach-Heilgersdorf
Closed Tue; Wed, Thu & Mon 10.00–13.00 & from 16.30, Fri–Sun from 10.00   DB Coburg 19km

HEILIGENSTADT 283

Aichinger

Brauerei Drei Kronen Erwin Aichinger
Marktplatz 5, 91332 Heiligenstadt
T/F 09198 522
Owner: Erwin Aichinger   Founded: 1888
Output: 700hl   Availability: 1 pub
REGULAR BEER:
Aichinger Spezialbier
SEASONAL BEER:
Aichinger Bock

Brewpub in the centre of this small town. Bus No. 8235 runs from Bamberg, Nos. 221 and 8235 from Ebermannstadt. No service at the weekend.

🍺 Aichinger
Marktplatz 5, 91332 Heiligenstadt
Daily 08.00–23.00; rooms available
DB Ebermannstadt 12km, Bamberg 23km

HEILMFURT (Malgersdorf) 284

Büchner

Gasthausbrauerei Stefan Büchner
84333 Malgersdorf-Heilmfurt
T/F 09954 303
www.brauerei-buechner.de

Owner: Stefan Büchner   Founded: 1895
Output: 350hl
REGULAR BEERS:
Heilmfurter Hell
Heilmfurter Märzen

Small brewery on a farm 1km south-west of Malgersdorf. Heilmfurt seems to consist solely of this farm, and it's so small it doesn't appear on many maps. It is possible to get to Malgersdorf by bus for Thursday opening but you can't return the same day. The pub may open on other days in hot weather.

🍴 **Heilmfurt**
84333 Malgersdorf-Heilmfurt
Closed Mon–Wed; Fri & Sat, Thu from 17.00,
Sun from 16.00
DB Eggenfelden 17km, Landau (Isar) 21km

HERGERTSWIESEN
(Eurasburg)   285

Landhausbräu Koller

Hergertswiesen 5, 86495 Eurasburg-
Hergertswiesen   **T** 08208 225
Owner: Ludwig Koller   Founded: 2000
REGULAR BEERS:
Landhausbräu Koller Helles
Landhausbräu Koller Dunkles
Landhausbräu Koller Weißbier

Brewpub in a hamlet on the St2051, a couple of kilometres east of Eurasburg. Buses Nos. 207 and 208 run from Friedberg, Mon–Fri only.

🍴 **Landhausbräu Koller**
Hergertswiesen 5, 86495 Eurasburg-
Hergertswiesen
Closed Wed; Thu–Sat & Mon from 16.00,
Sun & hols from 11.00; rooms available
DB Friedberg 12km

HERRMANNSDORF (Glonn) 286

Herrmannsdorfer Schweinsbräu

Herrmannsdorfer Landwerkstätten Glonn GmbH
Herrmannsdorf 7, 85625 Glonn-Herrmannsdorf
T 08093 90 94 40   **F** 08093 90 94 10
www.herrmannsdorfer.de
Owner: Karl Ludwig Schweisfurth
Founded: 1993   Output: 1,000hl

REGULAR BEERS:
Schweinsbräu Hell (4.8%)
Schweinsbräu Dunkel (4.8%)
Schweinsbräu Weißbier (5.2%)
SEASONAL BEERS:
Schweinsbräu Erntedankbier (5.6%),
Schweinsbräu Weihnachtsbier (5.6%),
Schweinsbräu Maibock (6.2%), **Schweinsbräu Faschings-Weiße** (6.3%), **Schweinsbräu Visionator**

One of many enterprises here – the brewery has an organic farm, butchers and restaurant for company. There's a beer garden which opens in fine weather at the weekend. We don't think any buses run to Hermannsdorf itself, but plenty run through Westerndorf less than 1km away.

🍴 **Zum Schweinsbräu**
Herrmannsdorf 7, 85625 Glonn-Herrmannsdorf
T 08093 90 94 45   **F** 08093 90 94 42
Closed Mon & Tue; Wed–Sun 18.00–23.00
DB Grafing Bf 8km

HERRNGIERSDORF   287

Schlossbrauerei

Schlossbrauerei Herrngiersdorf
Schloßallee 5, 84097 Herrngiersdorf
T 09452 20 41   **F** 09452 16 28
www.schlossbrauerei-herrngiersdorf.de
Owner: Paul Pausinger   Founded: 1131
Output: 5,000hl   Availability: c. 90 pubs
REGULAR BEERS:
Schlossbräu Jadwiga (4.8%)
Schlossbräu Publiner (4.9%)
Schlossbräu Trausnitz Pils (4.9%)
Schlossbräu Fanfaren Weiße Hell (5.6%)
Schlossbräu Fanfaren Weiße Dunkel (5.6%)
SEASONAL BEER:
Schlossbräu Sündenbock (7.3%, Lent)

The oldest privately owned brewery in the world. Despite its small size the brewery's beers can be found in a surprisingly large number of pubs. Translated, a *Sündenbock* is a scapegoat; Jadwiga, Queen of Poland in the 14th century, was made a saint in 1997. The bus journey from Eggmühl involves at least one change and can be a tortuous affair.

🍴 **Schlossbräukeller**
Bernhardstraße 6, 84097 Herrngiersdorf
T 09452 386

Closed Mon; Tue–Sun 11.00–24.00
DB Eggmühl 15km

HERRNSDORF (Frensdorf) 288

Barnikel

Brauerei Friedrich Barnikel
Dorfstraße 5, 96158 Frensdorf-Herrnsdorf
T 09502 293 **F** 09502 92 32 12
Owner: Friedrich Barnikel Founded: 1314
Output: 1,500hl Availability: 3 pubs
REGULAR BEERS:
Barnikel Lagerbier (4.8%)
Barnikel Weizen (5%)
Barnikel Rauchbier (5.4%)
Barnikel Dunkel (5.8%)
SEASONAL BEER:
Barnikel Bockbier

Small, family-run brewery, one of the oldest in
the region. During the week buses Nos. 215 and
8227 run from Bamberg, with the latter also
serving Hirschaid.

🍺 **Barnikel**
Dorfstraße 5, 96158 Frensdorf-Herrnsdorf
Closed Wed; Thu–Tue 09.00–23.00
DB Hirschaid 8km, Bamberg 15km

HERRNWAHLTHANN
(Hausen) 289

Stanglbräu

Gasthausbrauerei Stanglbräu
Dorfstraße 11, 93345 Hausen-Herrnwahlthann
T 09448 918 30 **F** 09448 91 83 14
www.allesbio.de/stanglbraeu
Owner: the Miller family Founded: 1997
Output: 400hl Availability: 2 pubs
REGULAR BEERS:
Stanglbräu Antonius Dunkel (4.9%)
Stanglbräu Michaeli Weizen (4.9%)
Stanglbräu Martinus Hell (5.1%)
SEASONAL BEERS:
Stanglbräu Hanfinger Urtrunk (4.8%),
Stanglbräu Pils (4.9%), **Stanglbräu
Doppelbock** (7.2%)

The original Stangl brewery closed in 1971 but
the name was revived in 1997 when the Miller
family resumed brewing in the original building.

Bus No. 6045 runs from Saal Mon–Sat, and there
are also buses from Regensburg.

🍺 **Stanglbräu**
Dorfstraße 11, 93345 Hausen-Herrnwahlthann
Closed Mon; Tue–Sun 10.00–24.00; rooms
available DB Saal (Donau) 10km

HERSBRUCK 290

Bürgerbräu

Bürgerbräu Hersbruck Deinlein & Co. KG
Lohweg 38, 91217 Hersbruck
T 09151 30 03 **F** 09151 28 39
E buergerbraeu.hersbruck@t-online.de
Owner: Ursula Weid Founded: 1920
Output: 20,000hl
REGULAR BEERS:
Hersbrucker Lagerbier
Hersbrucker Dampfsud Dunkel
Hersbrucker Edel-Pils
Hersbrucker Albweizen
Hersbrucker Albweizen Dunkel
Hersbrucker Export
Hersbrucker Märzen
SEASONAL BEERS:
**Hersbrucker Festbier, Hersbrucker Bock,
Hersbrucker Weizenbock**

Between the town centre and the river Pegnitz.
There's no brewery tap but the beers are easily
found in the town. Note that Hersbruck has a
station on either side of the river. On the north
side of the river and closest to the centre is the
main station, Hersbruck (rechts Pegnitz).
DB Hersbruck (rechts Pegnitz) 650m,
Hersbruck (links Pegnitz) 1.3km

HERZOGENAURACH 291

Heller

Brauerei Hans Heller
Hauptstraße 33, 91074 Herzogenaurach
T 09132 20 73 **F** 09132 77 30 14
www.brauerei-heller.de
Owner: Hans Heller Founded: 1874
Output: 5,000hl
REGULAR BEERS:
Heller's Schwarzes
Heller Pils

Heller Hefe-Weißbier
Heller Oeko-Bier
Heller Hell Export
SEASONAL BEERS:
Heller Festbier, Heller Kirchweih-Bier, Heller
Fest-Märzen, Heller Weihnachts-Festbier,
Heller Herzogenauracher Bock

Brewery and tap in the centre of town. There's a
good bus service from Erlangen (No. 201) that
runs daily.

🍺 **Heller**
Hauptstraße 33, 91074 Herzogenaurach
Mon–Wed & Fri 09.00–13.00 &15.00–22.00,
Thu & Sun 09.00–13.00, Sat 09.00–13.00 &
15.00–19.00
DB Erlangen 11km

HETZELSDORF (Pretzfeld) 292

Penning

Hetzelsdorf 9, 91362 Pretzfeld-Hetzelsdorf
T 09194 252
Owner: Karl Penning   Founded: 1620
Output: 3,000hl
REGULAR BEERS:
Hetzelsdorfer Fränkisches Vollbier (5%)
Hetzelsdorfer Pilsner (5%)
SEASONAL BEERS:
Hetzelsdorfer Festbier (5.5%), Hetzelsdorfer
Maibock (6.5%), Hetzelsdorfer
Weihnachtsbock (6.5%)

Formerly known as Penning-Zeißler, the brewery
can be reached by bus No. 235 from Pretzfeld
but the service only run Mon–Fri and is not much
use during the pub's opening hours.

🍺 **Penning**
Hetzelsdorf 9, 91362 Pretzfeld-Hetzelsdorf
Closed Mon & Tue; Wed–Fri 17.00–22.00, Sat &
Sun 10.00–22.00
DB Pretzfeld 4.5km, Forchheim 16km

HINTERGEREUTH (Ahorntal) 293

Stöckel

Brauerei Gebrüder Stöckel OHG
Hintergereuth 4, 95491 Ahorntal-Hintergereuth
T/F 09246 275
Owner: Helmut Stöckel   Founded: 1866

REGULAR BEERS:
Stöckel Pils (4.9%)
Stöckel Hell (5.1%)
Stöckel Landbier (5.1%)
Stöckel Weisse (5.5%)
SEASONAL BEER:
Stöckel Festbier

Small brewery and pub in a hamlet, not far from
the A9 Autobahn, but very difficult to get to and
from by public transport. The first bus of the day
to come in promptly forms the last bus out.

🍺 **Stöckel**
Hintergereuth 4, 95491 Ahorntal-Hintergereuth
Daily 09.00–24.00
DB Pegnitz 17km, Bayreuth Hbf 19km

HIRSCHAID 294

Kraus

Brauerei-Gasthof Kraus
Luitpoldstraße 11, 96114 Hirschaid
T 09543 8 44 40   **F** 09543 84 44 44
www.brauerei-kraus.de
Owners: the Kraus family   Founded: 1845
Output: 10,000hl   Availability: 20 pubs
REGULAR BEERS:
Kraus Leichtes (2.4%)
Kraus Vollbier (4.7%)
Kraus Lagerbier Hell (4.7%)
Kraus Edelpils (4.7%)
Kraus Hirschentrunk (5.5%)
Kraus Weißbier (5.5%)
SEASONAL BEERS:
Kraus Festbier (5.5%),
Kraus Bockbier (7.2%, winter)

Family-run brewery, pub and hotel in the centre
of town. Buses operate from Hirschaid to many
of the surrounding villages with breweries.

🍺 **Kraus**
Luitpoldstraße 11, 96114 Hirschaid
Closed Tue; Wed–Mon 08.00–24.00; rooms
available   DB Hirschaid 550m

HIRSCHAU 295

Schloßbrauerei Dorfner

Franz Dorfner Schloßbrauerei Hirschau
Mühlstraße 6, 92242 Hirschau

T 09622 22 12   F 09622 55 55
www.dorfner.schlossbrauerei.de
Owner: Franz Dorfner   Founded: 1812
Output: 7,000hl   Availability: c. 20 pubs
REGULAR BEERS:
Dorfner Schloß Leicht (3.1%)
Dorfner Hell (4.5%)
Dorfner Pils (4.8%)
Dorfner König Wenzel Schwarzbier (5.1%)
Dorfner Kristallweizen (5.1%)
Dorfner Hefe-Weisse (5.2%)
Dorfner Spezial (5.5%)
Dorfner Keller-Bier Spezial (5.5%)
SEASONAL BEER:
Dorfner Bock (7.5%, Dec–Apr)

Small brewery in a town renowned for its enormous hill of sand. The tap is around the corner. Hirschau can be reached by bus No. 6306 from Amberg seven days a week.

🍴 **Schloßhotel**
Hauptstraße 1, 92242 Hirschau
T 09622 701 00   F 09622 70 10 40
Closed Thu; Fri 15.00–24.00,
Sat, Mon–Wed 10.00–24.00,
Sun 09.00–24.00; rooms available
DB Amberg 15km

HÖCHSTADT an der Aisch   296

Blauer Löwe

Brauerei Blauer Löwe Gemeiner GmbH
Brückenstraße 9, 91315 Höchstadt an der Aisch
T 09193 82 19   F 09193 69 87 90
www.brauerei-blauer-loewe.de
Founded: 1633
Output: 5,000hl   Availability: 5 pubs
REGULAR BEERS:
Blauer Löwe Vollbier
Blauer Löwe Dunkel
Blauer Löwe Premium Pils
Blauer Löwe Weißbier
Blauer Löwe Märzen
SEASONAL BEERS:
Blauer Löwe Winterweiße, Blauer Löwe Festbier, Blauer Löwe Wintertraum

On the southern edge of the main part of town, the brewery and tap back onto each other. There's a surprisingly good service on bus No. 205 from Erlangen, seven days a week.

🍴 **Blauer Löwe**
Schillerplatz 8, 91315 Höchstadt an der Aisch
T 09193 13 30
Closed Mon; Tue–Sun 10.00–23.00
DB Erlangen 24km

Brauhaus Höchstadt

Brauhaus Höchstadt/Aisch e.G
Kellerstraße 7–11, 91315 Höchstadt an der Aisch
T 09193 83 67   F 09193 76 33
www.brauhaus-hoechstadt.de
Founded: 1926
Output: 10,000hl
Availability: 30 pubs
REGULAR BEERS:
Brauhaus Leichtes Schankbier (2.5%)
Brauhaus Hell (4.7%)
Brauhaus Schwarzbier (4.8%)
Brauhaus Pils (4.8%)
Brauhaus Hausbrauer (5.1%)
Brauhaus Weisse (5.2%)
Brauhaus Kellerberg (5.9%)
SEASONAL BEERS:
Brauhaus Festbier (5.2%),
Brauhaus Doppelbock (winter)

The larger of the town's two breweries, Brauhaus Höchstadt doesn't have an official tap, but around ten pubs in the town sell their beers.
DB Erlangen 24km

HOCHSTAHL (Aufseß)   297

Reichold

Hochstahl 24, 91347 Aufseß-Hochstahl
T 09204 271   F 09204 91 92 76
www.reichold.de
Owner: Hilmar Reichold
Founded: 1906   Output: 3,000hl
Availability: 8 pubs
REGULAR BEERS:
Reichold Weizen (4.9%)
Reichold Lager (5%)
Reichold Kellerbier (5.2%)
SEASONAL BEER:
Reichold Bock (7%, May)

Brewpub in a small village 3km east of Aufseß. Like nearby Kathi-Bräu, you can get here by bus on weekdays but will have to walk to Aufseß if you want to catch one back on the same day.

📍 **Reichold**
Hochstahl 24, 91347 Aufseß-Hochstahl
Closed Mon & Tue; Wed–Sun 08.00–24.00;
rooms available
DB Ebermannstadt 18km

HOF 298

Bürgerbräu

Bürgerbräu Hof Maria Ried GmbH & Co. KG
Ascher Straße 3–5, 95028 Hof
T 09281 736 60   **F** 09281 73 66 19
www.bbhof.de
Owner: Maria Ried   Founded: 1864
Output: 50,000hl
REGULAR BEERS:
Bürger Bräu Lager
Bürger Bräu Edel Pilsner (4.8%)
Bürger Bräu Edel-Weiße (4.9%)

Fairly large brewery that has drastically reduced
its range of beers in recent years. One improve-
ment, however, has been the opening of a tap in
a cellar under the brewery. They also have a
museum that's open daily.

📍 **Kuriosa Brauhaus Ausschank**
Ascher Straße 3, 95028 Hof
T 09281 14 45 84
Daily from 18.00
DB Hof Hbf 1.3km

Falter

Hirschbergerstraße 6, 95030 Hof-Unterkotzau
T 09281 76 90 90   **F** 09281 7 69 09 26
www.brauerei-falter.de
Owner: Werner Falter   Founded: 1927
Output: 15,000hl   Availability: 40 pubs
REGULAR BEERS:
Falter Hell (4.8%)
Falter Pils (5%)
Falter Weissbier Dunkel (5%)
Falter Weissbier (5.3%)
Falter Aitermoser (5.3%)
Falter Keller-Bier (6.2%)
SEASONAL BEERS:
Falter Weizen-Bock (6.8%, winter),
Falter Bock-Bier (winter)

Small brewery, hotel and tap in the northern
suburb of Unterkotzau. Bus No. 1 runs daily
from the main station.

📍 **Falter**
Hirschbergerstraße 6, 95030 Hof-Unterkotzau
T 09281 767 50   **F** 09281 767 51 90
Daily 11.00–14.00 & 17.00–21.00; rooms avail-
able   DB Hof-Neuhof 2.4km, Hof Hbf 4.5km

Meinel-Bräu

Familienbrauerei Georg Meinel GmbH
Alte Plauener Straße 24, 95028 Hof
T 09281 35 14   **F** 09281 776 21
www.meinel-braeu.de
Founded: 1731   Output: 10,000hl
REGULAR BEERS:
Meinel-Bräu Dark Lager (4.3%)
Meinel-Bräu Gold Lager (4.6%)
Meinel-Bräu Hefe-Weizen (4.7%)
Meinel-Bräu Classic Pils (5.2%)
Meinel-Bräu Märzen (5.6%)
SEASONAL BEERS:
Meinel-Bräu Absolvinator (7.5%, Lent),
Meinel-Bräu Doppelbock Hell (8%, winter)

The smallest of Hof's breweries is north of the
city centre. The tap is nearby, close to a bridge
over the river Saale.

📍 **Meinel's Bas**
Vorstadt 13, 95028 Hof
T 09281 14 13 66
Closed Thu in winter; other days 11.00–24.00
DB Hof-Neuhof 1.4km, Hof Hbf 2.2km

Scherdel

Privatbrauerei Scherdel Hof GmbH & Co. KG
Unterkotzauer Weg 14, 95028 Hof
T 09281 89 60   **F** 09281 896 44
www.scherdelbier.de
Owner: Brau Holding International, München
Founded: 1831   Output: 100,000hl
REGULAR BEERS:
Scherdel Light
Scherdel Leichte Weisse
Scherdel Lager (4.7%)
Scherdel Premium Pilsner (4.7%)
Scherdel Edelhell (5%)
Schwarzes Scherdel (5.1%)
Scherdel Helle Weisse (5.1%)
Scherdel Dunkle Weisse (5.1%)
Scherdel Kristall Weizen (5.1%)

Hof's largest brewery has no specific tap but their
beers can be found all over the city and beyond.
DB Hof-Neuhof 700m, Hof Hbf 2km

Zeltbräu

Privatbrauerei Zeltbräu GmbH
Schleizerstraße 28, 95028 Hof
T 09281 830 10   **F** 09281 83 01 99
www.zeltbraeu.de   Founded: 1856
REGULAR BEERS:
Zeltbräu Schmidt's Heiner Weisse-Leichte (2.7%)
Zeltbräu Hofer Hell (4.6%)
Zeltbräu Kristall Mild (4.8%)
Zeltbräu Kristall Pils Premium (4.8%)
Zeltbräu Schmidt's Heiner Weisse-Hell (5%)
Zeltbräu Schmidt's Heiner Weisse-Dunkel (5%)
Zeltbräu Hofer Gassenhauer Dunkel (5.3%)
Zeltbräu Bayrisch Edelgold Export (5.5%)
SEASONAL BEERS:
Zeltbräu Schlappenbier (6.5%, June),
Zeltbräu Hofatius Winterbock (6.7%, winter)

Zeltbräu is close to Meinel's brewery on the
north-side of the Saale. Like Scherdel they've
no tap but their beers aren't difficult to find.
[DB] Hof-Neuhof 1.2km, Hof Hbf 2.5km

HÖFEN (Rattelsdorf)   299

Zum Goldenen Adler

Höfen 21, 96179 Rattelsdorf-Höfen
T 09547 264   **F** 09547 288
Owners: Adam Endres   Founded: 1775
Output: 150hl   Availability: 1 pub
REGULAR BEER:
Goldenen Adler Lagerbier

The Golden Eagle is a brewpub, north-west of
Rattelsdorf. Höfen is on the same road as
Freudeneck and, like the latter, is served by bus
No. 8219 on weekdays.

🍺 **Zum Goldenen Adler**
Höfen 21, 96179 Rattelsdorf-Höfen
Closed Tue & Sat; Sun from 13.00,
Mon, Wed–Fri from 15.00   [DB] Ebing 4km

HOFHEIM (Unterfranken)   300

Raab

Privatbrauerei Michael Raab
Johannisstraße 11, 97461 Hofheim
T 09523 952 70   **F** 09523 95 27 50
www.brauerei-raab.de
Owner: Michael Raab   Founded: 1930
Output: 8,000hl   Availability: 10 pubs

REGULAR BEERS:
Raab Aecht Fränkisches Landbier (4.8%)
Raab Kellerbier (4.8%)
Raab Pils (4.8%)
Raab Zwergle (4.8%)
Raab Weissbier (5.2%)
Raab Märzen (5.5%)

The brewery was founded by the current owner's
grandfather. The railway to Hofheim closed in
the mid-1990s but the town can be reached by
bus No. 8168 from Haßfurt daily except Sunday.

🍺 **Zum Bräustüble**
Johannisstraße 11, 97461 Hofheim
T 09523 54 33
Closed Wed; Thu–Tue 11.00–24.00
[DB] Haßfurt 15km

HOHENALTHEIM   301

Bauer's

Bauer's Brauerei AG
Am Straußenhof 2, 86745 Hohenaltheim
T 09088 887   **F** 09088 552
www.bauers-brauerei.de
Founded: 2001
Output: 200hl   Availability: 1 pub
REGULAR BEERS:
Bauer's Vollbier Hell
Bauer's Weizen

Very small brewery in a pub near the centre of
the village. The pub only opens on 1 May and for
private functions but does have a beer garden in
the summer. The brewery inform us there's a bus
service from Nörlingen but we can find no details.

🍺 **Biergarten**
Am Straußenhof 2, 86745 Hohenaltheim
Closed 4 Oct–30 Apr. 1 May–3 Oct:
Sun 10.00–20.00, Mon–Sat 17.00–22.00
[DB] Möttingen 7km, Nördlingen 9km

HOHENSCHWÄRZ (Gräfenberg)   302

Hofmann

Hohenschwärz 16, 91322 Gräfenberg-
Hohenschwärz
T 09192 251   **F** 09192 69 06
Owners: Elfriede Hofmann & Gerlinde Nentwig

Founded: 1897   Output: 2,500hl
Availability: 5 pubs
REGULAR BEER:
Hofmann Hofmannstropfen Dunkel (5.2%)
SEASONAL BEER:
Hofmann Weihnachtsfestbier

Small brewery and tap in a village that has a much better bus service in than out, though it is possible to make a return journey from nearby Gräfenberg in one day.

🍺 **Hofmann**
Hohenschwärz 16,
91322 Gräfenberg-Hohenschwärz
Closed Tue; Wed–Sun 09.30–22.30,
Mon 15.00–22.00
DB Gräfenberg 4.5km

HOHENTHANN   303

Schloßbrauerei

Schloßbrauerei Hohenthann KG
Brauhausstraße 1, 84098 Hohenthann
T 08784 960 20   **F** 08784 96 02 99
www.hohenthanner.de
Owner: Rauschenecker Family   Founded: 1844
Output: 35,000hl   Availability: c.180 pubs
REGULAR BEERS:
Hohenthanner Tannen Leicht (2.9%)
Hohenthanner Leichte Weisse (2.9%)
Hohenthanner Premium Lager Hell (5%)
Hohenthanner Tannen-Pils Edelherb (5%)
Hohenthanner Weisse (5.3%)
Hohenthanner Holzhacker Hefe-Weisse Dunkel
(5.3%)
Hohenthanner Urstoff (5.4%)
Hohenthanner Dunkel Urtyp (5.4%)
SEASONAL BEERS:
Hohenthanner Winterfestbier (5.5%),
Hohenthanner St. Sixtus Doppelbock (6.5%)

Small regional brewery in the centre of town. The brewery tap is around the corner on the main street. Bus No. 6241 runs from the main station in Landshut Mon–Fri.

🍺 **Bräustüberl**
Rottenburgerstraße 4, 84098 Hohenthann
T 08284 96 99 35
Sat & Sun 10.00–24.00, Mon–Fri 10.00–14.00
& 16.00–24.00; rooms available
DB Landshut Hbf 15km

HOHENWART (Mespelbrunn)   304

Hohe-Wart-Bräu

Brewery: 63875 Mespelbrunn-Hohenwart
T 0172 699 59 95
Office: Gabelsbergerstraße 9, 63739 Aschaffen-
burg   **T** 06021 339 80   **F** 06021 33 98 10
www.hohewart-haus.de
Founded: 2004
REGULAR BEERS:
Hohe-Wart-Bräu Räuber-Hell
Hohe-Wart-Bräu Räuber-Dunkel
Hohe-Wart-Bräu Weizen-Hell
SEASONAL BEERS:
Hohe-Wart-Bräu Maibock, Hohe-Wart-Bräu
Weihnachtsbock, Hohe-Wart-Bräu Antonius-
Sartor-Starkbier

Brewpub in a remote forest building, about 2km up a track that leaves the St 2312 near Hessenthal. Although open every weekend, midweek opening is restricted to high summer, New Year and a few other days, weather permitting. Bus No. 40 runs from Aschaffenburg station to Hessental daily and apparently calls at the bottom of the track.

🍺 **Hohewart Haus**
63875 Mespelbrunn-Hohenwart
July, August, Boxing Day–Epiphany: daily
10.30–18.30.
Rest of year: closed Mon–Fri; Sat, Sun & hols
10.30–18.30, may open Wed–Fri in fine weather
DB Aschaffenburg Hbf 15km

HOLNSTEIN (Neukirchen)   305

Schloßbrauerei

Schloßbrauerei Holnstein KG
Holnstein 1, 92259 Neukirchen-Holnstein
T 09663 12 48   **F** 09663 24 42
www.schlossbrauerei-holnstein.de
Owner: Karola Haberler   Founded: 1502
REGULAR BEERS:
Holnsteiner Barons Urhell (4.8%)
Holnsteiner Schlossherrn Pils (5%)
Holnsteiner Baroness Weisse (5%)
Holnsteiner Ahnentrunk (5.2%)
SEASONAL BEER:
Honsteiner Ahnengold (5.2%)

Small brewery that recently celebrated its 500th anniversary. Bus No. 2448 runs from Neukirchen station on weekdays if you want to chance your arm looking for the beers in Holnstein, but we don't think there's a pub in the village.

DB Neukirchen (bei Sulzbach-Rosenberg) 4.5km

HOLZHAUSEN (Igling) 306

Holzhausener Landbrauerei

Hauptstraße 8, 86859 Igling-Holzhausen
T/F 08241 47 58
Founded: 1464   Output: 400hl
REGULAR BEERS:
Holzhausener Zwickel Leicht
Holzhausener Landbier
SEASONAL BEER:
Holzhausener St. Georgsbock

We must admit to being a bit uncertain about this one. Almost no sources list it as brewing but they've assured us on several occasions that they do. We do know the pub changed hands in 2004. If you want to check it out, there don't appear to be any buses.

🏠 **Brauereigasthaus**
Hauptstraße 8, 86859 Igling-Holzhausen
Closed Mon; Tue–Fri 17.00–24.00,
Sat & Sun 10.00–24.00
DB Buchloe 5.5km

HOLZKIRCHEN 307

Holzkirchner Oberbräu

Holzkirchner Oberbräu Friedrich Wochinger KG
Industriestraße 5, 83607 Holzkirchen
T 08024 64 70   **F** 08024 647 72
www.oberbraeu-holzkirchen.de
Owner: Friedrich Wochinger   Founded: 1605
Output: 50,000hl   Availability: 100 pubs
REGULAR BEERS:
Holzkirchner 2,8er (2.8%)
Holzkirchner Leichte Weisse
Holzkirchner Oberbräu Zwickl
Holzkirchner Oberbräu Urtyp Hell (5%)
Holzkirchner Hell (5%)
Holzkirchner Oberbräu Pils (5%)
Holzkirchner Laurenzi Export-Dunkel (5%)
Holzkirchner Anno 1605er Weisse (5%)
Holzkirchner Weisse-Hell (5.2%)
Holzkirchner Weisse-Dunkel (5.2%)

Holzkirchner Oberbräu Edel-Export
Holzkirchner Gold (5.5%)
SEASONAL BEER:
Holzkirchner Festbier
GAMS BEERS:
Gams Bier Hell, Gams Bier Export

Oberbräu moved to a new brewery on the western edge of town in 1996. The tap remains on the market square, south of the station.

🏠 **Zum Oberbräu**
Marktplatz 18, 83607 Holzkirchen
T 08024 47 31 66
Daily 10.00–24.00
DB Holzkirchen 950m

HORNECK (Elsendorf) 308

Horneck

Brauerei Horneck GmbH & Co. KG
Horneck 7, 84094 Elsendorf-Horneck
T 08753 503   **E** brauerei.horneck@t-online.de
Owner: Josef Stempfhuber   Founded: 1881
Output: 10,000hl   Availability: 7 pubs
REGULAR BEERS:
Hornecker Leichtes Weizen (3%)
Hornecker Hallertauer Hopfentrunk (4.5%)
Hornecker Braumeister Urhell (4.5%)
Hornecker Hell (4.8%)
Hornecker Pils (4.8%)
Hornecker Edel-Hell (5%)
Hornecker Dunkel (5%)
Hornecker Hefe-Weizen Export (5.2%)
Hornecker Hefe-Weizen Export-Dunkel (5.2%)
Hornecker Spezial (5.5%)

Self-sufficient brewery that has its own spring and produces its own malt and hops. There's no tap and the bus service to Horneck is not the best, to say the least, so be warned that your journey may be in vain if you just want a drink.
DB Abensberg 18km

HUPPENDORF (Königsfeld) 309

Grasser

Brauerei & Brennerei Johannes Grasser
Huppendorf 25, 96167 Königsfeld-Huppendorf
T 09207 270   **F** 09207 636
www.huppendorfer-bier.de

Owner: Johannes Grasser
Founded: 1750   Output: 7,500hl
Availability: 5 pubs
REGULAR BEERS:
Huppendorfer Hausbrauerart (4.6%)
Huppendorfer Pils (4.9%)
Huppendorfer Vollbier (5%)
Huppendorfer Hefeweizen (5.2%)
SEASONAL BEERS:
Huppendorfer Festbier (5.5%, Christmas),
Huppendorfer Josefi-Bock (7%, Mar),
Huppendorfer Kathrein-Bock (7.5%, winter)

Brewery and pub in a tiny village east of
Bamberg. The bus service from both Bamberg
and Ebermannstadt is poor, so you'll be better
off with your own transport.

🍺 Grasser
Huppendorf 25, 96167 Königsfeld-Huppendorf
Closed Tue; Wed–Mon 10.00–23.00; rooms
available
DB Ebermannstadt 20km, Bamberg 21km

HÜTTEN (Warmensteinach)   310

Hütten
Brauerei Hütten Michael Trassl OHG
Hütten 6–8, 95485 Warmensteinach-Hütten
T 09277 312   **F** 09277 13 69
www.brauerei-huetten.de
Owners: Horst & Wolfgang Nickl
Founded: 1887
Output: 4,000hl
Availability: 6 pubs
REGULAR BEERS:
Hütten Leichte Hefe Weisse (3.1%)
Hütten Pilsner (4.8%)
Hütten Hell (4.9%)
Hütten Märzen (5.2%)
Hütten Hefe Weisse (5.5%)
SEASONAL BEERS:
Hütten Festbier (5.2%), **Hütten Doppel-Bock** (7%)

Brewery in a hamlet on the main road east out
of Warmensteinach. The railway from Bayreuth
closed recently, so it's bus only these days,
although some do go through to Hütten. The
beers are sold in just six pubs, so we suggest
you contact the brewery if you want to avoid a
wasted journey.
DB Bayreuth 26km

HUTTHURM   311

Hutthurmer
Hutthurmer Bayerwald Brauerei
Marktplatz 5, 94116 Hutthurm
T 08505 94 05 55   **F** 08505 849
www.hutthurmer.de
Founded: 1577   Output: 80,000hl
REGULAR BEERS:
Hutthurmer Bayerwald Medium (2.9%)
Hutthurmer Bayerwald Leichte Weisse (2.9%)
Hutthurmer Bayerwald Premium Pils (4.8%)
Hutthurmer Bayerwald Urtyp Hell (4.9%)
Hutthurmer Bayerwald Bayrisch Hell (4.9%)
Hutthurmer Bayerwald Gourmet-Bier (4.9%)
Hutthurmer Bayerwald Hefe-Weisse (5.2%)
Hutthurmer Bayerwald Tradition-Dunkel (5.3%)
Hutthurmer Bayerwald Dunkle Weisse (5.4%)
Hutthurmer Bayerwald Tradition-Export (5.4%)
SEASONAL BEERS:
Hutthurmer Bayerwald Festbier (5.4%),
Hutthurmer Bayerwald Kulinator (Lent)

Substantial regional brewery in the south-
eastern part of the Bayerischer Wald. There are
plenty of journey opportunities by bus from
Passau Mon–Sat.

🍺 Bräustüberl
Marktstraße 16, 94116 Hutthurm
T 08505 91 94 74
Closed Tue; Wed–Mon 09.30–01.00
DB Passau Hbf 15km

ILLERTISSEN   312

Schloßbrauerei
Schloßbrauerei Illertissen R. Endres
Bräuhausstraße 17, 89257 Illertissen
T 07303 34 21   **F** 07303 425 28
www.schloss-brauhaus.de
Owner: Rudolf Endres   Founded: 1686
Output: 600hl   Availability: 2 pubs
REGULAR BEERS:
Schloßbrauerei Illertissen Hell (5%)
Schloßbrauerei Illertissen Dunkel (5%)
Schloßbrauerei Illertissen Hefeweizen (5%)

Small brewery on the western edge of the town
centre that supplies just one pub in addition to
the tap.

🍺 Schloß-Bräuhaus
Bräuhausstraße 17, 89257 Illertissen
Closed Mon; Tue 16.00–02.00, Wed–Sat 11.00–
14.00 & 16.00–22.00, Sun 10.00–22.00
DB Illertissen 800m

INGOLSTADT 313

Herrnbräu

Herrnbräu GmbH & Co. KG
Manchinger Straße 95, 85053 Ingolstadt
T 0841 63 10   **F** 0841 63 12 11
www.herrnbraeu.de
Founded: 1899   Output: 100,000hl
REGULAR BEERS:
Herrnbräu Leichtes Weizen (2.9%)
Herrnbräu Herrntrunk Helles (4.8%)
Herrnbräu Herrntrunk Dunkles (4.9%)
Herrnbräu Premium Pils (5%)
Herrnbräu Römergold (5.2%)
Herrnbräu Hefe Weißbier Dunkel (5.3%)
Herrnbräu Hefe Weissbier Hell (5.4%)
Herrnbräu Kristall Weizen (5.4%)
SEASONAL BEERS:
Herrnbräu Tradition (5.6%), **Herrnbräu
Schneewalzer Weisse** (5.6%), **Herrnbräu St.
Martini Weizenbock** (7%)

Large brewery in an industrial area south-west
of the city. Bus No. 21 runs from the city centre.
The old tap, The Weissbräuhaus, is in the heart
of the old town. We believe they may now be
owned by Brau Holding International.

🍺 Zur Sudpfanne
Manchinger Straße 95, 85053 Ingolstadt
T 0841 684 46
Closed Mon; Tue–Sun from 09.00
DB Ingolstadt Hbf 3km

🍺 Weissbräuhaus zum Herrnbräu
Dollstraße 3, 85049 Ingolstadt
T 0841 328 90   **F** 0841 336 20
Daily 09.00–24.00   DB Ingolstadt Hbf 2.5km

Ingobräu

Ingobräu Ingolstadt GmbH
Harderstraße 20, 85049 Ingolstadt
T 0841 310 80   **F** 0841 31 08 28
www.ingobraeu.de
Owners: F. Dittmar, M. Dittmar, H.-T. Lang
Founded: 1507   Output: 60,000hl

REGULAR BEERS:
Ingobräu Leichte Halbe (2.6%)
Ingobräu Donauthaler Weisse (2.8%)
Ingobräu Hell (5%)
Ingobräu Zwickel (5.2%)
Ingobräu Dunkel Weisse (5.2%)
Ingobräu Meistersud (5.3%)
Ingobräu Edel Weisse (5.4%)
SEASONAL BEERS:
Ingobräu Festbier (5.5%),
Ingobräu Honorator (7%)

The oldest of Ingolstadt's breweries was known
as Schaffbräu until 1978. The brewery and tap
are on the northern edge of the old town. Take
buses Nos. 10 or 11 from the main station.

🍺 Hahnenhof
Harderstraße 24, 85049 Ingolstadt
T 0841 322 02
Sun from 10.30, Mon–Sat from 08.30
DB Ingolstadt Nord 1km, Hbf 3km

Nordbräu

Nordbräu & Jesuiten Quelle GmbH
Gutsstraße 5, 85055 Ingolstadt-Oberhaunstadt
T 0841 95 59 60   **F** 0841 955 96 40
www.nordbraeu.de
Owners: the Wittmann family   Founded: 1693
Output: 200,000hl
REGULAR BEERS:
Nordbräu Leichte Weiße (2.7%)
Nordbräu Leichtes (3.1%)
Nordbräu Urtyp Dunkel (5%)
Nordbräu Urtyp Hell (5.1%)
Nordbräu Privat Pilsener (5.2%)
Nordbräu Schanzer Weiße (5.4%)
Nordbräu Edel-Weißes (5.6%)
Nordbräu '93er Weizenbier (5.6%)
SEASONAL BEERS:
**Nordbräu Festbier, Nordbräu Glühtrunk,
Nordbräu Eisbock**
FOR BRAUEREI HOPF, MIESBACH:
Schlierseer Hell (4.8%), **Schlierseer Dunkel** (5.7%)

Ingolstadt's largest brewery is in the northern
suburb of Oberhaunstadt. As well as their own
range they brew a couple of bottom-fermented
beers for Hopf of Miesbach. Bus No. 30 runs from
the ZOB via Nord station.

🍺 Zum Bräukeller
Gutsstraße 4, 85055 Ingolstadt-Oberhaunstadt
T 0841 555 41   **F** 0841 961 20 33

Closed Mon; Tue–Fri 10.00–14.00 & 17.00–
01.00, Sat & Sun 10.00–01.00
DB Ingolstadt Nord 3.3km, Hbf 7km

1516 Westparkbräu

Am Westpark 6, 85057 Ingolstadt-Friedrichshof
T 0841 956 87 77   **F** 0841 956 87 78
www.westparkbraeu.de
Founded: 2001
Output: 1,500hl
Availability: 1 pub
REGULAR BEERS:
1516 Blond (4.8%)
1516 Weißbier (5.2%)
SEASONAL BEERS:
1516 Dunkelblond (4.8%),
1516 Weihnachtsbier (5.8%),
1516 Maibock (6.8%), **1516 Dunkler Bock** (8%)

Brewpub on the western side of the city.
Unusually for a modern brewpub, the wheat
beer is only available bottled. Bus No. 16 runs
from the Hauptbahnhof.

Westparkbräu
Am Westpark 6, 85057 Ingolstadt-Friedrichshof
Daily 09.00–01.00
DB Ingolstadt Nord 3.8km, Hbf 6km

IRCHENRIETH   314

Hösl

Brauerei Johann Hösl
Braugasse 3, 92699 Irchenrieth
T/F 09659 666
Owners: Arne Luchner & Claudia Molter
Founded: before 1750
Output: 1,500hl
Availability: 7 pubs
REGULAR BEERS:
Irchenriether Zoigl (4.7%)
Irchenriether Echtes (4.8%)
Irchenriether Dunkles (4.8%)
Irchenriether Edel Weisse (5.1%)
Irchenriether Füchserl (5.2%)

Small brewery in the centre of Irchenrieth that
brews a Zoigl-style beer. No tap, but if you want
to look for the beers locally, bus No. 11 runs
from Weiden Mon–Sat.
DB Weiden (Oberpfalz) 9km

IRLBACH   315

Schloßbrauerei

Freiherr von Poschinger-Bray'sche
Schloßbrauerei Irlbach GmbH
Heckenweg 5, 94342 Irlbach
T 09424 940 30   **F** 09424 94 03 15
www.irlbacher.de
Owner: Franz Gabriel Freiherr von
Poschinger-Bray
Founded: 1811
Output: 100,000hl
REGULAR BEERS:
Irlbacher Premium Leichte Weisse (3.2%)
Irlbacher Graf Bray Klassik (4.9%)
Irlbacher Vollbier Hell (4.9%)
Irlbacher Pils (5.2%)
Irlbacher Hefeweissbier Hell (5.2%)
Irlbacher Schloßherrn Weisse Dunkel (5.2%)
Irlbacher Exzellent (5.6%)
Alt Irlbacher Spezial Dunkel (5.8%)
SEASONAL BEERS:
Irlbacher Winterfestbier (5.6%),
Irlbacher Gäubodenfestbier (5.7%)

Large brewery in a small town on the banks of the
Danube. Bus No. 1019 runs from Straßkirchen
during the week if you want to visit Irlbach and
try to find the beers locally.
DB Straßkirchen 3km

IRSEE (Allgäu)   316

Irseer Klosterbräu

Klosterring 1, 87660 Irsee
T 08341 43 22 00   **F** 08341 43 22 69
www.irsee.com
Owners: Herbert & Rosemarie Paulus
Founded: 1803   Output: 10,000hl
REGULAR BEERS:
Irseer Kloster-Pils (5%)
Irseer Kloster-Urtrunk (5.6%)
Irseer Kosterdunkel (5.6%)
Irseer Kloster-Urweiße (5.7%)
SEASONAL BEER:
Irseer Kloster-Starkbier (7%)

Brewery, pub and hotel in the former monastery
at Irsee. They also have a small brewery museum.
We think the closest you can get to Irsee by bus
is the B16 at Leinau, 2.5km away.

Klosterbräu

Klosterring, 87660 Irsee   **T** 08341 43 22 60
Daily 10.00–23.00; rooms available
DB Kaufbeuren 7km

JANDELSBRUNN   317

Lang

Privatbrauerei Josef Lang GmbH & Co. KG
Hauptstraße 17, 94118 Jandelsbrunn
T 08583 60 88 80   **F** 08583 608 88 50
www.jandelsbrunner.de
Founded: 1810   Output: 15,000hl
REGULAR BEERS:
Jandelsbrunner Leichte Weisse (2.9%)
Jandelsbrunner Pils (4.9%)
Jandelsbrunner Hell (5%)
Jandelsbrunner Dunkel (5.1%)
Jandelsbrunner Weisse (5.3%)
Jandelsbrunner Ur-Weizen (5.3%)
SEASONAL BEERS:
Jandelsbrunner Festbier (5.1%),
Jandelsbrunner Helyator (8%)

Small regional brewery in the south-western
corner of the Bayerischer Wald, 8km from the
Austrian border. Bus No. 6122 runs from Passau.

Kerber

Hauptstraße 8, 94118 Jandelsbrunn
T 08583 13 45   **F** 08583 28 86
Winter: closed Fri; Sat 17.00–23.00,
Sun–Thu 11.00–14.00 & 17.00–23.00
Summer: Fri–Sat 17.00–23.00, Sun–Thu 11.00–
14.00 & 17.00–23.00. Rooms available.
DB Passau Hbf 33km

JOCHSBERG (Leutershausen)   318

Reindler

Brauerei Reindler GmbH & Co. KG
Am Ring 5, 91578 Leutershausen-Jochsberg
T 09823 203   **F** 09823 930 46
Owners: the Reindler family   Founded: 1663
Output: 7,000hl
REGULAR BEERS:
Reindler Hell (4.9%)
Reindler Edel-Pils (4.9%)
Reindler Gold-Export (5.1%)
Reindler Spezial-Dunkel (5.5%)

SEASONAL BEERS:
Reindler Festbier, Reindler Seckenator

Brewery and tap in the centre of the village.
Closes on the last weekend of each month Fri–
Sun and Christmas/New Year. Bus No. 703 run
direct from Ansbach on weekdays, and there
are other options that involve changing.

Reindler

Am Ring 5, 91578 Leutershausen-Jochsberg
Closed last weekend of each month; Mon–Sun
09.00–23.00; rooms available
DB Ansbach 17km

KALLMÜNZ   319

Zum Goldenen Löwen

Zum Goldenen Löwen Wirtshaus und Brauerei
Alte Regensburger Straße 18, 93183 Kallmünz
T 09473 380   **F** 09473 900 90
Owners: Richard & Waltraut Luber
Founded: 1992
Output: 500hl
Availability: 1 pub
REGULAR BEERS:
Kallmünzer Dunkel
Kallmünzer Weisse

Brewpub close to the river in the picturesque
town of Kallmünz. Buses Nos. 15 and 42 run
from Regensburg Mon–Sat. You can also travel
by bus from Maxhütte-Haidhof and Regenstauf
but they're not as useful given the opening
hours of the pub.

Zum Goldenen Löwen

Alte Regensburger Straße 18, 93183 Kallmünz
Closed Mon; Tue–Sat 18.00–01.00, Sun & hols
11.00 – 14.30; rooms available
DB Regensburg Hbf 23km

KALTENBERG (Geltendorf)   320

Schloßbrauerei

König Ludwig GmbH & Co. KG Schloßbrauerei
Kaltenberg
Schloßstraße 8, 82269 Geltendorf-Kaltenberg
T 08193 93 30   **F** 08193 93 31 23
www.kaltenberg.de
Owner: Luitpold Prinz von Bayern
Founded: 1870   Output: 100,000hl

REGULAR BEERS:
Kaltenberg Pils (4.8%)
Kaltenberg Hell (4.9%)
König Ludwig Dunkel (5.1%)
Prinzregent Luitpold Weissbier Hell (5.5%)
Prinzregent Luitpold Weissbier Dunkel (5.5%)
Kaltenberg Spezial (5.6%)
Kaltenberg Ritterbock (9.5%)

The brewery is in the castle of the same name, still the residence of the Crown Prince of Bavaria. We have been told in the past that the only beer brewed here was the famous Dunkel but the brewery themselves listed all the above. They also own the similarly named brewery in Fürstenfeldbrück and Postbräu in Thannhausen. Buses Nos. 60 and 61 run to Kaltenberg from Geltendorf station.

Schloßrestaurant
Schloßstraße 8, 82269 Geltendorf-Kaltenberg
T 08193 68 28   **F** 08193 70 08 65
Closed Thu; Fri, Mon–Wed 17.00–22.30, Sat, Sun & hols 11.00–22.30
DB Geltendorf 6km

Ritterschwemme
Schloßstraße 11, 82269 Geltendorf-Kaltenberg
T 08193 75 75   **F** 08193 41 87
Jan–Oct: closed Mon; Tue–Sun 10.00–23.00
Nov–Dec: closed Mon & Tue; Wed–Sun 10.00–23.00   DB Geltendorf 6km

KALTENBRUNN (Itzgrund)   321

Schleicher

Coburger Straße 22, 96274 Itzgrund-Kaltenbrunn
T 09533 229   **F** 09533 15 67
www.brauerei-schleicher.de
Owner: Oskar Döllinger   Founded: 1880
Output: 5,000hl
REGULAR BEERS:
Schleicher Kaltenbrunner Vollbier (4.5%)
Schleicher Itzgrunder Landbier Dunkel (4.8%)
Schleicher Kaltenbrunner Pils (4.8%)
SEASONAL BEERS:
Schleicher Storchenbier (5.1%), **Schleicher Bock**

Small brewery in the centre of the village. The brewery tap has recently re-opened following several years out of use. Bus No. 8319 runs from Coburg via Creidlitz on weekdays.

Schleicher's Bräustübla
Coburger Straße 22, 96274 Itzgrund-Kaltenbrunn
Closed Mon; 10.00–24.00   DB Creidlitz 16km

KAPPEL (Burgwindheim)   322

Ibel-Bräu

Brauerei Hans Ibel
Kappel 1, 96154 Burgwindheim-Kappel
T 09551 295
Owner: Hans Ibel   Founded: 1650
Output: 2,500hl   Availability: 1 pub
REGULAR BEERS:
Ibel-Bräu Leichtbier (2.7%)
Ibel-Bräu Vollbier (4.6%)
Ibel-Bräu Pils (4.7%)
Ibel-Bräu Lagerbier (5%)
Ibel-Bräu Weizenbier (5%)
SEASONAL BEERS:
Ibel-Bräu Bock (Christmas)

Small brewery and tap in a hamlet on the old road from Bamberg to Würzburg. Bus No. 8223 runs from Bamberg but there's only one bus back after the pub opens on weekdays and none at the weekend.

Ibel
Kappel 1, 96154 Burgwindheim-Kappel
Daily from 17.00   DB Bamberg 24km

KARLSTADT am Main   323

Brauhaus im Wurzgrund

Im Wurzgrund 6, 97753 Karlstadt am Main
T 09353 98 23 66
E markus.metzger@hausgebraut.de
Owner: Heike Metzger   Founded: 1990
Output: 30hl
REGULAR BEERS:
Karschter Original (5%)
Karschter Räuchermännchen (5.2%)
SEASONAL BEERS:
Karschter Weihnachtsmännchen (7.8%),
Karschter Josefi-Bock (7.8%)

Tiny brewery in the basement of Heike and Markus Metzger's house. Markus Metzger lectures at the nearby brewing school. The beer is only available to take away.
DB Karlstadt (Main) 1km

KAUFBEUREN 324

Aktienbrauerei

Aktienbrauerei Kaufbeuren KG
Hohe Buchleuthe 3, 87600 Kaufbeuren
T 08341 430 40 **F** 08341 43 04 50
www.aktien-brauerei.de
Founded: 1308
Output: 125,000hl
REGULAR BEERS:
Kaiser Maximilian Leichte Weisse (2.8%)
Aktienbrauerei Original Schankbier (3.9%)
Aktienbrauerei Anno 1518 Lager Hell (5.1%)
Aktienbrauerei Kaufbeurer Hell (5%)
Aktienbrauerei Urbayrisch Dunkel (5%)
Aktienbrauerei Jubiläums-Pils (5%)
Aktienbrauerei Anno 1516 Landbier (5.1%)
Aktienbrauerei Anno 1308 Kellerbier (5.1%)
Aktienbrauerei Steingadener Dunkle Weisse
(5.1%)
Aktienbrauerei Anno 1885 Weissbier (5.2%)
Aktienbrauerei Anno 25 Hefe-Weisse (5.3%)
Aktienbrauerei Spezialbier Edel (5.8%)
SEASONAL BEERS:
Aktienbrauerei St. Blasius Weizenbock (7.2%),
Aktienbrauerei St. Martin Doppelbock (7.5%)

Large brewery on the western edge of town. The
brewery tap is in the centre, on the original site
of one of the breweries that merged over the
years to form Aktienbrauerei.

🍺 **Traube**
Kaiser-Max-Straße 23, 87600 Kaufbeuren
T 08341 23 68
Sun 10.00–14.00, Mon–Sat 10.00–22.00
DB Kaufbeuren 900m

KELHEIM 325

Aukofer-Bräu

Brauerei und Hotel Johann Aukofer KG
Alleestraße 27, 93309 Kelheim
T 09441 20 20 **F** 09441 2 14 37
www.hotel-brauerei-aukofer.de
Owner: Johann Aukofer
Founded: 1874
REGULAR BEERS:
Aukofer-Bräu Pils (4.8%)
Aukofer-Bräu Hell (5%)
Aukofer-Bräu Dunkel (5.1%)

Aukofer-Bräu Klösterl Weisse (5.5%)
Aukofer-Bräu Klösterl Weisse Dunkel (5.5%)
SEASONAL BEER:
Aukofer-Bräu Kelheimer Festbier (5.5%)

Brewery between the Altmühl and Donau rivers,
on the western side of town. There are rumours
they may have stopped brewing due to damage
sustained in the August 2005 floods. Any reports
welcome at GermanBreweries@aol.com. Buses
Nos. 6022 & 6035 run to Allestrasse from Saal.

🍺 **Hotel Aukofer-Bräu**
Alleestraße 27, 93309 Kelheim
Daily 10.00–23.00; rooms available
DB Saal (Donau) 6km

Schneider

Private Weißbierbrauerei G. Schneider & Sohn
Emil-Ott-Straße 1–5, 93309 Kelheim
T 09441 70 50 **F** 09441 70 51 90
www.schneider-weisse.de
Owner: Georg Schneider VI
Founded: 1872
Output: 300,000hl
REGULAR BEERS:
Schneider Weisse Leicht (3.3%)
Schneider Weisse Weizen-Hell (5.2%)
Schneider Weisse Kristall (5.3%)
Schneider Weisse Original (5.4%)
Schneider Aventinus (8%)
SEASONAL BEER:
Schneider Aventinus Weizen-Eisbock (12%)

World-famous wheat beer brewery that moved
to Kelheim from München in the 1940s. The official tap is still their original home in München
but there is a pub next to the brewery. Various
buses run from Saal to the centre of Kelheim.

🍺 **Weisses Brauhaus zu Kelheim**
Emil-Ott-Straße 3, 93309 Kelheim
T 09441 34 80 **F** 09441 34 49
Daily 10.00–24.00
DB Saal (Donau) 5.5km

🍺 **Weisses Brauhaus im Tal**
Tal 7, 80331 München/Altstadt-Lehel
T 089 290 13 80 **F** 089 29 01 38 15
Daily from 07.00
DB Marienplatz 200m, München Hbf 1.5km

KEMMERN 326

Wagner-Bräu

Wagner-Bräu GmbH & Co. KG
Hauptstraße 15, 96164 Kemmern
T 09544 67 46   **F** 09544 98 20 72
www.brauerei-wagner.de
Owners: Hubert & Lorenz Wagner
Founded: 1788   Output: 8,000hl
REGULAR BEERS:
Wagner-Bräu Pilsener (4.8%)
Wagner-Bräu Schwarzbier (4.8%)
Wagner-Bräu Ungespundetes Lagerbier (5%)
Wagner-Bräu Märzen (5.2%)
Wagner-Bräu Hefeweizen (5.3%)
SEASONAL BEER:
Wagner-Bräu Bock (6.6%)

Brewery and tap on the western side of the town.
They also have a Bierkeller off Mainstraße,
which overlooks the river. Although close to
Bamberg, the bus service to the town is
surprisingly poor, so you may find it easier to
walk from nearby Breitengüßbach.

🍺 **Wagner**
Hauptstraße 15, 96164 Kemmern
Closed Tue; Wed–Sat & Mon 16.00–23.00, Sun &
hols 15.00–23.00   DB Breitengüßbach 2.1km

KEMNATH 327

Klosterbrauerei

Klosterbrauerei Kemnath GmbH & Co. KG
Klosterhofstraße 6, 95478 Kemnath
T 09642 431   **F** 09642 83 56
www.klosterbrauerei-kemnath.de
Founded: 1660
Output: 5,000hl   **Availabilty:** 13 pubs
REGULAR BEERS:
Klosterbrauerei Kloster Hell (4.9%)
Klosterbrauerei Kloster Pils (5%)
Klosterbrauerei Kloster Weisse (5.2%)
Klosterbrauerei Kloster Märzen (5.8%)
SEASONAL BEERS:
Phantastisches Karpfen-Gold (5.1%, Sep–Apr),
Klosterbrauerei Kloster Festbier (5.6%)

Small brewery close the the Oberfranken/
Oberpfalz border. The tap is 7km north-west of
Kemnath, in the small village of Ahornberg. The
bus service to Ahornberg is very poor but it is

walkable from Immenreuth. The Phantastisches
Karpfen-Gold is named after a 2.8km walk along
local waterways, adorned with artistic
sculptures of carp.

🍺 **Zum Flötztal**
Ahornberg 18, 95505 Immenreuth-Ahornberg
T 09642 921 10   **F** 09642 92 11 55
Closed Tue; Wed–Mon 10.00–22.00
DB Immenreuth 2.8km

KIRCHENTHUMBACH 328

Heberbräu

Auerbacher Straße 14, 91281 Kirchenthumbach
T 09647 92 97 18   www.heberbraeu.de
Founded: 2003
REGULAR BEER:
Heberbräu Krawendorfer

Modern brewpub, located in the former tap of
the Heberbräu brewery which closed in 1962.
The old brewery building is now a museum. Bus
No. 6269 runs from Neuhaus station Mon–Sat,
but is only of much use on weekdays.

🍺 **Heberbräu**
Auerbacher Straße 14, 91281 Kirchenthumbach
T 09647 92 94 33   **F** 09647 92 94 34
Closed Thu–Fri, Mon & Tue from 17.00,
Sat & Sun from 14.00
DB Neuhaus (Pegnitz) 23km

KIRCHHEIM (Schwaben) 329

Lechler

Brandgasse 1, 87757 Kirchheim
T 08266 25 99   Owner: Lothar Lang
Founded: 1908   Output: 1,000hl
REGULAR BEERS:
Lechler Export-Hell
Lechler Export-Dunkel
Lechler Weizen

Small village brewery which we think just
supplies its own pub. Bus No. 819 runs from
Pfaffenhausen on weekdays.

🍺 **Lechler**
Brandgasse 1, 87757 Kirchheim
T 08266 304   Closed Wed; Thu–Tue from 09.00
DB Pfaffenhausen 7.5km

KLINGENBRUNN (Spiegelau) 330

Klingenbrunn

Brauerei Stangl Klingenbrunn
Frauenauer Straße 15,
94518 Spiegelau-Klingenbrunn
T 08553 60 18   F 08553 914 76
Owner: Hermine Mandl   Founded: 1850
Output: 3,000hl   Availability: 6 pubs
REGULAR BEERS:
Klingenbrunner Ur-Hell (4.6%)
Klingenbrunner Panduren-Dunkel (4.8%)
Klingenbrunner Pilsener (4.8%)
Klingenbrunner Spezial (5.3%)
SEASONAL BEER:
Klingenbrunner Fest-Bock Dunkel (6.8%)

This small village brewery is closer to Spiegelau station then the one that supposedly serves Klingenbrunn. There are several bus routes from Spiegelau to the village.

🍺 **Zum Ludwigstein**
Fatimaweg 2, 94518 Spiegelau-Klingenbrunn
T 08553 819
Closed Wed; Thu–Tue 10.00–01.00
DB Spiegelau 3.3km, Klingenbrunn 3.8km

KÖNIGSBRUNN 331

Charivari-Bräu

Aumühlestraße 33, 86343 Königsbrunn
T 08321 55 65
www.charivari-braeu.de
Founded: 2004
REGULAR BEERS:
Königsbrunner Gold
Königsbrunner Gold-Weiße
Königsbrunner Rubin

Brewpub on the south-western edge of town, close to the bypass. Bus No.100 runs from Mering on weekdays and there are frequent buses from Augsburg Hbf every day of the week. They also make their own bread and charcuteries.

🍺 **Charivari-Bräu**
Aumühlestraße 33, 86343 Königsbrunn
Mon & Tue 16.00–01.00, Wed 08.00–01.00,
Thu–Sat 11.00–01.00, Sun 10.00–01.00
DB Mering 8km, Augsburg Hbf 12km

KONZELL 332

Klett-Bräu

Brauerei Otto Kienberger
Dachauer Straße 8, 94357 Konzell
T 09963 805   F 09963 28 29
Owner: Otto Kienberger   Founded: 1705
Output: 5,000hl
REGULAR BEERS:
Klett-Bräu Leichtes Weizen
Klett-Bräu Urhell (4.9%)
Klett-Bräu Pils (5%)
Klett-Bräu Weißbier Dunkel (5%)
Klett-Bräu Konzeller Weiße (5.3%)
Klett-Bräu Märzen (5.5%)
SEASONAL BEERS:
Klett-Bräu Festbier, Klett-Bräu Dunkler Bock

Small brewery without a tap at the southern end of the village. The only realistic way of getting to Konzell and back by public transport is taking the train to Miltach and the bus from there. This has to be done early morning if you want to return the same day.
DB Miltach 15km

KÖSSLARN 333

Weißbräu

Marktplatz 23, 94149 Kößlarn
T 08536 256   F 08536 91 96 26
Owner: Sven Grünleitner   Founded: 1884
Output: 2,000hl   Availability: 9 pubs
REGULAR BEERS:
Kösslarner Köss Vollbier (4.2%)
Kösslarner Pils (4.2%)
Kösslarner Weiße (4.6%)
SEASONAL BEER:
Kösslarner Weizenbock (5.8%)

Small brewery which also brews some bottom-fermented beers, despite the 'Weiß' in the name. Although the nearest station is Bayerbach, 6km away, if you want to come by bus you'll need to go to either Pocking or Simbach.

🍺 **Weißbräu**
Marktplatz 23, 94149 Kößlarn
Closed Tue; Wed–Mon 09.00–24.00; rooms available
DB Pocking 18km, Simbach (Inn) 21km

KÖTTENSDORF (Scheßlitz) 334

Hoh

Köttensdorf 4, 96110 Scheßlitz-Köttensdorf
T 09542 627   **E** brauereihoh@freenet.de
Owner: Johannes Seeber   Founded: 1778
Output: 800hl   Availability: 1 pub
REGULAR BEER:
Hoh Lagerbier

Brewpub in a small village south of Scheßlitz.
There's no bus service to Köttensdorf. but
Straßgeich, which is served by various buses
from Bamberg, is only a mile away.

🍺 **Hoh**
Köttensdorf 4, 96110 Scheßlitz-Köttensdorf
Closed Wed; Thu, Fri, Mon & Tue from 15.30,
Sat from 15.00, Sun from 14.00
DB Bamberg 14km

KÖTZTING 335

Lindner-Bräu

Brauerei Heinrich Kolbeck
Weißenregener Straße 4, 93444 Kötzting
T 09941 14 29   **F** 09941 900 74
Owner: Heinrich Kolbeck   Founded: 1870
Output: 3,000hl
REGULAR BEERS:
Lindner-Bräu Kaitersberg Dunkel (5%)
Lindner-Bräu Kaitersberg Exportbier (5%)
SEASONAL BEERS:
Lindner-Bräu Festbier (5.5%), **Lindner-Bräu
Maibock, Lindner-Bräu Weihnachts-Bockbier** (7%)

Small brewery and tap south of the town on the
other side of the railway and river, in a layby
next to the main road through the valley.

🍺 **Kolbeck**
Weißenregener Straße 4, 93444 Kötzting
Closed Sun; Mon–Sat 11.00–01.00
DB Kötzting 900m

KRAUTHEIM (Volkach) 336

Düll

Privatbrauerei Friedrich Düll GmbH & Co. KG
Landstraße 4–8, 97332 Volkach-Krautheim
T 09381 5 07   **F** 09381 13 37

www.krautheimer.com
Owner: Friedrich Düll   Founded: 1654
Output: 30,000hl
REGULAR BEERS:
Krautheimer Light (2.9%)
Krautheimer Helles (4.9%)
Krautheimer Pilsner (5%)
Krautheimer Weißbier (5%)
Krautheimer Weißbier Dunkel (5%)
Krautheimer Urtyp-Dunkel (5.4%)
Krautheimer Landmärzen (5.6%)
SEASONAL BEERS:
Krautheimer Weihnachtsbier (5.6%),
Krautheimer Heller Bock (7.2%),
Krautheimer Dunkler Doppelbock (7.8%)

Large village brewery that apparently has plans
for a brewery tap. It's only possible to get to
Krautheim by bus on a weekday and at least
one change is required if you're using the train
for part of your journey.
DB Seligenstadt 15km, Schweinfurt 20km

KREUZBERG (Bischofsheim) 337

Klosterbrauerei

Klosterbrauerei Kreuzberg/Rhön
Kreuzberg 2, 97653 Bischofsheim-Kreuzberg
T 09772 9 12 40   **F** 09772 91 24 45
www.kreuzbergbier.de
Owner: Bayrische Franziskanerprovinz
Founded: 1731   Output: 6,000hl
REGULAR BEERS:
Kreuzberger Klosterbier Dunkel (5.4%)
Kreuzberger Klosterbier Pils (5.6%)
SEASONAL BEERS:
Kreuzberger Klosterbier Hefe-Weizen (5.6%),
Kreuzberger Klosterbier Weihnachtsbock (7.6%)

A genuine monastic brewery, owned by the
Franciscan Order, with the beer still brewed by
monks. The only public transport to Kreuzberg
is the seasonal Hochrhönbus (No. 8260) which
runs on Sundays and holidays from May to early
October, connecting out of trains at Bad
Neustadt and Gersfeld.

🍺 **Klosterschenke**
Kreuzberg 2, 97653 Bischofsheim-Kreuzberg
Nov–mid Dec closed. Mid-Dec–Oct daily
08.00–20.00; rooms available
DB Gersfeld 16km, Bad Neustadt 25km

KREUZWERTHEIM   338

Spessart

Spessart-Brauerei GmbH
Junkergasse 2, 97892 Kreuzwertheim
T 09342 857 00   **F** 09342 85 70 40
www.spessart-specht.de
Founded: 1887
REGULAR BEERS:
Spessart Schwarzer Specht (4.5%)
Spessart Premium Specht (4.9%)
Spessart Edel-Export (4.9%)
Spessart Hefe-Weizen Hell (4.9%)
Spessart Hefe-Weizen Dunkel (4.9%)
Spessart Weizen Kristall (4.9%)
Spessart Märzen Gold-Specht (5.2%)
SEASONAL BEER:
Spessart Jubilator (7%)

Specht, meaning woodpecker, is the bird that
originally gave the mountainous Spessart region
its name. The brewery and nearby tap are directly
opposite Wertheim station on the other side of
the river Main, around 400m away as the crow –
or the woodpecker – flies. Sadly, the beer nut
without a car will either have to trudge the 2km
or so via the river bridge, or catch a bus.

🍺 **Zum Stern**
Hauptstraße 22, 97892 Kreuzwertheim
T/F 09342 85 79 17
Closed Tue; Wed from 17.00,
Thu–Mon 11.00–14.00 & from 17.00
DB Wertheim 2km

KRONACH   339

Kaiserhof

Brauerei Kaiserhof Gebr. Kaiser GmbH & Co. KG
Friesener Straße 1, 96317 Kronach
T 09261 62 80 00   **F** 09261 62 80 08
www.kaiserhofbraeu.de
Owners: the Kaiser family   Founded: 1879
Output: 10,000hl   Availability: 30 pubs
REGULAR BEERS:
Kaiserhof Lucas Cranach Lagerbier (4.5%)
Kaiserhof Kellerbier (4.5%)
Kaiserhof Schmäußbräu (4.5%)
Kaiserhof Pilsner (4.8%)
Kaiserhof Schwedentrunk Dunkel (5.2%)

Kaiserhof Weisser Kaiser (5.3%)
Kaiserhof Schwarzer Kaiser (5.3%)
SEASONAL BEERS:
Kaiserhof Schützenfestbier (5.2%), **Kaiserhof
Festbier** (5.2%), **Kaiserhof Kronator** (7.5%)

The brewery is behind the tap in the centre of
Kronach, one of Franconia's most attractive
towns.

🍺 **Kaiserhof**
Friesener Straße 1, 96317 Kronach
T/F 09261 10 48
Closed Mon; Tue–Sun 10.00–14.00 & 17.00–24.00
DB Kronach 700m

KRONBURG   340

Kronburger

Brauerei Schweighart – Kronburger Bier
Hauptstraße 21, 87758 Kronburg
T 08394 237   **F** 08394 16 43
www.brauerei-kronburg.de
Owner: Florian Schweighart   Founded: 1891
Availability: 5 pubs
REGULAR BEERS:
Kronburger Pils (4.9%)
Kronburger Hell (5%)
Kronburger Zwickelbier (5%)
Kronburger Dunkel (5%)
Kronburger Hefeweissbier Hell (5.5%)
SEASONAL BEERS:
Kronburger Spezial (Fest-/Weihnachtsbier),
Kronburger Bock (7%, winter)

Small brewery and tap in the centre of the village.
Although there are two direct buses from
Memmingen on weekday lunchtimes, getting
back is a bit of a challenge.

🍺 **Zur Krone**
Hauptstraße 21, 87758 Kronburg
Closed Mon & Tue; Wed–Sun 10.30–22.30
DB Memmingen 12km

KÜHBACH   341

Kühbach

Brauerei Kühbach Freiherr von Beck-Peccoz
Grosshausener Straße 2, 86556 Kühbach
T 08251 896 60   **F** 08251 89 66 99
www.brauereikuehbach.de

Owner: Frederico Freiherr von Beck-Peccoz
Founded: 1862   Output: 25,000hl
Availability: 70 pubs
REGULAR BEERS:
Kühbacher Schloß-Weizen Leicht (3.3%)
Kühbacher Lager (4.8%)
Kühbacher Hell (5%)
Kühbacher Pils (5%)
Kühbacher X-Weizen (5.3%)
Kühbacher Export (5.5%)
Kühbacher Josefi Bier (5.5%)
Kühbacher Schloß-Weizen Hell (5.5%)
Kühbacher Schloß-Weizen Dunkel (5.5%)
SEASONAL BEERS:
Kühbacher Festbier (5.8%),
Kühbacher Peccator Doppelbock (7%)

The tap only opens in fine weather during the summer but the brewery have recommended Peterhof as an alternative. Bus No. 241 runs from Aichach on weekdays and there's an AST taxi service evenings and weekend.

🍽 **Biergarten im Schloßpark**
Grosshausener Straße 3, 86556 Kühbach
T 08251 87 17 57
Oct–Apr: closed. May–Sep: Sat from 12.00,
Sun & hols from 10.00, Mon–Fri from 16.00
DB Aichach 6km

🍽 **Peterhof**
Aichacher Straße 3, 86556 Kühbach
T 08251 34 88
Closed Mon; Tue–Sun from 11.00
DB Aichach 6km

KULMBACH   342

Bayerisches Brauereimuseum
Hofer Straße 20, 95326 Kulmbach
T 09221 805 14   **F** 09221 805 15
www.bayerisches-brauereimuseum.de
Founded: 2002
Output: 500hl   Availability: 1 pub
REGULAR BEER:
Brauereimuseum Museumsbier (5.5%)
SEASONAL BEERS:
Brauereimuseum Gartenweizen (5.3%)
Brauereimuseum Lebkuchenbier (5.3%)
Brauereimuseum Erntedank-Bier (5.5%)
Brauereimuseum Osterfestmärzen (5.5%)
Brauereimuseum Heller Bock (7.5%)

Museum and brewery at the former Mönchshof site, featuring Germany's only glass brewing kettles. The museum is open until 17.00 and the beers are sold in the Mönchshof Bräuhaus.

🍽 **Mönchshof Bräuhaus**
Hofer Straße 20, 95326 Kulmbach
T 09221 805 18
Closed Mon; Tue–Sun from 10.00
DB Kulmbach 1.5km

Kulmbacher
Kulmbacher Brauerei AG
Lichtenfelser Straße 9, 95326 Kulmbach
T 09221 70 50   **F** 09221 70 52 92
www.kulmbacher.de
Owner: Brau Holding International, München
Founded: 1846   Output: 2,100,000hl
EKU BEERS:
EKU Hell (4.9%), **EKU Pils** (4.9%),
EKU Export (5.4%), **EKU 28** (11%)
SEASONAL BEER:
EKU Festbier (5.6%)
KULMBACHER BEERS:
Kulmbacher Leicht (2.9%), **Kulmbacher Lager
Hell** (4.9%), **Kulmbacher Gold** (4.9%),
Kulmbacher Edelherb Premium Pils (4.9%),
Kulmbacher Feinmild (4.9%), **Kulmbacher
Export** (5.4%)
SEASONAL BEERS:
Kulmbacher Festbier (5.6%),
Kulmbacher Eisbock (9.2%)
KAPUZINER BEERS:
Kapuziner Weißbier-Leicht (3.1%), **Kapuziner
Weißbier** (5.4%), **Kapuziner Weißbier-Schwarz**
(5.4%), **Kapuziner Kristall-Weizen** (5.4%)
SEASONAL BEER:
Kapuziner Winter Weißbier (5.4%)
MÖNCHSHOF BEERS:
Mönchshof Urtypisches Schwarzbier (4.9%),
Mönchshof Lager (4.9%),
Mönchshof Original (4.9%),
Mönchshof Kellerbier (5.4%),
Mönchshof Maingold Landbier (5.4%),
Mönchshof Bockbier (6.9%)
SEASONAL BEER:
Mönchshof Weihnachtsbier (5.6%)

Franconia's largest brewery was formed in 1996 when Reichelbräu took over EKU, having already swallowed Sandlerbräu and Mönchshof. We think all beers are now brewed in the former Reichelbräu plant.

🍺 Mönchshof Bräuhaus
Hofer Straße 20, 95326 Kulmbach
T 09221 805 18
Closed Mon; Tue–Sun from 10.00
[DB] Kulmbach 1.5km

Kommunbräu

Kulmbacher Kommunbräu e.G.
Grünwehr 17, 95326 Kulmbach
T 09221 844 90   **F** 09221 45 66
www.kommunbraeu.de
Owners: Peter & Sonja Stübinger
Founded: 1994   Output: 1,000hl
Availability: 1 pub
REGULAR BEERS:
Kommunbräu Hell (4.9%)
Kommunbräu Bernstein (4.9%)
SEASONAL BEERS:
Kommunbräu Sommerbier (4.5%, Jun–Aug),
Kommunbräu Schutt-und-Asche (4.9%, Feb),
Kommunbräu Schwarze Tinte (4.9%, Mar),
Kommunbräu Hexenbier (4.9%, April),
Kommunbräu Brezenbier (5.5%, Jan & Oct),
Kommunbräu Kerwa-Bier (5.6%, Sep),
Kommunbräu Deflorator (7.1%, May),
Kommunbräu Delirium (7.4%, Dec)

Brewpub to the west of the town centre, below
the castle. The beers have adventurous names
such as 'Rubble and Ash' or 'Black Ink'. They also
have a small distillery.

🍺 Kommunbräu
Grünwehr 17, 95326 Kulmbach
Closed Tue; Wed–Mon 10.00–24.00
[DB] Kulmbach 900m

KUTZENHAUSEN 343

Rapp

Brauerei Rapp KG Brauerei und
Mineralbrunnen
Augsburger Straße 14, 86500 Kutzenhausen
T 08238 30 90   **F** 08238 30 92 00
www.brauerei-rapp.de
Owners: the Rapp family   Founded: 1893
REGULAR BEERS:
Rappen Leicht (3%)
Rappen Leichte Weisse (3%)
Rappen Pilsner (4.5%)
Rappen Lager (4.9%)
Rappen Hell (5%)
Rappen Pils (5%)
Rappen Weisse (5.5%)
Rappen Dunkle Weisse (5.5%)
Rappen Weizen (5.5%)
Rappen Export (5.5%)
Rappen Märzen (5.5%)
Rappen 1893 Dunkel (5.5%)
SEASONAL BEERS:
Rappen Fest (5.5%), **Rappen Weihnachtsbock**
(7%), **Rappen Rappiator**

Brewery that also produces mineral water and
soft drinks. The total annual output is around
1,000,000hl but we think only a small fraction of
that is beer. We're not aware of any brewery tap.
[DB] Kutzenhausen 1.1km

LAABER 344

Plank

Privatbrauerei Michael Plank
Marktplatz 1, 93164 Laaber
T 09498 87 07   **F** 09498 86 87
www.brauerei-plank.de
Owners: Maria & Michael Plank
Founded: 1617   Output: 5,000hl
REGULAR BEERS:
Plank Hefeweizen Leicht (2.9%)
Plank Helles Lager (4.9%)
Plank Red Lion (5%)
Plank Hadmar Export (5%)
Plank Weizen (5%)
SEASONAL BEER:
Plank Weizenbock (7.5%)

Brewery and tap in the centre of Laaber, close
to the river of the same name. The beers are
available in a few other pubs locally.

🍺 Plank
Marktplatz 1, 93164 Laaber
Closed Wed; Thu–Tue 10.00–01.00
[DB] Laaber 950m

LANDAU an der Isar 345

Krieger

Brauerei Wilhelm Krieger e.K.
Hauptstraße 88, 94405 Landau/Isar
T 09951 981 10   **F** 09951 98 11 22

Right: *Domstrasse, Bamberg*

www.brauerei-krieger.de
Owner: Helene Sturm
Founded: 1804
Output: 20,000hl
Availability: 60 pubs
REGULAR BEERS:
Krieger Isartaler Leichtes Weiße (2.9%)
Krieger Hell (4.8%)
Krieger Pils (4.9%)
Krieger Weissbier (5.3%)
Krieger Weissbier Dunkel (5.3%)
Krieger Ludwig der Kelheimer Dunkel (5.4%)
SEASONAL BEER:
Krieger Festbier (5.4%)

Situated in the old town south of the river Isar, Krieger's brewery features a small museum in the former maltings. The brewery tap is next door.

🍺 Zur Post
Hauptstraße 86, 94405 Landau/Isar
T 09951 594 41
Closed Mon; Tue–Sun 11.00–14.00 & 18.00–24.00; rooms available
DB Landau (Isar) 1.5km

LANDSHUT 346

Landshuter Brauhaus

Landshuter Brauhaus Koller-Fleischmann AG
Pulverturmstraße 2a, 84028 Landshut
T 0871 92 39 40   **F** 0871 923 94 29
www.landshuter-brauhaus.de
Founded: 1493
REGULAR BEERS:
Landshuter Brauhaus Leichte Weisse (2.7%)
Landshuter Brauhaus Premium Light (2.9%)
Landshuter Brauhaus Dunkel (4.4%)
Landshuter Brauhaus Hell (4.8%)
Landshuter Brauhaus Edelhell (4.8%)
Landshuter Brauhaus Hefe-Weisse (5%)
Landshuter Brauhaus Dunkle Weisse (5%)
Landshuter Brauhaus Hochzeits-Weisse (5.6%)
SEASONAL BEERS:
Landshuter Brauhaus Koller's Klassik (5.3%),
Landshuter Brauhaus Ostersud (5.3%),
Landshuter Brauhaus Hochzeits-Bier (5.3%),
Landshuter Brauhaus Festbier 2000 (5.3%),
Landshuter Brauhaus Prädikator (8%)

The brewery was formed in 1923 when Koller and Fleischmann breweries merged. Ainmiller is the former Fleischmann brewery and tap.

🍺 Ainmiller
Altstadt 195–197, 84028 Landshut
T 0871 211 63   **F** 0871 276 22 58
Closed Mon; Tue–Fri 11.00–14.00 & 17.30–24.00, Sat 10.00–24.00, Sun 11.00–14.00
DB Landshut Süd 1.9km, Hbf 2km

Wittmann

Brauerei Carl Wittmann OHG
Brewery: Bachstraße 12, 84036 Landshut
T 0871 94 30 60   **F** 0871 943 06 45
Office: Ländgasse 50, 84028 Landshut
T 0871 92 59 20   **F** 0871 925 92 50
www.brauerei-wittmann.de
Founded: 1616
REGULAR BEERS:
Wittmann 2,9 Medium (2.9%)
Wittmann Leichte Weisse (2.9%)
Wittmann Urhell (4.9%)
Wittmann Lager (4.9%)
Wittmann Premium Extra Pils (4.9%)
Carl Wittmann Dunkel (5%)
Wittmann Hefe-Weisse (5.3%)
Wittmann Schwarz-Weisse (5.3%)
SEASONAL BEERS:
Wittmann Dult-Bier (5.5%),
Wittmann Weihnachtsfestbier (5.5%),
Wittmann Ergolator (7.5%)

Medium-sized brewery near Landshut-Süd station. The tap is a couple of hundred metres away and the brewery offices are in the centre of the old town.

🍺 Zollhaus
Äußere Münchener Straße 83, 84036 Landshut
T 0871 439 10
Closed Wed; Thu–Tue 10.00–24.00
DB Landshut Süd 700m, Hbf 2.7km

LARSBACH (Wolnzach) 347

Lampl-Bräu

Bründlweg 1, 85283 Wolnzach-Larsbach
T 08442 20 68   **F** 08442 49 48
Owner: Gerhard Stanglmayr   Founded: 1998
Output: 400hl   Availability: 4 pubs
REGULAR BEERS:
Lampl-Bräu Hopfenzupferbier (4.9%)
Lampl-Bräu Lamperl-Pils (4.9%)
Lampl-Bräu Larsbacher Weiße (5%)

SEASONAL BEER:
Lampl-Bräu Nikolator

Microbrewery in the centre of Larsbach which, as far as we know, doesn't have a tap of its own but does supply four pubs. We don't think there are any bus services within 3km of the village.

DB Rohrbach (Ilm) 10km

LAUF an der Pegnitz   348

Dreykorn

Dreykorn Bräu KG
Mauergasse 9–13, 91207 Lauf/Pegnitz
T 09123 24 24   **F** 09123 835 59
Owner: Friedrich Vogel   Founded: 1831
Output: 8,000hl   Availability: 50 pubs
REGULAR BEERS:
Dreykorn Hell (4.8%)
Dreykorn Dunkel (4.8%)
Dreykorn Weissbier Hell (4.9%)
Dreykorn Weissbier Dunkel (4.9%)
Dreykorn Pils (5.2%)
SEASONAL BEERS:
Dreykorn Weihnachtsbier (5.5%),
Dreykorn St. Kunigunden Festbier(5.8%),
Dreykorn Bock (7%)

Brewery in the centre of town, behind the market square. Although there's no official tap, the beers are widely available in the town.

DB Lauf (rechts) 250m, Lauf (links) 900m

Simon

Weissbierbrauerei Simon KG
Heroldstraße 12, 91207 Lauf/Pegnitz
T 09123 23 23   **F** 09123 23 28
www.brauerei-simon.de
Owner: Kaiser-Bräu, Neuhaus
Founded: 1875
Output: 15,000hl
REGULAR BEERS:
Simon Erstes Laufer Weißbier Leicht (3.2%)
Simon Erstes Laufer Weißbier (5.2%)
SEASONAL BEER:
Simon Die Schwarze Kuni Weizenbock (7%)

Franconia's sole wheat beer-only brewery is on the opposite side of the railway from the town centre. The brewery tap doubles as an Italian restaurant and is very close to the Dreykorn brewery.

🍴 **Bräustübla La Trattoria da Carmelo**
Faulkner Straße 2, 91207 Lauf/Pegnitz
T 09123 31 34
Closed Mon; Tue–Sun 11.00–15.00 & 17.00–24.00
DB Lauf (rechts) 270m, Lauf (links) 900m

LAUINGEN (Donau)   349

Hirschbrauerei Schwarz

Hirschbrauerei Lauingen Schwarz KG
Herzog-Georg-Straße 30, 89415 Lauingen
T 09072 45 56   **E** brauerei.schwarz@aol.com
Owner: Herbert Schwarz   Founded: 1635
REGULAR BEERS:
Lauinger Hell
Lauinger Kellerbier
Lauinger Export
Lauinger Weizen
Lauinger Märzen Gold

Brewery on the main street, not far from the Danube. The brewery tap, whose name means 'Lucky Star', is a Chinese restaurant.

🍴 **Glücksstern**
Herzog-Georg-Straße 30, 89415 Lauingen
T 09072 39 11
Closed Mon; Tue–Sun 11.00–14.30 & 18.00–24.00
DB Lauingen 800m

LAUTERBACH (Buttenwiesen) 350

Lauterbach

Privatbrauerei Lauterbach Ehnle GmbH & Co KG
Badstraße 2–5, 86647 Buttenwiesen-Lauterbach
T 08274 99 79 50   **F** 08274 997 95 50
www.lauterbacher.de
Owner: Ludwig Ehnle   Founded: 1651
Output: 50,000hl   Availability: c. 85 pubs
REGULAR BEERS:
Lauterbacher Schlanke Weisse (2.7%)
Lauterbacher Pilsener (4.7%)
Lauterbacher Urtyp (4.8%)
Lauterbacher Kristall Weisse (5.1%)
Lauterbacher Brotzeit-Bier (5.2%)
Lauterbacher Keller-Bier (5.2%)
Lauterbacher Hefe Weisse (5.3%)
Lauterbacher Sautter's Hofbier (5.4%)
Lauterbacher Anno 1651 (5.5%)
Lauterbacher Helles Export (5.5%)

Lauterbacher Georg Bader Dunkel (5.5%)
Lauterbacher Stephani Weisse (5.5%)
Lauterbacher Bayrischer Haisl (5.5%)
SEASONAL BEERS:
Lauterbacher Festbier (6%, Oct–Dec),
Lauterbacher Weißer Bock (7.1%),
Gut Mergenthauer Dunkler Doppelbock (8.9%)

Regional brewery in a village south-west of
Donauwörth. The brewery tap is nearby, close to
the old railway station. Bus No. 405 runs from
Mertingen Bahnhof on weekdays.

🍎 **Brauereigaststätte**
Bahnhofstraße 16, 86647 Buttenwiesen-
Lauterbach
T 08274 69 18 59   **F** 08274 69 13 65
Daily from 11.00; rooms available
DB Mertingen Bahnhof 8km

LEINBURG   351

Bub
Marktplatz 14, 91227 Leinburg
T 09120 204   **F** 09120 83 40
www.leinburger-bier.de
Owner: Ernst Bub   Founded: 1617
Output: 10,000hl   Availability: 30 pubs
REGULAR BEERS:
Leinburger Hell (4.7%)
Leinburger Lager (4.8%)
Leinburger Pils (5%)
Leinburger Dunkel (5.2%)
Leinburger Weißbier (5.2%)
SEASONAL BEER:
Leinburger Festbier (5.4%, Christmas)

The oldest brewery in the Nürnberg area is
situated in the small town of Leinburg. There
are two pubs at the brewery. Bus No. 331 runs
daily from Röthenbach station.

🍎 **Bei Belle**
Marktplatz 14, 91227 Leinburg
T 09120 98 02
Closed Wed; Thu–Sat, Mon & Tue from 16.00,
Sun from 11.00
DB Röthenbach (Pegnitz) 7km

🍎 **Braugewölbe**
Marktplatz 14, 91227 Leinburg
T 09120 66 45
Closed Mon; Tue–Sat from 16.00, Sun from 11.00
DB Röthenbach (Pegnitz) 7km

LEIPHEIM   352

Hirschbräu Gaissmaier
Ulmer Straße 1, 89340 Leipheim
T 08221 714 11   **F** 08221 76 32
Owner: Anna Gaissmaier
Founded: 2003
Output: 1,500hl
Availability: 1 pub
REGULAR BEERS:
Hirschbräu Naturtrüb Hell (5.1%)
Hirschbräu Weizen (5.1%)
Hirschbräu Naturtrüb Dunkel (5.3%)
SEASONAL BEER:
Hirschbräu Dunkler Bock (6.7%)

This brewery was revived in 2003, the original
one dating from 1661 having closed in 1986.
Hirschbräu remains in the hands of the same
family who owned the first incarnation. One for
those who like a beer before breakfast.

🍎 **Hirschbräu**
Ulmer Straße 1, 89340 Leipheim
Daily 06.00–24.00; rooms available
DB Leipheim 250m

LEMBACH (Eltmann)   353

Thein
Steinhauser Straße 28, 97483 Eltmann-Lembach
T 09549 391
Owner: Leo Thein
Founded: 1866
Output: 2,000hl
REGULAR BEERS:
Thein-Bräu Lager
Thein-Bräu Dunkel
Thein-Bräu Pils
SEASONAL BEER:
Thein-Bräu Festbier

Small brewery and tap in the equally small
village of Lembach. Bus No. 8180 runs a few
times a day from Eltmann on weekdays.

🍎 **Thein**
Steinhauser Straße 28, 97483 Eltmann-Lembach
Closed Mon & Tue; Wed–Sun 09.00–23.00
DB Ebelsbach-Eltmann 9km

LENGENFELD (Velburg) 354

Winkler

Winkler Bräu GmbH & Co. KG
St. Martin Straße 6, 92355 Velburg-Lengenfeld
T 09182 170   **F** 09182 171 10
www.winkler-braeu.de
Owner: Hans Konrad Winkler & Georg Böhm
Founded: before 1628   Output: 7,000hl
Availability: 32 pubs
REGULAR BEERS:
Winkler-Bräu Pils (4.7%)
Winkler-Bräu Hefe-Pils (4.7%)
Winkler-Bräu Hell (4.9%),
Winkler-Bräu Export (5.1%)
Winkler-Bräu Martini-Trunk (5.2%)
Winkler-Bräu Kupfer-Spezial (5.4%)
SEASONAL BEER:
Winkler-Bräu Lengenfelder Glühbier (4%)
FOR ZUM HIRSCHEN, PARSBERG:
Hirschen's Keller-Pils (4.7%),
Hirschen's Blobb-Bier (5.2%)

Village brewery with a large tap and hotel
attached. Lengenfeld is very close to junction
93 of the A3. On weekdays buses No. 513 runs
from Neumarkt, No. 542 from Parsberg.

🍺 Winkler
St. Martin Straße 6, 92355 Velburg-Lengenfeld
Sun & hols 08.00–21.00, Mon–Sat 08.00–23.00;
rooms available
DB Parsberg 13km, Neumarkt (Oberpfalz) 16km

LEUPS (Pegnitz) 355

Gradl

Leups 6, 91257 Pegnitz-Leups
T 09246 247   **E** brauerei-gradl@gmx.de
Owner: Hans Wolfring   Founded: 1683
Output: 1,500hl   Availability: 3 pubs
REGULAR BEERS:
Leupser Dunkel (4.9%)
Leupser Pils (4.9%)
SEASONAL BEER:
Leupser Bock (May & Christmas)

Small brewery that supplies just two other pubs
in addition to the tap. Bus No. 388 runs from
Pegnitz once in the late afternoon, but the only
bus of the day back leaves Leups early morning!

🍺 Gradl
Leups 6, 91257 Pegnitz-Leups
Closed Tue; Wed–Mon 09.00–23.00.
DB Pegnitz 8km

LEUTENBACH 356

Drummer

Dorfstraße 10, 91359 Leutenbach
T 09199 403   **F** 09199 87 20
E brauerei.drummer@walberla.de
Owner: Peter Drummer   Founded: 1763
Output: 1,000hl   Availability: 1 pub
REGULAR BEER:
Drummer Dunkles Vollbier (4.8%)

Brewpub in a village on the edge of the Veldensteiner Forest. Bus No. 223 runs from Forchheim
station via Wiesenthau on weekdays.

🍺 Drummer
Dorfstraße 10, 91359 Leutenbach
Closed Mon; Tue–Sun 11.00–24.00; rooms
available
DB Wiesenthau 4.2km, Forchheim 10km

LEUTERSCHACH
(Marktoberdorf) 357

Allgäuer Brauhaus

Brewery: Schwendener Straße 18, 87616
Marktoberdorf-Leuterschach
T 08342 964 70   **F** 08342 964 72 70
Office: Beethovenstraße 18, 87435 Kempten
T 0831 205 00   **F** 0831 205 01 14
www.allgaeuer-brauhaus.de
Owner: Oetker Gruppe AG
Founded: 1394
Output: 400,000hl
REGULAR BEERS:
Allgäuer Brauhaus Fürstabt Weizen Leicht (2.9%)
Allgäuer Brauhaus Bayrisch Hell (4.7%)
Allgäuer Brauhaus 1394 Premium Lager (4.7%)
Allgäuer Brauhaus Teutsch Pils (4.8%)
Allgäuer Brauhaus Urbairisch Dunkel (5%)
Allgäuer Brauhaus Fürstabt Hefeweizen (5%)
Allgäuer Brauhaus Alt Kemptener Weisse (5%)
Allgäuer Brauhaus Fürstabt Kristallweizen (5%)
Allgäuer Brauhaus Urtyp Export (5.3%)
Allgäuer Brauhaus Büble Bier (5.5%)

SEASONAL BEERS:
Allgäuer Brauhaus Zwickel Naturtrüb (5%),
Allgäuer Brauhaus Allgäuer Jagdbier (5.5%),
Allgäuer Brauhaus Festbier (5.5%),
Allgäuer Brauhaus Winterfestbier (5.5%),
Allgäuer Brauhaus St. Magnus Heller Bock (7%),
Allgäuer Brauhaus Stifts-Weizenbock (7%),
Allgäuer Brauhaus Cambonator (7.2%)
ALTENMÜNSTER BEERS:
Altenmünster Hopfig Herb (4.9%),
Altenmünster Metzgerbier (4.9%),
Altenmünster Urig Würzig (4.9%),
Altenmünster Franz Joseph Jubelbier (5.5%)
SEASONAL BEERS:
Altenmünster Winterbier (5.5%),
Altenmünster Maibock (7.5%)

Allgäuer Brauhaus took over Sailerbräu (which also owned Kronenbrauerei Altenmünster) in 2003, and production of all Altenmünster beers was moved to Leuterschach. During 2004 and early 2005 Altenmünster beers were brewed in Kempten while the Leuterschach brewery was upgraded. In June 2005 Allgäuer Brauhaus in Kempten ceased brewing, all production moving to Leuterschach.

🍺 Zum Stift
Stiftsplatz 1, 87439 Kempten
T 0831 223 88   **F** 0831 512 15 54
Daily 10.00–01.00
DB Kempten-Ost 1.8km, Kempten Hbf 2km

LICHTENAU   358

Hauff-Bräu
Hauff-Bräu Lichtenau R. Weid KG
Hindenburgplatz 1, 91586 Lichtenau
T 09827 923 30   **F** 09827 92 33 33
www.hauff-braeu.de
Founded: 1489
Output: 60,000hl   Availability: c.250 pubs
REGULAR BEERS:
Hauff Urhell (4.7%)
Hauff Pils (5.1%)
Hauff Lichtenauer Weissbier (5.3%)
Hauff Klares Weizen (5.3%)
Hauff Frankenländer Landbier (5.3%)
Hauff Frankenländer Schwarzbier (5.3%)
Hauff Gold (5.6%).
SEASONAL BEER:
Hauff Festbier (5.6%)

Large regional brewery in the southern part of the town. No tap, but the beers are widely available in Lichtenau. Bus No. 711 runs from Ansbach on weekdays plus Saturday mornings. Sachsen station is only 3km away if you fancy the walk.
DB Sachsen 3km, Ansbach 9km

LICHTENBERG   359

Sonnenbräu
Nailaer Straße 20, 95192 Lichtenberg
T 09288 304   **F** 09288 92 46 25
Owner: Barbara Trier   Founded: 1765
Output: 2,500hl
REGULAR BEERS:
Sonnenbräu Sonnengold Pils (5%)
Sonnenbräu Hopfenperle Pils (5%)
Sonnenbräu Raubritter Dunkel (5%)
Sonnenbräu Sonnenweisse (5%)
Sonnenbräu Schloßherrn Export (5.5%)
Sonnenbräu Bayerisches Märzen (5.5%)
SEASONAL BEER:
Sonnenbräu Sonnengold Bockbier (6%)

The brewery has family connections with Schloßbrauerei Schwarzbach, and both brew beers with the same name, but they are run independently. Several bus routes run from Bad Steben on weekdays, No. 167 continuing through to Blankenstein in Thüringen.

🍺 Zur Sonne
Marktplatz 25, 95192 Lichtenberg
T 09288 95 79 85
Daily 09.00–14.00 & from 17.30
DB Bad Steben 2.9km, Blankenstein 3.3km

LINDENHARDT (Creußen) 360

Kürzdörfer
Brauerei-Gaststätte Heinrich Kürzdörfer
Lindenhardt 16, 95473 Creußen-Lindenhardt
T 09246 714   **F** 09246 98 91 55
www.brauerei-kuerzdoerfer.de
Owner: Heinrich Kürzdorfer   Founded: 1865
Output: 1,000hl   Availability: 1 pub
REGULAR BEERS:
Kürzdörfer Lindenhardter Landbier-Hell
Kürzdörfer Lindenhardter Vollbier-Dunkel

SEASONAL BEER:

Kürzdörfer Lindenhardter Bockbier (winter)

Brewpub in a small village west of Creußen with poor public transport connections. There's a bus from both Pegnitz and Bayreuth each weekday evening, plus a couple of ASTs from Creußen, and that's about it. Schnabelwaid station is a 6km walk if you feel up to it.

⚑ Kürzdörfer

Lindenhardt 16, 95473 Creußen-Lindenhardt
Closed Mon; Tue–Sat 11.00–23.00,Sun & hols 10.00–23.00
DB Creussen (Oberfranken) 8km

LOFFELD (Bad Staffelstein)　361

Staffelberg-Bräu

Mühlteich 4, 96231 Bad Staffelstein-Loffeld
T 09573 59 25　**F** 09573 317 05
www.staffelberg-braeu.de
Owners: the Geldner & Wehrfritz families
Founded: 1856　Output: 15,000hl
REGULAR BEERS:

Staffelberg-Bräu Hopfen-Gold Pils (4.7%)
Staffelberg-Bräu Landbier-Hell (5%)
Staffelberg-Bräu Loffelder-Dunkel (5%)
Staffelberg-Bräu Hefe-Weißbier (5.2%)
Staffelberg-Bräu Märzen (5.5%)
SEASONAL BEERS:

Staffelberg-Bräu Festbier (5.5%),
Staffelberg-Bräu Maibock (6.5%),
Staffelberg-Bräu Doppel-Bock (7%)

Attractive half-timbered brewery and tap on the edge of the small village. Buses run daily from Bad Staffelstein.

⚑ Bräustübl

Mühlteich 4, 96231 Bad Staffelstein-Loffeld
Closed Mon; Tue–Sun 10.00–22.00
DB Bad Staffelstein 4km

LOH (Dorfen)　362

Bräu z'Loh

Loh 7, 84405 Dorfen-Loh
T 08082 442　**F** 08082 84 69
Owner: Nikolaus Lohmeier
Founded: 1928
Availability: 10 pubs

REGULAR BEERS:

Bräu z'Loh Dunkel (4.8%)
Bräu z'Loh Pils (4.9%)
Bräu z'Loh Weißbier (5.1%)
Bräu z'Loh Export-Hell (5.2%)
Bräu z'Loh Märzen (5.6%)
SEASONAL BEER:

Bräu z'Loh Kirta-Bier (5.8%)

Small brewery in a hamlet near Schwindkirchen. It is possible to get to Loh by bus No. 81 in time for opening on Thursday and Friday but there are no buses back the same day.

⚑ Wirt z'Loh

Loh 6, 84405 Dorfen-Loh
T 08082 52 11　**F** 08082 94 94 97
Closed Mon–Wed; Thu–Sat from 18.00,
Sun from 12.00　DB Dorfen Bahnhof 6km

LOHBERG　363

Späth-Bräu

Späth-Bräu GmbH & Co. KG
Pfarrweg 8, 93470 Lohberg
T 09943 944 40　**F** 09942 94 44 29
www.osser-bier.de
Owner: August Späth　Founded: 1861
REGULAR BEERS:

Osser Leichte Weisse
Osser Hell (4.7%)
Osser Pils (4.9%)
Osser Weisse (4.9%)
Osser Gold (5.2%)
SEASONAL BEER:

Osser Weihnachtsbier (Dec)

Brewery in the small town of Lohberg, close to the Czech border. The beers are named after a nearby river. Bus No. 6073 runs from Lam station on weekdays.

⚑ Zur Kegelbahn

Pfarrweg 2, 93470 Lohberg　**T** 09943 569
Closed Mon;Tue–Sun 11.00–22.00　DB Lam 5km

LOHNDORF (Litzendorf)　364

Hölzlein

Ellertalstraße 13, 96123 Litzendorf-Lohndorf
T/F 09505 357
Owner: Heinrich Hölzlein　Founded: 1685

Output: 2,000hl   Availability: 2 pubs
REGULAR BEER:
Hölzlein Vollbier (4.7%)

Brewpub on the main road through the village. One other pub is supplied. Given its proximity to Bamberg, the bus service to Litzendorf is appalling, with just one bus to the village on weekday afternoons when the two brewery taps are open.

🍺 **Hölzlein**
Ellertalstraße 13, 96123 Litzendorf-Lohndorf
Closed Tue; Wed–Fri & Mon 15.00–23.00, Sat & Sun 10.00–23.00   DB Bamberg 11km

Reh

Privatbrauerei Reh OHG
Ellertalstraße 36, 96123 Litzendorf-Lohndorf
T 09505 210   **F** 09505 363
www.reh-bier.de
Owners: Anja & Elmar Reh   Founded: 1901
Output: 10,000hl
REGULAR BEERS:
Reh Landbier Hell (4.6%)
Reh Pils (4.9%)
Reh Ellertaler Zwickel (4.9%)
Reh Ellertaler Weisse (5.2%)
Reh Landbier Dunkel (5.5%)
SEASONAL BEERS:
Reh Bock Hell (7%, Lent),
Reh Bock Dunkel (7.3%, Nov–Jan)

The larger of Lohndorf's two breweries, Reh doesn't have an official tap but we've listed Landgasthof Ellertal as we think it's the only pub in the village that sells their beers.

🍺 **Landgasthof Ellertal**
Lohntalstraße 15, 96123 Litzendorf-Lohndorf
T 09505 922 90   **F** 09505 92 29 50
Closed Mon; Tue–Sat from 16.00, Sun & hols from 11.00; rooms available
DB Bamberg 11km

LOHR am Main   365

Lohrer

Lohrer Bier GmbH
Ludwigstraße 3, 97816 Lohr
T 09352 872 90   **F** 09352 76 99
www.lohrer-bier.de
Owner: Brau Holding International, München

Founded: 1878   Output: 60,000hl
Availability: c.150 pubs
REGULAR BEERS:
Lohrer Light (2.9%)
Lohrer Pils (4.9%)
Lohrer Export (4.9%)
Lohrer Keiler Weißbier Hell (4.9%)
Lohrer Keiler Weißbier Dunkel (4.9%)
Lohrer Winter Keiler (4.9%)
Lohrer Weissbier (4.9%)
Lohrer Schwarze (5.2%)
Lohrer Urtyp 1878 (5.2%)
SEASONAL BEER:
Lohrer Böckle (7%)

Known as Brauerei Stumpf until 2001, when the brewery was taken over by Würzburger Hofbräu. There's talk they don't brew anymore but they've told us they do.

🍺 **Bräustübl**
Alfred-Stumpf-Straße 2, 97816 Lohr
T 09352 73 28
Closed Wed; Thu–Tue 10.00–01.00
DB Lohr Bf 1.4km

LOIFLING (Cham)   366

Hofmark

Hofmark Brauerei Cham Paul Häring KG
Hofmarkstraße 15, 93403 Cham-Loifling
T 09971 33 01   **F** 09971 322 33
www.hofmark-bier.de
Founded: 1590   Availability: c.50 pubs
REGULAR BEERS:
Hofmark Original Hell (5.1%)
Hofmark Premium Pils (5.1%)
Hofmark Pilsner (5.3%)
Hofmark Öko-Pilsener (5.3%)
Hofmark Würzig-Herb (5.3%)
Hofmark Original Export (5.3%)
Hofmark Würzig-Mild (5.6%)
Hofmark Premium Weisse (5.6%)
Hofmark Dunkle Weisse (5.6%)
Hofmark Kristallweizen (5.6%)
SEASONAL BEER:
Hofmark Doppelbock
FOR HARRODS, LONDON:
Harrods 1849 Lager (5.6%)

Village brewery deep in the Bayerischer Wald that also supplies Harrods with their house lager. Confusingly, the postal address has recently changed from 93455 Traitsching-Loifling to 93403 Cham-Loifling. Loifling has no bus service but Nos. 710 and 6098 run on weekdays from Cham to the neighbouring village of Wilting.

🍺 **Zum Hofmark Bräu**
Hofmarkstraße 29, 93403 Cham-Loifling
Daily 09.00–01.00   DB Cham (Oberpfalz) 8km

LUDWIGSSTADT 367

Jahns-Bräu

Christoph Jahn Erben Brauerei Gmbh & Co. KG
Kronacher Straße 22, 96337 Ludwigsstadt
T 09263 990 00   **F** 09263 99 00 44
www.jahns-braeu.de
Founded: 1871   Output: 50,000hl
Availability: c.100 pubs
REGULAR BEERS:
Jahns Christoph's Landbier (4.8%)
Jahns Bräu Christoph's Zwickl-Bier (4.8%)
Jahns Pilsener (4.8%)
Jahns Nortwald Pils (4.8%)
Jahns Christoph's Premium Pils (4.8%)
Jahns Bräu Christoph's Kellergold (5.2%)
Jahns Export (5.2%)
Jahns Bräu Schützenbier (5.2%)
SEASONAL BEERS:
Jahns Festbier (5.4%), Jahns Löwen Bock (6.8%)
FALKENSTEINER BEERS:
Falkensteiner Hefeweizen Gold (5.2%),
Falkensteiner Hefeweizen Dunkel (5.2%)
FOR BURGBRÄU, LAUENSTEIN:
Burgbräu Unser Hell (4.6%),
Burgbräu Pilsener (4.7%)
FOR BRAUEREI LEHESTEN, LEHESTEN:
Lehestener Premium Pilsner (4.8%)

Regional brewery on the southern edge of town. The tap is no longer open but the beers are easily found locally.
DB Ludwigsstadt 1.3km

MAINBURG 368

Ziegler Bräu

Scharfstraße 22, 84048 Mainburg
T 08751 14 70   **F** 08751 55 39
www.ziegler-braeu-mainburg.de
Owner: Hermine Randeltshofer   Founded: 1892
Output: 5,000hl

REGULAR BEERS:
Ziegler Leichte Hopfazupfa Weisse (5.2%)
Ziegler Bräu Lager (4.7%)
Ziegler Bräu Pils (4.8%)
Ziegler Bräu Kellerbier
Ziegler Bräu Premium Hell (5.2%)
Ziegler Bräu Hopfazupfa Weisse (5.2%)
SEASONAL BEERS:
Ziegler Bräu Festbier,
Ziegler Bräu Herminator (6.8%, Lent)

Brewery on the western side of the town centre. The beer garden is around the corner and only opens during spring and summer in fine weather. Bus No. 6018 runs from Abensburg station on weekdays.

🍺 **Biergarten Zieglerbräu**
Kellerstraße 6, 84048 Mainburg
T 08751 58 48   Closed Oct–Apr & in wet weather;
Sun 10.00–23.00, Mon–Sat 16.30–23.00
DB Abensburg 22km

MAISACH 369

Maisach

Brauerei Maisach, Privatbrauerei J. Sedlmayer
Hauptstraße 24, 82216 Maisach
T 08141 39 55 70   **F** 08141 395 57 13
www.brauerei-maisach.de
Owner: Martina Wieser-Sedlmayr
Founded: 1556   Output: 20,000hl
Availability: c.100 pubs
REGULAR BEERS:
Maisacher Leicht (2.9%)
Maisacher Pils (4.8%)
Maisacher Räuber Kneißl Dunkel (5.1%)
Maisacher Kellerbier (5.3%)
Maisacher Perle (5.3%)
Maisacher Sedlmayr Weizen (5.3%)
SEASONAL BEER:
Maisacher Bock

Brewery on the main street with the tap and beer garden attached. Räuber Kneißl Dunkel is named after a local Robin-Hood-like thief who was beheaded in Augsburg in 1902.

🍺 **Bräustüberl Maisach**
Hauptstraße 24, 82216 Maisach
T 08141 942 10   **F** 08141 949 88
Mon–Fri 09.00–22.00, Sat & Sun 09.00–24.00
DB Maisach 800m

MALLERSDORF
(Mallersdorf-Pfaffenberg)   370

Klosterbrauerei

Klosterberg 1, 84066 Mallersdorf-Pfaffenberg/
Pfaffenberg
T 08772 6 91 84   **F** 08772 6 92 43
Founded: 1618
Output: 3,000hl   Availability: 1 pub
REGULAR BEERS:
Klosterbräu Mallersdorf Vollbier Hell (5%)
Klosterbräu Mallersdorf Zoigl Vollbier (5%)
SEASONAL BEERS:
Klosterbräu Mallersdorf Maibock,
Klosterbräu Mallersdorf Weihnachtsbock,
Klosterbräu Mallersdorf Doppelbock

One of only two convent breweries we know of,
the brewer here is Sister Doris. As far as we're
aware the brewery tap is the only pub to sell the
beers. We promise you won't have difficulty
spotting the convent from the station.

🍺 **Klosterbräustüberl**
Klosterberg 1, 84066 Mallersdorf-Pfaffenberg/
Pfaffenberg   **T** 08772 91 54 70
Closed Mon; Tue–Sun 09.00–21.00
DB Mallersdorf 1.3km

MARIAKIRCHEN (Arnstorf)   371

Schlossbräu

Lindner Schlossbräu Mariakirchen GmbH & Co.
Obere Hofmark 31, 94424 Arnstorf-Mariakirchen
T 08723 97 88 99   **F** 08723 97 88 98
www.schlossbraeu-mariakirchen.de
Founded: 2003
Output: 1,000hl   Availability: 1 pub
REGULAR BEERS:
Schlossbräu Mariakirchen Scheps (2.8%)
Schlossbräu Mariakirchen Hell (4.8%)
Schlossbräu Mariakirchen Dunkel (5.2%)
Schlossbräu Mariakirchen Weißbier (5.2%)
SEASONAL BEERS:
Schlossbräu Mariakirchen Festbier (5.8%),
Schlossbräu Mariakirchen Maibock (6.4%),
Schlossbräu Mariakirchen Bock (6.5%)

Brewpub in front of the moated 16th-century
Mariakirchen castle. Brewing started here in
2003 after the previously derelict building had
been renovated. The pub opens earlier on

summer weekends. There's only one bus a day,
weekdays only, and that gets to Mariakirchen
over two hours before opening. Arnstorf has a
better service but it's over 3km away. They may
organise transport for large groups if you phone
in advance.

🍺 **Schlossbräu**
Obere Hofmark 31, 94424 Arnstorf-Mariakirchen
Sun 12.00–23.30, Mon–Sat 16.00–23.30
DB Pfarrkirchen 19km

MARKT SCHWABEN   372

Schweiger

Privatbrauerei Schweiger GmbH & Co. KG
Ebersberger Straße 25, 85570 Markt Schwaben
T 08121 92 90   **F** 08121 929 88
www.schweiger-bier.de
Founded: 1896   Availability: c.500 pubs
REGULAR BEERS:
Schweiger Light Premium (2.9%)
Schweiger Leichte Sport Weisse (2.9%)
Schweiger Premium Pilsener (4.8%)
Schweiger Blond Lager (4.9%)
Schweiger Black Lager (4.9%)
Schweiger Helles Export (5.1%)
Schweiger Alt Bairisch Dunkel (5.1%)
Schweiger Schmankerl Weiße (5.1%)
Schweiger Schmankerl Weiße Dunkel (5.1%)

Brewery on the main road south out of Markt
Schwaben. The brewery tap re-opened in 2002
following several decades out of use. We believe
they may brew beers for the town's Widmann
brewery which closed in 2003.

🍺 **Schweiger**
Ebersberger Straße 26, 85570 Markt Schwaben
T 08121 22 18 15   **F** 08121 22 18 16
Closed Mon; Tue–Fri 11.00–01.00,
Sat 17.00–01.00, Sun & hols 10.00–01.00
DB Markt Schwaben 1km

MARKTHEIDENFELD   373

Martinsbräu

Martinsbräu Georg Mayr GmbH & Co. KG
Georg-Mayr-Straße 4, 97828 Marktheidenfeld
T 09391 500 80   **F** 09391 50 08 57
www.martinsbraeu.de

Founded: 1883   Output: 40,000hl
REGULAR BEERS:
Martin's Leicht (2.9%)
Martin's Hell (4.7%)
Martin's Gans-Bier (4.9%)
Martin's Pils (4.9%)
Martin's Dunkel (5.1%)
Martin's Hefe-Weißbier (5.1%)
Martin's Dunkles Hefe-Weißbier (5.1%)
Martin's Export (5.3%)
Martin's Märzen (5.4%)
SEASONAL BEERS:
Martin's Laurenzi Festbier (5.3%),
Martin's Doppelbock (7.5%)

The tap is in the heart of the old town, the brewery a few hundred metres to the north. Bus No. 8050 runs daily from Lohr station.

🍺 Bräustüble
Mitteltorstraße 1, 97828 Marktheidenfeld
T 09391 12 24   **F** 09391 91 46 25
Closed Thu; Fri–Wed 11.00–14.00 & 17.00–24.00
[DB] Lohr Bahnhof 20km

MARKTREDWITZ 374

Nothhaft
Brauerei Otto Nothhaft
Ottostraße 26–30, 95615 Marktredwitz
T 09231 20 77   **F** 09231 645 20
www.brauerei-nothhaft.de
Owner: Otto Nothhaft   Founded: 1882
Output: 20,000hl   Availability: c.80 pubs
REGULAR BEERS:
Nothhaft Leichtes Schankbier (2.9%)
Nothhaft Rawetzer Weißbier Leicht (3%)
Nothhaft Ur-Hell (4.9%)
Nothhaft Zwickelbier (4,9%)
Nothhaft Aloisius Dunkel (4.9%)
Nothhaft Edel-Pils (5%)
Nothhaft Rawetzer Zoigl (5.4%)
Nothhaft Rawetzer Premium (5.4%)
Nothhaft Rawetzer Weißbier (5.4%)
Nothhaft Rawetzer Weißbier Dunkel (5.4%)
SEASONAL BEER:
Nothhaft Antonius Starkbier (7.5%)

Small regional brewery on the southern side of the town centre with the brewery tap in front. One of several in the area to brew commercial Zoigl.

🍺 Am Strand
Ottostraße 32, 95615 Marktredwitz
Closed Mon; Tue–Sun 10.00–24.00
[DB] Marktredwitz 800m

MARKTSTEFT 375

Kesselring
Privatbrauerei Kesselring GmbH & Co. KG
Leithenbukweg 13, 97342 Marktsteft
T 09332 506 30   **F** 09332 50 63 10
www.kesselring-bier.de
Owners: the Himmel-Kesselring family
Founded: 1688
Output: 45,000hl
Availability: c.100 pubs
REGULAR BEERS:
Kesselring Steffen Leicht (2.9%)
Kesselring Hell (4.7%)
Kesselring Premium Pils (4.9%)
Kesselring Schlemmer Weißbier (5.1%)
Kesselring Schlemmer Schwarze (5.1%)
Kesselring Kristall Weizen Klar (5.1%)
Kesselring Urtyp Export (5.1%)
Kesselring Urfränkisches Landbier (5.1%)
Kesselring Premium Gold 1688 (5.3%)
SEASONAL BEERS:
Kesselring Fränkische Weihnacht (5.3%),
Kesselring Fastenbier (6.2%),
Kesselring Bockbier (6.2%)

Small regional brewery that brews wheat and dark beers for a former brewery whose identity they didn't divulge. Bus No. 8112 runs between Marktbreit and Kitzingen via Marktsteft on weekdays and stops outside the Golden Anchor.

🍺 Goldener Anker
Hauptstraße 47, 97342 Marktsteft
T 09332 44 35
Closed Tue; Wed–Mon 11.00–23.00
[DB] Marktbreit 4.5km, Kitzingen 5km

🍺 Zum Goldenen Hirschen
Hauptstraße 35, 97342 Marktsteft
T 09332 59 11 45
Closed Mon & Wed; Tue, Thu–Sun from 10.00; rooms available
[DB] Marktbreit 4.5km, Kitzingen 5km

MAROLDSWEISACH 376

Hartleb

Herrenstraße 9, 96126 Maroldsweisach
T 09532 240   **F** 09532 98 08 32
Owner: Irmgard Hartleb   Founded: 1520
Output: 800hl   Availability: 1 pub
REGULAR BEER:
Hartleb Vollbier

Brewpub in the centre of Maroldsweisach. Buses Nos. 8221 and 8226 run from Ebern on weekdays.

🍺 **Zum Grünen Baum**
Herrenstraße 9, 96126 Maroldsweisach
Closed Wed; Thu–Tue 09.00–24.00; rooms
available   DB Ebern 17km

MAXLRAIN (Tuntenhausen) 377

Schlossbrauerei

Schlossbrauerei Maxlrain Leo Graf von
Hohenthal und Bergen GmbH & Co. KG
Aiblinger Straße 1, 83104 Tuntenhausen-Maxlrain
T 08061 907 90   **F** 08061 90 79 80
www.maxlrain.de
Owner: Christina Prinzessin von Lobkowicz
Founded: 1636   Output: 40,000hl
Availability: 35 pubs
REGULAR BEERS:
Maxlrainer Erntebier (2.8%)
Maxlrainer Lagerbier (4.8%)
Maxlrainer Pils (4.9%)
Maxlrainer Aiblinger Schwarzbier (5%)
Maxlrainer Schloss Weisse (5%)
Maxlrainer Leo Weisse (5%)
Maxlrainer Zwickl Max (5.1%)
Maxlrainer Schloss Trunk (5.3%)
Maxlrainer Schloss Gold (5.3%)
SEASONAL BEERS:
Maxlrainer Kirtabier Märzen (5.5%), **Maxlrainer
Festbier** (5.5%), **Maxlrainer Jubilator** (7%, Lent)

Attractive brewery close to Maxlrain castle.
There are no buses to the village so you'll have
to find your own transport or be prepared to
walk from Bad Aibling.

🍺 **Bräustüberl Maxlrain**
Stachöder Weg 2, 83104 Tuntenhausen-Maxlrain
T 08061 924 22   **F** 08061 49 16 52
Closed Tue; Wed–Sun 10.00–23.00, Mon
10.00–14.00   DB Bad Aibling 5km

MECKATZ (Heimenkirch) 378

Meckatzer Löwenbräu

Meckatzer Löwenbräu Benedikt Weiß KG
Meckatz 10, 88178 Heimenkirch-Meckatz
T 08381 50 40   **F** 08381 504 43
www.meckatzer.de
Owner: the Weiß family   Founded: 1738
Output: 175,000hl   Availability: c. 500 pubs
REGULAR BEERS:
Meckatzer Leichtes Helles (2.9%)
Meckatzer Leichtes Weizen (3%)
Meckatzer Pils (4.8%)
Meckatzer Weiss-Gold (5.2%)
Meckatzer Weizen (5.2%)
Meckatzer Urweizen (5.2%)
SEASONAL BEERS:
Meckatzer Zwickelbier (5.4%, spring & autumn),
Meckatzer Fest-Märzen (5.4%, Christmas)

Large brewery that dominates the little village.
Bus No. 13 runs from Hergatz Mon–Sat and bus
No. 793 operates from Lindau on Sunday.

🍺 **Meckatzer Bräustüble**
Meckatz 8, 88178 Heimenkirch-Meckatz
T 08381 15 73
Closed Mon; Tue–Sun 09.00–24.00
DB Hergatz 7km

MELKENDORF (Litzendorf) 379

Winkler

Otterbachstraße 13, 96123 Litzendorf-Melkendorf
T 09505 224   **F** 09505 80 56 46
www.brauerei-winkler.onlinehome.de
Owner: Friedrich Winkler   Founded: 1889
Output: 700hl   Availability: 1 pub
REGULAR BEER:
Winkler Fränkisches Lagerbier

Brewpub in the centre of Melkendorf. There are
no buses to the village. Closed at Easter, for three
weeks in August, and over Christmas/New Year.

🍺 **Winkler**
Otterbachstraße 13, 96123 Litzendorf-Melkendorf
Closed Tue (Wed after hols); Wed–Fri & Mon
from 16.00, Sat, Sun & hols from 10.00; rooms
available
DB Bamberg 11km

MEMMELSDORF 380

Drei Kronen

Brauerei-Gasthof Drei Kronen Straub KG
Hauptstraße 19, 96117 Memmelsdorf
T 0951 94 43 30   **F** 0951 944 33 66
www.drei-kronen-memmelsdorf.de
Owner: Hans Ludwig Straub   Founded: 1457
Output: 1,000hl   Availability: 1 pub
REGULAR BEERS:
Drei Kronen Lager (4.3%)
Drei Kronen Stöffla Keller-Rauchbier (4.5%)
Drei Kronen Hefe-Pils (4.9%)
SEASONAL BEERS:
Drei Kronen Hefeweizen (4.4%), **Drei Kronen Melchior** (4.5%), **Drei Kronen Böckla** (6.2%)

Brewpub and hotel in the centre of the village. The owner is the manager of the Privater Braugasthof group which publishes a free booklet each year detailing all member breweries.

🍺 **Drei Kronen**
Hauptstraße 19, 96117 Memmelsdorf
Mon 17.00–23.00, Tue–Sat 11.00–23.00, Sun 11.00–15.00; rooms available
DB Bamberg 6km

Höhn

Hauptstraße 11, 96117 Memmelsdorf
T 0951 40 61 40   **F** 0951 406 14 44
www.gasthof-hoehn.de
Owner: Georg Höhn   Founded: 1783
Output: 350hl   Availability: 1 pub
REGULAR BEER:
Höhn Görchla (4.9%)
SEASONAL BEER:
Höhn Görchla Bock Naturtrüb

The smaller of Memmelsdorf's two brewpubs may feature a modernised tap but the brewery is still wood-fired. There's a good bus service from Bamberg seven days a week.

🍺 **Hohn**
Hauptstraße 11, 96117 Memmelsdorf
Closed Tue; Wed–Mon from 06.00; rooms available
DB Bamberg 6km

MEMMINGEN 381

Memminger

Memminger Brauerei GmbH
Dr.-Karl-Lenz-Straße 68, 87700 Memmingen
T 08331 856 60   **F** 08331 50 10
www.memminger-brauerei.de
Owner: Jochen Kesselschläger   Founded: 1911
Output: 215,000hl   Availability: c.2,000 pubs
REGULAR BEERS:
Memminger Leichte Weiße (3.1%)
Memminger Skip Pilsener (4.9%)
Memminger Lager Schwarz (5%)
Memminger Dunkle Weiße (5%)
Memminger Premium (5.1%)
Memminger Keller Pils (5.1%)
Memminger Kristallweizen (5.1%)
Memminger Weizen (5.1%)
Memminger Flight Hefeweizen (5.1%)
Memminger Gold (5.3%)
Memminger Kartäuser Weissbier (5.5%)
Memminger Kartäuser Spezialbier (5.7%)
Memminger Gaugraf Silach (5.7%)
Memminger Klausator (7.1%)
SEASONAL BEER:
Memminger Winterbier Spezial (5.7%)
FOR BRAUEREI WEITNAU, WEITNAU:
Alpkönig Dunkel (5%), **Alpkönig Hefe-Weizen** (5.1%), **Alpkönig Dunkle Weisse** (5.1%), **Original Weitnauer Märzen** (5.7%)
FOR ULMER-MÜNSTER BRAUEREI, ULM:
Ulmer-Münster Hirsch Bier Urhell (4.9%), **Ulmer-Münster Herrenpils** (4.9%), **Ulmer-Münster Gulden Classic** (5.1%)

Large brewery on the northern outskirts of Memmingen. The brewery tap is on the western side of the town centre.

🍺 **Engelkeller**
Königsgraben 9, 87700 Memmingen
T 08331 856 60
Closed Wed; Thu–Tue 10.00–24.00
DB Memmingen 900m

MERKENDORF
(Memmelsdorf) 382

Hummel

Brauerei Julius Hummel
Lindenstraße 9, 96117 Memmelsdorf-Merkendorf

T 09542 12 47   **F** 09542 12 62
www.brauerei-hummel.de
Owner: Julius Hummel   Founded: 1846
Output: 8,000hl
REGULAR BEERS:
Hummel-Bräu Kellerbier (4.9%)
Hummel-Bräu Pils (4.9%)
Hummel-Bräu Weißbier (5.2%)
Hummel-Bräu Dunkles Weißbier (5.2%)
Hummel-Bräu Märzen (5.4%)
Hummel-Bräu Räucherla (5.6%)
SEASONAL BEERS:
Hummel-Bräu Festbier (5.6%), **Hummel-Bräu Heller Maibock** (7%, May), **Hummel Weizen-Bock** (7.1%, Lent & Advent), **Hummel-Bräu Bock Dunkel** (7.5%, Nov–Dec), **Hummel Räucherator** (8.1%, Lent)

Village brewery and tap. Bus No.17 runs directly to Bamberg from Memmelsdorf but the outward journey usually involves a change.

🍺 **Hummel**
Lindenstraße 9, 96117 Memmelsdorf-Merkendorf
Closed Tue; Wed–Sat & Mon 09.00–24.00,
Sun & hols 09.00–12.00 & 15.00–24.00
DB Bamberg 10km

Wagner

Brauerei Wagner GmbH
Pointstraße 1, 96117 Memmelsdorf-Merkendorf
T 09542 620   **F** 09542 650
www.wagner-merkendorf.de
Owner: Richard Wagner   Founded: 1797
Output: 16,000hl   Availability: 16 pubs
REGULAR BEERS:
Wagner Pils (4.9%)
Wagner Ungespundetes Lagerbier (5.3%)
Wagner Weisse (5.3%)
Wagner Märzen (5.4%)
SEASONAL BEERS:
Wagner Festbier (5.7%), **Wagner Bock Hell** (7.5%, winter), **Wagner Bock Dunkel** (7.5%, winter)

The larger of Merkendorf's two breweries is around the corner from Hummel, close to the church. The tap is alongside the brewery.

🍺 **Wagner**
Pointstraße 1, 96117 Memmelsdorf-Merkendorf
Closed Mon; Tue–Sun 09.00–24.00
DB Bamberg 10km

MESSHOFEN (Roggenburg)   383

Kolb

Brauerei Kolb Messhofen
Illertisser Straße 24, 89297 Roggenburg-Meßhofen
T 07300 301
www.brauerei-kolb.de
Owner: Clemens Kolb   Founded: 1910
Output: 800hl
REGULAR BEERS:
Messhofener Weißbier (5%)
Messhofener Märzen (5%)
SEASONAL BEER:
Messhofener Festbier (5.5%)

Small brewery and tap on the main road through the village. We think the beers are only available here. The brewery tap closes on the last weekend of each month. The last bus from Meßhofen leaves around opening time.

🍺 **Kolb**
Illertisser Str. 24, 89297 Roggenburg-Meßhofen
Closed Mon, Tue & last weekend of the month;
Wed–Fri from 17.00, Sat & Sun from 09.30
DB Illertissen 12km, Krumbach 13km

MICKHAUSEN   384

Schloßbrauerei

Hauptstraße 32–34, 86866 Mickhausen
T 08204 10 13   **F** 08204 10 23
E schlossbrauerei-mickhausen@t-online.de
Owners: Helmut & Sophie Prinzing
Founded: 1613   Availability: 87 pubs
REGULAR BEERS:
Schloßbräu Schloß-Privat (4.5%)
Schloßbräu Hell (4.7%)
Schloßbräu Schloß-Pils (4.9%)
Schloßbräu Hefe-Weissbier (4.9%)
Schloßbräu Dunkle Weisse (4.9%)
Schloßbräu Kaiserritter (5.2%)

Small brewery in the centre of Mickhausen. The tap is 25km north-west of Mickhausen in Augsburg. From Augsburg Hauptbahnhof a change of bus is required to reach the pub which is opposite Bärenkeller school (No. 21 stops outside), but it's walkable from Neusäß station.

🍺 **Lerchenkrug**
Lerchenweg 61, 86156 Augsburg-Bärenkeller
T 0821 209 06 29
Closed Tue; Wed–Mon 10.00–24.00
[DB] Neusäß 2km, Augsburg Hbf 5km

MIESBACH   385

Hopf

Weißbierbrauerei Hopf GmbH
Schützenstraße 8–10, 83714 Miesbach
T 08025 295 90   **F** 08025 29 59 29
www.hopfweisse.de
Founded: 1910
Output: 45,000hl
Availability: 85 pubs
REGULAR BEERS:
Hopf Die Leichtere (3.3%)
Hopf's Red Weizen-Ale (4.7%)
Hopf Dunkle Weiße (5%)
Hopf Helle Weiße (5.3%)
Hopf Kristall Weiße (5.3%)
Hopf Wendelsteiner Hefeweissbier (5.4%)
Hopf's White Eisweissbier (5.5%)
Hopf's Ice Eisweissbierbock (7.5%)
SEASONAL BEER:
Hopf Weißer Bock (7%)

Wheat beer brewery in the foothills of the Alps.
The bottom-fermented Schlierseer Hell & Dunkel
are brewed for Hopf by Nordbräu in Ingolstadt.
The tap is in the town centre, close to the station,
the brewery on the other side of the railway.

🍺 **Weißbräustüberl**
Marienplatz 6, 83714 Miesbach
T 08025 37 89
Closed Mon; Tue–Sun 09.00–24.00
[DB] Miesbach 150m

MILTENBERG   386

Faust

Brauhaus Faust OHG
Hauptstraße 219, 63897 Miltenberg
T 09371 971 30   **F** 09371 97 13 99
www.faust.de
Owners: Cornelius & Johannes Faust
Founded: 1654   Output: 40,000hl
Availability: c.350 pubs

REGULAR BEERS:
Faust Das Leichte (2.6%)
Faust Pils (4.9%)
Faust Weizen Dunkel (5.2%)
Faust Weizen Hefe-Hell (5.3%)
Faust Export (5.3%)
Faust Schwarzviertler (5.2%)
Faust Kräusen (5.4%)
SEASONAL BEERS:
Faust Festbier (5.3%), Faust Weihnachtsbier
(5.4%), Faust Doppelbock Dunkel (7%)

Brewery formerly known as Löwenbrauerei
Miltenberg at the western end of the
picturesque high street. The tap is opposite,
down a lane towards the river.

🍺 **Faust Bräustüb'le**
Löwengasse 3, 63897 Miltenberg
T 09371 27 09   **F** 09371 949 94 92
Mid Oct–Mar: closed Mon; Tue–Thu 17.00–24.00,
Fri 15.00–03.00, Sat 11.00–03.00,
Sun & hols 11.00–23.00
Apr–Mid Oct: Sun–Tue 11.00–24.00,
Wed–Thu 11.00–01.00, Fri–Sat 11.00–03.00
[DB] Miltenberg 1.3km

Kalt-Loch-Bräu

Hauptstraße 201, 63897 Miltenberg
T 09371 22 83
Founded: 1580
Output: 4,000hl
REGULAR BEERS:
Kalt-Loch-Bräu Schloß-Pils (4.8%)
Kalt-Loch-Bräu Hefe-Weisse Dunkel (5%)
Kalt-Loch-Bräu Hefe-Weisse Hell (5.2%)
Kalt-Loch-Bräu Export (5.3%)
Kalt-Loch Fränkisches Landbier Dunkel (5.5%)
Kalt-Loch-Bräu Kalomator (8%)
SEASONAL BEERS:
Kalt-Loch-Bräu Festbier 1580 (5.6%),
Kalt-Loch-Bräu Weihnachts Doppelbock (7.5%)

Small brewery down the street from Faust, with
the tap next door. The Kalomator is available on
draught all year round.

🍺 **Kalt-Loch-Bräustüble**
Hauptstraße 201, 63897 Miltenberg
T 09371 24 81
Closed Wed; Thu–Tue 11.00–22.00
[DB] Miltenberg 1.2km

MINDELHEIM 387

Lindenbrauerei

Memminger Straße 21, 87719 Mindelheim
T 08261 14 02   **F** 08261 73 04 89
Owner: Adolf Müller   Founded: 1900
Output: 3,000hl   Availability: 4 pubs
REGULAR BEERS:
Lindenbräu Vollbier Hell (4.7%)
Lindenbräu Zwickelbier Naturtrüb (5%)
Lindenbräu Rittertrunk (5%)
Lindenbräu Spezialbier Hell (5.6%)
SEASONAL BEERS:
Lindenbräu Faschingsbier Narrentrunk (5%),
Lindenbräu Weihnacht Festbier (5.8%)

Small brewery on the western edge of town.
The brewery tap is alongside the river Mindel, a
little closer to the centre of Mindelheim. The
Faschingsbier Narrentrunk is a carnival special.

🍺 Drei König
Memminger Straße 1, 87719 Mindelheim
T 08261 43 34
Closed Tue; Wed–Mon 10.00–01.00
DB Mindelheim 1.5km

MISSEN (Missen-Wilhams) 388

Schäffler

Brauerei Schäffler Hanspeter Graßl KG
Hauptstraße 17, 87547 Missen-Wilhams/Missen
T 08320 92 00   **F** 08320 920 23
www.schaeffler-braeu.de
Owner: Hanspeter Graßl   Founded: 1868
Output: 10,000hl
REGULAR BEERS:
Schäffler Bräu Leichte Weisse
Schäffler Bräu Premium Gold
Schäffler Bräu Zwickl
Schäffler Bräu Premium Pils
Schäffler Bräu Schwarzer Peter
Schäffler Bräu Weissbier
Schäffler Bräu Dunkle Weisse Original
SEASONAL BEERS:
Schäffler Bräu Winterzauber, Schäffler Bräu
Oster-Festbier, Schäffler Bräu Weißer Bock

Small brewery in the Alps between Immenstadt
and Isny, with the brewery tap next door. There's
no bus service to the village, as far as we can tell.

🍺 Schäffler
Hauptstraße 15, 87547 Missen-Wilhams/Missen
T 08320 920 15   **F** 08320 920 16
Closed Wed (except Jul–Aug);
Thu–Tue from 09.00; rooms available
DB Immenstadt 11km

MITTENWALD 389

Mittenwald

Brauerei Mittenwald Johann Neuner GmbH & Co.
Innsbrücker Straße 13, 82481 Mittenwald
T 08823 10 07   **F** 08823 35 90
www.brauerei-mittenwald.de
Owner: Mathias Neuner
Founded: 1808
Output: 18,000hl
Availability: c. 100 pubs
REGULAR BEERS:
Mittenwalder Leicht (3.2%)
Mittenwalder Karwendel Hell (4.7%)
Mittenwalder Jäger Dunkel (4.7%)
Mittenwalder Premium Pils (4.7%)
Mittenwalder Kellerbier
Mittenwalder Berg Gold Export (5.2%)
Mittenwalder Edel Märzen (5.2%)
SEASONAL BEERS:
Mittenwalder Heller Bock (6.4%),
Mittenwalder Josefi Bock Dunkel (6.5%, Lent),
Mittenwalder Weihnachts-Bock Dunkel (6.5%)
WEDENFELSER BEER:
Werdenfelser Original,
Werdenfelser Weisse (5.3%)

Germany's highest privately owned brewery is
on the southern edge of town. The Kellerbier is
only available at the brewery tap which is divided
into two businesses (see below).

🍺 Postkeller
Innsbrücker Straße 13, 82481 Mittenwald
T 08823 17 29   **F** 08829 21 85
Closed Mon; Tue–Sun from 10.00

🍺 Alte Braustub'n
Innsbrücker Straße 13, 82481 Mittenwald
T 08823 17 29   **F** 08829 21 85
Closed Mon; Tue–Sun 11.00–14.30 & from 17.00
DB Mittenwald 800m

MITTERTEICH 390

Hösl

Hösl & Co. Brauhaus GmbH
Bahnhofstraße 1, 95666 Mitterteich
T 09633 922 20   **F** 09633 92 22 22
www.hoeslbier.de
Founded: 1516   Output: 60,000hl
REGULAR BEERS:
Hösl Leichtes Weissbier (2.9%)
Hösl Edelhell (4.5%)
Hösl Abt Andreas Traditionstrunk (4.9%)
Hösl Edel Pilsener (4.9%)
Hösl Urstoff (5.1%)
Hösl Weissbier (5.1%)
Hösl Dunkles Weissbier (5.1%)
Hösl Kristallweizen (5.1%)
Hösl Oberpfälzer Landgold
SEASONAL BEERS:
Hösl Winterbräu, Hösl Süffikus (6.5%)
FOR TRASSL-BRÄU, WARMENSTEINACH:
Steinachtaler Pils (4.9%),
Steinachtaler Lagerbier Hell (5.1%),
Steinachtaler Export (5.5%)

Brewery in the middle of Mitterteich with the
tap in front on the central square. Bus No. 6276
runs from Wiesau Mon–Sat.

🍺 Hösl
Bahnhofstraße 1, 95666 Mitterteich
T 09633 21 66
Closed Sat; Sun–Fri 10.00–01.00
DB Wiesau (Oberpfalz) 8km

Kommunbrauerei

Kirchplatz 12, 95666 Mitterteich
T 09633 890   **F** 09633 892 99
www.mitterteich.de
Owner: Stadt Mitterteich   Founded: 1516
Output: 1,000hl   Availability: 3 pubs
REGULAR BEER:
Zoigl

Communal brewery on the main square, opposite
Hösl. The three Zoigl houses are all nearby; they
each open on seven or eight weekends a year.
Opening dates are listed on the website. There
is a Zoigl festival on the last weekend in June.

🍺 Hartwich
Angergasse 1, 95666 Mitterteich
T 09633 23 08

🍺 Lugert
Bachstraße 12, 95666 Mitterteich
T 09633 91 92 07

🍺 Oppl
Oberer Marktplatz 11, 95666 Mitterteich
T 09633 33 26
DB Wiesau (Oberpfalz) 8km

MÖNCHSAMBACH
(Burgebrach) 391

Zehendner

Mönchsambach 18,
96138 Burgebrach-Mönchsambach
T 09546 380   **F** 09546 92 12 27
www.brauerei-zehendner.de
Founded: 1899
Output: 5,000hl   Availability: 8 pubs
REGULAR BEERS:
Mönchsambacher Lagerbier (5%)
Mönchsambacher Weizenbier (5%)
Mönchsambacher Export (5.2%)
SEASONAL BEERS:
**Mönchsambacher Maibock, Mönchsambacher
Weihnachtsbock**
FOR MAX-BRÄU, AMPFERBACH:
Max-Bräu Lagerbier, Max-Bräu Bockbier

Brewery and tap in a small village on the main
road west from Burgebrach. Bus No. 8223 runs
from Bamberg station daily except Sunday.

🍺 Zehendner
Mönchsambach 18,
96138 Burgebrach-Mönchsambach
Closed Mon; Tue–Sun 09.00–24.00
DB Bamberg 21km

MOOS (Plattling) 392

Arcobräu

Arcobräu Gräfliches Brauhaus GmbH & Co. KG
Schloßalle 1, 94554 Moos
T 09938 91 81 80   **F** 09938 91 81 55
www.arcobraeu.de
Owner: Graf. von Arco-Zinneberg
Founded: 1567   Output: 100,000hl
REGULAR BEERS:
Arcobräu Graf Arco light (2.9%)
Arcobräu Weissbier Leicht (2.9%)

Arcobräu Schloss Dunkel (4.7%)
Arcobräu Schloss Hell (4.9%)
Arcobräu Pilsener (4.9%)
Arcobräu Larry's Lager (4.9%)
Arcobräu Urfass (5.2%)
Arcobräu Weissbier Hell (5.3%)
Arcobräu Weissbier Dunkel (5.3%)
Arcobräu Fips Weizen (5.3%)
Arcobräu Larry's White (5.3%)
SEASONAL BEERS:
Arcobräu Christkindl (5.5%, Christmas),
Arcobräu Coronator (7.5%)

Large brewery on the southern edge of the village, with the tap more centrally located. Buses Nos. 6139 and 6148 run between Plattling and Osterhofen on weekdays and stop on the main road outside Moos.

🍺 Schloßwirtschaft Moos

Preysingstraße 23, 94554 Moos
T 09938 229   F 09938 13 48
Closed Mon; Tue–Sun 10.00–24.00
DB Osterhofen 9km, Plattling 9km

MOOS (Tüßling)   393

Bräu im Moos

Bräu im Moos 1, 84577 Tüßling-Moos
T 08633 10 41   F 08633 79 41
www.braeuimmoos.de
Owner: Eugen Münch   Founded: 1870
Output: 30,000hl
REGULAR BEERS:
Bräu im Moos Leichte Weisse (2.9%)
Bräu im Moos Edel-Pils (4.8%)
Bräu im Moos Hefe-Weizen (4.8%)
Bräu im Moos Dunkle Weisse (5%)
Bräu im Moos Dunkel (5.2%)
Bräu im Moos Export Hell (5.3%)
SEASONAL BEER:
Bräu im Moos Weihnachtsfestbier

Brewery, tap and museum in a tiny hamlet on the opposite side of the railway to the village of Mörmoosen. There's no public transport to Moos but it is walkable from Tüßling station.

🍺 Bräu im Moos

Bräu im Moos 1, 84577 Tüßling-Moos
Closed Mon & Jan–Feb; Tue–Sun 08.00–24.00
DB Tüßling 3.2km

MOOSBACH   394

Scheuerer

Private Landbrauerei Scheuerer
Bräugasse 7, 92709 Moosbach
T 09656 209   F 09656 731
www.moosbacher.com
Owner: Erhard Scheuerer   Founded: 1887
Output: 20,000hl   Availability: 30 pubs
REGULAR BEERS:
Moosbacher Leichte Weiße (2.4%)
Moosbacher Lager Hell (5%)
Moosbacher Pilsener (5%)
Moosbacher Weißbier (5%)
Moosbacher Schwarze Weiße (5%)
Moosbacher Zoigl (5.4%)
Moosbacher Kellerbier (5.4%)
Moosbacher Export (5.4%)
SEASONAL BEER:
Moosbacher Bock (6.8%)
FOR SCHLOSSBRAUEREI, FRIEDENFELS:
Friedenfelser Zoigl Schwarzer Ritter (5%)

Small regional brewery in the middle of Moosbach, a small town in the Oberpfälzer forest. Bus No. 6291 runs from Weiden but the last one out leaves before the brewery tap opens.

🍺 Bräustübl

Bräugasse 7, 92709 Moosbach
T 09656 17 42
Closed Sun; Mon–Sat from 17.00
DB Weiden (Oberpfalz) 25km

MOOSHAM (Mintraching)   395

Meyringer

Gutsbrauerei Hugo Meyringer
Regensburger Straße 5,
93098 Mintraching-Moosham
T 09406 10 47   F 09406 95 91 53
www.brauerei-meyringer.de
Founded: 1640
REGULAR BEERS:
Meyringer Georgi Leichtes Weizen (3%)
Meyringer Vollbier Hell (4.7%)
Meyringer Pilsner (4.7%)
Meyringer Georgi Weizen (4.9%)
Meyringer Export (5%)
SEASONAL BEER:
Meyringer Zwicklbier (4.7%, summer)

Small brewery on the western edge of the village, with the brewery tap a few hundred metres away. Bus No. 23 runs from Regensburg Hauptbahnhof to Sünching via Moosham.

Mooshamer Bierstüberl
Keltenweg 9, 93098 Mintraching-Moosham
T 09406 28 49 51
Closed Mon; Tue–Fri 11.00–14.00 & 17.00–24.00,
Sat, Sun & hols 09.00–24.00
DB Sünching 9km, Regensburg Hbf 17km

MOTTEN 396

Hochstiftliches Brauhaus
Hochstiftliches Brauhaus in Bayern
Brückenauer Straße 6, 97786 Motten
T 09748 710   **F** 09748 713 00
www.will-braeu.de
Owner: Hochstiftliches Brauhaus, Fulda
Founded: 1791   Output: 90,000hl
REGULAR BEERS:
Will-Bräu Pilsner (4.6%)
Will-Bräu Urtyp (4.8%)
Will-Bräu Pils de Luxe (4.9%)
Will-Bräu Hefe Weizen (5.3%)
Will-Bräu Ur-Weisse (5.3%)
Will-Bräu Kristall Weizen (5.3%)
SEASONAL BEERS:
Will-Bräu Festbier, Will-Bräu Ur-Bock (6.2%)

Until 1997, when it was taken over by Hochstifli-ches Brauhaus of Fulda, this brewery was called Will-Bräu. The beers still are. Bus No. 8054 runs from Fulda on weekday afternoons but you'll have to catch the first one if you want to return the same day.

Brauerei-Gasthof
Brückenauer Straße 8, 97786 Motten
T 09748 261   **F** 09748 12 82
Closed Tue; Wed–Mon 10.00–24.00
DB Fulda 21km

MÜHLDORF 397

Unertl
Weißbräu Unertl GmbH & Co. KG
Weißgerber Straße 7–15, 84453 Mühldorf
T 08631 376 80   **F** 08631 37 68 22
www.brauerei-unertl.de

Owners: Wolfgang Alois Unertl   Founded: 1929
Output: 14,200hl   Availability: c.100 pubs
REGULAR BEERS:
Unertl Leichte Weisse (3.2%)
Franz-Xaver Unertl Weisse Hell (4.9%)
Unertl Mühldorfer Weissbier (5%)
Unertl Bio-Dinkel Weisse (5.2%)
SEASONAL BEER:
Unertl Gourmet Weisse (5.6%)

Wheat beer brewery in the centre of Mühldorf, with the brewery tap nearby, set back off the long town square. The Bio-Dinkel Weisse is an organic brew made from spelt.

Beim Schreindl
Stadtplatz 67, 84453 Mühldorf
T 08631 16 44 77
Closed Sun; Mon–Sat 09.00–24.00
DB Mühldorf 1.1km

MÜHLENDORF (Stegaurach) 398

Mühlenbräu
Mühlenbräu Merklein
Brückenstraße 19, 96135 Stegaurach-Mühlendorf
T 0951 291 19   **F** 0951 29 00 30
Owner: Alfons Merklein
Founded: 1793
Output: 600hl
Availability: 1 pub
REGULAR BEERS:
Mühlenbräu Hell
Mühlenbräu Dunkel
Mühlenbräu Pils
SEASONAL BEERS:
Mühlenbräu Märzen (Lent),
Mühlenbräu Eremitentrunk (May),
Mühlenbräu Kirchweihbier (Sep),
Mühlenbräu Maibock Hell (May),
Mühlenbräu Bock Dunkel (winter)

Brewery and tap in a former watermill. The beers are only sold here and in the summer Bierkeller. Buses Nos. 12 and 8244 run from Bamberg daily.

Alte Mühle
Brückenstraße 19, 96135 Segaurach-
Mühlendorf
Closed Tue; Wed–Sun from 11.00,
Mon from 16.00; rooms available
DB Bamberg 10km

MÜHLFELD 399

Mühlfelder Brauhaus

Mühlfeld 13, 82211 Herrsching-Mühlfeld
T 08152 55 78   **F** 08152 80 18
www.muehlfelder-brauhaus.de
Owner: Hubert Gruber   Founded: 1989
Output: 2,000 hl   Availability: 7 pubs
REGULAR BEERS:
Mühlfelder Helles (5.2%)
Mühlfelder Weizen (5.4%)
SEASONAL BEER:
Mühlfelder Stärkstes Bier der Welt (25.4%)

Large brewpub in a small village just south of
Herrsching on the Amersee. In September 2005
they brewed what is claimed to be the strongest
beer in the world. Bus No. 9653 runs from
Herrsching station a few times each weekday
and we think there may also be another,
privately operated route.

🍺 **Mühlfelder Brauhaus**
Mühlfeld 13, 82211 Herrsching-Mühlfeld
Daily 11.00–24.00
DB Herrsching 1.7km

MÜHLHAUSEN (Oberpfalz) 400

Bender

Kirchgasse 7–9, 92360 Mühlhausen
T 09185 406   **F** 09185 90 21 15
Owner: Helga Atzler   Founded: 1482
Output: 2,500hl
REGULAR BEERS:
Bender Landl Hell (4.9%)
Bender Grafen-Pils (5%)
Bender Hefe-Weizen (5%)
Bender Hefe-Weizen Dunkel (5%)
SEASONAL BEERS:
Bender Festbier, Bender Landlator

Small brewery and tap in the centre of town,
formerly known as the Gräfliche Wolfsteinsche
Brauerei. Bus No. 515 runs to Mühlhausen from
Neumarkt daily.

🍺 **Bender**
Kirchgasse 7, 92360 Mühlhausen
Daily 10.00–13.00 & from 16.30
DB Neumarkt (Oberpfalz) 12km

MÜNCHEN 401

Augustiner

Augustiner-Bräu Wagner KG
Landsberger Straße 31–35,
80339 München-Schwanthalerhöhe
T 089 51 99 40   **F** 089 51 99 41 11
www.augustinerbraeu.de
Founded: 1328   Output: 400,000hl
REGULAR BEERS:
Augustiner-Bräu Pils (5%)
Augustiner-Bräu Lagerbier Hell (5.2%)
Augustiner-Bräu Weissbier (5.4%)
Augustiner-Bräu Dunkel (5.6%)
Augustiner-Bräu Edelstoff (5.6%)
SEASONAL BEERS:
Augustiner-Bräu Oktoberfestbier (6%),
Augustiner-Bräu Heller Bock (7%),
Augustiner-Bräu Maximator (7.5%)

München's oldest brewery was originally
housed in the Augustiner Großgaststätte but
today occupies a substantial part of Landsberger
Straße. The Großgaststätte is the official tap
but there's another pub at the brewery.

🍺 **Augustiner Bräustuben**
Landsberger Straße 19,
80339 München-Schwanthalerhöhe
T 089 50 70 47   **F** 089 502 25 69
Daily 10.00–24.00
Tram 18 & 19 Holzapfelstraße 70m
DB Hackerbrücke 450m, München Hbf 1km

🍺 **Augustiner Großgaststätte**
Neuhauser Straße 27,
80331 München-Altstadt-Lehel
T 089 23 18 32 57   **F** 089 260 53 79
Daily 10.00–24.00
DB Karlsplatz 200m, München Hbf 700m

Bavaria-Bräu

Theriesenhöhe 7, 80337 München/
Ludwigsvorstadt-Isarvorstadt
T 089 51 99 77 57   **F** 089 51 91 99 37
www.bavaria-braeu.de
Owner: Brau Holding International, München
Founded: 16.09.2005   Output: 3,000hl
Availability: 1 pub
REGULAR BEER:
Bavaria-Bräu Münchner Helles (5.2%)
Bavaria-Bräu Alt Münchner Weisse (5.4%)

Bavaria-Bräu Oktoberfestbier, Bavaria-Bräu Weihnachtsfestbier, Bavaria-Bräu Bock

Massive new brewpub built on the site of the Pschorr-Keller, opposite the Theresienwiese. It opened the day before the 2005 Oktoberfest.

🍺 Bavaria-Bräu
Theriesenhöhe 7, 80337 München/
Ludwigsvorstadt-Isarvorstadt
Daily 10.00–01.00
U U4 & U5 Theresienwiesen 200m
DB Hackerbrücke 750m, München–Hbf 1km

Forschungsbrauerei
Unterhachinger Straße 76,
81737 München-Altperlach
T 089 670 11 69
www.forschungsbrauerei.de
Owner: Stefan Jacob   Founded: 1930
Availability: 1 pub
REGULAR BEERS:
Forschungs-Pilsissimus (5.2%)
Forschungs-St. Jacobus Blonder Bock (7.5%)

Experimental brewery in south-east München whose beers are only available at the tap. Each autumn the pub closes in mid-October and doesn't re-open until sometime in March (the timing varies).

🍺 Forschungsbrauerei
Unterhachinger Straße 76, 81737 München-Altperlach
Closed Mon & mid Oct–Mar; Tue–Sat 11.00–23.00,
Sun & hols 10.00–22.00
DB München-Perlach 700m

Hofbräu
Staatliches Hofbräuhaus in München
Hofbräuallee 1, 81829 München/Trudering-Riem
T 089 92 10 50   F 089 90 64 26
www.hofbraeu-muenchen.de
Owner: Free State of Bavaria   Founded: 1589
Output: 218,000hl
REGULAR BEERS:
Hofbräu Münchner Kindl Weissbier Light (3.2%)
Hofbräu Original (5.1%)
Hofbräu Münchner Kindl Weissbier (5.1%)
Hofbräu Schwarze Weisse (5.1%)
Hofbräu Kristall Weisse (5.4%)
Hofbräu Dunkel (5.5%)

Hofbräu Münchner Sommer Naturtrüb (5.1%),
Hofbräu Oktoberfestbier (6%), **Hofbräu Festbier** (6%), **Hofbräu Maibock** (7.2%)

Probably München's most famous brewery, although by no means the largest, Hofbräu moved to their current site on the eastern edge of the city in 1988. The brewery was previously next to the Hofbräu Keller and, before that, in the world-famous pub.

🍺 Hofbräuhaus
Platzl 9, 80331 München/Altstadt-Lehel
T 089 290 13 60   F 089 22 75 86
Daily 08.00–23.30
DB Marienplatz 350m, München Hbf 1.6km

Löwenbräu
Nymphenburger Straße 4,
80335 München-Maxvorstadt
T 089 520 00   F 089 52 00 34 12
www.loewenbraeu.de
Owner: InBev   Founded: 1383
Output: 1,000,000hl
REGULAR BEERS:
Löwenbräu Schwarzbier Urtyp (4.8%)
Löwenbräu Kristallweizen (4.9%)
Löwenbräu Original (5.2%)
Löwenbräu Premium Pils (5.2%)
Löwenbräu Löwen Weisse (5.2%)
Löwenbräu Schwarze Weisse (5.2%)
Löwenbräu Dunkel (5.5%)
Löwenbräu Märzen (5.8%)
Löwenbräu Triumphator (7.6%)
SEASONAL BEER:
Löwenbräu Oktoberfestbier (6.1%)

Very large brewery north of the Hauptbahnhof whose beers are exported worldwide. The labyrinthine tap is next door.

🍺 Löwenbräukeller
Nymphenburger Straße 2,
80335 München-Maxvorstadt
T 089 52 60 21   F 089 52 89 33
Daily 10.00–24.00
U U1 & U7, Stiglmaierplatz 20m
DB München Hbf 750m

Paulaner/Hacker-Pschorr
Paulaner Brauerei GmbH & Co. KG
Hacker-Pschorr Bräu GmbH

Hochstraße 75, 81541 München/Au-Haidhausen
T 089 48 00 50   **F** 089 4800 54 09
www.paulaner.de
www.hacker-pschorr.de
Owner: Brau Holding International, München
Founded: 1634   Output: 2,080,000hl
PAULANER BEERS:
Paulaner Original Münchner Leicht (3.2%)
Paulaner Hefeweißbier Leicht (3.2%)
Paulaner Münchner Diät Bier (4.3%)
Paulaner Helles Gold (4.5%)
Paulaner Weißes Gold (4.5%)
Paulaner Original Münchner Hell (4.9%)
Paulaner Premium Pils (4.9%)
Paulaner Original Münchner Dunkel (5%)
Paulaner Nockherberger (5.2%, at the tap only)
Paulaner Hefeweißbier Dunkel (5.3%)
Paulaner Roggen (5.3%)
Paulaner Hefeweißbier Naturtrüb (5.5%)
Paulaner Weißbier Kristallklar (5.5%)
Paulaner Original Münchner Urtyp (5.5%)
Paulaner Original Münchner Märzen (5.8%)
Paulaner Salvator (7.5%)
SEASONAL BEER:
Paulaner Oktoberfestbier (6%)
HACKER-PSCHORR BEERS:
Hacker-Pschorr Leichte Weisse (3.2%)
Hacker-Pschorr Münchner Hell (4.9%)
Hacker-Pschorr Braumeister Pils (5%)
Hacker-Pschorr Münchner Dunkel (5%)
Hacker-Pschorr Dunkle-Weisse (5.3%)
Hacker-Pschorr Edelhell (5.5%)
Hacker-Pschorr Anno 1417 Kellerbier (5.5%)
Hacker-Pschorr Hefe Weisse (5.5%)
Hacker-Pschorr Kristall Weisse (5.5%)
Hacker-Pschorr Münchner Gold (5.5%)
Hacker-Pschorr Sternweisse (5.5%)
SEASONAL BEERS:
Hacker-Pschorr Oktoberfest-Märzen (5.8%),
Hacker-Pschorr Superior (6%), **Hacker-Pschorr
Hubertus Bock** (6.8%), **Hacker-Pschorr Weiss
Bock** (7%), **Hacker-Pschorr Animator** (7.8%),
FOR THURN UND TAXIS, REGENSBURG:
Thurn und Taxis Leichte Weisse (2.9%),
Thurn und Taxis Hell (4.7%), **Thurn und Taxis
St. Wolfgang Dunkel** (4.8%), **Thurn und Taxis
Pilsener** (4.9%), **Thurn und Taxis Weissbier
Hefetrüb** (5.3%), **Thurn und Taxis Kristallweizen**
(5.3%), **Thurn und Taxis Export** (5.3%),
Thurn und Taxis Fürstengold Märzen (5.3%),
Thurn und Taxis Weissbier Dunkel (5.5%)
SEASONAL BEER:
Thurn und Taxis Winter Festbier (6%)

München's largest brewery is south of the city
centre on the Nockherberg. Hacker-Pschorr
beers have been brewed here for some years.
It's widely assumed Thurn und Taxis beers also
originate here but we think they may well be
brewed elsewhere.

🍺 Paulaner am Nockherberg
Hochstraße 77, 81541 München/Au-Haidhausen
T 089 459 91 30   **F** 089 477 00 72
Daily 10.00-01.00
Ⓣ Ostfriedhof 300m
Ⓤ Kolumbusplatz 500m
Ⓓ München Hbf 2.5km

🍺 Altes Hackerhaus
Sendlinger Straße 14,
80331 München/Altstadt-Lehel
T 089 260 50 26   **F** 089 260 50 27
Daily 09.00–23.00
Ⓓ Marienplatz 200m, München Hbf 1km

Paulaner Bräuhaus

Paulaner Bräuhaus Bavaria Minibrauerei GmbH
Kapuzinerplatz 5, 80337 München/
Ludwigsvorstadt-Isarvorstadt
T 089 544 61 10   **F** 089 54 46 11 18
www.paulanerbraeuhaus.de
Owner: Brau Holding International, München
Founded: 1989   Output: 2,500hl
Availability: 1 pub
REGULAR BEERS:
Paulaner Bräuhaus Thomas Zwickl (4.7%)
Paulaner Hefe-Weissbier Naturtrüb (5.5%)
SEASONAL BEERS:
Paulaner Schwarzer Kapuziner (4.7%),
Pauline Dunkles Weissbier (5.2%),
Paulaner Schwarzes Zwicklbier (5.5%),
Paulaner Bräuhaus Oktoberfestbier (6.3%),
Paulaner Bräuhaus Maibock (7.2%)

Imposing brewpub on Kapuzinerplatz, the home
of Thomasbräu until the 1920s. There are further
seasonal beers in addition to those listed above
but we don't have any details.

🍺 Paulaner Bräuhaus
Kapuzinerplatz 5, 80337 München/
Ludwigsvorstadt-Isarvorstadt
Daily 09.00–01.00
Ⓤ U3 & U6 Goetheplatz 200m
Ⓓ München Hbf 1.2km

Spaten-Franziskaner

Spaten-Franziskaner-Bräu GmbH
Marsstraße 46–48, 80335 München-Maxvorstadt
T 089 512 20   **F** 089 51 22 24 00
www.spatenbraeu.de
www.franziskaner-weissbier.de
Owner: InBev   Founded: 1397
Output: 2,000,000hl
SPATEN BEERS:
Spaten Diät Pils (4.9%)
Spaten Pils (5%)
Spaten Münchner Hell (5.2%)
SEASONAL BEER:
Spaten Oktoberfestbier (5.9%)
FRANZISKANER BEERS:
Franziskaner Hefe-Weissbier Leicht (2.9%)
Franziskaner Hefe-Weissbier Hell (5%)
Franziskaner Hefe-Weissbier Dunkel (5%)
Franziskaner Weissbier Kristallklar (5%)

Close to the main station, Spaten-Franziskaner
is the second largest brewery in a city with more
than its fair share of big breweries. The two
ranges are marketed separately.

🍺 Bräustüberl Spaten
Marsstraße 16, 80335 München-Maxvorstadt
T/F 089 54 50 71 41
Closed Sun; Mon–Sat 10.00–01.00
DB München Hbf 350m

🍺 Spatenhaus
Residenzstraße 12, 80335 München/Altstadt-Lehel
T 089 290 70 60   **F** 089 291 30 54
No. 19 Nationaltheater 100m
DB Marienplatz 350m, München Hbf 1.4km
Daily 09.30–23.30

Unionsbräu

Unionsbräu Haidhausen
Einsteinstraße 42, 81675 München/Au-Haidhausen
T 089 47 76 77   **F** 089 470 58 48
www.unionsbraeu.de   Founded: 1990
Output: 1,500hl   Availability: 1 pub
REGULAR BEERS:
Unionsbräu Hell (5%)
Unionsbräu Dunkel (5%)
SEASONAL BEER:
Unionsbräu Unimator (7.8%)

Brewpub which resumed brewing in 1990 after a
sixty year hiatus, albeit on a much smaller scale.
Formerly owned by Löwenbräu, we think they

may now be independent. The pub is outside the
eastern exit of Max-Weber-Platz U-Bahn station.

🍺 Unionsbräu
Einsteinstraße 42, 81675 München/Au-Haidhausen
Sun 10.00–16.00, Mon–Sat 11.00–01.00
U U4 & U5 Max-Weber-Platz 20m
DB München Hbf 2km

MÜNCHSTEINACH   402

Loscher

Brauerei Loscher KG
Steigerwaldstraße 21–23, 91481 Münchsteinach
T 09166 607   **F** 09166 825
www.brauerei-loscher.de
Owner: Andreas Loscher   Founded: 1881
Output: 15,000hl
REGULAR BEERS:
Loscher Hell (4.8%)
Loscher Pils (4.8%)
Loscher Münchsteinacher Zwickel-Pils (4.8%)
Loscher Schwarzbier (4.9%)
Loscher Hefe-Weizen Dunkel (5.1%)
Loscher Hefe-Weißbier (5.2%)
Loscher Klares Weizen (5.2%)
Loscher Export (5.4%)

Brewery in a small town in the Steigerwald.
Bus No. 146 runs from Neustadt on weekdays
but the service is a little sparse.

🍺 Zur Krone
Steigerwaldstraße 21, 91481 Münchsteinach
T 09166 227   **F** 09166 99 67 72
Closed Mon; Tue–Sun 11.00–24.00
DB Neustadt (Aisch) Bf 10km

MÜNNERSTADT   403

Klosterbrauerei

Klosterbrauerei Münnerstadt GmbH
Brewery: Am Dicken Turm 14, 97702 Münnerstadt
Office: Birkenweg 2, 97647 Hausen-Roth
T 09779 810 10   **F** 09779 81 01 29
Owners: Tobias & Xaver Weydringer
Founded: 1381   Output: 4,100hl
Availability: 43 pubs
REGULAR BEERS:
Kloster Pils (4.7%)
Kloster Urstoff (5.4%)

Small brewery close to the oldest of the medieval towers that used to defend Münnerstadt. The beer is transported 35km north to Roth to be bottled by Rother Bräu, owned by the same family and the administrative base for both breweries. They don't have a tap.

DB Münnerstadt 300m

MURNAU 404

Griesbräu

Griesbräu zu Murnau
Obermarkt 37, 82418 Murnau
T 08841 14 22   F 08841 39 13
www.griesbraeu.de
Owner: the Gilg family   Founded: 2000
Output: 1,000hl   Availability: 1 pub
REGULAR BEERS:
Griesbräu Hell
Griesbräu Werdenfelser Ur-Dunkel
Griesbräu Weisse
SEASONAL BEERS:
Griesbräu Drachenblut Rauchbier, Griesbräu Murnauer Märzen, Griesbräu Maibock

Brewpub in the building formerly occupied by an earlier brewery of the same name which was taken over by Thomasbräu of München (now the Paulaner Brauhaus). Brewing resumed after an 83-year gap in 2000.

🍴 Griesbräu
Obermarkt 37, 82418 Murnau
Daily 10.00–01.00; rooms available
DB Murnau 850m

Karg

Brauerei Karg GmbH & Co. KG
Untermarkt 25–27, 82418 Murnau
T 08841 12 68   F 08841 12 09
www.brauerei-karg.de   Founded: 1912
Output: 20,000hl   Availability: 30 pubs
REGULAR BEERS:
Karg Leichtes Weißbier (2.9%)
Karg Original Murnauer Weißbier (5%)
Karg Dunkles Hefe-Weißbier (5.2%)
SEASONAL BEER:
Karg Original Murnauer Weizen-Bock (7%)

Wheat-beer-only brewery in the centre of town. The dark was until recently called Schwarzer Woipertinger.

🍴 Kargs Bräustüberl
Untermarkt 27, 82418 Murnau
T 08841 82 72   F 08841 909 98
Closed Mon; Tue–Sun 09.00–23.00
DB Murnau 1.1km

MÜRSBACH (Rattelsdorf) 405

Sonnen-Bräu

Zaugendorfer Straße 4,
96179 Rattelsdorf-Mürsbach
T 09533 98 10 17   F 09533 98 10 19
www.gasthaus-schmitt.de
Owner: Ralf Schmitt   Founded: 1868
Output: 350hl   Availability: 1 pub
REGULAR BEER:
Sonnen-Bräu Lager (4.8%)
SEASONAL BEER:
Sonnen-Bräu Festbier (5.6%)

Brewpub in the centre of the village. The only bus of the day to Mürsbach leaves Baunach around 13.00 on weekdays but you can walk from Rentweinsdorf station.

🍴 Zur Sonne
Zaugendorfer Straße 4,
96179 Rattelsdorf-Mürsbach
Closed Mon; Tue–Sun 10.00–24.00; rooms available
DB Rentweinsdorf 4km

NAABECK (Schwandorf) 406

Schloßbrauerei

Naabecker Str. 13, 92421 Schwandorf-Naabeck
T 09431 13 26   F 09431 13 25
www.naabecker.de
Owner: Wolfgang Rasel   Founded: 1620
Output: 40,000hl
REGULAR BEERS:
Naabecker Pils (4.6%)
Naabecker Hell (4.8%)
Naabecker Dunkel (5%)
Naabecker Märzen (5.5%)
Naabecker Spezial (5.5%)
SEASONAL BEERS:
Naabecker Bock (6.4%)

Castle brewery in the centre of the village, above the river Naab. They also own Weizenbrauerei

Plank in nearby Wiefelsdorf. There's no tap but there are occasional buses to Naabeck from Schwandorf.
DB Schwandorf 7km

NAILA 407

Bürgerbräu
Privatbrauerei Bürgerbräu Naila Wohn OHG
Hofer Straße 21, 95119 Naila
T 09282 960 90 **F** 09282 96 09 30
www.wohn-bier.de
Founded: 1464 Output: 20,000hl
NAILAER BEERS:
Nailaer Fichten Zäpfla (4.8%)
Nailaer Zwergla (4.9%)
Nailaer Wilder Mann Dunkler Bock (7.2%)
WOHN BEERS:
Wohn Lager Hell (4.7%)
Wohn Alt Nailaer Dunkel (4.8%)
Wohn Pilsner (4.9%)
Wohn Braumeister Original (5%)
Wohn Hefe Weissbier (5.4%)
SEASONAL BEERS:
Wohn Weihnachtsbier (5.6%),
Wohn Heller Bock (7.2%).

Brewery just south of the town centre. There's no official tap but the beers aren't hard to find in Naila.
DB Naila 350m

NANKENDORF
(Waischenfeld) 408

Schroll
Nankendorf 41, 91344 Waischenfeld-Nankendorf
T 09204 248 **F** 09204 91 92 66
www.brauerei-schroll.de
Owner: Georg Schroll Founded: 1848
Output: 2,200hl Availability: 5 pubs
REGULAR BEERS:
Schroll Nankendorfer Urhell (4.9%)
Schroll Nankendorfer Landbier (5.2%)
SEASONAL BEER:
Schroll Nankendorfer Bock (7%)

Brewpub in the middle of the village. There's only one direct bus from Ebermannstadt on weekdays but it is possible to get from both Ebermannstadt and Bayreuth using a combination of buses and ASTs.

🍺 **Schroll**
Nankendorf 41, 91344 Waischenfeld-Nankendorf
Closed Tue; Wed–Mon 09.00–23.00
DB Ebermannstadt 22km, Bayreuth 25km

NEDENSDORF
(Bad Staffelstein) 409

Reblitz
Brauerei Reblitz Kleines Brauhaus in Nedensdorf
Am Mahlberg 1, 96231 Bad Staffelstein-Nedensdorf
T 09573 965 00 **F** 09573 96 50 50
Owners: Adelhaid & Reinhold Reblitz
Founded: 1805 Output: 350hl
Availability: 1 pub
REGULAR BEER:
Nedensdorfer Dunkles Landbier (4.7%)
SEASONAL BEERS:
Nedensdorfer Hefeweißbier (4.7%, Apr–Oct),
Reblitz Bock (6.8%, Nov–Jan)

Small brewery and tap in a village on the other side of the river Main from Bad Staffelstein. There are a couple of local buses on weekdays but you'll probably find it just as quick to walk.

🍺 **Reblitz**
Am Mahlberg 1, 96231 Bad Staffelstein-Nedensdorf
Closed Mon; Tue–Fri from 16.00, Sat from 15.00,
Sun & hols from 10.00; rooms available
DB Bad Staffelstein 3km

NENNSLINGEN 410

Ritter St. Georgen
Ritter St. Georgenbrauerei Karl Gloßner GmbH
Marktplatz 1, 91790 Nennslingen
T 09147 246 **F** 09147 18 89
www.ritter-bier.de
Owner: Dietmar Gloßner Founded: 1645
Output: 10,000hl Availability: 14 pubs
REGULAR BEERS:
Ritter-Bier Leicht
Ritter-Bier Hell (4.9%)
Ritter-Bier Pils (4.9%)
Ritter-Bier Georgi-Sud (5.1%)
Ritter-Bier Weißer Franke (5.1%)
Ritter-Bier Schwarzer Ritter Dunkel (5.1%)

Ritter-Bier Märzen (5.5%)
Ritter-Bier Ritter 1645 (5.5%)
SEASONAL BEERS:
Ritter-Bier Kirchweihstoff, Ritter-Bier Weihnachtsbier, Ritter-Bier Weihnachtsbock, Ritter-Bier Maibock

Brewery in the centre of the village with the tap next door. Bus No. 616 runs from Weißenburg on weekdays.

🍺 **Bräustüble**

Marktplatz 1, 91790 Nennslingen
T 09147 94 04 48
Closed Tue; Wed, Thu & Mon 16.00–23.00,
Fri & Sat 11.00–13.00 & 16.00–23.00,
Sun 10.00–13.00 & 16.00–23.00
DB Weißenburg (Bayern) 14km

NESSELWANG 411

Post-Brauerei

Hauptstraße 25, 87484 Nesselwang
T 08361 309 60 **F** 08361 309 74
www.post-brauerei-nesselwang.de
Owner: Karl Meyer   Founded: 1650
Output: 15,000hl   Availability: 100 pubs
REGULAR BEERS:
Postbrauerei Lager Hell (4.75%)
Postbrauerei Edel Pils (4.8%)
Postbrauerei Allgäuer Landbier (4.8%)
Postbrauerei Postwirt's Dunkel (4.9%)
Postbrauerei Der Postillion Weißbier (4.9%)
Postbrauerei Posthorn Gold (5.1%)
Postbrauerei Geburtstagsbier (5.1%)
Postbrauerei Traditions Bock (6.5%)
SEASONAL BEERS:
Postbrauerei Frühlingsbote, Postbrauerei Osterbier (5.45%)**, Postbrauerei Weihnachtsbier** (5.45%)**, Postbrauerei Kirchweihbier** (5.45%)**, Postbrauerei Mai-Bock** (6.4%)

Brewery and tap in the centre of town. The bright yellow pub is difficult to miss. They have a small brewery museum downstairs. Nearby Bärenbräu stopped brewing in 2002.

🍺 **Post**

Hauptstraße 25, 87484 Nesselwang
T 08361 309 10 **F** 08361 309 73
Daily 07.00–23.00; rooms available
DB Nesselwang 600m

NEUBURG (An der Donau) 412

Juliusbräu

Augsburger Straße 135, 86633 Neuburg
T 08431 20 69
Owner: Gabriele Bauer   Founded: 1858
Output: 3,000hl
REGULAR BEERS:
Juliusbräu Lager-Hell
Juliusbräu Export
Juliusbräu Jubiläms-Bier
SEASONAL BEERS:
Juliusbräu Märzen-Spezial, Juliusbräu Festbier, Juliusbräu Bock

Small brewery south of the railway. The tap is between the station and town centre.

🍺 **Neuwirt**

Färberstraße 88, 86633 Neuburg
T 08431 20 78 **F** 08431 386 43
Closed Tue; Wed–Mon 10.00–01.00; rooms available
DB Neuburg (Donau) 650m

NEUHAUS (Adelsdorf) 413

Löwenbräu

Neuhauser Hauptstraße 3, 91325 Adelsdorf-Neuhaus
T 09195 72 21 **F** 09195 87 46
www.zum-loewenbraeu.de
Owner: Benno Wirth   Founded: 1747
Output: 3,000hl   Availability: 5 pubs
REGULAR BEERS:
Löwenbräu Neuhaus Leichtes (2.8%)
Löwenbräu Neuhaus Vollbier (4.7%)
Löwenbräu Neuhaus Edel-Pilsner (4.9%)
Löwenbräu Neuhaus Hausbräu (5%)
Aischgründer Karpfen-Weisse (5.2%)
SEASONAL BEER:
Löwenbräu Neuhaus Festbier (5.5%)

Small brewery and tap in the centre of the village with its own distillery. There are no direct buses from Erlangen but you can get to Neuhaus on weekdays by taking the No. 205 to Adelsdorf and changing there for a No. 246 or 247.

🍺 **Zum Löwenbräu**

Neuhauser Hauptstraße 3,
91325 Adelsdorf-Neuhaus

Mon & Tue 17.30–23.00, Wed–Sun 10.00–14.00
& 17.30–23.00; rooms available
DB Erlangen 16km

NEUHAUS an der Pegnitz 414

Kaiser-Bräu

Kaiser-Bräu GmbH & Co. KG
Brewery: Auwaldstraße, 91284 Neuhaus/Pegnitz
Office: Oberer Markt 1, 91284 Neuhaus/Pegnitz
T 09156 880   **F** 09156 88 50
www.kaiser-braeu.de
Owner: Josef Laus   Founded: 1929
Output: 400,000hl   Availability: c.600 pubs
REGULAR BEERS:
Kaiser Light (2.5%)
Kaiser Pils (4.8%)
Kaiser Hell (4.9%)
Kaiser Weiße (5.2%)
Kaiser Weizen Kristallklar (5.2%)
Kaiser Export (5.6%)
Kaiser Jura Gold Märzen (5.9%)
VELDENSTEINER BEERS:
Veldensteiner Original Lager (4.9%),
Veldensteiner Premium Pils (4.9%),
Veldensteiner Weißbier (5.1%),
Veldensteiner Zwick'l (5.4%),
Echt Veldensteiner Landbier (5.4%)
SEASONAL BEER:
Veldensteiner Festbier (6%)
FOR WEISS RÖSSL, ROSSSTADT:
Weiss Rössl Urstoff Hell (4.9%), **Weiss Rössl
Pilsener** (4.9%), **Weiss Rössl Hefeweizen**
(5.2%), **Weiss Rössl Export** (5.5%)

Large brewery that moved to its present site
alongside the station in 1991. We think they may
brew beer for the four pubs formerly supplied by
the Kommunbrauerei. They also own Dorn-Bräu
in Vach, Simon in Lauf and Weiss Rössl of
Roßstadt, although we believe only Simon still
brews. The brewery tap is in the castle that
dominates the town.

Hotel Burg Veldenstein
Burgstraße 12, 91284 Neuhaus/Pegnitz
T 09156 633   **F** 09156 17 49
Closed Mon; Tue–Sun from 11.00; rooms available
DB Neuhaus (Pegnitz) 400m

NEUHAUS (Windischeschenbach) 415

Kommunbrauerei

Wurzer Straße,
92670 Windischeschenbach-Neuhaus
www.zoiglbier.de
Owner: Kommunbraugenossenschaft Neuhaus
Founded: 1415   Output: 800hl
Availability: 5 pubs
REGULAR BEERS:
Zoiglbier (5%)

Communal brewery that supplies five Zoigl
houses around the village. Each house opens
around ten times a year from Friday to Monday.
Dates are posted on the website but you'll have
to phone ahead for opening hours.

Bahler
Marktplatz 12, 92670 Windischeschenbach-
Neuhaus
T/F 09681 39 16

Beim Käck'n
Marktplatz 18, 92670 Windischeschenbach-
Neuhaus
T/F 09681 23 12

Schafferhof
Burgstraße 6, 92670 Windischeschenbach-
Neuhaus
T 09681 82 19

Sholmichl
Marktplatz 20, 92670 Windischeschenbach-
Neuhaus
T 09681 13 97   **F** 09681 91 74 27
DB Windischeschenbach 900m

Teicher
Marktplatz 4, 92670 Windischeschenbach-
Neuhaus
T 09681 21 28
All: DB Windischeschenbach 900m

NEUHAUSEN (Holzheim) 416

Bärenbräu

Hohlgasse 2, 89291 Holzheim-Neuhausen
T 07302 31 13   **F** 07302 67 36
www.baerenbraeu-neuhausen.de
Owner: Peter Stephan   Founded: 1996

REGULAR BEERS:
Bärenbräu Bären Hell
Bärenbräu Bären Weisse
Bärenbräu Neuhauser Märzen Römer Türmle
SEASONAL BEERS:
Bärenbräu Whisky-Bier, Bärenbräu Bären
Festbier, Bärenbräu Bären Bock

Although modern, this small brewery operates on traditional lines. The owner was previously brewer at several local breweries. Bus No. 78 runs from Neu-Ulm station daily but the Sunday service is poor.

Bärenbräu

Hohlgasse 2, 89291 Holzheim-Neuhausen
Closed Mon (in winter); Tue–Sat 10.00–24.00,
Sun & hols 09.00–24.00   DB Neu-Ulm 7km

NEUMARKT (Oberpfalz)   417

Gansbräu

Gansbrauerei Ludwig Ehrnsperger
Ringstraße 4, 92318 Neumarkt
T 09181 90 58 85   F 09181 226 44
E gansbrauerei@t-online.de
Founded: 1600   Output: 15,000hl
REGULAR BEERS:
Gansbräu Urtyp (4.6%)
Gansbräu Hell (4.9%)
Gansbräu Dunkel (5%)
Gansbräu Pils (5%)
Gansbräu Kellerpils (5%)
Gansbräu Weizen (5%)
SEASONAL BEER:
Gansbräu Festbier

The smallest of Neumarkt's three breweries is on the edge of the old town, opposite the end of Bahnhofstraße. The brewery tap is alongside.

Oberer Ganskeller

Ringstraße 2, 92318 Neumarkt
T 09181 90 74 86   F 09181 209 38
Mon 17.00–01.00, Tue–Fri 11.00–01.00,
Sat 10.00–01.00, Sun 10.00–17.00
DB Neumarkt (Oberpfalz) 500m

Glossner

Brauerei Franz Xaver Glossner & Neumarkter
Mineralbrunnen e.K.
Schwesterhausgasse 8–16, 92318 Neumarkt
T 09181 23 40   F 09181 234 60

www.glossner.de
Owner: Franz Xaver Glossner   Founded: 1574
Output: 40,000hl   Availability: 250 pubs
REGULAR BEERS:
Glossner Helle Wolke Leichtes Weizen (2.8%)
Glossner Dunkle Wolke Mehrkornbier (2.8%)
Glossner Torschmied's Dunkel (4.9%)
Glossner Original Neumarkter Gold (5%)
Glossner Original Neumarkter Bio-Gold (5.1%)
Glossner Hopfengarten Edel-Pils (5.1%)
Glossner Hefe-Weiss (5.3%)
Glossner Neumarkter Schwarzbier (5.6%)
Glossner Kristall-Weizen (5.6%)
SEASONAL BEERS:
Glossner Mai-Glöckl Festbier (5.3%),
Glossner Weihnachts-Glöckl Festbier (5.5%),
Glossner Neumarkter Gold Festbier (5.5%),
Glossner Mariahilfberger Weizenbock (6.5%)
FOR ALTDORFER BRAUHAUS, ALTDORF:
Altdorfer Hell (4.8%), **Altdorfer Pils** (4.8%)

Brewery built into the old town wall that has been in the Glossner family for 14 generations. The tap features a small museum.

Neumarkter Bräustüberl

Schwesterhausgasse 9, 92318 Neumarkt
T 09181 221 45   F 09181 234 55
Closed Sun; Mon & Wed–Sat 09.00–19.00,
Tue 09.00–23.00
DB Neumarkt (Oberpfalz) 750m

Neumarkter Lammsbräu

Neumarkter Lammsbräu Gebr. Ehrensperger e.K.
Amberger Straße 1, 92318 Neumarkt (Oberpfalz)
T 09181 40 40   F 09181 404 49
www.lammsbraeu.de
Owner: Dr. Franz Ehrnsperger   Founded: 1628
Output: 85,000hl
REGULAR BEERS:
Neumarkter Lammsbräu Schankbier (2.4%)
Lammsbräu Leichtes Hefeweizen (2.7%)
Neumarkter Lammsbräu Urstoff (4.7%)
Neumarkter Lammsbräu Pilsner (4.8%)
Neumarkter Lammsbräu Edel Pils (4.8%)
Neumarkter Lammsbräu Dunkel (4.8%)
Neumarkter Lammsbräu Dinkel (5.1%)
Lammsbräu Hefeweizen Weisse (5.1%)
Lammsbräu Hefeweizen Schwarze (5.1%)
Neumarkter Lammsbräu Kristall Weizen (5.1%)

Large brewery north of the town centre. They also own the Kleines Brauhaus in Pleinfeld. There's no brewery tap but the beers are

available over a wide area.
🚉 Neumarkt (Oberpfalz) 1.5km

northern Franconia. Bus No. 8306 runs from Kronach to Mitwitz Mon–Sat.
🚉 Kronach 11km

NEUNBURG vorm Wald 418

Weißes Brauhaus

Weißes Brauhaus Wolfgang Mehringer GmbH
Bachgasse 26, 92431 Neunburg vorm Wald
T 09672 871 **F** 09672 51 20
www.mehringer-weissbier.de
Founded: 1354
Output: 10,000hl Availability: c. 100 pubs
REGULAR BEERS:
Weißes Brauhaus Leichte Weisse (2.8%)
Weißes Brauhaus Altbayerisches Weißbier (4.9%)
Weißes Brauhaus Hussiten Weiße (4.9%)
Weißes Brauhaus Weißbier Dunkel (5.1%)
SEASONAL BEER:
Weißes Brauhaus Ruprechtus (7.3%)
NEUNBURG BRAUHAUS BEERS:
Brauhaus Pils (4.8%), **Brauhaus Helles** (4.9%),
Brauhaus Export (5.2%)

Small brewery in the old town, with the tap in the next street. We think the Neunburg Brauhaus beers may be brewed for Frankbräu which stopped brewing in 1997. Take bus No. 43 from Bodenwöhr Nord or No. 2511 from Schwandorf.

🍺 **Weißbierkeller**
Webergasse 16, 92431 Neunburg vorm Wald
Closed Sun–Tue & Thu; Wed & Fri–Mon from 19.00
🚉 Bodenwöhr Nord 12km, Schwandorf 25km

NEUNDORF (Mitwitz) 419

Franken Bräu

Franken Bräu Lorenz Bauer GmbH & Co. KG
Neundorf 41, 96268 Mitwitz-Neundorf
T 09266 721 **F** 09266 63 41
www.frankenbraeu.de Founded: 1520
Output: 80,000hl Availability: 300 pubs
REGULAR BEERS:
Franken Bräu Pilsener-Premium (4.9%)
Franken Bräu Schwarzbier Premium (5.4%)
Franken Bräu Weissbier (5.4%)
Franken Bräu Festbier (5.4%)

Regional brewery in the small village of Neundorf, a mile or so north of Mitwitz. There's no tap but the beers are widely available in

NEUNHOF (Lauf) 420

Wiethaler

Welserplatz 6–7, 91207 Lauf-Neunhof
T 09126 76 51 **F** 09126 42 54
Owner: Sabine Wiethaler-Dorn Founded: 1498
Output: 2,500hl
REGULAR BEERS:
Wiethaler Lager Hell (4.8%)
Wiethaler Landbier Dunkel (4.9%)
Wiethaler Neunhofer Pils (4.9%)
Wiethaler Weisse (5.2%)
SEASONAL BEERS:
Wiethaler Festbier (4.9%), **Wiethaler Bockbier**

Small brewery with an attractive half-timbered tap. Bus No. 315 runs from Lauf on weekdays, with one service going through to Eschenau.

🍺 **Brauerei-Gasthof**
Welserplatz 6, 91207 Lauf-Neunhof
T 09126 54 60
Closed Mon; Tue–Sun 11.30–21.00
🚉 Eschenau 3.5km, Lauf (r. Pegnitz) 7km

🍺 **Bräustüberl**
Welserplatz 6a, 91207 Lauf-Neunhof
T 09126 308 90
Closed Tue; Wed–Fri & Mon 17.00–23.00,
Sat & Sun & hols 11.00–14.00 & 17.00–23.00
🚉 Eschenau 3.5km, Lauf (r. Pegnitz) 7km

NEUNKIRCHEN (Brand) 421

Vasold & Schmitt

Privatbrauerei Vasold & Schmitt GmbH & Co. KG
Schellenberger Weg 3, 91077 Neunkirchen
T 09134 994 10 **F** 09134 99 41 23
Founded: 1888 Output: 20,000hl
REGULAR BEERS:
Vasold Fränkisches Vollbier (4.5%)
Vasold Pilsener (4.7%)
Vasold Urtyp (4.8%)
Vasold Benedikt Dunkel (5.4%)
Vasold Märzen (5.4%)
SEASONAL BEER:
Vasold Festbier (5.8%)

The brewery is on the south-western side of town but we don't think they have a tap. Bus No. 209 runs daily between Erlangen and Eschenau via Neunkirchen.

[DB] Eschenau 7km, Erlangen 12km

NEUÖTTING 422

Müllerbräu

Burghauser Straße 2, 84524 Neuötting
T 08671 976 00 **F** 08671 97 60 20
www.muellerbraeu.de
Owner: Reinhard Müller Founded: 1768
Output: 20,000hl Availability: c. 100 pubs
REGULAR BEERS:
Müllerbräu Leichte Weiße (2.9%)
Müllerbräu Pils (4.9%)
Müllerbräu Altbayerisch Dunkel (5.2%)
Müllerbräu Neuöttinger Export (5.2%)
Müllerbräu Weiße (5.3%)
Müllerbräu Dunkle Weiße (5.3%)
SEASONAL BEERS:
Müllerbräu Bockser,
Müllerbräu Jahrtausend-Bock (8.9%)

Town centre brewery with a Mexican-themed tap. Various buses run to Burghauser Straße from Altötting station but none do so from Neuötting.

🍺 El Loguito
Burghauser Straße 2, 84524 Neuötting
T 08671 24 33 **F** 08671 710 42
Closed Sun; Mon–Sat 11.00–01.00; rooms available [DB] Altötting 2.5km, Neuötting 3.1km

NEUSTADT an der Aisch 423

Kohlenmühle

Gasthof Hausbrauerei Kohlenmühle GmbH & Co.
Bamberger Straße 53, 91413 Neustadt an der Aisch
T 09161 66 22 70 **F** 09161 662 27 77
www.kohlenmuehle.de
Owner: Lothar Hufnagel Founded: 10.01.2005
Output: 1,000hl Availability: 1 pub
REGULAR BEERS:
Kohlenmühle Helles Landbier
Kohlenmühle Weizen
SEASONAL BEER:
Kohlenmühle Roter 12er,
Kohlenmühle Koksbock

Brewpub on the western side of Neustadt that opened early in 2005. Various bus routes run from the station into town.

🍺 Kohlenmühle
Bamberger Straße 53, 91413 Neustadt an der Aisch
Closed Mon in winter; Tue–Sun 10.00–24.00; rooms available
[DB] Neustadt (Aisch) 2.3km

NEU-ULM 424

Barfüßer

Paulstraße 4, 89231 Neu-Ulm
T 0731 97 44 80 **F** 0731 974 48 20
www.barfuesser-brauhaus.de
Founded: 1996 Availability: 1 pub
REGULAR BEERS:
Barfüßer Blonde (4.9%)
Barfüßer Schwarze (4.9%)
Barfüßer Weiße (4.9%)

Modern brewpub and hotel with a large beer garden on the south bank of the Donau. One of a chain of four across southern Germany.

🍺 Barfüßer
Paulstraße 4, 89231 Neu-Ulm
Daily 11.00–24.00; rooms available
[DB] Neu-Ulm 700m

Schlössle

Brauerei und Gasthof Schlössle
Schlössleweg 3, 89231 Neu-Ulm/Offenhausen
T 0731 773 90 **F** 0731 972 75 57
www.schloessle.com
Owners: the Zoller family Founded: 1690
Output: 1,300hl Availability: 1 pub
REGULAR BEERS:
Schlössle Zwickel
Schlössle Hefeweizen
Schlössle Spezial-Märzen
SEASONAL BEER:
Schlössle Bock

Brewpub in the suburb of Offenhausen, formerly a village in its own right. The beers are only available at the tap.

🍺 Schlössle
Schlössleweg 3, 89231 Neu-Ulm/Offenhausen
T 0731 773 90 **F** 0731 972 75 57

Closed Wed; Thu–Tue 10.30–23.00
`DB` Neu-Ulm 1.8km

NITTENAU 425

Nittenau

Brauhaus Nittenau Josef Jacob
Brauhausstraße 5, 93149 Nittenau
T 09436 82 09   **F** 09436 30 06 38
www.nittenauer-bier.de
Owner: Josef Jakob   Founded: 1923
Output: 3,000hl   Availability: 15 pubs
REGULAR BEERS:
Nittenauer Hell (4.9%)
Nittenauer Pils (5%)
Nittenauer Export (5.5%)
Nittenauer Stockenfelser Geisterbräu (5.5%)
SEASONAL BEER:
Nittenauer Festbier (5.9%)

Small brewery close to the river Regen. The brewery tap closes for the last two weeks of October and the first two in November. Buses Nos. 43 and 106 operate from Bodenwöhr Nord, the former running through to Regenstauf and Regensburg.

🍺 Jakob

Hauptstraße 10, 93149 Nittenau
T 09436 82 24   **F** 09436 31 83
Closed Wed & 15th Oct–15th Nov;
Thu–Tue 07.00–23.00
`DB` Bodenwöhr Nord 13km

NÖRDLINGEN 426

Ankerbräu

Ankerbrauerei Nördlingen GmbH & Co. KG
Ankergasse 4, 86720 Nördlingen
T 09081 29 06 00   **F** 09081 290 60 20
www.ankerbrauerei.de
Founded: 1608   Output: 30,000hl
REGULAR BEERS:
Ankerbräu Nördlinger Premium Pils (4.7%)
Ankerbräu Nördlinger Lager Hell (5%)
Ankerbräu Nördlinger Premium Ice (5%)
Ankerbräu Nördlinger Edel-Tropfen (5.5%)
Ankerbräu Rieser Hefeweizen (5.5%)
Ankerbräu Rieser Dunkles Weizen (5.5%)
Ankerbräu Rieser Kristallweizen (5.5%)

SEASONAL BEERS:
Ankerbräu Nördlinger Weihnachtsbier (5.7%),
Ankerbräu Mille Centenium (5.8%),
Ankerbräu Goldrausch (10%)

Small regional brewery in the walled town of Nördlingen. The brewery tap is on the opposite side of the town centre, not far from the central market square.

🍺 Zum Fuchs

Bei den Kornschrannen 20, 86720 Nördlingen
T 09081 44 71   **F** 09081 225 11
Closed Tue; Wed–Mon 09.30–24.00
`DB` Nördlingen 600m

NÜRNBERG 427

Altstadthof

Nürnberger Altstadthof e.K.
Bergstraße 19–21, 90403 Nürnberg-Sebald
T/F 0911 244 98 59
www.altstadthof.de
Owner: Richard Engel   Founded: 1984
Output: 1,000hl
REGULAR BEERS:
Altstadthof Helles (4.8%)
Altstadthof Schwarze (4.8%)
Altstadthof Weisse (4.8%)
Altstadthof Rothebier (5.2%)
SEASONAL BEERS:
Altstadthof Dunkel Bock (6.6%),
Altstadthof Maibock (6.6%)

The first of Germany's modern brewpubs, Altstadthof was opened in 1984 by Neumarkter Lammsbräu and sold to the current owner in 1998. They also have a bakery and a small distillery.

🍺 Schwarzer Bauer

Bergstraße 19, 90403 Nürnberg-Sebald
T 0911 22 72 17
Daily 11.00–01.00
`Tram` No. 4 Tiergärtnertor 250m
`DB` Nürnberg Hbf 1.4km

Barfüßer

Hallplatz 2, 90402 Nürnberg-Lorenz
T 0911 20 42 42   **F** 0911 20 41 86
www.barfuesser-brauhaus.de
Founded: 1994
Output: 2,500hl   Availability: 1 pub

REGULAR BEERS:
Barfüßer Blonde (4.9%)
Barfüßer Schwarze (4.9%)

The first of the Barfüßer chain which now owns brewpubs in Heilbronn, Neu-Ulm and Ulm. Housed in the cellar of a large building close to the main station.

📍 **Barfüßer**
Hallplatz 2, 90402 Nürnberg-Lorenz
Daily 11.00–01.00
Ⓤ U1 & U11 Lorenzkirche 200m
DB Nürnberg Hbf 400m

Tucher

Tucher Bräu GmbH & Co. KG
Brewery: Schillerstraße 14,
90409 Nürnberg-Maxfeld
Office: Schwabacher Straße 106, 90763 Fürth
T 0911 977 60   **F** 0971 977 63 70
Owner: Oetker Gruppe AG   Founded: 1672
REGULAR BEERS:
Tucher Light (2.9%)
Tucher Leichtes Hefe Weizen (2.9%)
Tucher Original Urbräu (4.8%)
Tucher Pilsener (4.9%)
Tucher Diät Pils (4.9%)
Tucher Urfränkisch Dunkel (5.2%)
Tucher Helles Hefe Weizen (5.3%)
Tucher Dunkles Hefe Weizen (5.3%)
Tucher Kristall Weizen (5.3%)
Tucher Übersee Export (5.3%)
SEASONAL BEERS:
Tucher Sebaldus Festbier (5.9%),
Tucher Christ-Kindlsmarkt Bier (6%, Dec),
Tucher Lorenzi Bock Hell (7.2%, Lent),
Tucher Bajuvator (7.2%)

Tucher have a second brewery in Fürth, the former home of Patrizier. We believe both sites still brew but aren't certain which beers are brewed where. If you can help, please contact us at GermanBreweries@aol.com

📍 **Tucher-Bräu am Opernhaus**
Am Kartäusertor 1, 90402 Nürnberg-Lorenz
T 0911 20 46 49   **F** 0911 20 32 22
Daily 11.00–24.00
Ⓤ U2 & U21 Opernhaus 30m
DB Nürnberg Hbf 500m

Weizenbierglasmuseum

Nürnberg Weizenbierglasmuseum & Hausbrauerei
Schupfer Straße 39, 90482 Nürnberg-Laufamholz
T 0911 50 24 98   **F** 0911 50 24 76
www.museumsvielfalt-nuernberg.de
Owner: Walter Geißler   Founded: 1995
Output: 5hl   Availability: 1 pub
REGULAR BEERS:
Geißler Weisse (5.2%)
Geißler 1. Laufamholzer Weisse (5.2%)
SEASONAL BEERS:
Geißler Mören Leichte-Weisse (5.2%),
Geißler Weizenbier Dunkel (5.2%),
Geißler Rauchweizen (5.4%),
Geißler's Geißplosator Weizenbock (6.5%),
Geißler Viagrotor Sechskornbier (6.8%),
Geißler Ebriosus Weizen-Doppelbock (8.5%)

We think this is the smallest commercial brewery in Germany. It's housed among the largest collection of wheat beer glasses in the world. Both brewery and museum are open by prior arrangement only.

📍 **Weizenbierglasmuseum**
Schupfer Straße 39, 90482 Nürnberg-Laufamholz
DB Nürnberg-Laufamholz 350m

OBERAILSFELD (Ahorntal)   428

Held-Bräu

Oberailsfeld 19, 95491 Ahorntal-Oberailsfeld
T 09242 295   **F** 09242 74 30 30
www.held-braeu.de
Owner: Helmut Polster   Founded: 1680
Output: 4,000hl   Availability: 15 pubs
REGULAR BEERS:
Held-Bräu Hell (4.9%)
Held-Bräu Pils (4.9%)
Held-Bräu Hefeweizen (5.4%)
Held-Bräu Alt-Fränkisches Bauernbier (5.5%)
SEASONAL BEERS:
Held-Bräu Weizenbock, Held-Bräu Bock (Lent)

Village brewery and tap in the heart of Fränkische Schweiz. Oberailsfeld can be reached by bus from both Ebermannstadt and Pegnitz on weekdays but it involves a change.

📍 **Held-Bräu**
Oberailsfeld 19, 95491 Ahorntal-Oberailsfeld
Closed Wed; Thu–Tue 10.00–23.00; rooms available   DB Ebermannstadt 19km, Pegnitz 19km

---

t: Gasthof zum Fuchs in Nördlingen,
of the town's Ankerbrauerei.

OBERASBACH
(Gunzenhausen)   429

Schorschbräu

Oberasbach 16a,
91710 Gunzenhausen-Oberasbach
T 09831 18 68   **F** 09831 61 28 30
www.schorschbraeu.de
Owner: Georg Tscheuschner
Founded: 1999   Output: 1,000hl
REGULAR BEERS:
Schorschbräu Hell (5%)
Schorschbräu Dunkel (5%)
SEASONAL BEERS:
Schorschbräu Donnerweizen (13%),
Schorschbräu Donnerbock (13%)

Brewpub in a village close to Gunzenhausen
that until recently brewed the strongest beers
in Germany. There is a bus from Gunzenhausen
that arrives around opening time (No. 621) but
nothing back afterwards.

🍴 **Baumgärtner**
Oberasbach 16,
91710 Gunzenhausen-Oberasbach
T 09831 24 29
Closed Mon; Tue–Sat from 17.00, Sun from 11.00
🚉 Gunzenhausen 4.3km

OBERAUDORF   430

Alpenrose

Rosenheimerstraße 3, 83080 Oberaudorf
T 08033 30 85 96   **F** 08033 30 85 97
www.alpenrose-wirt.de
Owners: Frank & Mona Müller   Founded: 2005
REGULAR BEER:
Alpenrose Helles

Wirtshaus Alpenrose started brewing early in
2005 and currently produces just one beer. The
more established Brauerei Bals is a few doors
closer to the station.

🍴 **Alpenrose**
Rosenheimerstraße 3, 83080 Oberaudorf
Closed Mon; Tue–Fri 15.00–01.00,
Sat, Sun & hols 10.00–02.00
🚉 Oberaudorf 600m

Bals

Oberaudorfer Weißbierbrauerei Bals KG
Rosenheimerstraße 21, 83080 Oberaudorf
T 08033 14 50   **F** 08033 30 92 94
www.brauerei-bals.de
Owners: Astrid & Renate Bals   Founded: 1927
Output: 2,000hl
REGULAR BEERS:
Oberaudorfer Goldweizen
Oberaudorfer Dunkles Weizen

Small wheat beer brewery in the centre of the
border town of Oberaudorf. We think the beers
are only available in a few other pubs.

🍴 **Bräustüberl**
Rosenheimerstraße 19, 83080 Oberaudorf
Closed Wed; Thu–Tue 09.00–23.00
🚉 Oberaudorf 500m

OBERBERNBACH (Aichach)   431

Berabecka Boandl-Bräu

Hauptstraße 36, 86551 Aichach-Oberbernbach
T 08251 523 55   **F** 08251 524 18
www.boandlbraeu.de
Owner: Manfred Fritsch   Founded: 1994
Output: 350hl   Availability: 4 pubs
REGULAR BEER:
Boandl-Bräu Export Hell (SW 12.5%)
SEASONAL BEERS:
Boandl-Bräu Export Dunkel (SW 12.5%),
Boandl-Bräu Mannipulator Hell (SW 17%),
Boandl-Bräu Mannipulator Dunkel (ST 17%)

Brewpub run more like a British microbrewery
than a typical German example. Oberbernbach
is on the opposite side of the railway and river
Paar to Aichach.

🍴 **Bräustüberl**
Hauptstraße 36, 86551 Aichach-Oberbernbach
Closed Mon & Tue; Wed–Fri 17.00–01.00, Sat
10.00–13.00 & 17.00–01.00, Sun 10.00–13.00
🚉 Aichach 1.2km

OBERDACHSTETTEN   432

Haag

Hauptstraße 18, 91617 Oberdachstetten
T 09845 206   **F** 09845 410

www.brauerei-haag.de
Owners: Christa Haag-Lohner
Founded: 1720   Output: 2,500hl
REGULAR BEERS:
Haag Landbier (4.8%)
Haag Vollbier (4.9%)
Haag Pilsener (4.9%)
Haag Oberdachstetter Hefeweizen (5.6%)
SEASONAL BEER:
Haag Bockbier (7%)

Traditional brewery in the small town of Oberdachstetten. All draught beers come from the wood.

Haag
Hauptstraße 18, 91617 Oberdachstetten
Closed Mon; Tue–Sun 11.00–14.00 & from 17.00
DB Oberdachstetten 400m

OBERHACHING 433

Stadlbräu

Kybergstraße 19, 82041 Oberhaching
T 089 9544 75 65
www.bayerische-brauhaus-consulting.de
Founded: 2004
REGULAR BEERS:
Stadlbräu Dunkel Spezial (4.9%)
Stadlbräu Weißbier (4.9%)

Microbrewery; we don't think they supply any pubs regularly but the beers are available to take away from the brewery Mon–Thu 09.00–12.00 & 13.00–17.00 and Fri 09.00–13.00.
DB Deisenhofen 1.1km

OBERHAID 434

Wagner

Bamberger Straße 2, 96173 Oberhaid
T 09503 229   F 09503 41 51
Owner: Klaus Bendner   Founded: 1550
Output: 2,000hl
REGULAR BEERS:
Wagner-Bräu Kellerbier (4.8%)
Wagner-Bräu Vollbier (5.2%)
Wagner-Bräu Pils (5.2%)
Wagner-Bräu Märzen (5.8%)

Brewery and tap on the main road through town. We think the beers are only available at the tap and the brewery's Bierkeller.

Zum Hannla
Bamberger Straße 2, 96173 Oberhaid
Daily 10.00–01.00
DB Oberhaid 500m

OBERLEINLEITER
(Heiligenstadt) 435

Ott

Oberleinleiter 6,
91332 Heiligenstadt-Oberleinleiter
T 09198 99 76 49   F 09198 594
www.brauerei-ott.de
Owner: Manfred Ott   Founded: 1678
Output: 8,000hl   Availability: 6 pubs
REGULAR BEERS:
Ott Edel-Pils (4.9%)
Ott Export-Bier (5.1%)
Ott Obaladara (5.1%)
Ott Weißbier (5.2%)
SEASONAL BEERS:
Ott Festbier (5.8%, Nov–Jan),
Ott Bockbier (6.5%, Feb–May)

Village brewery and tap on the western side of Fränkische Schweiz. Bus No. 8235 runs from Bamberg and Ebermannstadt on weekdays.

Ott
Oberleinleiter 6,
91332 Heiligenstadt-Oberleinleiter
T 09198 271
Closed Mon; Tue–Sun 09.00–23.00
DB Ebermannstadt 15km, Bamberg 22km

OBERNDORF (Bad Abbach) 436

Berghammer

Donaustraße 55, 93077 Bad Abbach-Oberndorf
T 09405 96 21 79   F 09405 96 21 77
www.brauerei-berghammer.de
Owner: Johann Berghammer   Founded: 1800
Output: 1,150hl   Availability: 1 pub
REGULAR BEERS:
Berghammer Helles (5.6%)
Berghammer Weizen-Bier (5.6%)
Berghammer Kupfer (5.6%)
SEASONAL BEER:
Berghammer Bock Dunkel (7%)

Small brewery and tap near Bad Abbach. The pub is less than 1km from Gundelshausen station but unfortunately the Danube is in the way. You may find it more convenient to catch a bus from Regensburg than from Bad Abbach station.

🍺 Berghammer
Donaustraße 55, 93077 Bad Abbach-Oberndorf
T 09405 96 21 76
Closed Tue; Wed–Fri, Sun & Mon 12.00–24.00, Sat 12.00–19.00
DB Bad Abbach 7km

OBERREICHENBACH   437

Geyer
Brauerei & Brennerei Geyer
Hauptstraße 18, 91097 Oberreichenbach
T 09104 28 02   **F** 09104 82 44 19
andreas:geyer@o2online.de
Owner: Reinhard Geyer   Founded: 1894
Output: 1,200hl
REGULAR BEERS:
Oberreichenbacher Pils (4.8%)
Oberreichenbacher Helles Landbier (4.9%)
Oberreichenbacher Hausbräu (4.9%)
Oberreichenbacher Hefeweizen
SEASONAL BEER:
Oberreichenbacher Festbier

Half-timbered brewery, distillery and tap in the centre of the village. The only other pub supplied is the Felsenkeller on Tanzenhaider Weg. Although only 7km from Emskirchen, Erlangen's the best place to catch a bus from.

🍺 Geyer
Hauptstraße 18, 91097 Oberreichenbach
Closed Tue; Wed, Thu, & Mon 09.00–14.00 & 17.00–23.00, Fri–Sun 09.00–23.00; rooms available
DB Erlangen 22km

OBERROTH   438

Reittinger
Brauerei und Gastwirtschaft Josef Reitinger
Hauptstraße 26, 89294 Oberroth
T 08333 12 13
Owner: Josef Reitinger   Founded: 1860
Output: 1,000hl

REGULAR BEERS:
Reitinger Hell
Reitinger Dunkel
Reitinger Pils
Reitinger Hefe-Weizen
Reitinger Märzen
SEASONAL BEER:
Reitinger Bock

Small brewery in the centre of the village that we think only supplies the tap. Bus No. 920 runs from Illertissen on weekdays.

🍺 Reitinger
Hauptstraße 26, 89294 Oberroth
Daily from 08.00; rooms available
DB Illertissen 10km

OBERSCHLEICHACH
(Oberaurach)   439

Zenglein
Pfarrer-Baumann-Straße 23, 97514 Oberaurach-Oberschleichach
T 09529 922 40   **F** 09529 92 24 44
Owner: Friedrich & Karin Zenglein
Founded: 1846   Output: 2,000hl
REGULAR BEERS:
Zenglein Pils (4.7%)
Zenglein Zwickel (4.7%)
SEASONAL BEER:
Zenglein Bock

Brewery and tap in the centre of the village. We're not sure if the beers are sold in any other pubs. Bus No. 8178 from Haßfurt weekdays only is probably the best option for those without a car.

🍺 Zenglein
Pfarrer-Baumann-Straße 21, 97514 Oberaurach-Oberschleichach
Closed Tue & Wed; Thu–Mon from 09.00; rooms available   DB Haßfurt 13km

OBERSTDORF   440

Dampfbierbrauerei
Oberstdorfer Dampfbierbrauerei
Bahnhofplatz 6, 87561 Oberstdorf
T 08322 89 08   **F** 08322 88 77
www.dampfbierbrauerei.de
Owners: Christa & Michael Venzky

Founded: 1992   Output: 1,500hl
REGULAR BEERS:
Dampfbier Hell
Dampfbier Dunkel
SEASONAL BEERS:
Dampfbier Weizen, Dampfbier Märzen,
Dampfbier Bock

Brewpub alongside the railway station that also supplies the station bar with its steam beers. Its opening in 1992 ended 60 years of Oberstdorf being a brewery-free town.

🍺 **Dampfbierbrauerei**
Bahnhofplatz 6, 87561 Oberstdorf
Daily 11.00–01.00
DB Oberstdorf 20m

OBERTHÜRHEIM
(Buttenwiesen)   441

Oberthürheimer Bio-Bräu

Bioland-Hof Wagner
Ulrich-Von-Thürheim-Straße 56a, 86647 Buttenwiesen-Oberthürheim
T 08274 16 47   **F** 08274 92 87 40
Owner: Josef Wagner   Founded: 2000
REGULAR BEER:
Oberthürheimer Bio-Bräu (5.5%)

Very small brewery, part of a business producing organic food. They don't have a tap that we're aware of but the farm shop is open Tue & Sat 08.00–12.00, Fri 08.00–18.00. The only day you can get here by bus during opening hours is Friday.
DB Nordendorf 13km

OBERWALLENSTADT
(Lichtenfels)   442

Wichert

Alte Reichsstraße 50,
96215 Lichtenfels-Oberwallenstadt
T 09571 33 17   **F** 09571 94 85 12
Owners: Michael & Rainer Wichert
Founded: 1863   Output: 3,000hl
Availability: 1 pub
REGULAR BEERS:
Wichert Pils
Wichert Kellerbier

SEASONAL BEER:
Wichert Doppelbock (winter)

Brewpub close to the river Main in the village of Oberwallenstadt which has almost been swallowed up by Lichtenfels. Take buses Nos. 1 or 2 to Brückenberg if you don't fancy the walk.

🍺 **Wichert**
Alte Reichsstraße 50,
96215 Lichtenfels-Oberwallenstadt
Closed Mon; Tue–Sun 10.00–24.00
DB Lichtenfels 2.4km

OCHSENFURT   443

Kauzen-Bräu

Kauzen-Bräu GmbH & Co. KG
Uffenheimer Straße 17, 97199 Ochsenfurt
T 09331 872 50   **F** 09331 87 25 48
www.kauzen.de
Owner: Karl-Heinz Pritzl   Founded: 1809
Output: 75,000hl   Availability: c.200 pubs
REGULAR BEERS:
Kauzen Helles Landbier (4.8%)
Kauzen Premium Pils (5%)
Kauzen Weissbier Hell (5%)
Kauzen Weissbier Dunkel (5%)
Kauzen Kristall Weizen (5%)
Kauzen Alt Fränkisch (5.1%)
Kauzen Original 1809 (5.2%)
SEASONAL BEERS:
Kauzen Festbier (5.8%), **Kauzen Winter-Weisse** (7.1%), **Kauzen Bock** (7.1%)

Large regional brewery on the main road south out of the town. The tap is on the high street in the largely half-timbered centre of Ochsenfurt. A *Kauz* is a screech owl, the bird featured on the labels. They also distil a beer schnapps.

🍺 **Zum Kauzen**
Hauptstraße 37, 97199 Ochsenfurt
T 09331 22 37   **F** 09331 807 82
Closed Tue; Wed–Mon 07.30–24.00; rooms available   DB Ochsenfurt 450m

Oechsner

D. Oechsner Ankerbräu KG
Klinge 2, 97199 Ochsenfurt
T 09331 876 60   **F** 09331 87 66 33
www.oechsner.de
Owners: the Oechsner family   Founded: 1863

Output: 45,000hl   Availability: c.100 pubs
REGULAR BEERS:
Oechsner Lager (4.9%)
Oechsner Premium Pils (4.9%)
Oechsner Schwarzbier (5%)
Oechsner Hefeweizen (5.2%)
Oechsner Märzen Gold (5.5%)
SEASONAL BEER:
Oechsner Bock (7%)

Like Kauzen, Oechsner's brewery is south of the town centre, the tap being in the old town on the street leading to the old bridge over the Main.

🍺 Zum Anker
Brückenstraße 10, 97199 Ochsenfurt
T 09331 74 09   **F** 09331 98 07 15
Closed Mon; Tue–Sun 10.00–24.00; rooms available   DB Ochsenfurt 700m

OESLAU (Rödental)   444

Grosch

Gasthof Hotel Brauerei Grosch GmbH
Oeslauer Straße 115, 96472 Rödental-Oeslau
T 09563 75 00   **F** 09563 75 01 47
Owner: Kerstin Pilarzyk   Founded: 1492
Output: 3,000hl   Availability: 8 pubs
REGULAR BEERS:
Grosch Pilsner (4.9%)
Grosch Zwickl (5%)
Grosch Fuhrmannstrunk (5.3%)
SEASONAL BEERS:
Grosch Erntebier (3%, Apr–Sep),
Grosch Bock (7%, Nov–Mar)

Brewery and tap opposite the Rödental station, although they are in fact in Oeslau, Rödental being the name of the valley. They do brewery tours in English for groups of four or more.

🍺 Grosch
Oeslauer Straße 115, 96472 Rödental-Oeslau
Daily 08.00–23.00; rooms available
DB Rödental 50m

OETTINGEN   445

Oettinger

Oettinger Brauerei GmbH
Brauhausstraße 8, 86732 Oettingen
T 09082 70 80   **F** 09082 708 10

www.oettinger-bier.de
Owners: Oettinger Gruppe   Founded: 1731
Output: 1,500,000hl
REGULAR BEERS:
Original Oettinger Leicht (2.8%)
Original Oettinger Leichte Weiße (2.8%)
Original Oettinger Vollbier Hell (4.7%)
Original Oettinger Pils (4.7%)
Original Oettinger Alt (4.9%)
Original Oettinger Gold (4.9%)
Original Oettinger Schwarzbier (4.9%)
Original Oettinger Hefeweißbier (4.9%)
Original Oettinger Dunkles Weißbier (4.9%)
Original Oettinger Kristall Weizen (4.9%)
Original Oettinger Export (5.4%)
Original Oettinger Urtyp (5.6%)
SEASONAL BEER:
Original Oettinger Winterbier (5.6%)

The main brewery of the Oettinger group, still owned by the Kollmar family. Oettinger beers are also brewed in the company's breweries in Dessow, Gotha, Mönchengladbach & Wüstmark. Bottles are labelled with the brewery of origin. Buses Nos. 648 & 649 run from Gunzenhausen on weekdays.

🍺 Zur Post
Königstraße 14, 86732 Oettingen
T 09082 22 14   **F** 09082 92 15 47
Closed Wed; Thu–Tue 11.00–23.30
DB Gunzenhausen 25km

OSTERBERG   446

Deil

Privatbrauerei Deil
Babenhauser Straße 2, 89296 Osterberg
T 08333 94 69 40   **F** 08333 946 94 33
www.deil.de
Owner: Georg Deil   Founded: 1876
Output: 15,000hl
REGULAR BEERS:
Deil Urtyp
Deil Zwickel
Deil Pils
Deil Weizen-Hell
Deil Weizen-Dunkel
Deil Export
Deil Märzen

The brewery tap opens on roughly one weekend a month and on few other days during the year.

See the website or phone for details. Buses Nos. 712 and 925 run from Kelmünz on weekdays.

🍺 **Braumeisterei**
Babenhauser Straße 2, 89296 Osterberg
DB Kellmünz 6km

OSTHEIM vor der Rhön   447

Peter

Privatbrauerei Peter KG
Nordheimer Straße 14,
97645 Ostheim vor der Rhön
T 09777 910 10   **F** 09777 14 53
Owner: Sigrid Peter-Leopold   Founded: 1827.
Output: 10,000hl   Availability: c. 50 pubs
REGULAR BEERS:
Rhön Pils (4.9%)
Rhön Pils Exquisit (4.9%)
Rhön Kellerbier
Rhön Export (5.1%)
Rhön Weiße
FOR EICHBERG BRAUEREI, EISFELD:
Eisfelder Pils (4.9%),
Eisfelder Export (5.4%)

Small brewery on the western edge of town that specialises in Bionade, an organic lemonade that's become a cult drink. The tap is opposite. Bus No. 8153 runs from Mellrichstadt station on weekdays.

🍺 **Braustüble**
Nordheimer Straße 9,
97645 Ostheim vor der Rhön
T 09777 35 89 99
Closed Mon; Tue–Sun 10.00–24.00
DB Mellrichstadt 9km

Streck

Streck-Bräu e.K.
Ludwig-Jahn-Straße 11,
97645 Ostheim vor der Rhön
T 09777 92 65   **F** 09777 92 68
www.streck-bier.de
Owner: Axel Kochinki   Founded: 1718
Output: 25,000hl   Availability: c.300 pubs
REGULAR BEERS:
Streck's Ostheim Dunkel (4.5%)
Streck's Burgherren Pils (4.8%)
Streck's Export (5.2%)
Streck's Weizen (5.4%)

SEASONAL BEER:
Streck's Fest-Bock (7.2%)

The larger of Ostheim's two breweries is on the southern side of town. The tap in the centre of town was the former site of the brewery.

🍺 **Zur Krone**
Marktstraße 34, 97645 Ostheim vor der Rhön
T 09777 35 04 48   **F** 09777 35 04 49
Closed Thu; Fri–Wed 11.00–01.00
DB Mellrichstadt 8km

OTTOBEUREN   448

Kleines Brauhaus am Kloster

Luitpoldstraße 42, 87724 Ottobeuren
T 08332 92 50 02
Owner: Sonja Schimon   Founded: 09.04.2005
REGULAR BEERS:
Kleines Brauhaus am Kloster Hell
Kleines Brauhaus am Kloster Dunkel
SEASONAL BEER:
Kleines Brauhaus am Kloster Weizenbock

Recently opened brewpub in what we think was once the tap for the town's Benediktinerbrauerei. The owner is the daughter of Memminger's head brewer. They brew other seasonals in addition to the Weizenbock but we have no details. Bus No. 955 runs daily from Memmingen.

🍺 **Kleines Brauhaus am Kloster**
Luitpoldstraße 42, 87724 Ottobeuren
Daily 11.00–01.00   DB Memmingen 14km

PAHRES (Gutenstetten)   449

Hofmann

Privatbrauerei Hofmann GmbH & Co. KG
Dettendorfer Straße 1,
91468 Gutenstetten-Pahres
T 09163 998 70   **F** 09163 99 87 18
www.hofmann-bier.de
Owner: Georg Hofmann   Founded: 1663
Output: 30,000hl
REGULAR BEERS:
Hofmann Lager (4.5%)
Hofmann Helles Landbier (4.8%)
Hofmann Hopfengold Premium Pils (4.9%)
Hofmann Ex (4.9%)
Hofmann Alt Pahreser Dunkel (5%)

SEASONAL BEERS:
Hofmann Pils aus Pahres (5%), **Hofmann Fest-märzen** (5.3%), **Hofmann Weihnachts-Festbier** (5.3%), **Hofmann Weissbier** (5.4%), **Hofmann Kerwabier** (5.4%), **Hofmann Doppelbock** (7.5%)

Brewery in the small village of Pahres. Bus No. 127 runs from Neustadt Mon–Sat and there is one bus back after the tap opens.

🏠 Hofmann
Braugasse 1, 91468 Gutenstetten-Pahres
T 09163 998 70   **F** 09163 99 87 18
Closed Mon, Wed & Sat; Sun from 17.00, Tue, Thu & Fri from 18.00
DB Neustadt (Aisch) Bf 8km

PASSAU · 450

Andorfer
Weizenbierbrauerei Thomas Andorfer
Rennweg 2, 94034 Passau-Ries
T/F 0851 75 35 84
Owner: Thomas Andorfer   Founded: 1919
Output: 2,000hl
REGULAR BEER:
Andorfer Weizen (4.8%)
SEASONAL BEERS:
Andorfer Weizenbock (6.2%),
Andorfer Weizendoppelbock (7.7%)

Small wheat beer brewery on the hill above Brauerei Hacklberg. There are two ways to walk there from town – up the twisting Neue Rieser Straße or the more direct Alte Riese Straße. Alternatively, you can save your breath and use one of several bus routes that pass the pub.

🏠 Andorfer
Rennweg 2, 94034 Passau-Ries
T 0851 75 44 44
Closed Mon; Tue–Sun 09.30–24.00
DB Passau Hbf 2km

Hacklberg
Brauerei Hacklberg e.K.
Bräuhausplatz 3, 94034 Passau-Hacklberg
T 0851 501 50   **F** 0851 50 15 50
www.hacklberg.de
Founded: 1618   Output: 160,000hl
REGULAR BEERS:
Hacklberg Leicht

Hacklberg Jacobi Weißbier Leicht
Hacklberg Urhell (4.9%)
Hacklberg Zwickl (4.9%)
Hacklberg Hochfürst Pilsener (5%)
Hacklberg Ex
Hacklberg Dunkel Spezial (5.2%)
Hacklberg Edelhell Export (5.2%)
Hacklberg 375 Jahre Jubiläumsbier (5.5%)
Hacklberg Jacobi Weißbier Hell (5.5%)
Hacklberg Jacobi Weißbier Dunkel (5.5%)
SEASONAL BEERS:
Hacklberg Festbier (5.5%), **Hacklberg Weihnachtstrunk** (5.5%), **Hacklberg Dultfestbier** (5.5%), **Hacklberg Humorator** (7%)

Large, attractive brewery on the other side of the Danube from the railway station. The brewery tap is opposite.

🏠 Hacklberger Bräustüberl
Bräuhausplatz 7, 94034 Passau-Hacklberg
T 0851 583 82   **F** 0851 75 22 13
Sun 09.00–23.00, Mon–Sat 09.00–01.00
DB Passau Hbf 1.5km

Innstadt
Innstadt Brauerei Bierspezialitäten GmbH
Schmiedgasse 23, 94032 Passau-Innstadt
T 0851 38 90   **F** 0851 389 55
www.innstadt.de
Founded: 1318
Output: 77,000hl   Availability: c. 100 pubs
REGULAR BEERS:
Innstadt Leicht & Hell (2.9%)
Innstadt Leichte Weisse (2.9%)
Innstadt Original Hell (4.9%)
Innstadt Neues Helles (5%)
Innstadt Pilsener (5%)
Innstadt Extra Schwarz (5.1%)
Innstadt Export (5.2%)
Innstadt Original Edelsud (5.2%)
Innstadt Neue Weisse (5.2%)
Innstadt Hefe-Weißbier (5.3%)
Innstadt Dunkles-Weißbier (5.3%)
Innstadt Kristall Weizen (5.3%)
Innstadt Bock Weisse (7%)
SEASONAL BEERS:
Innstadt Festbier (5.4%), **Innstadt Stadl-Bier** (5.4%), **Innstadt d'Inn'Staade** (5.6%, winter), **Innstadt Kapuziner-Doppelbock** (7.2%)

Brewery in the suburb of Innstadt on the opposite side of the river Inn from the town centre. The tap has recently changed.

🍺 Inn.Bräu

Kapuzinerstraße 6, 94032 Passau-Innstadt
T 0851 966 49 46
Closed Sun; Mon–Sat 10.00–1.00
[DB] Passau Hbf 1.6km

Löwenbrauerei

Bayerische Löwenbrauerei Franz Stockbauer
Franz-Stockbauer-Weg 13, 94032 Passau/
Haidenhof-Süd
T 0851 700 50 **F** 0851 70 05 10
www.loewenbrauerei.de
Founded: 1874 Output: 100,000hl
REGULAR BEERS:
Löwenbrauerei Passau Leichtes Weizen (3%)
Löwenbrauerei Passau Leichtes Helles (3.1%)
Löwenbrauerei Passau Urtyp Hell (4.8%)
Löwenbrauerei Passau Pils (4.9%)
Löwenbrauerei Passau Spezial Dunkel (5.2%)
Löwenbrauerei Passau Dunkle Weisse (5.2%)
Löwenbrauerei Passau Export Hell (5.3%)
Löwenbrauerei Passau Hefe Weißbier (5.3%)
SEASONAL BEER:
**Löwenbrauerei Passau Maibier, Löwenbrauerei
Passau Festbier** (5.8%), **Löwenbrauerei
Weihnachts-Festbier**

The brewery is south of the station, the tap in
front on the square. We think they may brew
beers for Schlossbrauerei Haselbach.

🍺 Löwenbräu-Stüberl

Kleiner Exerzierplatz 16–17,
94032 Passau/Haidenhof-Süd **T** 0851 64 97
Sun 10.00–15.00, Mon–Sat 10.00–23.00
[DB] Passau Hbf 600m

Peschl

Brauerei E.F. Peschl
Brewery: Roßtränke 6, 94032 Passau-Altstadt
Office: Auerspergstraße 2, 94032 Passau/
Haidenhof-Nord
T 0851 540 41 **F** 0851 739 59
www.peschl-braeu.de Owner: Ernst Peschl
Founded: 1259 Output: 20,000hl
REGULAR BEERS:
Peschl Bräu Leicht (2.8%)
Peschl Bräu Leichte Weisse (2.9%)
Peschl Bräu Ur-Hell (4.7%)
Peschl Bräu Meistertrunk (4.9%)
Peschl Bräu Pils (4.9%)
Peschl Bräu Zwickelbier (4.9%)

Peschl Bräu Original 1855 (5.1%)
Peschl Bräu Altbairisches Weißbier (5.1%)
Peschl Bräu Dunkle Weisse (5.1%)
Peschl Bräu Gold Spezial (5.2%)
SEASONAL BEERS:
Peschl Bräu Festbier (5.3%),
Peschl Bräu Stephanus Doppelbock (7.5%)

The oldest of Passau's breweries is split
between two locations. Brewing and primary
fermentation takes place next door to the tap in
the old town. Administration, maturation and
filling are done in buildings next to the railway
on the western side of the station.

🍺 Peschl-Terrasse

Roßtränke 4, 94032 Passau-Altstadt
T 0851 24 89 **F** 0851 340 13
Closed Mon; Tue–Sun 10.00–24.00
[DB] Passau Hbf 600m

PEGNITZ 451

Brauer-Vereinigung

Brauer-Vereinigung Pegnitz GmbH
Am Buchauer Berg 4, 91257 Pegnitz
T 09241 20 35 **F** 09241 35 75
www.brauervereinigung.de Founded: 1923
Output: 5,000hl Availability: 22 pubs
REGULAR BEERS:
Böheim Hell
Böheim Pils
Böheim Altfränkisch Landbier
SEASONAL BEERS:
**Böheim Flinderer Spezialbier, Böheim Festbier,
Böheim Bock**

The brewery was founded by a group of local
communal brewers in 1923. Although there's no
brewery tap, the beers are easy to find in Pegnitz.
[DB] Pegnitz 1km

Jura-Bräu

Am Buchauer Berg 8–10, 91257 Pegnitz
T 09241 20 19 **F** 09241 25 22
www.jura-braeu.de
Owner: Wilhelm Knopf Founded: 1900
Output: 10,000hl Availability: 35 pubs
REGULAR BEERS:
Jura Lager
Jura Anno 1900
Jura Pils

SEASONAL BEER:
Jura Flindererbier

Next door to the Brauer-Vereinigung brewery, Jura-Bräu is slightly larger. Like the former, the brewery doesn't have a specific tap.

`DB` Pegnitz 1km

PFAFFENBERG
(Mallersdorf-Pfaffenberg)   452

Stöttner

Privatbrauerei Stöttner GmbH
Marktplatz 9, 84066 Mallersdorf-Pfaffenberg
T 08772 960 80   **F** 08772 96 08 40
www.stoettner.de
Owners: Andreas & Karl Stöttner   Founded: 1832
Output: 10,000hl   Availability: 30 pubs
REGULAR BEERS:
Stöttner Pfaffenberger Leichte Weisse (2.9%)
Stöttner Lager (4.8%)
Stöttner Neues Helles (4.8%)
Stöttner Pfaffenberger Ur-Pils (4.8%)
Stöttner Schwarzer Pfaff (5%)
Stöttner Export Hell (5.5%)
Stöttner Pfaffenberger Original Weisse (5.5%)
Stöttner Pfaffenberger Dunkle Weisse (5.5%)
Stöttner Pfaffen Gold (5.9%)
SEASONAL BEERS:
Stöttner Festbier (5.9%), **Stöttner Weißbierbock** (6.5%, Christmas), **Stöttner Pfaffenator** (7.6%, Lent)

Brewery in the centre of town that supplies a number of pubs locally in addition to the tap. The closest railway station is in the nearby village of Niederlindhardt.

Stöttner
Marktplatz 9, 84066 Mallersdorf-Pfaffenberg
Closed Mon & Tue; Wed–Sun 10.00–24.00
`DB` Niederlindhardt 1.3km

PFAFFENHAUSEN   453

Storchenbräu

Storchenbräu Hans Roth GmbH & Co. KG
Kirchplatz 5-7, 87772 Pfaffenhausen
T 08265 70 22   **F** 08265 70 25
www.storchenbraeu.de
Owner: Hans Roth   Founded: 1804
Output: 25,000hl   Availability: c.100 pubs

REGULAR BEERS:
Storchen Leicht (2.6%)
Storchenbräu Störchle (4.8%)
Storchen Bayrisch Hell (4.9%)
Storchenbräu Schwarzstörchle (4.9%)
Storchen Pils (5%)
Storchen Dunkel (5.3%)
Storchen Export (5.3%)
Storchen Spezial (5.9%)
SEASONAL BEER:
Storchenbräu Stephanus Bock Dunkel (6.4%)

Brewery close to the centre of the small town of Pfaffenhofen with the tap is alongside. Perhaps unsurprisingly, storks are regular visitors to the brewery's chimney.

Zum Storchen
Kirchplatz 7, 87772 Pfaffenhausen
T 08265 91 17 44
Closed Mon; Tue–Sun 11.00–14.00 & 17.00–24.00
`DB` Pfaffenhausen 600m

PFAFFENHOFEN an der Ilm   454

Müllerbräu

Müllerbräu GmbH & Co. KG
Hauptplatz 36, 85276 Pfaffenhofen
T 08441 785 50   **F** 08441 78 55 11
www.muellerbraeu.com
Founded: 1640   Output: 20,000hl
REGULAR BEERS:
Müllerbräu Heimer Leicht (2.9%)
Müllerbräu Ilmthaler Leichte Weiße (2.9%)
Müllerbräu Altbayrisch Hell (5%)
Müllerbräu Hopfenland Pils (5%)
Müllerbräu Müller's Weißbier Premium (5.5%)
Müllerbräu Müller's Dunkle Weiße (5.5%)
SEASONAL BEER:
Müllerbräu Bavariator (7%)

Small regional brewery on the central square. The brewery tap is at the other end of the Stadtplatz close to the town hall. Another pub with particularly early opening hours.

Müller
Hauptplatz 2, 85276 Pfaffenhofen
T 08441 493 70   **F** 08441 49 37 40
Sun 06.00–15.00, Mon–Sat 06.00–24.00; rooms available
`DB` Pfaffenhofen (Ilm) 850m

Urbanus

Brauhaus Pfaffenhofen a. d. Ilm Urban KG
Kellerstraße 36, 85276 Pfaffenhofen
T 08441 75 30 **F** 08441 753 34
www.brauhaus-pfaffenhofen.de
Founded: 1612 Output: 50,000hl
REGULAR BEERS:
Urbanus Leicht
Urbanus Leichte Weisse
Urbanus Premium Hell (4.9%)
Urbanus Edel-Pils (4.9%)
Urbanus Hopfen-Stoff (4.9%)
Urbanus Spezial Export (5.3%)
Urbanus Brauhaus-Weizen Hell (5.5%)
Urbanus Brauhaus-Weizen Dunkel (5.5%)
Urbanus Altbayrisch Dunkel (5.5%)
Urbanus Kellerweizen (5.5%)
SEASONAL BEERS:
Urbanus Festmärzen (5.5%),
Urbanus St. Urbanus Bock (7.5%)

The larger of Pfaffenhofen's two breweries,
Urbanus is near Müllerbräu on the western side
of the town centre. The Kellerweizen is made
with champagne yeast.

🍺 Zum Wohlherrn

Hauptplatz 13, 85276 Pfaffenhofen
T 08441 753 13
Sat 10.00–14.00, Sun–Fri 10.00–23.00
DB Pfaffenhofen (Ilm) 900m

Gässlbräu

Brauerei Alois Gässl GmbH & Co. KG
Alois-Gässl-Straße 1, 84347 Pfarrkirchen
T 08561 14 36 **F** 08561 718 12
www.gaesslbraeu.de Founded: 1630
Owner: Burgl Schiedermair Output: 8,000hl
REGULAR BEERS:
Gässl-Bräu Vollbier-Hell (4.7%)
Gässl-Bräu Pilsner (4.9%)
Gässl-Bräu Hefe-Weiss (5.1%)
Gässl-Bräu Hefe-Weiss Dunkel (5.1%)
Gässl-Bräu Export (5.2%)
SEASONAL BEER:
Gässl-Bräu Festbier (5.6%)

Small brewery in the town centre. We don't think
they have an official tap any more but the beers
are fairly easy to find around Pfarrkirchen.
DB Pfarrkirchen 350m

Pöllinger

Anton Pöllinger, Brauerei e.K.
Moosburger Straße 65, 84076 Pfeffenhausen
T 08782 960 60 **F** 08782 96 06 30
www.brauerei-poellinger.de
Owner: Hans-Peter Pöllinger-Rank
Founded: 1474 Output: 20,000hl
REGULAR BEERS:
Pfeffenhausener Helles (4.9%)
Pfeffenhausener Pils (4.9%)
Pfeffenhausener Kellerbier (5.2%)
Pfeffenhausener Export (5.2%)
Pfeffenhausener Anno 1402 (5.4%)
Pfeffenhausener Weizen (5.5%)
Pfeffenhausener Schwarze Weisse (5.5%)
SEASONAL BEER:
Pfeffenhausener Ur-Bock (6.9%)

Long-established brewery that nowadays
produces a far larger volume of soft drinks than
beer. Bus No. 6234 runs daily from Landshut.

🍺 Pöllinger

Moosburger Straße 23, 84076 Pfeffenhausen
T 0800 987 88 55 **F** 08782 83 80
Daily 08.00–23.00; rooms available
DB Landshut (Bayern) Hbf 21km

Leicht

Pferdsfeld 3, 96250 Ebensfeld-Pferdsfeld
T 09573 236
Owner: Kunigunda Leicht Founded: 1870
Output: 250hl Availability: 1 pub
REGULAR BEER:
Leicht Hell

Very small brewery in the little village of Pferdsfeld that just supplies its own pub. Bus No. 2 runs
a couple of times on weekday afternoons from
Ebensfeld but you can also walk from there or
Bad Staffelstein.

🍺 Leicht

Pferdsfeld 3, 96250 Ebensfeld-Pferdsfeld
Closed Thu; Fri–Sun from 11.00, Mon–Wed
from 16.00; rooms available
DB Bad Staffelstein 3.4km, Ebensfeld 3.6km

PFRONTEN-RIED 458

Falkenstein

Braugasthof Falkenstein
Allgäuerstraße 28, 87459 Pfronten-Ried
T 08363 96 06 58   F 08363 96 06 59
www.braugasthof-falkenstein.de
Founded: 2002
REGULAR BEERS:
Falkenstein Hell
Falkenstein Dunkel
Falkenstein Weizen
SEASONAL BEERS:
Falkenstein Märzenbier (Oct),
Falkenstein Weihnachtsbier (Dec),
Falkenstein Bockbier (Lent)

Brewpub in the former station hotel which has
also been a Wienerwald restaurant in its time.
Seasonal beers only join the regulars during
the colder months.

🍺 **Falkenstein**
Allgäuerstraße 28, 87459 Pfronten-Ried
Daily 10.00–01.00   DB Pfronten-Ried 150m

PIRK 459

Pirker

Pirker Brauhaus Dr. Hermann Schwab
Braugasse 1–7, 92712 Pirk
T 0961 423 91   E dr.hermann.schwab@gmx.de
Owner: Dr. Hermann Schwab   Founded: 1545
Output: 8,000hl   Availability: c.50 pubs
REGULAR BEERS:
Pirker Lager Hell
Pirker Edelpils
Pirker Helles Zoigl Kellerbier (4.9%)
Pirker Dunkles Zoigl Kellerbier (5.1%)
Pirker Märzen (5.1%)
Pirkator Zoigl-Doppelbock Dunkel (7.3%)

Small brewery in a village south of Weiden.
Buses run daily from Weiden, No. 4 during the
week and No. 94 at the weekend.

🍺 **Bräustüberl im Schlossgarten**
Rothenstädter Straße 7, 92712 Pirk
T 0961 470 50 55
Oct–Apr: closed Tue; Wed–Sat & Mon 17.00–
24.00, Sun 11.00–24.00
May–Sep: Mon–Sat 17.00–24.00, Sun 11.00–
24.00   DB Weiden (Oberpfalz) 5km

PLEINFELD 460

Kleines Pleinfelder Brauhaus

Sportpark 9–11, 91785 Pleinfeld
T 09144 96 00   F 09144 96 01 90
www.landhotel-sonnenhof.de   Founded: 1998
Output: 50hl   Availability: 1 pub
REGULAR BEERS:
Das Kleine Brauhaus Hell
Das Kleine Brauhaus Weizen
Das Kleine Brauhaus Märzen
SEASONAL BEER:
Das Kleine Brauhaus Doppelbock

Small brewery at the rear of the Landhotel
Sonnenhof, owned by Neumarkter Lammsbräu.
They brew infrequently (generally only in spring
and summer), and the beer is not always
available at the Hotel.

🍺 **Sonnenhof**
Sportpark 9–11, 91785 Pleinfeld
T 09144 96 00   F 09144 96 01 90
Daily 07.00–23.00; rooms available
DB Pleinfeld 1km

PLÖSSBERG 461

Riedl

Brauerei Hans Riedl Inhaber Angela Riedl e.K.
Kirchenstraße 2, 95703 Plößberg
T 09636 236   E brauerei.riedl@t-online.de
Owner: Angela Riedl   Founded: 1875
Output: 1,000hl   Availability: 1 pub
REGULAR BEERS:
Riedl-Bräu Zoigl (4.5%)
Riedl-Bräu Hell (4.8%)
Riedl-Bräu Pils (5%)
Riedl-Bräu Märzen (5.5%)
SEASONAL BEERS:
Riedl-Bräu Schnitzerhalbe (4.8%),
Riedl-Bräu Bock (6.8%, Lent)

Brewpub in the centre of Plößberg which still
uses a *Kühlschiff* (coolship). They also have a
small brewery museum. Bus No. 2705 runs from
Neuhaus station Mon–Sat.

🍺 **Riedl**
Kirchenstraße 2, 95703 Plößberg
Sun 10.00–12.00, Mon–Sat 10.00–12.00 &
14.30–24.00   DB Neustadt (Waldnaab) 16km

POING 462

Liebhart's Bräuhaus

Anzinger Straße 1, 85586 Poing
T 08121 85 47   **F** 08121 763 51
Owner: Horst Liebhart
Founded: 1996
Output: 300hl
REGULAR BEERS:
Liebus Bräu Kellerbier
Liebus Bräu Weisse
SEASONAL BEERS:
Liebus Bräu Sommerbier,
Liebus Bräu Dunkel,
Liebus Bräu Lieberator

Modern brewpub on the western side of town. Be warned that it had closed by October 2005, ostensibly for refurbishment, but there was still no life when two of the Guide's intrepid reporters visited in mid-January 2006, although all signs and menus were on display.

 Liebhart's Bräuhaus
Anzinger Straße 1, 85586 Poing
Closed Mon; Tue–Wed 11.30–15.00 & 17.00–01.00, Sat & Sun 11.30–01.00
DB Poing 750m

PÖSING 463

Drexler

Bräustraße 3, 93483 Pösing
T 09461 21 54   **F** 09461 40 10 68
Owner: Josef Drexler
Founded: 1850
Output: 3,000hl
Availability: 3 pubs
REGULAR BEERS:
Waldquell Urhell
Waldquell Dunkel
Waldquell Pils
Waldquell Kristall-Export

Small brewery in the little town of Pösing in the Bayerischer Wald. The tap is one of only three pubs where the beers are sold.

 Drexler
Bräustraße 3, 93483 Pösing
Closed Sun; Mon–Sat 17.00–23.00
DB Pösing 550m

POSSENFELDEN
(Schlüsselfeld) 464

Scheubel

Steigerwaldstraße 15,
96132 Schlüsselfeld-Possenfelden
T 09552 382
Owner: Georg Scheubel   Founded: 1638
Output: 2,000hl
REGULAR BEERS:
Scheubel Hell
Scheubel Edel-Pils
Scheubel Landbier

Small brewery on the northern side of the village, not to be confused with Stern-Bräu Scheubel in nearby Schlüsselfeld. The bus service to the village itself is very poor but No. 8227 runs to Elsendorf (less than 1km away) from Bamberg via Hirschaid on weekdays.

 Scheubel
Steigerwaldstraße 17,
96132 Schlüsselfeld-Possenfelden
Closed Tue & Wed; Thu–Mon 09.00–23.00
DB Hirschaid 25km

POTTENSTEIN 465

Hufeisen

Gasthaus-Brauerei Hufeisen
Hauptstraße 36–38, 91278 Pottenstein
T 09243 260   **F** 09243 74 29
www.hufeisen-braeu.de
Owner: Josef Wiegärtner   Founded: 1803
Output: 1,000hl
REGULAR BEERS:
Hufeisen Pottensteiner Urdunkel (5%)
Hufeisen Pottenstein's Premium Pils (5.1%)
Hufeisen Keller-Weizen (5.1%)

Small, half-timbered brewery and tap in the centre of Pottenstein. Unbelievably, they produce a wheat beer and milk drink called Dr. Moo. We'll leave you to imagine what that tastes like...

 Hufeisen
Hauptstraße 36–38, 91278 Pottenstein
Closed Mon; Tue–Sun 09.00–23.00
DB Pegnitz 13km

Mager

Hauptstraße 15–17, 91278 Pottenstein
T 09243 333   **F** 09243 75 86
Owner: Georg Mager   Founded: 1774
Output: 2,500hl   Availability: 15 pubs
REGULAR BEERS:
Mager Pils (4.8%)
Mager Ur-Hell (4.9%)
Mager Dunkel (5%)
Mager Märzen (5.1%)
SEASONAL BEER:
Mager Festbier (Christmas)

The larger of the two remaining breweries in
town is just down the street from Hufeisen.
Buses Nos. 389 and 393 run daily from Pegnitz
railway station.

🍺 Mager
Hauptstraße 17, 91278 Pottenstein
Daily 09.00–24.00; rooms available
DB Pegnitz 13km

PÖTTMES   466

Schloßbrauerei

Schloßbrauerei Pöttmes GmbH & Co. KG
Marktplatz 18–20, 86554 Pöttmes
T 08253 99 66 11   **F** 08253 65 48
Owner: Freiherr von Gumppenberg
Founded: 1402
REGULAR BEERS:
Pöttmes Light
Pöttmes Pils
Pöttmes Export Hell
Pöttmes Export Dunkel

Small brewery in the centre of town owned by
the Baron von Gumppenberg. The easiest way to
get to Pöttmes by public transport is probably
bus No. 301 from Augsburg but there are much
closer railway stations if you have a bike.
DB Augsburg Hbf 34km

PRIESENDORF   467

Schrüfer

Hauptstraße 31, 96170 Priesendorf
T 09549 317   **F** 09549 98 74 68
Owner: Otto Schrüfer   Founded: 1865
Output: 700hl   Availability: 1 pub

REGULAR BEER:
Schrüfer Vollbier (5%)

Small brewpub in the north-eastern corner of the
Streigerwald. Bus No. 8244 runs from Bamberg
a few times each weekday and once on Saturday.

🍺 Schrüfer
Hauptstraße 31, 96170 Priesendorf
Closed Wed; Thu, Fri, Mon & Tue 16.00–24.00,
Sat & Sun 14.00–24.00
DB Ebelsbach-Eltmann 13km, Bamberg 15km

PÜRKWANG (Wildenberg)   468

Metzgerbräu

Siegenburger Straße 5,
93359 Wildenberg-Pürkwang
T 09444 15 57   **F** 09444 883 70
Owner: Bernd Frühmorgen   Founded: 2003
REGULAR BEERS:
Metzgerbräu Hell
Metzgerbräu Dunkel
Metzgerbräu Weizen Hell
Metzgerbräu Weizen Dunkel

We don't know much about this place but believe
it's basically a butchers that sells the beer in the
shop and Bräustüberl (*Metzgerbräu* means butchers' brew). We strongly recommend you check
the opening hours beforehand. You can reach
Pürkwang by bus from Abensburg on weekdays.

🍺 Bräustüberl
Siegenburger Straße 5,
93359 Wildenberg-Pürkwang
Closed Mon, Tue, Wed & Sat; Tue from 18.00,
Fri from 09.30, Sun 11.00–14.00
DB Abensberg 13km

PYRAS (Thalmässing)   469

Pyraser

Pyraser Landbrauerei GmbH & Co. KG
Pyras 26, 91177 Thalmässing-Pyras
T 09174 474 70   **F** 09174 47 47 19
www.pyraser.de
Owner: Georg Bernreuther   Founded: 1870
Output: 100,000hl
REGULAR BEERS:
Pyraser Federleichte Weisse (2.8%)
Das Leichte Pyraser (3.7%)

Pyraser Kellerbier Naturtrüb (4.8%)
Pyraser Gutsherrn Pils (5.1%)
Pyraser Schwarzbier (5.2%)
Pyraser Angerwirts-Weizen (5.2%)
Pyraser Jubel-Weisse Altfränkisch (5.3%)
Pyraser Landbier Export Hell (5.4%)
Pyraser 6-Korn Bier (5.5%)
Pyraser Jubeltrunk Altfränkisch (5.6%)
SEASONAL BEERS:
Pyraser Hopfenpflücker Pils (5%),
Pyraser Burgfest Bier (6%),
Pyraser Kirchweih Bier (6%),
Pyraser Weihnachts-Festbier (6.1%),
Pyraser Weizenbock (6.5%),
Pyraser Josephi Bier (7.5%),
Pyraser Ultra (8.3%)

Large brewery in the village of Pyras. We think some beer is brewed by Engel in Crailsheim. It is possible to get to Pyras by bus but we're not sure if there's a pub in the village.

DB Hipoltstein 6km

RAIGERING (Amberg) 470

Sterk

Privatbrauerei Sterk
Hofmark 2, 92224 Amberg-Raigering
T 09621 221 19   F 09621 221 05
www.brauerei-sterk.de
Owner: Martin Josef Sterk
Founded: 1723
Output: 1,500hl
REGULAR BEERS:
Raigeringer Edelhell (4.9%)
Raigeringer Zoigl (5.1%)
Raigeringer Pils (5.1%)
Raigeringer Weisse (5.1%)
SEASONAL BEERS:
Raigeringer Festbier (5.4%, Jul, Aug & Dec),
Raigeringer Doppelbock (7.5%)

Small brewery and tap in the village of Raigering, nowadays almost a suburb of Amberg. Bus No. 6312 runs from Amberg station on weekdays and Saturday morning.

🍺 Sterk
Hofmark 1, 92224 Amberg-Raigering
Closed Tue; Wed–Fri & Mon, 10.00–14.00 & 16.00–24.00, Sat & Sun 10.00–24.00
DB Amberg 3.5km

RAIN 471

Kleinbrauerei Rain

Alte Bayerdillinger Straße 9, 86641 Rain
T 09090 25 57   F 09090 53 93
Founded: 2002
REGULAR BEERS:
Rainer Tilly-Hell
Rainer Lagerbier
Rainer Dunkel
Rainer Weizen
SEASONAL BEER:
Rainer Festbier

Microbrewery behind the Pledl drinks market on the southern edge of town. There's no brewery tap as such but the beer is sold in the Bierkutsch'n (The Brewer's Dray), a rock bar just up the street from the Ratsbrauerei.

🍺 Bierkutsch'n
Hauptstraße 52, 86641 Rain
T 09090 92 14 63
Closed Sun–Wed; Thu 19.30–01.00,
Fri & Sat 19.30–02.00
DB Rain 1.3km

Ratsbrauerei

Ratsbrauerei zum Bäuml
Hauptstraße 45, 86641 Rain
T 09090 70 56 52   F 09090 70 56 53
www.ratsbrauerei-rainamlech.de
Owners: Monika Schöneberg & Josef Bäuml
Founded: 23.10.2004
REGULAR BEERS:
Ratsbrauerei zum Bäuml Kellerbier
Ratsbrauerei zum Bäuml Dunkel
Ratsbrauerei zum Bäuml Weizen

Brewpub in the centre of town that lagers its beers in wooden casks, the only modern brewery in Germany we're aware of that does so. They brew seasonals in addition to the regular three.

🍺 Ratsbrauerei
Hauptstraße 45, 86641 Rain
Daily 11.00–24.00
DB Rain 1.3km

RAMMINGEN 472

Häpfenbräu

Am Bahnhof 4, 86871 Rammingen
T/F 08245 34 09
Founded: 1999
REGULAR BEERS:
Häpfenbräu Hell
Häpfenbräu Dunkel

Small brewery next to the station. We think it's more or less run as a hobby. The brewery tap is a beer garden that only opens in fine weather.

📂 Häpfenbräu Biergarten
Am Bahnhof 4, 86871 Rammingen
Closed Nov–Mar; daily from 17.00 in fine weather only
DB Rammingen (Bayern)

RECKENDORF 473

Schloßbrauerei

Schloßbrauerei Reckendorf GmbH & Co. KG
Mühlweg 16, 96182 Reckendorf
T 09544 942 10   **F** 09544 94 21 21
www.recken.de
Owner: Dominik Eichhorn   Founded: 1597
Output: 25,000hl   Availability: c.100 pubs
REGULAR BEERS:
Recken Light (2.8%)
Recken Lagerbier Hell (4.8%)
Recken Edel-Pils (4.8%)
Recken Dunkel (5%)
Recken Kellerbier (5%)
Recken Export (5%)
Recken Weissbier (5.2%)
Recken 1597 (5.3%)
SEASONAL BEER:
Recken Henrici-Bock (7.5%)

Comparatively small brewery in the lower part of town whose beers we've always found surprisingly easy to find. The tap is just up the street.

📂 Schloßbräu
Mühlweg 8, 96182 Reckendorf
T 09544 949 50
Closed Tue, Wed–Fri 09.00–23.00,
Sat 12.00–23.00, Sun & Mon 09.00–23.00
DB Reckendorf 650m

Schroll

Hauptstraße 38, 96182 Reckendorf
T 09544 203 38   **F** 09544 98 21 29
Owner: Rudolf Schroll   Founded: before 1870
Output: 2,000hl   Availability: 3 pubs
REGULAR BEER:
Schroll Edel-Trunk (4.9%)
SEASONAL BEER:
Schroll Bock (Lent)

Small brewery and tap on the main road through Reckendorf at the corner of the road to the station. The brewery's age is uncertain but it's known to date from before 1870.

📂 Schroll
Hauptstraße 38, 96182 Reckendorf
Closed Thu; Fri–Wed 09.00–23.00
DB Reckendorf 550m

REGEN 474

Falter

Privatbrauerei J. B. Falter
Am Sand 15, 94209 Regen
T 09921 882 30   **F** 09921 88 23 25
www.jb-falter.de
Founded: 1649
Output: 50,000hl   Availability: c.70 pubs
REGULAR BEERS:
Falter's Leichte Weisse (2.8%)
Falter's Privat Hell (4.9%)
Falter's Lager (4.9%)
Falter's Privat Pils (4.9%)
Falter's Export Hell (5.3%)
Falter Weissbier Premium Gold (5.5%)
Falter's Weißer Bock (6.5%)
Falter's Regenator
SEASONAL BEERS:
Falter's Wiesen Festbier, Falter's Pichelsteiner Festbier, Falter's Weihnachts Festbier, Falter's Weihnachts-Doppelbock

Fairly large brewery on the banks of the Schwarzer Regen (literally: Black Rain) in the centre of the town. The brewery tap is next door.

📂 Falter
Am Sand 14, 94209 Regen
T 09921 942 30   **F** 09921 94 23 35
Daily 10.00–23.00
DB Regen 1km

REGENSBURG 475

Bischofshof

Brauerei Bischofshof e.K.
Heitzerstraße 2, 93049 Regensburg
T 0941 200 10   **F** 0941 200 11 90
www.bischofshof.de
Founded: 1649   Output: 180,000hl
REGULAR BEERS:
Bischofshof Leichte Weisse (2.9%)
Bischofshof Pils (4.7%)
Bischofshof Urhell (4.8%)
Bischofshof Regensburger Premium (5%)
Bischofshof Original 1649 (5.1%)
Bischofshof Hefe-Weissbier Hell (5.1%)
Bischofshof Hefe-Weissbier Dunkel (5.1%)
Bischofshof Kristall Weizen (5.4%)
FOR KLOSTERBRAUEREI, WELTENBURG:
Weltenburger Urtyp Hell (4.9%),
Weltenburger Pils (4.9%),
Weltenburger Hefe-Weißbier Dunkel (5.3%),
Weltenburger Hefe-Weißbier Hell (5.4%),
Weltenburger Barock Hell (5.6%)

Large brewery south-west of the town centre with
the tap in one corner. They brew Weltenburger
beers for Klosterbrauerei Weltenburg but not
Weltenbuger Kloster beers. The three Malteser
wheat beers they advertise are brewed by
Stuttgarter Hofbräu.

🍺 Braustuben
Dechbettener Straße 50, 93049 Regensburg
T 0941 214 73   **F** 0941 222 24
Daily 10.00–24.00
DB Regensburg Hbf 2km

Fürstliches Brauhaus

Thurn & Taxis Vertriebsgesellschaft mbH
Waffnergasse 6–8, 93047 Regensburg
T 0941 280 43 30   **F** 0941 2804 33 99
www.fuerstlichesbrauhaus.de
Owner: Brau Holding International, München
Founded: 2005   Output: 1,000hl
Availability: 1 pub
REGULAR BEERS:
Fürstliches Brauhaus Regensburger Hell (4.7%)
Fürstliches Brauhaus Marstall Dunkel (4.8%)
Fürstliches Brauhaus Pils
Fürstliches Brauhaus Roggen
Fürstliches Brauhaus Weisse (5.5%)

SEASONAL BEER:
Fürstliches Brauhaus Postmeister Doppelbock

Brewpub which opened in autumn 2005 in one
part of the St. Emeram palace. They are owned
by Paulaner who bought and closed the Thurn &
Taxis brewery in Regensburg in 1997. Paulaner in
turn are owned by Brau Holding International.

🍺 Fürstliches Brauhaus
Waffnergasse 6–8, 93047 Regensburg
Daily 09.00–01.00
DB Regensburg Hbf 1km

Johann Albrecht

Schwarze-Bären-Straße 6, 93047 Regensburg
T 0941 510 55   **F** 0941 56 34 36
www.brauhaus-joh-albrecht.de/reg.html
Founded: 1993   Output: 500hl
Availability: 1 pub
REGULAR BEERS:
Johann Albrecht Messing Hell
Johann Albrecht Kupfer Dunkel
Johann Albrecht Weizen

One of six Johann Albrecht brewpubs dotted
around the country, this one sits just south of
the heart of old Regensburg. They may brew
occasional seasonal beers.

🍺 Johann Albrecht
Schwarze-Bären-Straße 6, 93047 Regensburg
Daily 11.00–01.00
DB Regensburg Hbf 750m

Kneitinger

Brauerei J. Kneitinger
Kreuzgasse 7, 93047 Regensburg
T 0941 59 30 20   **F** 0941 593 02 99
www.kneitinger.de
Founded: 1530   Output: 25,000hl
Availability: 8 pubs
REGULAR BEERS:
Kneitinger Dunkel (5.2%)
Kneitinger Edel-Pils (5.2%)
SEASONAL BEER:
Kneitinger Bock (6.8%, Oct–Apr)

Traditional brewery on the western side of the
city centre with the tap in front on Arnulfsplatz.
They also have a large Bierkeller next to the site
of the old Thurn & Taxis brewery on Galgenbergstraße, just south of the main station.

🍺 Kneitinger
Arnulfsplatz 3, 93047 Regensburg
T 0941 524 55   **F** 0941 599 99 82
Daily 09.00–01.00
DB Regensburg Hbf 1.5km

Spitalbrauerei
Am Brückenfuß 1–3, 93059 Regensburg
T 0941 83 00 60   **F** 0941 843 68
www.spitalbrauerei.de
Founded: 1226   Output: 15,000hl
Availability: 20 pubs
REGULAR BEERS:
Spital Hell (4.7%)
Spital Dunkel (5.4%)
Spital St. Katherinen Spezial (5.4%)
Spital Pils (5.5%)
Spital Weizen (5.5%)
SEASONAL BEERS:
Spital Festbier (5.7%), **Spital Weizenbock** (7%),
Spital Maibock (7.2%)

Regensburg's oldest brewery is located on an
island in the Danube close to Germany's oldest
bridge, the 850-year-old Steinerne Brücke.
Part of a 13th-century hospital complex, the
Katharinenspital, it is one of only a few hospital
breweries to have survived beyond the 19th
century. Beer was originally given as a good-
night drink to the patients.

🍺 Spitalgarten
St. Katharinenplatz 1, 93059 Regensburg
T 0941 847 74   **F** 0941 890 31 68
Daily 09.00–24.00
DB Regensburg Hbf 1.7km

REICHELSHOFEN
(Steinsfeld)   476

Landwehr-Bräu
Landwehr-Bräu Wilhelm Wörner GmbH & Co.
Reichelshofen 31, 91628 Steinsfeld-Reichelshofen
T 09865 989 70   **F** 09865 989 89
www.landwehr-braeu.de
Owner: Wilhelm Wörner   Founded: 1755
Output: 30,000hl   Availability: 40 pubs
REGULAR BEERS:
Landwehr Light (2.7%)
Landwehr Hell (4.7%)
Landwehr Kellerbier (4.7%)

Landwehr Gold (4.9%)
Landwehr Pilsner (4.9%)
Landwehr Toppler-Pils (4.9%)
Landwehr Edel (5%)
Landwehr Dunkel (5.2%)
SEASONAL BEERS:
Landwehr Weihnachtsbier (5.2%), **Landwehr
Kirchweihbier** (5.4%), **Landwehr Festbier** (5.8%),
Landwehr Dunkler Bock (6.6%)

Brewery, tap and hotel in a small village north
of the famous medieval town of Rothenburg ob
der Tauber. Bus No. 857 runs from Rothenburg
station on weekdays.

🍺 Landwehrbräu
Reichelshofen 31, 91628 Steinsfeld-Reichelshofen
T 09865 98 90   **F** 09865 98 96 86
Closed Jan; Feb–Dec: Sun–Sat 07.00–23.00;
rooms available
DB Rothenburg ob der Tauber 8km

REISBACH (Vils)   477

Lang
Brauerei Xaver Lang OHG
Marktplatz 27, 94419 Reisbach
T 08734 922 40   **E** brauerei-lang@t-online.de
Owners: Katharina Lang, Annemarie Lang-Koller
Founded: 1670   Output: 12,000hl
REGULAR BEERS:
Lang Leichtes Weizen
Lang Hell (4.7%)
Lang Dunkel (4.7%)
Lang Pils (4.9%)
Lang Hefe-Weizen Hell (5.2%)
Lang Dunkles Hefe-Weizen (5.2%)
SEASONAL BEERS:
Lang Volksfestbier, Lang Weihnachtsbier

Small brewery in the centre of Reisbach. Bus
No. 6151 operates from Landau on weekdays
but isn't particularly convenient for the opening
hours of the tap, although you'll find other pubs
that sell the beer nearby.

🍺 Schlappinger Hof
Marktplatz 40–42, 94419 Reisbach
T 08734 921 10
Closed Wed; Thu–Tue 10.30–14.00 & 16.00–24.00;
rooms available
DB Landau (Isar) 18km

REISCHACH 478

Berger

Brauerei Max Berger
Öttinger Straße 3, 84571 Reischach
T 08670 218   **F** 08670 722
Owner: Karl Berger   Founded: 1878
Output: 1,000hl
REGULAR BEERS:
Berger Hell
Berger Dunkel
Berger Märzen
Small brewery in the centre of the village that
we think just supplies the tap. Bus No. 6223
runs from Neuötting station on weekdays.

Berger
Öttinger Straße 3, 84571 Reischach
T 08670 52 34
Closed Wed & Sat; Thu, Fri, Mon & Tue from 16.30,
Sun 10.00–13.00 & 17.00–21.00
DB Neuötting 5km

RETTENBERG 479

Engelbräu

Engelbräu Rettenberg Hermann Widenmayer KG
Burgberger Straße 7, 87549 Rettenberg
T 08327 930 00   **F** 08327 93 00 40
www.engelbraeu.de
Owner: Hermann Widenmayer   Founded: 1668
Output: 50,000hl   Availability: c.150 pubs
REGULAR BEERS:
Engelbräu Leichtes Weizen (2.9%)
Engelbräu Urtyp-Hell (4.9%)
Engelbräu Grünten-Pils (4.9%)
Engelbräu Hefe-Weizen Hell (5%)
Engelbräu Grünten-Gold (5.2%)
Engelbräu Urtyp-Dunkel (5.5%)
Engelbräu Hefe-Weizen Dunkel (5.5%)
Engelbräu Jubiläums-Bier (5.5%)
SEASONAL BEERS:
Engelbräu Kellerbier (5.4%), **Engelbräu
Wintergold** (5.6%), **Engelbräu Doppelbock
Dunkel** (7.8%)

Small regional brewery in the centre of the
village. The tap is alongside, on the main road
through Rettenberg. There's one bus on
weekdays from Sonthofen but that's not much
use if you want to return the same day.

Engel
Burgberger Straße 9, 87549 Rettenberg
T 08327 206   **F** 08327 71 83
Mon & Tue from 16.30, Wed–Sun from 10.00
DB Immenstadt 7km

Zötler Bier

Adlerbrauerei Rettenberg Herbert Zötler GmbH
Grüntenstraße 2, 87549 Rettenberg
T 08327 92 10   **F** 08327 74 87
www.zoetler.de
Founded: 1447   Output: 90,000hl
REGLAR BEERS:
Zötler Hefe-Weizen Leicht (2.9%)
Zötler Bayerisch Hell (4.7%)
Zötler Joe's Lagerbier (4.7%)
Zötler Privat-Pils (4.7%)
Zötler Vollmond-Bier (4.9%)
Zötler Gold (5.1%)
Zötler Korbinian Dunkel (5.1%)
Zötler Hefe-Weizen Dunkel (5.1%)
Zötler Hefe-Weizen (5.2%)
SEASONAL BEERS:
Zötler Fest-Bier (5.5%),
Zötler St. Stephans Bock Dunkel (7.1%)

Modern brewery owned by the same family
since 1447, a feat bettered by only nine other
businesses in the world. The tap was the original
site of the brewery, which is now on the road east
out of the village.

Adler-Post
Burgberger Straße 8, 87549 Rettenberg
T 08327 226   **F** 08327 12 35
Closed Wed; Thu–Tue 11.30–14.00 & from
17.00; rooms available
DB Immenstadt 7km

REUNDORF (Frensdorf) 480

Müller-Bräu

Lange Straße 2, 96158 Frensdorf-Reundorf
T 09502 280
Owner: Andreas Müller   Founded: 1874
Output: 950hl   Availability: 2 pubs
REGULAR BEERS:
Müller-Bräu Kellerbier (5%)
Müller-Bräu Pils (5%)
SEASONAL BEER:
Müller-Bräu Bockbier (6.5%, Nov–Dec)

Small brewery that switches tap twice a year: in winter they open the pub at the brewery and in summer the drinking's done at their Bierkeller. Bus No. 8227 runs from Bamberg on weekdays and Saturday mornings but isn't much use given the opening times.

🍺 Müller-Bräu

Lange Straße 2, 96158 Frensdorf-Reundorf
Early Mar–mid Nov closed.
Mid-Nov–early Mar: closed Thu; Sat & Sun from 15.00, Mon–Wed & Fri from 16.00

🍺 Schmausen-Keller

Am Bahnhof, 96158 Frensdorf-Reundorf
T 09502 608
Mid Oct–mid Mar & Mon if wet: closed.
Mid-Mar–mid-Oct: Mon–Sat from 16.00, Sun from 11.00
DB Bamberg 11km

REUTBERG (Sachsenkam)   481

Klosterbrauerei

Klosterbrauerei Reutberg eG
Am Reutberg 3, 83679 Sachsenkam-Reutberg
T 08021 258   F 08021 17 06
www.klosterbrauerei-reutberg.de
Founded: 1677
Output: 20,000hl
Availability: 30 pubs
REGULAR BEERS:
Reutberger Kloster Weisse (4.9%)
Reutberger Export Hell (5.1%)
Reutberger Export Dunkel (5.2%)
Reutberger Kloster Märzen (5.3%)
SEASONAL BEERS:
Reutberger Heller Bock (6.7%),
Reutberger Josefi-Bock (6.9%, Lent)

A former monastic brewery that is now owned by a co-operative with 4,000 members. Bus No. 9553 runs between Holzkirchen and Bad Tölz a few times each weekday and stops at the monastery.

🍺 Kloster-Bräustüberl

Am Reutberg 2, 83679 Sachsenkam-Reutberg
T 08021 86 86   F 08021 50 78 81
Daily from 09.00
DB Bad Tölz 9km, Holzkirchen 11km

REUTH bei Erbendorf   482

Schloßbrauerei

Schloßbrauerei Reuth GmbH
Hauptstraße 22, 92717 Reuth
T 09682 22 06   F 09682 40 53
www.schlossbraureuth.de   Founded: 1742
Output: 15,000hl   Availability: 30 pubs
REGULAR BEERS:
Reuther Leichtes Hefeweißbier (2.9%)
Reuther Schwarzes Lager (4.8%)
Reuther Lager (4.9%)
Reuther Öko Lager (4.9%)
Alt Reuther Zoigl (5%)
Reuther Schloss-Pils (5%)
Reuther Hefeweißbier (5%)
Alt Reuther Spezial (6%)
SEASONAL BEER:
Reuther Baronator (9%)

Castle brewery next to the railway near Reuth station. They don't have a tap but the beers can be found locally.
DB Reuth (b. Erbendorf) 250m

RHAN (Schönthal)   483

Rhanerbräu

Rhanerbräu GmbH & Co. KG
Rhan 9, 93488 Schönthal-Rahn
T 09978 801 10   F 09978 512
www.rhaner.de
Founded: 1283   Output: 25,000hl
REGULAR BEERS:
Rhaner Leichte Weisse (2.9%)
Rhaner Pils (4.9%)
Rhaner Export Hell (5.1%)
Rhaner Export Dunkel (5.1%)
Rhaner Panduren Weisse (5.2%)
Rhaner Schwarzer Pandur (5.2%)
SEASONAL BEER:
Rhaner Weihnachtsbier (5.2%)

Bayerischer Wald brewery in a small village near Schönthal. The tap is in 15km south of Rhan in Cham, near the railway station, which makes it fairly easy to reach. Panduren were the Baron von der Trenck's personal bodyguards, a rough bunch of warriors, originally hailing from the Balkans and wreaking havoc in Bavaria in the mid-18th century.

*Right: Storchsgasse with Altenburg
castle in the distance*

🍺 **Rhaner Bräustüberl**
Ludwigstraße 5, 93413 Cham
T 09971 70 09   Daily 14.00–23.30
DB Cham (Oberpfalz) 400m

RIEDELSBACH
(Neureichenau)   **484**

Sitter-Bräu

Landhotel Gut Riedelsbach
94089 Neureichenau-Riedelsbach
T 08583 960 40   **F** 08583 96 04 13
www.sitterbraeu.de
Owners: Bernard & Petra Sitter
Founded: 1998
REGULAR BEERS:
Sitter-Bräu Blonde
Sitter-Bräu Schwarze
Sitter-Bräu Pils

Hotel and brewpub next to the Austrian border
in a remote corner of the Bayerischer Wald, a few
kilometres west of Neureichenau. Surprisingly,
you can get there by bus on weekdays but it does
involve a change in Neureichenau.

🍺 **Sitter-Bräu**
94089 Neureichenau-Riedelsbach
Closed Thu; Fri–Wed 08.00–01.00; rooms
available
DB Passau Hbf 44km

RIEDENBURG   **485**

Riedenburger

Riedenburger Brauhaus Michael Krieger KG
Hammerweg 5, 93339 Riedenburg
T 09442 644   **F** 09442 31 26
www.riedenburger.de
Owner: Martha & Michael Krieger
Founded: 1866   Output: 18,000hl
Availability: 30 pubs
REGULAR BEERS:
Riedenburger Leicht Hefeweizenbier (2.9%)
Riedenburger Helles Naturtrüb (4.6%)
Riedenburger Pilsner Naturtrüb (4.7%)
Riedenburger Pils (4.9%)
Riedenburger Einkorn Edelbier (5%)
Riedenburger 5-Korn Ur-Bier (5%)
Riedenburger Weisse Premium (5.1%)

Riedenburger Michaeli Dunkel Weizen (5.2%)
Riedenburger Export Hefeweizenbier (5.3%)
Riedenburger Emmer Bier (5.5%)
SEASONAL BEER:
Riedenburger Edel-Bock (7.8%)
FOR BENEDIKTINER ABTEI, PLANKSTETTEN:
Plankstettener Dinkel Naturtrüb (4.9%),
Plankstettener Dunkles Naturtrüb (5%),
Plankstettener Spezial Naturtrüb (5.3%)
SEASONAL BEER:
Plankstettener Mai-Bock (6.8%)

Organic brewery that has brewed Plankstetten
beers since 1997. It's one of only two breweries
we're aware of that brews with emmer, an
ancient form of wheat in common use in Europe
until the 20th century. The tap is on the opposite
side of the river to the brewery.

🍺 **Krieger's Bräustüberl**
Mühlstraße 37b, 93339 Riedenburg
T 09442 15 00   **F** 09442 15 06
Closed Mon; Tue–Sun 10.00–24.00; rooms
available   DB Saal (Donau) 23km

Riemhofer

Brauerei Riemhofer GmbH & Co. KG
Austraße 45, 93339 Riedenburg
T 09442 919 80   **F** 09442 91 98 91
www.riemhofer.com
Owner: Friedrich Riemhofer   Founded: 1683
Output: 15,000hl   Availability: 30 pubs
REGULAR BEERS:
Riemhofer Unser Gebremstes Weizen
Riemhofer Helles Vollbier
Riemhofer Schwanenpower Edel-Pils
Riemhofer Schwanen-Weisse
Riemhofer Altbayerisches Export Weizen
Riemhofer Exclusiv Weisse
Riemhofer Spezial
Riemhofer 300 Jahr-Bier

The brewery was originally located in the tap
but moved to its current location on the north-
western edge of town in 1959. The Gebremstes
Weizen is a reduced-alcohol low calorie beer.
Bus No. 6022 runs daily from Saal station.

🍺 **Schwan**
Marktplatz 5, 93339 Riedenburg
T 09442 12 72   **F** 09442 28 07
Closed Fri; Sat–Thu 07.00–24.00; rooms
available
DB Saal (Donau) 23km

RÖBERSDORF (Hirschaid) 486

Weber

Ringstraße 46, 96114 Hirschaid-Röbersdorf
T/F 09543 7882
Owner: Friedrich Weber   Founded: 1800
Output: 2,100hl   Availability: 1 pub
REGULAR BEERS:
Röbersdorfer Mild (4.7%),
Röbersdorfer Landbier Hell (5.2%),
Röbersdorfer Lager (5.2%),
Röbersdorfer Rauchbier (5.2%).
SEASONAL BEERS:
Röbersdorfer Märzen (5.4%),
Röbersdorfer Bock (6.8%).

Brewpub on the northern side of the village.
Bus No. 8227 runs from Bamberg and other
stations in the area but the last one leaves the
village early afternoon.

🍺 Weber
Ringstraße 46, 96114 Hirschaid-Röbersdorf
Closed Wed; Thu–Tue 09.00–24.00
DB Hirschaid 6km

RODING 487

Brantl

Brauerei Brantl e.K.
Regensburger Straße 16, 93426 Roding
T 09461 12 28   F 09461 73 47
Owner: Josef Brantl   Founded: 1932
Output: 4,000hl
REGULAR BEERS:
Brantl Bräu Vollbier Hell
Brantl Bräu Edel Pils
Brantl Bräu Hefe-Weizen
Brantl Bräu Export
Brantl Bräu Märzen
SEASONAL BEERS:
Brantl Bräu Festbier, Brantl Bräu Bock

Small brewery in the centre of town. Despite
the different addresses, the tap is a couple of
hundred metres up the same street.

🍺 Brantl-Bräu
Schulstraße 1, 93426 Roding
T 09461 675
Closed Wed; Thu–Tue 09.00–24.00; rooms
available   DB Roding 2.7km

Greiner

Brauerei Greiner GmbH
Chamer Straße 10, 93426 Roding
T 09461 945 40   F 09461 94 54 24
www.greinerbraeu.de
Founded: 1926   Output: 20,000hl
Availability: 20 pubs
REGULAR BEERS:
Greiner Helles (4.8%)
Greiner Rodinger Schwarzbier (4.8%)
Greiner Anker Pilsner (4.9%)
Greiner Anker Gold Export (5.2%)
Greiner Rodinger Weisse (5.3%)
Greiner Alte Braukunst Weizen Dunkel (5.3%)
SEASONAL BEER:
Greiner Festbier (5.2%)

The larger of Roding's two breweries, Greiner
and its tap are to the east of the town centre.
Buses Nos. 200 & 230 run into town from the
station on weekdays.

🍺 Zum Goldenen Anker
Chamer Straße 10, 93426 Roding
T 09461 26 98   F 09461 94 54 24
Closed Fri; Sat–Thu 09.00–01.00,
Sun 09.00–01.00   DB Roding 2.7km

ROSENHEIM 488

Auerbräu

Owner: Brau Holding International, München
Founded: 1889
REGULAR BEERS:
Auerbräu Rosenheimer Leichte Weiße (2.9%),
Auerbräu Rosenheimer Helles (5%), **Auerbräu
Rosenheimer Pils** (5%), **Auerbräu 111 Zwickl** (5%),
Auerbräu Rosenheimer Bajuwaren Dunkel (5.5%),
Auerbräu Rosenheimer Hefe-Weißbier (5.5%),
Auerbräu Johann Auer Dunkle-Weiße (5.5%),
Auerbräu 111 Hefe Flaschl Weisse (5.5%),
Auerbräu Rosenheimer Export (5.5%)
SEASONAL BEERS:
Rosenheimer Herbfest-Marzen (5.5%),
Rosenheimer Weizenbock (7%)

Large brewery close to the station. They asked
not to be included in the Guide.

🍺 Auerstüberl
Münchener Straße 80, 83022 Rosenheim
Daily from 09.00
DB Rosenheim 300m

215

Flötzinger-Bräu

Flötzinger-Bräu Privatbrauerei Franz
Steegmüller
Herzog-Heinrich-Straße 7, 83022 Rosenheim
T 08031 366 30   **F** 08031 36 63 90
www.floetzinger-braeu.de
Owner: Franz Steegmüller
Founded: 1543
REGULAR BEERS:
Flötzinger-Bräu Leichte Weisse (2.5%)
Flötzinger-Bräu Leicht (2.9%)
Flötzinger-Bräu Pils (4.8%)
Flötzinger-Bräu Hell (5.2%)
Flötzinger-Bräu Export Dunkel (5.3%)
Flötzinger-Bräu Hefe-Weizen (5.3%)
Flötzinger-Bräu Hefe-Weizen Dunkel (5.3%)
Flötzinger-Bräu 1543 Hefe-Weisse (5.5%)
Flötzinger-Bräu Sanfte Weisse (5.5%)
Flötzinger-Bräu FS (5.6%)
Flötzinger-Bräu Märzen (5.6%)
SEASONAL BEER:
Flötzinger-Bräu Josefi-Bock (7.5%)
FOR BIERBICHLER, ROSENHEIM:
Bierbichler Weißbier (5.5%)

Flötzinger's brewery is just west of the town
centre, the tap is across the street. We believe
they brew the beer for Weißbräu Bierbilcher
whose tap is nearby on Gillitzerstraße.

🍺 **Flötzinger Löchl**
Samerstraße 17, 83022 Rosenheim
T 08031 124 08
Closed Wed; Thu–Tue 10.00–01.00
DB Rosenheim 600m

ROSSACH (Großheirath)   489

Kommunbrauerei

Coburger Str. 25, 96269 Großheirath-Rossach
T 09565 21 38 (brewer Adolf Lorenz)
Founded: c.1700   Output: 185hl
REGULAR BEERS:
Kommunbrauerei Rossach Hell
Kommunbrauerei Rossach Pils
SEASONAL BEER:
Kommunbrauerei Rossach Bock

Communal brewery whose beer is brewed
almost exclusively for private consumption by
residents of the village who have been handed
down the right to brew. It is normally only

available to the general public at the Kellerfest
on Whit Sunday.
DB Creidlitz 9km, Bad Staffelstein 10km

ROSSDORF am Forst (Strullendorf)   490

Sauer

Sutte 5, 96129 Strullendorf-Roßdorf am Forst
T 09543 15 78   **F** 09543 85 02 04
www.brauerei-sauer.de
Founded: 1784
Output: 2,000hl
REGULAR BEERS:
Rossdorfer Urbräu (4.6%)
Rossdorfer Pils (4.7%)
Rossdorfer Weißbier (5%)
SEASONAL BEER:
Rossdorfer Bock (7%, winter)

Small brewery and tap in a village east of
Bamberg. There are no buses to Roßdorf but it's
just about walkable from Strullendorf. Annual
holiday during October.

🍺 **Sauer**
Sutte 5, 96129 Strullendorf-Roßdorf am Forst
Closed Mon; Tue–Sun from 11.00
DB Strullendorf 4.5km, Bamberg 9km

ROSSFELD (Bad Rodach)   491

Gemeinschaftsbrauerei

Gemeinschaftsbrauerei Roßfeld e.V.
Roßfeld 77, 96476 Bad Rodach-Roßfeld
T 09564 32 07
Founded: 1784
Output: 400hl
REGULAR BEER:
Roßfeld Hausbrauerbier

Communal brewery. Like the Kommunbrauerei
in Rossach, the beer is brewed for consumption
by Althausbrauer and Neuhausbrauer (old and
new home-brewers), residents who have the
right to brew beer or purchase it without paying
tax. In this case we don't think it's ever available
to the general public so you're advised to
befriend a local if you want to try the beer.
DB Bad Rodach 3.3km

ROTH vor der Rhön (Hausen) 492

Rother Bräu

Rother Bräu Bayerische Exportbierbrauerei
Roth Ida Schneider GmbH
Birkenweg 2, 97647 Hausen-Roth
T 09779 810 10　**F** 09779 81 01 29
www.rother-braeu.de
Owners: Fritz & Georg Weydringer
Founded: 1788　Output: 29,000hl
Availability: 260 pubs
REGULAR BEERS:
Rother-Bräu Vollbier (4.5%)
Rother-Bräu Pilsener (4.7%)
Rother-Bräu Öko-Ur-Pils (4.7%)
Rother-Bräu Öko-Urtrunk (4.7%)
Rother-Bräu Export (5.2%)
Rother-Bräu Öko Ur-Weizen (5.3%)
SEASONAL BEERS:
Rother-Bräu Festbier (5.7%, Christmas),
Rother-Bräu Rhönator (7%, Christmas)

Small regional brewery which also bottles the
beers and administers for Klosterbrauerei
Münnerstadt. The Öko beers are organic. Bus
No. 8250 runs from Mellrichstadt on weekdays
but the return service is very poor.

🍴 **Bräustüble**
Hauptstraße 7, 97647 Hausen-Roth
T 09779 63 97　**F** 09779 85 89 94
Daily 10.00–23.00 (24.00 Fri–Sun); rooms
available　DB Mellrichstadt 17km

ROTH (Mittelfranken) 493

Stadtbrauerei

Büchenbacher Weg 8-10, 91154 Roth
T 09171 89 23 79　**F** 09171 887 46
www.stadtbrauereiroth.de　Founded: 1924
Owner: the town of Roth　Output: 12,000hl
REGULAR BEERS:
Stadtbrauerei Roth Markgrafen Hell (4.6%)
Stadtbrauerei Roth Ratibor Dunkel (5%)
Stadtbrauerei Roth Schloß Pilsner (5%)
Stadtbrauerei Roth Kellerbier (5.2%)
Stadtbrauerei Roth Edle Weisse (5.3%)
Stadtbrauerei Edle Weisse Dunkel (5.3%)
SEASONAL BEERS:
Stadtbrauerei Roth Festbier (5.3%),
Stadtbrauerei Roth Bockbier (winter)

Brewery owned by the town of Roth, just north
of the mainline station alongside the river
Rednitz. The tap, in the centre of town, is closer
to the station on the Hipoltstein branch line.

🍴 **Goldener Schwan**
Hauptstraße 48, 91154 Roth
T 09171 89 23 01　**F** 09171 85 15 85
Daily 11.00–24.00
DB Lohgarten-Roth 400m, Roth 1.2km

ROTHENFELS 494

Bayer Bräu

Hauptstraße 77, 97851 Rothenfels
T 09393 408　**F** 09393 14 88
Owner: Alfred Bayer　Founded: 1896
Output: 3,000hl　Availability: 40 pubs
REGULAR BEERS:
Bayer Bräu Pilsener (5%)
Bayer Bräu Jubiläums-Export (5%)
Bayer Bräu Schwarzes Röslein (5.2%)
Bayer Bräu Spessarträuber Weissbier (5.2%)
Bayer Spessarträuber Dunkles Weissbier (5.2%)
Bayer Bräu Rothenfelser Raubritter (5.5%)
SEASONAL BEER:
Bayer Bräu Bayerator Doppelbock (7.5%)

Small brewery in the smallest town in Bayern.
In the early 19th century, the densely wooded
Spessart region was infamously made unsafe
by hordes of *Spessarträuber* (Spessart robbers)
and *Raubritter* (robber barons). The tap closes
for two weeks in November. Bus No. 8050 runs
daily from Lohr station.

🍴 **Bayer Bräustüble**
Hauptstraße 77, 97851 Rothenfels
T 09393 484
Closed Tue; Wed–Sat & Mon from 16.00,
Sun & hols from 10.00; rooms available
DB Lohr Bf 14km

ROTHMOOS (Halfing) 495

Rothmoos

Brauerei Rothmoos Anton Kirnberger GmbH
Rothmoos 2, 83128 Halfing-Rothmoos
T 08055 906 60　**F** 08055 90 66 66
www.rothmooser.de　Founded: 1927
Owner: Anton Kirnberger　Output: 5,000hl

REGULAR BEERS:
Rothmooser Premium Hell (5%)
Rothmooser Hefe-Weißbier (5.2%)
SEASONAL BEERS:
Rothmooser Festbier (5.4%),
Rothmooser Weißbier-Bock (7.4%)

Formerly known as Schmiedbräu, this small brewery is in a tiny hamlet 3km west of Halfing which appears on few maps. The tap is in the slightly larger hamlet of Egg, some 500m south of Rothmoos. The nearest bus stop is 2km away in Gunzenham but isn't much use for the pub.

🍺 **Rothmooser Bräustüberl**
Egg 5, 83128 Halfing-Egg
T 08055 903 99 30   **F** 08055 903 99 31
Closed Mon; Tue–Sat from 18.00, Sun from 11.00
DB Bad Endorf 8km

RÖTTENBACH 496

Sauer
Hauptstraße 45, 91341 Röttenbach
T 09195 79 10   **F** 09195 64 37
E brauerei.sauer@t-online.de
Owner: Herbert Sauer   Founded: 1890
Output: 3,000hl
REGULAR BEERS:
Sauer Pils
Sauer Export
SEASONAL BEER:
Sauer Festbier

Small brewery and tap on the main road through the town. Bus No. 205 runs regularly from Erlangen, seven days a week.

🍺 **Sauer**
Hauptstraße 45, 91341 Röttenbach
T 09195 92 81 94
Closed Wed; Thu–Tue 13.00–01.00
DB Erlangen 12km

RÖTZ 497

Genossenschaftsbrauerei
Genossenschaftsbrauerei Rötz e.G.
Hussenstraße 17, 92444 Rötz
T 09976 14 25   **F** 09976 799
Founded: 1812
Output: 5,000hl   Availability: 15 pubs

REGULAR BEER:
Genossenschafts-Vollbier Hell (4.9%)
SEASONAL BEER:
Genossenschafts-Guttensteiner Halbe (4.9%)

Small brewery run as a co-operative by local publicans. There's no specific tap but the beer can be found in a number of local pubs. Bus No. 230 runs a couple of times from Pösing on weekdays, as does the No. 320 from Cham.
DB Pösing 15km, Cham (Oberpfalz) 19km

RÜDENHAUSEN 498

Wolf
Brauerei Karl Heinrich Wolf Rüdenhausen
Paul-Gerhard-Platz 7, 97355 Rüdenhausen
T 09383 440
Owner: Karl Heinrich Wolf
Founded: 1746
Output: 800hl
REGULAR BEERS:
Wolf Rüdenhäuser Urtyp-Dunkel (4.5%)
Wolf Rüdenhäuser Pils (4.6%)

Brewpub in the centre of Rüdenhausen which we believe to be the only outlet for the beers. Bus No. 8111 runs from Kitzingen on weekdays.

🍺 **Wolf**
Paul-Gerhard-Platz 7, 97355 Rüdenhausen
Closed Mon; Tue–Sun 11.00–14.30 & 17.00–23.00; rooms available
DB Kitzingen 15km

RUNDING 499

Schloßbrauerei
Dorfplatz 6, 93486 Runding
T 09971 16 15
Owner: Otto Kopp
Founded: 1386
Output: 1,500hl
REGULAR BEERS:
Rundinger Schlossbräu Hell
Rundinger Schlossbräu Export
SEASONAL BEER:
Rundinger Schlossbräu Festbier

Small brewery and tap in the centre of the village. The railway station is a fair walk but there are direct buses to Runding from Cham on weekdays.

🍺 **Schloßbrauerei**
Dorfplatz 6, 93486 Runding
Daily 08.00–23.00; rooms available
DB Runding 3km, Cham (Oberpfalz) 9km

SACHSENDORF (Aufseß) 500

Stadter

Brauerei-Gasthof Benedikt Stadter
Schloßstraße 26, 91347 Aufseß-Sachsendorf
T 09274 786 www.brauerei-stadter.de
Owner: Benedikt Stadter Founded: 1884
Output: 400hl Availability: 1 pub
REGULAR BEER:
Stadter Dunkles Landbier

Very small brewery with the tap nearby. They
also own a guesthouse in the village. Bus No.
8235 runs once a day on weekdays from both
Bamberg and Ebermannstadt but the return
journey is more complicated.

🍺 **Stadter**
Hauptstraße 26, 91347 Aufseß-Sachsendorf
T 09274 81 93
Closed Mon; Tue–Sun 10.00–22.00
DB Ebermannstadt 20km, Bamberg 30km

SAMBACH (Pommersfelden) 501

Hennemann

Brauerei Hans Hennemann
Sambach 33, 96178 Pommersfelden-Sambach
T/F 09502 43 07
Owner: Hans Hennemann Founded: 1780
Output: 1,000hl
REGULAR BEERS:
Hennemann Lagerbier (4.9%)
Hennemann Zwickelbier (4.9%)
SEASONAL BEER:
Hennemann Bockbier Dunkel (6.8%)

Brewpub in the middle of the village. Bus No.
8227 runs from Bamberg on weekdays but the
return service is limited.

🍺 **Hennemann**
Sambach 33, 96178 Pommersfelden-Sambach
Closed Mon & Tue; Wed & Thu 11.00–14.00 &
17.00–23.00, Fri–Sun 10.00–23.00
DB Bamberg 18km

SANDERSDORF (Altmannstein) 502

Schloßbrauerei

de Bassus Schloßbrauerei zu Sandersdorf
Schambachtal GmbH
Nürnberger Straße 13, 93336 Altmannstein-
Sandersdorf
T 09446 90 29 30 F 09446 90 29 39
www.schlossbrauerei-sandersdorf.de
Founded: 1550
Output: 15,000hl Availability: 25 pubs
REGULAR BEERS:
Baron Augustus Urtyp Hell (4.9%)
Baron Tassilo Premium Pils (4.9%)
Baron Ferdinand Weizen Hell (5.1%)
Baron Ferdinand Weizen Dunkel (5.1%)
Baron Maximilian Premium Lager (5.3%)
Baron Dominicus Spezial Dunkel (5.6%)
SEASONAL BEER:
de Bassus Bock (7.5%)

Small brewery on the main road out of the village.
The barons in the beer names all hail from the
de Bassus family. Bus No. 9221 runs daily from
Ingolstadt ZOB and stops outside the tap.

🍺 **Zur Sonne**
Marienplatz 10, 93336 Altmannstein-Sandersdorf
T 09446 12 36
Daily 09.00–24.00; rooms available
DB Ingolstadt Hbf 30km

SCHALCHEN (Tacherting) 503

Weissbräu Schwendl

Weissbräu Schwendl GmbH & Co. KG
Trostberger Straße 130,
83342 Tacherting-Schalchen
T 08621 23 00 F 08621 636 26
www.weissbraeu-schwendl.de
Owners: the Schwendl family Founded: 1935
Availability: c.80 pubs
REGULAR BEERS:
Schalchner Leichte Weisse (2.9%)
Schalchner Weisse (4.9%)
Schalchner Dunkle Weisse (4.9%)
Schalchner Bonsai Weißbier (5%)
SEASONAL BEER:
Schalchner Weisser Bock (6.9%)

Small wheat beer brewery and tap on the main

road from Traunstein to Altötting. Despite the address, we think they may technically be in the village of Lengloh rather than Schalchen.

📍 **Weissbräu Schwendl**
Trostberger Straße 130,
83342 Tacherting-Schalchen
Closed Sat; Sun–Fri 08.00–24.00
DB Schalchen 300m

SCHAMMELSDORF
(Litzendorf)   504

Knoblach

Brauerei Knoblach GmbH
Kremmeldorfer Straße 1,
96123 Litzendorf-Schammelsdorf
T 09505 267   **F** 09505 61 84
Owner: Michael Knoblach   Founded: 1880
Output: 2,000hl
REGULAR BEERS:
Knoblach Schammelsdorfer Weißbier (4.9%)
Knoblach Schammelsdorfer Kellerbier (5%)
Knoblach Schammelsdorfer Lagerbier (5.1%)
Knoblach Schammelsdorfer Räuschla (5.1%)

Brewpub in the centre of the village which we think supplies a couple of other pubs. Bus No. 27 runs from Bamberg on weekdays but the return journey is likely to involve a change.

📍 **Knoblach**
Kremmeldorfer Straße 1,
96123 Litzendorf-Schammelsdorf
Closed Mon; Tue–Fri 15.30–23.00, Sat, Sun & hols 09.00–23.00
DB Bamberg 10km

SCHEDERNDORF
(Stadelhofen)   505

Will

Brauerei Wirtshaus Biergarten Konrad Will
Schederndorf 19, 96187 Stadelhofen-Schederndorf
T 09504 262   **F** 09504 283
www.schederndorf.de
Owner: Konrad Will   Founded: 1742
Output: 3,000hl   Availability: 5 pubs
REGULAR BEERS:
Schederndorfer Landbier Dunkel (5.2%)
Schederndorfer Hefeweizen (5.2%)

SEASONAL BEER:
Schederndorfer Bockbier (7.5%, Nov–Dec)

Small brewery and tap in an equally small village close to the A70. Closes for two weeks over Christmas and New Year. There's no public transport to Schederndorf, the nearest bus stop being in Steinfeld, 3km to the south.

📍 **Will**
Schederndorf 19, 96187 Stadelhofen-Schederndorf
Closed Tue; Wed–Sat & Mon 11.00–24.00,
Sun & hols 10.00–24.00
DB Bad Staffelstein 20km, Bamberg 27km

SCHERNECK (Rehling)   506

Schloßbrauerei

Scherneck 1, 86508 Rehling-Scherneck
T 08237 255   **F** 08237 95 96 56
www.schloss-scherneck.de
Owner: Dr. Christian Siedler, Freiherr von Schätzler
Founded: 1719   Output: 3,000hl
Availability: 10 pubs
REGULAR BEERS:
Schernecker Bernstein-Pils (4.6%)
Schernecker Helles Zwickel-Bier (5.3%)
Schernecker Dunkles Keller-Bier (5.3%)
Schernecker Naturtrüber Doppel-Bock (7.1%)

Castle brewery and tap on a wooded hill south of Rehling. Bus No. 305 runs from Augsburg Mon–Sat and stops at the nearby village of Au.

📍 **Schlößbräustüberl**
Scherneck 1, 86508 Rehling-Scherneck
T 08237 63 50
Winter: closed Mon; Tue–Sun 10.00–01.00
Summer daily 10.00–01.00
DB Augsburg Hbf 14km

SCHESSLITZ   507

Drei Kronen

Brauerei Drei Kronen Scheßlitz
Hauptstraße 39, 96110 Scheßlitz
T 09542 15 64   **F** 09542 92 15 95
www.kronabier.de
Owner: Ludwig Lindner   Founded: 1669
Output: 1,500hl   Availability: 4 pubs
REGULAR BEERS:
Schäazer Kronabier Lagerbier (5.1%)

Schäazer Premium Pils (5.2%)
Schäazer Weisse (5.3%)
SEASONAL BEERS:
Schäazer Weihnachts-Festbier (5.5%),
Schäazer Festbier (5.6%), **Schäazer Weizenbock**
(6.8%), **Schäazer Kronabier Bock** (8%)

Small brewery and tap on the main road through
the town. Bus No. 8224 runs daily from Bamberg.

🍺 **Drei Kronen**
Hauptstraße 39, 96110 Scheßlitz
Closed Wed; Thu–Tue 09.00–14.00 & 17.00–01.00
DB Bamberg 14km

Senger

Oberend 11, 96110 Scheßlitz
T 09542 10 64
Owner: Hans Senger   Founded: 1854
Output: 500hl   Availability: 1 pub
REGULAR BEER:
Senger Vollbier Dunkel

Tiny brewpub formerly known as Barth-Senger,
though we believe the first part of the name has
been officially dropped. Schmitt-Bräu just up the
street no longer brew themselves but we think
they do have some beers contract-brewed.

🍺 **Senger**
Oberend 11, 96110 Scheßlitz
Closed Mon, Tue–Fri & Sun 10.00–23.00,
Sat 10.00–17.00
DB Bamberg 14km

SCHEYERN   508

Klosterbrauerei

Schyrenplatz 1, 85298 Scheyern
T 08441 75 20   F 08441 75 22 10
www.kloster-scheyern.de
Owner: Benediktinerabtei Scheyern
Founded: 1119   Output: 2,000hl
Availability: 3 pubs
REGULAR BEERS:
Klosterbier Hell
Klosterbier Dunkel
Klosterbier Weizen
SEASONAL BEERS:
**Klosterbier Hopfenzupferbier, Klosterbier
Märzen, Klosterbier Doppelbock Dunkel**

Brewing resumed in late 2005 after a ten-year

hiatus, albeit on a small scale. Hasen-Bräu in
Augsburg have brewed the beers of the Scheyern
Benedictine abbey since 1995 and will continue
to do so as there is not enough capacity here. Bus
No. 9241 runs from Pfaffenhofen on weekdays.

🍺 **Klosterstub'n**
Schyrenplatz 1, 85298 Scheyern
T 08441 278 90   F 08441 27 89 27
Daily 10.00–23.00; rooms available
DB Pfaffenhofen (Ilm) 6km

SCHIERLING   509

Spezial-Brauerei

Spezial-Brauerei Schierling GmbH
Hauptstraße 15–17, 84069 Schierling
T 09451 30 12   F 09451 33 61
Founded: 1834   Output: 25,000hl
REGULAR BEERS:
Schierlinger Hell (4.9%)
Schierlinger Roggen (4.9%)
Schierlinger Pils (5%)

Small regional brewery, formerly a subsidiary of
Thurn und Taxis. Nowadays they are owned by
Kuchlbauer of Abensberg. Bus No. 25 runs from
Eggmühl station daily except Sunday.

🍺 **Bräustüberl**
Rathausplatz 7, 84069 Schierling
T/F 09451 36 68
Sat 11.00–14.00, Sun–Fri 11.00–4.00 & 16.00–01.00
DB Eggmühl 3.8km

SCHLAMMERSDORF
(Hallerndorf)   510

Witzgall

Schlammersdorfer Straße 17, 91352
Hallerndorf-Schlammersdorf
T 09545 74 52
Owner: Helmut Witzgall   Founded: 1811
Output: 1,200hl   Availability: 1 pub
REGULAR BEERS:
Witzgall Vollbier (4.6%)
Witzgall Lagerbier (5.3%)
Brewpub in the centre of Schlammersdorf. We
think the lagerbier is only available at their
Keller on the outskirts of the village. Bus No.
265 runs from Eggolsheim station on weekdays.

🍺 **Witzgall**
Schlammersdorfer Straße 17, 91352
Hallerndorf-Schlammersdorf
Closed Thu; Fri–Wed 09.00–23.00
DB Eggolsheim 3km

SCHLAMMERSDORF
(Oberpfalz)   511

Püttner

Hauptstraße 11, 95519 Schlammersdorf
T 09205 292   **F** 09205 988 10 38
www.brauerei-puettner.de
Owner: Christine & Johannes Püttner
Founded: 1819   Output: 9,000hl
REGULAR BEERS:
Püttner Bräu Lager Hell (4.7%)
Püttner Bräu Pils (4.9%)
Püttner Bräu Püt (4.9%)
Püttner Bräu P2000
Püttner Bräu Jo Püt
Püttner Bräu Gold Export (5.2%)
Püttner Bräu Weißbier (5.4%)
Püttner Bräu Böckl

Small brewery and recently refurbished tap in
the middle of the village. It is possible to get to
Schlammersorf by bus on weekdays but there
are no buses out after the pub opens.

🍺 **Püttner**
Hauptstraße 11, 95519 Schlammersdorf
Closed Mon & Tue; Wed–Fri 11.00–14.00 & from
16.30, Sat, Sun & hols from 10.00; rooms available
DB Kemnath-Neustadt 11km

SCHLICHT (Vilseck)   512

Winkler-Bräu

Winkler-Bräu Schlicht GmbH & Co.
Winklergasse 1, 92249 Vilseck-Schlicht
T 09662 233   **F** 09662 13 56
Founded: 1782   Output: 15,000hl
REGULAR BEERS:
Winkler-Bräu Schlichter Ursprung Hell
Winkler-Bräu Schlichter Pils
Winkler-Bräu Schlichter Kupfer Gold
Winkler-Bräu Schlichter Hefeweiße
Winkler-Bräu Schlichter Klosterweizen
SEASONAL BEER:
Winkler-Bräu Schlichter Doppelbock

Brewery in Oberpfalz with a tap 35km away in
the Oberfranken village of Bronn, near Pegnitz.
Several bus routes run from Pegnitz to Bronn on
weekdays. The brewery is around 1.7km from
Vilseck station.

🍺 **Brauhaus Bronn**
Klumpertalstraße 49, 91257 Pegnitz-Bronn
T 09241 60 37
Closed Tue; Wed–Mon 10.00–14.00 & 17.00–24.00
DB Pegnitz 8km

SCHLÜSSELFELD   513

Adler-Bräu

Brauerei zum Adler Hans Amtmann
Marktplatz 6, 96132 Schlüsselfeld
T 09552 359   **F** 09552 60 15
Owner: Hans Amtmann
Founded: 1866
Output: 2,000hl
REGULAR BEER:
Adler-Bräu Vollbier (4.8%)
SEASONAL BEER:
Adler-Bräu Festbier

Small brewery and tap in the centre of town.
Buses Nos. 8223 and 8227 run from Bamberg on
weekdays and there are also a few on route No.
145 from Neustadt.

🍺 **Schwarzer Adler**
Marktplatz 6, 96132 Schlüsselfeld
Mon 09.00–14.00, Tue–Sun 09.00–23.00
DB Neustadt (Aisch) 28km, Bamberg 30km

Stern-Bräu

Stern-Bräu Günter Scheubel
Kirchplatz 12, 96132 Schlüsselfeld
T 09552 320
www.brauerei-scheubel.de
Owner: Günter Scheubel   Founded: 1828
Output: 2,000hl   Availability: 1 pub
REGULAR BEERS:
Scheubel Vollbier Hell (5%)
Scheubel Hausbrauerbier Ungespundet (5%)
SEASONAL BEER:
Scheubel Festbier Dunkel (5.5%)

One of two breweries in the area called Scheubel,
the other is in Possenfelden, 4km east of
Schlüsselfeld. We don't know if they're related.

🍺**Scheubel**
Kirchplatz 12, 96132 Schlüsselfeld
Daily 09.00–23.00
DB Neustadt (Aisch) 28km, Bamberg 30km

SCHNAID (Hallerndorf) 514

Friedel

Schnaid 10, 91352 Hallerndorf-Schnaid
T 09543 34 58
www.friedels-keller.de
Owner: Luitgard Friedel-Winkelmann
Founded: 1461   Output: 1,000hl
REGULAR BEERS:
Friedels Zwickelbier (4.9%)
Friedels Hefeweizen (5%)

Small brewery in the centre of Schnaid, with a
tap next door and a Bierkeller on the hill south of
the village. Bus No. 265 runs from Eggolsheim
station on weekday afternoons but the return
service is fairly limited.

🍺**Friedel**
Schnaid 10, 91352 Hallerndorf-Schnaid
Closed Mon & Tue; Wed–Sun 09.00–23.00
DB **Eggolsheim** 8km

🍺**Friedels Keller am Kreuzberg**
Kreuzberg, 91352 Hallerndorf
T/F 09545 47 36
Oct–Mar: closed Mon–Thu; Fri–Sun from 11.00
Apr–Sep daily from 11.00
DB Eggolsheim 8km

SCHNAITTACH 515

Kanone

Brauerei Kanone, Lohr GmbH & Co. KG
Bayreuther Straße 3, 91220 Schnaittach
T 09153 366   F 09153 59 99
www.brauerei-kanone.de
Owner: Gerda Löhr-Küchler   Founded: 1886
Output: 6,000hl   Availability: 6 pubs
REGULAR BEERS:
Kanone Pils (4.9%)
Kanone Weizen Hell (4.9%)
Kanone Weizen Dunkel (4.9%)
Kanone Hell (5.1%)
Kanone Dunkel (5.2%)
Kanone Zwickel (5.3%)

SEASONAL BEER:
Kanone Bock (6.8%)

Small brewery in the centre of town. The half-
timbered tap closes for two weeks in late July.

🍺**Kanone**
Bayreuther Straße 3, 91220 Schnaittach
Closed Sun, Mon–Fri 09.00–19.00,
Sat 09.00–14.00   DB Schnaittach Markt 550m

Schaffer-Bräu

Badstraße 5, 91220 Schnaittach
T 09153 253
www.brauerei-schaffer.de
Owners: the Schaffer family   Founded: 1895
Output: 7,000hl
REGULAR BEERS:
Schaffer-Bräu Lager (4.9%)
Schaffer-Bräu Pilsner (5%)
Schaffer-Bräu Rothenburg Gold (5.3%)
SEASONAL BEER:
Schaffer-Bräu Bockbier (7.3%)

Slightly the larger of Schnaittach's two
breweries, Schaffer-Bräu is located on the
western edge of the town. The former tap at
Erlanger Straße 29 is now an Italian restaurant
but the beers are easy to find locally.
DB Schnaittach Markt 1km

SCHÖLLKRIPPEN 516

Barbarossa Bräu

Aschaffenburger Straße 18, 63825 Schöllkrippen
T 06024 54 54   F 06024 84 67
www.brauhaus-barbarossa.de
Owner: Frank Ziemen   Founded: 1990
Output: 500hl   Availability: 2 pubs
REGULAR BEER:
Barbarossa Hell (5.2%)
SEASONAL BEERS:
Barbarossa Leichtes Landbier (3%), **Barbarossa
Frühlingsbier** (3.2%, Apr), **Barbarossa Honig
Bier** (4.9%, Mar), **Barbarossa Alt** (5%, summer),
Barbarossa Dunkel (5.1%), **Barbarossa Weizen
Dunkel** (5.1%, Jan–Jun), **Barbarossa Weizen
Hell** (5.1%, Jul–Dec), **Barbarossa Marleusbier**
(5.2%), **Barbarossa Michaeli Bier** (5.2%, Sep),
Barbarossa Rotbier (5.8%, Jul), **Barbarossa
Fastenbier** (6.5%, Lent), **Barbarossa
Weihnachtsdoppelbock** (8.1%)

Modern brewpub close to the centre of town. Schöllkrippen is the terminus of the private Kahlgrundbahn from Kahl.

🏠 Brauhaus Barbarossa

Aschaffenburger Straße 18, 63825 Schöllkrippen
Closed Mon; Tue–Sat 17.00–01.00, Sun & hols 11.00–24.00   DB Schöllkrippen 400m

SCHÖNBRUNN (Steigerwald)   517

Bähr

Brauerei Fritz Bähr
Zettmannsdorfer Straße 24, 96185 Schönbrunn
T 09546 379   **F** 09546 92 14 51
www.baehr-keller.de
Owner: Fritz Bähr   Founded: before 1900
Output: 2,500hl   Availability: 3 pubs
REGULAR BEER:
Bähr Pils (4.9%)
SEASONAL BEER:
Bähr Bockbier (7.5%, May)

Small brewery and tap on the main road through the village. Their Bierkeller is nearby and we think they may brew a Kellerbier for it.

🏠 Landgasthof Bähr

Zettmannsdorfer Straße 24, 96185 Schönbrunn
Closed Mon; Tue–Sun 09.00–14.00 & 16.00–24.00; rooms available
DB Bamberg 20km

🏠 Bähr-Keller

Friedhofsweg, 96185 Schönbrunn
Closed Oct–Apr & in wet weather;
Sat & Sun 14.00–23.00, Mon–Fri 16.00–23.00
DB Bamberg 20km

Wernsdörfer

Brauerei & Gastwirtschaft Andreas Wernsdörfer
Obere Bachgasse 5, 96185 Schönbrunn
T 09546 389   **F** 09546 59 22 03
www.brauerei-wernsdoerfer.de
Owner: Andreas Wensdörfer   Founded: 1789
Output: 800hl   Availability: 4 pubs
REGULAR BEER:
Wernsdörfer Landbier (5%)

The smaller of Schönbrunn's two breweries, Wernsdörfer is just around the corner from Bähr. Bus No. 8244 runs from Bamberg on weekdays.

🏠 Wernsdörfer

Obere Bachgasse 5, 96185 Schönbrunn
Closed Tue; Wed–Mon 09.00–24.00; rooms available
DB Bamberg 20km

SCHÖNBRUNN (Wunsiedel)   518

Lang-Bräu

Lang-Bräu OHG
Bayreuther Straße 18–19,
95632 Wunsiedel-Schönbrunn
T 09232 21 97   **F** 09232 79 12
www.lang-braeu.de
Owners: Irma Hopf & Gerda Lang
Founded: 1853
Output: 20,000hl
Availability: 25 pubs
REGULAR BEERS:
Lang Schönbrunner Hopfen Medium (2.9%)
Lang Schönbrunner Weissbier Medium (3.1%)
Lang-Bräu Fichtelgebirgs-Hell (4.5%)
Lang-Bräu Siebensternchen-Pils (5%)
Lang-Bräu Fichtelgebirgs-Pils (5%)
Lang-Bräu Schönbrunner Weissbier (5.2%)
Lang Schönbrunner Weissbier Dunkel (5.2%)
Lang Schönbrunner Burggraf Dunkel (5.5%)
Lang-Bräu Fichtelgebirgs-Spezial (5.5%)
Lang-Bräu Erotik Bier (5.5%)
SEASONAL BEERS:
Lang-Bräu Fichtelgebirgs-Festbier (5.5%),
Lang-Bräu Benedikt XVI (7.5%),
Lang-Bräu Schönbrunner Urbock (7.5%),
Lang Schönbrunner Urbock Dunkel (7.5%),
Lang-Bräu Maibock Dunkel (7.5%)

Brewery on the main road through Schönbrunn, with a tap around the corner. For reasons known only to themselves the bottled pale and light wheat beers have their labels stuck on upside down. It's also the label which makes one of their beers 'erotic'. We can't trace a bus service to the village but believe there is one.

🏠 Bräustübl

Brunnenstraße 10, 95632 Wunsiedel-Schönbrunn
T 09232 28 13
Closed Sat in winter; Sun–Fri 09.00–24.00; rooms available
DB Marktredwitz 10km

SCHONGAU 519

Schongauer Brauhaus

Altenstädter Straße 13, 86956 Schongau
T 08861 90 95 86   **F** 08861 90 95 87
Owner: Peter Just   Founded: 2003
REGULAR BEERS:
Schongauer Haustrunk
Schongauer Weisse

Modern brewpub in what looks like a barn, on
the opposite side of the town centre to the
station. We believe they brew seasonal beers in
addition to the regulars.

🍺 **Schongauer Brauhaus**
Altenstädter Straße 13, 86956 Schongau
Sun 10.00–14.00 & 17.00–23.00,
Mon–Sat 11.00–14.00 & 17.00–24.00
DB Schongau 1.1km

SCHÖNRAM (Petting) 520

Schönram

Private Landbrauerei Schönram
Salzburger Straße 10–14, 83367 Petting-Schönram
T 08686 988 00   **F** 08686 98 80 40
www.brauerei-schoenram.de
Owner: Alfred Oberlindober junior
Founded: 1780   Output: 40,000hl
Availability: c.30 pubs
REGULAR BEERS:
Schönramer Surtaler Leichter Typ (3.4%)
Schönramer Hell (5%)
Schönramer Original Altbayrisch Dunkel (5%)
Schönramer Pils (5%)
Schönramer Festweisse (5.6%)
Schönramer Gold (5.7%)
SEASONAL BEERS:
Schönramer Festbier (6.1%),
Schönramer Bock (7.1%)

Brewery on the main road through Schönram.
The tap is due to be re-open in June 2006
following refurbishment. Bus No. 9519 runs
from Laufen station on weekdays but you may
find it easier to make your way from Teisendorf.

🍺 **Bräustüberl**
Salzburger Straße 10, 83367 Petting-Schönram
T 08686 273   Closed Wed; Thu–Tue from 09.00
DB Teisendorf 5.5km, Laufen 8km

SCHÖNSEE 521

Haberl

Brauerei Hans Haberl
Am Graben 1, 92539 Schönsee
T 09674 508
Owner: Hans Haberl   Founded: 1883
Output: 5,000hl
REGULAR BEERS:
Haberl-Bräu Hell (4.8%)
Haberl-Bräu Pils (4.9%)
Haberl-Bräu Reichenstein Ur-Weisse (4.9%)
Haberl-Bräu Export (5.1%)
Haberl-Bräu Märzen (5.1%)
SEASONAL BEER:
Haberl-Bräu Festbier

Small brewery on the northern side of town, with
the tap a couple of streets away. Bus No. 6273
runs from Nabburg on weekday afternoons but
you'll have to stay the night if you want to return
by bus after the pub opens.

🍺 **Haberl**
Hauptstraße 9, 92539 Schönsee
T 09674 214   **F** 08252 911 38
Closed Mon; Tue–Sun 17.30–23.00; rooms
available
DB Nabburg 35km

SCHROBENHAUSEN 522

Gritschenbräu

Gritschenbräu Schrobenhausen KG,
Brauerei Höcht & Söhne
Augsburger Straße 2, 86529 Schrobenhausen
T 08252 834 94   **F** 08252 834 32
www.gritschenbraeu.de
Owners: Annemarie & Franz Höcht
Founded: 1593   Output: 10,000hl
REGULAR BEERS:
Gritschenbräu Pils (4.9%)
Gritschenbräu Hell (5.1%)
Gritschenbräu Export (5.3%)
Gritschenbräu Altbayerisch Dunkel (5.4%)

Small brewery and tap on the opposite side of the
river Paar to Schrobenhausen's walled old town.

🍺 **Gritschenbräu-Stüberl**
Augsburger Straße 2, 86529 Schrobenhausen
T/F 08252 47 56

Closed Mon; Tue–Sun from 10.00
DB Schrobenhausen 1.4km

SCHRÖTTING
(Michelsneukirchen) 523

Schröttinger

Schröttinger Bräu Wolfgang Krottentaler e.K.
Schrötting 1, 93185 Michelsneukirchen-Schrötting
T 09467 253   **F** 09467 14 12
Owner: Wolfgang Krottenthaler
Founded: 1899   Output: 7,000hl
REGULAR BEERS:
Schröttinger Bräu Hell
Schröttinger Bräu Pils
Schröttinger Bräu Weisse
Schröttinger Bräu Dunkles Weisse
Schröttinger Bräu Märzen
SEASONAL BEER:
Schröttinger Bräu Festbier

Brewery in a hamlet a mile or so north-west of
Michelsneukirchen. The tap is in Falkenstein,
8km west of Schrötting. Bus No. 6072 runs from
Cham station to Falkenstein via Michelsneukirchen on weekdays.

🍺 Schröttinger Bräu
Marktplatz 7, 93167 Falkenstein
T 09462 321
Closed Mon; Tue–Sun 09.00–01.00; rooms
available
DB Cham (Oberpfalz) 24km

SCHWABACH 524

Leitner

Leitner Bräu GmbH & Co. KG
Nürnberger Straße 19, 91126 Schwabach
T 09122 926 50   **F** 09122 92 65 20
Owners: the Leitner family   Founded: 1530
Output: 8,000hl   Availability: 30 pubs
REGULAR BEERS:
Leitner-Bräu Lager (4.8%)
Leitner-Bräu Golden (4.9%)
Leitner-Bräu Hefeweizen Hell (4.9%)
Leitner-Bräu Zwicklbier
Leitner-Bräu Pils (5%)
Leitner-Bräu Schwabacher Weisse (5%)
Leitner-Bräu Prinz-Albrecht-Trunk (5.1%)

SEASONAL BEERS:
Halloween Beer (5%), **Weihnachtsfestbier** (5%),
Märzen (5.1%), **Bürgerfestbier** (5.3%)

Family-run brewery and tap in the centre of
Schwabach. The tap has recently extended its
opening hours and is now much easier to visit
on weekdays.

🍺 Leitner-Bräu-Stub'n
Nürnberger Straße 19, 91126 Schwabach
T 09122 87 56 85
Closed Mon; Tue–Sun 09.00–23.00
DB Schwabach 1.3km

SCHWANDORF 525

Schmidt-Bräu

Schmidt-Bräu GmbH & Co. KG
Marktplatz 8, 92421 Schwandorf
T 09431 30 55   **F** 09431 436 79
www.schmidtbraeu.de
Owner: Marianne Ruhland   Founded: 1858
Output: 40,000hl   Availability: c.100 pubs
REGULAR BEERS:
Schmidt-Bräu Schmidtchen (2.7%)
Schmidt-Bräu Vollbier Hell (4.7%)
Schmidt-Bräu Pils (4.8%)
Schmidt-Bräu Export Hell (5.2%)
Schmidt-Bräu Jacobus Export Dunkel (5.2%)
Schmidt-Bräu Zünftige Weisse (5.2%)
Schmidt-Bräu Zünftige Schwarze (5.2%)
Schmidt-Bräu Zünftige Kristall-Weisse (5.3%)

Small regional brewery on the market square
with the tap in front. If you happen to be in town
on the rest day (Thu) you won't have difficulty
finding the beers elsewhere.

🍺 Schmidtbräu
Marktplatz 7, 92421 Schwandorf
T 09431 26 32
Closed Thu; Fri–Wed 09.00–01.00
DB Schwandorf 650m

SCHWEINFURT 526

Brauhaus Schweinfurt

Klingenbrunnstraße 22–26, 97422 Schweinfurt
T 09721 536 11   **F** 09721 536 33
www.brauhaus-schweinfurt.de
Founded: 1903   Output: 50,000hl

Availability: 220 pubs
REGULAR BEERS:
Brauhaus Leichte (2.9%)
Brauhaus Lager (4.8%)
Brauhaus Alpha-Bier (4.8%)
Brauhaus Pilsener (4.9%)
Brauhaus Kellerbier (5.3%)
Brauhaus Elchbier (5.3%)
Brauhaus Weissbier (5.3%)
Brauhaus Schwarz-Weisse (5.3%)
Brauhaus Perlweizen (5.3%)
Brauhaus Franken Gold (5.4%)
SEASONAL BEERS:
Brauhaus Advents-Bier (5.4%), **Brauhaus Volksfest-Bier** (5.7%), **Brauhaus Kirchweihbier** (5.7%), **Brauhaus Maibock** (7.5%), **Brauhaus Antonator** (7.5%)

Small regional brewery just north of the town centre. The brewery tap is at the top of the market square.

🍺 **Brauhaus am Markt**
Markt 30, 97421 Schweinfurt
T 09721 163 16   **F** 09721 29 91 49
Daily 11.00–24.00
DB Schweinfurt Stadt 850m, Hbf 1.7km

Roth

Brauerei Roth GmbH
Obere Straße 24, 97421 Schweinfurt
T 09721 10 34   **F** 09721 281 44
www.rothbier.com
Founded: 1831   Output: 20,000hl
Availability: 65 pubs
REGULAR BEERS:
Roth Light (2.9%)
Roth Pilsner (4.8%)
Roth Runner (4.8%)
Roth Schwarzbier (4.8%)
Roth Weißbier (5.4%)
Roth Schwarzes Weißbier (5.4%)
Roth Marzen (5.6%)
SEASONAL BEERS:
Roth Volksfest-Bier (5.6%), **Roth Festbier** (5.7%)

The smaller of Schweinfurt's two remaining breweries, Roth is situated in the old town, just up from the market square. A third brewery, Brauhaus Tabasco on Albrecht-Dürer-Platz, has stopped brewing but may resume in the future.

🍺 **Zum Roth**
Obere Straße 24, 97421 Schweinfurt

T 09721 163 39
Closed Mon; Tue–Sun 11.00–14.00 & from 17.00
DB Schweinfurt Stadt 850m, Hbf 1.8km

SEEMANNSHAUSEN
(Gangkofen)   527

Klosterbräu

Seemannshausen 8, 84140 Gangkofen-Seemannshausen
T 08722 312   **F** 08722 314
www.klosterbraeu-seemannshausen.de
Owner: Lene Obermayr   Founded: 1355
Output: 3,000hl
REGULAR BEERS:
Klosterbräu Pater Dunkel
Klosterbräu Pater Export
Klosterbräu Pater Gold Märzen
SEASONAL BEER:
Klosterbräu Pater Festbier

Small brewery in the former monastery in the hamlet of Seemannshausen. Note the restricted opening hours of the tap. Bus No. 51 runs from Eggenfelden on weekdays.

🍺 **Bierkeller**
Seemannshausen 8,
84140 Gangkofen-Seemannshausen
Closed Mon–Thu; Fri–Sun 15.00–23.00
DB Eggenfelden 19km

SEINSHEIM   528

Seinsheimer-Kellerbräu

Bierbrauerei F. Engelhardt und W. Zippel GbR
In den Kirchengaden am Rathausplatz,
97342 Seinsheim
T/F 09332 12 19
www.seinsheimer-kellerbier.de
Owners: Frank Engelhardt & Wilfred Zippel
Founded: 2002
REGULAR BEER:
Seinsheimer Kellerbier (4.9%)
SEASONAL BEERS:
Seinsheimer Hefeweizen (4.9%),
Seinsheimer Maibock (6.5%),
Seinsheimer Weihnachtsbock (6.8%)

Tiny brewery that's run as a semi-commercial hobby. No tap but the beers are available from

the brewery on brewing days (normally Fri, but sometimes Sat). There's just one bus a day from Marktbreit on weekday evenings.
DB Marktbreit 7km

SELB 529

Brauhaus Ploss

Schillerstraße 23, 95100 Selb
T 09287 89 03 42 **F** 09287 912 31
www.brauhaus-ploss.de
Owner: Klaus Peter Ploß
Founded: 1998 Availability: 2 pubs
REGULAR BEERS:
Brauhaus Ploss Lager
Brauhaus Ploss Selber Weisse
SEASONAL BEERS:
Brauhaus Ploss Sommerbier, Brauhaus Ploss Zoigl, Brauhaus Ploss Rauchbier, Brauhaus Ploss Roggenbier, Brauhaus Ploss Festbier

Modern brewpub set up by one of owners of the former Rauh & Ploß brewery, which used to stand across the street. They also have a small distillery.

🍺 **Brauhaus Ploss**
Schillerstraße 23, 95100 Selb
Closed Sun; Mon–Sat 10.30–01.30
DB Selb Stadt 600m

SESSLACH 530

Kommunbrauhaus

Brewery: Pfarrgasse 105, 96145 Seßlach
T 09569 452
Office: Marktplatz 98, 96145 Seßlach
T 09569 922 50 **F** 09569 98 08 08
www.sesslach.de
Owner: Stadt Seßlach Founded: 1335
Output: 1,500hl Availability: 2 pubs
REGULAR BEER:
Seßlacher Pilsner (SW 12%)
SEASONAL BEER:
Seßlacher Bockbier (SW 16%)

Communal brewhouse in the small walled town of Seßlach. It supplies two pubs nearby and the beer is available direct from the brewery on Fri 16.00–18.00. Bus No. 8301 runs daily from Coburg.

🍺 **Reinwand**
Maximiliansplatz 99, 96145 Seßlach
T 09569 304
Closed Wed; Thu–Tue 09.00–24.00
DB Coburg 15km

🍺 **Roter Ochse**
Maximiliansplatz 95, 96145 Seßlach
T 09569 12 20 **F** 09569 15 10
Closed Mon & Thu; Fri–Sun, Tue & Wed 10.00–14.00 & 17.00–24.00; rooms available
DB Coburg 15km

SIEGENBURG 531

Schmidmayer-Bräu

Siegenburger Spezialitätenbrauerei
Hopfenstraße 3, 93354 Siegenburg
T 09444 97 22 22 **F** 09444 97 21 56
www.spezialitaetenbrauerei.de
Owner: Simon Wittmann Founded: 1275
Output: 12,000hl Availability: 50 pubs
REGULAR BEERS:
Schmidmayer-Bräu Holledauer Florian (5.2%)
Schmidmayer Siegenburger Kellerbier (5.2%)
Schmidmayer-Bräu Schimmel Weisse (5.3%)

Small, attractive brewery in the centre of Siegenburg, with the tap next door. Bus No. 6018 runs from Abensberg station on weekdays.

🍺 **Bräustüberl**
Hopfenstraße 3, 93354 Siegenburg
T 09444 453 **F** 09444 86 14
Closed Mon; Tue–Sun 10.00–24.00
DB Abensburg 9km

SIMMERBERG
(Weiler-Simmerberg) 532

Aktienbrauerei

Alte Salzstraße 45, 88171 Weiler-Simmerberg
T 08387 10 16 **F** 08387 27 12
E brauerei-simmerberg@t-online.de
Founded: 1793 Output: 5,000hl
Availability: 20 pubs
REGULAR BEERS:
Simmerberger Bio-Hell (4.8%)
Simmerberger Bräustatt Pils (4.8%)
Simmerberger Rapunzel Pils (4.8%)
Simmerberger Rapunzel Export (5.1%)

Simmerberger Bräustatt Gold (5.2%)
Simmerberger Rödler-Trunk (5.2%)
Simmerberger Weizen Hell (5.4%)
Simmerberger Weizen Dunkel (5.4%)

Small brewery in the centre of the village. The tap, it is often claimed, brews itself but all beers actually come from Aktienbrauerei. Bus No. 12 runs daily from Röthenbach station.

🍺 Bräustatt und Taferne
Ellhofer Straße 2, 88171 Weiler-Simmerberg
T 08387 38 06   **F** 08387 17 76
Daily 11.00–24.00
DB Röthenbach (Allgäu) 4km

SONTHOFEN 533

Hirschbräu
Hirschbräu Privatbrauerei Höss GmbH & Co. KG
Grüntenstraße 7, 87527 Sonthofen
T 08321 663 30   **F** 08321 66 33 20
www.hirschbraeu.de
Founded: 1657
Output: 30,000hl
Availability: 80 pubs
REGULAR BEERS:
Hirschbräu Der Leichte Hirsch (2.6%)
Hirschbräu Allgäuer Öko-Bier (4.7%)
Hirschbräu Neuschwansteiner (4.7%)
Hirschbräu Edelhirsch Premium-Pils (4.9%)
Hirschbräu Holzar-Bier (5.2%)
Hirschbräu Hirsch-Gold (5.2%)
Hirschbräu Weisser Hirsch (5.2%)
Hirschbräu Dunkler Hirsch (5.2%)
SEASONAL BEERS:
Hirschbräu Oberstdorfer Bier (5.2%),
Hirschbräu Weihnachts-Bier (5.2%),
Hirschbräu Mai-Bock (6.5%),
Hirschbräu Doppel-Hirsch (7.2%)

Town-centre brewery with the tap around the corner on the road leading from the station. The beers are fairly widely available in the region.

🍺 Hirsch
Hirschstraße 2, 87527 Sonthofen
T 08321 672 80   **F** 08321 67 28 28
Closed Tue; Wed–Mon from 10.00; rooms available
DB Sonthofen 450m

SPALT 534

Stadtbrauerei
Brauereigasse 3, 91174 Spalt
T 09175 796 10   **F** 09175 79 61 55
www.spalter-bier.de
Founded: 1879
Output: 70,000hl
REGULAR BEERS:
Spalter Hopfen Leicht (2.9%)
Spalter Leichte Weisse (2.9%)
Spalter Vollbier Hell (4.8%)
Spalter Weisse (4.9%)
Spalter Premium Pils (5%)
Spalter Edel-Export (5.2%)
Spalter Edel-Export Dunkel (5.2%)
SEASONAL BEERS:
Spalter Weihnachtsbier (5.6%),
Spalter Bockbier Hell, Spalter Bockbier Dunkel

Regional brewery in the centre of town, with the historic Hans-Gruber-Keller close by. Bus No. 606 runs from the station at Georgensgmünd but the Sunday service is limited.

🍺 Hans Gruber Keller
Hans-Gruber-Keller 1, 91174 Spalt
T/F 09175 340   Daily 10.00–24.00
DB Georgensgmünd 8km

SPANBERG (Eggenfelden) 535

Brunner-Bräu
Spannberg 3, 84307 Eggenfelden-Spanberg
T 08721 68 01   **F** 08721 123 75
www.brunner-braeu.de
Owner: Wolfram Brunner   Founded: 1990
Output: 500hl   Availability: 1 pub
REGULAR BEERS:
Brunner-Bräu Spanberger Hell
Brunner-Bräu Spanberger Weissbier
SEASONAL BEERS:
Brunner-Bräu Spanberger Volksfestbier,
Brunner-Bräu Spanberger Brunator

Brewpub in the hamlet of Spanberg, 3km west of Eggenfelden, close to an airfield. There's plenty of room for confusion here as there's another Spanberg 3km east of Eggenfelden, the latter a satellite of Herbertsfelden. Bus No. 6220 runs on weekdays but isn't much use given the opening times.

🍺 Brunner-Bräu

Spanberg 3, 84307 Eggenfelden-Spanberg
Winter: closed Mon–Wed; Thu–Fri 18.00–24.00,
Sat 17.00–24.00, Sun & hols 15.00–24.00
Summer: Mon–Fri 18.00–24.00, Sat 17.00–24.00,
Sun & hols 15.00–24.00
DB Eggenfelden 3.3km

SPEIDEN (Eisenberg)   536

Kössel-Bräu

Kössel-Bräu Mariahilfer Sudhaus
Mariahilfer-Straße 17, 87637 Eisenberg-Speiden
T 08364 85 56   **F** 08362 92 16
www.koessel-braeu.de
Owner: Anton Kössel   Founded: 1992
Output: 2,000hl   Availability: 2 pubs
REGULAR BEERS:
Kössel-Bräu Mariahilfer Vollbier (4.8%)
Kössel-Bräu Mariahilfer Weizen (5.2%)
SEASONAL BEERS:
Kössel-Bräu Mariahilfer Natur-Pils (summer),
Kössel-Bräu Mariahilfer Festbier (Christmas),
Kössel-Bräu Mariahilfer Helles Starkbier (7%),
Kössel-Bräu Antonator Doppelbock (Lent)

Brewpub in the former Mariahilf brewery which
closed in 1965, a fact reflected in the names of
the beers. Shuts for the four weeks before
Boxing Day. Speiden is within easy walking
distance of Weizern-Hopferau station.

🍺 Mariahilfer Sudhaus

Mariahilfer-Straße 17, 87637 Eisenberg-Speiden
Closed Mon; Tue–Fri 15.30–24.00,
Sat & Sun 10.00–24.00
DB Weizern-Hopferau 1km

STADTSTEINACH   537

Schübel

Brauerei Leonhard Schübel oHG
Knollenstraße 12, 95346 Stadtsteinach
T 09225 955 90   **F** 09225 95 59 65
www.schuebel-braeu.de
Owner: Jürgen Münch & Andrea Schübel-Münch
Founded: 1872   Output: 5,000hl
Availability: 20 pubs
REGULAR BEERS:
Schübel Florian Trunk (4.9%)

Schübel Nordeck Trunk (4.9%)
Schübel Pils (4.9%)
Schübel Edelweiße (4.9%)
Schübel Dunkel (5%)
SEASONAL BEERS:
Schübel Leonhardor (7.2%, Lent),
Schübel Bock (7.2%, winter)

Small brewery and maltings close to the centre
of Stadtsteinach. There's no official tap but the
beers are easily found in the town. Several bus
routes run from Untersteinach on weekdays.
DB Untersteinach (bei Stadtsteinach) 4.3km

STAFFELBACH (Oberhaid)   538

Hertlein

Hallstädter Straße 12, 96173 Oberhaid-Staffelbach
T/F 09503 78 90
Owner: Veronika Wolter   Founded: c. 1750
Output: 400hl
REGULAR BEER:
Hertlein Lagerbier

Brewpub in the centre of the village. Bus No.
8229 runs between Bamberg and Ebelsbach via
Oberhaid and Staffelbach on weekdays.

🍺 Hertlein

Hallstädter Straße 12, 96173 Oberhaid-Staffelbach
Sat 15.00–18.30, Sun 15.00–23.00,
Mon–Fri 17.00–23.00
DB Oberhaid 5km, Ebelsbach-Eltmann 8km

STEGAURACH   539

Hausbräu

Hausbräu Stegaurach
Ruhlstraße 6, 96135 Stegaurach
T 0951 29 97 09   **F** 0951 29 00 02
www.hausbraeu-stegaurach.de
Owner: H. Jürgen Winkler
Founded: 14.08.2000   Availability: 4 pubs
REGULAR BEERS:
Hausbräu Stegaurach Pils (4.5%)
Hausbräu Stegaurach Lager (5.2%)
Hausbräu Stegaurach Rauchbier (5.6%)
SEASONAL BEERS:
Hausbräu Stegaurach Rauchbock Hell (6.5%),
Hausbräu Rauchbock Dunkel (6.5%),
Hausbräu Stegaurach Bock Dunkel (6.5%)

The only microbrewery we're aware of that also hires marquees. They tell us the Pelikan in Bamberg is the best place for their beer. It's also available at Catwheezle's Castle (Steinweg 8, 96050 Bamberg, daily from 19.30).

🏠 Pelikan

Untere Sandstraße 45, 96049 Bamberg
T 0951 60 34 10
Fri 17.00–02.00, Sat 17.00–03.00,
Sun–Thu 17.00–01.00
DB Bamberg 1.8km

STEIN (Traun) 540

Schlossbrauerei

Schlossbrauerei Stein Wiskott GmbH & Co. KG
Schloßhof 2, 83371 Stein
T 08621 983 20   **F** 08621 98 32 40
www.steiner-bier.de
Founded: 1489
Output: 40,000hl
REGULAR BEERS:
Steiner Medium (2.9%)
Steiner Pils (4.8%)
Steiner Stoaner Zwerg Pils (4.8%)
Heinz vom Stein Hefe-Weißbier Hell (4.9%)
Heinz vom Stein Hefe-Weißbier Dunkel (4.9%)
Steiner Kloster Seeon Ur-Dunkel (5.2%)
Steiner Heinz vom Stein Kellerbier (5.3%)
Steiner Stoaner Zwerg Export (5.3%)
Steiner Export Hell (5.3%)
SEASONAL BEER:
Steiner Adventsbier,
Steiner Märzen (5.5%), **Stein-Bock** (7%)

Small regional brewery close to the castle. The brewery tap is nearby at the crossroads in the centre of the village. We suspect the Stoaner Zwerg beers may be re-badged Pils and Export. They also brew a Bio-Weizen for an unknown Austrian brewery.

🏠 Zur Post

Hauptstraße 5, 83371 Stein
T 08621 22 39   **F** 08621 64 78 34
Closed Mon; Tue–Sun 11.00–22.30;
rooms available
DB Stein (Traun) 200m

STEINFELD (Stadelhofen) 541

Hübner-Bräu

Steinfeld 69, 96187 Stadelhofen-Steinfeld
T 09207 259   **F** 09207 338
www.huebner-braeu.de
Owner: Thomas Will   Founded: 1904
Output: 5,000hl   Availability: 20 pubs
REGULAR BEER:
Hübner-Bräu Vollbier (4.7%)
SEASONAL BEER:
Hübner-Bräu Festbier (5%)

Small brewery in what must be one of the largest villages in Germany without street names. They also distil their own schnapps. Bus No. 8231 runs from Bamberg a couple of times a day.

🏠 Hübner-Bräu

Steinfeld 69, 96187 Stadelhofen-Steinfeld
Jan–Mar: closed Fri; Sat–Thu 09.00–23.00
Apr–Dec: closed Thu; Fri 12.00–23.00,
Sat–Wed 09.00–23.00
DB Bamberg 27km

STETTFELD 542

Adler Bräu

Hauptstraße 19, 96188 Stettfeld
T 09522 369   **F** 09522 702 77
Owner: Norbert Merklein
Founded: 1730
Output: 10,000hl
REGULAR BEERS:
Adler Bräu Alt Frankisches Lager (4.8%)
Adler Bräu Stöpflder Zwickel (5%)
Adler Bräu Stöpflder Classic (5%)
Adler Bräu Stettfelder Pils (5%)
SEASONAL BEER:
Adler Bräu Stettfelder Bock (7.1%)

Small brewery and tap on the main road through the village. Bus No. 8229 runs from Bamberg to Ebelsbach via Stettfeld on weekdays.

🏠 Bräustübla

Hauptstraße 19, 96188 Stettfeld
Closed Tue; Wed–Mon 10.00–23.00
DB Ebelsbach-Eltmann 4km

STIEBARLIMBACH
(Hallerndorf) 543

Roppelt

Stiebarlimbach 9, 91352 Hallerndorf-
Stiebarlimbach
T 09195 72 63   **F** 09195 43 83
www.brauerei-roppelt.de
Owner: Franz Roppelt   Founded: 1850
Output: 3,000hl   Availability: 2 pubs
REGULAR BEERS:
Roppelt Kellerbier (4.9%)
Roppelt Weißbier (5%)
SEASONAL BEER:
Roppelt Festbier

Small brewery that supplies just its tap and
Bierkeller. At the time of writing the pub was
closed for refurbishment and the Keller was
opening Fri–Tue from 11.00 and Wed–Thu from
15.30. Bus No. 265 runs from Eggolsheim
station on weekdays.

🍺 Roppelt
Stiebarlimbach 9, 91352 Hallerndorf-
Stiebarlimbach
Closed Wed & Thu; Fri–Tue 09.00–24.00
DB Eggolsheim 9km, Hirschaid 9km

🍺 Roppelt-Keller
Stiebarlimbach, 91352 Hallerndorf-
Stiebarlimbach
Closed Oct–Apr & in wet weather; Sat from 15.00,
Sun & hols from 14.00, Mon–Fri from 16.00
DB Eggolsheim 9km, Hirschaid 9km

STIERBERG
(Obertaufkirchen) 544

Stierberg

Stierberg 14, 84419 Obertaufkirchen-Stierberg
T 08082 18 51   **F** 08082 72 91
www.brauerei-stierberg.de
Owner: Annemarie Kammhuber-Hartinger
Founded: 1908
REGULAR BEERS:
Stierberg Hell
Stierberg Dunkel
Stierberg Eispils
Stierberg Export
Stierberg Märzen

Small brewery and tap in a tiny hamlet south of
Obertaufkirchen. Getting to Stierberg by bus
can take an age and you may find it more
convenient to catch one to nearby Frauenornau.

🍺 Brauereigasthof
Stierberg 12, 84419 Obertaufkirchen-Stierberg
Closed Sat; Sun–Fri from 10.00
DB Schwindegg 5km

STRASSKIRCHEN (Salzweg) 545

Gutsbräu

Scheibe 1, 94121 Salzweg-Straßkirchen
T 08505 934 10   **F** 08505 934 11
E chr-boehm@t-online.de
Owner: Christian Böhm   Founded: 2000
Output: 250hl   Availability: 3 pubs
REGULAR BEERS:
Gutsbräu Braunbier (SW 12%)
Gutsbräu Weißbier (SW 12%)
SEASONAL BEERS:
Gutsbräu Helles Kellerbier (SW 11.5%),
Gutsbräu Weizenbock (SW 16%),
Gutsbräu St. Ägidi Fastenbock (SW 18.5%)

Brewpub on the northern edge of the village,
in the former premises of the Hellmannsberger
brewery which closed in 1906. All the beers are
organic. Various bus routes run from Passau.

🍺 Gutsbräu
Scheibe 1, 94121 Salzweg-Straßkirchen
Closed Tue; Wed–Sat & Mon 17.00–24.00,
Sun & hols 10.00–24.00
DB Passau Hbf 9km

STRAUBING 546

Karmeliten

Karmeliten Brauerei Karl Sturm GmbH & Co. KG
Senefelder Straße 21, 94315 Straubing-Hofstetten
T 09421 78 19 0   **F** 09421 78 19 13
www.karmeliten-brauerei.de
Founded: 1367   Output: 50,000hl
REGULAR BEERS:
Karmeliten Kloster Pils (4.7%)
Karmeliten Kloster Urtyp (4.9%)
Karmeliten Kloster Gold (5.1%)
Karmeliten AS Weisse Hell (5.4%)
Karmeliten AS Weisse Dunkel (5.4%)

Karmeliten Kloster Dunkel (5.5%)
SEASONAL BEERS:
Karmeliten Festbier, Karmeliten Doppelbock (8%)

Long-established brewery which moved to the current premises close to the B20 in 1980. They don't have a tap but the beers are very easy to find locally.

DB Itting 1.7km, Straubing 4km

Röhrl

Brauerei Gebrüder Röhrl GmbH & Co. KG
Heerstraße 13, 94315 Straubing
T 09421 993 70   **F** 09421 821 90
www.roehrlbraeu.de
Founded: 1431   Output: 70,000hl
REGULAR BEERS:
Röhrl's Gäuboden Landbier (4.8%)
Röhrl's Helles Premium (4.8%)
Röhrl's Premium (4.9%)
Röhrl's Kristall Pils (5%)
Röhrl's Alt-Straubinger Schwarzbier (5%)
Röhrl's Straubinger Weisse Naturtrüb (5.2%)
Röhrl's Straubinger Weisse Original (5.3%)
Röhrl's Straubinger Weisse Dunkel (5.3%)
Röhrl's Straubinger Blauweisse (5.3%)
SEASONAL BEERS:
Röhrl's Bruder Straubinger Festbier (5.6%),
Röhrl's Bockbier (7.3%)

Slightly larger than Karmeliten, Röhrl's brewery stands alongside the tap, to the east of the town centre. They have a second brewery in Frontenhausen.

🍺 Zum Weißbräu
Heerstraße 11, 94315 Straubing
T 09421 96 81 80
Closed Tue; Wed–Mon 10.00–01.00
DB Straubing 700m

STUBLANG (Bad Staffelstein) 547

Dinkel

Frauendorfer Straße 18,
96231 Bad Staffelstein-Stublang
T 09573 64 24   **F** 09573 51 60
www.dinkel-stublang.de
Owner: Andreas Dinkel   Founded: 1880
Output: 500hl   Availability: 1 pub
REGULAR BEER:
Dinkel Dunkles

Brewpub on the edge of the village. A daily bus service from Bad Staffelstein is provided by local operators.

🍺 Dinkel
Frauendorfer Straße 18,
96231 Bad Staffelstein-Stublang
Closed Wed; Thu–Tue 09.00–23.00;
rooms available
DB Bad Staffelstein 6km

Hennemann

Löwenbräu Hennemann
Dorfbrunnen 13, 96231 Bad Staffelstein-Stublang
T 09573 961 00   **F** 09573 96 10 55
www.brauerei-hennemann.de
Owner: Peter Hennemann   Founded: 1862
Output: 300hl   Availability: 1 pub
REGULAR BEER:
Hennemann Vollbier

Stublang's other brewery is more central but, like Dinkel, the sole beer is only available at the tap.

🍺 Hennemann
Dorfbrunnen 13, 96231 Bad Staffelstein-Stublang
Closed Mon; Tue–Sun 09.00–23.00; rooms
available   DB Bad Staffelstein 6km

SULZBACH-ROSENBERG 548

Fuchsbeck

Orth-Bräu GmbH & Co. KG 'Zum Fuchsbeck'
Hagtor 1, 92237 Sulzbach-Rosenberg
T 09661 45 18   **F** 09661 81 22 15
www.fuchsbeck.de
Owners: Erna & Wilhelm Haller   Founded: 1834
Output: 8,000hl   Availability: 20 pubs
REGULAR BEERS:
Fuchsbeck Schlanke Schwarze (2.8%)
Fuchsbeck Hell (4.5%)
Fuchsbeck Pils (5%)
Fuchsbeck Kristall Weizen (5.1%)
Fuchsbeck Weissbier (5.2%)
Fuchsbeck Export (5.4%)
SEASONAL BEERS:
Fuchsbeck Festbier (5.5%), **Fuchsbeck Bock** (7%),
Fuchsbeck Primus Weizenbock (7.5%)

Small brewery and tap just below the castle, officially called Orth-Bräu but known to one and all as Fuchsbeck. They brew the only low-alcohol dark wheat beer that we're aware of.

🏠 **Zum Fuchsbeck**
Hagtor 1, 92237 Sulzbach-Rosenberg
Closed Wed; Thu–Sat, Mon & Tue 09.00–01.00,
Sun 09.00–12.00
DB Sulzbach-Rosenberg 700m

Sperber-Bräu

Rosenberger Straße 14,
92237 Sulzbach-Rosenberg
T 09661 870 90   **F** 09661 87 09 77
www.sperberbraeu.de
Owner: Christian Sperber   Founded: 1894
REGULAR BEERS:
Sperber Bräu Leichte Weisse (3.5%)
Sperber Bräu Helles Vollbier (5%)
Sperber Bräu Rosenberger Pils (5%)
Sperber Bräu Zoiglbier (5%)
Sperber Bräu Steiger Schwarze (5%)
Sperber Bräu Graf Gebhard Weisse (5.2%)
SEASONAL BEERS:
Sperber Bräu Weihnachtsfestbier (5.7%),
Sperber Bräu Frühlingsfestbier (5.7%),
Sperber Bräu Annaberg-Festbier (5.8%),
Sperber Bräu Herzog Christian August (7.2%)

Brewery, pub and hotel in the centre of
Sulzbach-Rosenberg's old town. The refurbished
tap has the feel of a modern brewpub. The
Protestant Herzog Christian August signed a
treaty in 1652 which allowed Protestants and
Catholics alternating use of schools and churches.

🏠 **Sperber-Bräu**
Rosenberger Straße 14,
92237 Sulzbach-Rosenberg
Daily 06.30–01.00; rooms available
DB Sulzbach-Rosenberg 750m

TANN   549

Weideneder

Weideneder Bräu Vertriebs GmbH & Co. KG
Marktplatz 43, 84367 Tann
T 08572 960 10   **F** 08572 96 01 16
www.weideneder.com
Owner: Fritz Weideneder   Founded: 1889
Output: 17,000hl   Availability: 150 pubs
REGULAR BEERS:
Weideneder Leichte Weisse (3%)
Weideneder Bayrisch Hell (4.9%)
Weideneder Meister Pils (4.9%)

Weideneder Privat Hell (5.1%)
Weideneder Hell Export (5.2%)
Weideneder Dunkel Export (5.2%)
Weideneder Weizengold (5.2%)
Weideneder Schankl Weisse (5.2%)
Weideneder Papst-Bier (5.4%)
SEASONAL BEERS:
Weideneder Festbier (5.5%),
Weideneder Weihnachtsbier (5.5%),
Weideneder Awetator (6.4%)

Small regional brewery on the market square.
The brewery tap around the corner is run by an
Italian. Several bus routes run to Tann from
Simbach, though none are frequent.

🏠 **Bräustüberl**
Nopplinger Straße 1, 84367 Tann
T 08572 76 33
Closed Tue; Wed–Fri, Sun & Mon 11.00–14.00 &
17.00–24.00, Sat 17.00–24.00
DB Marktl 10km, Simbach (Inn) 13km

TAUFKIRCHEN (Vils)   550

Brauereigenossenschaft

Guts- und Brauereigenossenschaft e.G.
Bräuhausstraße 3, 84416 Taufkirchen
T 08084 23 77   **F** 08084 72 36
Founded: 1642
Output: 12,000hl   Availability: 35 pubs
REGULAR BEERS:
Taufkirchner Leichtes (3%)
Taufkirchner Leichtes Weißbier (3.1%)
Taufkirchner Hell (4.9%)
Taufkirchner Pils (5%)
Taufkirchner Weißbier (5.2%)
Taufkirchner Märzen (5.2%)
SEASONAL BEER:
Taufkirchner Bock (6.9%)

Brewery co-operative formed to supply local
pubs. There's a tap at the brewery and they
recommended two other pubs in the town.
Bus No. 9403 runs from Dorfen on weekday
afternoons.

🏠 **Bräustüberl**
Bräuhausstraße 3, 84416 Taufkirchen
T/F 08084 411
Closed Mon; Tue–Sun from 10.00

🏠 **Wagnerwirt**
Marktplatz 5, 84416 Taufkirchen

T 08084 94 68 49
Closed Thu; Fri–Wed from 09.00; rooms available

📍 **Weißbräu**
Erdinger Straße 8, 84416 Taufkirchen
T 08084 545
Closed Wed; Thu–Tue 10.00–01.00

All: DB Dorfen Bahnhof 11km

TAXA (Odelzhausen) — 551

Schloßbrauerei Odelzhausen

Schloßbrauerei Odelzhausen GmbH & Co. KG
Am Schloßberg 1, 85235 Odelzhausen-Taxa
T 08134 998 70
E schlossbrauerei-odelzhausen@web.de
Owners: Hans Eser   Founded: 1450
Output: 2,000hl   Availability: 10 pubs
REGULAR BEERS:
Odelzhausen Traditions Hell (4.9%)
Odelzhausen Traditions Dunkel (4.9%)
SEASONAL BEER:
Odelzhausen Operator Doppelbock (7%)

Brewery and tap in the grounds of Odelzhausen castle, which despite the name is actually in the village of Taxa, on the opposite side of the A8 to Odelzhausen. Bus No. 721 runs from Dachau on weekdays plus Saturday mornings.

📍 **Schloßbräustüberl**
Am Schloßberg 1, 85235 Odelzhausen-Taxa
T 08134 998 71 00   **F** 08134 998 71 50
Daily 09.00–24.00; rooms available
DB Dachau Bahnhof 21km

TEGERNSEE — 552

Herzogliches Brauhaus

Herzoglich Bayerisches Brauhaus Tegernsee KG
Schloßplatz 1, 83684 Tegernsee
T 08022 180 20   **F** 08022 18 02 44
Founded: 1803   Output: 60,000hl
REGULAR BEERS:
Tegernseer Leichtes
Tegernseer Hell (4.8%)
Tegernseer Dunkel Export (5.5%)
Tegernseer Spezial (5.6%)
Tegernseer Heller Bock (6.8%)
Tegernseer Quirinus Doppelbock (7%)

Former monastery on the shores of the Tegernsee, which has been a royal palace since the 19th century and houses this well-known brewery and tap.

📍 **Herzogliches Bräustüberl**
Schloßplatz 1, 83684 Tegernsee
T 08022 41 41   **F** 08022 34 55
Daily 09.00–23.00
DB Tegernsee 750m

TEISENDORF — 553

Wieninger

Privatbrauerei M.C. Wieninger GmbH & Co. KG
Poststraße 1, 83317 Teisendorf
T 08666 80 20
F 08666 80 27 69
www.wieninger.de
Founded: 1666   Output: 130,000hl
REGULAR BEERS:
Wieninger Feder-Weizen (2.9%)
Wieninger Hefe Weißbier (4.9%)
Wieninger Bayerisch Hell (5%)
Wieninger Dunkles Lagerbier (5%)
Wieninger Guidobald Dunkel (5%)
Wieninger Ruperti Pils (5%)
Wieninger Weißbier Naturtrüb Premium (5%)
Wieninger Helles Lagerbier (5.2%)
Wieninger Bräufaß (5.2%)
Wieninger Hefe Weißbier Dunkel (5.2%)
Wieninger Guidobald Gold (5.3%)
SEASONAL BEERS:
Wieninger Weihnachts-Festbier (5.7%),
Wieninger Höglwörther Maifestbier (5.8%),
Wieninger Weißbier-Bock (7.1%),
Wieninger Impulsator (7.5%).

Large regional brewery on the western edge of the small town of Teisendorf. The tap is nearby on the main road. The Guidobald beers are so named to honour Guidobald Count von Thun, archbishop and founder of the brewery.

📍 **Alte Post**
Marktstraße 9, 83317 Teisendorf
T 08666 92 91 71
Closed Tue; Wed–Sat and Mon 10.00–01.00, Sun & hols 09.00–01.00
DB Teisendorf 900m

TEISNACH 554

Ettl-Bräu

Bahnhofstraße 2, 94244 Teisnach
T 09923 80 13 20   **F** 09923 80 13 23
www.brauerei-ettl.de
Founded: 1543   Output: 8,000hl
REGULAR BEERS:
Ettl Teisnacher Leichte Weisse (3.1%)
Ettl Pils (4.5%)
Ettl Hell (4.8%)
Ettl Teisnacher Weisse (5.2%)
Ettl Spezial (5.4%)
SEASONAL BEERS:
Ettl Märzen (5.4%, Lent), **Ettl Festbier** (5.4%, summer), **Ettl Weihnachts-Festbier** (5.4%, Christmas)

Small brewery on the main road through the valley. The tap has now closed but the beers are sold in a few pubs in the town. Bus No. 6195 runs from Regen Mon–Sat, and there are one or two buses a day plus occasional tourist trains from Gotteszell.
DB Gotteszell 10km, Regen 16km

TEUGN 555

Dantscher

Brauerei Franz Dantscher
Kirchplatz 12, 93356 Teugn
T 09405 96 21 10
E rupert-dantscher@t-online.de
Owner: Rupert Dantscher   Founded: 1828
Output: 3,000hl
REGULAR BEERS:
Dantscher Vollbier Hell
Dantscher Bertl's Pils
Dantscher Export Hell
Dantscher Spezial Hell
Dantscher Märzen

Small brewery and traditional tap in the centre of Teugn. Buses run from Saal station but aren't much use if you want to drink in the tap and return the same day.

🍺 **Dantscher**
Kirchplatz 12, 93356 Teugn
Closed Tue & Wed; Thu, Fri & Mon from 17.00, Sat from 11.00, Sun 10.00–12.00 & from 16.00
DB Saal (Donau) 7km

THALMANNSFELD (Bergen) 556

Felsenbräu

Felsenbräu Thalmannsfeld W. Gloßner KG
Felsenweg 2, 91790 Bergen-Thalmannsfeld
T 09147 942 66   **F** 09147 94 26 79
www.felsenbraeu.com
Owner: the Gloßner family
Founded: 1928   Output: 30,000hl
REGULAR BEERS:
Felsen-Bräu Leicht
Felsen-Bräu Leichtes Weizen
Felsen-Bräu Felsentrunk (4.9%)
Felsen-Bräu Schwarzes (5.1%)
Felsen-Bräu Hefeweizen (5.1%)
Felsen-Bräu Braune Weisse (5.1%)
Felsen-Bräu Edel Pils (5.2%)
Felsen-Bräu Märzen
Felsen-Bräu Privat Export (5.3%)
SEASONAL BEERS:
Felsen-Bräu Weihnachtsbier, Felsen-Bräu Weizenbock, Felsen-Bräu Felsator

Along with the Pflugbrauerei in Hörvelsingen, Felsenbräu still produces its own ice that's then stored and used for refrigeration. There are a few buses (No. 616) from Weißenburg on weekdays but none back after the tap opens.

🍺 **Bräustüberl**
Kirchenweg 3, 91790 Bergen-Thalmannsfeld
T 09147 350
Closed Mon & Tue; Wed–Sun from 18.00
DB Weißenburg 18km

THANNHAUSEN 557

Postbräu

Münz u. Postbräu König Ludwig GmbH & Co. KG
Schreieggstraße 8, 86470 Thannhausen
T 08281 90 50   **F** 08281 905 99
www.postbraeu.de
Owner: Luitpold Prinz von Bayern
Founded: 1450   Output: 60,000hl
REGULAR BEERS:
Postbräu Leichte Weisse (2.9%)
Postbräu Postherren Pils (4.6%)
Postbräu Hell (4.9%)
Postbräu Export Dunkel (5%)
Postbräu Weisse (5.2%)
Postbräu Dunkle Weisse (5.2%)

SEASONAL BEER:
Postbräu Thannator (7.5%)
FOR BRAUEREI MÜNZ, GÜNZBURG:
Münz Altdeutsches (4.5%)
Münz Edel Pilsener (4.5%)
Münz Hefe-Weizen (5%)
Münz Edle Weiße (5%)
Münz Edel Export (5%)
Münz Märzen (5.1%)
FOR SCHLOSSBRAUEREI KALTENBERG:
Prinzregent Luitpold Weissbier Light (2.9%),
Prinzregent Luitpold Weissbier Hell (5.5%),
Prinzregent Luitpold Weissbier Dunkel (5.5%),
Prinzregent Luitpold Weissbier Kristall (5.5%)

Recently acquired by Schlossbrauerei Kaltenberg, Postbräu now brew some wheat beer for them as well as all beers for Münz of Günzberg. The brewery tap is in a four-star hotel in the centre of town. Bus No. 600 runs daily from Augsburg to Krumbach via Thannhausen.

Schreiegg's Post
Postgasse 1, 86470 Thannhausen
T 08281 995 10   **F** 08281 99 51 51
Closed Mon; Tue 18.00–22.00, Wed–Sun
12.00–14.00 & 18.00–22.00; rooms available
DB Krumbach (Schwaben) 10km

THEINHEIM (Rauhenebrach) 558

Bayer

Schulterbachstraße 15,
96181 Rauhenebrach-Theinheim
T 09554 293   **F** 09554 88 93
www.bayer-theinheim.de
Owner: Michael Bayer   Founded: 1718
Output: 750hl   Availability: 1 pub
REGULAR BEER:
Bayer Kellerbier
SEASONAL BEER:
Bayer Bock (Christmas)

Brewpub on the main road through the village. They also have a small distillery. Bus No. 8244 runs from Bamberg on weekdays but there are limited services out of Theinheim in the afternoon.

Zum Grünen Baum
Schulterbachstraße 15,
96181 Rauhenebrach-Theinheim
Closed Mon; Tue–Sun from 09.00
DB Bamberg 26km

THUNDORF 559

Gemeindebrauhaus

Brewery: Kirchplatz 1, 97711 Thundorf
Contacts: Egon Klöffel, Esther-von-Rosenbach-
Straße 16, 97711 Thundorf   **T** 09724 384
Thomas Bretscher, Esther-von-Rosenbach-
Straße 21, 97711 Thundorf   **T** 09724 90 61 18
www.thundorf.de/brau.htm
Owner: Hausbrauerverein Thundorf
Founded: 1680   Output: 90hl
REGULAR BEERS:
Thundorfer Hausbrauerbier

Small communal brewhouse whose sole beer is normally only available for sale to the general public at the brewery festival on Ascension Day but prior warning to either of the above contacts may reap rewards. Local residents are allowed to brew 200 litres of beer tax-free.
DB Münnerstadt 14km

THÜNGEN 560

Burgbrauerei

Burgbrauerei Herzog von Franken
Hauptstraße 3, 97289 Thüngen
T 09360 99 08 08
Owners: Günther & Dr. Susan Schubert
Founded: 1846   Output: 10,000hl
REGULAR BEER:
Herzog von Franken Pils (4.9%)

The former Schloßbrauerei Thüngen was taken over by Eder (now Eder & Heylands) in 1991. Brewing ceased in 1998 but restarted around 2003, following acquisition by the owners of the Arnsteiner brewery. We think the other Herzog beers are brewed in Arnstein. There's no brewery tap that we're aware of. Bus No. 8099 runs from Karlstadt station on weekdays.
DB Karlstadt (Main) 9km

THURNAU 561

Thurnauer Schloßbräu

Am Schloßpark 2, 95349 Thurnau
T 09228 99 65 99
Founded: 2004

REGULAR BEER:
Thurnauer Schloßbräu Dunkel

Brewpub near the castle that currently produces just one beer. Bus No. 8435 runs from Kulmbach on weekdays but there are none back after the pub opens. There are ASTs at the weekend.

🍺 **Thurnauer Schloßbräu**
Am Schloßpark 2, 95349 Thurnau
Closed Mon; Tue–Sat from 18.00, Sun from 11.30
DB Kulmbach 13km

TIEFENELLERN (Litzendorf) 562

Hönig

Ellerbergstaße 15, 96123 Litzendorf-Tiefenellern
T 09505 391   F 09505 95 06 83
www.brauerei-hoenig.de
Owners: Konrad & Peter Hönig   Founded: 1478
Output: 6,000hl   Availability: 7 pubs
REGULAR BEERS:
Hönig Lagerbier Ungespundet (4.8%)
Hönig Pils (4.8%)
Hönig Postillon Weiße (4.9%)
Hönig Posthörnla Rauchbier (5.4%)
SEASONAL BEER:
Hönig Bockbier Hell (7.2%, Christmas)

Small brewery and tap on the main road through the village. The bus service from Bamberg is very poor, to say the least.

🍺 **Zur Post**
Ellerbergstaße 15, 96123 Litzendorf-Tiefenellern
Closed Thu; Fri–Wed 10.00–23.00
DB Bamberg 14km

TIRSCHENREUTH 563

Schels

Brauerei Bernhard Schels
Regensburger Straße 21, 95643 Tirschenreuth
T 09631 12 67   F 09631 52 34
Owner: Rainer Schels   Founded: 1893
REGULAR BEERS:
Tirschenreuther Leichtes Weizen
Tirschenreuther Hell
Tirschenreuther Pilsener
Tirschenreuther Hefeweizen
Tirschenreuther Spezial Export

Brewery in the town centre, on the old main road from the south. There's no brewery tap that we're aware of. Bus No. 6267 runs from Wiesau on weekdays.
DB Wiesau (Oberpfalz) 14km

TITTING 564

Gutmann

Brauerei Fritz Gutmann
Am Kreuzberg 1, 85135 Titting
T 08423 996 60   F 08423 99 66 40
www.brauerei-gutmann.de
Owner: Fritz Gutmann   Founded: 1707
Output: 90,000hl
REGULAR BEERS:
Gutmann Leichtes Hefeweizen (2.8%)
Gutmann Untergärig (4.9%)
Gutmann Spezial (5.1%)
Gutmann Hefeweizen (5.2%)
Gutmann Dunkles Hefeweizen (5.2%)
SEASONAL BEERS:
Gutmann Festbier (5.5%),
Gutmann Weizenbock (7.2%)

Regional brewery a few miles from the Franconian border. Bus No. 9224 runs from Eichstätt town station on weekday afternoons but the last bus leaves before the brewery tap opens.

🍺 **Bräustüberl**
Am Kreuzberg 4, 85135 Titting
T 08423 98 56 50   F 08423 98 56 46
Closed Tue & Wed; Thu–Sat & Mon from 15.00, Sun from 10.00
DB Eichstätt Stadt 18km

TRABELSDORF (Lisberg) 565

Beck

Beck-Bräu OHG
Steigerwaldstraße 8, 96170 Lisberg-Trabelsdorf
T 09549 252   F 09549 10 34
www.beck-braeu.de
Owner: Herbert Beck   Founded: 1895
Output: 3,500hl   Availability: 16 pubs
REGULAR BEERS:
Beck Hell (4.7%)
Beck Weisse (4.8%)
Beck Lisberger Lager (4.9%)

Beck Pilsner (4.9%)
Beck Jahrhundertbier-Dunkel (5%)
Beck Zwickelbier
Beck Trabelsdorfer Schloßgold (5.2%).
SEASONAL BEERS:
Beck Vollmondbier, Beck Bockbier (winter)

Small brewery and tap on the southern side of the village. Bus No. 8244 from Bamberg stops outside the pub.

Beck-Bräu

Steigerwaldstraße 8, 96170 Lisberg-Trabelsdorf
Closed Mon; Tue–Sun from 17.00
DB Oberhaid 10km, Bamberg 13km

TRAUNSTEIN 566

Hofbräuhaus

Hofbräuhaus Traunstein Josef Sailer KG
Hofgasse 6–11, 83278 Traunstein
T 0861 98 86 60   F 0861 988 66 66
www.hb-ts.de
Owners: Bernhard & Dietrich Sailer
Founded: 1612   Output: 100,000hl
REGULAR BEERS:
HB Leichte Weiße (3.3%)
HB Hofbräu Leicht (3.4%)
HB Fürsten Pils (5.1%)
HB 1612er Zwicklbier (5.3%)
HB Fürsten Quell (5.3%)
HB Altbairisch Dunkel (5.3%)
HB Fürsten Trunk (5.5%)
HB Hofbräu Weiße (5.5%)
HB Altbairisch Ur-Weizen (5.5%)
HB Gastro Weiße (5.5%)
SEASONAL BEER:
HB Trunator Vollmond-Bock (7.5%)

Large brewery in the centre of town. They opened a number of brewpubs throughout Germany in the mid-1990s but we think all may now have been sold, although they do still sell HB beers. The nearby tap is a recent addition.

Hofbräuhaus Bräustüberl

Stadtplatz 20, 83278 Traunstein
T 0861 43 79   F 0861 909 76 81
Tue (Nov–Apr) 10.00–15.00,
Wed–Mon 10.00–23.00 (daily May–Oct)
DB Traunstein 800m

Maximiliansbräu

Maximiliansbräu (vormals Kiesel-Bräu) GmbH
Haslacher Straße 39, 83278 Traunstein
T 0861 988 00   F 0861 988 01 05
www.maximiliansbrauerei.de
Owner: Wolfgang Hover   Founded: 1883
Output: 25,000hl
REGULAR BEERS:
Maximiliansbräu Hell (4.8%)
Maximiliansbräu Premium Pils (5%)
Maximiliansbräu Weißbier Hefe Hell (5.3%)
SEASONAL BEER:
Maximiliansbräu Winterbier (5.7%)
CHIEMSEER BEERS:
Chiemseer Dunkle Weisse (5.3%), Chiemseer Braustoff (5.6%), Chiemseer Helle Weisse (5.6%)
SEASONAL BEER:
Chiemseer Maibock (7.1%)

Brewery south-west of the town centre, trading as Kiesel-Bräu until 2001. The Chiemseer beers are also marketed as Wolpertinger. They don't have a brewery tap that we know of.
DB Traunstein 700m

Schnitzlbaumer

Privatbrauerei Schnitzlbaumer KG
Mühlenstraße 8, 83278 Traunstein
T 0861 34 00   F 0861 145 50
www.schnitzlbaumer.de
Owner: Gabriele & Robert Schnitzlbaumer
Founded: 1575   Output: 17,000hl
Availability: 25 pubs
REGULAR BEERS:
Schnitzlbaumer Edel-Pils (4.9%)
Schnitzlbaumer Export-Hell (5.2%)
Schnitzlbaumer Export-Dunkel (5.2%)
Schnitzlbaumer Schnitzei Weiße (5.2%)
SEASONAL BEER:
Schnitzlbaumer Bernhardus Bock (6.2%)

Brewery in the lower part of town with the tap above, just off the main square. The Brauerei-Ausschank features two decorative brewing coppers.

Brauerei-Ausschank

Taubenmarkt 11a–13, 83278 Traunstein
T 0861 98 66 50   F 0861 986 65 20
Daily 09.00–01.00
DB Traunstein 850m

Wochinger-Bräu

Wochinger-Bräu Jakob Wochinger & Sohn GmbH
St.-Oswald-Straße 4, 83278 Traunstein
T 0861 98 60 60   **F** 0861 986 06 99
www.wochingerbraeu.de
Owners: Rudi & Theo Wochinger
Founded: 1587   Output: 5,000hl
REGULAR BEERS:
Wochinger-Bräu Pils (4.9%)
Wochinger-Bräu Export-Dunkel (4.9%)
Wochinger-Bräu Hefe-Weisse (5.1%)
Wochinger-Bräu Urtrunk (5.3%)
Wochinger-Bräu Export-Hell (5.3%)
SEASONAL BEER:
Wochinger-Bräu Urbock (6.5%)

The smallest of Traunstein's breweries, just south
of the town centre. The tap stands alongside.

🍺 **Wochinger Brauhaus**
St.-Oswald-Straße 4, 83278 Traunstein
T 0861 30 45   **F** 0861 149 76
Closed Mon (Oct–Apr); Tue–Sun from 10.00
(daily May–Sept)   DB Traunstein 750m

Haberstumpf

Bergstraße 31, 95367 Trebgast
T 09227 351   **F** 09227 22 73
www.brauerei-haberstumpf.de
Owner: Hans Wernlein   Founded: 1531
Output: 1,500hl   Availability: 11 pubs
REGULAR BEERS:
Haberstumpf Lager Hell (4.9%)
Haberstumpf Landkrönla (4.9%)
Haberstumpf Kellerkrönla Naturtrüb (4.9%)
Haberstumpf Kupferkrönla Dunkel (4.9%)
Haberstumpf Trebgaster Zunft Pils (5.3%)
Aecht's Haberstumpf Zwick'l (5.3%)
SEASONAL BEERS:
Haberstumpf Fasten-Bock Dunkel (6.5%),
Haberstumpf Doppel-Bock

Small brewery on the hill road west out of
Trebgast. As well as the tap, they have a beer
garden which opens Mon–Fri from 16.00 and
Sun from 15.00 in fine weather.

🍺 **Hockerstube**
Bergstraße 31, 95367 Trebgast
Closed Sun; Mon–Fri from 16.00, Sat 10.00–13.00
DB Trebgast 1km

Schäff

Altmühltaler Mineralbrunnen GmbH
Bahnhofstraße 48, 91757 Treuchtlingen
T 09142 80 30   **F** 09142 803 55
Founded: 1364
SCHÄFF BEERS:
Schäff Hell (4.8%)
Schäff's Dunkle Weisse (5.2%)
Schäff's Helle Weisse (5.4%)
ALTMÜHLTALER BEERS:
Altmühltaler Hell (4.8%), **Altmühltaler Pils**
(4.8%), **Altmühltaler Gold-Export** (5.8%)
FEUERFEST BEER:
Feuerfest Edel-Bier (10.5%)

A bit of a puzzle, this one. Some sources say it
closed years ago but our guess is it still brews,
albeit mostly for supermarkets, etc. The above
beers are certainly brewed somewhere. Any
definite information would be most welcome at
GermanBreweries@aol.com.

🍺 **Schäffbräu-Stüberl**
Heinrich-Aurnhammer-Straße 11,
91757 Treuchtlingen   **T** 09142 97 58 50
Sat 15.00–01.00, Sun 10.00–14.00 & 17.00–01.00,
Mon–Fri 17.00–01.00
DB Treuchtlingen 700m

Bauer

Weißbierbrauerei Bauer
Unterer Markt 7, 84371 Triftern
T 08562 12 50
Owner: Lore Bauer   Founded: 1890
Output: 250hl   Availability: 1 pub
REGULAR BEERS:
Bauer Leichtes Weizen
Bauer Weizen
SEASONAL BEER:
Bauer Weizenbock (winter)

Brewpub in the centre of Triftern that produces
only wheat beer. Bus No. 6217 runs from
Pfarrkirchen Monday to Saturday.

🍺 **Weißbräu**
Unterer Markt 7, 84371 Triftern
Closed Tue; Wed–Mon 09.00–14.00 &
17.00–24.00   DB Pfarrkirchen 7km

TROSSENFURT (Oberaurach) 570

Roppelt

An der Steige 2, 97514 Oberaurach-Trossenfurt
T 09522 18 40   **F** 09522 95 08 63
Owner: Michael Roppelt   Founded: 1701
Output: 1,500hl   Availability: 1 pub
REGULAR BEERS:
Roppelt-Bräu Lagerbier (4.9%)
Roppelt-Bräu Hausbrauerbier (5.1%)
Roppelt-Bräu Pilsner (5.1%)
SEASONAL BEER:
Roppelt-Bräu Festbier

Brewpub close to a bridge over the river Aurach.
Bus No. 8169 runs from Ebelsbach-Eltmann
station on weekdays but Haßfurt is also an option.

🍺 Roppelt
An der Steige 2, 97514 Oberaurach-Trossenfurt
Closed Tue; Wed–Mon 09.00–23.00
DB Ebelsbach-Eltmann 8km, Haßfurt 20km

UEHLFELD 571

Prechtel

Hauptstraße 24, 91486 Uehlfeld
T 09163 228   **F** 09163 12 29
Owner: Walter Prechtel   Founded: c.1900
Output: 1,500hl
REGULAR BEERS:
Prechtel Schnapperla Kellerbier (4.5%)
Prechtel Landbier (4.7%)
Prechtel Weissbier (5%)
SEASONAL BEERS:
Prechtel Festbier, Prechtel Bock (Lent)

Small brewery and tap on the main road
through the village. Bus No. 127 runs from
Neustadt station daily except Sunday.

🍺 Prechtel
Hauptstraße 24, 91486 Uehlfeld
Closed Mon; Tue–Sun 08.00–24.00
DB Neustadt (Aisch) 17km

Zwanzger

Burghaslach Straße 10, 91486 Uehlfeld
T/F 09163 78 49
Owner: Rainer Zwanzger   Founded: 1639
Output: 1,500hl   Availability: 5 pubs

REGULAR BEERS:
Zwanzger Vollbier (4.5%)
Zwanzger Pils (4.7%)
Zwanzger Hausbräu Unfiltiert (4.7%)
Zwanzger Uehlfelder Weisse (5.5%)

Just around the corner from Prechtel, Zwanzger
is of a similar size, supplying four pubs in
addition to the tap. Uehlfeld is at the northern
end of the Aischgründer Bierstraße.

🍺 Zwanzger
Burghaslach Straße 10, 91486 Uehlfeld
T 09163 98 97 56
Closed Mon; Tue–Sun 09.30–24.00; rooms
available   DB Neustadt (Aisch) 17km

UETZING (Bad Staffelstein) 572

Dinkel

Serkendorfer Straße 11,
96231 Bad Staffelstein-Uetzing
T/F 09573 78 75
Owner: Marianne Dinkel
Founded: before 1870   Output: 150hl
REGULAR BEER:
Dinkel Dunkel

Although others say not, we believe they still
brew here, albeit only for villagers with the right
to brew or buy tax-free beer – at least, that's
what they told us. There are some local buses to
Uetzing on weekdays if you're up for a challenge.
DB Bad Staffelstein 8km

UMMENHOFEN (Jengen) 573

Rössle-Bräu

St. Antonius Straße 35,
86860 Jengen-Ummenhofen
T 08246 755
www.roessle-braeu.de
Owner: Robert Kunz   Founded: 1869
Output: 600hl
REGULAR BEERS:
Rössle-Bräu Zunftherrn Pils (4.9%)
Rössle-Bräu Zunftherrn Export (5%)

Small brewery which we think supplies the brewery tap and nowhere else. The closest you can get
by bus is Jengen, around a mile to the north of
Ummenhofen, and the service there is very poor.

🍎 **Rössle**
St. Antonius Str. 34, 86860 Jengen-Ummenhofen
T 08246 321
Sun 10.00–12.00, Mon–Sat 14.00–22.00
[DB] Buchloe 6km

UNTERBAAR (Baar)　574

Schloßbrauerei

Hauptstraße 18, 86674 Baar-Unterbaar
T 08276 589 80　**F** 08276 58 98 69
www.schlossbrauerei-unterbaar.de
Owner: Freiherr Groß von Trockau
Founded: 1608　Output: 150,000hl
Availability: 350 pubs
REGULAR BEERS:
Unterbaarer Leicht (3%)
Unterbaarer Leichtes Weizen (3%)
Unterbaarer Hell (5%)
Unterbaarer Dunkel (5.3%)
Unterbaarer Meister Pils (5.5%)
Unterbaarer Hefetrübes Weizen (5.5%)
Unterbaarer Helles Weizen (5.5%)
Unterbaarer Dunkles Weizen (5.5%)
Unterbaarer Export (5.7%)
Unterbaarer Anno 2000 (5.7%)
Unterbaarer Märzen (5.8%)
SEASONAL BEERS:
**Unterbaarer Weihnachtsmärzen, Unterbaarer
Weizenbock, Unterbaarer St. Laurentius Bock**

Regional brewery, owned by the Baron von
Trockau, that produces beers of above-average
strength. Bus No. 410 runs from Meitingen
station on weekdays and stops outside the tap,
which was closed for refurbishment at the time
of writing.

🍎 **Bräustüberl**
Postweg 2, 86674 Baar-Unterbaar
T 08276 304　Closed Tue; Wed–Mon from 08.30
[DB] Meitingen 12km

UNTERGREUTH (Frensdorf)　575

Büttner

Untergreuth 8, 96158 Frensdorf-Untergreuth
T 09502 342
Owner: Michael Büttner　Founded: 1782
Output: 1,500hl　Availability: 1 pub

REGULAR BEER:
Büttner Vollbier Hell

In the same family since 1782, this brewpub
only opens at the weekend and the beer is only
available on draught. The opening times make
it very difficult to reach the pub by bus.

🍎 **Büttner**
Untergreuth 8, 96158 Frensdorf-Untergreuth
Closed Mon–Thu; Fri from 17.00, Sat, Sun &
hols from 14.00　[DB] Bamberg 10km

UNTERLEITERBACH (Zapfendorf)　576

Hennemann

Brauerei Gasthof Hennemann
Schloßstraße 2, 96199 Zapfendorf-Unterleiterbach
T 09547 261　**F** 09547 52 42
www.brauerei-gasthof-hennemann.de
Owner: Albert Hennemann　Founded: 1927
Output: 500hl　Availability: 1 pub
REGULAR BEERS:
Hennemann Dunkles Export (5.1%)
Hennemann Lätterbacher Weisse
SEASONAL BEER:
Hennemann Weizenbock

Brewpub and distillery in a village next to the
railway from Bamberg to Lichtenfels. There's no
station and only the odd bus so you'll probably
find it best to walk if you've no car.

🍎 **Zum Schwan**
Schloßstr. 2, 96199 Zapfendorf-Unterleiterbach
Closed Tue; Wed, Thu & Mon 16.00–24.00, Fri–
Sun 09.00–24.00; rooms available
[DB] Zapfendorf 2.5km

UNTERNBIBERT (Rügland)　577

Reuter

Hauptstraße 17, 91622 Rügland-Unternbibert
T/F 09828 229
Owner: Ludwig Reuter　Founded: 1717
Output: 900hl　Availability: 4 pubs
REGULAR BEER:
Unternbiberter Vollbier Bernstein (4%)

Known as Brauerei Dietz until the 1970s, this
small brewery and tap are on the main road

through the village. Bus No. 707 runs from Ansbach station on weekdays.

🍺 Reuter

Hauptstraße 17, 91622 Rügland-Unternbibert
Closed Tue & 3rd Sun of the month; Sat & Sun from 10.00, Mon, Wed–Fri from 16.30
DB Ansbach 17km

UNTERNEUHAUSEN (Weihmichl) 578

Weinzierl

Hauptstr. 2, 84107 Weihmichl-Unterneuhausen
T 08708 260   F 08708 17 34
www.brauerei-weinzierl.de
Owner: Franz Heidenreich   Founded: 1825
Output: 3,000hl
REGULAR BEERS:
Weinzierl Spezial-Hell (4.8%)
Weinzierl Pils (4.8%)
Weinzierl Export Weissbier (5.2%)
Weinzierl Neuhauser Weisse (5.2%)
SEASONAL BEERS:
Weinzierl Festbier (5.5%),
Weinzierl Weizenbock

Small brewery in a former monastery. The tap closed in 1945 but we think the Bahnhofsgaststätte on Stollnrieder Straße sells the beers. Bus No. 6234 runs daily from Landshut.
DB Landshut (Bayern) Hbf 16km

UNTERNEUKIRCHEN 579

Leidmann

Private Landbrauerei Sebastian Leidmann
Pinsmaierstraße 1, 84579 Unterneukirchen
T 08634 80 87   F 08634 80 97
Owner: Sebastian Leidmann   Founded: 1933
REGULAR BEERS:
Leidmann Alzthaler Leichte Weisse
Leidmann Goldenes Land Export
Leidmann Landbier Hefe Weisse
Leidmann Landbier Dunkel Weisse
SEASONAL BEERS:
Leidmann Fest Märzen, Leidmann Weisse Bock

Brewery in the village of Unterneukirchen. They used to contract-brew Original Keltisches Emmerbier but we think this has stopped.

Bus No. 34 runs from Tüßling once on weekdays but the return journey is a little complicated.

🍺 Leidmann

Pinsmaierstraße 1, 84579 Unterneukirchen
Closed Mon; Tue–Sat from 10.00, Sun from 09.00
DB Tüßling 7.5km, Altötting 9km

UNTERNEUSES (Ebensfeld) 580

Martin

Unterneuses 6b, 96250 Ebensfeld-Unterneuses
T 09573 43 82   F 09573 23 56 52
Owner: Hans-Georg Martin   Founded: 1868
Output: 250hl   Availability: 1 pub
REGULAR BEER:
Martin Vollbier (4.7%)

Small brewery on the main road through the village with the sole outlet being the nearby tap. Several bus routes run from Ebensfeld on weekdays but it is also walkable.

🍺 Martin

Viehtriebweg 3, 96250 Ebensfeld-Unterneuses
Closed Wed; Thu, Fri, Mon & Tue 16.00–24.00, Sat & Sun 10.00–24.00; rooms available
DB Ebensfeld 2.4km, Bad Staffelstein 3.7km

UNTERSCHLEICHACH (Oberaurach) 581

Löwenbräu Neeb

Michelsberg 1, 97514 Oberaurach-Unterschleichach
T 09529 277   F 09529 12 90
Owner: Beate Althoff   Founded: 1929
Output: 5,000hl
REGULAR BEERS:
Steigerwald Vollbier Bier (4.7%)
Steigerwald Vollbier Dunkel (4.8%)
Steigerwald Bauernbier (4.8%)
Steigerwald Pilsener (5.1%)
Steigerwald Weisse (5.2%)
SEASONAL BEER:
Steigerwald Aurator (7.5%, spring)

Brewery, tap and hotel at the crossroads in the centre of the village. We suggest bus No. 8178 from Haßfurt on weekdays but there are a couple of alternatives from Zeil and Ebelsbach-Eltmann.

🍺 **Löwenbräu Neeb**
Michelsberg 1, 97514 Oberaurach-
Unterschleichach
Closed Wed in winter; Thu–Tue 10.00–24.00;
rooms available
DB Haßfurt 14km

UNTERSIEMAU 582

Murmann
Coburger Straße 2–6, 96253 Untersiemau
T 09565 811   **F** 09565 69 82
E brauerei-murmann@t-online.de
Owner: Eberhard Murmann
Founded: 1862
Output: 6,000hl
REGULAR BEERS:
Murmann Halbe M
Murmann Hausbrauerbier
Murmann Lager
Murmann Dunkel
Murmann Pils
Murmann Premium
Murmann Hefeweizen
SEASONAL BEER:
Murmann Festbier

Small brewery in the centre of Untersiemau.
The tap in front is now closed. If you want to
look for the beers in the village, bus No. 8319
runs daily from Creidlitz station.
DB Creidlitz 4.3km

UNTERZAUNSBACH
(Pretzfeld) 583

Meister
Unterzaunsbach 8, 91362 Pretzfeld-
Unterzaunsbach
T 09194 91 26   **F** 09194 79 68 50
Owner: Georg Meister   Founded: 1865
Output: 1,500hl   Availability: 1 pub
REGULAR BEER:
Meister Vollbier (4.8%)
SEASONAL BEER:
Meister Festbier (5.5%, Christmas)
Brewpub on the main road through the tiny
village. Bus No. 222 runs from Forchheim via
Pretzfeld on weekdays.

🍺 **Meister**
Unterzaunsbach 8,
91362 Pretzfeld-Unterzaunsbach
Closed Tue; Wed–Mon 09.00–23.00
DB Pretzfeld 4.7km, Forchheim 17km

URSBERG 584

Klosterbräuhaus
Klosterbräuhaus Ursberg GmbH
Dominikus-Ringeisen-Straße 2, 86513 Ursberg
T 08281 99 89 62   **F** 08281 99 89 69
www.klosterbraeuhaus.de
Founded: 1623   Output: 3,000hl
REGULAR BEERS:
Ursberger Schankbier
Ursberger Hell
Ursberger Dunkel
Ursberger Zwickelbier
Ursberger Pils
Ursberger Weizen
Ursberger Dunkles Weizen
SEASONAL BEERS:
Ursberger Märzen, Ursberger Aloisius-Bock

Brewery and tap in a convent but, unlike at
Mallersdorf, the nuns here don't do the brewing.
They also have a recently refurbished three-star
hotel. Bus No. 600 runs daily from Augsburg to
Krumbach via Ursberg.

🍺 **Klosterbräuhaus**
Dominikus-Ringeisen-Straße 2, 86513 Ursberg
T 08281 998 90   **F** 08281 99 89 59
Daily 07.30–23.00; rooms available
DB Krumbach (Schwaben) 7.5km

USTERSBACH 585

Ustersbacher
Privatbrauerei Ustersbach A. Schmid KG
Hauptstraße 40, 86514 Ustersbach
T 08236 58 90   **F** 08236 589 15
www.ustersbacher.com
Owner: Kasper Schmid   Founded: 1605
Output: 180,000hl
REGULAR BEERS:
Ustersbacher Leichte Helle (3.2%)
Ustersbacher Leichte Weisse (3.3%)
Ustersbacher Urhell (4.9%)

Ustersbacher Pilsner (4.9%)
Ustersbacher Privat Pils (4.9%)
Ustersbacher Altbayerisch Dunkles (5.3%)
Ustersbacher Dunkle Weisse (5.3%)
Ustersbacher Bayerisch Hefeweizen (5.5%)
Ustersbacher Kristallweizen (5.5%)
Ustersbacher Edel Export (5.5%)
SEASONAL BEERS:
Ustersbacher Reischenau Gold (5.5%),
Ustersbacher 400 Jubiläumsbier (5.5%),
Ustersbacher Weihnachtsbier (5.8%),
Ustersbacher Ustator Weizenbock (8.9%)

Large regional brewery owned by the Schmid family for over 400 years and now in the hands of the 13th generation. Bus No. 600 from Augsburg stops outside the brewery.

🍺 Bräustüble

Hauptstraße 40, 86514 Ustersbach
T 08236 773
Closed Sat; Sun–Fri 09.30–23.00
DB Gessertshausen 7.5km

VESTENBERG
(Petersaurach)   586

Löwenbräu

Löwenbräu Vestenberg Simon Dorn & Sohn oHG
Brauhausstraße 9, 91580 Petersaurach-Vestenberg
T 09802 72 15
Owners: Karl & Margarete Dorn
Founded: c.1500   Output: 3,000hl
REGULAR BEERS:
Löwenbräu Vestenberg Vollbier (4.5%)
Löwenbräu Vestenberg Pilsner (4.7%)
Löwenbräu Vestenberg Gold Export (5.4%)
Löwenbräu Vestenberg Export Dunkel (5.4%)
SEASONAL BEER:
Löwenbräu Vestenberg Doppelbock (winter)

Small brewery in the middle of the village. Bus No. 751 runs to Vestenberg from Anbach on weekdays but it is walkable from Wicklesgreuth.

🍺 Brauereigaststätte

Brauhausstraße 9, 91580 Petersaurach-Vestenberg
Closed Mon; Tue–Sat 09.00–23.00,
Sun 17.00–23.00
DB Wicklesgreuth 3km, Ansbach 10km

VIECHTACH   587

Gesellschaftsbrauerei

Gesellschaftsbrauerei Viechtach oHG
Bahnhofstraße 5, 94234 Viechtach
T 09942 16 63   F 09942 65 22
www.vit-online.de/brauerei
Founded: 1553   Output: 30,000hl
REGULAR BEERS:
Viechtacher Vollbier-Hell (4.8%)
Viechtacher Bergkristall Pils (5%)
Viechtacher Weiße (5.2%)
Alt Viechtacher Dunkel (5.5%)
Viechtacher Märzen (5.5%)
SEASONAL BEERS:
Viechtacher Festbier (4.8%),
Viechtacher Bock Dunkel (7%)

Brewery which has been both a communal and a co-operative brewery but is now run on more commercial lines. The tap is in Linden, 10km south-east of Viechtach on the B85, which can be reached by bus from Gotteszell on weekdays.

🍺 Linden

Schloßanger 20, 94244 Geiersthal-Linden
T 09942 26 74
Closed Mon; Tue–Sun 10.00–24.00
DB Gotteszell 9km, Regen 15km

VIERETH (Viereth-Trunstadt)   588

Mainlust

Hauptstraße 9, 96191 Viereth-Trunstadt/Viereth
T 09503 74 44   F 09503 615
www.mainlust.com
Owner: Helmut Bayer   Founded: 1848
Output: 700hl   Availability: 1 pub
REGULAR BEERS:
Mainlust Vollbier
Mainlust Märzen

Brewpub on the main road through the village that still maintains traditional rural Franconian opening hours. Bus No. 8229 runs a few times a day from Bamberg on weekdays and it's just about walkable from Oberhaid.

🍺 Mainlust

Hauptstraße 9, 96191 Viereth-Trunstadt/Viereth
Closed Fri; Sat & Sun 08.00–24.00, Mon–Thu 06.00–24.00; rooms available
DB Oberhaid 4.8km, Bamberg 10km

VIERZEHNHEILIGEN
(Bad Staffelstein)   589

Trunk

Brauerei Trunk Vierzehnheiligen
Vierzehnheiligen 3, 96231 Bad-Staffelstein-
Vierzehnheiligen
T 09571 34 88
Owners: Alfred & Andreas Trunk
Founded: 1803   Output: 4,000hl
REGULAR BEERS:
Nothelfer Pils (4.7%)
Nothelfer Lager (4.7%)
Nothelfer Trunk Dunkel (5.1%)
SEASONAL BEERS:
Nothelfer Erntebier (4.7%, summer), **Nothelfer
Festbier** (Christmas), **Nothelfer Silberbock** (7%)

Sometimes known as the Alte Klosterbrauerei,
this little brewery sits near the church of the
fourteen saints (Vierzehnheiligen), on a hill
south of Lichtenfels. Local buses run on
weekdays from both Bad Staffelstein and
Lichtenfels to a car park lower down the hill.

🍺 **Klosterbräustübchen**
Vierzehnheiligen 3, 96231 Bad-Staffelstein-
Vierzehnheiligen
Daily 10.00–20.00
DB Lichtenfels 4km, Bad Staffelstein 6km

VILSHOFEN   590

Wolferstetter

Brauerei Wolferstetter Georg Huber KG
Bürg 26, 94474 Vilshofen
T 08541 58 80   **F** 08541 588 15
www.wolferstetter-brauerei.de
Owner: Georg Andreas Huber   Founded: 1542
Output: 120,000hl
REGULAR BEERS:
Wolferstetter Hopfen Leicht (3%)
Wolferstetter Leichtes Weizen (3%)
Wolferstetter Josef Groll Pils (4.7%)
Wolferstetter Edel Hell (5%)
Wolferstetter Dunkel Spezial (5.1%)
Wolferstetter Urtyp Export Hell (5.1%)
Wolferstetter Export Hefe Weizen (5.5%)
Wolferstetter Dunkles Weizen (5.5%)
SEASONAL BEERS:
Wolferstetter Winter Premium (5.2%),

Wolferstetter Festbier (5.2%), **Wolferstetter
Weizen Bock, Wolferstetter Bock** (7.7%)

Large brewery in the centre of Vilshofen. The
beer is transported to a site south of the town
for bottling and filling. Josef Groll Pils is named
after the local brewer credited with creating
this style back in 1842.

🍺 **Wolferstetter Keller**
Bürg 21, 94474 Vilshofen
T 08541 17 29   **F** 08541 27 30
Closed Wed; Thu-Tue 10.00–14.00 & from 17.30
DB Vilshofen (Niederbayern) 550m

VOHENSTRAUSS   591

Behringer

Weißbierbrauerei Behringer
Marktplatz 35, 92648 Vohenstrauß
T 09651 18 70
Owner: Rudolf Fiebig   Founded: 1898
Output: 700hl
REGULAR BEER:
Behringer Weißbier

Brewpub in the centre of Vohenstrauß that
produces beer mostly for sale on the premises.
The above phone number hasn't worked for a
couple of years but we understand the pub is still
open, though whether it still brews is anyone's
guess (answers to GermanBreweries@aol.com).
Bus No. 6291 runs from Weiden daily (once on
Sunday).

🍺 **Behringer**
Marktplatz 35, 92648 Vohenstrauß
Closed Mon; Tue–Thu 10.00–13.30 & 16.00–
01.00, Fri & Sat 10.00–01.00, Sun 09.00–12.00
& 16.00–01.00
DB Weiden (Oberpfalz) 18km

WAISCHENFELD   592

Heckel

Vorstadt 20, 91344 Waischenfeld
T 09202 493
Owner: Alfons Heckel   Founded: 1890
Output: 350hl   Availability: 1 pub
REGULAR BEER:
Heckel Vollbier Hell

Brewpub in the centre of the village. It's possible to get here using bus No. 231 from Ebermannstadt on weekdays but you'll need to arrive early if you want an easy journey back.

🏠 Heckel
Vorstadt 20, 91344 Waischenfeld
Daily 09.00–13.00 & 16.30–22.00
DB Ebermannstadt 19km

WALDSASSEN 593

Ziegler

Ziegler-Brauerei GmbH
Stationsweg 50, 95652 Waldsassen
T 09632 92 30 00
E ziegler.brauerei@t-online.de
Owner: Felicitus Hart   Founded: 1847
Output: 12,000hl
REGULAR BEERS:
Ziegler-Bräu Böhms Böhmisches Hell
Ziegler-Bräu Böhms Böhmisches Dunkel
Ziegler-Bräu Pils
Ziegler-Bräu Kappl Weisse
Ziegler-Bräu Export
SEASONAL BEER:
Ziegler-Bräu Heller Bock
FOR POGORAUSCH GBR, MÜNCHEN:
Pogorausch Pralles Pils Herb (5%),
Pogorausch Pralles Pils Mild (5%),
Pogorausch Geiler Bock (7.5%)

Small brewery on the northern outskirts of Waldsassen with a tap opposite the monastery in the centre of town. Bus No. 6276 runs from Wiesau station on weekdays.

🏠 Ziegler's Gaststätte
Johannisplatz 6, 95652 Waldsassen
T 09632 91 67 47
Mon 10.00–14.00, Tue–Sun 10.00–24.00
DB Wiesau (Oberpfalz) 15km

WALDSTETTEN 594

Goldener Engel

Engelbrauerei Waldstetten
Raiffeisenstraße 4, 89367 Waldstetten
T 08223 12 74   **F** 08223 57 05
www.engelbrauerei.de
Owners: Johann Mayer   Founded: 1665

Output: 750hl
REGULAR BEERS:
Goldener Engel Dunkel
Goldener Engel Zwickel
Goldener Engel Pils
Goldener Engel Weiße
Goldener Engel Märzen

Brewpub in the centre of town. The Zwickel and Dunkel are only available at the pub. There are a few buses on weekdays from Ichenhausen but it's walkable if you'd otherwise have a long wait.

🏠 Goldener Engel
Raiffeisenstraße 4, 89367 Waldstetten
Wed 10.00–13.00, Thu, Fri, Sun–Tue from 10.00, Sat 10.00–17.00; rooms available
DB Ichenhausen 3.2km

WALKERTSHOFEN 595

Schorer

Grimoldsrieder Straße 1, 86877 Walkertshofen
T/F 08239 507
Owner: Franz Schorer   Founded: 1846
Output: 1,000hl
REGULAR BEERS:
Schorer Stauden Pilsner
Schorer Staudengold
Schorer Staudenweisse
SEASONAL BEER:
Schorer Festbier Märzen

Small brewery on the western edge of Walkertshofen that we believe supplies just the tap. Bus No. 604 runs from Gessertshausen station on weekdays and a couple of times at the weekend, and there are occasional tourist trains.

🏠 Schorer
Grimoldsrieder Straße 1, 86877 Walkertshofen
Closed Mon–Wed; Thu & Fri from 19.00, Sat from 14.00, Sun 09.00–12.00 & from 18.00
DB Gessertshausen 20km

WALLERSTEIN 596

Fürst Wallerstein

Fürst Wallerstein Brauhaus AG
Berg 78, 86757 Wallerstein
T 09081 70 75   **F** 09081 70 48
www.fuerst-wallerstein.de

Owner: S. D. Fürst zu Oettingen-Wallerstein
Founded: 1598   Output: 80,000hl
Availability: c.250 pubs
REGULAR BEERS:
Fürst Wallerstein Fürsten Medium (2.9%)
Fürst Wallerstein Zwickel (4.7%)
Fürst Wallerstein Fürsten Hell (4.8%)
Fürst Wallerstein Fürsten Pils (4.9%)
Fürst Wallerstein Weißbierpils (5.1%)
Fürst Wallerstein Landsknecht-Bier (5.2%)
Fürst Wallerstein Fürsten Felsen-Quell (5.2%)
Fürst Wallerstein Fürsten Hefe-Weizen (5.2%)
Fürst Wallerstein Hefe-Weizen Dunkel (5.2%)
Fürst Wallerstein Classic (5.4%)
SEASONAL BEER:
Fürst Wallerstein Winter-Böckle (7.5%)

Regional brewery owned by the Prince of
Oettingen-Wallerstein. We believe they may
also brew beers for Scheible-Bräu of Alerheim.
Bus No. 868 runs from Nördlingen daily.

🍺 **Fürstlicher Keller**
Berg 78, 86757 Wallerstein
T 09081 27 59 09   **F** 09081 27 59 08
Daily from 11.00. Rooms available.
DB Nördlingen 6km

WALTERSHAUSEN (Saal) 597

Lang
Privatbrauerei Lang
Charlotte-von-Kalb-Straße 13,
97633 Saal-Waltershausen
T 09762 92 92   **F** 09762 92 94
www.brauerei-lang.de
Owner: Werner Lang   Founded: 1844
Output: 5,000hl
REGULAR BEERS:
Lang Lager (4.7%)
Lang Pils (4.9%)
Lang Mephisto Weisse (4.9%)
Lang Kupferbier (5%)

Small brewery on the road south out of the
village with a tap just around the corner. The
owner also has a large drinks market which
stocks well over 100 beers. Bus No. 8304 runs
from Bad Neustadt on weekdays but you won't
get long if you want to visit the tap.

🍺 **Bräustüble**
Martin-Luther-Straße 7,
97633 Saal-Waltershausen

T 09762 93 09 41
Closed Mon; Tue–Fri 17.00–24.00,
Sat 13.00–24.00, Sun 10.00–24.00
DB Bad Neustadt 14km

WARTENBERG 598

Reiter-Bräu
Untere Hauptstraße 2, 85456 Wartenberg
T 08762 735 80   **F** 08762 73 58 50
www.hotelgasthof-reiter.de
Owner: Ferdinand Reiter
Founded: 1716
Output: 5,000hl
REGULAR BEERS:
Reiter-Bräu Hell
Reiter-Bräu Pils
Reiter-Bräu Weizen Hell
Reiter-Bräu Weizen Dunkel
Reiter-Bräu Export Hell
Reiter-Bräu Export Dunkel
SEASONAL BEER:
Reiter-Bräu Bock

Brewery, hotel and pub on the old road north
out of the village. Bus No. 501 runs between
Erding and Moosburg via Wartenberg on
weekdays and does run late enough to allow
you to visit the tap.

🍺 **Reiter-Bräu**
Untere Hauptstraße 2, 85456 Wartenberg
Closed Thu; Fri & Mon–Wed from 18.00, Sat &
Sun from 12.00; rooms available
DB Moosburg 8km, Erding 14km

WATTENDORF 599

Dremel
Hauptstraße 21, 96196 Wattendorf
T 09504 271   **F** 09504 923 90 19
www.brauerei-dremel.de
Owner: Günther Dremel   Founded: 1865
Output: 500hl   Availability: 1 pub
REGULAR BEERS:
Dremel Hell (4.5%)
Dremel Dunkel (4.5%)

The smaller of Wattendorf's two brewpubs. The
opening hours make this a very difficult place to
visit by public transport.

Zum Schwan
Hauptstraße 21, 96196 Wattendorf
Closed Mon & Sat; Sun & hols 10.00–24.00,
Tue–Fri 17.00–24.00
DB Lichtenfels 18km, Bamberg 24km

Hübner
Brauereigasthof Hübner
Hauptstraße 28, 96196 Wattendorf
T 09504 207   F 09504 591
www.brauerei-huebner.de
Owner: Johannes Hübner   Founded: 1806
Output: 1,000hl   Availability: 1 pub
REGULAR BEERS:
Hübner-Bräu Dunkel
Hübner-Bräu Zwicklpils
SEASONAL BEER:
Hübner-Bräu Maibock

Brewpub across the street from Dremel. There
are two buses on weekdays from Lichtenfels and
one from Bamberg. The return service is even
worse.

Hübner
Hauptstraße 28, 96196 Wattendorf
Closed Wed; Thu–Tue 11.00–24.00
DB Lichtenfels 18km, Bamberg 24km

WEIDEN (Oberpfalz)   600

Bräuwirt
Unterer Markt 9, 92637 Weiden
T 0961 48 13 30   F 0961 481 33 50
www.braeuwirt.de   Founded: 1993
Output: 1,000hl   Availability: 1 pub
REGULAR BEERS:
Bräuwirt St. Georgs Zoigl Hell
Bräuwirt St. Georgs Zoigl Dunkel
Bräuwirt Hefeweizen Hell
SEASONAL BEER:
Bräuwirt Bock

Brewpub in an old building in the lower part of
the central market square. We think they may
brew other seasonal beers, in addition to the
Bock.

Bräuwirt
Unterer Markt 9, 92637 Weiden
Daily 10.00–01.00
DB Weiden (Oberpfalz) 1.1km

Gambrinus
Gambrinus-Brauerei Weiden Rohrwild e.K.
Keplerstraße 15–23, 92637 Weiden
T 0961 67 03 30   F 0961 670 33 20
www.gambrinus-weiden.de
Owner: Ernst Rohrwild   Founded: 1927
Output: 30,000hl
REGULAR BEERS:
Gambrinus Sparta
Gambrinus Leichte Weisse
Gambrinus Hell (4.9%)
Gambrinus Dunkel (4.9%)
Gambrinus Max-Reger-Dunkel (4.9%)
Gambrinus Zwickelbier (4.9%)
Gambrinus Premium Pils (5%)
Gambrinus Helles Hefe-Weizen (5.1%)
Gambrinus Dunkles Hefe-Weizen (5.1%)
Gambrinus Perl-Weizen (5.1%)
Gambrinus Märzen
SEASONAL BEERS:
Gambrinus Bockbier Hell (7%),
Gambrinus Bockbier Dunkel (7%)

Brewery and tap in a largely residential area
north of the station, on the opposite side of the
main railway line to the town centre. Named
after the supposed inventor and 'Patron Saint
of Beer'.

Gambrinus
Keplerstraße 21, 92637 Weiden
T 0961 223 00   Daily 08.00–24.00
DB Weiden (Oberpfalz) 1.4km

WEIGELSHOFEN (Eggolsheim)   601

Pfister
Brauerei Gasthof Pfister GmbH
Eggerbachstraße 22, 91330 Eggolsheim-
Weigelshofen
T 09545 942 60   F 09545 94 26 50
www.brauerei-pfister.de
Owners: Elisabeth Pfister   Founded: 1848
Output: 1,700hl
REGULAR BEERS:
Pfister Weißbier (4.6%)
Pfister Landbier (4.9%)
Pfister Schwarz Kellerbier (4.9%)
SEASONAL BEER:
Pfister Bock (Christmas)

Brewery pub and hotel on the main road through the village. We think the only other outlet for the beer is their Keller on the outskirts of the village. Bus No. 220 runs from the centre of Eggolsheim (a mile from the station) on weekdays.

🍺 Pfister
Eggerbachstraße 22, 91330 Eggolsheim-Weigelshofen
Closed Tue; Wed 17.00–01.00,
Thu–Mon 11.00–01.00; rooms available
DB Eggolsheim 5km

WEIHER (Viereth-Trunstadt)   602

Kundmüller
Weiher 13, 96191 Viereth-Trunstadt/Weiher
T 09503 43 38   **F** 09503 78 68
www.kundmueller.de
Owner: Anna Kundmüller   Founded: 1835
Output: 8,000hl   Availability: 3 pubs
REGULAR BEERS:
Weiherer Lager (4.7%)
Weiherer Pils (4.7%)
Weiherer Rauch (5.1%)
Weiherer Weisse (5.2%)
SEASONAL BEER:
Weiherer Bock (6.6%, winter)

Small brewery and distillery in a village with no public transport. We suggest the best bet, if you're without your own transport, is a bus to either Viereth or Trabelsdorf, both around 2.5km from Weiher.

🍺 Kundmüller
Weiher 13, 96191 Viereth-Trunstadt/Weiher
Closed Wed; Thu–Tue from 09.00; rooms available
DB Bamberg 12km

WEILER im Allgäu   603

Post
Post Brauerei Weiler A. Zinth KG
Käsgasse 17, 88171 Weiler im Allgäu
T 08387 921 00   **F** 08387 92 10 70
www.post-brauerei.de
Owner: Anton Zinth
Founded: 1650
Output: 25,000hl

REGULAR BEERS:
Post Allgäu-Weisse Leicht (2.9%)
Post Förderstoff (4.9%)
Post Pilsener (4.9%)
Post Edel Privat (5.2%)
Post Zwickel-Bier (5.2%)
Post Hefe-Weizen (5.4%)
Post Weizen Dunkel (5.4%)

Small regional brewery whose beers are fairly easy to find over much of the Allgäu. The tap was the original home of the brewery. Bus No. 12 runs daily from Röthenbach station.

🍺 Zur Post
Fridolin-Holzer-Straße 4, 88171 Weiler im Allgäu
T 08387 10 70   **F** 08387 92 31 60
Closed Wed; Thu–Tue 11.30–14.00 & from 17.00; rooms available
DB Röthenbach (Allgäu) 7km

WEILHEIM   604

Dachsbräu
Murnauer Straße 5, 82362 Weilheim
T 0881 22 61   **F** 0881 38 14
www.dachsbier.de
Owner: Ulrich Klose
Founded: 1879
Output: 8,000hl
Availability: 25 pubs
REGULAR BEERS:
Dachsbräu Leichtes Hefe-Weizen (3.5%)
Dachsbräu Dunkel (5%)
Dachsbräu Weizen (5%)
Dachsbräu Hell (5.5%)
Dachsbräu Weilheimer Urhell (5.5%)
SEASONAL BEERS:
Dachsbräu Weilheimer Festbier (6%),
Dachsbräu Weizenbock (7%),
Dachsbräu Ulimator (7.5%)

Small brewery on the opposite side of the town centre to the railway station. The tap is alongside and has a pleasant shaded beer garden.

🍺 Dachs Bräustüberl
Murnauer Straße 5, 82362 Weilheim
T 0881 26 93
Closed Sun & hols; Mon–Fri 09.00–24.00, Sat 09.00–15.00
DB Weilheim (Oberbayern) 900m

WEISBRUNN (Eltmann) 605

Bräutigam

Dorfstraße 12, 97483 Eltmann-Weisbrunn
T 09522 16 28
Owner: Baptist Bräutigam   Founded: c.1850
Output: 400hl   Availability: 1 pub
REGULAR BEER:
Bräutigam Pilsner
SEASONAL BEER:
Bräutigam Festbier

Owned by the Bräutigam family since 1901 but
founded at least 50 years earlier, this small
brewpub is in a small village south of Eltmann.
There are a few buses a day to the Weisbrunn,
seemingly all from different places.

🍺 **Bräutigam**
Dorfstraße 12, 97483 Eltmann-Weisbrunn
Closed Tue & Wed; Thu–Mon 09.00–23.00
DB Ebelsbach-Eltmann 6km

WEISMAIN 606

Püls Bräu

Burgkunstadter Straße 41–43, 96260 Weismain
T 09575 922 90   **F** 09575 92 29 30
www.weismainer.de
Owners: Hans & Hans Josef Püls
Founded: 1798   Output: 100,000hl
Availability: c.400 pubs
REGULAR BEERS:
Weismainer Feinherb (2.9%)
Weismainer Urhell (4.6%)
Weismainer Landbier (5%)
Weismainer Premium (5%)
Weismainer Krone Pils (5.2%)
Weismainer Weiße (5.2%)
Weismainer 1798er Kellertrunk (5.4%)
SEASONAL BEERS:
Weismainer Treib-Stoff (7.5%),
Weismainer Abt Knauer Bock (7.5%)

Large brewery now owned by the sixth generation of the Püls family. There's no official tap but
the beers are available over much of northern
Franconia. If you want to try the beers in
Weismain, bus No. 1 runs from Burgkunstadt on
weekdays.
DB Burgkunstadt 6km

WEISSENBRUNN 607

Gampertbräu

Gampertbräu Gebr. Gampert GmbH & Co. KG
Braustraße 2–4, 96369 Weißenbrunn
T 09261 603 30   **F** 09261 60 33 42
www.gampertbraeu.de
Owners: Birgit & Christian Höfner
Founded: 1514   Output: 100,000hl
Availability: c.150 pubs
REGULAR BEERS:
Gampertbräu Förster-Leicht (2.7%)
Gampertbräu Förster-Hell (4.4%)
Gampertbräu Förster-Pils (4.9%)
Gampertbräu Förster-Weisse (5.4%)
Gampertbräu Förster-Gold (5.5%)
Gampertbräu Förster-Dunkel (5.5%)
Gampertbräu Förster-Märzen (5.5%)
SEASONAL BEERS:
Gampertbräu Schützenfestbier (5.5%),
Gampertbräu Osterfestbier (5.5%),
Gampertbräu Weihnachtsfestbier (5.5%)

Large brewery on the main road through
Weißenbrunn. The tap is around 500m down
the street, on the road towards Kulmach. Buses
run from both Neuses and Kronach.

🍺 **Frankenwald**
Kulmbacher Straße 2, 96369 Weißenbrunn
T 09261 42 14
Closed Thu; Fri–Wed 10.00–22.00; rooms
available
DB Neuses (bei Kronach) 4km, Kronach 7km

WEISSENBURG 608

Schneider

Bachgasse 15, 91781 Weißenburg
T 09141 24 07   **F** 09141 729 37
www.schneider-bier.de
Owner: Thomas Schneider   Founded: 1772
Output: 3,000hl   Availability: 10 pubs
REGULAR BEERS:
Schneider-Bräu Weizen Leicht
Schneider-Bräu Helles
Schneider-Bräu Schwarz
Schneider-Bräu Pils
Schneider-Bräu Weizen
Schneider-Bräu Märzen

SEASONAL BEERS:

Schneider-Bräu Festbier, Schneider-Bräu Bock

Traditional brewery and tap at the opposite end of the old town to the station. They also have a small brewing museum.

🍺 **Zur Kanne**

Bachgasse 15, 91781 Weißenburg
T 09141 38 44
Closed Mon; Tue & Wed 17.30–24.00,
Thu–Sun 10.30–14.00 & 17.30–24.00
DB Weißenburg (Bayern) 850m

Sigwart

Brauerei Hermann Sigwart KG
Roßmühle 10, 91781 Weißenburg
T 09141 857 50   **F** 09141 85 75 19
www.brauerei-sigwart.de
Owner: Wolfgang Aurnhammer
Founded: 1451   Output: 20,000hl
REGULAR BEERS:
Sigwart Leichtes
Sigwart Weißenburger Leichte Weiße
Sigwart Hell (4.9%)
Sigwart Pils (4.9%)
Sigwart Hefe-Weizen Hell (4.9%)
Sigwart Weißenburger Weiße (5.1%)
Sigwart Weißenburger Dunkle Weiße (5.1%)
Sigwart Spezial Märzen

The larger of Weißenburg's two breweries, Sigwart is a couple of hundred metres north of Scheider. The nearby tap used to house the brewery.

🍺 **Sigwart-Bräustüberl**

Luitpoldstraße 17, 91781 Weißenburg
T 09141 16 26
Closed Tue; Wed–Mon 10.00–23.00
DB Weißenburg (Bayern) 750m

WEISSENHORN   609

Hasenbrauerei

Brauereigasthof zum Hasen
Brewery: Reichenbacher Straße 21,
89264 Weißenhorn
T 07309 423 55
Office: Hauptstraße 13, 89264 Weißenhorn
T 07309 24 12   **F** 07309 24 70
www.gasthof-hasen.de

Owner: Anton Walser   Founded: 1872
Output: 500hl
REGULAR BEERS:
Weißenhorner Dunkel
Weißenhorner Pils
Weißenhorner Weizen
Weißenhorner Märzen

Small brewery which we believe is actually on Reichenbacher Straße, west of the town centre. The tap is in the heart of the old town. Bus No. 76 runs daily from Senden station. The Hare pub offers 'Speating', a copyrighted programme of *speak*ing and learning a foreign language (Italian, Spanish, French or Russian) while ea*ting*.

🍺 **Zum Hasen**

Hauptstraße 13, 89264 Weißenhorn
T 07309 24 12   **F** 07309 24 70
Closed Mon; Tue–Sun 10.00–14.00 & from 17.00
DB Senden 10km

WEISSENOHE   610

Klosterbrauerei

Klosterbrauerei Weißenohe GmbH & Co. KG
Klosterstraße 20, 91367 Weißenohe
T 09192 591   **F** 09192 80 52
www.klosterbrauerei-weissenohe.de
Owners: the Winkler family   Founded: 1052
Output: 20,000hl   Availability: 40 pubs
REGULAR BEERS:
Weißenoher Pils (4.9%)
Weißenoher Classic Export (5%)
Weißenoher Export Dunkel (5%)
Weißenoher Klosterbier Altfränkische (5.1%)
Weißenoher Klostersud (5.2%)
Weißenoher Kloster Spezial (5.2%)
Weißenoher Eucharius Märzen (5.2%)
FOR HANF & NATUR, MARIENHEIDE:
Cannabis-Club-Sud Hanfbier (4.9%)

Brewery in the former monastery at Weißenohe which has been owned by the Winkler family since 1827. It is purported to date from 1052, a couple of years after Weltenburg was supposedly founded and 12 years after Weihenstephan. The cannabis beer is brewed like a normal beer, to which edible hemp is added.

🍺 **Wirtshaus der Klosterbrauerei**

Klosterstraße 20, 91367 Weißenohe
T 09192 63 57

Closed Mon & winter Tue; Tue 15.00–24.00,
Wed–Sun 11.00–24.00   DB Weißenohe 300m

WEISSENSTADT   611

Michael

Privatbrauerei Michael
Kirchenlamitzer Str. 64–66, 95163 Weißenstadt
T 09253 265   **F** 09253 85 97
www.brauerei-michael.de   Founded: 1906
Owners: Beate Michael & Hermann Michael
Output: 4,000hl   Availability: c.20 pubs
REGULAR BEERS:
Michael Egerthaler Leicht (2.9%)
Michael Weißenstädter See Weisse Light
Michael M. Lager
Michael Premium Pilsner (4.9%)
Michael Fränkisches Kellerbier
Michael Weißenstädter See Weisse
Michael Bär Bier Pils (5.2%)
Michael Bär Bier Dinkel (5.6%)

Small brewery on the lakeside town of
Weißenstadt. There's no tap but the beers are
available locally. Bus No. 6351 runs a couple of
times on weekdays from Münchberg.
DB Münchberg 14km

WELTENBURG (Kelheim)   612

Klosterbrauerei

Klosterbrauerei Weltenburg GmbH
Asamstraße 32, 93309 Kelheim-Weltenburg
T 09441 73 91   **F** 09441 289 28
www.weltenburger.de
Owner: Kloster Weltenburg   Founded: 1050
REGULAR BEERS:
Weltenburger Kloster Barock Dunkel (4.7%)
Weltenburger Kloster Anno 1050 (5.5%)
SEASONAL BEERS:
Weltenburger Kloster Winter-Traum (5.2%),
Weltenburger Kloster Asam Bock (6.9%)

The second oldest brewery in the world and
possibly the most attractively situated. Its
scenic location in a bend on the Danube was
almost the cause of its downfall in 2005 when the
monastery was flooded. The five 'Weltenburger'
beers are brewed by Bischofshof in Regensburg,
'Weltenburger Kloster' beers are brewed here.

Bus No. 6018 runs from Abensberg on weekdays
but you'll have to walk the last kilometre or so.

Klosterschenke
Asamstraße 32, 93309 Kelheim-Weltenburg
T 09441 675 70   **F** 09441 67 57 26
Closed mid Nov–mid Mar, Closed Mon & Tue in
Mar & Nov; Wed–Sun 08.00–19.00 (daily Apr–Oct)
DB Abensburg 11km

WERNECK   613

Wernecker

Wernecker Bierbrauerei
Schönbornstraße 2–4, 97440 Werneck
T 09722 915 00   **F** 09722 91 50 50
www.wernecker-bier.de   Founded: 1621
Owner: Hans Jörg Lang   Output: 20,000hl
REGULAR BEERS:
Wernecker Bayerisch Hell (4.6%)
Wernecker Bayerisch Dunkel (4.9%)
Wernecker Premium Pils (4.9%)
Balthasar Neumann Hefe Weisse (5.2%)
Balthasar Neumann Schwarze Weisse (5.2%)
Wernecker Laurentius Kellerbier (5.5%)
SEASONAL BEERS:
Wernecker Maibaumbier (5.5%),
Wernecker Weihnachtsbier (5.5%),
Wernecker Fränkischer Land-Bock (7.8%)

Brewery and tap in the centre of Werneck. Bus
No. 8134 runs on weekdays from Schweinfurt to
Werneck via Waigolshausen but the walk from
the latter should be easy enough for most
people. Balthasar Neumann was one of the
most famous German architects; he built
Werneck castle in 1733–44.

Brauereigashof
Schönbornstraße 2, 97440 Werneck
T 09722 910 80   **F** 09722 91 08 10
Daily 11.00–24.00; rooms available
DB Waigolshausen 2.5km

WERTINGEN   614

Schwanen-Bräu

Schwanen-Bräu H. Carry KG
Schmiedgasse 1–2, 86637 Wertingen
T 08272 23 23   **F** 08272 61 42
www.schwanenbraeu.com

Owner: Fritz Carry   Founded: 1880
Output: 4,000hl   Availability: 15 pubs
REGULAR BEERS:
Schwanen-Bräu Hell (5%)
Schwanen-Bräu Wertinger Original (5%)
Schwanen-Bräu Dunkel (5.2%)
Schwanen-Bräu Pils (5.2%)
Schwanen-Bräu Carry's Monatsbier (5.2%)
Schwanen-Bräu Kellerbier (5.7%)
Schwanen-Bräu Spezial (5.7%)
SEASONAL BEER:
Schwanen-Bräu Festbier (5.7%, Christmas)

Small brewery off the main street, with the tap
at the front. They have a small museum. Buses
Nos. 400 and 402 run from Mertingen on weekdays and there are buses from Augsburg all week.

🍺 **Zum Schwanen**
Hauptstraße 8, 86637 Wertingen
T 08272 99 37 88   **F** 08272 99 29 82
Daily from 10.00; rooms available
DB Meitingen 14km

WETTELSHEIM
(Treuchtlingen)   615

Strauß

Bahnhofstraße 20, 91757 Treuchtlingen-
Wettelsheim
T 09142 83 89   **F** 09142 43 22
www.wettelsheimer-bier.de
Owner: Karl Strauß   Founded: 1797
Output: 10,000hl
REGULAR BEERS:
Wettelsheimer Hell (4.9%)
Wettelsheimer Pils (5%)
Wettelsheimer Märzen (5.5%)
SEASONAL BEERS:
Wettelsheimer Bock Hell (6.6%, Christmas),
Wettelsheimer Bock Dunkel (6.6%, Christmas)

Family-run brewery whose tap is a beer garden
south-west of the village that only opens in the
summer (in fine weather). Wettelsheimer Keller
is near the point where Ansbacher Straße
becomes Treuchtlinger Straße, within walking
distance of Treuchtlingen station.

🍺 **Wettelsheimer Keller**
Kellerhaus, 91757 Treuchtlingen-Wettelsheim
T 09142 77 40
Oct–Apr closed.

May–Jun & Sep: Thu–Sun from 10.00
Jul & Aug: Mon–Wed from 16.00, Thu–Sun from
10.00
DB Treuchtlingen 2.2km

WEYBERHÖFE (Sailauf)   616

Weyberbräu

Biergarten-Restaurant Weyberbräu
Kurfürst-Eppstein-Ring 6,
63877 Sailauf-Weyberhöfe
T 06093 99 63 10   **E** weyberbraeu@primanet.de
Owners: Sonja & Roland Pfeiffer
Founded: 05.12.1998   Output: 1,000hl
Availability: 1 pub
REGULAR BEERS:
Weyberbräu Hell (4.9%)
Weyberbräu Dunkel (4.9%)
Weyberbräu Weizen (4.9%)
SEASONAL BEERS:
Weyberbräu Bock (6.4%)

Brewpub in what looks like a designer barn.
They also have their own distillery. Weyberhöfe
is on the opposite side of the A3 from Hösbach
station. Bus No. 45 runs from Hösbach if you
can't manage the walk.

🍺 **Weyberbräu**
Kurfürst-Eppstein-Ring 6,
63877 Sailauf-Weyberhöfe
Closed Mon & Tue; Wed–Sun 12.00–23.00
DB Hösbach 1.5km

WIEFELSDORF (Schwandorf) 617

Plank

Weißbierbrauerei Plank GmbH
Wiefelsdorfer Straße 1,
92421 Schwandorf-Wiefelsdorf
T 09431 504 50   **F** 09431 556 23
Owner: Wolfgang Rasel   Founded: 1888
Output: 15,000hl
REGULAR BEERS:
Die Leichte Jura (2.9%)
Jura Pfiff (4.9%)
Jura Weizen (5%)
Jura Weizen Dunkel (5%)
SEASONAL BEER:
Jura Weizen-Bock

Wheat beer brewery whose proprietor also owns the nearby Schloßbrauerei Naabeck. Buses Nos. 108 and 110 run from Schwandorf on weekdays but the service isn't great.

🍺 Plank

Wiefelsdorfer Straße 1,
92421 Schwandorf-Wiefelsdorf
Closed Mon & Tue; Wed–Sun 11.00–21.00
DB Schwandorf 8km

WIESEN (Bad Staffelstein)   618

Hellmuth

Wiesen 14, 96231 Bad Staffelstein-Wiesen
T 09573 43 95   F 09573 34 02 53
www.gasthaus-hellmuth.de
Owner: Georg Hellmuth   Founded: 1836
Output: 400hl   Availability: 1 pub
REGULAR BEER:
Hellmuth Eierberg Urstoff (5%)
SEASONAL BEER:
Hellmuth Wiesner Weiße (Apr–Nov)

Small brewery in a village of around 300 people where both pubs brew. They recently started producing a wheat beer for the warmer months.

🍺 Hellmuth

Wiesen 14, 96231 Bad Staffelstein-Wiesen
Closed Mon; Tue–Sun from 10.30; rooms available
DB Bad Staffelstein 4km, Ebensfeld 4.5km

Thomann

Altmainstraße 5, 96231 Bad Staffelstein-Wiesen
T/F 09573 52 96   www.gasthaus-thomann.de
Owners: Alfons & Brigitte Thomann
Founded: before 1870   Output: 400hl
Availability: 1 pub
REGULAR BEERS:
Thomann Dunkel

Wiesen's other brewpub. There are a couple of local buses on weekday afternoons from Bad Staffelstein and Edelsfeld but you're likely to use Shank's pony at least one way.

🍺 Thomann

Altmainstraße 5, 96231 Bad Staffelstein-Wiesen
Closed Tue; Wed – Fri 16.00–23.00, Sat–Mon 11.00–23.00; rooms available
DB Bad Staffelstein 4km, Ebensfeld 4.5km

WIESEN (Unterfranken)   619

Bürgerliches Brauhaus

Hauptstraße 97, 63831 Wiesen
T 06096 373   F 06096 10 89
www.brauhaus-wiesen.de
Founded: 1888
Output: 14,000hl   Availability: 85 pubs
REGULAR BEERS:
Wiesener Pils (4.7%)
Wiesener Öko Pils (4.7%)
Wiesener Räuber Weisse (5.2%)
Wiesener Räuber Weisse Dunkel (5.2%)
Wiesener Öko Räuber Weisse (5.3%)
Wiesener Altfränkisches Landbier (5.6%)
Wiesener Keller Bier (5.6%)
Wiesener Export (5.6%)
Wiesener Märzen (5.6%)
SEASONAL BEERS:
Wiesener Frühlingsbock (7.5%),
Wiesener Räuber Bock (7.5%)

Brewery on the northern edge of Wiesen with the tap in the centre of the village. Bus No. 46 runs from Heigenbrücken on weekdays and there's an AST service on Saturdays.

🍺 Kreuzwirt

Hauptstraße 43, 63831 Wiesen
T 06096 98 40 50
Closed Mon; Tue–Sun 11.30–14.00 & 17.30–22.00
DB Heigenbrücken 14km

WIESETH   620

Fischer

Brauerei Fischer GmbH & Co. KG
Hauptstraße 18, 91632 Wieseth
T 09822 74 11   F 09822 60 55 81
www.fischer-landbraeu.de
Owner: Angela Hüttner   Founded: 1607
Output: 3,000hl   Availability: 18 pubs
REGULAR BEERS:
Fischer Landbräu Das Helle (4.9%)
Fischer Landbräu Das Pils (4.9%)
Fischer Landbräu Das Landbier (5.2%)
Fischer Landbräu Das Spezial (5.5%)
SEASONAL BEER:
Fischer Landbräu Das Bockbier (7.4%)

Small brewery in the centre of Wieseth. We assume the tap at the brewery has now closed as they listed the following pub in Feuchtwangen (10km west of Wieseth) as the tap. If you want to go to Wieseth, take bus No. 802 from Ansbach on weekdays. Bus No. 813 runs from Dinkelsbühl to Feuchtwangen Mon–Sat.

🍺 Sindel-Buckel

Spitalstraße 28, 91555 Feuchtwangen
T 09852 25 94   **F** 09852 34 62
Daily 09.00–24.00; rooms available
DB Dinkelsbühl 13km

WIESMÜHL (Engelsberg)   621

Wieser

Brauerei Josef Wieser & Co. OHG
Wiesmühl 8, 84549 Engelsberg-Wiesmühl
T 08634 80 12   **F** 08634 80 31
www.brauerei-wieser.de   Founded: 1824
Owner: Fritz Wieser   Output: 10,000hl
REGULAR BEERS:
Wieser Edel-Pils
Wieser Export Hell
Wieser Export Dunkel
Wieser Josephi Weizen

Small brewery across the street from the station in the tiny village of Wiesmühl. The tap offers accommodation, and there's an ecology garden to visit.

🍺 Brauhaus Wiesmühl

Wiesmühl 9, 84549 Engelsberg-Wiesmühl
T 08634 625 70   **F** 08634 62 57 20
Daily from 07.00   DB Wiesmühl (Alz) 100m

WINDISCHESCHENBACH   622

Kommunbrauerei

Braugasse 1, 92670 Windischeschenbach
www.zoiglbier.de
Founded: 1455   Availability: 11 pubs
REGULAR BEER:
Zoigl

The largest communal brewery in Oberpfalz. Eleven pubs and Zoiglstuben sell the beer, three on an almost daily basis. If you time your visit right you can drink in five pubs in one day. Details of opening dates are posted on the above website. Finding Zoigl really isn't the challenge it once was...

🍺 Binner

Kleiau 3, 92670 Windischeschenbach
T 09681 14 98
DB Windischeschenbach 1km

🍺 Zum Fiedlschneider

Stadtplatz 15, 92670 Windischeschenbach
DB Windischeschenbach 950m

🍺 Beim Gloser

Lehnerberg 2, 92670 Windischeschenbach
T 09681 31 70   **F** 09681 37 21
DB Windischeschenbach 850m

🍺 Loistl

Neustädter Straße 8, 92670 Windischeschenbach
T 09681 35 07
Closed Sat & Sun; Mon–Fri from 17.00
DB Windischeschenbach 900m

🍺 Oberpfälzer Hof

Hauptstraße 1, 92670 Windischeschenbach
T 09681 788   **F** 09681 82 23
Closed Wed; Thu–Tue 11.00–14.00 & 16.00–21.30; rooms available
DB Windischeschenbach 900m

🍺 Zum Posterer

An der Alten Post 5, 92670 Windischeschenbach
T 09681 91 80 88
DB Windischeschenbach 950m

🍺 Da Roude

Stadtplatz 3, 92670 Windischeschenbach
T 09681 914 00   **F** 09681 914 11
DB Windischeschenbach 900m

🍺 Schloßhof

Schloßhof 13, 92670 Windischeschenbach
T 09681 26 60
DB Windischeschenbach 950m

🍺 Stern

Neustädter Str. 24, 92670 Windischeschenbach
DB Windischeschenbach 850m

🍺 Weißer Schwan

Pfarrplatz 1, 92670 Windischeschenbach
T 09681 12 30
Closed Sat; Sun–Fri 07.00–24.00
DB Windischeschenbach 900m

🍺 Wolframstub'n

Braugasse, 92670 Windischeschenbach
T 09681 12 41
DB Windischeschenbach 800m

Würth

Bahnhofstraße 7–9, 92670
Windischeschenbach
T 09681 12 20   **F** 09681 37 52
www.brauerei-wuerth.de
Owner: Ludwig Würth   Founded: 1880
Output: 3,000hl
REGULAR BEERS:
Würth Hell (4.5%)
Würth Pils (4.9%)
Würth Zoigl (5.3%)
Würth Dunkles Zoigl (5.3%)
Würth Spezial (5.3%)
SEASONAL BEERS:
Würth Festbier (4.9%),
Würth Weihnachtsbier (5.2%)

Small brewery south of the town centre, near
the railway station. The brewery tap is in front.

🍺 **Würth**
Bahnhofstraße 7, 92670 Windischeschenbach
T 09681 13 73
Closed Wed, Thu–Tue 09.00–23.00
DB Windischeschenbach 300m

WINKLARN   623

Betz

Johann-Metzler-Straße 19, 92559 Winklarn
T 09676 234
Owner: Maria Betz   Founded: 1890
Output: 5,000hl
REGULAR BEERS:
Betz Frauenstein Hell (4.8%)
Betz Frauenstein Pils (5%)
Betz Frauenstein Gold (5.2%)

Small village brewery. The brewery tap is 6km
north-west of Winklarn in Oberviechtach and is
run by a member of the Betz family. Bus No. 6273
runs from Nabburg to Oberviechtach on weekdays but the best service is from Weiden.

🍺 **Zur Post**
Marktplatz 1, 92526 Oberviechtach
T 09671 15 03   **F** 09671 913 85
Closed Wed; Thu–Tue 09.00–14.00 & 17.00–
23.00; rooms available
DB Nabburg 22km, Weiden 40km

WOLFSHÖHE (Neunkirchen)   624

Wolfshöher

Brauerei Wolfshöhe Weber GmbH & Co. KG
Wolfshöhe 3, 91233 Neunkirchen-Wolfshöhe
T 09153 40 40   **F** 09153 404 16
www.wolfshoeher.de
Owner: H. Stephan Weber   Founded: 1872
Output: 90,000hl   Availability: c.400 pubs
REGULAR BEERS:
Wolfshöher Leicht (2%)
Wolfshöher Hefeweissbier Leicht (2%)
Wolfshöher Premium Kellerbier (4%)
Wolfshöher Schwarzbier (4%)
Wolfshöher Pilsner (4%)
Wolfshöher Premium (4%)
Wolfshöher Hell (4.9%)
Wolfshöher Premium Pils (4.9%)
Wolfshöher Kristallweizen (4.9%)
Wolfshöher Hefeweissbier Hell (5%)
Wolfshöher Hefeweissbier Dunkel (5%)
Wolfshöher Altes (5.5%)
Wolfshöher Vollmond Bier (5.5%)
SEASONAL BEERS:
Wolfshöher Festbier (5%),
Wolfshöher Weihnachts-Festbier (5%),
Wolfshöher Annafest-Bier (5.7%)

Regional brewery in the hamlet of Wolfshöhe
that's apparently reduced the alcohol content
of many of its beers. The tap has recently re-
opened following several years out of use and
serves the Altes direct from the Lagertank.

🍺 **Bräustüberl**
Wolfshöhe 14, 91233 Neunkirchen-Wolfshöhe
T 09153 92 52 50
Closed Mon; Tue–Sun 10.00–23.00
DB Rollhofen 700m

WOLNZACH   625

Bürgerbräu

Bürgerbräu Wolnzach AG
Am Brunnen 2, 85283 Wolnzach
T/F 08442 95 55 14
www.buergerbraeu-wolnzach.de
Founded: 1999
Output: 3,500hl   Availability: 4 pubs
REGULAR BEERS:
Wolnzacher Dunkles (4.9%)

Wolnzacher Hell (5.1%)
Wolnzacher Hell Naturtrüb (5.1%)
Wolnzacher Weizen (5.2%)
SEASONAL BEERS:
Wolnzacher Festbier (5.4%), **Wolnzacher Nikolausbier** (5.4%), **Wolnzacher Maibock** (6.5%), **Wolnzacher Aktionator** (7.8%)

Microbrewery on the northern side of town. The brewery tap is on the corner of the main road and may have changed its name to Bürgerbräuwirt since the brewery first contacted the Guide. The bus service from Rohrbach appears to be poor.

🍴 **Hetzgerwirt**
Hopfenstraße 45, 85283 Wolnzach
T 08442 606 07
Closed Wed; Thu, Sat, Mon & Tue 17.00–24.00, Fri & Sun 11.00–24.00
DB Rohrbach (Ilm) 4.7km

WUNSIEDEL 626

Hönicka-Bräu

Hönicka-Bräu GmbH & Co. KG
Hofer Straße 31, 95632 Wunsiedel
T 09232 20 44   **F** 09232 20 42
www.hoenicka.de
Founded: 1778   Output: 10,000hl
REGULAR BEERS:
Hönicka Wunsiedler Weißbier Leicht (3.2%)
Hönicka Unser Landbier (4.8%)
Hönicka Luisenburg Pils (4.9%)
Hönicka Wunsiedler Weißbier (5.4%)
Hönicka Wonnesud (5.4%)
SEASONAL BEERS:
Hönicka Hönickator Doppelbock (7.4%)

Small brewery on the western side of Wunsiedel. There's no official tap but the beers are easily found in the town. We refuse to believe the bus service is as bad as it appears on www.bahn.de
DB Wunsiedel-Holenbrunn 3.5km

WÜRGAU (Scheßlitz) 627

Hartmann

Fränkische-Schweiz-Straße 26, 96110 Scheßlitz-Würgau
T 09542 92 03 00   **F** 09542 92 03 09
www.brauerei-hartmann.de

Owner: Ambros Hartmann   Founded: 1550
Output: 15,000hl
REGULAR BEERS:
Hartmann Hell (4.8%)
Hartmann Edelpils (5.2%)
Hartmann Felsentrunk (5.2%)
Hartmann Felsen-Weisse (5.2%)
Hartmann Erbschänk 1550 (5.2%)
SEASONAL BEERS:
Hartmann Felsenkeller (4.9%, summer),
Hartmann Festbier (5.5%, Christmas),
Hartmann Bock Hell (7%, winter)
Hartmann Bock (7%, winter)

Brewery and tap on the main road through the village. Bus No. 8231 runs daily from Bamberg but the service is fairly limited, particularly at the weekend.

🍴 **Hartmann**
Fränkische-Schweiz-Straße 26,
96110 Scheßlitz-Würgau
Closed Tue; Wed–Mon 08.00–24.00; rooms available
DB Bamberg 18km

WÜRZBURG 628

Brauhaus

Burkarderstraße 2–4, 97082 Würzburg-Altstadt
T 0931 431 59   **F** 0931 4148 63
www.brauhausbar.de
Owner: Michael Will   Founded: 1989
Output: 1,000hl   Availability: 1 pub
REGULAR BEERS:
Brauhaus Hell
Brauhaus Dunkel
Brauhaus Weizen
SEASONAL BEER:
Brauhaus Bock

Formerly known as the Fränkisches Brauhaus am Spitäle, this brewpub opposite the old bridge over the river has swapped Franconia for America. If you don't fancy the trek from the station, take a tram to the Rathaus and walk across the bridge.

🍴 **Brauhaus**
Burkarderstraße 2–4, 97082 Würzburg-Altstadt
Closed Sun; Mon–Sat 20.00–01.00
Tram Rathaus 400m
DB Würzburg Hbf 1.6km

Würzburger Hofbräu

Höchberger Straße 28, 97082 Würzburg-Zellerau
T 0931 410 90   **F** 0931 410 91 32
www.wuerzburger-hofbraeu.de
Owner: Brau Holding International, München
Founded: 1643   Output: 350,000hl
REGULAR BEERS:
Würzburger Hofbräu Light (2.9%)
Julius Echter Leichte Weiße (2.9%)
Würzburger Hofbräu Premium Pilsner (4.9%)
Würzburger Hofbräu Schwarzbier (4.9%)
Würzburger 1643 Original Lager (4.9%)
Julius Echter Hefe-Weißbier Hell (4.9%)
Julius Echter Weißbier Dunkel (4.9%)
Julius Echter Kristallweizen (4.9%)
Würzburger Hofbräu Export (5.2%)
SEASONAL BEERS:
Würzburger Jubiläumsbier Dunkel (4.9%),
Würzburger Hofbräu Festbier (5.9%, Nov–Dec),
Würzburger Hofbräu Sympator (7.9%)
FOR FÜRSTLICHE BRAUEREI, WÄCHTERSBACH:
Fürst Ysenburg Schwarzbier (4.5%),
Wächtersbacher Fürsten-Pils (4.8%),
Wächtersbacher Hopfen Herbes (4.8%),
Wächtersbacher Export Classic (4.9%),
Wächtersbacher Jubiläumsbier (4.9%)
FOR BRAUEREI HEIL, TÜCKELHAUSEN:
Jagdherren Pils (4.8%)
FOR WERNER BRÄU, POPPENHAUSEN:
Werner Premium Light Pils (2.7%), Werner
Altfränkisch Landbier (4.9%), Werner Privat
Diät Pils (4.9%), Werner Premium Pilsener
(4.9%), Werner Schwarze Premium (5%),
Werner Export (5.2%), Werner Hefe-Weisse Hell
(5.2%), Werner Hefe-Weisse Dunkel (5.2%),
Werner Kristall Weizen (5.2%)
SEASONAL BEERS:
Werner Festbier (5.2%),
Werner Privat Bock Dunkel

Large brewery that we believe brews for several
other breweries. The only slight doubts we have
are the Werner beers but we have pretty good
information this is where they come from. We
think Lohrer beers are still brewed in Lohr but
are prepared to be proved wrong.

🍺 Hofbräukeller

Jägerstraße 17, 97082 Würzburg-Zellerau
T 0931 4 29 70   **F** 0931 41 36 69
Daily from 10.30
Tram Nos. 2 & 4 Wörthstraße 250m
DB Würzburg Hbf 2.1km

ZEIL (Main) 629

Göller

Brauerei Göller 'Zur Alten Freyung'
Brewery: Speiersgasse 21, 97475 Zeil
Office: Wildgarten 12, 97475 Zeil
T 09524 300 40   **F** 09524 30 04 22
www.brauerei-goeller.de
Owner: Franz-Josef Göller   Founded: 1514
Output: 50,000hl   Availability: 60 pubs
REGULAR BEERS:
Göller Brotzeitseidla (4.3%)
Göller Hausbrauerbier (4.3%)
Göller Lager (4.9%)
Göller Kellerbier (4.9%)
Göller Original (4.9%)
Göller Pilsner (4.9%)
Göller Steinhauer Weisse (4.9%)
Göller Dunkel (5.2%)
Göller Rauchbier (5.2%)
Göller Freyungs-Weisse (5.2%)
Göller Dunkle Weisse (5.2%)
SEASONAL BEERS:
Göller Leichte Weisse (3.7%, summer),
Göller Herbst Bock (7%, Oct–Mar),
Göller Weizen Bock (7%, Oct–Mar)

Brewery which has grown so large the administrative, filtering and filling departments have
moved to new premises on the western edge of
town. The tap is the only one we've seen with
vines growing on the front.

🍺 Göller

Speiersgasse 21, 97475 Zeil
T 09524 95 54
Closed Tue from September to May;
Wed–Mon 09.00–01.00
DB Zeil 900m

ZELL 630

Schloßbrauerei Schwarzfischer

Oberzeller Straße 1, 93199 Zell
T 09468 325   **F** 09468 103 75
Owner: Alfons Schwarzfischer   Founded: 1825
Output: 3,000hl
REGULAR BEERS:
Schwarzfischer Vollbier Hell
Schwarzfischer Pils
Schwarzfischer Edelstoff

SEASONAL BEER:
Schwarzfischer Festbier

Small brewery and tap in the centre of the village. Despite its distance from Zell, Regensburg is the best place to start if you've no transport of your own. Buses Nos. 219 and 818 run on weekdays.

🍺 **Schwarzfischer**
Oberzeller Straße 1, 93199 Zell
Closed Mon; Tue–Sun 09.00–24.00; rooms available   DB Regensburg Hbf 35km

ZENTBECHHOFEN
(Höchstadt)   631

Friedel
Höchstadter Straße 1, 91315 Höchstadt-
Zentbechhofen   **T** 09502 209   **F** 09502 42 90
Owner: Michaela Baier   Founded: 1467
Output: 2,000hl
REGULAR BEERS:
Friedel Vollbier (4.8%)
Friedel Pilsener (5%)
Friedel Märzen (5.3%)
Friedel Lagerbier (5.5%)
SEASONAL BEER:
Friedel Festbier, Friedel Bock

Brewpub in the village of Zentbechhofen, not the easiest place to get to and from by bus. There's one a day on weekdays from both Bamberg and Hirschaid but you're likely to have to return another way.

🍺 **Friedel**
Höchstadter Straße 1,
91315 Höchstadt-Zentbechhofen
Closed Tue; Wed, Thu & Mon 16.00–23.00,
Fri–Sun 10.00–23.00
DB Hirschaid 11km, Bamberg 20km

ZETTMANNSDORF
(Schönbrunn)   632

Seelmann
Zettmannsdorfer Hauptstraße 18,
96185 Schönbrunn-Zettmannsdorf
T 09546 66 84   **F** 09546 87 42
E georg.seelmann@t-online.de
Owner: Georg Seelmann   Founded: 1847
Output: 1,000hl   Availability: 1 pub

REGULAR BEERS:
Seelmann Bräu Zwickel
Seelmann Bräu Export
SEASONAL BEER:
Seelmann Bräu Bock (Nov–Jan)

Brewpub whose beers are only available draught. There are plenty of buses from Bamberg (No. 8244) on weekday afternoons but only one out of the village after opening, and that involves a change. The guide understands that the brewery may have closed.

🍺 **Seelmann**
Zettmannsdorfer Hauptstraße 18, 96185
Schönbrunn-Zettmannsdorf
Closed Mon; Tue–Fri from 16.00,
Sat, Sun & hols from 10.00   DB Bamberg 22km

ZIRNDORF   633

Zirndorf
Brauerei Zirndorf GmbH
Rote Straße 8–10, 90513 Zirndorf
T 0911 977 60   **F** 0911 977 63 70
www.zirndorfer.de
Owner: Oetker Gruppe AG   Founded: 1674
Output: 80,000hl
REGULAR BEERS:
Zirndorfer Landbier (5%)
Zirndorfer Landweizen (5.3%)

Large brewery close to the centre of Zirndorf that's now owned by the Brau und Brunnen, part of the Oetker empire. Despite rumours to the contrary we're pretty sure they still brew here.

🍺 **Zur Lustigen Lena**
Rote Straße 8, 90513 Zirndorf
T 0911 689 05 86   **F** 0911 689 05 87
Closed Mon; Tue–Sat 17.00–01.00,
Sun 11.00–01.00   DB Zirndorf 350m

ZÖSCHINGEN   634

Behnle Bräu
Wehrstraße 14, 89447 Zöschingen
T 09077 95 03 11   **F** 09077 95 03 15
www.behnle-braeu.de
Owner: Thorsten Behnle-Napierala
Founded: 2002   Output: 500hl
Availability: 6 pubs

REGULAR BEERS:
Behnle Bräu Kellerbier (5.5%)
Behnle Bräu Export Hell (5.5%)
Behnle Bräu Weizen Hell (5.5%)
Behnle Bräu Weizen Dunkel (5.5%)
SEASONAL BEERS:
Behnle Bräu Weizenbock (6.5%),
Behnle Bräu Weihnachtsnock (6.8%)

Microbrewery in a village close to the Bavarian border with Baden-Württemberg. There's no tap at the brewery but they do have a drinks market there. All six pubs that sell the beers are over the border. We've listed the Goldenes Rad in Langenau, 25km south-west of Zöschingen, as that was the first on the list the brewery sent us.

🍎 Goldenes Rad
Hindenburgstraße 89, 89129 Langenau
T 07345 66 93
Closed Tue; Wed–Mon 10.00–14.00 & 17.00–24.00
DB Langenau (Württemberg) 1.2km

ZUSMARSHAUSEN 635

Schwarzbräu

Schwarzbräu GmbH & Co. Verwaltungs KG
Marktplatz 6, 86441 Zusmarshausen
T 08291 880   **F** 08291 88 44
www.schwarzbraeu.de   Founded: 1648
Output: 130,000hl   Availability: 118 pubs
REGULAR BEERS:
Schwarzbräu Light & Fit (2.8%)
Schwarzbräu Weizen Light (2.9%)
Schwarzbräu Feines Helles (4.9%)
Schwarzbräu Dunkel (5%)
Schwarzbräu Pilsener (5%)
Schwarzbräu Schweden Pils (5%)
Schwarzbräu Keller Pils (5%)
Schwarzbräu Exquisit (5.3%)
Schwarzbräu Schweden Weizen (5.3%)
Schwarzbräu Weizen Hell (5.4%)
Schwarzbräu Weizen Dunkel (5.4%)
Schwarzbräu Urtyp (5.5%)

SEASONAL BEER:
Schwarzbräu Schweden Bock Dunkel (7.1%)

Large brewery and tap on the market square. If you want to come here by bus you'd be best off going to Augsburg. Route No. 506 runs from the main station Mon–Sat.

🍎 Schwarzbräu
Marktplatz 4, 86441 Zusmarshausen
T 08291 10 29
Closed Thu; Fri–Wed 09.00–22.00
DB Augsburg Hbf 25km

ZWIESEL 636

Dampfbierbrauerei

1. Dampfbierbrauerei Zwiesel GmbH & Co. KG
Regener Straße 9–11, 94227 Zwiesel
T 09922 846 60   **F** 09922 84 66 55
www.dampfbier.de
Owner: Dr. Pfeffer
Founded: 1889
Output: 20,000hl
REGULAR BEERS:
Pfefferbräu Hell (4.9%)
Pfefferbräu Nationalpark Pilsener (5%)
Pfefferbräu Dampfbier (5%)
Pfefferbräu Fahnenschwinger Export (5.2%)
Pfefferbräu Hefe-Weisse (5.3%)
Pfefferbräu Dunkles-Weissbier (5.3%)
Pfefferbräu Wolfgang Weisse
SEASONAL BEERS:
Pfefferbräu Bock (6.5%),
Pfefferbräu Silvator (7.5%)

'Steam beer' brewery on the south-western edge of Zwiesel, a town famous for its glass and winter sports. The town's other brewery, Janka-Bräu, closed on New Year's Eve 2004.

🍎 Bräustüberl
Regener Straße 6, 94227 Zwiesel
T 09922 66 86   **F** 09922 86 96 35
Closed Mon; Tue–Sun 10.00–23.00
DB Zwiesel (Bayern) 1.5km

Berlin

GERMANY'S LARGEST CITY (pop. 3,388,000) and once again its capital, Berlin is one of the country's three city states (Bremen and Hamburg are the others), surrounded by Brandenburg. To say its recent history has been turbulent is an understatement – it's hard to think of many cities that endured quite what Berlin went through during the 20th century. Happily, the scars are starting to heal and the united Berlin today is a vibrant, confident city and a fantastic place to spend a few days or more.

Many first-time visitors are struck by just how green the place is – a quarter of the city area is either woodland or water. Another feature is the general lack of very high buildings – although the 368m tall *Fernsehturm* (TV tower) on Alexanderplatz is a prominent exception. Museums, galleries and other tourist attractions abound and are far too numerous to mention here; you'll find them in any guidebook. Accommodation is plentiful but can be expensive.

Berlin's nightlife is legendary and will probably live up to your expectations. The best areas for clubs and late/all-night bars are currently Mitte and Prenzlauer Berg, as well as Kreuzberg and around Hackescher Markt.

The beer scene is dominated by Kindl and Schultheiss, although the former was due to close as we went to press, with most production likely to move to the latter. In addition, Berlin still has the comparatively small Bürgerbräu and more than a dozen modern brewpubs and microbreweries. We've listed each entry under its district to help you find them. Travel information can be found in the city's pub guide *(see pp. 431).*

CHARLOTTENBURG

Luisen-Bräu

Luisenplatz 1, 10585 Berlin-Charlottenburg
T 030 341 93 88   **F** 030 342 50 66
www.luisenbraeu.com
Owner: Karl Heinz Grießbach   Founded: 1987
Output: 1,600hl   Availability: 1 pub
REGULAR BEERS:
Luisen-Bräu Hell (4.8%)
Luisen-Bräu Dunkel (4.8%)
SEASONAL BEER:
Luisen-Bräu Rauchbier (5.2%)

The oldest of the city's modern brewpubs, Luisen-Bräu is in the western district of Charlottenburg, close to the palace. The wheat beer sold in the pub is brewed elsewhere.

🍺 **Luisen-Bräu**
Luisenplatz 1, 10585 Berlin-Charlottenburg
Fri & Sat 09.00–02.00, Sun–Thu 09.00–01.00
🇺 U7 Richard-Wagner-Platz 600m
🇸 Berlin-Charlottenburg 1.7km

FRIEDRICHSHAGEN

Bürgerbräu

Berliner Bürgerbräu GmbH
Müggelseedamm 164–166,
12587 Berlin-Friedrichshagen
T 030 64 08 21 11   **F** 030 645 31 35
www.berliner-buergerbraeu.de
Founded: 1869   Output: 150,000hl
REGULAR BEERS:
Bürgerbräu Hauptmann von Köpenick (5%)

Berliner Bürgerbräu Premium Pils (5%)
Bürgerbräu Bernauer Schwarzbier (5.2%)
Berliner Bürgerbräu Rotkehlchen (5.3%)
SEASONAL BEERS:
Berliner Bürgerbräu Dunkler Bock (6.8%),
Berliner Bürgerbräu Maibock (6.8%)
FOR KADEWE, BERLIN:
KaDeWe Premium Pilsner (5%)

Large brewery in the east of the city, on the north-western shore of the Großer Müggelsee. They still brew Berliner Weisse but it's only available in cans with syrup already added. They also brew for KaDeWe, Berlin's luxury department store.

🍴 Bräustübl

Müggelseedamm 164,
12587 Berlin-Friedrichshagen
T 030 645 57 16
Closed Mon; Tue–Sat 12.00–24.00,
Sun 11.00–24.00
Nos. 60 & 61 Müggelseedamm/
   Bölschestraße 100m
Ⓢ S3 Berlin-Friedrichshagen 1.2km

HOHENSCHÖNHAUSEN

Schultheiss

Berliner Schultheiss-Brauerei GmbH
Indira-Ghandi-Straße 66–69,
13053 Berlin-Hohenschönhausen
T 030 960 90   F 030 960 92 80
www.schultheiss.de
Owner: Oetker Gruppe AG   Founded: 1842
Output: 1,300,000hl
REGULAR BEERS:
Schultheiss Original Berliner Weisse (3.3%)
Schultheiss Diät Schankbier (3.8%)
Schultheiss Lager (5%)
Schultheiss Lager Schwarz (5%)
Schultheiss Pilsener (5%)
Aecht Patzenhofer Premium Pilsner (5%)
SEASONAL BEER:
Schultheiss Urbock (6.5%)
FOR BERLINER PILSENER, BERLIN:
Berliner Pilsener (5%)
FOR ENGELHARDT BRAUEREI, BERLIN:
Engelhardt Pilsener (5%)

Very large, modern brewery opposite Weißensee cemetery. The only tap we're aware of is inside the brewery and only open to brewery visitors

but we promise you won't have any problem finding Schultheiss beer on sale in Berlin!
No. M13 Sportforum 100m
Ⓢ Landsberger Allee 2km

KÖPENICK

Schloßplatzbrauerei

Schloßplatzbrauerei Köpenick
Brewery: Schloßplatz, 12555 Berlin-Köpenick
Office: Birkheidering 6, 12527 Berlin-Treptow
T 030 674 70 15   F 030 674 06 46
Founded: 08.04.2004   Availability: 1 pub
REGULAR BEERS:
Schloßplatzbrauerei Hell (5.3%)
Schloßplatzbrauerei Kupfer (5.3%)
SEASONAL BEERS:
Schloßplatzbrauerei Frühjahr Märzen (5.8%),
Schloßplatzbrauerei Frühjahrsbock (6.2%),
Schloßplatzbrauerei Herbstbock Dunkel (6.2%),
Schloßplatzbrauerei Winterbock Hell (6.2%),
Schloßplatzbrauerei Rauchbock (6.8%),
Schloßplatzbrauerei Doppelbock (7.2%),
Schloßplatzbrauerei Doppelrauchbock (7.6%)

One of the oddest breweries we're aware of, this tiny brewpub is in a glass-fronted building in the middle of Köpenick's central square. They seem to be fond of Bocks.

🍴 Schloßplatz

Schloßplatz, 12555 Berlin-Köpenick
T 0176 24 39 95 68 (mobile)   Daily 12.00–23.00
Schloßplatz Köpenick 50m,
   Rathaus Köpenick 80m
Ⓢ S3 Berlin-Köpenick 1.5km

KREUZBERG

Südstern

Hasenheide 69, 10967 Berlin-Kreuzberg
T 030 69 00 16 24
www.brauhaus-suedstern.de
Founded: 31.12.2005
REGULAR BEERS:
Südstern Hell
Südstern Dunkel
Südstern Weizen

Brewpub backing onto the Hasenheide park. It opened as Brauhaus Braams in 2002, but the original incarnation closed in 2004. Seasonal beers are brewed in addition to the above but we don't yet have details.

🍴 Südstern
Hasenheide 69, 10967 Berlin-Kreuzberg
Daily 10.00–01.00
[U] U7 Südstern 150m

MITTE

Georgbræu

Spreeufer 4, 10178 Berlin-Mitte
T 030 242 42 44   **F** 030 242 58 70
www.georgbraeu.de
Owner: Peter Härig   Founded: 1992
Output: 1,500hl   Availability: 1 pub
REGULAR BEERS:
Georg Pils Hell
Georg Pils Dunkel

Large brewpub next to the river Spree near the Nikolai-Kirche in an area of the city that's very popular with tourists. Just the two regular beers and no seasonals.

🍴 Georgbræu
Spreeufer 4, 10178 Berlin-Mitte
Jan–Mar: daily from 12.00;
Apr–Dec: daily from 10.00
Nos. M4, M5 & M6 Spandauer/
    Marienkirche 400m
[U] Ⓢ DB Alexanderplatz 700m

Lemkes

Lemkes Spezialitätenbrauerei
S-Bahnbogen 143, Dircksenstraße,
10178 Berlin-Mitte
T 030 24 72 87 27   **F** 030 24 72 87 28
www.brauerei-lemke.de
Owner: Oliver Lemke   Founded: 1999
Output: 500hl   Availability: 2 pubs
REGULAR BEERS:
Lemke Original
Lemke Pilsner
SEASONAL BEERS:
Lemke Champagnerbier (Jul)**, Lemke Zwickel** (Jul)**, Lemke Schwarzbier, Lemke Altbier, Lemke Pale Ale, Lemke Amber Ale, Lemke Red Ale, Lemke Schwanbier, Lemke Weizen** (May)**, Lemke Porter, Lemke Stout, Lemke Märzen** (Mar)**,**

Lemke Festbier, Lemke Weihnachtsbier (Dec)**, Lemke Weizenbock, Lemke Maibock** (May)**, Lemke Herbst-Festbock** (Oct)**, Lemke Eisbock** (Jan)**, Lemke Barley Wine**

Adventurous brewpub in an arch beneath the S-Bahn, producing a large variety of seasonal beers. Those we're aware of are listed above, but there are more. They also own nearby Brauhaus Mitte.

🍴 Lemkes
S-Bahnbogen 143, Dircksenstraße,
10178 Berlin-Mitte
Daily from 12.00
Ⓢ Hackescher Markt 100m

🍴 Tiergartenquelle
S-Bahnbogen 432, Bachstraße 6,
10555 Berlin-Tiergarten
Mon–Fri from 17.00, Sat & Sun from 12.00
[U] U9 Hansaplatz 500m   Ⓢ Tiergarten 100m

Marcus-Bräu

Mikrobrauerei Barkowsky – Brauhaus Alexanderplatz 'Marcus-Bräu'
Münzstraße 1–3, 10178 Berlin-Mitte
T 030 247 69 85   **F** 030 67 81 94 33
www.marcus-braeu.de
Owners: the Barkowsky family   Founded: 2000
Output: 150hl   Availability: 1 pub
REGULAR BEERS:
Marcus-Bräu Pils
Marcus-Bräu Preußen Dunkel
SEASONAL BEERS:
Marcus-Bräu Honey-Sun, Marcus-Bräu Euro-Pils, Marcus-Bräu Bock Hell, Marcus-Bräu Bock Dunkel

Very small brewpub near Alexanderplatz. The tiny brewery is built into the bar. They also supply home-brewing kits.

🍴 Marcus-Bräu
Münzstraße 1–3, 10178 Berlin
Mon–Fri 11.00–03.00, Sat & Sun 16.00–03.00
[U] Ⓢ DB Berlin Alexanderplatz 250m

Mitte

Brauhaus Mitte GmbH
Karl-Liebknecht-Straße 13, 10178 Berlin-Mitte
T 030 30 87 89 89   **F** 030 30 87 89 88
www.brauhaus-mitte.de
Owner: Oliver Lemke   Founded: 1993
Output: 1,700hl

REGULAR BEERS:
Brauhaus Pils
Brauhaus Dunkel
Brauhaus Hefeweizen Hell
SEASONAL BEERS:
Brauhaus Zwickel (Jul),
Brauhaus Märzen (Mar),
Brauhaus Maibock (May),
Brauhaus Weihnachtsbock (Dec)

First-floor brewpub on the southern side of the
S-Bahn, west of Alexanderplatz station. Known
as Leopold's Brauhaus until it was acquired by
Lemke's in 2004.

Mitte
Karl-Liebknecht-Straße 13,
10178 Berlin-Mitte   Daily 11.00–24.00
U S DB Berlin Alexanderplatz 150m

---

*We intend to post regular updates to the
Guide at* **www.german-breweries.com**
*If you find anything you think we should
be told about we can be contacted at*
GermanBreweries@aol.com.

NEUKÖLLN

Kindl
Berliner Kindl Brauerei
Werbellinstraße 50, 12053 Berlin-Neukölln
T 030 68 99 20   **F** 030 68 99 22 12
www.berliner-kindl.de
Owner: Oetker Gruppe AG   Founded: 1872
Output: 1,350,000hl
REGULAR BEERS:
Berliner Kindl Weisse (2.7%)
Berliner Kindl Pils (4.6%)
Potsdamer Rex Pils (4.6%)
Märkischer Landmann Schwarzbier (4.9%)
Berliner Kindl Jubiläums Pilsener (5%)
SEASONAL BEERS:
Berliner Kindl Bock Hell (7%),
Berliner Kindl Bock Dunkel (7%)
FOR BÄRENBIER VERTRIEB, BERLIN:
Bärenpils (4.6%)

Very large brewery that's sadly planned for
closure in 2006. Beer production will move to at
least one of Oetker's numerous other breweries,
with Schultheiss likely to brew the lion's share.

Ⓤ U8 Boddinstraße 430m
Ⓢ Hermannstraße 1.4km

Brauhaus in Rixdorf

Glasower Straße 27, 12051 Berlin-Neukölln
T 030 626 88 80   **F** 030 62 84 00 73
www.brauhaus-in-rixdorf.de
Owners: Benjamin Lehmann & Martin Mundt
Founded: 1988   Output: 800hl
Availability: 2 pubs
REGULAR BEERS:
Rixdorfer Hell (5.2%)
Rixdorfer Dunkel (5.3%)
SEASONAL BEERS:
Rixdorfer Weizenbier (5.2%, summer),
Rixdorfer Festbier (5.5%), **Rixdorfer
Weihnachtsbier** (5.6%, Christmas), **Rixdorfer
Doppelbock** (6.1%, winter)

Brewpub in a former house in the south-eastern
district of Neukölln. The seasonal Doppelbock
is much weaker than most.

🍺 Brauhaus in Rixdorf
Glasower Straße 27, 12051 Berlin-Neukölln
Closed Mon in winter; (Mon) Tue-Sat 12.00–01.00,
Sun 10.00–23.00
Ⓤ Ⓢ Hermannstraße 600m

Schoppe Bräu

Waldowstraße 16, 13156 Berlin-
Niederschönhausen
T 030 32 52 85 51   **F** 030 32 52 85 52
www.schoppebraeu.de
Owner: Thorsten Schoppe
Founded: 01.10.2004

It's hard to keep track of this one. Thorsten
Schoppe was involved with the Bier-Company
until they closed in 2003. In 2002 he founded
Brauhaus Braams but that closed in 2004. Then
came this tiny brewery which specialises in
contract-brewing very small quantities of beer,
generally for private customers (hence the lack
of a beer listing). On the eve of 2006 Braams re-
opened, this time as Brauhaus Südstern. Whether
brewing survives here remains to be seen.
🚋 No. M1 Waldemarstraße 100m
Ⓤ Ⓢ Pankow 2.9km

Brauhaus in Spandau

Neuendorfer Straße 1, 13585 Berlin-Spandau
T 030 353 90 70   **F** 030 35 39 07 11
www.brauhaus-spandau.de
Founded: 1994
Output: 2,400hl   Availability: 1 pub
REGULAR BEER:
Spandauer Havelbräu (5.2%)
SEASONAL BEERS:
Spandauer Landbier (Aug), **Spandauer Dunkles
Weizen** (Jun–Jul), **Spandauer Potz-Blitz-Bier** (Jan),
Spandauer Rotbier (Feb), **Spandauer Märzen**
(Mar), **Spandauer Mondscheinbier** (Apr),
Spandauer Weihnachtsfestbier, **Spandauer
Maibock** (May), **Spandauer Maronator** (Sep–Nov)

Sprawling, two-storey brewpub in the former
laundry of Spandau barracks. Oddly enough,
the red-brick building looks like it was designed
to be a brewery.

🍺 Brauhaus im Spandau
Neuendorfer Straße 1, 13585 Berlin-Spandau
Fri & Sat 11.00–01.00, Sun 10.00–24.00,
Mon 16.00–24.00, Tue–Thu 11.00–24.00;
rooms available
Ⓤ U7 Altstadt Spandau 200m
Ⓢ Berlin-Spandau 900m

Alter Fritz

Karolinenstraße 12, 13507 Berlin-Tegel
T 030 433 50 10   **F** 030 433 82 27
www.restaurant-alter-fritz.de
Owner: Alter Fritz Gaststättenbetriebs GmbH
Founded: 1992   Output: 1,000hl
Availability: 1 pub
REGULAR BEERS:
Alter Fritz Kupfer
Alter Fritz Messing
SEASONAL BEERS:
Alter Fritz Weizen (summer),
Alter Fritz Bockbier (winter)

Single-storey brewpub in the north-western
district of Tegel. The building dates from 1410.
Don't be misled – Tegel airport is around 7km
south of here by road.

📖 Alter Fritz

Karolinenstraße 12, 13507 Berlin-Tegel
Fri 16.00–02.00, Sat 11.00–02.00,
Sun 11.00–01.00, Mon–Thu 16.00–01.00
U U6 Alt-Tegel 1.1km S S8 Berlin-Tegel 1.6km

TIERGARTEN

Brewbaker

S-Bahnbogen 415, Flensburger Straße,
10557 Berlin-Tiergarten
T 030 39 90 51 56
www.brewbaker.de
Owner: Michael Schwab   Founded: 2005
REGULAR BEERS:
Brewbaker Pils
Brewbaker Weizen

Small, recently opened pub and brewery under
the S-Bahn near Tiergarten station. The beer
range always includes a Pils and a Weizen but
the recipes change with the seasons, becoming
darker in the winter. There should be a different
special beer each week. Closes for a week over
Christmas and New Year.

📖 Brewbaker

S-Bahnbogen 415, Flensburger Straße,
10557 Berlin-Tiergarten
T 030 39 90 51 56
Mon–Fri 10.00–23.00, Sat & Sun 16.00–23.00
S Bellevue 100m

Lindenbräu

Lindenbräu am Potsdamerplatz
Sony Center, Bellevuestraße 3–5,
10785 Berlin-Tiergarten
T 030 25 75 12 80   F 030 25 75 12 99
www.lindenbraeu-berlin.de
Owner: Dr. Peter Wunderlich   Founded: 2000
Output: 2,000hl   Availability: 1 pub

REGULAR BEER:
Hofbräu Weiße

Large brewpub in the Sony Center. Hofbräuhaus
Traunstein had some involvement initially but
we think it's now independent. Express trains
should be stopping at the new station downstairs by the time you read this.

📖 Lindenbräu

Sony Center, Bellevue Straße 3–5,
10785 Berlin-Tiergarten
Fri & Sat 11.00–02.00, Sun–Thu 11.00–01.00
U S Potsdamer Platz 200m

WEDDING

Eschenbräu

Triftstraße 67, 13353 Berlin-Wedding
T 030 462 68 37
www.eschenbraeu.de
Owner: Martin Eschenbrenner   Founded: 2002
REGULAR BEERS:
Eschenbräu Pils
Eschenbräu Dunkles
Eschenbräu Weizen
SEASONAL BEERS:
Eschenbräu Dunkler Bock (Feb), **Eschenbräu
Rauchbier** (Easter), **Eschenbräu Hopfenblume**
(Apr), **Eschenbräu Bayrisch Hell** (Jun),
Eschenbräu Roter Wedding (Jul), **Eschenbräu
Schwarze Molle** (Sep), **Eschenbräu Alter
Schwede** (Dec)

Microbrewery off the south side of Triftstraße,
behind a block of flats. Below is a Bierkeller and
there's a beer garden opposite.

📖 Eschenbräu

Triftstraße 67, 13353 Berlin-Wedding
Mon–Fri from 17.00, Sat & Sun from 19.00
U U6 Wedding 500m S Wedding 600m

Brandenburg

THE LARGEST OF EASTERN Germany's six states, Brandenburg also surrounds the smallest, Berlin, although the latter has a larger population. In 1996 there was a referendum on the question of whether the two should merge. Berliners voted in favour but Brandenburgers rejected the resolution by a decisive majority.

Although you could be forgiven for thinking otherwise, the state capital is Potsdam. Sometimes called the Versailles of the north, this palace-laden city is Brandenburg's most popular tourist destination. Other attractions include the town of Brandenburg itself and the Spreewald, a large wetland area to the east of Lübbenau, where transport is largely by boat.

Almost three-quarters of the breweries here are modern brewpubs, the majority less than ten years old, but there should be plenty to occupy the enthusiast, particularly lovers of dark beers.

Transport: Public transport in the state is good, Brandenburg's rail network having suffered less from closures than others in the east since the fall of the Wall. For €24 up to five adults can travel on most train, tram, bus and underground services in Berlin and Brandenburg. Tickets are valid from 09.00 until 03.00 the following day, Monday to Friday, and all day at the weekend. As usual, check which services are valid before travelling.

DESSOW 638

Dessow

Brauerei Dessow, Zweigniederlassung der Oettinger Brauerei GmbH
Neuruppiner Straße 2, 16845 Dessow
T 033974 650   **F** 033974 651 45
Owner: Oettinger Gruppe   Founded: 1777
Output: 250,000hl
REGULAR BEERS:
Märkisches Pils (4.9%)
Kyritzer Mord und Totschlag (5.3%)
Märkisches Export (5.4%)
Märkisches Urbräu (5.6%)
SEASONAL BEER:
Märkischer Bock (6.8%)
FOR OETTINGER, OETTINGEN:
Original Oettinger Leicht (2.8%),
Original Oettinger Leichte Weiße (2.8%),
Original Oettinger Vollbier Hell (4.7%),
Original Oettinger Pils (4.7%),
Original Oettinger Alt (4.9%),
Original Oettinger Gold (4.9%),
Original Oettinger Schwarzbier (4.9%),
Original Oettinger Hefeweißbier (4.9%),
Original Oettinger Dunkles Weißbier (4.9%),
Original Oettinger Kristall Weizen (4.9%),
Original Oettinger Export (5.4%),
Original Oettinger Urtyp (5.6%)
SEASONAL BEER:
Original Oettinger Winterbier (5.6%)

Large brewery in the village of Dessow. In common with the other breweries in the Group, Oettinger beers are brewed here according to demand. Refreshingly, the bottles state the brewery of origin. We don't think there's a tap.
DB Dessow (Mark) 600m

DREBKAU 639

Kirchers Brauhaus

Brauhausstraße 42, 03116 Drebkau
T 035602 701 **F** 035602 223 88
Owners: Andreas & Thomas Kircher
Founded: 1996 Output: 1,600hl
Availability: c.25 pubs
REGULAR BEERS:
Kirchers Spreewald Porter (4.8%)
Kirchers Spreewald Lager (4.9%)
Kirchers Spreewald Dunkel (4.9%)

Microbrewery and pub in the centre of Drebkau, a small town in southern Brandenberg's brown-coal field. The tap currently opens at weekends only but they do supply a number of other local pubs.

🍺 **Kirchers Brauhaus**
Brauhausstraße 42, 03116 Drebkau
Closed Mon–Fri; Sat & Sun 11.00–22.00
DB Drebkau 400m

FINSTERWALDE 640

Radigk's

Radigk's Wirtshausbräu
Sonnewalder Straße 13, 03238 Finsterwalde
T 03531 22 86 **F** 03531 70 99 38
www.radigks.de
Owner: Bernhard Radigk Founded: 1997
Output: 800hl
REGULAR BEERS:
Radigk's Pilsener (5.1%),
Radigk's Spezial (5.1%).
SEASONAL BEERS:
Radigk's Radikator (6.8%)
Radigk's 111 (7%)

Brewpub with two bars – the Brauhaus and Wirtshaus. The Brauhaus (which oddly enough, features the brewery) opens at 18.00. Radigk's is on the opposite side of the railway to the town centre.

🍺 **Radigk's**
Sonnewalder Straße 13, 03238 Finsterwalde
Closed Mon; Tue–Sun from 11.00
DB Finsterwalde (Niederlausitz) 400m

Sieben Brunnen

Brunnen Straße 2, 03238 Finsterwalde
T 03531 85 26 www.siebenbrunnen.de
Founded: 2002
REGULAR BEER:
Sieben Brunnen Dunkel

The Seven Springs pub and bowling alley is to the west of Finsterwalde's centre. They installed a small brewery in 2002 and currently brew just one beer, a dark.

🍺 **Sieben Brunnen**
Brunnen Straße 2, 03238 Finsterwalde
Closed Mon; Tue–Sun 12.00–14.30 & from 16.00
DB Finsterwalde (Niederlausitz) 1.1km

FORST (Lausitz) 641

Worrich's Pub

Worrich's Pub – 1. Forster Brauhaus
Albertstraße 20, 03149 Forst (Lausitz)
T 03562 98 41 22 Founded: 2004
REGULAR BEER:
Schwarze Jule

Small brewpub near the station. The Polish border runs along the Lausitzer Neiße river, less than a mile from the pub. The beer commemorates the S-Bahn/narrow-gauge train, Black Jules, that ran in this little town until 1965.

🍺 **Worrich's Pub**
Albertstraße 20, 03149 Forst (Lausitz)
Closed Mon; Tue–Sun from 18.00
DB Forst (Lausitz) 150m

FRANKFURT (Oder) 642

Frankfurter Brauhaus

Lebuser Chaussee 3, 15234 Frankfurt (Oder)
T 0335 66 19 15 **F** 0335 66 19 14
www.frankfurter-brauhaus.de
Founded: 2004 Output: 1,500,000hl
REGULAR BEERS:
Spitzkrug Pils (4.6%)
Pilsator Pilsener (5%)
Frankfurter Pilsener (5.2%)
Frankfurter Export (5.4%)

Large brewery built in the 1980s as Oderland Brauerei but closed in 2003. A management buyout saw it re-open in 2004. We've been quoted an annual output of 1,500,000hl but would be surprised if it's anything like that. They brew other beers in addition to the above, but these are only canned or plastic-bottled (we don't do those). There's no brewery tap.

DB Frankfurt (Oder) 4km

FÜRSTLICH DREHNA   643

Schloßbrauerei

Schloßbrauerei Fürstlich Drehna GmbH
Lindenplatz 10, 03246 Fürstlich Drehna
T 035324 303 30   F 035324 303 31
Founded: 1745   Output: 15,000hl
REGULAR BEERS:
Schloß-Bräu Fürst Lynar (4.6%)
Schloß-Bräu Edelhell (4.8%)
Schloß-Bräu Mondschein-Bier (4.8%)
Schloß-Bräu Herren Pils (5%)
Schloß-Bräu Odin-Trunk (5.4%)
SEASONAL BEERS:
Schloß-Bräu Weihnachtsbier (4.8%),
Schloß-Bräu Maibock (5.8%),
Schloß-Bräu Dunkler Bock (7.1%)

Small brewery that we think stopped brewing for a while but now does so again. They don't have a tap but bus No. 598 runs from Finsterwalde on weekdays if you fancy looking for the beers.
DB Finsterwalde (Niederlausitz) 20km

GOLZOW (Chorin)   644

Uckermärker

Uckermärker Brauerei GmbH
Dorfstraße 43, 16230 Chorin-Golzow
T 03334 42 05 57   F 03334 42 92 02
www.choriner.de
Owners: Gudrun & Mark Mangold
Founded: 1996   Output: 1,000hl
Availability: 12 pubs
REGULAR BEERS:
Choriner Classic Pils (5%)
Choriner Herb Pils (5%)
Choriner Dunkel (5%)
Choriner Schwarzbier (5%)

SEASONAL BEERS:
Choriner Weizenbier (5%), **Choriner Weihnachts-bier** (5.5%), **Choriner Bock** (6.4%, May & Oct)

Microbrewery in a village north of Eberswalde. The tap only opens for brewery visits but the beers are available in a dozen other pubs.
DB Golzow (bei Eberswalde) 1km

KOLONIE (Jänschwalde)   645

Zur Linde

Brauhaus zur Linde
Lindenstraße 1, 03197 Jänschwalde-Kolonie
T 035607 502   F 035607 509
Owners: Marianne & Andreas Labsch
Founded: 2001
REGULAR BEERS:
Lindenbräu Pils
Lindenbräu Dunkel

Brewpub in the village of Kolonie, a few hundred metres east of Jänschwalde. We don't think they supply anyone else with beer.

🍴 Zur Linde
Lindenstraße 1, 03197 Jänschwalde-Kolonie
Closed Tue & Wed; Thu–Fri from 16.00,
Sat & Sun 10.00–14.00 & from 16.00
DB Jänschwalde 1.5km

KÖNIGS WUSTERHAUSEN   646

Kavalierhäuser

Kavalierhäuser Schloß Königs Wusterhausen
Schloßplatz 1, 15711 Königs Wusterhausen
T 03375 21 20 90   F 03375 212 09 50
www.schloss-koenigs-wusterhausen.de
Founded: 2004
Output: 250hl   Availability: 1 pub
REGULAR BEER:
Wusterhausener Zwölfender (6%)
SEASONAL BEERS:
Wusterhausener Märzen (7%),
Wusterhausener Bockbier (8.5%)

A small brewery in a former hunting lodge next to Königs Wusterhausen palace. The regular beer is a top-fermented Dunkel of above-average strength.

🍴 Schlossrestaurant
Schloßplatz 1, 15711 Königs Wusterhausen
Closed Mon; Tue–Sat 12.00–24.00,
Sun 12.00–22.00
DB Königs Wusterhausen 500m

LÜBBENAU 647

Babben

Brauhaus und Pension Babben
Brauhausgasse 2, 03222 Lübbenau
T 03542 21 26   **F** 03542 87 26 27
www.babben-bier.de
Owner: Roberto Babben   Founded: 1996
Output: 400hl   Availability: 7 pubs
REGULAR BEERS:
Babben Spezialbier Dunkel
Babben Pils
SEASONAL BEERS:
Babben Weizen, Babben Märzen,
Babben Festbier (Christmas), **Babben Bock**

Microbrewery in the former premises of Stadtbrauerei Lübbenau which was owned by the
current proprietor's family from 1928 until 1962,
and closed in 1974. Six pubs are supplied in
addition to the tap and they also have a distillery.

🍺 Babben
Brauhausgasse 2, 03222 Lübbenau
Nov–mid-Mar closed; mid-Mar–Oct from 17.00;
rooms available
DB Lübbenau (Spreewald) 1km

LUCKENWALDE 648

Luckenwalder

Luckenwalder Spezialitäten-Brauerei
Haag 11, 14943 Luckenwalde
T 03371 63 20 12   **F** 03371 63 29 23
Owner: Maximilian Hösl   Founded: 1906
Output: 4,000hl
REGULAR BEERS:
Luckenwalder Pilsner Premium (4.8%)
Luckenwalder Goldsiegel Spezial
SEASONAL BEERS:
Weihnachtstraum Spezial, Edel Bock

Known as the 'Wirte-Genossenschaftsbrauerei'
until 2001, this small brewery has the same owner
as the Luckenwalder Spezialitätenbrauerei and
Gardelegen Spezialitätenbrauerei. Luckenwalder
beers have the same names as Peniger's, and we
wouldn't be surprised if only one of them brews...
They don't have a tap.
DB Luckenwalde 1.1km

NEUZELLE 649

Klosterbrauerei

Klosterbrauerei Neuzelle GmbH
Brauhausplatz 1, 15898 Neuzelle
T 033652 81 00   **F** 033652 810 70
www.neuzeller-bier.de
Owner: Helmut Fritsche   Founded: 1589
Output: 50,000hl   Availability: 50 pubs
REGULAR BEERS:
Neuzeller Dunkel (1.7%)
Neuzeller Schwarzer Abt (3.9%)
Neuzeller Schlaubetaler Landbier (4.8%)
Neuzeller Mönchs-Pils (4.8%)
Neuzeller Bock (6.2%)
Neuzeller Closter Zell (6.3%)
Neuzeller Porter (7%)
'WELLNESS' BEERS:
Neuzeller Anti Aging Bier (4.8%),
Neuzeller Marathon (4.8%),
Neuzeller Original Badebier (5.2%)

Regional brewery that started life in the nearby
monastery. The current building dates from 1902
when it was completely rebuilt following a fire.
They specialise in what they term 'wellness beers'
and are not averse to upsetting the brewing
establishment. The tap is a hotel on the western
side of Neuzelle. One of the services on offer is
a beer bath. No, honestly!

🍺 Kummerower Hof
Kummroer Straße 41, 15898 Neuzelle
T 033652 81 10   **F** 033652 811 13
Daily 11.00–22.00; rooms – and baths! – available
DB Neuzelle 3.3km

PLAUE (Brandenburg) 650

Kneipe Pur

Bräuhaus Kneipe Pur
Lewaldstraße 23a, 14774 Brandenburg-Plaue
T 03381 40 34 66
www.kneipepur.de
Founded: 1997   Output: 400hl
REGULAR BEER:
Pur Bräu 1912er Plausch (4.9%)
SEASONAL BEERS:
Pur Bräu Schwarzbier, Pur Bräu Altbier, Pur Bräu
Pilsener, Pur Bräu Weizenbier, Pur Bräu
Braunbier, Pur Bräu Rauchbier, Pur Bräu

Roggenbier, Pur Bräu Rotbier, Pur Bräu
Bitterbier, Pur Bräu Honigbier, Pur Bräu
Lakritzbier, Pur Bräu Knoblauchbräu, Pur Bräu
Wacholderbier, Pur Bräu Porter, Pur Bräu
Stout, Pur Bräu Märzen, Pur Bräu Festbier, Pur
Bräu Winterwarmerbier, Pur Bräu Weizenbock,
Pur Bräu Bockbier

Brewpub with an adventurous taste in seasonal
beers, including liquorice, honey, juniper and
various fruits. The garlic beer appears on
Fathers' Day. Although officially a suburb of
Brandenburg, we've listed Plaue separately as
it's 10km west of the city centre. Take bus E
from Kirchmöser station to Genthiner Straße,
then walk down Patendamm to the pub (800m).

Kneipe Pur
Lewaldstraße 23a, 14774 Brandenburg-Plaue
Closed Mon & Tue; Wed–Sun from 18.00
DB Kirchmöser 5km

POTSDAM 651

Braumanufaktur
Braumanufaktur Forsthaus Templin
Templiner Straße 102,
14473 Potsdam-Templiner Vorstadt
T 033209 21 79 79   F 033209 21 79 80
www.braumanufaktur.de
Owners: Jörg Kirchhoff & Thomas Köhler
Founded: 2004   Output: 1,000hl
Availability: 10 pubs
REGULAR BEERS:
Braumanufaktur Lager (4.5%)
Braumanufaktur Potsdamer Stange (4.8%)
Braumanufaktur Bio-Pils (4.8%)
SEASONAL BEERS:
Braumanufaktur Weizen (5%), **Braumanufaktur
Märzen** (5.5%), **Braumanufaktur Maibock**
(6.5%), **Braumanufaktur Erntebock** (6.5%),
Braumanufaktur Nikolator (6.5%)

Brewpub on the Templiner See that has revived
Potsdamer Stange, a beer named after the tall
glasses in which it's served. Bus No. 607 runs
daily from Potsdam Hbf or you can walk from
Pirschheide station along the railway dam
across the lake. There's also a seasonal
steamboat service.

Forsthaus Templin
Templiner Straße 102, 14473 Potsdam-
Templiner Vorstadt

Fri & Sat 11.00–01.00, Sun–Thu 11.00–23.00
DB Potsdam Pirschheide 2km, Hbf 5km

Hofbrauerei Krongut Bornstedt
Ribbeckstraße 6–7, 14469 Potsdam-Bornstedt
T 0331 55 06 50   F 0331 550 65 15
www.krongut-bornstedt.de
Owner: Krongut Bornstedt Parkgesellschaft
Founded: 2002   Output: 1,000hl
REGULAR BEER:
Bornstedter Büffel Helles (5.4%)
Bornstedter Büffel Braunbier (5.4%)
SEASONAL BEERS:
Bornstedter Büffel Weizen (5%),
Bornstedter Büffel Märzen (6.5%),
Bornstedter Büffel Bock (7%)

Small brewery in a cellar of the Krongut
Bornstedt manor house, a few hundred metres
from Sanssouci palace.

Brau- und Brennhaus
Ribbeckstraße 6–7, 14469 Potsdam-Bornstedt
Daily 11.00–23.00
Tram No. 92 Kirschallee 600m
DB Potsdam Hbf 3.7km

Meierei
Gasthausbrauerei Meierei im Neuen Garten
Am Neuen Garten 10, 14469 Potsdam-Nauener
Vorstadt
T 0331 704 32 11   F 0331 704 32 13
www.meierei-potsdam.de
Owners: Hannelore & Jürgen
Solkowski   Founded: 27.06.2003
Output: 1,000hl   Availability: 1 pub
REGULAR BEER:
Meierei Hell (5.2%)
SEASONAL BEERS:
**Meierei Top Secret Bier, Meierei Vampbier,
Meierei Potsdamer Landbier** (5.2%), **Meierei
Potsdamer Schwarze** (5.2%), **Meierei Rotbier**
(5.5%), **Meierei Osterbier** (5.5%), **Meierei
Weihnachtsfestbier** (5.5%), **Meierei Märzen**
(5.6%), **Meierei Mittsommerbier** (5.9%),
Meierei Neumondbier (5.9%), **Meierei Maibock**
(6.8%), **Meierei Sollator Herbstbock** (6.8%)

Brewpub in a former pumping house on the
shores of the Jungfernsee. Take bus No. 692
from the city centre to Höhenstraße. Annual
holiday mid-January to mid-February.

Meierei

Am Neuen Garten 10,
14469 Potsdam-Nauener Vorstadt
Winter: closed Mon; Tue–Sat 12.00–22.00,
Sun 10.00–20.00
Summer: Mon–Sat 10.00–23.00, Sun 10.00–22.00
DB Potsdam Hbf 3.8km

PRITZWALK 652

Preussen Pils

Brauhaus Preussen Pils GmbH
Meyenburger Tor 3–5, 16928 Pritzwalk
T 03395 305 40   F 03395 30 54 91
www.preussenpils.de
Founded: 1795   Output: 30,000hl
REGULAR BEERS:
Preussen Pils Premium (4.9%)
Preussen Schwarzbier Premium (5.2%)
BRANDENBURGER BEERS:
Brandenburger Landbier (4.8%),
Brandenburger Bauernbier Dunkel (4.9%),
Brandenburger Export (5.4%)
SEASONAL BEER:
Brandenburger Dunkler Bock (6.9%)
PRITZWALKER BEER:
Pritzwalker Schraube Pils (4.8%)
FOR BÄRENQUELL BRAUEREI, BERLIN:
Bärenquell Pilsener Spezial (4.8%)

Attractive brewery, just over the river Domnitz
from the town centre. It was extensively
modernised in the mid-1990s. The tap is in a
former maltings.

Alte Mälzerei

Meyenburger Tor 5, 16928 Pritzwalk
T 03395 31 02 84   F 03395 30 60 93
Closed Mon; Tue–Sun 10.00–23.00
DB Pritzwalk 1.2km

RHEINSBERG 653

Zum Alten Brauhaus

Gasthausbrauerei zum Alten Brauhaus,
Privatbrauerei Rheinsberg
Rhinhöher Weg 1, 16831 Rheinsberg
T 033931 720 80   F 033931 720 81
www.brauerei-rheinsberg.de
Owner: Horst Mücke   Founded: 1994

Output: 2,000hl
REGULAR BEERS:
Kronprinzen Pils
Kronprinzen Pils Naturtrüb
Kronprinzen Pils Naturtrüb Dunkel

Brewpub that occupies the buildings of the
former Brauerei Rheinsberg which closed in
1983. You shouldn't have any trouble finding it
from the station.

Zum Alten Brauhaus

Rhinhöher Weg 1, 16831 Rheinsberg
T 033931 720 88   F 033931 720 82
Daily from 11.00
DB Rheinsberg (Mark) 150m

SCHLEPZIG 654

Spreewälder

Spreewalder Privatbrauerei 1788
Dorfstraße 53, 15910 Schlepzig
T 035472 662 51   F 035472 662 50
www.spreewaldbrauerei.de
Owner: Dr. Torsten Roemer   Founded: 1998
Output: 1,000hl   Availability: 10 pubs
REGULAR BEERS:
Spreewälder Pils (5%)
Spreewälder Dunkel (5%)
SEASONAL BEERS:
Spreewälder Zwickel Pils (5%), **Spreewälder
Hefeweizen-Hell** (5%), **Spreewälder Hefeweizen-
Dunkel** (5%), **Spreewälder Spreelator**

Brewpub close to the river Spree in a complex
that includes a distillery, hotel, restaurant and
conference centre. All are housed in refurbished
brick and timber buildings. Bus No. 506 runs
from Lübben on weekdays.

Brauhaus

Dorfstraße 53, 15910 Schlepzig
Sat & Sun from 11.00, Mon–Fri from 11.30;
rooms available
DB Lübben (Spreewald) 15km

WARNITZ (Oberuckersee) 655

Burgwall Bräu

Lindenalle 54, 17291 Oberuckersee-Warnitz
T 039863 71 49
Founded: 1999

Warnitzer Burgwall Bräu Hell
Warnitzer Burgwall Bräu Dunkel

Tiny brewery in the Deutsche Eiche pub, in the lakeside village of Warnitz. We don't think their beers are available anywhere else.

Deutsche Eiche
Lindenalle 54, 17291 Warnitz
Closed Wed; Thu–Tue 11.00–22.00
DB Warnitz (Uckermark) 300m

Sans Souci, Friedenskirche, Brandenburg, Potsdam.

275

Bremen

www.bremen.de
www.bremen-tourism.de

THE FREE HANSEATIC CITY of Bremen, one of the city states, is the smallest of Germany's 16 Länder, in terms of both population and area. The state also encompasses the town of Bremerhaven, a large port at the mouth of the Weser river, 40 miles north of Bremen itself. The late-medieval Rathaus, still standing in its original glory, together with the Roland statue in front of it were awarded World Heritage status by UNESCO in 2004.

To many foreigners Bremen means just two things – musicians and beer. Although the former were fictional, brewing is one of the main industries here, with the enormous Beck/Haake-Beck brewery employing around 1,500 people. In addition to this behemoth, two brewpubs can be found locally. A third, Koggen-Bräu in Bremerhaven, closed towards the end of 2005.

Transport: Trains are generally only of use to the beer hunter as a means of getting to and from the city, but Bremen has an excellent bus and tram network.

Beck/Haake-Beck

Am Deich 18–19, 28199 Bremen-Neustadt
T 0421 509 40   F 0421 509 46 67
www.becks.de
www.haake-beck.de
Owner: InBev   Founded: 1826
Output: 5,000,000hl
BECK'S BEERS:
Beck's (4.9%)
Beck's Gold (4.9%)
HAAKE-BECK BEERS:
Haake-Beck Edel-Hell (4.7%),
Haake-Beck Kräusen (4.8%),
Haake-Beck Pils (4.8%),
Haake-Beck Export (5.2%)
SEASONAL BEER:
Haake-Beck Maibock (7.2%)
HEMELINGER BEER:
Hemelinger Spezial Schankbier (4.7%)

Massive brewery on the western bank of the river Weser. Although marketed separately, Beck and Haake-Beck share their premises and owner, and are thus listed as one brewery. The two pubs below are in the historic centre of the city, south of the cathedral.

Beck's in'n Snoor
Im Schnoor 34–36, 28195 Bremen-Mitte
T 0421 32 31 30   F 0421 337 81 92
Daily 11.00–23.00
Tram Domsheide 250m   DB Bremen Hbf 1.4km

Haake Beck Ausspann
Im Schnoor 1–2, 28195 Bremen-Mitte
T 0421 32 11 24
Daily 11.00–24.00
Tram Domsheide 250m   DB Bremen Hbf 1.4km

*ft: Zoigl has reached almost mythical status in recent years.
nuela Zimmermann pours another at Zum Posterer in
ndischeschenbach.*

Borgfelder Landhaus

Warfer Landstraße 73, 28357 Bremen-Borgfeld
T 0421 277 71 47   **F** 0421 277 71 49
www.borgfelder-landhaus.de
Owner: Fredi Cordes   Founded: 1998
Output: 1,000hl   Availability: 12 pubs
REGULAR BEERS:
Borgfelder Urtrüb (4.8%)
Lilienthaler Dunkel (4.8%)
SEASONAL BEERS:
Borgfelder Frühlingsbier (spring), **Borgfelder Sommerweizen** (summer), **Borgfelder Herbststurm** (autumn), **Borgfelder Winterbock** (winter)

Thriving brewpub right on the state border, in the northern suburb of Borgfeld. It supplies a number of other outlets in the region. Bus No. 630 from the station stops outside the pub and the terminus of tram line No. 4 is half a mile to the south.

🍺 **Borgfelder Landhaus**
Warfer Landstraße 73, 28357 Bremen-Borgfeld
Closed Mon; Tue–Sat 12.00–24.00,
Sun 12.00–23.00
Tram No. 4 Borgfeld 800m   DB Bremen Hbf 8km

Schüttinger

Schüttinger – Erste Bremer Gasthausbrauerei
Hinter dem Schütting 12–13,
28195 Bremen-Mitte
T 0421 337 66 33   **F** 0421 337 66 99
www.schuettinger.de
Founded: 1990
Output: 1,200hl
Availability: 1 pub
REGULAR BEERS:
Schüttinger Hell
Schüttinger Dunkel

Brewpub in the old town. They recently brewed a special to celebrate their 15th anniversary but we don't think seasonal beers are a regular feature.

🍺 **Schüttinger**
Hinter dem Schütting 12–13, 28195 Bremen-Mitte
Sat & Sun from 11.00, Mon–Fri from 12.00
Tram Domsheide 170m
DB Bremen Hbf 1.1km

Hamburg

A HANSEATIC CITY STATE like Bremen, Hamburg is the second largest city in Germany. An economic powerhouse, many major industries are centered around the port, the second largest in Europe. The majority of the country's major newspapers and magazine publishers are based in the city – appropriately in the former brewing district.

Most people will have heard of the Reeperbahn, but Hamburg has much more to offer than a red-light district, boasting many museums, galleries, theatres and other cultured attractions. The Kunsthalle, in particular, should not be missed.

Like Bremen, Hamburg's brewing scene is dominated by one giant, with the odd brewpub thrown in for good measure. In this case the biggie is Holsten, where all the sugar turns to...

Transport: The city's transport network includes one of the few true underground systems in the country and an S-Bahn system based on three routes.

ALTONA

Holsten

Holsten-Brauerei AG
Holstenstraße 224, 22765 Hamburg-Altona
T 040 38 10 10   **F** 040 38 10 17 51
www.holsten.de
Owner: Carlsberg Breweries, Denmark
Founded: 1879   Output: 3,200,000hl
REGULAR BEERS:
Holsten Pilsener (4.8%)
Holsten Diät Pils (4.9%)
Holsten Edel (4.9%)
Holsten Knight (5.2%)
Holsten Export (5.4%)
SEASONAL BEER:
Holsten Maibock (7%).
ASTRA BEER:
Astra Urtyp (4.9%)

Huge brewery alongside the railway in the Altona district, now under Danish ownership. Astra Urtyp was brewed by Bavaria-St. Pauli until they were taken over by Holsten in 1998. They don't have a specific tap.
[DB] Holstenstraße 150m

MESSBERG

Gröninger

Willy-Brand-Straße 47 (formerly Ost-West-Straße), 20457 Hamburg-Meßberg
T 040 33 13 81   **F** 040 32 38 40
www.groeninger-hamburg.de
Owner: Jens Stacklies   Founded: 1988

Überseebrücken, Port Hamburg.

Output: 3,500hl
REGULAR BEER:
Gröninger Pils (5.1%)

Cellar brewpub that produces just one beer – a copper-coloured Pils. Upstairs is the Brauhaus (the brewery is in the Braukeller) which only opens in the evening (not Sun). They also own Brauhaus Hanseat.

Gröninger Braukeller
Willy-Brand-Straße 47 (formerly Ost-West-Straße), 20457 Hamburg-Meßberg
Closed Sun & hols; Mon–Fri from 11.00, Sat from 17.00
U Meßberg 200m   DB Hamburg Hbf 1.1km

Hanseat

Zippelhaus 4, 20457 Hamburg-Meßberg
T 040 32 25 52   F 040 32 38 40
www.brauhaus-hanseat.de
Owner: Jens Stacklies   Founded: 1993
Output: 1,500hl
REGULAR BEER:
Hanseaten Weisse (5.2%)

Opposite the Zoll canal, Brauhaus Hanseat is a wheat beer-only brewpub, owned by nearby Gröninger. The two back on to each other and are connected by an underground passage.

Hanseat
Zippelhaus 4, 20457 Hamburg-Meßberg
Closed Sun & hols; Mon–Sat 17.00–24.00
U Meßberg 300m
DB Hamburg Hbf 1.2km

Johann Albrecht

Adolphsbrücke 7, 20457 Hamburg-Meßberg
T 040 36 77 40   F 040 36 79 15
www.brauhaus-joh-albrecht.de/ham.html
Founded: 1991
Output: 2,000hl
Availability: 1 pub
REGULAR BEERS:
Johann Albrecht Messing
Johann Albrecht Kupfer

The first and most northerly of the six Johann Albrecht brewpubs is alongside the Alsterfleet, a few hundred metres from the Binnenalster. We think they brew occasional seasonal beers.

Johann Albrecht
Adolphsbrücke 7, 20457 Hamburg-Meßberg
Daily 11.00–01.00
DB Jungfernstieg 350m, Hbf 1.3km

Hessen (Hesse)

A HILLY, HEAVILY FORESTED state, Hessen features some of Germany's most attractive countryside. Although Frankfurt is the largest city, the capital is Wiesbaden, situated at the centre of Hessen's wine region.

Attractions for the tourist include: Frankfurt, a compact, bustling city and the country's financial centre with strong international and global links; Rüdesheim, an attractive town on the Rhine, famous for its wine; the Odenwald and Taunus regions, both featuring some wonderful scenery; Fritzlar, a beautiful medieval town.

Hessen currently has 64 breweries, many of which are modern brewpubs. There are some more venerable establishments, notably the Hofbrauhaus Arolsen, which claims an ancestry dating back to 1131. The largest of the lot is Binding's huge plant in Frankfurt.

Transport: Frankfurt naturally has the best public transport system. The rail and bus network throughout the state is generally good, although some areas are relatively poorly served, in large part due to the terrain. A day ticket for Hessen currently costs €25 for up to five people, and can be used from 09.00 on weekdays and all day at the weekend. The usual restrictions apply – please check it's valid for your intended journey.

ALSFELD 658

Alsfeld
Brauerei Alsfeld AG
Grünberger Straße 68, 36304 Alsfeld
T 06631 960 20 **F** 06631 96 02 10
www.alsfelder.de Founded: 1858
Output: 100,000hl Availability: c.350 pubs
REGULAR BEERS:
Alsfelder Schwarzbier (4.9%)
Alsfelder Rathaus Pilsner (4.9%)
Alsfelder Pilsener (4.9%)
Alsfelder Export (5%)
Alsfelder Helles (5.2%)
Alsfelder Weizen Hefe-Hell (5.2%)
Alsfelder Weizen Hefe-Dunkel (5.2%)
Alsfelder Weizen Kristall (5.2%)

Large brewery on the south-western outskirts of Alsfeld. There's no tap but plenty of pubs in the medieval town centre sell the beers.
DB Alsfeld (Oberhessen) 1km

ALT-HASSLOCH (Rüsselsheim) 659

Kleines Rüsselsheimer Brauhaus
An der Wied 1, 65428 Rüsselsheim/Alt-Haßloch
T 06142 56 24 30 **F** 06142 574 85
www.ruesselsheimerbrauhaus.de
Owner: Horst Gampert Founded: 1993
Output: 1,000hl
REGULAR BEERS:
Haßlocher Hell (4.5%)
Haßlocher Dunkel (4.5%)
Haßlocher Weizenbier (4.7%)
SEASONAL BEERS:
Haßlocher Maibock, Haßlocher Weihnachtsbock

Modern brewpub in a half-timbered building dating from 1740. Take buses Nos. 51 or 52 from Rüsselsheim station to Am Borngraben.

🍽 **Kleines Rüsselsheimer Brauhaus**
An der Wied 1, 65428 Rüsselsheim/Alt-Haßloch
Sun & hols from 11.00, Mon–Sat from 12.00
DB Rüsselsheim 3.5km

ALTENHASSLAU
(Linsengericht) — 660

Brauhaus Linsengericht

Metzgerstraße 2, 63589 Linsengericht-Altenhaßlau   **T** 06051 70 13 14
www.brauhaus-linsengericht.de
Owners: J. Bock, J. Weingärtner & S. Weingelt
Founded: 2004   Output: 300hl
Availability: 1 pub
REGULAR BEERS:
Haselaner Weizen (5.3%)
Haselaner Hell (5.3%)
Haselaner Dunkel (5.3%)

Microbrewery that doesn't yet have a tap. The beers are available from the brewery Tue & Fri 17.00–19.00, and Sat 12.00–14.00.
DB Gelnhausen 1.4km

AUERBACH (Bensheim) — 661

Burggraf Bräu

Darmstädter Straße 231,
64625 Bensheim-Auerbach
T 06251 725 25   **F** 06251 756 60
www.burggraf-braeu.de
Founded: 1993   Output: 800hl
REGULAR BEERS:
Burggraf Bräu Pils
Burggraf Bräu Hefeweizen Hell
Burggraf Bräu Märzen Dunkel
SEASONAL BEERS:
Burggraf Bräu 11er Landbier, Burggraf Bräu Maibock, Burggraf Bräu Weihnachtsbock

Brewpub and restaurant on the old main road from Heidelberg to Frankfurt. We think they may do other seasonal beers.

🍽 **Burggraf-Bräu**
Darmstädter Straße 231,
64625 Bensheim-Auerbach

Mon–Fri 11.00–15.00 & 17.00–01.00,
Sat 17.00–01.00, Sun 11.00–24.00
DB Bensheim-Auerbach 650m

BABENHAUSEN — 662

Michelsbräu

Privatbrauerei Michelsbräu GmbH
Fahrstraße 83–85, 64832 Babenhausen
T 06073 720 40   **F** 06073 72 04 11
www.michelsbraeu.de
Owners: Günther & Dr. Susan Schubert
Founded: 1815   Output: 30,000hl
REGULAR BEERS:
Michel's Pilsener (4.9%)
Michel's Kellerbier (4.9%)
Michelsbräu Hexe (5.2%)
Michel's Export (5.4%)
SEASONAL BEER:
Michelsbräu Hexator Doppelbock (7.2%)

One of three breweries owned by the Schuberts; the others are in Arnhausen and Thüngen. The Swan pub is just down the street.

🍽 **Zum Schwanen**
Fahrstraße 67, 64832 Babenhausen
T 06073 72 50 52
Sat from 17.30, Sun–Fri 11.30–14.30 & from 17.30
DB Babenhausen (Hessen) 900m

BAD AROLSEN — 663

Hofbrauhaus Arolsen

Privatbrauerei Brüne GmbH
Kaulbachstraße 33, 34454 Bad Arolsen
T 05691 22 04   **F** 05691 69 42
www.hofbrauhaus-arolsen.de
Owner: Andreas, Dirk & Heinrich Brüne
Founded: 1131   Output: 10,000hl
Availability: 20 pubs
REGULAR BEERS:
Arolser Pils (4.9%)
Alt Waldecker Dunkel (5.5%)
SEASONAL BEER:
Waldecker Edelbock (7.5%, Oct)

One of the world's oldest breweries, the court brewery and its tap are down a cobbled street, close to the Baroque Residenzschloss.

🍺 Zum Hofbrauhaus
Kaulbachstraße 33, 34454 Bad Arolsen
T 05691 20 28
Mon from 16.30, Tue–Fri 11.00–14.00 & from
16.30, Sat, Sun & hols from 11.00; rooms
available   DB Bad Arolsen 1.6km

BAD HOMBURG   664

Graf Zeppelin

Bad Homburger Brauhaus GmbH & Co. KG
Hofgut Kronenhof, Zeppelinstraße 10,
61352 Bad Homburg
T 06172 28 86 62   **F** 06172 28 86 60
www.badhomburger-brauhaus.de
Owner: Hans-Georg Wagner   Founded: 2000
Output: 1,000hl   Availability: 1 pub
REGULAR BEERS:
Kronenhof Hell
Kronenhof Dunkel
SEASONAL BEERS:
Kronenhof Dinkel-Bier (spring), **Kronenhof
Bernstein Weizen** (summer), **Kronenhof
Quattro-Bier** (autumn), **Kronenhof Mai-Bock**
(May), **Kronenhof Nikolaus-Bock** (Dec)

Brewpub on a farm just south of Bad Homburg.
They also stable show-jumping horses here and
the site was the location for a large airship
display in 1910, hence the name.

🍺 Graf Zeppelin
Hofgut Kronenhof, Zeppelinstraße 10,
61352 Bad Homburg
Mon–Fri 11.00–24.00, Sat 11.00–01.00,
Sun & hols 11.00–23.00
DB Bad Homburg 1.3km

BAD NAUHEIM   665

Schluckebier

Gasthausbrauerei Schluckebier
Rittershausstraße 5, 61231 Bad Nauheim
T 06032 842 62
Owner: Alfred Volp   Founded: 2000
Output: 400hl
REGULAR BEERS:
Schlucke Hell
Schlucke Dunkel
Schlucke Weizen

Owned by a local drinks and pub company,
this modern pub in a cellar has a small brewing
plant that produces beer solely for sale on the
premises.

🍺 Schluckebier
Rittershausstraße 5, 61231 Bad Nauheim
Daily 09.00–02.00   DB Bad Nauheim 400m

BAD ORB   666

Kärrners

Kärrners Hausbrauerei
Jahnstraße 8/Kurparkstraße 7, 63619 Bad Orb
T 06052 25 15   www.kaerrners.de
Owner: Helmut Prehler   Founded: 1998
REGULAR BEERS:
Kärrners Hell
Kärrners Weisse
SEASONAL BEERS:
**Kärrners Schwarzbier, Kärrners Oktoberfestbier,
Kärrners Maibock, Kärrners Celebrator
Doppelbock**

Modern brewpub in the spa resort of Bad Orb,
just south of the town centre. The pub has
entrances off two streets. Bus No. 81 runs daily
from Wächtersbach station.

🍺 Kärrners
Jahnstraße 8/Kurparkstraße 7, 63619 Bad Orb
Closed Mon; Tue–Sat from 17.30, Sun from 17.00
DB Wächtersbach 7km

BAD WILDUNGEN   667

Bad Wildunger Brauhaus

Frankenberger Straße 2, 34537 Bad Wildungen
T 05621 741 50   **F** 05621 96 02 83
www.brauhaus-bad-wildungen.de
Founded: 1992   Output: 400hl
REGULAR BEERS:
Engelsbräu Hell
Engelsbräu Dunkel
SEASONAL BEER:
Engelsbräu Hefe (summer)

This brewpub is beneath the Hornberg at the
western edge of Bad Wildingen, just off the
road to Frankenberg. Bus No. 1 runs from the
station if you don't fancy the long walk uphill.

🍺 Bad Wildunger Brauhaus
Frankenberger Straße 2, 34537 Bad Wildungen
Closed Tue; Wed–Sat & Mon 18.00–23.00,
Sun 08.30–15.00   DB Bad Wildungen 3km

BEERFELDEN 668

Felsenkeller
Privatbrauerei Felsenkeller
Eberbacher Weg 68, 64743 Beerfelden
T 06068 22 32   **E** beerfelder@aol.com
Owner: Andreas Schmucker   Founded: 1782
REGULAR BEERS:
Beerfelder Leicht
Beerfelder Kellerbier
Beerfelder Kräusenpils
Beerfelder Felsenpils Premium
Beerfelder Weizen
Beerfelder Export
Beerfelder Märzen
SEASONAL BEER:
Beerfelder Bock

Hessen's most southerly brewery, Felsenkeller
doesn't have a tap of its own but the beers are
sold in a number of pubs locally. Bus No. 50 runs
daily from Michelstadt via Hetzbach station,
some services continuing through to Eberbach.
DB Hetzbach 4km, Eberbach 14km

BRAUNFELS 669

Obermühle
Brauhaus Obermühle
Gebrüder-Wahl-Straße 17–19, 35619 Braunfels
T 06442 43 82   **F** 06442 339 04 31
www.obermuehle-braunfels.de
Owner: Uwe Schönwetter   Founded: 2003
Output: 250hl   Availability: 1 pub
REGULAR BEER:
Schloßbräu Brauner Schlawiner (4.9%)

Brewpub and hotel on the western side of Braunfels, a picturesque town dominated by its castle.
Bus No. 180 runs from the station to the town on
weekdays. A *Schlawiner* is a bit of a rogue.

🍺 Obermühle
Gebrüder-Wahl-Straße 17–19, 35619 Braunfels
Closed Mon; Tue–Sat 17.00–01.00, Sun 11.00–24.00;
rooms available   DB Leun/Braunfels 3.2km

DARMSTADT 670

Darmstädter
Darmstädter Privatbrauerei GmbH
Göbelstraße 7, 64293 Darmstadt
T 06151 928 80   **F** 06151 92 88 49
www.darmstaedter.de
Owner: Wolfgang Koehler
Founded: 1847
Output: 60,000hl
REGULAR BEERS:
Darmstädter Leichtes (2.6%)
Darmstädter 1847 Zwickel (4.8%)
Darmstädter Pilsener Premium (4.8%)
Darmstädter Braustüb'l Pilsner (4.8%)
Darmstädter Braustüb'l Weissbier Hell (4.8%)
Darmstädter Weissbier Hefe Hell (4.8%)
Darmstädter Weissbier Hefe Dunkel (4.8%)
Darmstädter Weissbier Kristall (4.8%)
Darmstädter Helles Export (5.2%)
Darmstädter Märzen Dunkel (5.6%)
SEASONAL BEER:
Darmstädter Braustüb'l Winter-Bock (6.5%)

Not surprisingly, railways feature heavily in
Darmstädter's advertising as it's located
directly opposite the Hauptbahnhof. The tap is
in front of the brewery. They also own the much
smaller Brauerei Grohe.

🍺 Braustüb'l
Göbelstraße 7, 64293 Darmstadt
T 06151 87 65 87   Daily 10.00–01.00
DB Darmstadt Hbf 100m

Grohe
Brauerei Grohe GmbH
Nieder-Ramstädter-Straße 3, 64283 Darmstadt
T 06151 444 55   **F** 06151 430 44
www.grohe-gastro.de
Owner: Wolfgang Koehler
Founded: 1838
Output: 5,000hl
REGULAR BEERS:
Grohe Pils (4.8%)
Grohe Export-Hell (5.1%)
Grohe Märzen (5.1%)
SEASONAL BEER:
Grohe Bock Dunkel (6.2%, winter)

Street-corner brewery and tap just south of the
city centre. It was bought by the owner of the

Darmstädter brewery in the late 1980s. They have another pub next door that opens Monday to Saturday evenings only.

🍺 Grohe
Nieder-Ramstädter-Straße 3, 64283 Darmstadt
T 06151 42 52 55   **F** 06151 71 66 44
Mon–Sat 10.00–24.00, Sun & hols 16.00–24.00
🚋 Schulstraße 100m   DB Darmstadt Hbf 2.4km

Ratskeller
Darmstädter Ratskeller Hausbrauerei GmbH
Marktplatz 8, 64283 Darmstadt
T 06151 264 44   **F** 06151 241 77
Founded: 1989   Output: 1,500hl
REGULAR BEERS:
Ratsbräu Pemium Hell (5.4%)
Ratsbräu Spezial Dunkel (5.8%)
Ratsbräu Hefeweizen (5.8%)
SEASONAL BEER:
Ratsbräu Coronator

Brewpub in the old town hall, on the opposite side of the Marktplatz to the Schloss. As far as we're aware they brew just one seasonal beer.

🍺 Ratskeller
Marktplatz 8, 64283 Darmstadt
Daily 10.00–24.00
🚋 Schloß 100m   DB Darmstadt Hbf 2.1km

DÖRNHAGEN (Fuldabrück)   671

Fuldabrücker Landbrauerei
Rundstraße 1a, 34277 Fuldabrück-Dörnhagen
T 05665 300 88   **F** 05665 92 22 43
E fuldabruecker-landbrauerei@t-online.de
Owner: Harald Hess   Founded: 15.12.1995
Output: 1,000hl   Availability: 2 pubs
REGULAR BEERS:
Hess'isches Landbier Pils (4.8%)
Hess'isches Landbier Dunkel (4.8%)
SEASONAL BEERS:
Hess'isches Landbier Festbier (5.8%, autumn),
Hess'isches Landbier Nikolausbier (7.8%)

Small brewpub and distillery in the centre of the village. On summer Sundays they open at 15.00. Bus No. 38 runs from Guxahagen on weekdays, and if you want to avoid the walk at other times, you'll need to take a series of trams and buses from Kassel.

🍺 Fuldabrücker Landbrauerei
Rundstraße 1a, 34277 Fuldabrück-Dörnhagen
Closed Tue; Wed–Fri & Sun/Mon from 17.00,
Sat 10.00–12.00 & from 17.00
DB Guxhagen 3.4km

EGELSBACH   672

Schuhbeck's Check Inn
Flugplatz Egelsbach, Hans-Fleißner-Straße,
63329 Egelsbach
T 06103 485 93 80   **F** 06103 4859 38 20
www.schuhbecks-check-inn.de
Owner: Alfons Schuhbeck   Founded: 2001
REGULAR BEERS:
Schubeck's Hell
Schubeck's Dunkel
Schubeck's Hefeweizen

Brewery, restaurant, bar and beer garden at Egelsbach airfield. The owner is a renowned chef and the author of numerous cookery books.

🍺 Schuhbeck's Check Inn
Flugplatz Egelsbach, Hans-Fleißner-Straße,
63329 Egelsbach
Daily 11.00–01.00
DB Egelsbach 1.3km

ELTVILLE   673

Kleines Eltviller Brauhaus
Kleines Eltviller Brauhaus Otto Binding GmbH
Schwalbacher Sraße 41–43, 65343 Eltville
T 06123 55 90   **F** 06123 638 12
www.eltviller-brauhaus.de
Founded: 1984   Output: 1,500hl
REGULAR BEERS:
Eltviller Hefe-Hell (5.2%)
Eltviller Hefe-Dunkel (5.2%)
SEASONAL BEERS:
Eltviller Schwarzbier (5.2%, Lent), **Eltviller Weizen** (5.2%, summer), **Eltviller Herbstbier** (5.2%, autumn), **Eltviller Märzen** (5.8%), **Eltviller Maibock** (6.5%, May)

Among the first of the new wave of German brew-pubs, Eltviller Brauhaus is still going strong after more than 20 years. They also brew for two former local brewpubs – Rathsbräu in Wiesbaden and Waldmühle Brauhaus in Kiedrich.

🍺 **Kleines Eltviller Brauhaus**
Schwalbacher Sraße 41–43, 65343 Eltville
Closed Mon; Tue–Sat from 17.00, Sun & hols
from 11.00   DB Eltville 600m

ERBACH   674

Erbacher

Erbacher Premium Pils Bräu GmbH
Auf der Kandelwiese 1, 64711 Erbach
T 06062 940 30   **F** 06062 94 03 40
Owner: Oetker Gruppe AG   Founded: 1762
Output: 50,000hl   Availability: c.200 pubs
REGULAR BEER:
Erbacher Premium Pils (4.9%).

Regional brewery taken over by Binding in
1988 and now in the hands of the Oetker Group.
The brewery is on the northern edge of town,
close to the border with Michelstadt, the tap
below the station in the centre of Erbach. They
now brew just the one beer.

🍺 **Brauereiausschank**
Jahnstraße 1, 64711 Erbach
T 06062 57 32   **F** 06062 91 31 53
Daily 11.00–24.00
DB Erbach (Odenwald) 500m

ESCHWEGE   675

Eschweger Klosterbrauerei

Klosterstraße 1, 37269 Eschwege
T 05651 307 30   **F** 05651 30 73 24
www.eschweger-klosterbrauerei.de
Founded: 1839   Output: 75,000hl
REGULAR BEERS:
Eschweger Kloster-Urtyp (4.8%)
Eschweger Klosterbräu Premium Pils (4.8%)
Eschweger Klosterbräu Export (5.4%)
JACOBINUS BEERS:
Jacobinus Classic (4.8%), **Jacobinus
Schwarzbier** (4.8%), **Jacobinus Hefe-Weizen**
(5.7%), **Jacobinus Kristall-Weizen** (5.7%),
Jacobinus Dunkles Weizen (5.7%).

Brewery in the centre of Eschwege that as far as
we know doesn't have a tap. Buses Nos. 228 and
232 run into the town from Eschwege West station.
DB Eschwege West 5km

FRANKFURT (Main)   676

Bier-Hannes

Bier-Hannes Brauerei zur Mainkur GmbH
Hanauer Landstraße 568,
60386 Frankfurt-Fechenheim
T 069 412890   **F** 069 412864
www.bier-hannes.de
Owners: Peter Kaminsky, Hannes Zimmermann
Founded: 1989   Output: 2,000hl
Availability: c.10 pubs
REGULAR BEERS:
Bier-Hannes Export Dunkel
Bier-Hannes Zwickel Pils
Bier-Hannes Hefe-Weizen
SEASONAL BEERS:
**Bier-Hannes Märzen, Bier-Hannes Maibock,
Bier-Hannes Krollebock, Bier-Hannes
Weihnachtsbock**

Microbrewery in a western suburb north of the
Main. The beers are sold in a number of pubs
besides the tap, as well as several local drinks
markets.

🍺 **Bier-Hannes**
Hanauer Landstraße 568,
60386 Frankfurt-Fechenheim
Closed Sun & hols; Mon–Sat 16.00–24.00
DB Frankfurt (Main)-Mainkur 250m

Binding-Henninger

Binding-Brauerei AG/Henninger-Bräu AG
Darmstädter Landstraße 185,
60598 Frankfurt-Sachsenhausen
T 069 606 50   **F** 069 606 52 09
www.binding.de
Owner: Oetker Gruppe AG   Founded: 1870
Output: 2,000,000hl   Availability: c.8,000 pubs
REGULAR BEERS:
Binding Lager (4.5%)
Binding Römer Pils (4.9%)
Binding Römer Pilsener Spezial (5%)
Binding Export (5.3%)
SEASONAL BEER:
Binding Carolus der Starke (7.5%, Christmas)
HENNINGER BEERS:
Henninger Kaiser Pilsener (4.8%), **Henninger
Diät Pils** (4.9%), **Henninger Highlander** (5.3%),
Henninger Export (5.5%)
KUTSCHER BEER:
Kutscher Alt (4.8%)

SCHÖFFERHOFER WHEAT BEERS:
Schöfferhofer Hefeweizen (5%), **Schöfferhofer Dunkles Hefeweizen** (5%), **Schöfferhofer Kristallweizen** (5%)

Huge brewery in the south of the city, probably best known outside Germany for their non-alcoholic Clausthaler range. Henninger closed their brewery and moved here in 2002. The Schöfferhofer beers were previously brewed in Kassel. The tap in the old town, a recent addition, opened in December 2005.

Binding am Goethehaus
Weißadlergasse 15, 60311 Frankfurt-Altstadt
T 069 15 39 30 00   **F** 069 153 93 00 10
Daily 10.00–01.00
DB Hauptwache 350m, Frankfurt Hbf 1.2km

Wäldches

Wäldches Bräu GmbH
Rotfeder-Ring Halle 16, Westhafen, 60327 Frankfurt-Gutleutviertel
T 069 52 05 22   **F** 069 51 72 49
www.waeldches-am-main.de
Owner: Helmuth Weinert   Founded: 1988
Output: 1,500hl
REGULAR BEER:
Wäldches Hell

Brewpub in a former pumping station, still not open as we went to press but expected to do so in the summer of 2006. Originally in the suburb of Ginnheim, the brewery was forced to move at the end of 2004. In the meantime the beer has been brewed by Weyberbräu in Weyberhöfe. Bus No. 33 should run to the pub once it's open.

Wäldches Pumpwerk
Rotfeder-Ring Halle 16, Westhafen, 60327 Frankfurt-Gutleutviertel
DB Frankfurt (Main) Hbf 1.6km

Zwölf Apostel

Zu den Zwölf Apostel
Rosenberger Straße 1, 60313 Frankfurt-Innenstadt
T 069 28 86 68   **F** 069 28 42 29
www.12apostel.net
Owners: Terezija Zelic   Founded: 1988
Output: 2,000hl
REGULAR BEERS:
Zwölf Apostel Bräu Hell
Zwölf Apostel Bräu Dunkel

SEASONAL BEER:
Zwölf Apostel Bräu Bock

Street-corner brewpub to the north-east of the city centre. We think the Twelve Apostles brew additional seasonal beers to the one listed above.

Zwölf Apostel
Rosenberger Straße 1, 60313 Frankfurt-Innenstadt
Daily 11.30–01.00
DB Konstablerwache 330m, Hbf 2.2km

FRIEDBERG   677

Friedberger Brauhaus

St. Florian Bräu GmbH
Kaiserstraße 37–39, 61169 Friedberg
T 06031 621 12   **F** 06031 633 97
www.friedberger-brauhaus.de
Owner: Walter Groß   Founded: 1989
Output: 1,500hl
REGULAR BEERS:
St. Florian Bräu Hell
St. Florian Bräu Dunkel
SEASONAL BEERS:
St. Florian Bräu Weizen Dunkel (Apr–Sep),
St. Florian Bräu Doppelbock Dunkel (winter)

Town-centre brewpub on Friedberg's main street. Although founded in 1988, brewing didn't begin until the following year. We don't think they supply anywhere else.

Friedberger Brauhaus
Kaiserstraße 37–39, 61169 Friedberg
Mon–Sat 11.00–24.00, Sun 11.00–22.00
DB Friedberg (Hessen) 900m

FRITZLAR   678

Brauhaus 18·80

Fritzlarer Dombräu GmbH
Brewery: Auf der Lache 4, 34560 Fritzlar
T 05622 91 88 09   **F** 05622 79 99 04
Office: Giessener Straße 56, 34560 Fritzlar
www.brauhaus1880.de
Owners: Jürgen Albers & Herbert Eifert
Founded: 2003   Output: 1,000hl
Availability: 2 pubs
REGULAR BEERS:
18·80 Hell, 18·80 Dunkel, 18·80 Hefeweizen

SEASONAL BEERS:
18·80 Sommerbier, 18·80 Altfränkisches Braunbier, 18·80 Schwarzbier, 18·80 Märzen, 18·80 Festbier, 18·80 Maibock, 18·80 Bonifatius Weizenbock, 18·80 Donator

Brewpub on the southern edge of Fritzlar. They have a second pub inside the medieval walled town centre. If you like your half-timbered buildings, you could do worse than come here.

🍺 Brauhaus 18·80
Auf der Lache 4, 34560 Fritzlar
Mon–Fri 17.00–24.00, Sat from 15.00, Sun from 11.00
DB Fritzlar 750m

🍺 Schenke 18·80
Jordan 1, 34560 Fritzlar
T 05622 918 80 12   **F** 05622 918 80 13
Mon–Sat from 17.00,
Sun 10.00–14.00 & from 17.00
DB Fritzlar 1.2km

FULDA 679

Hochstift

Hochstiftliches Brauhaus Fulda GmbH
Leipzigerstraße 12, 36037 Fulda
T 0661 835 00   **F** 0661 83 50 70
www.hochstift.de
Founded: 1848   Output: 300,000hl
REGULAR BEERS:
Hochstift Gold (4.8%)
Hochstift Schwarzer Hahn Landbier (4.9%)
Hochstift Pils (4.9%)
SEASONAL BEERS:
Hochstift Weihnachtsbier (5.6%)

Large regional brewery that also owns Hochstift Brauhaus in Motten and Bürgerbräu in Lauterbach. Two further breweries in its control (Auerhahn-Bräu and Salch) no longer brew.

🍺 Felsenkeller
Leipzigerstraße 12, 36037 Fulda
T 0661 727 84   **F** 0661 742 61
Mon–Thu 11.00–14.00 & 17.00–24.00,
Fri–Sun 11.00–24.00
DB Fulda 700m

Wiesenmühle

Brauhaus Wiesenmühle GmbH & Co. KG
Wiesenmühlenstraße 13, 36037 Fulda
T 0661 92 86 80   **F** 0661 928 68 39
www.wiesenmuehle.de
Founded: 1990   Output: 1,800hl
REGULAR BEER:
Wiesenmühlenbier
SEASONAL BEERS:
Mühlen Dunkel (Nov–Apr), **Mühlen Weizen** (May–Oct), **Mühlen Faschingsbier** (Feb), **Mühlen Fastenbier** (Mar), **Mühlen Osterbier** (Easter), **Mühlen Octoberfestbier** (Oct), **Mühlen Rauchbier** (Nov), **Mühlen Nikolausbier** (Dec), **Mühlen Silvesterbier** (New Year's Eve), **Mühlen Jännerbock** (Jan), **Mühlen Maibock** (May), **Mühlen Weihnachtsbock** (Dec)

Brewpub and hotel to the west of the city centre in a former mill on the river Fulda. Just the one regular beer but there are usually two seasonal beers available. The waterwheel still works, generating electricity for the mill.

🍺 Wiesenmühle
Wiesenmühlenstraße 13, 36037 Fulda
Daily 11.00–01.00; rooms available
DB Fulda 1.5km

GADERNHEIM (Lautertal) 680

Lautertaler Hausbrauerei

Nibelungenstraße 735,
64686 Lautertal-Gadernheim
T 06254 71 77
www.lautertaler-hausbrauerei.de
Founded: 1999   Availability: 1 pub
REGULAR BEERS:
Lautertaler Schwarzbier
Lautertaler Pils
Lautertaler Weizen

Pub on the main road through the village, with the brewery in an outhouse alongside. Bus No. 665 runs daily from Bensheim station to Gadernheim.

🍺 Lautertaler Hausbrauerei
Nibelungenstraße 735,
64686 Lautertal-Gadernheim
Closed Tue; Wed–Fri & Mon from 16.00, Sat from 12.00, Sun from 11.00
DB Bensheim 12km

GIESSEN 681

Alt-Giessen

Gasthausbrauerei Alt-Giessen
Westenlage 30–32, 35390 Gießen
T 0641 96 26 10   **F** 0641 962 61 66
www.altgiessen.de
Founded: 1991   Output: 2,000hl
REGULAR BEERS:
Alt-Giessen Helles
Alt-Giessen Dunkles
Alt-Giessen Hefe-Weizen

Large brewpub on the ring road at the south-western edge of the town centre. As far as we know they don't brew any seasonal beers.

🍺 **Alt-Giessen**
Westenlage 30–32, 35390 Gießen
Mon–Thu 11.30–01.00, Fri & Sat 11.30–02.00,
Sun 11.30–01.00   DB Giessen 700m

Giessener Brauhaus

Giessener Brauhaus A. & W. Denninghoff KG
Teichweg 8, 35396 Gießen-Wieseck
T 0641 500 80   **F** 0641 50 08 44
www.denninghoffs.de
Owner: Klaus Denninghoff   Founded: 1899
Output: 60,000hl   Availability: 400 pubs
DENNINGHOFF'S BEERS:
Denninghoff's Alt (4.8%)
Denninghoff's Premium (5%)
Denninghoff's Weisse Hefetrüb (5.2%)
Denninghoff's Weisse Dunkel (5.2%)
Denninghoff's Weisse Kristall (5.2%)
SEASONAL BEER:
Denninghoff's Wintertraum
GIESSENER BEERS:
Giessener Pilsner (4.9%), **Giessener Export** (5.2%)
FOR GUIDO FRANK, LICH:
Ice Cap Beer (5.5%), **Ice Cap Strong Beer** (7.4%)
FOR KRONENBRAUEREI HAUBACH, DILLENBURG
Haubach Pils (5.2%)

Modern brewery which moved from the centre of Gießen to the northern outskirts in 1976. The tap is on the eastern edge of the pedestrianised town centre. The ice cap beers are brewed using glacial ice imported from Greenland.

🍺 **Giessener Stube**
Neuen Bäue 8, 35390 Gießen
T 0641 376 94   **F** 0641 95 03 09

Closed Sun & hols; Mon–Sat 11.00–24.00
DB Gießen 1.3km

GROSS-BIEBERAU 682

Biberland

Brauhaus Biberland GmbH & Co. KG
Am Schaubacher Berg 17, 64401 Groß-Bieberau
T 06162 91 90 96   **F** 06162 91 90 98
www.biberland.de   Owner: Bernd Müller
Founded: 19.08.2000   Availability: 1 pub
REGULAR BEERS:
Biberland Hell
Biberland Dunkel
Biberland Weizen
SEASONAL BEERS:
**Biberland Märzen, Biberland Oktoberfestbier,
Biberland Bock**

Modern brewpub at the northern tip of the town. Several bus routes run from Reinheim station to Groß-Bieberau daily.

🍺 **Biberland**
Am Schaubacher Berg 17, 64401 Groß-Bieberau
Mon–Fri 11.30–14.00 & 18.00–24.00,
Sat 15.00–24.00, Sun 11.30–24.00
DB Reinheim (Odenwald) 2.8km

GROSS-UMSTADT 683

Umstädter Brauhaus

Zimmerstraße 28, 64823 Groß-Umstadt
T 06078 33 45   **F** 06078 715 53
www.umstaedter-brauhaus.de
Owner: Heinrich Eidmann   Founded: 1988
Output: 800hl   Availability: 1 pub
REGULAR BEERS:
Umstädter Pils (4.8%)
Umstädter Export (5.1%)
Umstädter Weisse (5.3%)
SEASONAL BEERS:
Umstädter Märzen, Umstädter Bock

Single-storeyed brewpub built on the site of the former Brenner brewery which closed in 1984. The beers aren't available anywhere else.

🍺 **Umstädter Brauhaus**
Zimmerstraße 28, 64823 Groß-Umstadt
Mon–Sat 18.00–24.00, Sun 16.00–24.00
DB Groß-Umstadt 900m

HALDORF (Edermünde) 684

Edermünder Brauscheune

Grifter Straße 3a, 34295 Edermünde-Haldorf
T 05665 96 98 96 **F** 05665 96 98 99
www.brauscheune.de
Owner: Karl-Friedrich Klitsch
Founded: 01.05.2000 Output: 800hl
REGULAR BEERS:
Edermünder Hell
Edermünder Dunkel
Edermünder Hefeweizen Hell
Edermünder Hefeweizen Dunkel
SEASONAL BEERS:
Edermünder Märzen, Edermünder Bock

Brewpub in the village of Haldorf, just to the
south-west of Edermünde. The brewer came
from the former Schöfferhofer brewery in Kassel.

🍺 **Edermünder Brauscheune**
Grifter Straße 3a, 34295 Edermünde-Haldorf
Closed Mon; Tue–Thu 16.00–01.00,
Fri 14.00–01.00, Sat, Sun & hols 12.00–01.00
DB Grifte 1.8km

HERBORN 685

Bärenbräu

HB Herborner Bärenbräu GmbH
Alte Marburgerstraße 2–8, 35745 Herborn
T 02772 70 20 **F** 02772 702 30
www.herborner-bier.com
Founded: 1879 Output: 70,000hl
REGULAR BEERS:
Herborner Bärenbräu Classix Dunkles (4.5%)
Herborner Bärenbräu Pils (4.7%)
Herborner Bärenbräu Export (4.9%)
Herborner Bären-Weisse (5.4%)
FOR SCHLOSSBRAUEREI, BRAUNFELS:
Braunfelser Pils (4.7%)

Regional brewery north of the station, on the
opposite side of the railway and dual carriageway to the medieval town centre. They don't have
a tap but most pubs in Herborn sell the beers.
DB Herborn (Dillkreis) 600m

IDSTEIN 686

Alte Feuerwache

Idsteiner Brauhaus Alte Feuerwache GmbH
Schulgasse 6, 65510 Idstein
T 06126 95 81 12 **F** 06126 93 86 66
www.brauhaus-alte-feuerwache.de
Founded: 30.07.2004
REGULAR BEERS:
Alte Feuerwache Helles
Alte Feuerwache Dunkles
SEASONAL BEERS:
Alte Feuerwache Pils, Alte Feuerwache Weizen,
Alte Feuerwache Märzen, Alte Feuerwache
Oktoberfestbier, Alte Feuerwache
Weihnachtsbier, Alte Feuerwache Bockbier

Brewpub in a former fire station north of the
town centre. The half-timbered building
complete with tower dates from 1924 but
appears much older.

🍺 **Alte Feuerwache**
Schulgasse 6, 65510 Idstein
Mon–Sat 11.30–24.00, Sun 11.00–23.00
DB Idstein (Taunus) 1.2km

KASSEL 687

Kleines Schweinchen

Konrad-Adenauer-Straße 117b,
34132 Kassel-Brasselsberg
T 0561 400 24 05 **F** 0561 94 04 85 55
www.steinernes-schweinchen.de
Owner: Thomas Nähler Founded: 2000
Availability: 1 pub
REGULAR BEERS:
Schweinchen-Bräu Hell
Schweinchen-Bräu Dunkel

The Little Piglet brewpub is located in the old
servants' quarters of the Steinernes Schweinchen hotel. Take bus No. 52 from either the
Hauptbahnhof or Wilhelmshöhe to Brasselsberg.

🍺 **Kleines Schweinchen**
Konrad-Adenauer-Straße 117b,
34132 Kassel-Brasselsberg
Daily from 17.00; rooms available
DB Kassel-Wilhelmshöhe 5km

Martini

Martini-Brauerei GmbH
Kölnische Straße 94–104, 34119 Kassel-West
T 0561 788 50   **F** 0561 788 52 68
www.martini-brauerei.de
Founded: 1859   Output: 140,000hl
REGULAR BEERS:
Kasseler Premium Pils (4.8%)
Martini Edel-Pils (4.8%)
Martini Naturtrüb (4.8%)
Martini Meister Pilsener (5.1%)
Martini Weissbier Hell (5.2%)
Martini Weissbier Dunkel (5.2%)
Martini Weissbier Kristallklar (5.2%)
SEASONAL BEERS:
Martini Winterbier (4.9%),
Martini Martinator (7.7%)
FOR WIEDERHOLTS, NÖRTEN-HARDENBERG:
Nörten-Hardenberger Pils (4.8%), **Nörten-Hardenberger Export** (5.2%), **Nörten-Hardenberger Hefe-Weißbier** (5.2%)

Large brewery to the south-west of the Hauptbahnhof, with the tap opposite. The Nörten-Hardenberg beers are brewed for Wiederholts brewery which stopped brewing in 1991.

🍺 **Braupfanne**
Kölnische Straße 93, 34119 Kassel-West
T 0561 134 77
Closed Sun & hols; Mon–Sat 11.00–24.00
🚃 Annastraße 250m   🚆 Kassel Hbf 1km

KNALLHÜTTE (Baunatal)   688

Hütt

Hütt-Brauerei Bettenhauser GmbH & Co. KG
Knallhütte 1, 34225 Baunatal-Knallhütte
T 0561 49 90 70   **F** 0561 499 07 50
www.huett.de
Owner: Frank Bettenhauser   Founded: 1752
Output: 82,739hl   Availability: 354 pubs
REGULAR BEERS:
Hütt Pils (4.8%)
Hütt Luxus Pils (4.9%)
Hütt Knallhütter Schwarzes Gold (4.9%)
Hütt Naturtrüb (4.9%)
Hütt Urknall (4.9%)
Hütt Grimms (4.9%)
Hütt Weizen-Kristall (5%)
Hütt Export (5.1%)

Hütt Hefeweizen (5.2%)
Hütt Hefeweizen Dunkel (5.2%)
SEASONAL BEER:
Hütt Winterbock (7%)

Brewery, tap and beer garden close to the A44/A49 interchange, on the opposite side of the A49 to the Volkswagen factory. It's debatable whether Knallhütte is separate from Rengershausen but we think it is. Bus No. 50 runs from Kassel Hbf on weekdays – get off at Lohkaserne. They also own Hessisches Löwenbier in Malsfeld.

🍺 **Brauhaus Knallhütte**
Knallhütte 1, 34225 Baunatal-Knallhütte
T 0561 49 20 76   **F** 0561 475 69 05
Fri & Sat 11.00–23.00, Sun–Thu 11.00–22.00
🚆 Baunatal-Rengershausen 2.2km,
   Kassel Hbf 9km

KRONBERG   689

Kronberger Brauhaus

Katharinenstraße 4, 61476 Kronberg
T 06173 32 13 54   **F** 06173 32 13 53
www.kronberger-brauhaus.de
Owner: Margot Schmidt   Founded: 2000
Output: 800hl
REGULAR BEERS:
Kronberger Helles
Kronberger Dunkles
SEASONAL BEERS:
**Kronberger Weizen, Kronberger Märzen,
Kronberger Festbier, Kronberger Maibock,
Kronberger Weihnachtsbock**

Brewpub in the centre of Kronberg, an attractive town in the foothills of the Taunus region – and the terminus of the S4 S-Bahn line from Frankfurt.

🍺 **Kronberger Brauhaus**
Katharinenstraße 4, 61476 Kronberg
Sat from 11.00, Sun–Fri from 17.00
Ⓢ Kronberg (Taunus) 600m

LAMPERTHEIM   690

Alte Kelter

Alte Kelter Hausbrauerei Lampertheim
Römerstraße 123, 68623 Lampertheim
T 06206 133 57   **E** wolfgang.tanzer@gmx.de
Owner: Wolfgang Tanzer   Founded: 2005

REGULAR BEERS:
Lampertheim No. 1 Mild (5%)
Lampertheim No. 1 Extra Herb (5%)
Lampertheim No. 2 Dunkel (5%)
SEASONAL BEER:
Lampertheim No. 3 Bockbier (8.5%)

The Old Wine-Press started brewing beer in January 2005. This half-timbered pub in the centre of Lampertheim also has a very pleasant beer garden.

Alte Kelter
Römerstraße 123, 68623 Lampertheim
Closed Tue; Wed–Sat & Mon 18.00–24.00,
Sun 17.00–24.00   DB Lampertheim 1.3km

LAUTERBACH   691

Lauterbacher-Auerhahn

Lauterbacher Burgbrauerei
Auerhahn-Bräu Schlitz GmbH
Cent 8, 36341 Lauterbach
T 06641 18 00   **F** 06641 180 90
www.lauterbacher-auerhahn.de
Founded: 1527.   Output: 90,000hl
LAUTERBACHER BEERS:
Lauterbacher Pils (4.9%)
Lauterbacher Erbpils (4.9%)
Lauterbacher Bier-Strolch (5.2%)
Lauterbacher Export (5.3%)
Lauterbacher Hefe-Weizen (5.3%)
Lauterbacher Edel-Weizen (5.3%)
SEASONAL BEER:
Vogelsberger Festtagsbier (5.3%)
AUERHAHN BEERS:
Auerhahn Pils (4.9%),
Auerhahn Urhahn Helles Alt (4.9%),
Auerhahn Bütten-Alt (4.9%),
Auerhahn Dark (4.9%),
Auerhahn Vogelsberger Urstoff (4.9%),
Auerhahn Export (5.3%)

Town-centre brewery owned by Hochstiftliches Brauhaus Fulda. Auerhahn beers were brewed in Schlitz until all production was transferred here in 1998.

Zum Felsenkeller
Cent 6, 36341 Lauterbach
T 06641 25 90
Sat from 17.00, Sun–Fri 11.00–14.00 & from 17.00
DB Lauterbach (Hessen) Nord 1.3km

LICH   692

Licher

Licher Privatbrauerei Jhring-Melchior GmbH
In den Hardtberggärten, 35423 Lich
T 06404 820   **F** 06404 821 17
www.licher.de
Owner: Bitburger Getränkegruppe
Founded: 1854   Output: 860,000hl
REGULAR BEERS:
Licher Leicht Pilsner (2.8%)
Licher Premium Pilsner (4.9%)
Licher Export (5.4%)
SEASONAL BEER:
Licher Doppelbock (7.6%, winter)

Very large brewery close to the railway station, owned by Holsten for a few years but now in Bitburger's hands. They don't have a tap but the beers are widely available throughout much of Hessen and beyond.
DB Lich (Oberhessen) 350m

MAINZ-KASTEL   693

Brauhaus Castel

Otto-Suhr-Ring 27, 55252 Mainz-Kastel
T 06134 249 99   **F** 06134 627 09
www.brauhaus-castel.de
Owner: Sabine Sonne   Founded: 1990
Output: 1,500hl   Availability: 1 pub
REGULAR BEERS:
Castel Hell (4.5%)
Castel Dunkel (4.8%)
Castel Weizen (4.9%)
SEASONAL BEERS:
Castel Festbier (5%), **Castel Märzen** (5.2%),
Castel Maibock (6.5%), **Castel Castelator** (6.8%)

Modern brewery and tap in Mainz-Kastel, officially a suburb of Wiesbaden. There are buses to Otto-Suhr-Ring from both Wiesbaden and Mainz, as well as Kastel station.

Brauhaus Castel
Otto-Suhr-Ring 27, 55252 Mainz-Kastel
Mon–Sat 11.00–24.00, Sun 10.00–24.00
DB Mainz-Kastel 1.9km, Mainz Hbf 4km

MALSFELD 694

Hessisches Löwenbier

Hessisches Löwenbier Brauerei GmbH & Co. KG
Brauereistraße 5, 34323 Malsfeld
T 05661 704 10　**F** 05661 70 41 35
www.hessisches-loewenbier.de
Owner: Frank Bettenhauser　Founded: 1615
REGULAR BEERS:
Hessisches Löwen Premium-Pilsner (5%)
Hessisches Löwen Naturtrüb
Hessisches Löwen Export
Hessisches Löwen Hefe-Weizen Hell (5.3%)

Known as Genossenschaftsbrauerei Malsfeld
until it closed in 2003, this small brewery
changed names when it re-opened in 2004 after
it had been acquired by the owner of the Hütt-
Brauerei in Knallhütte. We think the Goldener
Löwe in the neighbouring village of Beiseforth
(Mühlenstraße 1) may shortly re-open as the tap.
DB Malsfeld 1.1km

MICHELSTADT 695

Dörr

Hochstraße 15, 64720 Michelstadt
T 06061 23 47
E michelstaedter-bier@t-online.de
Owner: Georg Dörr　Founded: 1821
Output: 8,000hl
REGULAR BEERS:
Michelstädter Dunkel
Michelstädter Pilsener
Michelstädter Export
Michelstädter Ratsherrn Jubiläumsbier
SEASONAL BEER:
Michelstädter Bock

Small brewery on the opposite side of the town
centre to the tap which was its original home.
The beers can be found in several other pubs
locally.

🍺 **Zum Deutschen Haus**
Bahnhofstraße 20, 64720 Michelstadt
T 06061 36 99
Closed Mon; Tue–Sun 11.30–14.30 & 17.00–22.00
DB Michelstadt 600m

Rathausbräu

Michelstädter Rathausbräu GmbH
Mauerstraße 1–3, 64720 Michelstadt
T 06061 56 66　**F** 06061 56 65
www.rathausbraeu.de
Owner: Thomas Schwarz　Founded: 1995
REGULAR BEERS:
Rathausbräu Pils
Rathausbräu Weizen
Rathausbräu Märzen
SEASONAL BEERS:
Rathausbräu Altbier, Rathausbräu Narrhallabräu,
Rathausbräu Maibock, Rathausbräu
Weizendoppelbock, Rathausbräu Nikolator

Brewpub in the old town, close to the town hall
from which it takes its name. They distil their
own beer schnapps.

🍺 **Rathausbräu**
Mauerstraße 1–3, 64720 Michelstadt
Daily 11.00–01.00
DB Michelstadt 850m

NIDDA 696

Niddaer Marktbräu

Gasthofbrauerei-Hotel zur Traube
Markt 21, 63667 Nidda
T 06043 40 47 40　**F** 06043 40 47 41
www.hotel-zur-traube.de
Founded: 1998
REGULAR BEERS:
Marktbräu Hell
Marktbräu Dunkel
SEASONAL BEERS:
Marktbräu Hefeweizen, Marktbräu Narrenalt,
Marktbräu Maibier, Marktbräu Weihnachtsbock

The Hotel zur Traube was destroyed by a fire in
January 1996. A brewery was added when the
place was rebuilt, opening two years later.

🍺 **Zur Traube**
Markt 21, 63667 Nidda
T 06043 404 70　**F** 06043 40 47 10
Mon–Thu 11.00–14.30 & 17.00–24.00, Fri
11.00–14.30 & 17.00–01.00, Sat 11.00–01.00,
Sun 11.00–24.00; rooms available
DB Nidda 850m

OBER-MOSSAU (Mossautal) 697

Schmucker

Privat-Brauerei Schmucker GmbH & Co. KG
Hauptstraße 89, 64756 Mossautal/Ober-Mossau
T 06061 70 20   **F** 06061 20 81
www.schmucker-bier.de
Owner: F. M. Lippmann   Founded: 1780
Output: 200,000hl
REGULAR BEERS:
Schmucker Leicht (2.8%)
Schmucker Meister Pils (4.8%)
Schmucker Schwarzbier (4.8%)
Schmucker Kellerbier (4.8%)
Schmucker Gold (4.8%)
Schmucker Diät Pils (4.9%)
Schmucker Privat Export (5%)
Schmucker Hefe-Weizen (5%)
Schmucker Hefe-Weizen Dunkel (5%)
Schmucker Kristall-Weizen (5%)
Schmucker Märzen (5.5%)
SEASONAL BEERS:
Schmucker Rosé-Bock (8%), **Schmucker Doppel-Bock Dunkel** (8%)

Large brewery in the centre of the village, owned by the Schmucker family since 1895. Bus No. 31 runs from Michelstadt station to the brewery a few times on weekdays and is supplemented by ASTs. The Rosé-Bock receives its reddish hue from various special malts that are used in the brewing process.

🍺 Schmucker

Hauptstraße 91, 64756 Mossautal/Ober-Mossau
T 06061 941 10   **F** 06061 28 61
Closed Mon; Tue–Sun 11.30–24.00; rooms available
DB Michelstadt 7km

OBERURSEL 698

Alt-Oberurseler Brauhaus

Ackergasse 13, 61440 Oberursel
T 06171 543 70   **F** 06171 569 00
www.meinbier.de
Owner: Thomas Studanski   Founded: 1994
Output: 1,200hl   Availability: 1 pub
REGULAR BEER:
Oberurseler Brauhaus Pils

SEASONAL BEERS:
Oberurseler Brauhaus Erntebier, Oberurseler Brauhaus Kupferbier, Oberurseler Brauhaus Altbier, Oberurseler Brauhaus Hefeweizen, Oberurseler Brauhaus Winterweiße, Oberurseler Brauhaus Vollmondbier, Oberurseler Brauhaus Holloweeen-Bier, Oberurseler Brauhaus Märzenbier, Oberurseler Brauhaus Fastenbock, Oberurseler Brauhaus Maibock, Oberurseler Brauhaus Weihnachtsbock, Oberurseler Brauhaus St. Ursula Doppelbock

Brewpub in the centre of town that we think has connections with Vetter in Heidelberg. Oberursel is on the Frankfurt underground network.

🍺 Alt-Oberurseler Brauhaus

Ackergasse 13, 61440 Oberursel
Mon–Thu 11.30–24.00, Fri & Sat 11.30–01.00, Sun 10.00–23.00
U U3 Oberursel-Portstraße 500m
DB Oberursel (Taunus) 800m

PFUNGSTADT 699

Pfungstädter

Pfungstädter Brauerei Hildebrand KG
Eberstädter Straße 89, 64319 Pfungstadt
T 06157 80 20   **F** 06157 80 25 00
www.pfungstaedter.de
Founded: 1831   Output: 450,000hl
REGULAR BEERS:
Pfungstädter Leicht (2.4%)
Pfungstädter Edel-Pils Premium (4.9%)
Pfungstädter Golden Premium (4.9%)
Pfungstädter Extra Mild (4.9%)
Pfungstädter Justus Weizen Hefe Hell (4.9%)
Pfungstädter Justus Weizen Dunkel (4.9%)
Pfungstädter Justus Weizen Kristall (4.9%)
Pfungstädter 1831 Schwarzbier (5.3%)
Pfungstädter Export (5.3%)
SEASONAL BEERS:
Pfungstädter Maibock (6.5%),
Pfungstädter St. Nikolaus Bock (7%)

Very large regional brewery whose beers are available over much of Hessen and in neighbouring states. Bus route P runs from Eberstadt station to Pfungstadt.

🍺 Brauerei-Ausschank

Mühlstraße 1, 64319 Pfungstadt
T 06157 95 55 91   Daily 11.00–23.00
DB Darmstadt-Eberstadt 2.1km

RÖHRIGSHOF (Philippsthal) 700

Extra

Hattorfer Straße 1, 36269 Philippsthal-Röhrigshof
T 06620 91 95 80   F 06620 91 95 79
www.extra-brauhaus.de
Owner: Volker Borowski   Founded: 2002
Availability: 1 pub
REGULAR BEERS:
Extra Brauhaus Lager
Extra Hattorfer Rauchbier

American-themed roadside pub with a tiny
brewery built into the bar. Bus No. 311 runs
from Bad Hersfeld on weekdays and Saturday
mornings but the return service isn't much use.

Extra
Hattorfer Straße 1, 36269 Philippsthal-Röhrigshof
Sat from 13.00, Sun from 08.00
DB Bad Hersfeld 20km

SCHLÜCHTERN 701

Brauhaus Schlüchtern

Höbäckerweg 3, 36381 Schlüchtern
T 06661 711 21   F 06655 74 99 10
www.brauhaus-schluechtern.de
Owner: Normen Müller   Founded: 1995
Output: 1,000hl   Availability: 6 pubs

REGULAR BEERS:
Brauhaus Pils
Brauhaus Dunkles Vollbier

Microbrewery and tap on the southern side of
town, close to the river Kinzig. The beers are
available in five other pubs in the valley. We
think they also brew some seasonals.

Brauhaus Schlüchtern
Höbäckerweg 3, 36381 Schlüchtern
Mon 15.00–01.00, Tue–Thu 11.00–01.00,
Fri & Sat 11.00–02.00, Sun & hols 10.00–01.00
DB Schlüchtern 1km

SELIGENSTADT 702

Glaabsbräu

Privatbrauerei Glaab GmbH & Co. KG
Frankfurterstraße 9, 63500 Seligenstadt
T 06182 92 60   F 06182 92 62 00
www.glaabsbraeu.de
Owners: Richard & Robert Glaab
Founded: 1744   Output: 60,000hl
REGULAR BEERS:
Glaabsbräu Pilsener (4.9%)
Glaabsbräu Kristallweizen (4.9%)
Glaabsbräu Hefeweizen Hell (5%)
Glaabsbräu Hefeweizen Dunkel (5%)
Glaabsbräu 1744 Kellertrübes (5.3%)
Glaabsbräu Dunkles (5.3%)
Glaabsbräu Export (5.3%)

SEASONAL BEER:
Glaabsbräu Doppel-Bock (7.5%, Oct–Dec)

Brewery behind its original home, the Roman Emperor pub in the old town centre. A couple of hundred metres away is the river Main which marks the border with Bayern.

🍺 **Zum Römischen Kaiser**
Frankfurterstraße 9, 63500 Seligenstadt
T 06182 222 96
Mon–Fri 11.30–14.00 & 17.30–23.00,
Sat 10.00–24.00   Sun 10.00–23.00
DB Seligenstadt 750m

Kleines Brauhaus

Seligenstädter Klein Brauerei GmbH & Co. KG
Eisenbahnstraße 6, 63500 Seligenstadt
T 06182 82 97 29   **F** 06182 89 90 95
www.kleinesbrauhaus.de   Owner: Peter Klein
Founded: 1999   Output: 800hl
REGULAR BEERS:
Kleines Helles
Kleines Dunkles
Kleines Weizen
SEASONAL BEERS:
Kleines Dunkles Weizen, Kleines Roggenbier, Kleines Weihnachtsfestbier, Kleines Maibock

Brewpub conveniently situated for Seligenstadt railway station – it's directly opposite. We don't think the beers are sold anywhere else.

🍺 **Kleines Brauhaus**
Eisenbahnstraße 6, 63500 Seiligenstadt
Mon–Sat 16.00–24.00, Sun 11.00–24.00
DB Seligenstadt 50m

TREYSA (Schwalmstadt)   703

Schwalm Bräu

Privat Brauerei Friedrich Haaß KG
Ascheröde Straße 9, 34613 Schwalmstadt-Treysa
T 06691 230 51   **F** 06691 230 53
www.schwalmbraeu.de
Founded: 1820   Output: 10,000hl
REGULAR BEERS:
Schwalm Bräu Dunkles Landbier (4.6%)
Schwalm Bräu Ur-Typ (4.8%)
Schwalm Bräu Pilsener (4.8%)
Schwälmer Weizen Hefe-Hell (5.1%)
Schwälmer Weizen Hefe-Dunkel (5.1%)
Schwälmer Weizen Kristall (5.3%)

SEASONAL BEER:
Schwalm Bräu Bockbier (6.8%)

Small brewery on the western side of Treysa, owned by the Haaß family since 1890. The tap is just down the street.

🍺 **Am Brauhaus**
Ascheröde Straße 1, 34613 Schwalmstadt-Treysa
T 06691 15 59   Daily from 17.00
DB Treysa 500m

WEILBURG   704

Helbig

Brauerei August Helbig KG
Ahäuser Weg 8–10, 35781 Weilburg
T 06471 390 81   **F** 06471 15 99
www.brauerei-helbig.de
Founded: 1822   Output: 10,000hl
REGULAR BEERS:
Weilburger Pils (4.8%)
Weilburger Lord Pils (4.8%)
Weilburger Altdeutsch Dunkel (5%)
Weilburger Weißbier
Weilburger Dunkles Weißbier
Weilburger Kristall-Weizen
SEASONAL BEER:
Weilburger Festbier

Small brewery on the opposite side of the river Lahn to the railway station, close to Germany's only canal tunnel, built in the 1840s to avoid the long detour around the town which is virtually encircled by the river. The tap is in the old town in the shadow of the castle that dominates Weilburg.

🍺 **Weilburger Hof**
Schwanengasse 14, 35781 Weilburg
T 06471 71 53
Closed Mon; Tue–Sun 11.30–14.00 & 17.30–22.00
DB Weilburg 1km

WILLINGEN (Upland)   705

Rössel Bräu

Dampfbierhaus Rössel Bräu
Waldecker Straße 26, 34508 Willingen (Upland)
T 05632 63 40   **F** 05632 41 76
www.dampfbierhaus.de
Founded: 2002

REGULAR BEERS:
Rössel Bräu Dampfbier Hell
Rössel Bräu Dampfbier Dunkel
Rössel Bräu Hefeweizen

Small brewpub on the main road through Willingen, one of the most northerly winter sports resorts in central Europe. We don't know of any seasonal beers.

Dampfbierhaus
Waldecker Straße 26, 34508 Willingen (Upland)
Daily from 11.00
DB Willingen 1.2km

Willinger Brauhaus

Willinger Brauhaus GmbH & Co. KG
In den Kämpen 2, 34508 Willingen (Upland)
T 05632 988 70 **F** 05632 98 87 28
www.willinger-brauhaus.de
Founded: 1989 Output: 3,800hl
REGULAR BEERS:
Willinger Landbier Dunkel (4.8%)
Willinger Pils (4.8%)
Willinger Hefeweizen (5.5%)
SEASONAL BEER:
Willinger Weihnachtsbock (7%)

Large brewpub close to the station that also owns a nearby hotel and the Brauhaus zum Löwen in Mühlhausen, Thüringen.

Willinger Brauhaus
In den Kämpen 2, 34508 Willingen (Upland)
Fri & Sat 10.30–03.30, Sun–Thu 10.30–01.00
DB Willingen 200m

WITZENHAUSEN 706

Schinkel's Brauhaus

Burgstraße 18, 37213 Witzenhausen
T 05542 91 12 10 **F** 05542 91 12 11
www.schinkels-brauhaus.de
Owner: Rainer Schinkel Founded: 1997
Output: 900hl Availability: 2 pubs
REGULAR BEERS:
Witzenhüsser Kräusen
Schinkel's Dunkel
Witzenhäuser Weizen

Brewpub close to the centre of Witzenhausen, on the opposite side of the river Werra to the railway station. They don't brew any seasonal beers.

Schinkel's Brauhaus
Burgstraße 10, 37213 Witzenhausen
Daily from 17.00
DB Witzenhausen Nord 1.6km

WOLFHAGEN 707

Alte Brauerei

Alte Brauerei Wolfhagen GmbH
Gerichtsstraße 2, 34466 Wolfhagen
T 05692 99 36 87 **F** 05692 99 43 34
www.brauerei-wolfhagen.de
Founded: 2000 Output: 500hl
Availability: 6 pubs
REGULAR BEERS:
Ur-Wolfhager
Wolfsbräu
Schwarzer Wolf
SEASONAL BEER:
Wolfhagen Bockbier

Microbrewery adjoining the Café am Kornmarkt, in the centre of Wolfhagen. There was apparently a brewery on the site as far back as 1491. The Ur-Wolfhager is brewed to a recipe from 1799.

Alte Brauerei
Gerichtsstraße 2, 34466 Wolfhagen
T 05692 99 38 37 **F** 05692 98 78 48
Closed Mon; Tue–Sun 18.00–01.00
DB Wolfhagen 900m

WOLZHAUSEN (Breidenbach) 708

Thome

Brauerei H. Thome KG
Sandstraße 2, 35236 Breidenbach-Wolzhausen
T 06465 915 30 **F** 06465 91 53 22
Founded: 1868 Output: 10,000hl
REGULAR BEER:
Thome Pils

One of the country's smallest Pils-only producers, we don't think they have a tap. If you want to find out for yourself, bus No. 491 runs daily from Wallau station.
DB Wallau (Lahn) 8km

Mecklenburg-Vorpommern
(Mecklenburg Western Pommerania)

NORTH-EASTERN STATE, the most sparsely populated in Germany. The Baltic Sea forms the northern border, giving Mecklenburg-Vorpommern a longish coastline that attracts people from all over the country. The capital is Schwerin, a lovely old city situated on one of Germany's largest lakes.

The islands of Rügen and Usedom are particularly popular destinations, the former home to one of two narrow-gauge steam railways in the region, and the latter to the History of Technology Museum – the V1 and V2 rockets were once developed here. Many towns and cities are well worth a visit, not least Stralsund and Wismar, both UNESCO World Heritage sites.

As you might expect given the low population density, breweries are few in number, with just four surviving from the DDR era. The majority are modern brewpubs, built to cater for tourists.

Transport: Public transport isn't bad, particularly along the coast, but the region's not as well served as some. A Mecklenburg-Vorpommern day ticket currently costs €22 for up to five people, time restrictions being the same as in most other states. As ever, check which services it's valid on.

AHLBECK 709

Ahlbecker Kellerbräu
Seestraße 14, 17419 Ahlbeck
T 038378 282 32   **F** 038378 671 00
www.hotel-seestern.de
Owner: Dietrich Holst   Founded: 1997
REGULAR BEER:
Kellerbräu Hell

Brewpub in the cellar of the Seestern hotel. Ahlbeck (sometimed prefixed 'Seebad') is a seaside resort on the island of Usedom, and home to Germany's oldest pier.

Holsten-Keller
Seestraße 14, 17419 Ahlbeck
Closed Thu; Fri–Wed 11.00–22.00; rooms available
DB Ahlbeck Ostseetherme 700m

ALT REDDEVITZ
(Middelhagen) 710

Kliesow's Reuse
Dorfstraße 23a, 18586 Middelhagen-Alt Reddevitz
T 038308 21 71   **F** 038308 255 27
www.gasthof-kliesows-reuse.de
Owner: Heidi Kliesow   Founded: 1998
Output: 350hl   Availability: 1 pub
REGULAR BEER:
Reusenbräu Dunkel

Pub and restaurant in former farm buildings that also has a small brewery. They shut for four months during winter. The nearest railway is the narrow-gauge Rügensche Kleinbahn which operates daily. Bus No. 24 runs from Göhren a couple of times a day.

Kliesow's Reuse
Dorfstraße 23a, 18586 Middelhagen-Alt Reddevitz
Nov–Feb: closed.
Mar–Oct: closed Tue; Wed–Mon 09.00–22.00
DB Philippshagen 4km, Göhren 5.5km

DARGUN 711

Darguner
Darguner Brauerei GmbH
Brauereistraße 3, 17159 Dargun
T 039959 30 10   **F** 039959 301 61
www.brauerei-dargun.de

Owner: Harboe Brewery, Skælskør, Denmark
Founded: 1991   Output: 450,000hl
REGULAR BEERS:
Darguner Schwarzbier (4.8%)
Darguner Pilsener (5%)
Darguner Dunkel (5.2%)
Darguner Klosterbräu Premium (5.2%)
Dargun 98'er Pilsener (5.2%)
SEASONAL BEERS:
Darguner Ernte-Bräu (5.2%),
Darguner Oster-Bier (5.2%),
Darguner Weihnachtsbier (5.2%),
Darguner Mai-Bock (7.5%)

Large, modern brewery, founded by the Danish brewer Harboe in 1991. We think they brew a number of other beers that are sold in cans and plastic bottles. Public transport to Dargun seems to be lacking.
DB Demmin 14km

HERINGSDORF   712

Usedomer Brauhaus

Privatbrauerei zu Heringsdorf
Platz des Friedens, 17424 Heringsdorf
T 038378 614 20   **F** 038378 611 00
www.usedomer-brauhaus.de
Founded: 2004
REGULAR BEERS:
Usedomer Hell
Usedomer Schwarzbier
Usedomer Weizen

Brewpub in part of the Ostseeresidentz hotel. Like many other towns on Usedom, Heringsdorf is sometimes preceded by 'Seebad'.

🍺 **Usedomer Brauhaus**
Platz des Friedens, 17424 Heringsdorf
Daily from 12.00; rooms available
DB Seebad Heringsdorf 800m

KRUMMENHAGEN
(Steinhagen)   713

Rumpelstilz

Back- und Brauscheune Rumpelstilz
Dorfstraße 19, 18442 Steinhagen-Krummenhagen
T 038327 613 34   **F** 038327 613 46
E rumpelstilz-brauscheune@t-online.de

Owner: Burkhardt Steinfurth
Founded: 11.04.2003
REGULAR BEER:
Rumpelstilz Dunkel

Pub in the small village of Krummenhagen that brews its own beer and also bakes its own bread. We think the closest you can get by public transport is Zarrendorf, the best part of an hour away on foot.

🍺 **Rumpelstilz**
Dorfstraße 19, 18442 Steinhagen-Krummenhagen
Winter: Mon–Fri 18.00–22.00, Sat–Sun 11.00–22.00
Summer: daily 11.00–22.00
DB Zarrendorf 4.5km

KÜHLUNGSBORN   714

Ostsee Brauhaus

Strandstraße 41, 18225 Kühlungsborn
T 038293 40 60   **F** 038293 406 30
www.ostsee-brauhaus.de
Owner: Jörg Mehl   Founded: 1999
Output: 1,300hl   Availability: 1 pub
REGULAR BEERS:
Kühlungsbräu Helles (4.9%)
Kühlungsbräu Weizenbier (5.1%)
SEASONAL BEERS:
Kühlungsbräu Osterbier (4.9%, Oct),
Kühlungsbräu Festbier (5.1%, Oct),
Kühlungsbräu Weihnachtsbier (5.1%, winter),
Kühlungsbräu Maibock (6.8%, May)

Brewpub and hotel, one of half a dozen owned by Jörg Mehl. The nearest station is on the 'Molli', a narrow-gauge, steam-hauled railway that runs from Bad Doberan.

🍺 **Ostsee Brauhaus-Hotel**
Sandstraße 41, 18225 Kühlungsborn
Winter: Mon–Fri 17.00–24.00, Sat/Sun 11.00–24.00
Summer: daily 11.00–24.00; rooms available
DB Ostseebad Kühlungsborn Ost 400m

LÜBZ   715

Lübzer

Mecklenburgische Brauerei Lübz GmbH
Parchimer Straße 31, 19386 Lübz
T 038731 362 00   **F** 038731 362 95
www.luebzer.de

Owner: Carlsberg Breweries   Founded: 1877
Output: 900,000hl
REGULAR BEERS:
Lübzer Life (4.9%)
Lübzer Pils (4.9%)
Lübzer Export (5.4%)
Lübzer Bock (7%)

Easily Mecklenburg-Vorpommern's largest brewery, once owned by Holsten but now in the hands of the Danes. The tap is in the town centre, on the opposite side of the river Elde to the brewery.

📍 Alter Amtsturm
Am Markt 23, 19386 Lübz
T 038731 203 85
Daily 11.00–23.00
[DB] Lübz 800m

MIDDELHAGEN (Rügen)   716

Zur Linde

Landgasthof zur Linde Rügen
Dorfstraße 20, 18586 Middelhagen
T 038308 55 40   **F** 038308 554 90
www.landgasthof-zur-linde-ruegen.de
Owner: Steffen Leistert   Founded: 2001
Output: 150hl   Availability: 1 pub
REGULAR BEERS:
Zur Linde Biolandbier Hell (3.5%)
Zur Linde Biolandbier Dunkel (3.5%)

Supposedly the oldest pub on Rügen, Zur Linde had a small brewery installed in 2001. Middelhagen is within walking distance of the Philippshagen halt on the island's steam railway, and there are regular buses from Göhren which also have mainline connections. The beers are brewed from organic ingredients, and the hotel also offers a range of health treatments.

📍 Zur Linde
Dorfstraße 20, 18586 Middelhagen
Daily 12.00–23.00; rooms available
[DB] Philippshagen 2km, Göhren 3.5km

NEUBRANDENBURG   717

Alter Schlachthof

Brauhaus am Alten Schlachthof
Rostocker Straße 33, 17033 Neubrandenburg
T 0395 563 07 89

www.alter-schlachthof.com
Founded: 2003
REGULAR BEERS:
Alter Schlachthof Hell
Alter Schlachthof Dunkel
Alter Schlachthof Weizen

Brewpub in a former abattoir west of the walled city centre, next door to a similarly named neon-lit hip-hop disco, American diner, pizzeria and large beer garden. We believe they also brew seasonal beers.

📍 Alten Schlachthof
Rostocker Straße 33, 17033 Neubrandenburg
Daily from 17.00
[DB] Neubrandenburg 1.3km

ROSTOCK   718

Rostocker

Hanseatische Brauerei Rostock GmbH
Doberaner Straße 27, 18057 Rostock/
Kröpeliner Tor-Vorstadt
T 0381 45 64 50   **F** 0381 456 46 11
www.rostocker.de
Owner: Oetker Gruppe AG   Founded: 1878
Output: 400,000hl
REGULAR BEERS:
Rostocker Pilsener (4.9%)
Rostocker Hansebräu (4.9%)
Rostocker Dunkel (4.9%)
Rostocker Export (5.5%)
Rostocker Bock-Hell (6.9%)
Rostocker Bock-Dunkel (6.9%)
Freibeuter Starkbier (9%)

Large regional brewery owned by Beck's for much of the 1990s but now in the hands of Dr. Oetker (under Brau und Brunnen). The tap is next door.

📍 Braukeller
Doberaner Straße 26, 18057 Rostock/
Kröpeliner Tor-Vorstadt
T 0381 456 46 05
Closed Sun; Mon–Sat 15.00–22.00
[Tram] Doberaner Platz 250m
[DB] Rostock Parkstraße 1.2km, Hbf 1.6km

Trotzenburg

Ostsee Brauhaus AG 'Trotzenburg'
Tiergartenallee 6, 18059 Rostock-Hansaviertel

T 0381 20 36 00　**F** 0381 203 60 29
www.brauhaus-trotzenburg.de
Owner: Jörg Mehl　Founded: 19.11.2001
Output: 2,000hl　Availability: 1 pub
REGULAR BEERS:
Trotzenburger Helles (4.9%)
Trotzenburger Osterbier (4.9%)
SEASONAL BEERS:
Trotzenburger Weizen (5.1%),
Trotzenburger Oktoberfestbier (5.1%),
Trotzenburger Winterbier (5.1%),
Trotzenburger Maibock (6.8%)

Brewpub opposite the Zoo, rescued from
dereliction in the late 1990s. The beer range is
the same as in the Ostsee Brauhaus in Kühlungsborn. Jörg Mehl also owns brewpubs in Gladbeck,
Gummersbach, Lüdenscheid and Wuppertal.

🍺 Trotzenburg
Tiergartenalle 6, 18059 Rostock-Hansaviertel
Mon–Thu 11.00–23.00, Fri & Sat 11.00–01.00,
Sun 10.00–21.00
Tram Nos. 3 & 6 Zoo 20m
DB Thierfelder Straße 900m, Hbf 3.5km

SCHWERIN　719

Schweriner Schloßbrauerei

Schweriner Schloßbrauerei, Zweigniederlassung
der Oettinger Brauerei GmbH
Schweriner Straße 61, 19061 Schwerin-Wüstmark
T 0385 686 80　**F** 0385 686 81 00
Owner: Oettinger Gruppe　Founded: 1850
Output: 400,000hl
REGULAR BEERS:
Von Raven Pilsener (4.8%)
Schweriner Pilsener (4.9%)
Mecklenburger Landbier (5.1%)
Von Raven Export (5.4%)
Schweriner Export (5.5%)
Petermännchen Pils (5.6%)
SEASONAL BEER:
Schweriner Bock (7.1%)
FOR OETTINGER, OETTINGEN:
Original Oettinger Leicht (2.8%),
Original Oettinger Leichte Weiße (2.8%),
Original Oettinger Vollbier Hell (4.7%),
Original Oettinger Pils (4.7%),
Original Oettinger Alt (4.9%),
Original Oettinger Gold (4.9%),
Original Oettinger Schwarzbier (4.9%),

Original Oettinger Hefeweißbier (4.9%),
Original Oettinger Dunkles Weißbier (4.9%),
Original Oettinger Kristall Weizen (4.9%),
Original Oettinger Export (5.4%),
Original Oettinger Urtyp (5.6%)
SEASONAL BEER:
Original Oettinger Winterbier (5.6%)

Oettinger's most northerly brewery, in the suburb of Wüstmark. In common with the other large
breweries in the group the full range of Oettinger
beers is brewed here as required, bottles stating
the brewery of origin. No brewery tap.
DB Schwerin Süd 700m, Wüstmark 1.1km

Zum Stadtkrug

1. Altstadtbrauhaus Zum Stadtkrug
Wismarsche Straße 126, 19053 Schwerin
T 0385 593 66 93　**F** 0385 593 66 94
www.altstadtbrauhaus.de
Owner: H.-Ulrich Trosien　Founded: 1994
Output: 500hl　Availability: 1 pub
REGULAR BEERS:
Schweriner Alstadtbräu Hell (4.9%)
Schweriner Alstadtbräu Dunkel (4.9%)

Brewpub in the centre of Schwerin. It was known
as Brauhaus Schall & Knall until 1999, the name
changed upon re-opening in 2001.

🍺 Zum Stadtkrug
Wismarsche Straße 126, 19053 Schwerin
Mon–Thu 11.30–23.00, Fri & Sat 11.30–24.00,
Sun & hols 11.30–21.00
Tram Marienplatz 150m　DB Schwerin Hbf 650m

STRALSUND　720

Stralsunder

Stralsunder Brauerei GmbH
Greifswalder Chaussee 84–85, 18439 Stralsund
T 03831 25 50　**F** 03831 25 55 13
www.stralsunder-brauerei.de
Owners: Jürgen & Oliver Nordmann
Founded: 1827　Output: 88,000hl
Availability: 650 pubs
REGULAR BEERS:
Stralsunder Lager (4.7%)
Stralsunder Pils (4.9%)
SEASONAL BEERS:
Stralsunder Traditions-Bock (6.5%, Sep–Mar),
Stralsunder Frühlings-Bock (6.5%, Mar–Jun)

STÖRTEBECKER BEERS:
Störtebecker Hanse Porter (4%),
Störtebecker Pilsener (4.9%),
Störtebecker Schwarzbier (5%),
Störtebecker Bernstein-Weizen (5.3%)

Regional brewery south of the town centre that owns the 'Zum Alten Fritz' chain of pubs which are sometimes quoted as brewing but do not (the four pubs sell Zwickelfritz beers which we think are Stralsund beers re-badged). Take bus No. 3 to Voigdehäger Weg if you don't wish to walk. Klaus Störtebecker was a Robin-Hood-type pirate, active in the North and Baltic Seas in the late 14th century and executed in 1401.

🍺 **Zum Alten Fritz**
Greifswalder Chaussee 84–85, 18439 Stralsund
T 03831 25 55 00   **F** 03831 25 55 13
Daily 11.00–01.00
DB Stralsund 2.5km

UECKERMÜNDE 721

Brauhaus Ueckermünde

Markt 3–4, 17373 Ueckermünde
T 039771 800   **F** 039771 804 09
www.stadtkrug-ueckermuende.de
Owner: Horst Drücker   Founded: 20.05.2005
REGULAR BEERS:
Stadtkrug-Bräu Pils
Stadtkrug-Bräu Hefebier

Tiny brewery in the Stadtkrug hotel and restaurant on Ueckermünde's historic market square. We don't think the beers are sold anywhere else.

🍺 **Stadtkrug**
Markt 3–4, 17373 Ueckermünde
Daily 06.30–23.30; rooms available
DB Ueckermünde 1.5km

VIELANK 722

Vielanker Brauhaus

Vielanker Brauhaus GmbH & Co. KG
Lindenplatz 1, 19303 Vielank
T 038759 335 88   **F** 038759 335 90
www.vielanker-brauhaus.de
Owner: Kai Hagen   Founded: 2001
Output: 5,000hl

REGULAR BEERS:
Vielanker Pils (4.8%)
Vielanker Dunkel (5%)
Vielanker Schwarzbier (5.5%)
SEASONAL BEERS:
Vielanker Weizen (5%),
Vielanker Maibock (6.5%),
Vielanker Doppelbock Dunkel (7.5%)

Large brewpub in the centre of the village. The pub actually opens at 08.00, but they don't serve beer until 11.00. We don't think there are any buses to Vielank so you'll need your own wheels if you want to come here.

🍺 **Vielanker Brauhaus**
Lindenplatz 1, 19303 Vielank
Daily 11.00–24.00; rooms available
DB Pritzier 17km, Ludwigslust 30km

WISMAR 723

Brauhaus am Lohberg

Gasthausbrauerei Wismar GmbH
Kleine Hohe Straße 15, 23966 Wismar
T 03841 25 02 38   **F** 03841 28 28 88
Founded: 1995   Availability: 1 pub
REGULAR BEERS:
Wismarer Pilsener (4.8%)
Wismarer Roter Eric (4.8%)
Wismarer Mumme (4.8%)
SEASONAL BEERS:
Wismarer Herbstfestbier (5.8%),
Wismarer Weihnachtsbier (5.8%),
Wismarer Maibock (6.9%),
Wismarer Jubiläums-Mumme (10%).

Brewpub on the western side of the town centre, close to the old harbour. Beer was apparently first brewed on the site in 1452. Wismar, a Hanseatic League town with superb Gothic brick architecture, has been a UNESCO world heritage site since 2002.

🍺 **Brauhaus am Lohberg**
Kleine Hohe Straße 15, 23966 Wismar
Winter: Mon–Fri from 17.00, Sat & Sun from 11.00
Summer: daily from 11.00
DB Wismar 650m

Niedersachsen
(Lower Saxony)

FORMED IN 1946 by the amalgamation of four states, Niedersachsen is Germany's second largest state after Bayern. It has borders with nine others plus Holland, and a substantial coastline on the North Sea. Aside from south-eastern parts, Niedersachsen is almost entirely flat.

The Fresian islands, seven of which have ferry services to the mainland, are popular with German holidaymakers. The Harz montains, south-east of the state capital Hannover, are a delight, and come as something of a shock if you've spent much time in the flatter regions. Those with a fondness for all things half-timbered should make for Celle and Goslar in particular, although there are dozens of small towns and villages worth a visit.

Breweries are concentrated in the south-east. Western and northern parts are about the most sparsely populated area of the country in brewing terms. Two-thirds of breweries are less than 20 years old, the result of the recent trend for brewpubs.

Transport: Transport in the region is pretty good, with a number of Autobahns and main railway lines criss-crossing the state. A Niedersachsen day ticket costs €17 for one person and €24 for up to five. It's subject to the usual time restrictions on weekdays, but is also valid for travel in Bremen and Hamburg. As ever, check which services you can use it on.

ALLERSHEIM (Holzminden)   724

Allersheim

Brauerei Allersheim GmbH
Allersheim 6, 37603 Holzminden-Allersheim
T 05531 12 50   F 05531 12 51 09
www.brauerei-allersheim.de
Founded: 1854   Output: 100,000hl
REGULAR BEERS:
Allersheimer Urpils (4.8%)
Allersheimer Bügel Pils (4.9%)
Allersheimer Dunkles Landbier (5%)
Allersheimer Hefe Weißbier Hell (5.1%)
Allersheimer Hefe Weißbier Dunkel (5.1%)
SEASONAL BEERS:
Allersheimer Maibock (6.5%, spring),
Allersheimer Dunkler Bock (7%, Oct–Feb)

Large red-brick brewery in a small village just outside Holzminden. We don't think they have a tap but the beers are readily available in Holzminden itself.
DB Holzminden 3.4km

ALTENAU   725

Kolberg

Brauerei Paul Kolberg KG
Breite Straße 29, 38707 Altenau
T 05328 217   Owner: Hartmut Kolberg
Founded: 1617   Output: 9,000hl
REGULAR BEERS:
Kolberg Harzer Urstoff (5%)
Altenauer Dunkel-Bier (5%)
Altenauer Edel-Pils (5%)
Altenauer Export (5.2%)
SEASONAL BEERS:
Altenauer Maibock (6.5%),
Altenauer Doppelbock (7.5%)

---

ft: *The main square in Lüneburg.*

Small brewery on the main road through Altenau that produces a slightly greater volume of soft drinks than beer. They don't have a tap but bus No. 861 runs daily from Goslar via the station at Oker if you wish to try the beers locally.

🚉 Oker 15km

BAD GANDERSHEIM 726

Ratsbrauhaus

Markt 10, 37581 Bad Gandersheim
T 05382 10 61 **F** 05382 52 59
www.ratsbrauhaus.de
Owners: Karsten & Rita Köhler Founded: 1999
REGULAR BEERS:
Köhler's Bräu Hell (5.1%)
Köhler's Bräu Dunkel (5.1%)
Köhler's Bräu Weizen

The first of Karsten & Rita Köhlers town-hall brewpubs; others have since been opened in Alsfeld and Hannoversch Münden, although the former now has its beers brewed by the latter.

🍺 **Ratsbrauhaus**
Markt 10, 37581 Bad Gandersheim
Closed Mon; Tue–Fri from 17.00,
Sat from 15.00, Sun from 11.00
🚉 Bad Gandersheim 600m

BAD MÜNDER 727

Kornhus

Hausbrauerei Kornhus
Marktstraße 13, 31848 Bad Münder
T 05042 30 74 **F** 05042 73 12
www.hausbrauerei-kornhus.de
Owner: Klaus Pöhlker Founded: 1989
Output: 1,000hl
REGULAR BEERS:
Kornhus Hell
Kornhus Spezial Dunkel

Brewpub and distillery in the centre of Bad Münder. They have connections with Rampendahl in Osnabrück. The station is south of the town but bus No.10 runs between the two Mon–Sat if you'd rather avoid the walk.

🍺 **Kornhus**
Marktstraße 13, 31848 Bad Münder
Sat & Sun from 11.00,

Mon–Fri 11.00–14.30 & from 17.30
🚉 Bad Münder (Deister) 2.5km

BAGBAND (Großefehn) 728

Ostfriesen-Bräu

Voerstad 8, 26629 Großefehn-Bagband
T 04946 203 **F** 04946 10 55
www.ostfriesenbraeu.de
Founded: 23.04.1999
Output: 1,200hl Availability: 2 pubs
REGULAR BEER:
Ostfriesen-Bräu Landbier Dunkel (4.8%)
SEASONAL BEER:
Ostfriesen-Bräu Bagbander Bockbier (6%)

Brewpub in a former dairy. The current brew kettles were originally in Wenkers Brauhaus in Dortmund, moving here in 2000. Bus No. 460 runs from Leer station on weekdays and connects with bus No. 467 at Bagband Mühle for the last leg into the village.

🍺 **Ostfriesen-Bräu**
Voerstad 8, 26629 Großefehn-Bagband
Nov–Mar: Mon–Thu 16.00–22.00,
Fri–Sun 11.00–22.00
Apr–Oct: daily 11.00–23.00
🚉 Leer (Ostfriesland) 20km

BENNIGSEN (Springe) 729

Bennexer Brauhaus

Hauptstraße 23a, 31832 Springe-Bennigsen
T 05045 66 31 **F** 05045 96 20 53
Owner: Detlef Witt Founded: 2003
REGULAR BEERS:
Bennexer Pils
Bennexer Dunkel
Bennexer Weizen
SEASONAL BEERS:
Bennexer Sommerbier (3.8%, Jun–Aug),
Bennexer Landbier (5.2%, Feb–Apr),
Bennexer Export Hell (5.2%, Sep–Nov),
Bennexer Maibock (6.5%, May–Jun),
Bennexator Doppelbock (8.3%, Dec–Jan)

Brewpub in the centre of Bennigsen, usually with four beers available. It may open earlier at the weekend.

🍺 **Bennexer Brauhaus**
Hauptstraße 23a, 31832 Springe-Bennigsen
Closed Wed; Thu–Tue 16.00–01.00
DB Benningsen 500m

BODENWERDER   730

Münchhausen Brauhaus

Große Straße 5, 37619 Bodenwerder-Kemnade
T 05533 40 78 40   **F** 05533 40 78 50
www.muenchhausen-brauhaus.de
Founded: 2002
REGULAR BEERS:
Münchhausen Altstadt Bier
Münchhausen Hieronymus Pilsener
SEASONAL BEERS:
**Münchhausen Kloster Altbier, Münchhausen
Weizenbier**

Half-timbered brewpub named after the
eccentric baron who hailed from Bodenwerder.
Bus No. 520 runs daily from the level crossing at
Emmerthal.

🍺 **Münchhausen Brauhaus**
Große Straße 5, 37619 Bodenwerder-Kemnade
Sun 13.00–24.00, Mon–Sat 15.00–02.00
DB Emmerthal 15km

BRAUNSCHWEIG   731

Feldschlößchen

Brauerei Feldschlößchen GmbH
Wolfenbütteler Straße 33, 38102 Braunschweig
T 0531 700 30   **F** 0531 700 32 36
www.feldschloesschen.de/bs
Owner: Carlsberg Breweries, Denmark
Founded: 1871   Output: 1,500,000hl
REGULAR BEERS:
Feldschlößchen Pilsner Premium (4.9%)
Duckstein (4.9%)

Niedersachsen's largest brewery is west of the
Hauptbahnhof, opposite Braunschweig's main
park. They don't have a tap but their website
lists a number of pubs locally – we recommend
you head for the city centre.
Tram Nos. 4 & 8 Bürgerpark 100m
DB Braunschweig Hbf 1km

Zum Löwen

Weisenhausdamm 13, 38100 Braunschweig
T 0531 12 45 11   **F** 0531 12 45 55
www.schadts-brauerei-gasthaus.de
Founded: 1991   Availability: 1 pub
REGULAR BEERS:
Schadt's Pilsener (4.8%)
Schadt's Weizen (5%)
Schadt's Märzen (5%)
SEASONAL BEER:
Schadt's Bockbier (6.5%, May & Oct)

City-centre brewpub owned by nearby Schadt's.
Despite taking their names from the parent pub,
the beers are brewed here.

🍺 **Zum Löwen**
Weisenhausdamm 13, 38100 Braunschweig
Closed Sun; Mon–Fri 12.00–14.30 & 17.30–
24.00, Sat 12.00–24.00
Tram Bohlweg/Damm 150m
DB Braunschweig Hbf 1.6km

Schadt's

Schadt's Brauerei Gasthaus OHG
Marstall 2/Höhe 28, 38100 Braunschweig
T 0531 40 03 49   **F** 0531 12 45 55
www.schadts-brauerei-gasthaus.de
Founded: 1985   Availability: 1 pub
REGULAR BEERS:
Schadt's Pilsener (4.8%)
Schadt's Weizen (5%)
Schadt's Märzen (5%)
SEASONAL BEER:
Schadt's Bockbier (6.5%, May & Oct)

One of the country's earlier new-wave brewpubs,
situated just north of the cathedral. Schadt's
opened a second outlet in the city in 1991 (see
above).

🍺 **Schadt's**
Marstall 2/Höhe 28, 38100 Braunschweig
Sun 17.00–01.00, Mon–Sat 11.00–01.00
Tram Rathaus 250m   DB Braunschweig Hbf 2km

Wolters

Hofbrauhaus Wolters AG
Wolfenbütteler Straße 39, 38102 Braunschweig
T 0531 271 80   **F** 0531 271 83 60
www.hofbrauhaus-wolters.de
Owner: InBev   Founded: 1627
Output: 800,000hl

REGULAR BEERS:
Wolters Pilsener (4.8%)
Wolters Pilsener Premium (4.8%)
Wolters Schwarzer Herzog (5%)

Very large brewery next to the railway, just up the street from Feldschlößchen. Like their neighbour they don't have a tap, so you're best off looking for the beers in the city centre.

Tram Nos. 4 & 8 Jahnplatz 50m
DB Braunschweig Hbf 1.3km

BUXTEHUDE 732

Buxtehuder Brauhaus

Kirchenstraße 13, 21614 Buxtehude
T 04161 37 75   F 04161 526 32
www.buxtehuder-brauhaus.de
Owners: Matthias Laser   Founded: 1990
Output: 700hl
REGULAR BEERS:
Buxtehuder Pilsener (4.7%)
Buxtehuder Dunkel (4.9%)
SEASONAL BEERS:
Buxtehuder Märzen (5.1%, Mar),
Buxtehuder Hefeweizen (5.3%, Easter–Sep),
Buxtehuder Festbier (5.4%, Oct),
Buxtehuder Maibock (5.8%, May),
Buxtehuder Weihnachtsbock (6.3%, Dec)

Brewpub in the heart of the old town, opposite the St. Petri church. We don't think they supply any other pubs.

🍺 Buxtehuder Brauhaus
Kirchenstraße 13, 21614 Buxtehude
Sat & Sun from 10.00, Mon–Fri from 11.30
DB Buxtehude 1.3km

CELLE 733

Betz

Brauerei Carl Betz GmbH
Waldweg 101–103, 29221 Celle-Neuenhäusen
T 05141 850 25   F 05141 851 43
www.celler-bier.de
Founded: 1893
Output: 4,500hl   Availability: 21 pubs
REGULAR BEERS:
Celler Urtrüb (4.9%)
Celler Pilsener (4.9%)

Celler Dunkel (5.2%)
Celler Gold (5.2%)
Celler Weißbier (5.2%)
Celler Bekenner-Bock (6.9%)

Small brewery south-west of the town centre, close to the railway. The tap features four bowling alleys. Bus No. 2 runs from the station but be warned that it takes a circuitous route on the way out to Waldweg.

🍺 **Zur Tenne**
Waldweg 105, 29221 Celle-Neuenhäusen
T 05141 848 70
Closed Sun; Mon–Sat from 15.30
DB Celle 1.8km

EINBECK 734

Einbecker

Einbecker Brauhaus AG
Papenstraße 4–7, 37574 Einbeck
T 05561 79 70   F 05561 79 71 19
www.einbecker.com
Founded: 1378   Output: 790,000hl
REGULAR BEERS:
Einbecker Pilsener Premium (4.8%)
Einbecker Dunkel (4.9%)
Einbecker Gold (4.9%)
Einbecker Brauherren Premium Pils (4.9%)
Einbecker Diät-Pils (4.9%)
Einbecker Spezial (5.2%)
Einbecker Ur-Bock Hell (6.5%)
Einbecker Ur-Bock Dunkel (6.5%)
SEASONAL BEER:
Einbecker Mai-Ur-Bock (6.5%
FOR GÖTTINGER BRAUHAUS, GÖTTINGEN:
Göttinger Pilsener (4.9%),
Göttinger Edel-Pils (4.9%)

The last remaining brewery in Einbeck, the town that gave rise to Bock (at one time more than 700 local people had the right to brew beer). They also own the Martini brewery in Kassel and the Göttinger Brauhaus, but we think the latter's beers are brewed here. There's no tap but bus No. 230 runs from the station on weekdays and Saturday mornings if you want to drink locally.
DB Einbeck-Salzderhelden 5km

FALLERSLEBEN (Wolfsburg) 735

Altes Brauhaus

Altes Brauhaus zu Fallersleben
Schloßplatz 4, 38442 Wolfsburg-Fallersleben
T 05362 31 40   **F** 05362 663 07
www.brauhaus-fallersleben.de
Owner: Heidrun Gehrmann   Founded: 1987
Output: 1,450hl   Availability: 2 pubs
REGULAR BEERS:
Fallersleber Schloßbräu (4.8%)
Fallersleber Krauterbier (4.9%)
Fallersleber Bürgermeisterbräu (5%)
Fallersleber Weizen (5.3%)
SEASONAL BEERS:
Fallersleber Königs-Bräu (4.8%), **Fallersleber Brauhaus Alt** (4.9%), **Fallersleber Rauchbier** (5%)

Brewpub in the centre of Fallersleben, housed in a building that's seemingly all roof. If you drive a Volkswagen, the chances are it was built up the road in the massive factory at Wolfsburg. Fallersleben was also the birthplace of the liberal-nationalist poet Hoffmann von Fallersleben. In 1841 he penned the text of the German national anthem on Heligoland, then under British rule.

🍺 **Altes Brauhaus**
Schloßplatz 4, 38442 Wolfsburg-Fallersleben
Daily 11.00–01.00; rooms available
DB Fallersleben 650m

GIFHORN 736

Gifhorner Brauhaus

Schützenplatz 1, 38518 Gifhorn
T 05371 96 08 60   **F** 05371 96 08 66
www.gifhorner-brauhaus.de
Owner: Werner Beilke   Founded: 1994
Output: 2,500hl
REGULAR BEERS:
Gifhorner Brauhaus Gold
Gifhorner Brauhaus Dunkel

Large brewpub in the town centre that we believe also supplies the Hopfenspeicher in nearby Calberlah. We're don't know of any seasonal beers but think they may brew some. Be warned that Gifhorn station (as opposed to Gifhorn Stadt) is about 4.5km from the pub.

🍺 **Gifhorner Brauhaus**
Schützenplatz 1, 38518 Gifhorn
Sun from 10.00, Mon–Sat from 17.00; rooms available   DB Gifhorn Stadt 1.1km

GOSLAR 737

Brauhaus Goslar

An der Abzucht 1a, 38640 Goslar
T 05321 68 58 04   **F** 05321 68 58 05
www.brauhaus-goslar.de
Owner: Odin Paul   Founded: 2004
Availability: 11 pubs
REGULAR BEERS:
Goslarer Gose Hell (4.9%)
Goslarer Gose Dunkel (4.9%)
FOR BRAUHAUSSTUBEN, LAUENTHAL:
Lauenthaler Zwergenbräu
FOR KAISER KLEE, GOSLAR:
Kaiser Klee Gold

Small brewery that brews two types of Gose, Goslar's contribution to the brewing world but generally associated with Leipzig. Although not their official tap, we've listed Kaiser Klee as they brew a special beer for the pub. Goslar and its historic ore mine are UNESCO world heritage sites.

🍺 **Kaiser Klee**
Gemeindehof 6, 38640 Goslar
T 05321 211 66
Daily 11.00–15.00 & 17.30–23.00
DB Goslar 950km

HAHNENKLEE (Goslar) 738

Paul-Lincke-Treff

Oberförster-Hermann-Müller-Weg 6, 38644 Goslar-Hahnenklee
T 05325 22 72   **F** 05325 52 82 48
www.paul-lincke-haus.de   Founded: 2003
REGULAR BEER:
Hahnenkleer Edelbräu

Very small pub in the cellar of the former home of the Berlin folksong and operetta composer Paul Lincke. They've installed a tiny brewery, opening just one evening a week. Perhaps surprisingly, it is possible to get here by bus from Goslar on a Friday night (route No. 830) – and you can even get back.

🍺 Paul-Lincke-Treff

Oberförster-Hermann-Müller-Weg 6, 38644
Goslar-Hahnenklee
Closed Sat–Thu; Fri from 20.00
[DB] Goslar 17km

HANN. MÜNDEN 739

Ratsbrauhaus

Markt 3, 34346 Hann. Münden
T 05541 95 71 07
www.ratsbrauhaus.de
Owners: Karsten & Rita Köhler
Founded: 12.11.2003 Availability: 2 pubs
REGULAR BEERS:
Köhler's Bräu Hell
Köhler's Bräu Dunkel
Köhler's Bräu Weizen

The latest addition to the Köhler Ratsbrauhaus chain, not surprisingly located in Hann. Münden's town hall. They also supply the Ratsbrauhaus in Alfeld.

🍺 Ratsbrauhaus

Markt 3, 34346 Hann. Münden
Closed Mon; Tue–Sun from 11.00
[DB] Hann. Münden 1km

HANNOVER 740

Ernst August

Brauhaus Ernst August e.K.
Schmiedestraße 13, 30159 Hannover-Mitte
T 0511 36 59 50 **F** 0511 32 57 41
www.brauhaus.net
Owner: Sybille Aulich Founded: 1986
Output: 5,000hl Availability: 2 pubs
REGULAR BEER:
Hanöversch Pilsener Naturtrüb (4.7%)

Large, city-centre brewpub in a modern block of buildings. They brew just one beer but sell an awful lot of it. Note the exceptionally lengthy opening hours.

🍺 Ernst August

Schmiedestraße 13, 30159 Hannover-Mitte
Fri & Sat 08.00–05.00; Sun–Thu 08.00–03.00
[U] Markthalle/Landtag 200m
[DB] Hannover Hbf 750m

Gilde

Gilde Brauerei AG, Hildesheimer Straße 132,
30173 Hannover-Südstadt
T 0511 980 80 **F** 0511 980 84 67
www.gildebrau.de
Owner: InBev Founded: 1526
REGULAR BEERS:
Gilde Lüttje Lagen (2.8%)
Gilde Pilsener (4.9%)
Gilde Ratskeller Premium Pils (4.9%)
Lindener Spezial (5.1%)

Huge brewery in the southern part of the city, in InBev's hands since 2003. The tap is on the square opposite, close to the underground tram station at Altenbekenerdamm. The Lüttje Lagen is a low-alcohol dark beer to be drunk in tandem with a (weakish) schnapps – see Beer Styles, page 17.

🍺 Gilde Brauhaus

Heinrich-Heine-Platz 1, 30173 Hannover-Südstadt
T 0511 80 59 24
Daily 11.00–24.00
[U] Altenbekenerdamm 50m
[DB] Hannover-Bismarckstraße 1.1km

Herrenhäuser

Brauerei Herrenhausen KG
Herrenhäuser Straße 83–99,
30419 Hannover-Herrenhausen
T 0511 790 70 **F** 0511 279 57 59
www.herrenhaeuser.de
Owners: the Middendorff family
Founded: 1868 Output: 300,000hl
REGULAR BEERS:
Herrenhäuser Lüttje Lage (3%)
Herrenhäuser Icebeer (4.6%)
Herrenhäuser Pilsener (4.9%)
Herrenhäuser Weizenbier (5.5%)

Large, family-owned brewery in the north-western suburb of Herrenhausen. The tap is at the city end of the brewery, close to the tram stop at Herrenhäuser Markt.

🍺 Braustübchen

Markgrafstraße 1, 30419 Hannover-Herrenhausen
T 0511 79 46 61
Daily from 10.00
[Tram] 4 & 5 Herrenhäuser Markt 50m
[DB] Hannover-Leinhausen 600m

Right: The gleaming brewing coppers inside Lüneburg's Mälzer Brauhaus.

HÜNZINGEN (Walsrode) 741

Schnuckenbräu

Schnuckenbräu-Meyer Bräu KG
Hünzingen 3, 29664 Walsrode-Hünzingen
T 05161 97 01 44   **F** 05161 97 01 49
www.schnuckenbraeu.de
Owner: Bernd Meyer   Founded: 2000
Output: 650hl   Availability: 5 pubs
REGULAR BEERS:
Schnucken Dunkel (4.8%)
Schnucken Pils (4.8%)
Schnucken Weiße (5%)
SEASONAL BEERS:
Schnucken Ginsenggold (5%), **Schnucken Märzen** (6.2%), **Schnucken Maibock** (7%), **Schnucken Weihnachtsbock** (7.2%)

Microbrewery and tap in the four-star Forellenhof hotel. The owner formerly worked for Brauerei Beck (not the one in Trabelsdorf). Bus No. 500 runs from Walsrode station to Hünzingen. Schnucken are a special breed of sheep, typical of the Lüneburg heathlands.

🍴 **Forellenhof/Schnuckenstube**
Hünzingen 3, 29664 Walsrode-Hünzingen
T 05161 97 00   **F** 05161 97 01 23
Daily from 10.00; rooms available
DB Walsrode 4.6km

JEVER 742

Jever

Friesisches Bräuhaus zu Jever GmbH & Co. KG
Elisabethufer 18, 26441 Jever
T 04461 130   **F** 04461 137 10
www.jever.de
Owner: Oetker Gruppe AG   Founded: 1848
Output: 1,300,000hl
REGULAR BEERS:
Jever Light (2.7%)
Jever Pilsener (4.9%)
Jever Dark (4.9%)

Very large brewery whose flagship Pilsener can be found over much of the country. Owned by the now defunct Bavaria St. Pauli brewery for around 70 years, it's now in the hands of Dr. Oetker subsidiary Brau und Brunnen.
DB Jever 800m

LAUENAU 743

Rupp-Bräu

Feggendorfer Straße 10, 31867 Lauenau
T 05043 22 75   **F** 05043 15 07
www.ruppbraeu.de
Owner: Jürgen Rupp   Founded: 1474
Output: 4,500hl   Availability: 28 pubs
REGULAR BEERS:
Rupp Bräu Dunkles Leichtbier (2.8%)
Rupp Bräu Pilsener (4.8%)
Rupp Bräu Dunkel (5.4%)
SEASONAL BEERS:
Rupp Bräu Doppelbock Hell (7.2%, May–Oct),
Rupp Bräu Doppelbock Dunkel (7.2%, winter)

Small brewery and tap on the northern edge of town. Lauenau is just off junction 37 of the A2 and can be reached by bus No. 2602 from Haste and Bad Nenndorf.

🍴 **Felsenkeller**
Feggendorfer Straße 10, 31867 Lauenau
Daily 10.00–24.00; rooms available
DB Bad Nenndorf 8km

LÜBEN 744

Tennenbräu

Lüben 1, 29378 Wittingen-Lüben
T 05831 71 20   **F** 05831 75 15
www.luebener-tenne.de
Owners: the Wolter Family   Founded: 1995
REGULAR BEER:
Original Lübener Tennenbräu

Two connected pubs in the small village of Lüben, close to the Mecklenburg-Vorpommern border. If you want to try the beer here you'll need your own transport.

🍴 **Lübener Tenne/Gasthaus Wolter**
Lüben 1, 29378 Wittingen-Lüben
Daily 09.00–22.00   DB Wittingen 7km

LÜNEBURG 745

Mälzer

Mälzer Brau- und Tafelhaus Wiegmann & Klemz
Heilgengeiststraße 43, 21335 Lüneburg-Altstadt
T 04131 477 77   **F** 04131 478 87

www.maelzer-brauhaus.de
Founded: 1997   Availability: 2 pubs
REGULAR BEERS:
Mälzer Brauhaus Pils (5.2%)
Mälzer Brauhaus Märzen (5.4%)
SEASONAL BEERS:
Mälzer Brauhaus Hefeweizen (5%),
Mälzer Brauhaus Doppelbock (7.9%)

Multi-level brewpub in a former wine merchants on the south side of the old town. A couple of doors along is the former Lüneburger Kronen-Brauerei, nowadays a brewery museum and restaurant.

🍺 Mälzer
Heilgengeiststraße 43, 21335 Lüneburg-Altstadt
Sun & hols from 11.00, Mon–Sat from 09.00
DB Lüneburg 900m

Nolte

Gasthausbrauerei & Brennerei Nolte
Dahlenburger Landstraße 102–104, 21337
Lüneburg-Neu Hagen
T 04131 522 32   F 04131 587 74
www.gasthausbrauerei-nolte.de
Owners: Hannelore & Hans-Walter Nolte
Founded: 1997
REGULAR BEERS:
Nolte Hell
Nolte Dunkel

Brewpub and distillery on the western side of Lüneburg. Take bus No. 12 to Ahornweg if you want to avoid the walk from the station (it also runs to Am Sande, close to Mälzer).

🍺 Nolte
Dahlenburger Landstraße 102–104, 21337
Lüneburg-Neu Hagen
Mon–Sat from 16.00, Sun 11.00–14.30 & from 16.00
DB Lüneburg 1.6km

LÜNNE   746

Landhaus

Landhaus Brauerei Bochert GmbH
Heinrich-Schulte-Straße 2, 48480 Lünne
T 05906 920 60   F 05906 920 61
www.landhaus-brauerei.de
Founded: 1997   Output: 2,000hl

REGULAR BEERS:
Emsländer Pilsener
Emsländer Braunes
SEASONAL BEERS:
Emsländer Zwickelbier, Emsländer Dinkelbier,
Emsländer Weißbier, Emsländer Märzen,
Emsländer Oktoberfestbier, Emsländer
Maibock, Emsländer Nikolator

Formerly known as the Emsländer Brauhaus, this brewpub in the south-western corner of the state opens only at the weekend and closes for three months at the start of the year. The few buses that run to Lünne do so when the pub shuts.

🍺 Landhaus
Heinrich-Schulte-Straße 2, 48480 Lünne
Jan–Mar: closed. Apr–Dec: closed Mon–Thu;
Fri from 16.00, Sat & Sun from 10.00
DB Leschede 11km, Rheine 18km

NEUHAUS (Oste)   747

Alt Neuhaus

Bei der Kirche 1, 21785 Neuhaus
T 04752 84 10 31   F 04752 84 10 35
www.ulex.de
Owner: Olaf Schlichting   Founded: 11.06.2005
Output: 200hl   Availability: 1 pub
REGULAR BEERS:
Cronemeyers Hell (5%)
Cronemeyers Dunkel (5%)

The Ulex distillery started brewing beer in 2005 having already been long established as a spirit manufacturer. Those with a sense of adventure may like to try their absinthe. Buses to Neuhaus are few and far between.

🍺 Alt Neuhaus
Bei der Kirche 1, 21785 Neuhaus
T 04752 84 10 33
Closed Tue; Wed–Mon 17.00–01.00
DB Cadenberge 4.5km

NORDDEICH (Norden)   748

Diekster Bräu

Dörperweg 22, 26506 Norden-Norddeich
T 04931 918 10 51   F 04931 142 31
www.diekster-brauhaus.de
Founded: 2003   Availability: 1 pub

REGULAR BEERS:
Diekster Pils
Diekster Dunkel
Diekster Weizen

Brewpub and bowling alley in the Ocean Wave entertainment complex. Seasonal beers are brewed in additional to the regular three.

🍺 **Diekster Bräu**
Dörperweg 22, 26506 Norden-Norddeich
Daily from 11.00
DB Norddeich 1.5km

NORDHORN   749

Grafschafter Brauhaus

Vechteaue 2, 48529 Nordhorn
T 05921 72 39 88   **F** 05921 99 08 02
www.alteweberei.de
Founded: 1999
Output: 1,000hl   Availability: 3 pubs
REGULAR BEERS:
Grafschafter Pils (4.8%)
Grafschafter Braunbier (4.9%)
Grafschafter Helles Hefe-Weizen (5.1%)
SEASONAL BEERS:
Grafschafter Sommer-Spezial (4.5%),
Grafschafter Celtic Stout (5%),
Grafschafter Weihnachts-Doppelbock (9.7%)

Brewpub in a former textile mill close to the town centre. There's also a museum devoted to the building's previous existence. Bus No. 100 runs daily from Bad Bentheim.

🍺 **Grafschafter Brauhaus**
Vechteaue 2, 48529 Nordhorn
Closed Mon; Tue–Fri 17.00–02.00,
Sat & Sun 16.00–24.00   DB Bad Bentheim 16km

OSNABRÜCK   750

Rampendahl

Hausbrauerei Rampendahl Osnabrück
Hasestraße 35, 49074 Osnabrück-Innenstadt
T 0541 245 35   **F** 0541 281 41
www.rampendahl.de
Owner: Deutsch Kroner Heimathaus,
Hotelbetriebsgesellschaft mbH   Founded: 1988
Output: 2,500hl   Availability: 3 pubs

REGULAR BEERS:
Rampendahl Hell (4.8%)
Rampendahl Spezial (5.2%)
Rampendahl Weizen (5.2%)
SEASONAL BEERS:
Rampendahl Weizen (5.4%),
Rampendahl Maibock (5.6%)

City-centre brewpub, close to the cathedral. You can catch a bus from Hauptbahnhof/ZOB to Theater if you'd prefer not to walk, but it's not likely to save much time.

🍺 **Rampendahl**
Hasestraße 35, 49074 Osnabrück-Innenstadt
Daily from 11.00   DB Osnabrück Hbf 1.5km

PEINE   751

Härke

Privatbrauerei Härke KG
Am Werderpark 5, 31224 Peine
T 05171 40 50   **F** 05171 40 51 30
www.haerke-brauerei.de
Owner: Hans-Peter Härke   Founded: 1890
Output: 100,000hl   Availability: 250 pubs
REGULAR BEERS:
Härke Niedersachsen Pils (4.7%)
Härke Pils (4.9%)
Härke Dunkel (5.2%)

Family-run brewery, possibly the largest in the country that still uses a *Kühlschiff* (coolship) to cool the wort. The tap is behind the brewery, on a pedestrian street from the station to the centre.

🍺 **Härke-Brauerei-Ausschank**
Gröpern 5, 31224 Peine
T 05171 63 06   **F** 05171 484 14
Closed Sun; Mon–Sat 11.00–23.00
DB Peine 300m

RINTELN   752

Hartinger

1. Rintelner Lokalitätenbrauerei GmbH & Co. KG
Waldkateralee 27, 31737 Rinteln
T 05751 179 80   **F** 05751 17 98 83
www.waldkater.com
Owner: Richard Hartinger   Founded: 1989
Output: 1,200hl

REGULAR BEERS:
Hartinger Öko Pils (4.2%)
Hartinger Öko Hell (4.5%)
Hartinger Öko Dunkel (4.5%)
SEASONAL BEER:
Hartinger Öko Ernteweizen (4.5%, summer)

Brewery in the Waldkater hotel, situated at the edge of the forest on the northern side of town. All the beers are organic.

🏠 **Der Waldkater**
Waldkaterallee 27, 31737 Rinteln
Daily 11.00–24.00; rooms available
DB Rinteln 1.5km

RÖCKE (Bückeburg) 753

Klüsker Waldbräu

Am Klusbrink 19, 31675 Bückeburg-Röcke
T 05722 951 20   **F** 05722 95 12 50
www.kluesker.de
Owner: Harald Strüwe   Founded: 2002
Output: 180hl   Availability: 3 pubs
REGULAR BEERS:
Klüsker Weizen (4.8%)
Klüsker Hell (4.9%)
Klüsker Dunkel (5.2%)
SEASONAL BEER:
Klüsker Maibock (6.7%)

Small brewery in the Große Klus hotel, in the forest on the old road between Minden and Bückeberg. Take buses Nos. 10 or 510 from Minden to the village of Clus – the hotel is about 400m towards Röcke. They also recommend the Hof-Apotheke on Bückeberg's central square.

🏠 **Grosse Klus**
Am Klusbrink 19, 31675 Bückeburg-Röcke
Mon–Sat 16.00–23.00, Sun & hols 11.00–14.30 & 18.00–23.00; rooms available
DB Minden (Westfalen) 4.2km

🏠 **Hof-Apotheke**
Marktplatz 5, 31675 Bückeburg
T 05722 90 97 61   **F** 05722 95 99 50
Daily from 10.00; rooms available
DB Bückeberg 850m

SATKAU (Clenze) 754

Wendland Bräu

Satkau 1, 29459 Clenze-Satkau
T 05844 630   **F** 05844 97 64 02
www.wendland-braeu.de
Owners: Mathias Edler & Udo Krause
Founded: 2003
REGULAR BEER:
Wendland Bräu Märzen

Microbrewery in a hamlet west of Clenze that seemingly has plans for expansion. They currently brew one beer and advised us that Wendel in Lüchow (20km east of Satkau) is the best place to try it. Bus No. 1937 runs from Salzwedel to Lüchow on weekdays.

🏠 **Wendel**
Lange Straße 46, Lüchow
T 05841 97 97 77
Closed Mon; Tue–Sun 10.00–24.00
DB Salzwedel 14km

SOLTAU 755

Johann Albrecht

Winsener Straße 34d, 29614 Soltau
T 05191 97 63 13   **F** 05191 97 63 17
www.brauhaus-joh-albrecht.de/sol.html
Founded: 1998   Availability: 1 pub
REGULAR BEERS:
Johann Albrecht Messing
Johann Albrecht Kupfer

Brewpub north-west of the town centre, one of a chain of six across the country. We believe they may brew occasional seasonal beers.

🏠 **Johann Albrecht**
Winsener Straße 34d, 29614 Soltau
Daily 12.00–01.00
DB Soltau (Han.) 1.7km

STADTHAGEN 756

Schaumburger

Schaumburger Privat-Brauerei
St. Annen 11, 31655 Stadthagen
T 05721 977 00   **F** 05721 97 70 40

www.schaumburger.com
Owners: Stephan Wiksner & Wilhelm Lambrecht
Founded: 1873   Output: 60,000hl
Availability: 500 pubs
REGULAR BEERS:
Schaumburger Lüttje Lagen (3%)
Schaumburger Pilsener (4.8%)
Schaumburger Edel-Herb (4.8%)
Schaumburger Landbier (4.8%)
Schaumburger Keller-Bier (4.8%)
SEASONAL BEER:
Schaumburger Privat-Bock (6.5%)

Located on the southern edge of Stadthagen,
this small regional brewery is the only one
outside Hannover to brew Lüttje Lage. The tap
is in the old town, on the central market square.

🍺 **Schwarzer Adler**
Am Markt 23, 31655 Stadthagen
T 05721 50 00
Closed Wed; Thu–Tue from 10.00
DB Stadthagen 1.6km

STUHR   757

Stuhrer Mühle

Blockener Straße 10, 28816 Stuhr
T 0421 56 27 65   **F** 0421 56 33 30
Owner: Dieter & Gabriele Meinken
Founded: 1988
REGULAR BEERS:
Mühlen-Bräu Hell
Mühlen-Bräu Dunkel

Brewpub in the centre of Stuhr. From Bremen
take tram No. 1 to Roland-Center, then bus No.
55 to Moselallee. Occasional tourist trains stop
at the station opposite the pub.

🍺 **Stuhrer Mühle**
Blockener Straße 10, 28816 Stuhr
Mon–Sat 11.30–14.30 & 17.30–24.00,
Sun 11.30–24.00
DB Bremen Hbf 10km

*The opening hours of German pubs, particu-
larly those in less populous areas, can and
do change from year to year. If you find times
different to those we've listed, please let us
know at* **GermanBreweries@aol.com**.

USLAR   758

Bergbräu

Privatbrauerei Haffner GmbH & Co. KG
Rosenstraße 10, 37170 Uslar
T 05571 922 20   **F** 05571 92 22 25
www.bergbraeu.de
Owner: Heinrich Haffner   Founded: 1868
Output: 25,000hl
REGULAR BEERS:
Bergbräu Henry (4.5%)
Bergbräu Altstadt Dunkel (4.9%)
Bergbräu Pils (4.9%)
Bergbräu Haffner's Hefe-Weizen (4.9%)
SEASONAL BEERS:
Bergbräu Maibock (6%),
Bergbräu Doppelbock (6.5%)

Sometimes known as the Sollinger
Bergbrauerei, this family-owned brewery on
the western side of Uslar has no official tap but
their beers can easily be found locally.
DB Uslar 1.5km

VECHTA   759

Stierbräu

Kreuzweg 9, 49377 Vechta
T 04441 91 88 83   **F** 04441 99 92 32
www.stierbraeu.de
Owner: Dr. Pablo Meissner   Founded: 2004
Output: 600hl
REGULAR BEERS:
Stierbräu Hell (5.3%)
Stierbräu Dunkel (5.5%)
SEASONAL BEERS:
Stierbräu Ale,
Stierbräu Stout,
Stierbräu Schwarzbier,
Stierbräu Rauchbier,
Stierbräu Weizen

Microbrewery on the outskirts of the town
centre. New brewing equipment was installed
in December 2005, allowing a substantial
increase in capacity. The tap was still being
worked on in early 2006 but is expected to have
opened by the time you read this.

🍺 **Stierbräu**
Kreuzweg 9, 49377 Vechta
DB Vechta 1.3km

VEHLEN (Obernkirchen) 760

Meierhöfer

Hausbrauerei Meier
Ahnser Straße 1, 31683 Obernkirchen-Vehlen
T 05724 39 77 26 **F** 05724 39 77 27
Owner: Holger Meier Founded: 1999
REGULAR BEERS:
Meierhöfer Hell
Meierhöfer Dunkel
SEASONAL BEERS:
Meierhöfer Weizen, Meierhöfer Bock

Microbrewery, apparently run as a semi-commercial hobby. They don't have a tap and beer is only available from the brewery in barrels or 2-litre bottles. Bus No. 2026 runs from Bückeberg station on weekdays.
DB Bückeberg 3.7km

WERDUM 761

Küsten-Brauerei

Ostfriesische Küsten-Brauerei zu Werdum
Buttforder Straße 1, 26427 Werdum
T 04974 91 49 49 **F** 04974 13 39
www.watt-n-bier.de
Owners: the Pieperjohanns family
Founded: 15.04.2000
REGULAR BEERS:
Watt'n Bier Pilsener
Watt'n Bier Dunkel
SEASONAL BEERS:
Watt'n Bier Weizen (summer), **Watt'n Bier Bock**

Brewpub run by the adjacent Werdumer Hof hotel. Bus No. 4444 runs daily from Esens to the fire station in Werdum, a few minutes walk from the pub.

🍺 **Küsten-Brauerei**
Buttforder Straße 1, 26427 Werdum
Daily 11.00–24.00
DB Esens (Ostfriesland) 9km

WIENHAUSEN 762

Mühlengrund

Braugasthaus Mühlengrund
Mühlenstraße 1, 29342 Wienhausen
T 05149 331 **F** 05149 13 83
www.braugasthaus-muehlengrund.de
Owners: Friedrich-Wilhelm Gänsehals
Founded: 1998 Availability: 1 pub
REGULAR BEERS:
Wienhäuser Naturtyp Hell
Wienhäuser Naturtyp Dunkel
SEASONAL BEERS:
Wienhäuser Maibock, Wienhäuser Winterbock

This brewpub has featured in the *Guinness Book of Records* for housing the smallest mobile brewery in the world (it is on wheels). The house wheat beer is brewed in Franconia. Annual holiday first three weeks of January. Bus No. 50 runs from Celle and is probably of most use on Sundays.

🍺 **Mühlengrund**
Mühlenstraße 1, 29342 Wienhausen
Nov–Apr: closed Mon & first 3 weeks of Jan;
Sun from 12.00, Tue–Sat from 18.00
May–Oct: Mon from 18.00, Tue–Sat 12.00–14.00
& from 18.00, Sun from 12.00 DB Celle 12km

WITTINGEN 763

Wittinger

Privatbrauerei Wittingen GmbH
Ernst-Stackmann-Straße 7, 29378 Wittingen
T 05831 25 50 **F** 05831 255 69
www.wittinger.com
Owner: Christian Schulz-Hausbrandt
Founded: 1429 Output: 380,000hl
Availability: 1,200 pubs
REGULAR BEERS:
Wittinger Pils (4.9%)
Wittinger Premium (4.9%)
Wittinger Stackmann's Dunkel (5%)
Wittinger 1429 (5.6%)
SEASONAL BEER:
Wittinger Doppelbock (8%)

Large regional brewery on the western edge of the town centre. They don't have a tap but the beers can be found in most pubs in Wittingen.
DB Wittingen 1.5km

Nordrhein-Westfalen
(North Rhine-Westphalia)

GERMANY'S ENGINE-ROOM, this heavily industrialised state accounts for around a quarter of the country's GDP. Much of central and south-western Nordrhein-Westfalen is covered with huge conurbations, including one of Europe's largest, the former coal-mining and steel-producing Ruhrgebiet – it's possible to travel more than 50 miles without ever leaving a built-up area. Major cities include Köln, Essen, Dortmund and Düsseldorf, the state capital.

You could be forgiven for thinking such an industrial landscape would offer little of interest to the tourist but that's not the case. Many of the cities are attractions in their own right, notably Köln and Düsseldorf. There are also some very hilly areas with some stunning scenery, particularly to the east and south-west of Köln.

There are two beer specialities in the region that provoke fierce local loyalty. In the dark corner is Alt, particularly associated with Düsseldorf but brewed by a number of breweries north of the city and beyond. In the pale corner is Kölsch, Köln's golden speciality, protected by an *appellation contrôlée*. The Guide retains a diplomatic silence on its preference.

Transport: Public transport is excellent, particularly in the Rhein and Ruhr regions where inter-urban trams and buses complement the rail network. The day rail ticket for Nordrhein-Westfalen is called 'SchönerTagTicket' and, as usual, is valid from 09.00 on weekdays and all day at the weekend and on public holidays. At the time of writing the cost for one person was €21, and up to five people would need to pay €27.

ALT-WALSUM (Duisburg) 764

Walsumer Brauhaus Urfels

Römerstraße 109, 47179 Duisburg/Alt-Walsum
T 0203 991 94 50   F 0203 991 94 51
www.brauhaus-urfels.de   Founded: 1997
REGULAR BEERS:
Walsumer Hell
Walsumer Dunkel

Officially in Duisburg, we've listed this brewpub under Alt-Walsum as any punter turning up at Duisburg Hbf in the hope of finding the pub nearby would be disappointed. Bus No. 919 stops outside but you'll need to take a tram from either Duisburg or Dinslaken to catch it.

Walsumer Brauhaus Urfels
Römerstraße 109, 47179 Duisburg/Alt-Walsum
T 0203 991 94 50
Fri & Sat 11.30–02.00, Sun & hols 10.00–23.00,
Mon 11.30–23.00, Tue–Thu 11.30–24.00
No. 903 Walsum-Rathaus 1.4km
DB Dinslaken 6km, Duisburg Hbf 14km

ALTENRÜTHEN (Rüthen) 765

Altenrüthener

Altenrüthener Hausbrauerei
Altenrüthener Straße 7, 59602 Rüthen-Altenrüthen
T 02952 33 71   F 02952 33 70
www.altenruethenerhausbrauerei.de
Owner: Sybille Lisicin-Jezerac   Founded: 1994
Output: 500hl   Availability: 4 pubs
REGULAR BEERS:
Altenrüthener Hell (4.8%)
Altenrüthener Dunkel (4.8%)
SEASONAL BEERS:
Altenrüthener Weizen (4.8%, summer),
Altenrüthener Bock (7.2%, May)

Brewpub in the centre of the village that supplies several other pubs. You can travel by bus from either Lippstadt or Meschede on weekdays but you'll have to change at least once.

🍺 **Zur Braustube**
Altenrüthener Straße 7, 59602 Rüthen-Altenrüthen
Closed Tue; Wed–Sat & Mon from 17.00,
Sun from 11.00
DB Lippstadt 22km, Meschede 23km

ANRATH (Willich) 766

Schmitz-Mönk

Hausbrauerei Schmitz-Mönk
Jakob-Krebs-Straße 28, 47877 Willich-Anrath
T 02156 25 31   Founded: 1999   Output: 1,000hl
REGULAR BEERS:
Mönk Light
Mönk Alt (4.5%)
SEASONAL BEER:
Mönk Bock (7.1%)

Beer had been brewed at this pub in the centre of Anrath for the best part of a century until closure in 1990. Happily revived, we believe all beers are variants of Alt.

🍺 **Schmitz-Mönk**
Jakob-Krebs-Straße 28, 47877 Willich-Anrath
Closed Tue; Wed–Mon 10.00–13.30 & 16.00–01.00
DB Anrath 1.2km

BAD LAASPHE 767

Bosch

Privatbrauerei Bosch GmbH & Co. OHG
Steinackerstraße 15, 57334 Bad Laasphe
T 02752 476 20   **F** 02752 47 62 44
www.brauerei-bosch.de
Owner: Hans-Eberhard Bosch   Founded: 1705
Output: 50,000hl   Availability: 40 pubs
REGULAR BEERS:
Bosch Lager (4.9%)
Bosch Pils (4.9%)
Bosch Braunbier (5%)
Bosch Porter (5.3%)
Bosch Weizen (5.4%)
SEASONAL BEERS:
Bosch Maibock (6.8%),
Bosch Doppelbock (8%, winter)

Situated just north of Bad Laasphe's town centre, the brewery had previously been housed in the tap but moved as long ago as 1857. Zur Sonne is nearby, in the heart of the old town.

🍺 **Zur Sonne**
Königstraße 32, 57334 Bad Laasphe · **T** 02752 92 43
Closed Wed; Thu–Tue 11.30–14.00 & from 17.00
DB Bad Laasphe 900m

BAD MÜNSTEREIFEL 768

Kleines Eifeler-Brauhaus

Markt 6–8, 53902 Bad Münstereifel
T 02253 62 03   **F** 02253 54 33 02
www.eifelburg.de
Owner: Franz Schmitz   Founded: 1997
REGULAR BEERS:
Münstereifeler Primus-Landbier Hell
Münstereifeler Eifel-Manna Schwarzbier
Münstereifeler Primus-Weizenbier

Unusual brewpub tucked away at the rear of a delicatessen in the centre of Bad Münstereifel. We believe all beers are organic and think they may also brew some seasonals.

🍺 **Kleines Eifeler-Brauhaus**
Markt 6–8, 53902 Bad Münstereifel
Daily 11.00–20.00   DB Bad Münstereifel 700m

BECKUM 769

Stiefel-Jürgens

Brauhaus Stiefel-Jürgens
Hühlstraße 4–6, 59269 Beckum
T 02521 33 51   **F** 02521 95 03 41
Owner: Heinrich Jürgens   Founded: 1680
Output: 800hl
REGULAR BEERS:
Stiefel-Jürgens Obergäriges Lagerbier (4.8%)
Stiefel-Jürgens Kellerbier (4.8%)
Stiefel-Jürgens Stephanus-Bräu Pils (4.8%)
Stiefel-Jürgens Hefeweizen (4.8%)
Stiefel-Jürgens Ur-Alt Dunkel (4.8%)
SEASONAL BEER:
Stiefel-Jürgens Winterbräu (5.2%)

Despite its location in the centre of Beckum, this long-established brewpub only opens in the evening. Several routes run from Neubeckum to the bus station in Beckum.

🕯 Stiefel-Jürgens
Hühlstraße 4–6, 59269 Beckum
Closed Mon; Tue–Sun 17.30–23.00
DB Neubeckum 6km

BIELEFELD 770

Johann Albrecht

Hagenbruchstraße 8, 33602 Bielefeld-Mitte
T 0521 623 51 **F** 0521 623 99
www.brauhaus-joh-albrecht.de/bie.html
Founded: 1993
Output: 2,000hl Availability: 1 pub
REGULAR BEERS:
Johann Albrecht Messing
Johann Albrecht Gold
Johann Albrecht Kupfer

Brewpub in Bielefeld's old town, probably the most traditional in style of the six that the chain owns across the country. If you wish to catch a tram from the station be warned that they're underground at that point.

🕯 Johann Albrecht
Hagenbruchstraße 8, 33602 Bielefeld-Mitte
Sun 11.00–01.00, Mon–Sat 12.00–01.00
DB Rathausplatz 400m, Bielefeld Hbf 1.1km

BIELSTEIN (Wiehl) 771

Erzquell

Erzquell Brauerei Bielstein Haas & Co. KG.
Bielsteiner Straße 108, 51674 Wiehl-Bielstein
T 02262 820 **F** 02262 821 06
www.erzquell.de
Founded: 1900 Output: 250,000hl
REGULAR BEERS:
Zunft Kölsch Light (2.4%)
Erzquell Pils Light (2.4%)
Zunft Kölsch (4.8%)
Kupfer Alt (4.8%)
Erzquell Pils (4.8%)

One of two similarly named breweries owned by the same company (the other is west of Siegen in Nierschelderhütte), this brewery is the farthest from Köln entitled to brew Kölsch. They don't have a tap but if you want to look for the beers locally, catch bus No. 302 from Dieringhausen.
DB Dieringhausen 5km

BIGGE (Olsberg) 772

Josefsbräu

Integrationsfirma Josefheim Bigge-Josefsbräu
Heinrich-Sommer-Straße 13, 59939 Olsberg-Bigge
T 02962 80 02 56 **F** 02962 80 02 22
www.josefsheim-bigge.de
Owner: Josefs-Gesellschaft Founded: 2000
Output: 5,000hl
REGULAR BEERS:
Josefsbräu Kellerbier (4.8%)
Josefsbräu Dunkel (5.2%)
Josefsbräu Pilsener (5.2%)
Josefsbräu Märzen (5.2%)
SEASONAL BEERS:
Weizen (5.2%), **Bockbier** (7%)

Microbrewery owned by the JG Group, a Catholic organisation that runs institutions for the physically disabled. They don't have a tap but do run a shop opposite Bigge station at Hauptstraße 66. It's open Mon–Sat 09.30–12.30 and 14.30–18.30 on weekday afternoons.
DB Bigge 250m, Olsberg 1.2km

BOCHOLT 773

Bocholter Brauhaus

Kaiser-Wilhelm-Straße 25, 46395 Bocholt
T 02871 26 10 41 **F** 02871 26 10 43
www.bocholterbrauhaus.de
Owners: Norbert Engelen & Dominik Wegenaer
Founded: 1998 Output: 1,500hl
Availability: 1 pub
REGULAR BEERS:
Georgius Hell (4.5%)
Georgius Dunkel (4.5%)
Georgius Weizen (4.5%)
SEASONAL BEERS:
Georgius Dunkel (4.6%, autumn),
Georgius Fastenbier (5.2%, Lent),
Georgius Winterbock (6.5%, winter)

Large brewpub just south of the ring-road, not far from the railway station. The three regular beers are of unusually low strength for west Germany.

🕯 Bocholter Brauhaus
Kaiser-Wilhelm-Straße 25, 46395 Bocholt
Sat 11.30–01.00, Sun 10.30–23.00,
Mon–Fri 16.30–01.00 DB Bocholt 300m

BOCHUM — 774

Moritz Fiege

Privatbrauerei Moritz Fiege GmbH & Co. KG
Scharnhorststraße 21–25,
44787 Bochum-Innenstadt
T 0234 689 80   **F** 0234 689 81 11
www.moritzfiege.de
Owners: Hugo & Jürgen Fiege   Founded: 1878
Output: 140,000hl
REGULAR BEERS:
Moritz Fiege Leicht (2.6%)
Moritz Fiege Schwarzbier (4.9%)
Moritz Fiege Pils (4.9%)
Moritz Fiege Gründer-Hell (5.1%)

Large brewery on the north side of the railway, just east of the Haubtbahnhof. The tap is in the city centre, close to the Pauluskirche.

🍺 Stammhaus Fiege

Bongardstraße 23, 44787 Bochum-Innenstadt
T 0234 417 46 88
Closed Thu; Fri/Sat & Mon–Wed 11.00–15.00 & 17.00–23.00, Sun 11.00–15.00
U U35 Rathaus 130m
DB Bochum Hbf 500m

Tauffenbach

Hausbrauerei Tauffenbach
Gerberstraße 19–21, 44787 Bochum-Innenstadt
T 0234 68 76 16   **F** 0234 609 40
www.tauffenbach.de
Owner: Johannes Dörlemann   Founded: 1993
Output: 2,000hl
REGULAR BEERS:
Tauffenbach Hell (5%)
Tauffenbach Spezial (5.2%)

Brewpub in a former mill near the ring road, close to the St. Elisabeth hospital. The owner is also the proprietor of a distillery and of Hausbrauerei Boente in Recklinghausen.

🍺 Tauffenbach

Gerberstraße 19–21, 44787 Bochum-Innenstadt
Closed Sun & Mon; Sat 17.00–05.00, Tue–Sat 17.00–01.00
U U35 Rathaus 350m
DB Bochum Hbf 700m

BONN — 775

Bönnsch

Sterntorbrücke 4, 53111 Bonn-Zentrum
T 0228 65 06 10   **F** 0228 65 89 64
www.brauhaus-boennsch.de
Owner: Kurt Klein & Harald Voit   Founded: 1988
Output: 1,300hl   Availability: 1 pub
REGULAR BEER:
Bönnsch Naturtrüb (4.6%)
Bönnsch Na Klar (4.6%)
Bönnsch Weizen (5%)
SEASONAL BEER:
Bönnsch Winterbier (5.6%)

City-centre brewpub close to Oxford Street (ok, Straße). Köln has Kölsch, now Bonn has Bönnsch – available both filtered and unfiltered.

🍺 Bönnsch

Sterntorbrücke 4, 53111 Bonn-Zentrum
Fri & Sat 11.00–03.00, Sun & hols 12.00–24.00, Mon–Thu 11.00–01.00
Tram Stadthaus 100m   **DB** Bonn Hbf 600m

Brauhaus am Ennert

An den Hecken 1, 53229 Bonn-Küdinghoven
T 0228 43 17 84   **F** 0228 948 05 56
www.brauhausamennert.de
Owners: Detlef Kasparek & Uwe Lorbetzki
Founded: 1997   Availability: 1 pub
REGULAR BEER:
Ennert-Bräu Helles
SEASONAL BEER:
Ennert-Bräu Dunkles
Ennert-Bräu Weizen
Ennert-Bräu Märzen
Ennert-Bräu Weihnachtsbier
Ennert-Bräu Maibock

Brewpub at the edge of a forest close to the A59. The closest you can get by public transport is to Ennertbad by bus No. 537, then it's an 800m walk to the pub.

🍺 Brauhaus am Ennert

An den Hecken 1, 53229 Bonn-Küdinghoven
Apr–Sep: Sat, Sun & hols from 12.00; Mon–Fri from 16.30. Oct–Mar: Sat from 15.00, Sun & hols from 12.00; Mon–Fri from 17.30.
Tram No. 62 Küdighoven 1.4km
DB Bonn-Beuel 3.5km, Bonn Hbf 5km

BOTTROP   776

Bottich

Brauhaus Bottich GmbH
Gladbecker Straße 78, 46236 Bottrop-Stadtmitte
T 02041 77 44 60   **F** 02041 774 46 39
www.brauhaus-bottrop.de
Owners: Gisbert Suden & Mouika Hane
Founded: 1992   Output: 1,900hl
Availability: 1 pub
REGULAR BEERS:
Bottich Pilsener (4.8%)
Bottich Dunkel (4.8%)

Modern brewpub and hotel north of Bottrop's
town centre. Buses Nos. CE91 and 259 stop
outside but you may find it quicker to walk from
the station.

🍺 **Bottich**
Gladbecker Straße 78, 46236 Bottrop-
Stadtmitte
Sun 11.00–24.00, Mon–Sat 17.00–01.00,
rooms available
DB Bottrop Hbf 2.1km

BRAAM-OSTWENNEMAR   777

Brauhof Wilshaus

Baumstraße 46, 59071 Hamm/Braam-
Ostwennemar
T 02385 88 55   **F** 02385 60 41
www.brauhof-wilshaus.de
Owner: Heinz Wilhelm Wilshaus
Founded: 2001
REGULAR BEERS:
Wilshaus Helles
Wilshaus Dunkel
Wilshaus Weizen
SEASONAL BEER:
Wilshaus Bock

Idyllically situated on the edge of some
woodland next to a pond, this half-timbered
brewpub is off Soester Straße, west of Braam-
Ostwennemar. Bus No. 6 from Hamm station
stops about a mile away at Grüner Winkel.
There's also an hourly taxi-bus to Baumstraße
which connects out of the No. 28 and terminates
500m away from the pub.

🍺 **Brauhof Wilshaus**
Baumstraße 46, 59071 Hamm/Braam-
Ostwennemar
Closed Mon & Tue; Wed–Sat from 16.00,
Sun from 11.00
DB Hamm (Westfalen)

BRUCHHAUSEN (Olsberg)   778

Hofbrauerei Bruchhausen

Freiherr von Fürstenberg-Gaugreben'sche
Hofbrauerei, Gaugreben'scher Weg 1,
59939 Olsberg-Bruchhausen
T 02962 88 08 12   **F** 02962 97 67 29
www.fuerstenberg-gaugreben.de
Owner: Hubertus Freiherr von Fürstenberg
Founded: 1992   Output: 800hl
REGULAR BEERS:
Bornsteiner Landbier-Hell (4.8%)
Bornsteiner Dunkel-Spezial (4.8%)

Brewery and pub in the former dairy of
Bruchhausen castle. The building also houses a
horse-drawn-carriage museum. Bus No. R31
runs from Olsberg station on weekdays.

🍺 **Gutsschänke**
Gaugreben'scher Weg 1, 59939 Olsberg-
Bruchhausen
Closed Mon; Tue–Fri 11.00–22.00,
Sat, Sun & hols 11.00–22.00
DB Olsberg 8km

BRÜHL   779

Bischoff'sche Brauerei

Weilerhof, Weilerstraße, 50321 Brühl-Vochem
T 02232 273 66   **F** 02232 21 03 83
Owner: Wilhelm Bischoff   Founded: 1961
Output: 2,000hl
REGULAR BEERS:
Bischoff Kölsch (4.9%)
Bischoff Karthäuserbräu Naturtrüb (4.9%)

Small brewery just off Weilerstraße, between
Vochem and Fischentich. They don't have a tap
so the beers may be hard to find.
Tram Brühl-Vochem 1.3km
DB Kierberg 1.9km, Brühl 3.3km

CASTROP-RAUXEL   780

Rütershoff

Schillerstraße 33, 44575 Castrop-Rauxel/
Obercastrop
T 02305 24923
www.brauhaus-ruetershoff.de
Owner: Elmar Boek
Founded: 2005
REGULAR BEERS:
Castroper Urtrüb (4.8%)
Castroper Dunkel (4.8%)
Castroper Pilsener (4.8%)

Pub on the other side of the Stadtgarten from
the centre of this former mining town. They
started brewing in the spring of 2005 and now
produce three regular beers.

🍺 **Rütershoff**
Schillerstraße 33, 44575 Castrop-Rauxel/
Obercastrop
Daily from 11.00
DB Castrop-Rauxel Süd 950m, Hbf 3.7km

COESFELD   781

Stephanus

Brauhaus Stephanus oHG
Overhagenweg 1, 48653 Coesfeld
T 02541 10 00   F 02541 856 25
www.brauhausstephanus.de
Founded: 1990
Output: 2,000hl
Availability: 2 pubs
REGULAR BEER:
Stephanus-Bräu Naturtrüb
SEASONAL BEERS:
Stephanus-Bräu Fastenbier,
Stephanus-Bräu Maibock,
Stephanus-Bräu Weihnachts-Doppelbock

The first modern brewpub in the Münsterland,
Brauhaus Stephanus is on the opposite side of
the station to the town centre.

🍺 **Stephanus**
Overhagenweg 1, 48653 Coesfeld
Daily 11.00–24.00
DB Coesfeld (Westfalen) 1.2km

DAHL (Hagen)   782

Vormann

Braugasse 3–5, 58091 Hagen-Dahl
T 02337 445   F 02337 798
www.vormann-brauerei.de
Owner: Christian Vormann   Founded: 1877
Output: 5,000hl
REGULAR BEERS:
Vormann Dahler Urbräu (5%)
Vormann Alt aus Dahl (5%)
Vormann Pils (5%)
Vormann Sauerländer Weizenbier (5%)
Vormann's Vorder (5.2%)
SEASONAL BEER:
Vormann Doppelbock (8%, spring & autumn)

Traditional and fiercely independent brewery in
the scenic Volme valley. The tap is in front on the
main road. Officially a suburb of Hagen, we've
listed Dahl as a village in its own right due to the
distance and topography between the two.

🍺 **Brauerei-Ausschank**
Dahlerstraße 61, 58091 Hagen-Dahl
T 02337 48 26 55
Closed Mon; Tue–Sat 17.00–24.00,
Sun 11.00–15.00 & 17.00–23.00   DB Dahl 250m

DETMOLD   783

Strate

Privatbrauerei Strate Detmold GmbH & Co. KG
Palaisstraße 1–13, 32756 Detmold
T 05231 229 08   F 05231 251 96
www.brauerei-strate.de
Owners: the Strate family   Founded: 1863
Output: 150,000hl
REGULAR BEERS:
Detmolder Pilsener (4.8%)
Detmolder Landbier (4.8%)
Detmolder Hefeweizen (5%)

Large, architecturally attractive brewery just
west of the centre of Detmold. The tap is in the
middle of the old town, close to the picturesque
castle.

🍺 **Strate's Brauhaus**
Lange Straße 35, 32756 Detmold
T 05231 99 99 45
Fri 11.30–01.00, Sat 10.00–01.00,
Sun–Thu 11.30–24.00   DB Detmold 900m

Sudhaus

Am Gelskamp 15, 32756 Detmold
T 05231 30 66 30   **F** 05231 30 66 31
www.sudhaus-detmold.de
Founded: 24.05.2003
REGULAR BEERS:
Sudhaus Hell
Sudhaus Dunkel

Brewpub in one of a number of reconstructed half-timbered buildings in an otherwise industrial part of town. Catch bus Nos. 704 or 750 to Pinneichen.

🍺 **Sudhaus**
Am Gelskamp 15, 32756 Detmold
Closed Mon; Tue–Thu from 17.00,
Fri from 14.00, Sat & Sun from 10.00
DB Detmold 2km

DORTMUND 784

Brinkhoff

Brauerei Brinkhoff GmbH
Lütgendortmunder Hellweg 242,
44388 Dortmund-Lütgendortmund
T 0231 61 83 01   **F** 0231 618 33 00
www.brinkhoffs.de
www.wickueler.de
Owner: Oetker Gruppe AG   Founded: 1873
Output: 2,500,000hl
BRINKHOFF'S BEERS:
Brinkhoff's No. 1 Premium Pilsener (5%),
Brinkhoff's Dunkel (5%)
DORTMUNDER UNION BEERS:
Dortmunder Union Siegel Pils (4.8%),
Dortmunder Union Export (5.3%)
RITTER BEERS:
Ritter Pils (4.8%), **Ritter Bartholomäus Dunkle-Pilsener** (4.8%), **Ritter First Premium-Pils** (4.8%), **Ritter Export** (5.3%)
FOR HIRSCHBRAUEREI, DÜSSELDORF:
Düssel Alt (4.8%)
FOR SCHLÖSSER, DÜSSELDORF:
Schlösser Das Alt (4.8%), **Schlösser Jonges Naturtrübe Alt** (4.8%)
FOR WICKÜLER, WUPPERTAL:
Wicküler Pilsener (4.9%), **Wicküler D-Pils** (4.9%)

Ultra-modern brewery in a western suburb of the city, built in 1994 for the Dortmunder Ritterbrauerei which merged with the Dortmunder

Unionbrauerei the following year (the current name dates from 2002). They produce beers for several defunct breweries in the region but may well have closed by the time you read this.

🍺 **Brinkhoff's No.1**
Markt 6, 44137 44137 Dortmund/Innenstadt-West
T 0231 52 58 15   **F** 0231 14 39 15
Daily 11.00–24.00
U Reinoldkirche 250m
DB Dortmund Hbf 750m

DAB

Dortmunder Actien-Brauerei AG
Steigerstraße 20, 44145 Dortmund/Innenstadt-Nord
T 0231 840 00   **F** 0231 840 03 40
www.dab.de
www.kronen.de
Owner: Oetker Gruppe AG
Founded: 1867
Output: 4,000,000hl
DAB BEERS:
Stades Leicht (2.8%)
DAB Pilsener (4.8%)
DAB Diät Pils (4.8%)
DAB Original (4.8%)
DAB Strong (4.9%)
DAB Export (5%)
HANSA BEERS:
Hansa Alt (4.8%), **Hansa Pils** (4.8%), **Hansa Hefe Weizen** (4.9%), **Hansa Export** (5%)
FOR BRAUEREI ANDREAS, HAGEN:
Andreas Pils (4.9%)
FOR KRONEN BRAUEREI, DORTMUND:
Dortmunder Kronen Pilsener (4.8%),
Dortmunder Kronen Classic (4.8%),
Dortmunder Kronen Export (5%)
FOR REWE GROSSHANDEL, DORTMUND:
Freigraf Alt (4.8%), **Freigraf Pilsener** (4.8%),
Freigraf Export (5%)
FOR DORTMUNDER STIFTS BRAUEREI:
Dortmunder Stifts Pils (4.9%)
FOR DORTMUNDER THIER BRAUEREI:
Dortmunder Thier Pils (4.9%)

Massive brewery north of the main station that may shortly become the largest in Germany if the planned closure of Brinkhoff takes place and all their production moves here. Zum Alten Markt is the former Thier tap, Wenkers is Kronen's and was a brewpub until 2000.

🍺 Zum Alten Markt

Markt 3, 44137 44137 Dortmund/Innenstadt-West
T 0231 57 22 17   **F** 0231 52 57 83
Sun 15.00–23.00, Mon–Sat 11.00–01.00
Ⓤ Reinoldkirche 250m
DB Dortmund Hbf 750m

🍺 Wenkers Brauhaus

Betenstraße 1, 44137 Dortmund/Innenstadt-West
T 0231 52 75 48   **F** 0231 52 75 49
Sat from 10.00, Sun–Fri from 11.30
Ⓤ Reinoldkirche 250m
DB Dortmund Hbf 800m

Hövels

Hövels Hausbrauerei GmbH
Hoher Wall 5–7, 44137 Dortmund/Innenstadt-
West   **T** 0231 914 54 70   **F** 0231 9145 47 20
www.hoevels-hausbrauerei.de
Owner: Oetker Gruppe AG   Founded: 1989
Output: 3,000hl
REGULAR BEERS:
Clarissen Alt (4.8%)
Hövels Original Bitterbier (5.5%)
SEASONAL BEERS:
Hövels Jubiläumsbier (5%),
Hövels Sommerbier (5.5%)
FOR WENKERS BRAUHAUS, DORTMUND:
Wenkers Urtrüb (5%),
Wenkers Schwarzbier, Wenkers Bock

Brewpub on the ring road near the old Thier
brewery. We believe all the above beers bar the
seasonals may also (or indeed, only) be brewed
by DAB, but they've assured us the pub is still
brewing.

🍺 Hövels

Hoher Wall 5–7, 44137 Dortmund/Innenstadt-
West   Daily 11.00–24.00
Ⓤ Städtische Kliniken 350m
DB Dortmund Hbf 800m

DUISBURG   785

König

König-Brauerei GmbH
Friedrich-Ebert-Straße 255–263,
47139 Duisburg-Beeck
T 0203 45 50   **F** 0203 455 25 15
www.koenig.de
Owner: Bitburger Getränkegruppe

Founded: 1858   Output: 2,300,000hl
REGULAR BEER:
König Pilsener (4.9%)

Huge brewery north of the docks, formerly
owned by Holsten but now part of the Bitburger
Group. They don't have a tap but their sole beer
can be found all over the country (and beyond)
and is usually known as KöPi.
Tram No. 901 Brauerei 20m
DB Duisburg-Ruhrort 2.1km, Hbf 6.5km

Schacht 4/8

Brauhaus Schacht 4/8 GmbH
Düsseldorfer Straße 21,
47051 Duisburg-Dellviertel
T 0203 28 10 00   **F** 0203 210 10
www.brauhaus-schacht-4-8.de
Owner: Gerald Friedauer   Founded: 1995
Output: 1,500hl   Availability: 1 pub
REGULAR BEERS:
Schacht 4/8 Gruben Gold Zwickel (4.6%)
Schacht 4/8 Ruhr Pott Pils (4.8%)
Schacht 4/8 Ärwin's Weizen Gold (4.8%)
Schacht 4/8 Mulvany's Dunkel (5%)
SEASONAL BEERS:
Schacht 4/8 Märzen (5.2%, Mar), Schacht 4/8
Festbier (5.2%, Sep), Schacht 4/8 Maibock (6%,
May), Schacht 4/8 Hibernator (7.5%, Dec)

Located in the centre of Duisburg, this brewpub
is named after a former local coal mine. The
proprietor also owns Hibernia in Gelsenkirchen,
Mühleimer Brauhaus in Mühleim and Zeche
Jacobi in Oberhausen. All brew the same range
of beers.

🍺 Schacht 4/8

Düsseldorfer Straße 21, 47051 Duisburg-
Dellviertel
Fri & Sat 09.00–02.00, Sun–Thu 09.00–00.30
Ⓤ König-Heinrich-Platz 300m
DB Duisburg Hbf 750m

Webster

Am Dellplatz 14, 47051 Duisburg-Dellviertel
T 0203 230 78   **F** 0203 28 40 79
www.webster-brauhaus.de
Owner: Fredulux Bräu GmbH   Founded: 1992
Output: 1,000hl   Availability: 2 pubs
REGULAR BEERS:
Webster Blond
Webster Braun

SEASONAL BEERS:

Webster Skinny (autumn–spring), **Webster Weizen** (summer), **Webster Festbier** (autumn), **Webster Nikolausbier** (winter), **Webster Websterator** (spring)

Brewpub just south of the pedestrianised city centre, across the street from St. Joseph's church.

🍺 Webster

Am Dellplatz 14, 47051 Duisburg-Dellviertel
Fri & Sat 11.30–02.00, Sun–Thu 12.00–01.00
U Steinische Gasse 350m
DB Duisburg Hbf 1.1km

DURCHHOLZ (Witten) 786

Wolfs-Bier

Durchholzerstraße 168, 58456 Witten-Durchholz
T 02302 42 98 89 www.wolfsbier.de
Founded: 2003 Availability: 2 pubs
REGULAR BEER:
Wolf Dunkel (5.6%)

A hobby brewery that now operates on a semi-commercial basis. They no longer supply Dorfschänke in Sprockhövel but the beer is available in nearby Bommerholz. For the pub, bus 379 runs from Bochum-Langendreer via Witten.

🍺 Am Stöter

Bommerholzer Straße 107,
58456 Witten-Bommerholz
T/F 02302 73604
Mon–Fri 15.00–21.30, Sat, Sun & hols 11.30–21.30;
rooms available
DB Witten Hbf 6km

DÜSSELDORF 787

Füchschen

Brauerei im Füchschen
Ratinger Straße 28, 40213 Düsseldorf-Altstadt
T 0211 13 74 70 **F** 0211 137 47 47
www.fuechschen.de
Owner: Peter König Founded: 1858
Output: 15,000hl Availability: 30 pubs
REGULAR BEERS:
Füchschen Alt (4.5%)
Silberfüchschen Weizen (5.4%)
SEASONAL BEER:
Füchschen Weihnachtsbier (5.2%)

The smallest of Düsseldorf's Altbier brewers, the Little Fox is to the north of the old town, not far from the Hofgarten.

🍺 Füchschen

Ratinger Straße 28, 40213 Düsseldorf-Altstadt
T 0211 86 79 60 **F** 0211 32 86 39
Fri & Sat 09.00–01.00,
Sun–Thu 09.00–24.00
U Heinrich-Heine-Allee 350m
DB Düsseldorf Hbf 1.8km

Johann Albrecht

Niederkasseler Straße 104,
40547 Düsseldorf-Niederkassel
T 0211 57 01 29 **F** 0211 556 05 77
www.brauhaus-joh-albrecht.de/due.html
Founded: 1992
Output: 1,000hl Availability: 1 pub
REGULAR BEERS:
Johann Albrecht Messing
Johann Albrecht Gold
Johann Albrecht Kupfer
SEASONAL BEERS:
Johann Albrecht Weizen (summer), **Johann Albrecht Nickelbier** (winter), **Johann Albrecht Maibock** (spring)

Brewpub in the suburb of Oberkassel, on the opposite side of the Rhine from the city. If you're without car, take a tram/U-bahn to Belsenplatz and change for bus No. 833 to Heinsbergstraße.

🍺 Johann Albrecht

Niederkasseler Straße 104,
40547 Düsseldorf-Niederkassel
Daily 12.00–01.00
Tram Belsenplatz 1.3km
DB Düsseldorf Hbf 4.7km

Schlüssel

Hausbrauerei zum Schlüssel
Bolkerstraße 41–47, 40213 Düsseldorf-Altstadt
T 0211 828 95 50 **F** 0211 13 51 59
www.zumschluessel.de
Founded: 1850 Output: 17,000hl
REGULAR BEER:
Original Schlüssel Alt (5%)

City-centre brewery and tap. The brick-fronted building was built in the 1950s to replace the earlier pub which was destroyed during World War II.

📍 **Zum Schlüssel**

Bolkerstraße 41–47, 40213 Düsseldorf-Altstadt
Fri & Sat 10.00–01.00, Sun–Thu 10.00–24.00
Ⓤ Heinrich-Heine-Allee 150m
DB Düsseldorf Hbf 1.6km

Schumacher

Brauerei Ferdinand Schumacher
Oststraße 123, 40210 Düsseldorf-Stadtmitte
T 0211 828 90 20   **F** 0211 8289 02 44
www.brauerei-schumacher.de
Owner: Gertrud Schnitzler-Ungermann
Founded: 1838   Output: 40,000hl
Availability: 20 pubs
REGULAR BEERS:
Schumacher Jung (2.9%)
Schumacher Alt (4.6%)
SEASONAL BEER:
Schumacher Latzenbier (5.5%, three days a year)

The oldest brewery in the city and the only Altbier producer outside the old town. Latzenbier is a strong Alt that is only sold on the third Thursday in March, September and December.

📍 **Schumacher Stammhaus**

Oststraße 123, 40210 Düsseldorf-Stadtmitte
T 0211 32 60 04
Fri & Sat 10.00–01.00, Sun–Thu 10.00–24.00
Ⓤ Oststraße 150m   DB Düsseldorf Hbf 600m

Uerige

Uerige Obergärige Hausbrauerei GmbH
Bergerstraße 1, 40213 Düsseldorf-Altstadt
T 0211 86 69 90   **F** 0211 13 28 86
www.uerige.de
Founded: 1862   Output: 20,000hl
REGULAR BEERS:
Ueriges Alt (4.5%)
Ueriges Weizen (4.5%)
SEASONAL BEERS:
Ueriges Sticke (6.5%),
Ueriges Doppel Sticke (8.5%)

Brewpub in the heart of the old town. Sticke only appears on the third Tuesday in January and October – we're not sure about the Doppel Sticke.

📍 **Im Uerigen**

Bergerstraße 1, 40213 Düsseldorf-Altstadt
Daily 10.00–24.00
Ⓤ Heinrich-Heine-Allee 300m
DB Düsseldorf Hbf 1.7km

EICHEN (Kreuztal)   788

Eichener

Eichener Brauerei Gebrüder Schweisfurth GmbH
Eichener Straße 38–40, 57223 Kreuztal-Eichen
T 02732 55 10   **F** 02732 55 11 77
www.eichener.de
Owner: Krombacher Brauerei   Founded: 1888
Output: 150,000hl
REGULAR BEERS:
Eichener Zwickelbier (4.8%)
Eichener Pils (4.8%)
Eichener Landbier (5%)
Eichener Gold (5.4%)
Eichener Schwarzbier (5.6%)
SEASONAL BEERS:
Eichener Maibock (6.9%),
Eichener Festbock (6.9%)
FOR RHENANIA BRAUEREI, KREFELD:
Rhenania Alt (4.8%)

Large brewery, although somewhat small in comparison to its near neighbour, Krombacher, which bought Eichener in 2002. We don't think they have a tap.
DB Eichen (Kreis Siegen) 400m

ESLOHE   789

Esloher Brauhaus

St.-Rochus-Weg 1, 59889 Eslohe
T 02973 976 50   **F** 02973 97 65 22
www.essel-braeu.de
Owner: Werner Schulte   Founded: 1988
Output: 650hl   Availability: 2 pubs
REGULAR BEERS:
Essel-Bräu Hell
Essel-Bräu Dunkel
SEASONAL BEERS:
Essel-Bräu Maibock,
Essel-Bräu Weinhnachtsbock

Brewery, tap and hotel in three buildings around a courtyard. The Brauhaus is not always open and is across the yard from the Domschänke which usually acts as the tap. Bus No. S70 runs from Meschede Monday to Saturday but you'll need to change on a Sunday. From Grevenbrück you can catch bus No. R68 daily.

📍 **Domschänke**

St.-Rochus-Weg 1, 59889 Eslohe

Closed Mon & Tue; Wed–Fri from 16.30,
Sat, Sun & hols from 11.00, rooms available
DB Meschede 20km, Grevenbrück 21km

ESPELKAMP 790

Espelkamp

Espelkamper Bräu GmbH & Co. KG
General-Bishop-Straße 16, 32339 Espelkamp
T 05772 93 93 93   **F** 05772 93 93 91
www.brauhaus-espelkamp.de
Owner: Ingolf Steinkamp   Founded: 1998
Availability: 1 pub
REGULAR BEERS:
Espelkamp Steinpils
Espelkamp Steinweizen
SEASONAL BEER:
Espelkamp Landbier Dunkel (Oct–Apr)

Modern brewpub north of the station and town
centre. For some reason the decor includes an
old English red telephone kiosk...

🍺 **Espelkamp**
General-Bishop-Straße 16, 32339 Espelkamp
Closed Mon; Tue–Fri 12.00–14.00 & from 17.00,
Sat from 15.00, Sun 11.00–14.00 & from 17.00
DB Espelkamp 1.4km

ESSEN 791

Borbecker Dampfbier-Brauerei

Heinrich-Brauns-Straße 9–15, 45355 Essen/
Borbeck-Mitte
T 0201 63 00 70   **F** 0201 630 07 22
www.dampfe.de   Founded: 1989
REGULAR BEERS:
Borbecker Helles Dampfbier (4.8%)
Borbecker Zwickelbier (5%)
Borbecker Dunkles Salonbier (5%)

The former Essener Kronen-Brauerei, converted
to a pub in the late 1980s. Brewing is apparently
done in the kettles of the old brewery, although
we suspect some beer may be brewed by Stauder.
Any info welcome at GermanBreweries@aol.com.

🍺 **Dampfe**
Heinrich-Brauns-Straße 9–15, 45355 Essen/
Borbeck-Mitte
Fri & Sat 11.00–01.00, Sun–Thu 11.00–24.00
DB Essen-Borbeck 150m

Rüttenscheider

Rüttenscheider Hausbrauerei GmbH
Girardetstraße 2, 45131 Essen-Rüttenscheid
T 0201 79 00 60   **F** 0201 79 00 70
www.ruettenscheider-hausbrauerei.de
Owner: Volkmar Kampl   Founded: 1993
Output: 1,000hl   Availability: 1 pub
REGULAR BEERS:
Rüttenscheider Keller (4.9%)
Rüttenscheider Weizen (4.9%)

Brewpub in the south of the city, not far from
the Grugapark and tradefair grounds. We don't
believe they brew any seasonal beers.

🍺 **Rüttenscheider**
Girardetstraße 2, 45131 Essen-Rüttenscheid
Fri & Sat 17.00–01.00, Sun–Thu 17.00–24.00
U Martinstraße 300m   DB Essen Hbf 2.3km

Stauder

Privatbrauerei Jacob Stauder GmbH & Co. KG
Stauderstraße 88, 45326 Essen/Altenessen-Süd
T 0201 361 60   **F** 0201 361 61 33
www.stauder.de
Founded: 1867   Output: 200,000hl
REGULAR BEERS:
Stauder Pils (4.6%)
Stauder Spezial (5%)
FOR STERN BRAUEREI, ESSEN:
Stern Pils (4.8%), **Stern Export** (5.2%)

Large brewery in the north of the city. Among
the beers they advertise on their website is
Borbecker Helles Dampfbier which may, or may
not, be brewed by Borbecker Dampfbier-
Brauerei. We don't think they have a tap.
U Altenessen Mitte 1km
DB Essen-Altenessen 2.1km, Hbf 6km

FRECHEN 792

Hüchelner Urstoff

Hüchelner Urstoff Brauhaus GmbH & Co. KG
Ägidiusstraße 56, 50226 Frechen
T/F 02234 522 48   **www.urstoff-schaenke.de**
Owner: Werner Hintermeier   Founded: 1750
Output: 5,000hl   Availability: 15 pubs
REGULAR BEERS:
Stecken Kölsch (4.5%)
Bartmann's Kölsch (4.7%)
Hüchelner Urstoff (4.7%)

Small brewery and tap in what was once the village of Hücheln which has now been swallowed by Frechen. Take bus No. 731 from Frechen-Königsdorf station to Hücheln-Krankenhaus.

🍺 Urstoff-Schänke
Ägidiusstraße 56, 50226 Frechen
T/F 02234 95 17 18
Closed Mon; Tue–Sun from 17.00
DB Frechen-Königsdorf 3km

GELSENKIRCHEN   793

Hibernia

Brauhaus Hibernia GmbH
Bahnhofsvorplatz 2, 45879 Gelsenkirchen
T 0209 20 85 31   **F** 0209 14 66 77
www.brauhaus-hibernia.de
Owner: Gerald Friedauer   Founded: 1991
Output: 2,500hl   Availability: 2 pubs
REGULAR BEERS:
Hibernia Gruben Gold Zwickel (4.6%)
Hibernia Ruhr Pott Pils (4.8%)
Hibernia Ärwin's Weizen Gold (4.8%)
Hibernia Mulvany's Dunkel (5%)
SEASONAL BEERS:
Hibernia Märzen (5.2%, Mar), **Hibernia Festbier** (5.2%, Sep), **Hibernia Maibock** (6%, May), **Hibernia Hibernator** (7.5%, Dec)

Brewpub just outside Gelsenkirchen's main station, one of four in the Ruhr owned by Gerald Fridauer. All brew the same range of beers.

🍺 Hibernia
Bahnhofsvorplatz 2, 45879 Gelsenkirchen
Fri & Sat 09.00–01.00, Sun–Thu 09.00–24.00
DB Gelsenkirchen Hbf 100m

GEMÜND (Schleiden)   794

Gemünder

Gemünder Brauerei GmbH & Co. KG
Kölner Straße 69, 53937 Schleiden-Gemünd
T 02444 27 23   **F** 02444 36 42
Owners: the Scheidtweiler family
Founded: 1961   Output: 20,000hl
Availability: 70 pubs
REGULAR BEERS:
Gemünder Alt (5.1%)
Gemünder Obergärig (5.1%)

Gemünder Pilsener (5.1%)
Krönes Eifeler Landbier (5.1%)
Gemünder Spezial (5.1%)
SEASONAL BEER:
Eifel-Böckchen (6.3%)

Small brewery in the Urft valley, on the road from Kall. The tap is in the small pedestrianised area in the centre of the village. Buses Nos. 379 and 829 run here from Kall station.

🍺 Gemünder Quadrat M
Dreibornerstraße 22, 53937 Schleiden-Gemünd
T 02444 91 58 84
Closed Mon; Tue–Sun 09.30–01.00
DB Kall 6km

GLADBECK   795

Brauhaus Gladbeck

Brauerei Hotel Alte Post Gladbeck GmbH
Humboldtstraße 2, 45964 Gladbeck-Mitte
T 02043 208 40   **F** 02043 20 84 30
www.brauhaus-gladbeck.de
Owner: Jörg Mehl   Founded: 2003
Output: 700hl   Availability: 1 pub
REGULAR BEERS:
Gladbecker Hell (4.8%)
Gladbecker Dunkel (4.9%)
Gladbecker Lupulus Pils (4.9%)
SEASONAL BEERS:
Gladbecker Festbier (5.1%, Sep), **Gladbecker Winterbier** (5.3%, Dec), **Gladbecker Maibock** (6.8%, May)

Brewery, pub and 3-star hotel in a former post office in the centre of Gladbeck. One of six brewpubs around north Germany owned by Jörg Mehl.

🍺 Alte Post
Humboldtstraße 2, 45964 Gladbeck-Mitte
Fri & Sat 10.00–01.00, Sun–Thu 10.00–24.00, rooms available
DB Gladbeck Ost 500m, West 1km

GREVENSTEIN (Meschede)   796

Veltins

Brauerei C. & A. Veltins GmbH & Co.
An der Streue, 59872 Meschede-Grevenstein
T 02934 95 90   **F** 02934 95 94 93
www.veltins.de

Founded: 1824   Output: 2,400,000hl
Availability: c.17,000 pubs
REGULAR BEERS:
Veltins Leicht (2.4%),
Veltins Pilsener (4.8%).

Massive Pils brewery that dominates the northern part of the village. If you'd like to visit Grevenstein, bus No. 367 runs from Freienohl station daily.
DB Freienohl 9km

GUMMERSBACH   797

Brauhaus Gummersbach

Hindenburgstraße 15, 51643 Gummersbach
T 02261 29 00 10   F 02261 290 01 29
www.brauhaus-gummersbach.de
Owner: Jörg Mehl   Founded: 13.12.2002
REGULAR BEERS:
Oberberg Bräu (4.8%)
Oberberg Pils (4.8%)
SEASONAL BEERS:
Oberberg Osterbräu (5.4%, Easter),
Oberberg Weizenbier (5.5%, summer),
Oberberg Weihnachtsbräu (5.5%, Christmas),
Oberberg Maibock (7%, May)

Modern brewpub and hotel between the station and town centre. Owner Jörg Mehl also has other breweries in Gladbeck, Kühlunsborn, Lüdenscheid, Rostock and Wuppertal.

🍺 Brauhaus Gummersbach
Hindenburgstraße 15, 51643 Gummersbach
Fri & Sat 09.00–01.00, Sun 11.00–24.00,
Mon–Thu 09.00–24.00; rooms available
DB Gummersbach 250m

GÜTERSLOH   798

Gütersloher Brauhaus

Unter den Ulmen 9, 33330 Gütersloh-Innenstadt
T 05241 251 66   F 05241 247 93
www.guetersloher-brauhaus.de
Founded: 1990
Output: 1,500hl   Availability: 1 pub
REGULAR BEER:
Gütersloher Spezial-Pilsener

After it opened in 1990 as Ulmenbräu, a serious fire in 1996 almost led to the demise of this

brewpub. Just the one regular beer, but we suspect they may brew some seasonals.

🍺 Gütersloher Brauhaus
Unter den Ulmen 9, 33330 Gütersloh-Innenstadt
Sun 10.30–14.00 & 17.30–23.00,
Mon–Sat from 17.30
DB Gütersloh Hbf 1.1km

HALTERN   799

Peters Bauernstube

Lavesumer Straße 256, 45721 Haltern
T 02364 41 67   F 02364 16 98 60
www.peters-bauernstube.de
Owners: Christa & Paul Peters   Founded: 2004
REGULAR BEERS:
Treckeberger Helles
Treckeberger Dunkel
SEASONAL BEERS:
Treckeberger Klosterbier, Treckeberger Winterbier, Treckeberger Weihnachtsbier

Bakery, brewery and pub on the road between Haltern and Lavesum, very close to the A43 Hohe Mark services. Annual holday over Christmas/New Year. Take bus No. 275 from Haltern station to Am Treckeberg.

🍺 Peters Bauernstube
Lavesumer Straße 256, 45721 Haltern
Closed Mon & Tue; Wed–Sun 09.00–19.00
DB Haltern (Westfalen) 3.6km

HEISTERBACHERROTT
(Königswinter)   800

Alte Bürgerstube

Dollendorfer Straße 384,
53639 Königswinter-Heisterbacherrott
T 02244 91 88 41   F 02244 91 88 09
www.brauhaus-siegengebirge.de
Owner: Steffen Klaus   Founded: 13.08.2004
Output: 1,000hl
REGULAR BEERS:
Siebengebirgsbräu Naturtrüb
Siebengebirgsbräu Dunkel
SEASONAL BEER:
Siebengebirgsbräu Weihnachtsbier

This brewpub, which opened in the summer of 2004, is on the main road through Heisterbacherrott. Bus No. 521 runs frequently from Niederdollendorf station but be warned that the return route is the No. 520.

Alte Bürgerstube

Dollendorfer Straße 384,
53639 Königswinter-Heisterbacherrott
Sat 11.00–24.00, Sun & hols 10.00–23.00,
Mon–Fri 11.00–14.00 & 16.00–24.00
DB Niederdollendorf 5km

ISERLOHN 801

Iserlohn

Privatbrauerei Iserlohn GmbH
Grüner Talstraße 40–50,
58644 Iserlohn-Obergrüne
T 02371 95 70   **F** 02371 95 72 99
www.iserlohner.de
Owners: G. Heutelbeck, C. Ilske & P. Michaelis
Founded: 1899   Output: 400,000hl
REGULAR BEERS:
Iserlohner Pilsener (4.8%)
Iserlohner Blond (4.9%)
Iserlohner Dunkel (4.9%)
SEASONAL BEER:
Iserlohner Winter (5.9%)

Large brewery in the suburb of Obergrüne. It's once again independent following a management buyout in 2003, having previously been part of the Brau und Brunnen stable. Buses Nos. 1 & 7 run to Grüner Talstraße from Iserlohn station, the former continuing through to Letmathe.

Braustüb'l

Grüner Talstraße 53, 58644 Iserlohn-Obergrüne
T 02371 95 56 99
Closed Mon; Tue–Fri & Sun 12.00–14.30 &
17.30–23.30, Sat 17.30–23.30
DB Iserlohn 2.3km, Letmathe 4.3km

ISSUM 802

Diebels

Brauerei Diebels GmbH & Co. KG
Brauerei-Diebels-Straße 1, 47661 Issum
T 02835 300   **F** 02835 301 45
www.diebels.de
Owner: InBev   Founded: 1878
Output: 1,500,000hl

REGULAR BEERS:
Diebels Light (2.9%)
Diebels Premium Altbier (4.8%)
Diebels Pils (4.9%)
SEASONAL BEER:
Diebels Plato 13 (6%)

By far the largest producer of Altbier in the world. Diebels recently expanded the range by brewing for the first time a Pils. The tap, attached to the brewery, opened in 1995. Buses Nos. 31 & 32 from Geldern station stop outside.

Diebels Live

Brauerei-Diebels-Straße 1, 47661 Issum
T 02835 303 96
Fri & Sat 11.00–03.00, Sun–Thu 11.00–23.30
DB Geldern 8km

JÜLICH 803

Herzogen Brauhaus

Herzogen Brauhaus & Destillerie GmbH
Schützenstraße 22, 52428 Jülich
T 02461 72 83
Founded: 1986
REGULAR BEERS:
Herzogen Bure Bier Natur
Herzogen Bure Weissbier

Microbrewery and distillery in the centre of Jülich which also produces its own mustard and vinegar. The tap is on the next street. There are unconfirmed reports they no longer brew.

Brauhaus Victoria

Grünstraße 17, 52428 Jülich
T 02461 27 90
Closed Wed; Thu–Tue 17.00–24.00
DB Jülich 1.3km

KALKAR 804

Kalkarer Mühle

Mühlenstege 8, 47546 Kalkar
T 02824 932 30   **F** 02824 932 40
www.kalkarer-muehle.de
Founded: 2000   Availability: 1 pub
REGULAR BEERS:
Kalkarer Mühlenbier Pils
Kalkarer Mühlenbier Dunkel

Brewpub next to a restored windmill on the eastern edge of town. Bus No. 47 runs from the station at Goch but isn't much use during winter opening hours.

🍺 Kalkarer Mühle
Mühlenstege 8, 47546 Kalkar
Nov–Mar: closed Mon; Tue–Sun 17.00–23.00
Apr–Oct: daily 11.00–23.00
DB Goch 12km

KAMP-LINTFORT　805

Kolpinghaus
Prinzenstraße 64, 47475 Kamp-Lintfort/Lintfort
T/F 02842 2628
www.kolpinghaus-lintfort.de
Owner: Werner Poschmann　Founded: 2005
Availability: 1 pub
REGULAR BEERS:
Zunft-Bräu Weizen (4.7%)
Zunft-Bräu Hell (4.8%)
Zunft-Bräu Dunkel (4.8%)
Zunft-Bräu Bock (7.2%)

Brewpub in Kamp-Lintfort's Kolpinghaus, a charitable centre that helps people with rehabilitation and job-training. Bus No. 1 runs to the town from Rheinberg station.

🍺 Zunftstuben
Prinzenstraße 64, 47475 Kamp-Lintfort/Lintfort
Mon, Tue, Thu & Fri 11.30–14.00 & 17.00–02.00,
Wed 11.30–14.00, Sat 15.00–02.00,
Sun 11.00–02.00
DB Rheinberg (Rheinland) 7km

KELLERSHOHN (Lohmar)　806

Zum Pfaffen
Klasberg 2, 53797 Lohmar-Kellershohn
T 02205 853 96　**F** 02205 89 97 88
www.max-paeffgen.de
Owner: Max Pfäffgen　Founded: 2001
REGULAR BEER:
Pfaffen (4.5%)

Microbrewery just west of the hamlet of Kellershohn, around 3km south-west of Rösrath. The owner is a member of the Pfäffgen brewing family who started Pfaffen after a dispute. The tap is 20km away in Köln.

🍺 Zum Pfaffen
Heumarkt 62, 50667 Köln/Altstadt-Nord
T 0221 257 77 65　**F** 0221 257 99 47
Closed Mon; Tue–Sun 12.00–24.00
Tram Heumarkt 150m
DB Köln Hbf 700m

KIRCHHEIM (Euskirchen)　807

Steinbach
Waldgasthaus Steinbach e.K.
Talsperrenstraße 105, 53881 Euskirchen-Kirchheim
T 02255 66 03　**F** 02255 313 36
Founded: 1994　Output: 1,000hl
REGULAR BEERS:
Steinbach Naturblond
Steinbach Naturdunkel
Steinbach Weizen

Officially a suburb of Euskirchen, we've listed Kirchheim in its own right due to the distance between the two. This brewpub is 2km south of the village, alongside Steinbach reservoir. Bus No. 874 runs from Euskirchen to Kirchheim and we think some services may run to the reservoir in summer.

🍺 Steinbach
Talsperrenstraße 105, 53881 Euskirchen-Kirchheim
Daily 11.00–22.00
DB Arloff 3.5km, Euskirchen 11km

KIRCHHELLEN (Bottrop)　808

Brauhaus am Ring
Brauhaus Kirchhellen GmbH
Kirchhellener Ring 80–82, 46244 Bottrop-Kirchhellen
T 02045 41 21 41　**F** 02045 41 21 51
www.brauhaus-am-ring.de
Founded: 08.12.2001　Availability: 1 pub
REGULAR BEERS:
Kirchhell
Kirchdunkel

Large modern brewpub near the centre of Kirchhellen, officially a suburb of Bottrop which is 9km to the south. Bus No. C50 runs between the latter and Dorsten via Kirchhellen. Junction

40 of the A31 is less than a mile away if you are coming by car.

🍺 Brauhaus am Ring
Kirchhellener Ring 80–82, 46244 Bottrop-Kirchhellen
Closed Tue; Wed/Thu & Sun/Mon 11.00–01.00, Fri & Sat 11.00–02.00
DB Feldhausen 3.7km, Gladbeck West 6km

KÖLN   809

Braustelle
Owner: Peter Esser
Christianstraße 2, 50825 Köln-Ehrenfeld
T 0221 285 69 32
www.braustelle.com
Founded: 17.12.2001
Output: 250hl   Availability: 1 pub
REGULAR BEERS:
Braustelle Helios Kölsch
Braustelle Weizen
Braustelle Ehrenfelder Alt
SEASONAL BEERS:
Braustelle Neujahrsbier (Jan), **Braustelle Fastenbier** (Mar), **Braustelle Frühlingserwachen** (Apr), **Braustelle Maibock** (May), **Braustelle Weizen Dunkel** (Jun), **Braustelle Sommerwiese** (Jul), **Braustelle Hibiscusbier** (Jul), **Braustelle Lustiger Augustin** (Aug), **Braustelle Schwarzer September** (Sep), **Braustelle Erntedankbier** (Oct), **Braustelle St. Martins Bier** (Nov), **Braustelle Weihnachtsbier** (Dec)

Street-corner brewpub in the western district of Ehrenfeld, and the only place in Köln to brew Alt. Don't be surprised to find additional seasonals.

🍺 Braustelle
Christianstraße 2, 50825 Köln-Ehrenfeld
Closed Sun & hols; Mon–Sat 18.00–01.00
Tram U Leyendeckerstraße 100m
DB Köln-Ehrenfeld 900m

Dom
Dom-Brauerei GmbH
Alteburger Straße 145–155, 50968 Köln-Bayenthal
T 0221 37 60 80   F 0221 376 08 11
www.dom-koelsch.de
Founded: 1894
Output: 300,000hl   Availability: c.3,000 pubs

REGULAR BEERS:
Dom Kölsch (4.8%)
Dom Pils (4.8%)
FOR GANSER BRAUEREI, LEVERKUSEN:
Ganser Kölsch (4.8%)
FOR GIESLER BRAUEREI, BRÜHL:
Giesler Kölsch (4.8%)
FOR BRAUEREI METZMACHER, FRECHEN:
Rats Kölsch (4.8%)
FOR SCHRECKENSKAMMER, KÖLN:
Schreckenskammer Kölsch (4.8%)

Waste not, want not. Dom moved from their old home (Tacitusstraße 15, 500m south of here) to the former Küppers brewery and tap in 2001, the former occupant having moved in with the rest of the Kölner Verbund Brauereien.

🍺 Dom
Alteburger Straße 157, 50968 Köln-Bayenthal
T 0221 934 78 10   F 0221 934 78 19
Daily 11.00–24.00
Tram No. 16 Schönhauser Straße 400m
DB Köln Hbf 3.5km

Früh
Cölner Hofbräu P. Josef Früh KG
Brewery: Robert-Bosch-Straße 15, 50769 Köln-Merkenich
Office: Am Hof 12–14, 50667 Köln-Altstadt Nord
T 0221 261 30   F 0221 261 34 99
www.frueh.de
Founded: 1904   Output: 460,000hl
Availability: c.1,000 pubs
REGULAR BEER:
Früh Kölsch (4.8%)

Very large brewery which moved from its old home near the cathedral to a more spacious site in the far north of the city many years ago. The famous Brauhaus still houses the offices.

🍺 Früh am Dom
Am Hof 12–14, 50667 Köln-Altstadt Nord
T 0221 261 32 11   F 0221 261 32 99
Daily 08.00–01.00   DB Köln Hbf 400m

Gaffel (Altstadt)
Privatbrauerei Gaffel Becker & Co.
Eigelstein 41, 50668 Köln-Altstadt Nord
T 0221 16 00 60   F 0221 16 00 61 96
www.gaffel.de
Founded: 1302   Output: 400,000hl

REGULAR BEERS:
Gaffel Kölsch Light (2.4%)
Gaffel Kölsch (4.8%)
Gaffel 1396 (6%)

Gaffel's main brewery is alongside the railway, just north of the Hauptbahnhof, although filling is done elsewhere in the city. They have a second brewery in the Porz district. Their tap in the old market square is smaller than those of Köln's other major brewers.

🍴 **Gaffel-Haus**
Alter Markt 20–22, 50667 Köln-Altstadt Nord
T 0221 257 76 92
Daily 11.00–01.00
Tram Heumarkt 250m   DB Köln Hbf 600m

Gaffel (Porz)

Privatbrauerei Gaffel Becker–Braustätte Porz
Welserstraße 16, 51149 Köln-Porz
T 02203 933 90
Founded: 1877   Output: 150,000hl
RICHMODIS BEER:
Richmodis Kölsch (4.8%)
FOR BRAUHAUS ZUR GARDE, DORMAGEN:
Bürger Kölsch (4.8%)
Garde Kölsch (4.8%)

Gaffel's second brewery, formerly owned by Richmodis. We don't know if the above beers are exclusively brewed here or whether these and Gaffel's other beers are brewed at both sites.
DB Köln-Frankfurter Straße 850m

Hellers

Brauerei Heller GmbH
Roonstraße 33, 50674 Köln-Neustadt
T 0221 24 25 45   **F** 0221 23 92 00
www.hellers-brauhaus.de
Owner: Hubert Heller   Founded: 1991
Output: 2,200hl   Availability: 6 pubs
REGULAR BEERS:
Hellers Kölsch (4.5%)
Hellers Wiess (4.5%)
Hellers Weizen (5%).
SEASONAL BEERS:
Hellers No. 33 (5.5%),
Hellers Eurobock (6.5%, May & Oct)

Microbrewery and tap opposite Zülpicher Platz, south-west of the city centre. We think there was an earlier Brauhaus on this site as they gave us a founding date of 1877.

🍴 **Hellers**
Roonstraße 33, 50674 Köln-Neustadt
T 0221 240 18 81
Closed Sun & hols; Mon–Thu 18.00–01.00,
Fri & Sat 18.00–03.00
Tram Zülpicher Platz 200m
DB Köln Süd 450m

Kölner Verbund Brauereien

Kölner Verbund Brauereien GmbH & Co. KG
Bergisch-Gladbach Straße 116–134, 51065
Köln-Mühlheim
T 0221 96 29 90   **F** 0221 9629 94 33
www.gilden.de
www.kueppers-koelsch.de
www.sester.de
www.sion-koelsch.de
Owner: Oetker Gruppe AG   Founded: 1890
Output: 750,000hl
GILDEN BEER:
Gilden Kölsch (4.8%)
KÜPPERS BEERS:
Küppers Kölsch (4.8%), **Kölner Wieß** (4.8%)
KURFÜRSTEN BEERS:
Kurfürsten Kölsch (4.8%),
Kurfürsten Maximilian Kölsch (4.8%)
PETERS & BAMBECK BEER:
Peters Kölsch (4.8%)
RÖMER BEER:
Römer Kölsch (4.8%)
SION BEER:
Sion Kölsch (4.8%)
SESTER BEER:
Sester Kölsch (4.8%)
FOR DAB, DORTMUND:
Hansa Kölsch (4.9%)

The former Bergische Löwen-Brauerei is the home to this ever-expanding group of Kölsch producers. We've listed taps for three of them below.

🍴 **Gilden Brauhaus**
Clevischer Ring 121, 51063 Köln-Mühlheim
T 0221 640 63 39   **F** 0221 640 63 71
Daily 11.00–01.00
Tram No. 4 Von-Sparr-Straße 600m
DB Köln-Hbf 6km

🍴 **Peters Brauhaus**
Mühlengasse 1, 50667 Köln-Altstadt Nord
T 0221 257 39 50   **F** 0221 257 39 62
Daily 11.00–00.30
Tram Heumarkt 350m   DB Köln Hbf 500m

🍺 Sion Brauhaus
UnterTaschenmacher 5, 50667 Köln-Altstadt Nord
T 0221 257 85 40
Fri & Sat 10.00–01.00, Sun–Thu 10.00–00.30
🚋 Heumarkt 400m   **DB** Köln Hbf 450m

Malzmühle
Brauerei zur Malzmühle Schwartz KG
Heumarkt 6, 50667 Köln-Altstadt Nord
T 0221 21 01 18   **F** 0221 240 88 67
www.muehlen-koelsch.de
Owner: Josef Schwartz   Founded: 1858
Output: 50,000hl
REGULAR BEERS:
Mühlen Kölsch (4.8%)

Brewery at the southern end of the old town with
the tap in front, facing the Heumarkt. In keeping
with its name, the Malt Mill also brews a 2%
Malzbier, apparently along more traditional lines
than the sickly black liquid found elsewhere.

🍺 Malzmühle
Heumarkt 6, 50667 Köln-Altstadt Nord
T 0221 21 01 17
Sun 11.00–23.00, Mon–Sat 10.00–24.00
🚋 Heumarkt 70m   **DB** Köln Hbf 950m

Päffgen
Brauerei Päffgen GmbH & Co. KG
64–66 Friesenstraße, 50670 Köln-Altstadt Nord
T 0221 13 54 61   **F** 0221 139 20 05
www.paeffgen-koelsch.de
Owner: Rudolf Päffgen   Founded: 1883
Output: 6,000hl
REGULAR BEER:
Päffgen Kölsch (4.8%)

By some margin the smallest of Köln's
traditional breweries, Päffgen is on the western
side of the city centre, with the pub in front.

🍺 Päffgen
64–66 Friesenstraße, 50670 Köln-Altstadt Nord
Daily 10.00–24.00
U Friesenplatz 150m   **DB** Köln Hbf 1.2km

Reissdorf
Brauerei Heinrich Reissdorf GmbH & Co. KG
Emil-Hofmann-Str. 4–10, 50996 Köln-Hahnwald
T 02236 965 50   **F** 02236 965 52 35
www.reissdorf.de
Founded: 1894   Output: 600,000hl

REGULAR BEER:
Reissdorf Kölsch (4.8%)

Located in the southern suburb of Hahnwald,
Reissdorf brews the best-selling Kölsch brand.
The tap is further north, between Barbarossa-
platz and the Altstadt.

🍺 Reissdorf
Kleiner Griechenmarkt 40,
50676 Köln-Altstadt Süd
T 0221 21 92 54
Daily from 16.00
U Poststraße 200m   **DB** Köln Süd 800m

Sünner
Gebrüder Sünner GmbH & Co. KG
Kalker Hauptstraße 260, 51103 Köln-Kalk
T 0221 98 79 90   **F** 0221 87 83 81
www.suenner-koelsch.de
Owner: L. Becker, I. Müller Sünner, G. Schulz
Founded: 1830   Output: 60,000hl
REGULAR BEERS:
Sünner Kölsch (4.8%)
Sünner Hefeweizen (4.9%)
FOR BRAUEREI SCHOPEN, BEDBURG:
Schopen Pils (4.8%), Severin Kölsch (4.8%)

Attractive brewery on the main road through
Kalk, a suburb on the eastern bank of the Rhine.
The only outlet at the brewery is a beer garden
that opens in the summer. The main tap is now
in the old town, just off Heumarkt.

🍺 Sünner im Walfisch
Salzgasse 13, 50667 Köln-Altstadt Nord
T 0221 257 78 79   **F** 0221 257 78 09
Fri 15.00–02.00, Sat & Sun 11.00–02.00,
Mon–Thu 17.00–01.00
🚋 Heumarkt 200m   **DB** Köln Hbf 750m

🍺 Zechengarten
Kalker Hauptstraße 260, 51103 Köln-Kalk
Oct–Mar: closed
Apr–Sep: Fri from 15.00, Sat from 13.00,
Sun & hols from 11.00, Mon–Thu from 16.00
U U1 & U9 Kalk Kapelle 200m
DB Köln Hbf 4.5km

Weißbräu
Weiss Bräu Brauerei Betriebs GmbH
Am Weidenbach 24, 50676 Köln-Altstadt Süd
T 0221 23 18 23   **F** 0221 24 79 93
www.weissbraeu.com

Owner: Christian Berger   Founded: 1991
Output: 1,400hl   Availability: 1 pub
REGULAR BEERS:
Weiss Bräu Lecker Kölsch (4.9%)
Weiss Bräu Hefeweizen (5%)
Weiss Bräu St. Pantaleons Schwarze (5.1%)
SEASONAL BEERS:
Weiss Bräu Oktoberfestbier (5.8%), **Weiss Bräu Maibock** (6%), **Weiss Bräu Winterbier** (6.5%)

Brewpub not far from Barbarossaplatz, one of a number set up by Hofbrauhaus Traunstein in the late 1980s/early 1990s. It's now independent.

🍺 **Weißbräu**
Am Weidenbach 24, 50676 Köln-Altstadt Süd
Daily 11.00–01.00
🚊 Eifelstraße 150m, Barbarossaplatz 250m
DB Köln Süd 500m

KORSCHENBROICH   810

Bolten
Privatbrauerei Bolten GmbH
Rheydter Straße 138, 41352 Korschenbroich-Neersbroich
T 02161 61 79 00   **F** 02161 617 90 33
www.bolten-brauerei.de
Owner: Michael Hollmann   Founded: 1266
REGULAR BEERS:
Boltens Alt (4.8%)
Boltens Ur-Alt (4.8%)
Niederrhein Alt (4.8%)
Boltens Landbier (4.9%)
Boltens Ur-Weizen (5.4%)

Nordrhein-Westfalen's oldest brewery, although things have changed a bit since 1266. The Landbier was formerly known as Rubins, the name change following an increase in strength. Bus No. 016 from the station stops here.

🍺 **Poseidon**
Rheydter Straße 110, 41352 Korschenbroich-Neersbroich   **T** 02161 611 53
Daily 10.00–14.00 & 17.00–21.00
DB Korschenbroich 1.5km

KREFELD   811

Gleumes
Brauerei August Gleumes GmbH
Sternstraße 12–14, 47798 Krefeld-Stadtmitte
T 02151 60 15 39   **F** 02151 80 28 05
www.brauerei-gleumes.de
Founded: 1807
Output: 3,000hl   Availability: 25 pubs
REGULAR BEERS:
Gleumes Hell (4.9%)
Gleumes Lager (4.9%)
Gleumes Weizen (4.9%)

Small brewery and tap just north of Friedrichsplatz, one of the few traditional breweries of this size to survive in northern Germany.

🍺 **Gleumes**
Sternstraße 12, 47798 Krefeld-Stadtmitte
T 02151 205 21
Sat & Sun 11.30–01.00,
Mon–Fri 11.30–14.30 & 17.00–01.00
🚊 No. 44 Friedrichsplatz 180m
DB Krefeld Hbf 1.7km

KROMBACH (Kreuztal)   812

Krombacher
Krombacher Brauerei GmbH & Co. KG
Hagener Straße 261, 57223 Kreuztal-Krombach
T 02732 88 00   **F** 02732 88 02 54
www.krombacher.de
Founded: 1803   Output: 5,000,000hl
REGULAR BEERS:
Krombacher Fairlight (2.9%)
Krombacher Extra Mild (4.8%)
Krombacher Pils (4.8%)

Enormous brewery in the village of Krombach which also owns nearby Eichener. Their Pils is arguably the most widely availably beer in the country. If you want to take a closer look, bus No. R10 stops outside the brewery.
DB Eichen (Kreis Siegen) 2.5km, Littfeld 3km

Unfortunately, due to the nature of its subject this Guide will always be out of date. Help us keep it as up-to-date as possible at **GermanBreweries@aol.com.**

KUHLEMÜHLE (Warburg) 813

Warburger

Warburger Brauerei GmbH
Kuhlemühlerweg, 34414 Warburg-Kuhlemühle
T 05641 900 00   **F** 05641 90 00 29
www.warburger-brauerei.de
Owner: the Kohlschein family   Founded: 1721
Output: 30,000hl
REGULAR BEERS:
Warburger Pilsener (4.8%)
Warburger Urtyp (5%)
Warburger Landbier (5%)

In 1984 Warburger moved from their old home
at the tap in Warburg to Kuhlemühle, 3km east
of the town, next to the railway to Kassel. The
buildings used to be part of a paper mill.

🍺 **Brauhaus Kohlschein**
Hauptstraße 60, 34414 Warburg
T 05641 607 00
Closed Mon; Tue–Sun 11.00–16.00 & from 18.00
DB Warburg (Westfalen) 1.4km

LANGENBERG 814

Hohenfelder

Privat-Brauerei Hohenfelder GmbH
Wiedenbrücker Straße 155, 33449 Langenberg
T 05248 800 40   **F** 05248 80 04 50
www.hohenfelder.de
Founded: 1845   Output: 90,000hl
REGULAR BEERS:
Hohenfelder Lappmann's Dunkel (4.7%)
Hohenfelder Pilsener (4.8%)
Hohenfelder Kellerbier (4.8%)
Hohenfelder Weizen (5%)
SEASONAL BEERS:
Hohenfelder Wintertraum (5.2%, Oct–Jan),
Hohenfelder Maximum (7.8%)

Large brewery on the main road north out of
Langenberg, close to the village of Selhorst.
Bus No. R11 runs between Rheda-Wiedenbück
and Lippstadt stations, stopping outside the
brewery, but we don't know if there's a pub
nearby.
DB Rheda-Wiedenbrück 8km, Lippstadt 14km

LANGENFELD 815

Lohmann

Opladener Straße 19, 40764 Langenfeld-
Hagelkreuz
T 02173 916 10   **F** 02173 145 43
www.landhotel-lohmann.de
Owners: the Lohmann family   Founded: 2001
REGULAR BEERS:
Lohmann Bräu Altbier
Lohmann Bräu Hefeweizen
SEASONAL BEERS:
**Lohmann Bräu Oktoberfestbier, Lohmann Bräu
Maibock, Lohmann Bräu Doppelbock**

Very small brewery in Landhotel Lohmann in the
suburb of Hagelkreuz, close to junction 2 of the
A542. We don't think their beers are available
outside the hotel's restaurant. Bus No. 231 brings
you here from Langenfeld station.

🍺 **Lohmann**
Opladener Straße 19, 40764 Langenfeld-
Hagelkreuz
Closed Wed; Thu–Tue 11.30–14.00 & 17.30–
22.00, rooms available
DB Langenfeld (Rheinland) 2.6km

LIPPSTADT 816

Lippstädter Brauhaus

Lippstädter Brauerei Thombansen
Lange Straße 3, 59555 Lippstadt
T 02941 80 08 15
www.lippstaedter-brauerei.de
Owner: Daniel Thombansen
Founded: 01.09.2001   Availability: 4 pubs
REGULAR BEERS:
Lippstädter Hell (4.5%)
Lippstädter Dunkel (4.5%)
Lippstädter Pils (4.5%)
SEASONAL BEERS:
Lippstädter Weizen (4.5%),
Lippstädter Frühlingsbock (6.5%),
Lippstädter Winterbock (6.5%)

Brewpub in the centre of town, close to the river
Lippe. The brewery opened first, the pub
following a couple of years later.

🍺 **Brauhaus Thombansen**
Lange Straße 3, 59555 Lippstadt

Closed Sun; Mon–Sat from 17.00
`DB` Lippstadt 800m

LITTFELD (Kreuztal)   817

Ilsen-Bräu

Ludger's Kleine Brauerei
In den Erlen 29, 57223 Kreuztal-Littfeld
T 02732 823 96   **F** 02732 817 42
www.ilsenbraeu.de
Owner: Ludger Groß-Bölting   Founded: 1994
Output: 200hl
REGULAR BEER:
Ilsen-Bräu Privat (4.8%).

One of the more unusual breweries in this guide.
All the brewing equipment used to be portable,
although we're not sure if that's still the case.
The tap only opens for events (advertised on the
website), or for groups (by prior arrangment).

Ludger's Bierstube
In den Erlen 29, 57223 Kreuztal-Littfeld
`DB` Littfeld 400m

LÜBBECKE   818

Barre

Privatbrauerei Ernst Barre GmbH
Berliner Straße 122–124, 32312 Lübbecke
T 05741 270 10   **F** 05741 27 01 23
www.barre.de
Owners: the Barre & Holle families
Founded: 1842   Output: 210,000hl
REGULAR BEERS:
Barre Dunkel (4.8%)
Barre Altstadt Alt (4.8%)
Barre Pilsener (4.8%)
Barre Weizen (4.8%)
SEASONAL BEER:
Barre Maibock (6.9%)

Large brewery on the southern outskirts of town,
owned by the Barre family since it was founded.
The tap is opposite, part of a complex that also
includes a museum and shop.

Barre's Brauwelt
Berliner Straße 121–123, 32312 Lübbecke
T 05741 230 49 50   **F** 05741 230 49 51
Closed Mon; Tue–Thu 12.00–22.00, Fri & Sat
12.00–24.00, Sun 10.00–16.00
`DB` Lübbecke (Westfalen) 1.5km

LÜDENSCHEID   819

Schillerbad

Brauhaus Schillerbad GmbH
Jockuschstraße 3, 58511 Lüdenscheid
T 02351 362 00   **F** 02351 36 20 30
www.brauhaus-schillerbad.de
Owner: Jörg Mehl   Founded: 01.11.1994
Output: 2,000hl   Availability: 1 pub
REGULAR BEERS:
Medardusbräu (4.9%)
Medardus Schwattes (5.1%)
Medardus Aroma-Pils (5.1%)
Medardus Weizenbier (5.2%)
SEASONAL BEERS:
Medardus Festbier (5.1%, Sep), **Medardus
Osterbräu** (5.4%, Easter), **Medardus Weihnachts-
bier** (5.7%, Christmas), **Medardus Winterbier**
(5.8%, winter), **Medardus Maibock** (6.8%, May)

Large, modern brewpub, in a former swimming
pool, just south of the Stern shopping centre.
Owner Jörg Mehl has five other brewpubs in the
country, each with similarly designed motifs.

Schillerbad
Jockuschstraße 3, 58511 Lüdenscheid
Fri & Sat 09.00–01.00, Sun–Thu 09.00–24.00,
rooms available
`DB` Lüdenscheid 800m

LÜTTE (Lemgo-Voßheide)   820

Lütter Krug

An der Haselbeke 30, 32657 Lemgo-Voßheide/
Lütte
T 05261 137 80
www.lemgoer-bier.de
Owner: Thomas Arndt-Duprée   Founded: 2002
REGULAR BEERS:
Lütter Schwarzbier (4.8%)
Lütter Bernstein (5%)
SEASONAL BEERS:
Lütter Maibock, Lütter Winterbock

Very small brewery and tap in the hamlet of
Lütte. Although regular hours are restricted,
they will open for groups of 15 or more at other
times. Closes for a month following Christmas
and in September. Take bus No. 732 from Lemgo
to Hasebecker Weg, about 800m from the pub.

🍺 Lütter Krug
An der Haselbeke 30, 32657 Lemgo-Voßheide/
Lütte
Closed Fri–Tue; Wed & Thu from 18.00
DB Lemgo 5km

MAUEL (Windeck) 821

Maueler Hofbräu
Hotel Maueler Hofbräu GmbH
Preschlinallee 11, 51570 Windeck-Mauel
T 02292 913 30   F 02292 91 33 33
www.gasthof-willmeroth.de
Owner: K. & T. Willmeroth   Founded: 2003
Output: 200hl   Availability: 1 pub
REGULAR BEER:
Maueler Hofbräu Naturtrüb (5.4%)
SEASONAL BEER:
Maueler Maibock

The Willmeroth family have owned this hotel
and restaurant in the Sieg valley since it was
built in 1882 but the small brewery is a recent
addition. Buses Nos. 343 and 579 run from
Schladern station on weekdays.

🍺 Willmeroth
Preschlinallee 11, 51570 Windeck-Mauel
Closed Wed; Mon, Tue, Thu & Fri & 10.00–14.00
& 17.00–01.00, Sat–Sun & hols 10.00–01.00;
rooms available
DB Schladern (Sieg) 1.4km

MENNRATH
(Mönchengladbach) 822

Zum Stefanus
Brauerei und Gasthaus Zum Stefanus
Mennrath 59, 41179 Mönchengladbach-
Mennrath
T 02161 58 01 54   F 02161 57 27 85
www.zum-stefanus.de
Owner: Michael Stefan Kolonko   Founded: 1999
Output: 350hl   Availability: 1 pub
REGULAR BEERS:
Stefanus Hell (5%)
Stefanus Weizen (5.2%)
Stefanus Dunkel (5.4%)
SEASONAL BEERS:
Stefanus Festbier (5.6%, Sep),

Stefanus Bockbier Hell (7.2%, Lent),
Stefanus Bockbier Dunkel (7.2%, Christmas)

Street-corner pub in the village of Mennrath.
A brewery was installed in 1999 which now
produces three regular beers plus seasonals.
Bus No. 026 runs from Wickrath.

🍺 Zum Stefanus
Mennrath 59, 41179 Mönchengladbach-
Mennrath
Closed Mon; Tue–Sun 12.00–14.00 & 17.00–24.00
DB Wickrath 2.2km

MOERS 823

Moerser Brauhaus
Orsoyer Allee 1, 47445 Moers/Eick-Ost
T 02841 981 13 66   F 02841 981 12 55
www.moerserbrauhaus.de
Owner: Andrea Becker   Founded: 16.04.2005
Availability: 1 pub
REGULAR BEER:
Moerser Bernstein (4.8%)
SEASONAL BEERS:
Moerser Sommerbier (4.8%),
Moerser Winterbier (6%)

Modern brewpub in the northern suburb of
Eick, next to the railway but a long way from the
station. Take buses Nos. 68 or 911 from Moers to
Utfort-Rathaus, then continue for about 500m
north up Rheinberger Straße to the pub.

🍺 Moerser Brauhaus
Orsoyer Allee 1, 47445 Moers/Eick-Ost
Daily 10.00–23.00
DB Moers 3.5km

MÖNCHENGLADBACH 824

Mönchengladbach
Brauerei Mönchengladbach,
Zweigniederlassung der Oettinger Brauerei
GmbH
Senefelderstraße 25–29, 41066
Mönchengladbach-Neuwerk
T 02161 576 90   F 02161 576 91 11
www.oettinger-bier.de
Owner: Oettinger Gruppe
FOR OETTINGER, OETTINGEN:
Original Oettinger Leicht (2.8%)

Original Oettinger Leichte Weiße (2.8%)
Original Oettinger Vollbier Hell (4.7%)
Original Oettinger Pils (4.7%)
Original Oettinger Alt (4.9%)
Original Oettinger Gold (4.9%)
Original Oettinger Schwarzbier (4.9%)
Original Oettinger Hefeweißbier (4.9%)
Original Oettinger Dunkles Weißbier (4.9%)
Original Oettinger Kristall Weizen (4.9%)
Original Oettinger Export (5.4%)
Original Oettinger Urtyp (5.6%)
SEASONAL BEER:
Original Oettinger Winterbier (5.6%)
FOR CARLSBERG BREWERIES:
Carlsberg Beer (4.6%),
Gatz Altbier (4.8%),
Hannen Alt (4.8%),
Tuborg Pilsener (4.9%)
SEASONAL BEER:
Tuborg Weihnachts-Pilsener (4.9%)

The former home of Hannen, Carlsberg sold their
Mönchengladbach brewery to Oettinger in 2003.
Oettinger continue to brew here for Carlsberg,
as well as producing the full range of their own
beers. Bus No. 015 runs from the Hauptbahnhof
if you really want to see the brewery.
DB Mönchengladbach Hbf 4.5km

MORSBACH   825

Knoorz-Bräu

Kirchstraße 13, 51597 Morsbach
T 02294 325
Owner: Herbert Stausberg
Founded: 2002
REGULAR BEERS:
Knoorz-Bräu Hell
Knoorz-Bräu Dunkel
SEASONAL BEERS:
Knoorz-Bräu Pils, Knoorz-Bräu Weizen

Pub close to the centre of the small town. We
believe they had their beers brewed elsewhere
for several years before they started brewing for
themselves. Bus No. 347 runs from Wissen on
weekdays but the last one out leaves quite early.

Zur Republik
Kirchstraße 13, 51597 Morsbach
Closed Thu; Fri–Wed 17.00–24.00
DB Wissen (Sieg) 10km

MÜLHEIM (Ruhr)   826

Mülheimer Brauhaus

Humboldtring 24, 45472 Mülheim/Heissen-
Fullerum
T 0208 78 04 60   F 0208 780 46 46
www.muelheimer-brauhaus.de
Owner: Gerald Fridauer   Founded: 1999
Output: 1,000hl
REGULAR BEERS:
Mülheimer Gruben Gold Zwickel (4.6%)
Mülheimer Ruhr Pott Pils (4.8%)
Mülheimer Ärwin's Weizengold (4.8%)
Mülheimer Mulvany's Dunkel (5%)
SEASONAL BEERS:
Mülheimer Märzen (5.2%, Mar), Mülheimer
Festbier (5.2%, Sep), Mülheimer Maibock (6%,
May), Mülheimer Hibernator (7.5%, Dec)

Previously known as Mayr's Brauhaus, this
modern brewpub is on the first floor of the
Rhein-Ruhr-Zentrum, a large shopping centre
next to junction 20 of the A40. It was recently
taken over by Gerald Fridauer, who owns
several other Ruhr brewpubs.

Mülheimer Brauhaus
Humboldtring 24, 45472 Mülheim/Heissen-
Fulerum
Fri & Sat 09.00–01.00, Sun–Thu 09.00–24.00
U U18 Humboldtring 400m
DB Essen Hbf 4.5km, Mülheim Hbf 4.8km

MÜNSTER   827

Pinkus Müller

Brauerei Pinkus Müller GmbH & Co. KG
Kreuzstraße 4–10, 48143 Münster-Altstadt
T 0251 451 51   F 0251 571 36   www.pinkus.de
Owners: Barbara & Hans Müller   Founded: 1816
Output: 20,000hl
REGULAR BEERS:
Pinkus Leicht (2.8%)
Müller's Lagerbier (4.6%)
Pinkus Original Alt (5%)
Pinkus Pils (5%)
Pinkus Hefeweizen (5%)
Pinkus Special (5.1%)
Pinkus Jubilate (5.5%)

Small brewery and tap on the opposite side of the
old town to the station. This brewery was the first

in the world to be certified organic. Take buses Nos. 5 or 6 to Rosenplatz (return from Tibusstraße).

Pinkus Müller
Kreuzstraße 4–10, 48143 Münster-Altstadt
Closed Sun & hol; Mon–Sat 11.30–24.00
DB Münster Hbf 1.6km

NEUSS   828

Frankenheim
Privatbrauerei Frankenheim GmbH & Co. KG
Brewery: Kreitzweg 10, 41472 Neuss-Holzheim
Office: Wielandstraße 12, 40211 Düsseldorf
T 0211 16 90 20   **F** 0211 36 50 54
www.frankenheim.de
Founded: 1873   Output: 500,000hl
REGULAR BEER:
Frankenheim Alt (4.8%)

Very large, modern brewery in the suburb of Holzheim. They moved here from Düsseldorf in 1991 but the tap and offices are still at the site of the old brewery. If you like to drink your beer close to the source, they also have an outlet in Holzheim.

Brauereiausschank Frankenheim
Wielandstraße 16, 40211 Düsseldorf-Pempelfort
T 0211 351447   **F** 0211 164 0516
Fri & Sat 10.30–01.00, Sun–Thu 10.30–24.00
Tram Pempelforter Straße 50m
DB Düsseldorf Hbf 1.2km

Brauereiausschank Neuss-Holzheim
Bahnhofstraße 50, 41472 Neuss-Holzheim
T 02131 856 90   **F** 02131 805 90
Fri & Sat 10.30–01.00, Sun–Thu 10.30–24.00
DB Holzheim (bei Neuss) 130m

OBERHAUSEN   829

Zeche Jacobi
Promenade 30, 46047 Oberhausen-Neue Mitte
T 0208 80 22 00   **F** 0208 80 22 10
www.brauhaus-zeche-jacobi.de
Owner: Gerald Friedauer   Founded: 1996
REGULAR BEERS:
Zeche Jacobi Gold Zwickel (4.6%)
Zeche Jacobi Ruhr Pott Pils (4.8%)
Zeche Jacobi Ärwin's Weizen Gold (4.8%)
Zeche Jacobi Mulvany's Dunkel (5%)

SEASONAL BEERS:
Zeche Jacobi Märzen (5.2%, Mar),
Zeche Jacobi Festbier (5.2%, Sep),
Zeche Jacobi Maibock (6%, May),
Zeche Jacobi Hibernator (7.5%, Dec)

Named after a local mine *(Zeche)* that closed in 1979, this Ruhrgebiet brewpub is part of the CentrO development on the site of a steelworks. The owner has other breweries in Duisburg, Gelsenkirchen and Mühlheim. Take bus Nos. 939 or 989 from the station.

Zeche Jacobi
Promenade 30, 46047 Oberhausen-Neue Mitte
Fri & Sat 10.00–02.00, Sun–Thu 10.00–00.30
DB Oberhausen Hbf 3.3km

OBERVEISCHEDE (Olpe)   830

Müller
Privatbrauerei Müller
Oberveischeder Straße 13a,
57462 Olpe-Oberveischede
T/F 02722 89 00 50
Owners: the Müller family
Founded: 1996   Output: 750hl
REGULAR BEERS:
Veischeder Landbier Hell (4.8%)
Veischeder Landbier Dunkel (5.2%)

Microbrewery behind Landhotel Sangermann. The beers are sold there and in a couple of other pubs (we think). Bus No. SB3 runs between Olpe and Altenhundem via Oberveischede on weekdays and Saturday mornings.

Sangermann
Oberveischeder Straße 13,
57462 Olpe-Oberveischede
T 02722 81 66   **F** 02722 891 00
Mon from 18.00, Tue–Sun 10.00–14.00 & from 18.00; rooms available
DB Olpe 10km, Altenhundem 12km

OELDE   831

Pott's
Pott's Naturpark-Brauerei GmbH
In der Geist 120, 59302 Oelde
T 02522 933 20   **F** 02522 933 22 80
www.potts.de

Owner: Rainer Pott   Founded: 1769
Output: 90,000hl   Availability: c.500 pubs
REGULAR BEERS:
Pott's Gold (4.8%)
Pott's Pilsener (4.8%)
Alt Pott's Landbier (4.8%)
Pott's Weizen (5.3%)

Pott's moved from the centre of Oelde to this site on the southern edge of town in 1996. In 2003 they opened a brewery museum. The brewery is a few hundred metres from junction 21 of the A2 and bus No. 473 runs from the station.

Pott's Brau und Backhaus
In der Geist 120, 59302 Oelde
T 02522 937 70   **F** 02522 93 77 11
Daily 11.00–22.00
DB Oelde 2.4km

OTTBERGEN (Höxter)   832

Meierhof

Meierhof Privatbrauerei GmbH & Co. KG
Kirchwinkel 10, 37671 Höxter-Ottbergen
T 05275 13 69   **F** 05275 85 33
www.meierhof-brauerei.de
Founded: 1987
Output: 5,000hl   Availability: 82 pubs
REGULAR BEERS:
Alt Meierhof Dunkel (4.8%)
Echt Meierhof Landbier-Hell (5%)
Meierhof Bio-Weizen (5.4%)
SEASONAL BEERS:
Meierhof Höxterbier (4.8%),
Meierhof Festbier (5.6%, May & Oct),
Meierhof Weihnachtsbier (5.9%),
Meierhof Meierator (7.8%)

Microbrewery near the village church that's clearly experienced some success as they now supply more than 80 pubs. The tap is west of the station and now only opens at the weekend.

Spalting
Brakeler Straße 61, 37671 Höxter-Ottbergen
T 05275 98 50 50   **F** 05275 985 05 27
Closed Mon–Thu; Fri–Sun & hols 11.00–14.00 & 17.00–24.00; rooms available
DB Ottbergen 1.2km

PADERBORN   833

Paderborner

Paderborner Brauerei Haus Cramer KG
Halberstädter Straße 45, 33106 Paderborn-Kernstadt
T 05251 70 70   **F** 05251 70 71 05
www.paderborner-brauerei.de
Owner: Albert Cramer   Founded: 1871
Output: 800,000hl
REGULAR BEERS:
Paderborner Goldpilsener (4.8%)
Paderborner Pilsener (4.9%)
Paderborner Export (5.5%)
FOR BRAUEREI ISENBECK, HAMM:
Isenbeck Premium Dark (4.8%), **Isenbeck Pils** (4.8%), **Isenbeck Premium Dry** (4.9%)
FOR BRAUEREI WEISSENBURG, LIPPSTADT:
Weissenburger Pilsener (4.8%)

Very large brewery south of the city, owned by the proprietor of the massive Warsteiner brewery. The tap is north of the centre, close to Neuhäuser Tor.

Paderborner Brauhaus
Kisau 2, 33098 Paderborn
T 05251 28 25 54   **F** 05251 28 14 87
Fri 17.00–02.00, Sat 11.30–02.00,
Sun 11.30–01.00, Mon–Thu 17.00–01.00
DB Paderborn Hbf 1.2km

POPPENBECK (Havixbeck)   834

Klute's

Münsterländische Brauerei Klute AG
Poppenbeck 28, 48329 Havixbeck-Poppenbeck
T 02507 983 90   **F** 02507 98 39 33
www.klutes.de   Founded: 1993
REGULAR BEERS:
Klute's Hell (4.8%)
Klute's Landbier (4.8%)
SEASONAL BEERS:
Klute's Schwarzbier, Klute's Maibock, Klute's Weihnachtsbier

Poppenbeck is a small village of two parts, Klute's being near the northern bit, at the junction of the L550 and L874. The brewing equipment was formerly used by Karmeliter-Bräu in Bad Neustadt. We don't think there are any buses to the pub.

🍺 Klute's
Poppenbeck 28, 48329 Havixbeck-Poppenbeck
Sun 09.00–24.00, Mon 17.00–24.00,
Tue–Sat 12.00–24.00
DB Havixbeck 2.9km

RATINGEN 835

Ratinger Brauhaus
Bahnstraße 15, 40878 Ratingen
T 02102 219 81
Owner: Hans-Willi Poensgen   Founded: 2005
REGULAR BEER:
Ratinger Alt (4.8%)

The former Schinderhannes pub, brewing
commenced here in early 2005. The beer range
is so far limited to an Alt, an understandable
choice given the proximity to Düsseldorf.

🍺 Ratinger Brauhaus
Bahnstraße 15, 40878 Ratingen
Closed Mon; Tue–Fri from 16.00,
Sat & Sun from 11.00
DB Ratingen Ost 650m

RECKLINGHAUSEN 836

Boente
Hausbrauerei Boente, Recklinghäuser
Brauhaus GmbH
Augustinessenstraße 4, 45657 Recklinghausen
T 02361 176 09   F 02361 18 43 24
www.hausbrauerei-boente.de
Owner: Johannes Dörlemann   Founded: 1988
Output: 2,000hl
REGULAR BEERS:
Boente's Zwickelbier (4.8%)
Boente's Spezial (5.2%)

Owned by Johannes Dörlemann who also has
his own large distillery and the Tauffenbach
brewpub in Bochum. Boente is named after a
distillery of the same name which occupied the
building until 1988.

🍺 Boente
Augustinessenstraße 4, 45657 Recklinghausen
Sun 10.00–02.00, Mon–Sat 11.00–02.00
DB Recklinghausen Hbf 800m

REINEBERG (Hüllhorst) 837

Niedermeiers Hof
Buchenweg 6a, 32609 Hüllhorst-Reineberg
T 05741 30 15 45   F 05741 23 36 84
www.niedermeiershof.de
Owner: Ingrid Kujat   Founded: 2004
REGULAR BEERS:
Niedermeiers Pilsener
Niedermeiers Urtrüb

Half-timbered brewpub in the village of
Reineberg, only a couple of kilometres south of
Barre's brewery and tap. Bus No. 604 runs from
Lübbecke on weekdays and Saturday mornings,
with an AST service operating at other times.

🍺 Niedermeiers Hof
Buchenweg 6a, 32609 Hüllhorst-Reineberg
Closed Mon & Tue; Wed–Sat from 12.00,
Sun from 09.00   DB Lübbecke (Westfalen) 3.7km

RHEDER (Brakel) 838

Schloßbrauerei Rheder
Gräflich von Mengersen'sche Dampfbrauerei
Nethetalstraße 10, 33034 Brakel-Rheder
T 05272 392 30   F 05272 39 23 20
www.schlossbrauerei-rheder.de
Owner: Elmar Freiherr von Spiegel
Founded: 1686   Output: 20,000hl
REGULAR BEERS:
Schloßbräu Rheder Pils (4.9%)
Schloßbräu St. Annen Dunkel (5%)
Schloßbräu Rheder Export (5.3%)
Schloßbräu Husaren-Trunk (5.3%)
SEASONAL BEERS:
Schloßbräu Dampfbier (brewery festival only),
Schloßbräu Bock (6.8%, Lent), **Schloßbräu
Doppelbock** (7.3%, winter)

Brewery in the grounds of Rheder castle, close
to the centre of the village. The beers are sold at
the upmarket horse stables bar in Bad Driburg,
15km west of Rheder, as well as in the castle's
orangery on summer Sunday afternoons.

🍺 'Pferdestall' im Gräflichen Parkhotel
Im Kurpark, Brunnenstraße, 33014 Bad Driburg
T 05253 95 22 43   F 05253 95 22 04
Daily 09.00–23.00, rooms available
DB Bad Driberg (Westfalen) 900m

RHEINBACH   839

Brauhaus Rheinbach

Wilhelmsplatz 1, 53359 Rheinbach
T 02226 91 38 00   **F** 02226 91 38 01
www.brauhaus-rheinbach.de
Owner: Peter Schemerka   Founded: 1998
Output: 1,000hl   Availability: 2 pubs
REGULAR BEERS:
Rheinbacher Hell
Rheinbacher Dunkel
SEASONAL BEERS:
Rheinbacher Hefeweißbier,
Rheinbacher Weihnachtsfestbier

Situated between the station and the town-
centre, this brewpub now supplies one other
pub but has reduced its range of seasonal beers.

🍺 **Brauhaus Rheinbach**
Wilhelmsplatz 1, 53359 Rheinbach
Daily 11.00–01.00
DB Rheinbach 350m

RÖTTGERSBACH (Duisburg)   840

Mattlerhof

Wehofer Straße 42, 47169 Duisburg-Röttgersbach
T 0203 995 87 77   **F** 0203 995 87 99
www.brauhaus-mattlerhof.de
Owner: Antonio Link   Founded: 28.04.2002
REGULAR BEERS:
Mattler Blond
Mattler Braun
Mattler Weizen

Brewpub in Mattlersbusch park. We've listed
Röttgersbach separately from Duisburg as it's
10km north of the latter and takes at least 45
minutes by tram and bus. From Holten station,
take a bus to Holten Markt, then change for a
No. 905 to Niederrhein Therme – the pub's
about 350m to the south.

🍺 **Mattlerhof**
Wehofer Straße 42, 47169 Duisburg-Röttgersbach
Fri & Sat 12.00–01.00, Sun 11.00–22.30,
Mon–Thu 12.00–22.00
DB Oberhausen-Holten 3km

SCHMERLECKE (Erwitte)   841

Braumühle

Braumühle am Alten Hellweg
Windmühlenweg 3, 59597 Erwitte-Schmerlecke
T 02945 20 05 60   **F** 02945 20 05 61
www.brau-muehle.de   Owner: Elmar Claes
Founded: 2000   Availability: 1 pub
REGULAR BEERS:
Braumühle Söller Hell (4.8%)
Braumühle Söller Dunkel (4.8%)

Brewpub in a 175-year-old windmill on the edge
of the village. Schmerlecke can be reached by
bus from both Bad Sassendorf and Lippstadt
but it may require a bit of patience.

🍺 **Braumühle**
Windmühlenweg 3, 59597 Erwitte-Schmerlecke
Closed Mon; Tue–Fri 17.00–24.00,
Sat 15.00–24.00, Sun & hols 11.00–23.00
DB Bad Sassendorf 7km, Lippstadt 12km

SCHWELM   842

Schwelm

Neumarkt 1, 58332 Schwelm
T 02336 490 80   **F** 02336 49 08 46
www.schwelmer.com   Owner: Dr. Rolf Lohbeck
Founded: 1830   Output: 60,000hl
REGULAR BEERS:
Schwelmer Alt (4.2%)
Schwelmer Pils (4.7%)
Schwelmer Bernstein (4.8%)
Schwelmer Hefe Weizen (5.2%)
SEASONAL BEER:
Schwelmer Dunkler Bock (6.5%)

The previous owner Veltins planned to close
this brewery in 2000, so it's fortunate the
brewery is here today. The new owner seems to
mean business, having invested more than
€5,000,000, so far.

🍺 **Schwelmer Braustübchen**
Untermauerstraße 15, 58332 Schwelm
T 02336 34 73
Daily from 10.00
DB Schwelm 750m

SELBECKE (Hagen)　　843

Mäckinger Bräu

Museumsgaststätten im Westfälischen
Freilichtmuseum Hagen
Mäckingerbach, 58091 Hagen-Selbecke
T 02331 701 00　　**F** 02331 706 57
www.hausletmathe.de　　Founded: 1998
REGULAR BEERS:
Mäckinger Pils (5%)
Mäckinger Weizen Dunkel (5%)

Impressive reconstructed brewery inside the
open-air museum at Selbecke. The museum
itself opens at 09.00 and is well worth a visit in
its own right. It's the best part of a mile from
Freilichtmuseum bus stop (No. 512 from Hagen).

🍺 **Braustube**
Mäckingerbach, 58091 Hagen-Selbecke
T 02339 701 00　　**F** 02339 706 57
Closed Nov–Mar.
Apr–Oct: closed Mon; Tue–Sun 11.00–17.00
DB Hagen-Oberhagen 3km, Hagen Hbf 5km

SIEGBURG　　844

Siegburger Brauhaus

Siegburger Abteibrauerei GmbH
Holzgasse 37–39, 53721 Siegburg
T 02241 559 99　　**F** 02241 559 97
www.siegburger-abteibrauerei.de
Owners: Edith & Peter Palmer　　Founded: 1993
Output: 2,000hl　　Availability: 2 pubs
REGULAR BEERS:
Siegburger Pils
Siegburger Weizen

Brewery in the Red Lion pub, east of the market
square, also known as the Abteibrauerei (after
the nearby abbey). We don't think they do any
seasonal beers.

🍺 **Zum Roten Löwen**
Holzgasse 37–39, 53721 Siegburg
Fri 12.00–01.00, Sat 11.00–01.00,
Sun–Thu 12.00–24.00
DB Siegburg 850m

SIEGEN　　845

Irle

Brauhaus Johann Friedrich Irle GmbH
Hauptstraße 18, 57074 Siegen/Kaan-Marienborn
T 0271 66 04 60　　**F** 0271 660 46 13
www.der-biermacher.de
Owner: Klaus Irle　　Founded: 1693
REGULAR BEERS:
Irle Edel-Pils (5%)
Irle Johann-Friedrichs Zwickelbier Hell (5%)
Irle Johann-Friedrichs Zwickelbier Dunkel (5%)
SEASONAL BEERS:
Irle Cääner Blondes, Irle Landweizen,
Irle Bockbier, Irle Winterbock

The Irle brewery re-invented itself in 2000 with
the opening of what is effectively a brewpub
within part of the old brewery. Irle Edel-Pils is
still available elsewhere but the other beers are
only sold here.

🍺 **Irle**
Hauptstraße 18, 57074 Siegen/Kaan-Marienborn
T 0271 681 98 34
Closed Sun–Wed; Thu–Sat 18.00–02.00
DB Siegen 2.7km

SOEST　　846

Zwiebel

Ulricherstraße 24, 59494 Soest
T 02921 44 24　　**F** 02921 168 74
www.brauhaus-zwiebel.de
Owner: Manfred Wieners　　Founded: 1993
Output: 1,200hl　　Availability: 2 pubs
REGULAR BEERS:
Soester Hell (4.8%)
Soester Dunkel (4.8%)
Soester Weizen (5.4%)
SEASONAL BEERS:
Soester Märzen,
Soester Maibock,
Soester Weihnachtsbock

Housed in a 400-year-old half-timbered
building in the southern part of the town centre,
the Onion also supplies the Aloisius restaurant
just across the street. Catch a bus to Haarhofs-
gasse, if you'd prefer not to walk from the station.

🍺 Zwiebel
Ulricherstraße 24, 59494 Soest
Sun 11.30–22.00, Mon–Sat 11.30–23.00
DB Soest 1.2km

SONNEBORN (Barntrup)　　847

Röhr Bräu

Brauerei Röhr Bräu
Grießemer Straße 2a, 32683 Barntrup-Sonneborn
T 05263 38 11　　**F** 05263 95 52 55
www.roehrbraeu.de
Owner: Gerhard Röhr　　Founded: 1996
REGULAR BEERS:
Röhr Bräu Pils
Röhr Bräu Dunkel
Röhr Bräu Weizen

Modern brewpub at the southern end of the village, a few hundred metres from the Lower Saxony border. It's a bit of an ordeal getting to the village by public transport while the pub is open and is likely to involve an AST, but it can be done.

🍺 Brauhaus Sonneborn
Grießemer Straße 2a, 32683 Barntrup-Sonneborn
Closed Mon; Tue–Thu 17.00–23.00,
Fri & Sat 17.00–01.00, Sun 11.00–20.00
DB Bad Pyrmont 12km, Hameln 17km

STEINFURT　　848

Rolinck

Privatbrauerei A. Rolinck GmbH & Co. KG
Wettringer Straße 41, 48565 Steinfurt
T 02551 640　　**F** 02551 641 17
www.rolinck.de
Founded: 1820　　Output: 250,000hl
REGULAR BEERS:
Rolinck Pilsener Premium (4.8%)
Rolinck Friedensreiter Bräu (4.8%)
Alex Rolinck Feines Lagerbier (4.9%)
Rolinck Weizen (5.4%)

Large regional brewery below Burgsteinfurt. They don't have an official tap but their beers can be found over much of northern Nordrhein-Westfalen.
DB Burgsteinfurt 1.4km

SUNDERN (Hiddenhausen)　　849

Herforder

Brauerei Felsenkeller Herford GmbH & Co.
Gebrüder-Uekerman-Straße 1, 32120
Hiddenhausen-Sundern
T 05221 96 50　　**F** 05221 96 52 02
www.herforder.de
Founded: 1878　　Output: 650,000hl
REGULAR BEERS:
Herforder Pils (4.8%)
Herforder Mild Plus (4.9%)
Herforder Felsenkeller Dunkel (4.9%)
Herforder Export (5.2%)
SEASONAL BEERS:
Herforder Maibock (6%),
Herforder Weihnacht (5.8%)

Despite the name, this very large brewery is actually in the village of Sundern, between Herford and Hiddenhausen. Buses Nos. 646–648 from Herford station stop near the tap.

🍺 Herforder Wirtschaft am Felsenkeller
Bünder Straße 38, 32120 Hiddenhausen-Sundern
T 05221 622 24　　**F** 05221 69 04 89
Sat 17.00–24.00, Sun–Fri 11.00–24.00
DB Herford 2.4km

SUTTROP (Warstein)　　850

Suttroper Brauhof

Gasthausbrauerei Suttroper Brauhof
Steinrücken 7, 59581 Warstein-Suttrop
T 02902 70 08 88　　**F** 02902 70 08 89
www.suttroper.de
Owner: Jürgen Gudemann　　Founded: 1998
REGULAR BEERS:
Suttroper Hell (4.8%)
Suttroper Dunkel (4.8%)
SEASONAL BEERS:
**Suttroper Festbier, Suttroper Maibock,
Suttroper Bock**

Brewpub in a 17th-century farmhouse on the southern side of the village. Take bus No. R76 from Meschede to Warstein Bahnhof, then change for No. R77. You've time for a quick beer if you want to return the same day.

🍺 Suttroper Brauhof
Steinrücken 7, 59581 Warstein-Suttrop

Closed Mon & Tue; Wed–Sun from 18.00
DB Meschede 16km

TROISDORF 851

Stadtbrauerei

Wilhelm-Hamacher-Platz 24, 53840 Troisdorf
T 02241 80 05 55   F 02241 80 05 52
www.stadtbrauerei.de
Owner: Manfred Hausmann   Founded: 1994
Output: 1,000hl   Availability: 1 pub
REGULAR BEERS:
Troisdorfer (4.9%)
Troisdorfer Troilsch (4.9%)
Troisdorfer Troi-Pi (5.1%)
SEASONAL BEERS:
Troisdorfer Light (2%), **Troisdorfer Pils** (5.1%),
Troisdorfer Weizen (5.1%), **Troisdorfer
Schwarzbier** (5.1%), **Troisdorfer Wies'n Bier** (6%)

Brewpub in the Bürgerhaus, a modern buiding
on Troisdorf's central square. The Troilsch is not
entirely dissimilar to a certain speciality of Köln.
Only the Pils is bottom-fermented.

🍺 Stadtbrauerei

T 02241 80 05 55   F 02241 80 05 52
Wilhelm-Hamacher-Platz 24, 53840 Troisdorf
Fri & Sat 11.00–01.00, Sun–Thu 11.00–24.00
DB Troisdorf 400m

UNNA 852

Lindenbrauerei

Massener Straße 33–35, 59423 Unna
T 02303 25 11 20   F 02303 229 32
www.lindenbrauerei.de
Founded: 31.08.2002   Availability: 1 pub
REGULAR BEERS:
Linden Hell
Linden Dunkel

The original Lindenbrauerei closed in 1979 but
the site found further use as an arts and cultural
centre. A small brewery was installed in 2002,
reviving the name. Confusingly, some of the old
brewery's beers are still brewed elsewhere.

🍺 Schalander

Massener Straße 33–35, 59423 Unna
Fri & Sat 19.00–03.00, Sun–Thu 19.00–01.00
DB Unna 800m

VELBERT 853

Velberter Brauhaus

Friedrichstraße 102, 42551 Velbert
T 02051 525 00   F 02051 661 57
Founded: 1995
REGULAR BEER:
Velberter Brauhaus Alt

Small, street-corner brewpub that produces
just one beer. Various bus routes take you to
Velbert, including No. 649 from Neviges station
and express buses from Wuppertal and Essen.

🍺 Velberter Brauhaus

Friedrichstraße 102, 42551 Velbert
Daily 10.00–01.00
DB Velbert-Neviges 6km

VREDEN 854

Vredener Brauhaus

Vredener Brauhaus GmbH & Co. KG
Markt 1, 48691 Vreden
T 02564 96 83 80   F 02564 968 38 38
www.vredener-brauhaus.de
Founded: 09.06.2000
REGULAR BEERS:
Vredener Hell
Vredener Dunkel
Vredener Weizen

Brewpub in the central square that also produces
its own beer vinegar (there's a joke there, somewhere). Buses Nos. S70 & N12 run from Ahaus.

🍺 Vredener Brauhaus

Markt 1, 48691 Vreden
Closed Tue; Wed–Mon 11.00–01.00
DB Ahaus 15km

WARSTEIN 855

Warsteiner

Brewery: Im Waldpark, 59581 Warstein
Office: Domring 4–10, 59581 Warstein
T 02902 880   F 02902 88 12 99
www.warsteiner.de
Owner: Albert Cramer   Founded: 1753
Output: 5,000,000hl

Availability: c.35,000 pubs
REGULAR BEERS:
Warsteiner Light (2.4%)
Warsteiner Premium Verum (4.8%)

Along with Krombacher, contender for brewer of Germany's most consumed beer. Both brewery and tap are south of the town at the edge of the Warsteiner forest. They also own Paderborner. Take bus No. R76 from Meschede.

🍺 Haus Waldfrieden
Am Tüppel 10, 59581 Warstein
T 02902 98 10   **F** 02902 88 14 26
Daily 10.00–24.00; rooms available
DB Meschede 12km

WELZ (Linnich)   856

Rainer

Brauerei und Brennerei Jakob Rainer & Sohn
Kreisstraße 31–33, 52441 Linnich-Welz
T 02462 64 45   **F** 02462 16 87
www.brauerei-rainer.de
Owner: Berthold Rainer   Founded: 1828
Output: 2,000hl
REGULAR BEERS:
Lambertus Dunkel
Lambertus Schwarzbier
Lambertus Zwickel
Lambertus Pils
SEASONAL BEERS:
Lambertus Oktoberbier, Lambertus Maibock,
Lambertus Weihnachtsbock
FOR FELSENKELLER, MONSCHAU:
Felsenkeller Felsenquell Pils, Felsenkeller
Zwickelbier Dunkel
FOR GUT HÖHNE, BURBACH:
Gut Höhne Pils, Gut Höhne Alt

Small courtyard brewery and tap in the village of Welz, south-west of Linnich. Buses run from both Jülich and Linnich on weekdays.

🍺 Brauereiausschank
Kreisstraße 31–33, 52441 Linnich-Welz
T 02462 82 61
Closed Tue; Wed–Fri & Mon 17.00–01.00,
Sat 18.00–01.00, Sun 10.00–01.00
DB Linnich Bahnhof 4km, Lindern 7km

WESTHEIM (Marsberg)   857

Westheimer

Gräflich zu Stolberg'sche Brauerei Westheim
Kasseler Straße 7, 34431 Marsberg-Westheim
T 02994 88 90   **F** 02994 889 80
www.brauerei-westheim.de
Owner: Josef Freiherr von Twickel
Founded: 1862   Output: 80,000hl
Availability: 271 pubs
REGULAR BEERS:
Westheimer Wildschütz Klostermann (4.8%)
Westheimer Graf Stolberg Dunkel (4.8%)
Westheimer Premium Pilsener (4.8%)
SEASONAL BEERS:
Westheimer Märzen, Westheimer Winter

Large brewery owned by the Baron von Twickel. The tap is close to the station in Marsberg, 6km south-west of Westheim.

🍺 Deutsches Haus
Haupstraße 8, 34431 Marsberg
T 02992 24 12
Closed Mon; Tue–Sat 17.00–01.00,
Sun 10.00–14.00 & 17.00–01.00
DB Marsberg 250m

WOLLERSHEIM (Nideggen)   858

Cramer

Familienbrauerei Johann Cramer & Cie. KG
Zehnthofstraße 66, 52385 Nideggen-Wollersheim
T 02425 204   **F** 02425 72 99
www.cramer-bier.de
Founded: 1791   Output: 13,000hl
REGULAR BEERS:
Cramer Obergärig (4.8%)
Cramer Edel-Pils (4.8%)

Small, family-run brewery at the northern end of the Eifel mountains. The tap is in the village of Steckenborn, close to the Rur reservoir, 20km west of Wollersheim, but was closed at the time of writing.

🍺 Steckenborner Hof
In Steckenborn 40, 52152 Simmerath-Steckenborn
T 02473 27 20
Currently closed
DB Nideggen Brücke 13km

WULFEN (Dorsten)   859

Metzler

Hausbrauerei Metzler
Linnertweg 1, 46286 Dorsten-Wulfen
T 02369 86 14   **F** 02369 233 76
www.brauereiware.de
Owner: Ewald Metzler   Founded: 2000
Output: 500hl
REGULAR BEERS:
Metzler Hell
Metzler Dunkel

Metzler's main business is the supply of brewing equipment to small commercial and serious hobby brewers. However, they also brew a couple of beers themselves, supplemented by occasional seasonals. We don't think there's a tap and don't have any information on availability.
DB Wulfen (Westfalen) 700m

WÜLFRATH   860

Alt Wülfrath

Schwanenstraße 12, 42489 Wülfrath
T 02058 38 67   **F** 02058 735 77
www.brauhaus-alt-wuelfrath.de
Owner: Irene Brass   Founded: 1997
REGULAR BEERS:
Wolverother Helles
Wolverother Rotes
Wolverother Schwarzbier
SEASONAL BEERS:
Wolverother Weizenbier Hell, Wolverother Weizenbier Dunkel, Wolverother Honigbier, Wolverother Weihnachtsbier, Wolverother Potenzbier, Wolverother Buddyvator

Town-centre brewpub that produces more seasonal beers than we've listed. The best direct bus service is No.746 from Mettmann but there are alternatives from Wuppertal-Vohwinkel and Velbert-Neviges, generally involving a change.

🍺 Alt Wülfrath
Schwanenstraße 12, 42489 Wülfrath
Closed Mon; Tue–Fri & Sun from 17.00,
Sat 10.00–14.00 & from 17.00
DB Mettmann-Zentrum 5.5km

WUPPERTAL-BARMEN   861

Wuppertaler Brauhaus

Wuppertaler Brauhaus GmbH
Kleine Flurstraße 5, 42275 Wuppertal-Barmen
T 0202 25 50 50   **F** 0202 255 05 25
www.wuppbrau.de
Owner: Jörg Mehl   Founded: 1997
Output: 4,000hl   Availability: 1 pub
REGULAR BEERS:
Wupper Hell (4.9%)
Wupper Dunkel (4.9%)
Wupper Weizen (5.3%)
SEASONAL BEERS:
Wupper Oktoberfestbier (5.1%),
Wupper Maibock (5.7%),
Wupper Weihnachtsbock (5.7%)

The largest of Jörg Mehl's six brewpubs. Like Brauhaus Schillerbad, it's located in a former swimming pool. If you fancy something a litttle different, come here by Schwebebahn, a monorail suspended above the Wupper river.

🍺 Wuppertaler Brauhaus
Kleine Flurstraße 5, 42275 Wuppertal-Barmen
Fri & Sat 11.00–01.00, Sun–Thu 11.00–24.00
Monorail Werthe Brücke 400m
DB Wuppertal-Barmen 900m

Rheinland-Pfalz
(Rhineland-Palatinate)

ONE OF GERMANY'S MOST picturesque states, Rheinland-Pfalz has within its borders part of the Eifel and Hunsrück mountain ranges and some of Germany's most scenic river valleys. The capital is Mainz, a lovely old city that stands at the confluence of the Main and Rhein.

Six of Germany's 13 wine-growing regions lie within the state, producing between them almost two-thirds of the country's wine. Not surprisingly, many towns and villages have wine festivals and these can rival some beer festivals for raucous behaviour.

Among the many non-beery highlights on offer, the Guide recommends the following: a journey by train down the Rhein valley from Koblenz to Bingen and Mainz (and perhaps back by boat); Trier and its Roman remains; a visit to one of the countless wine festivals.

Just over half of Rheinland-Pfalz's 40 breweries are modern micros and brewpubs. The remainder are generally small-to-medium, family-run businesses. There's one major exception to this: Bitburger – their Pils accounts for about 80% of all beer brewed in the state.

Transport: The transport system in Rheinland-Pfalz is heavily influenced by the topography, and areas away from major river valleys are often poorly served, in particular by rail. That said, villages with breweries are generally easily reached. A DB Rheinland-Pfalz day ticket costs €23 for up to five people and is also valid in Saarland. As usual, please check to see where you can use it.

BELLHEIM 862

Bellheimer

Bellheimer Privatbrauerei Karl Silbernagel AG
Karl-Silbernagel-Straße 20-22, 76756 Bellheim
T 07272 70 10   **F** 07272 70 11 77
www.bellheimer.de
Owner: Actris AG   Founded: 1865
Output: 50,000hl
REGULAR BEERS:
Bellheimer Lord Light (2.9%)
Bellheimer Silber Pils (4.8%)
Bellheimer Naturtrüb (4.8%)
Bellheimer Lord Pils (4.9%)
Bellheimer Edel-Export (5.2%)
Bellheimer Hefeweizen (5.2%)
Bellheimer Kristallweizen (5.2%)
SEASONAL BEERS:
Pfälzer Festbier (5.5%), **Doppelbock** (7%)

Bellheimer merged with the Park brewery in Pirmasens in 1995 but the two remain separate as far as beer production is concerned. The tap closes for two weeks in January and August.

🏠 **Braustübl**
Hauptstraße 78, 76756 Bellheim
T 07272 55 00
Closed Mon & Tue; Wed–Sun 11.30–14.00 & 17.30–22.00
DB Bellheim 1.4km

BITBURG 863

Bitburger

Bitburger Brauerei Theobald Simon GmbH
Brewery: Brauereistraße, 54634 Bitburg
Office: Römermauer 3, 54634 Bitburg
T 06561 140   **F** 06561 14 22 89

www.bitburger.de
Owner: Bitburger Getränkegruppe
Founded: 1817   Output: 4,125,000hl
REGULAR BEERS:
Bitburger Light (2.8%)
Bitburger Premium Pils (4.8%)

Huge brewery on the south side of town. The offices and tap are close to the centre of Bitburg, on the site of the original brewery. Buses Nos. 400 & 405 run from Bitburg-Erdorf.

🍺 **Zum Simonbräu**
Am Markt 7, 54634 Bitburg
T 06561 33 33   **F** 06561 37 33
Daily from 10.00; rooms available
[DB] Bitburg-Erdorf 6km

FRANKENTHAL   864

Brauhaus zur Post

Neumayerring 45, 67227 Frankenthal
T 06233 22 02 86   **F** 06233 22 03 69
www.brauhaus-zur-post.de
Owner: Bischoff, Winnweiler   Founded: 2001
Availability: 1 pub
REGULAR BEERS:
Brauhaus zur Post Hell
Brauhaus zur Post Dunkel
Brauhaus zur Post Weizen

One of two brewpubs owned by Bischoff of Winnweiler, this street-corner pub is just south of Frankenthal's main station. Seasonal beers are brewed in addition to the regulars.

🍺 **Brauhaus zur Post**
Neumayerring 45, 67227 Frankenthal
Mon–Sat 11.00–01.00, Sun 10.00–24.00
[DB] Frankenthal Hbf 300m

GÖCKLINGEN   865

Göcklinger Hausbräu

Münsterweg 2, 76831 Göcklingen
T 06349 53 35   **F** 06349 96 31 07
www.goecklinger-hausbraeu.de
Owner: Reiner Weißgerber   Founded: 2004
Output: 800hl   Availability: 1 pub
REGULAR BEERS:
Göcklinger Hell (5%)
Göcklinger Dunkel (5%)

REGULAR BEERS:
Göcklinger Schwarzbier (5.5%),
Göcklinger Festbier (5.5%),
Göcklinger Maibock (6.5%),
Göcklinger Weihnachtsbock (6.5%)

Small brewery and purpose-built pub which opened in August 2004. Both the brewery and village have a cockerel (*Gockel* in German) on their emblems. Bus No. 543 runs from Landau.

🍺 **Göcklinger Hausbräu**
Münsterweg 2, 76831 Göcklingen
May–Oct: closed Wed; Thu–Tue from 11.00
Nov–Apr: closed Wed; Mon, Tue, Thu & Fri from 16.00, Sat & Sun from 11.00
[DB] Landau (Pfalz) Hbf 9km

GRÜNSTADT   866

Grünstadt

Hausbrauerei Grünstadt
Turnstraße 11, 67269 Grünstadt
T 06359 96 01 50   **F** 06359 84 07 98
www.hausbrauerei-gruenstadt.de
Founded: 1999   Availability: 1 pub
REGULAR BEERS:
Grünstadter Helles
Grünstadter Dunkles
Grünstadter Weizen
SEASONAL BEERS:
Grünstadter Bockbier,
Grünstadter Doppelbock

Town-centre brewpub, a few minutes walk from Grünstadt station. We think they brew a few more seasonal beers than we've listed.

🍺 **Grünstadt**
Turnstraße 11, 67269 Grünstadt
Mon–Thu 10.00–24.00, Fri & Sat 10.00–01.00, Sun 09.00–22.00, hols 11.00–22.00
[DB] Grünstadt 250m

HACHENBURG   867

Westerwald

Westerwald Brauerei Heiner Schneider KG
Gehlerter Weg 10, 57627 Hachenburg
T 02662 80 80   **F** 02662 808 80
www.hachenburger.de
Founded: 1861   Output: 200,000hl

REGULAR BEERS:
Hachenburger Light (2.8%)
Hachenburger Schwarze (4.8%)
Hachenburger Pils (5.1%)
Hachenburger Ur-Trüb (5.1%)
Hachenburger Weizen (5.5%)
SEASONAL BEER:
Hachenburger Special (5.8%)

Large regional brewery south of the centre. The tap in the heart of the old town is reputedly the oldest stone-built pub in Germany.

📍 Zur Krone
Alter Markt 3, 57627 Hachenberg
T 02662 94 78 90   **F** 02662 947 89 24
Daily from 10.00; rooms available
DB Hachenburg 500m

HAHNSTÄTTEN   868

Nassauische

Nassauische Privatbrauerei GmbH
Rößlerstraße 3, 65623 Hahnstätten
T 06430 40 01   **F** 06430 40 03
Owners: Hermann Schmidt & Gerd Siebel
Founded: 1842   Output: 22,500hl
Availability: 40 pubs
REGULAR BEERS:
Nassauer Schlök (4.6%)
Oraniensteiner Premium-Pils (4.6%)
Nassauer Traditions-Pilsener (4.7%)
Nassauer Kellerpils (4.7%)
Nassauer Alt (4.8%)
Nassauer Export Privat (4.9%)
Nassauer Landbier (5.2%)
Hahnstätter Hefeweizen Hell (5.2%)
Hahnstätter Weizen Dunkel (5.3%)
SEASONAL BEER:
Nassauer Schwarzbier (5.2%)
FOR PRINZ HENDRICK, EDE, HOLLAND:
Prinz Hendrick Pilsener

Small brewery on the western side of the town. The tap is nearby, on the main road through the valley. Bus No. 284 runs daily from Limburg.

📍 Nassauer Hof
Aarstraße 35, 65623 Hahnstätten
T 06430 92 89 29
Daily 11.00–14.00 & from 17.00
DB Limburg (Lahn) 10km

HINTERWEIDENTHAL   869

Brauhaus Ehrstein

Im Handschuhteich 3, 66999 Hinterweidenthal
T 06396 168 00 00
Owner: August Ehrstein   Founded: 2000
Output: 250hl   Availability: 1 pub
REGULAR BEERS:
Brauhaus Ehrstein Hell
Brauhaus Ehrstein Dunkel
SEASONAL BEERS:
Brauhaus Ehrstein Weizen,
Brauhaus Ehrstein Bock

Small pub and brewery on the western side of the village. Be warned that Hinderweidental has three stations but two of them (Hinterweidenthal-Bahnhof and Hinterweidenthal-Ort) are only open when the line to Bundenthal-Rumbach is in use.

📍 Brauhaus Ehrstein
Im Handschuhteich 3, 66999 Hinterweidenthal
Closed Mon; Tue–Fri 15.00–24.00 (May–Oct from 15.00), Sat 15.00–24.00, Sun & hols
11.00–24.00   DB Hinterweidenthal 900m

JOCKGRIM   870

Froschbräu

Buchstraße 5, 76751 Jockgrim
T/F 07271 54 78   www.froschl.de
Owner: Bärbel Dreyer   Founded: 1999
REGULAR BEERS:
Fröschl Hell
Fröschl Dunkel
Fröschl Weizen Hell
Fröschl Weizen Dunkel
SEASONAL BEERS:
Fröschl Oktoberfestbier, Fröschl Maibock,
Fröschl Weihnachtsbock

'Frogbrew' is just over the level crossing from the station, on the opposite side of the railway to the town. Unusually, they brew both dark and pale wheat beers all year round. They also offer accommodation.

📍 s' Fröschl
Buchstraße 5, 76751 Jockgrim
Tue–Fri from 16.00; Sat–Mon from 18.00
DB Jockgrim 200m

KAISERSLAUTERN 871

Brauhaus am Markt

Stiftsplatz 2–3, 67655 Kaiserslautern-Innenstadt
T 0631 619 44   **F** 0631 89 14 14
www.brauhaus-am-markt.com
Owner: Bischoff, Winnweiler   Founded: 2000
Availability: 1 pub
REGULAR BEERS:
Brauhaus am Markt Hell
Brauhaus am Markt Dunkel
Brauhaus am Markt Weizen

The first of the two brewpubs owned by Bischoff
to open, Brauhaus am Markt is opposite the
Stiftskirche in the city centre. The three regular
beers are usually supplemented by a seasonal.

🍺 **Brauhaus am Markt**
Stiftsplatz 2–3, 67655 Kaiserslautern-Innenstadt
Mon–Sat 09.00–01.00; Sun 10.00–24.00
DB Kaiserslautern Hbf 1.1km

KIRCHHEIMBOLANDEN 872

Brauhaus am Turm

Schloßstraße 1, 67292 Kirchheimbolanden
T 06352 700333
Founded: 2002   Output: 250hl
REGULAR BEERS:
Brauhaus am Turm Hell
Brauhaus am Turm Dunkel
Brauhaus am Turm Weizen
SEASONAL BEER:
Brauhaus am Turm Bock

Just inside the old town walls, this brewpub
takes its name from the Grauer Turm (grey tower) –
a tower that forms part of the fortifications.

🍺 **Brauhaus am Turm**
Schloßstraße 1, 67292 Kirchheimbolanden
Daily from 17.00   DB Kirchheimbolanden 700m

KIRN 873

Kirner

Kirner Privatbrauerei Endres GmbH & Co. KG
Kallenfelser Straße 2–4, 55606 Kirn
T 06752 13 40   **F** 06752 13 41 43
www.kirner.de

Founded: 1798   Output: 120,000hl
Availability: c.1,700 pubs
REGULAR BEERS:
Kirner Kyr (2.8%)
Kirner Pils (4.8%)
Kirner Pur (4.8%)
Kirner 1798 (5.5%)
Kirner Weizen (5.5%)

Large brewery just north of the town centre.
The beers are widely available throughout
much of the region. The tap is between the
market square and the brewery.

🍺 **Braustübchen**
Steinweg 25, 55606 Kirn   **T** 06752 65 23
Closed Wed; Thu–Tue from 09.00
DB Kirn 500m

KOBLENZ 874

Königsbacher

Königsbacher
An der Königsbach 8, 56075 Koblenz-Stolzenfels
T 0261 139 70   **F** 0261 139 72 22
www.koenigsbacher.de
Owner: Karlsberg, Homburg   Founded: 1689
Output: 150,000hl
REGULAR BEERS:
Königsbacher Alt (4.6%)
Königsbacher Pils (4.8%)
Königsbacher Spezial (5.3%)
SEASONAL BEER:
Maibock (6.8%)
ZISCHKE KELLERBIER:
Zischke Original (4.8%), **Zischke Dunkel** (5.4%),
Zischke Gold Märzen (5.4%)
FOR BRAUEREI NETTE, WEISSENTHURM:
Nette Edel-Pils (4.8%)

Large brewery and tap south of Koblenz, overlooking both the river Rhein and the main railway
line south. They moved from their old home on
Braugasse in 1885 (now the Altes Brauhaus).
Bus No. 650 from Koblenz Hbf stops outside.

🍺 **Brauerei-Ausschank**
An der Königsbach 8, 56075 Koblenz-Stolzenfels
T 0261 91 56 50   **F** 0261 915 65 15
Mon–Thu 09.00–23.00, Fri & Sat 09.00–24.00,
Sun & hols 09.00–22.00
DB Koblenz Hbf 3.5km

LANDAU 875

Landauer Brauhof

Industriestraße 10, 76829 Landau
T 06341 850 09   **F** 06341 89 02 10
www.brauhof.de
Owner: Sarah Roth   Founded: 1989
Output: 1,500hl   Availability: 2 pubs
REGULAR BEERS:
Landauer Helles
Landauer Dunkles
Landauer Hefeweizen

A former warehouse, this brewpub is between the main station and town centre. They used to brew a number of seasonal beers but have recently changed hands and may no longer do so.

Landauer Brauhof
Industriestraße 10, 76829 Landau
Mon–Thu 11.00–01.00, Fri & Sat 11.00–02.00,
Sun & hols 09.00–24.00
DB Landau (Pfalz) Hbf 550m

LAUTERECKEN 876

Lauterecker Brauhaus

Bahnhofstraße 1, 67742 Lauterecken
T/F 06382 85 88
www.veldenz-braeu.de
Owner: Friedhelm Jung   Founded: 2001
REGULAR BEERS:
Veldenz-Bräu Hell
Veldenz-Bräu Dunkel
SEASONAL BEERS:
Veldenz-Bräu Maibock, Veldenz-Bräu
Weihnachtsbock

The former station restaurant, Lauterecker Brauhaus is naturally extremely handy for the train. Those of an athletic disposition can work-up a thirst on the trolleys that can be hired for use on the closed railway lines out of the town.

Lauterecker Brauhaus
Bahnhofstraße 1, 67742 Lauterecken
Nov–Mar: closed Mon; Tue–Sun 09.00–24.00
Apr–Oct: daily 09.00–24.00
DB Lauterecken-Grumbach 0m

LUDWIGSHAFEN 877

Mayer Bräu

Privatbrauerei Gebr. Mayer GmbH & Co. KG
Schillerstraße 8, 67071 Ludwigshafen-Oggersheim
T 0621 67 50 77   **F** 0621 67 50 81
www.mayerbraeu.de
Owners: the Mayer family   Founded: 1846
Output: 35,000hl
REGULAR BEERS:
Mayer's Pilsener (4.7%)
Mayer's 150er Black & Dry (4.7%)
Carl Daniel Mayer Keller Bier (4.7%)
Mayer's Stammhaus Bier (5.1%)
Mayer's Schiller (5.3%)
Mayer's Hefe Weizen (5.3%)
Mayer's Hefe Weizen Dunkel (5.3%)
Mayer's Kristall Weizen (5.3%)
SEASONAL BEERS:
Mayer's Sommer Bier (4.6%, summer), **Mayer's Fastnachtsbier** (5%, Feb), **Mayer's Festbier** (5.1%, Christmas), **Mayer's Osterbier** (5.1%, Easter), **Mayer's Halali Edelbock** (7.4%, winter)

Family-run brewery and tap in the western suburb of Oggersheim. Ludwigshafen is the home of the massive BASF chemical works.

Hauswirtschaft
Schillerstraße 8,
67071 Ludwigshafen-Oggersheim
T 0621 67 50 83
Closed Wed; Thu–Tue 11.00–14.00 & from 17.00
Tram Nos. 4 & RHB Hans-Warsch-Platz 200m
DB Ludwigshafen-Oggersheim 550m

Weißes Häus'l

Großwiesenstraße 3,
67065 Ludwigshafen-Mundenheim
T 0621 54 20 87
Founded: 2004
REGULAR BEERS:
Weißes Häus'l Hell
Weißes Häus'l Weizen
SEASONAL BEER:
Weißes Häus'l Bock

The Little White House is a long-established restaurant south of the city, on the left bank of the Rhein. They started brewing in 2004 but their strangest claim to fame is as the record-holders for the longest noodle ever made!

Buses Nos. 170 & 581 stop a few hundred metres from the pub.

🍺 Weißes Häus'l

Großwiesenstraße 3,
67065 Ludwigshafen-Mundenheim
Closed Thu; Fri–Wed from 11.00
DB Ludwigshafen-Rheingönheim 6km, Mitte 9km

MACHERN (Bernkastel-Kues)   878

Kloster Machern

An der Zeltinger Brücke,
54470 Bernkastel-Kues/Machern
T 06532 951 50   F 06532 95 15 15
www.brauhaus-kloster-machern.de
Owners: Hermann Saxler & Jürgen Thetard
Founded: 01.05.2004
REGULAR BEERS:
Kloster Machern Hell (5.2%)
Kloster Machern Hefeweizen (5.3%)
Kloster Machern Dunkel (5.4%)

Brewpub in the former monastery at Machern, on the opposite bank of the Mosel to Zeltingen. We think they may close for a few weeks during the winter. Bus No. 300 from Wittlich stops at Zeltingen bridge.

🍺 Kloster Machern

An der Zeltinger Brücke,
54470 Bernkastel-Kues/Machern
Jan & Feb: **Mon–Thu** 16.00–01.00,
        Fri–Sun 11.00–01.00
Mar–Dec: daily 11.00–01.00
DB Wittlich Hbf 7km

MAINZ   879

Eisgrub-Bräu

1. Mainzer Gasthausbrauerei GmbH
Weißliliengasse 1a, 55116 Mainz-Altstadt
T 06131 22 11 04   F 06131 23 45 58
www.eisgrub.de   Founded: 1989
Output: 1,500hl   Availability: 1 pub
REGULAR BEERS:
Eisgrub-Bräu Helles Märzen (4.9%)
Eisgrub-Bräu Dunkles Pils (4.9%)
SEASONAL BEERS:
Eisgrub-Bräu Dunkles Märzen (4.9%),
Eisgrub-Bräu Weihnachtsbier Gambrinus (5%)

Brewpub in Mainz's former ice-houses after which the brewery is named, above the railway tunnels that burrow under the old town. If you don't want to walk up the hill from the station, there are buses which stop nearby.

🍺 Eisgrub-Bräu

Weißliliengasse 1a, 55116 Mainz-Altstadt
Sun–Thu 09.00–02.00, Fri & Sat 09.00–01.00
DB Mainz-Süd 500m, Mainz Hbf 1.3km

MANNEBACH   880

Mannebacher Brauhaus

Hauptstraße 1, 54441 Mannebach
T 0658 1992 77   F 0658 1992 79
www.mannebacher.de
Owner: Hans-Günther Felten
Founded: 01.05.1994   Availability: 1 pub
REGULAR BEERS:
Mannebacher Hell (4.8%)
Mannebacher Landbier Dunkel (5.2%)
SEASONAL BEERS:
Mannebacher Weizen,
Mannebacher Roggen,
Mannebacher Dreikornbier,
Mannebacher Bock

Village brewpub and hotel in the Saargau, between the Mosel and Saar valleys. Antique furniture features in both hotel and pub. Buses Nos. 241 and 243 run from Nittel to Saarburg via Mannebach Brücke on weekdays.

🍺 Mannebacher Brauhaus

Hauptstraße 1, 54441 Mannebach
Closed Wed; Thu–Tue from 11.00;
rooms available
DB Saarburg (Bezirk Trier) 6km, Nittel 7km

MARIENSTATT   881

Marienstatter Brauhaus

Abtei Marienstatt, 57629 Streithausen-
Marienstatt
T 02662 953 35 00   F 02662 953 53 33
www.abtei-marienstatt.de
Owner: Abtei Marienstatt
Founded: 01.05.2004
Output: 500hl
Availability: 1 pub

REGULAR BEER:
Marienstatter Klosterbräu Dunkel (5.5%)
SEASONAL BEERS:
Marienstatter Klosterbräu Weizen (5.2%),
Marienstatter Klosterbräu Märzen (5.5%)

Brewpub in the Cistercian abbey at Marienstatt. There was an earlier brewery here which closed in 1908. They close for four weeks holiday from early February. Bus No. 8410 runs from Hachenburg a couple of times each weekday.

Marienstatter Brauhaus
Abtei Marienstatt,
57629 Streithausen-Marienstatt
Closed Mon; Tue–Sat 11.00–23.00,
Sun & hols 10.30–23.00   DB Hachenburg 3.5km

REGULAR BEERS:
Zils-Bräu Hell
Zils-Bräu Dunkel
SEASONAL BEER:
Zils-Bräu Weizen

Hotel, brewery, distillery and pub in the centre of Naurath. We don't think there are any buses to the village. Don't confuse this place with Naurath (Wald), a village about 15km south-west of here.

Zils-Bräu
Waldstraße 1, 54340 Naurath (Eifel)
Closed Mon; Tue–Sun from 11.30; rooms available
DB Hetzerath 4.5km

MENDIG   882

Vulkan

Vulkan Brauerei Mendig GmbH
Laacher-See-Straße 2,
56743 Mendig-Niedermendig
T 02652 52 03 90   **F** 02652 52 03 91
www.vulkan-brauhaus.de
Owner: Peter Weber   Founded: 1987
Output: 3,000hl   Availability: 10 pubs
REGULAR BEERS:
Vulkan Bräu Hell (4.9%)
Vulkan Bräu Dunkel (4.9%)
SEASONAL BEER:
Vulkan Bräu Weizen (5.3%, summer)

Microbrewery and tap taking its name from the local volcano (extinct, we hope), Vulkan is in the former Brauerei Wölker on the northern edge of town. The lagering cellars are reputedly the deepest in the world.

Vulkan
Laacher-See-Straße 2, 56743 Mendig-Niedermendig   **T** 02652 52 03 30
Daily 11.00–23.00   DB Mendig 1.4km

NAURATH (Eifel)   883

Zils-Bräu

Waldstraße 1, 54340 Naurath (Eifel)
T 06508 917 10   **F** 06508 16 16
www.zils-braeu.de
Owner: Alwin & Frank Zils   Founded: 1999

NEUSTADT (Weinstraße)   884

Neustadter Brauhaus

Martin-Luther-Straße 60, 67433 Neustadt-Stadt
T 06321 18 51 55   **F** 06321 18 51 66
www.brauhaus-neustadt.de
Owner: Olaf Klapproth   Founded: 1999
Output: 1,500hl   Availability: 1 pub
REGULAR BEERS:
Neustadter Hell
Neustadter Dunkel
Neustadter Weizen
SEASONAL BEER:
Neustadter Bock

Tucked away off Martin-Luther-Straße behind a Lidl supermarket, this large brewpub is built on the site of the Pfalzbrauerei which closed in 1969.

Neustadter Brauhaus
Martin-Luther-Straße 60, 67433 Neustadt-Stadt
Daily 11.00–24.00
DB Neustadt (Weinstraße)-Böbig 750m, Hbf 1.4km

NIEDERLAHNSTEIN (Lahnstein)   885

Maximilians Brauwiesen

Didierstraße 25, 56112 Lahnstein-Niederlahnstein
T 02621 92 60 60   **F** 02621 92 60 61
www.maximilians-brauwiesen.de
Owners: the Ohlig family   Founded: 1995
Availability: 1 pub

REGULAR BEERS:
Brauwiesen Helles
Brauwiesen Braunes
Wiesenweizen
SEASONAL BEERS:
Brauwiesen Dunkles Winterweizen (Jan–Feb),
Brauwiesen Märzen (Mar–Apr), **Brauwiesen
Spezial** (Oct), **Brauwiesen Maibock** (May),
Brauwiesen Nikolator (Nov–Dec)

Large, castellated brewpub in a mainly
industrial part of town. The substantial garden
slopes down to the Rhein and offers views
across the valley to the Königsbacher brewery.

🍺 **Maximilians Brauwiesen**
Didierstraße 25, 56112 Lahnstein-Niederlahnstein
Oct–Mar: closed Mon; Tue–Sat 11.00–01.00;
Sun 11.00–24.00
Apr–Sep: Mon–Sat 11.00–01.00; Sun 11.00–24.00
DB Niederlahnstein 1km

NIEDERSCHELDERHÜTTE
(Mudersbach) **886**

Erzquell

Erzquell Brauerei Siegtal Haas & Co. KG
Kölner Straße 1–5, 57555 Mudersbach-
Niederschelderhütte
T 0271 350 10   **F** 0271 350 11 30
www.erzquell.de
Founded: 1885   Output: 150,000hl
REGULAR BEERS:
Erzquell Pils (4.8%)
Kupfer Alt (4.8%)

The smaller of the two Erzquell breweries is just
inside the Rheinland-Pfalz border, overlooking
the river Sieg west of Niederschelden station.
We think they just brew the two beers above
but they may do the same range as Bielstein.
DB Niederschelden 400m

OBERLAHNSTEIN
(Lahnstein) **887**

St. Martin

St. Martin Brauerei Dr. R. Fohr KG
Sandstraße 1, 56112 Lahnstein-Oberlahnstein
T 02621 917 40   **F** 02621 91 74 34
www.st-martin-brauerei.de   (until 31.12.2006)

www.lahnsteiner-brauerei.de (from 01.01.2007)
Owners: Dr. Rainer Fohr & Dr. Markus Fohr
Founded: 1667   Output: 12,000hl
REGULAR BEERS:
Lahnsteiner Alt (4.9%)
Lahnsteiner Obergärig (4.9%)
Lahnsteiner Fürsten Pils (4.9%)
Lahnsteiner Zwickel Bier (4.9%)
Lahnsteiner Schwarzbier (4.9%)
Lahnsteiner Weizenbier (4.9%)
Lahnsteiner Fest-Export (5.3%)
Lahnsteiner Schnee Bock (7.2%)
Lahnsteiner Martinator (8%)

Small brewery in the centre of Oberlahnstein
which will change its name to Lahnsteiner
Brauerei from 1 January 2007. They've recently
revised their beer range – oddly, the Schnee
Bock (snow bock) is now available all year.
Some beers are re-badged for others. The tap is
a couple of streets away.

🍺 **Winzerhaus**
Burgstraße 34, 56112 Lahnstein-Oberlahnstein
T 02621 28 96   **F** 02621 18 76 66
Closed Mon; Tue–Sun from 17.00
DB Oberlahnstein 350m

OTTERSHEIM (Landau) **888**

Ottersheimer Bärenbräu

Waldstraße 35a, 76879 Ottersheim
T 06348 75 95   **F** 06348 12 71
Owner: Matthias Rüde   Founded: 2000
Output: 2,000hl
REGULAR BEERS:
Ottersheimer Bärenbräu Hell (5.2%)
Ottersheimer Bärenbräu Dunkel (5.2%)
Ottersheimer Bärenbräu Pils (5.2%)
Ottersheimer Bärenbräu Weizen (5.3%)
SEASONAL BEERS:
Ottersheimer Bärenbräu Frühlingsbier (5.3%),
Ottersheimer Bärenbräu Weihnachtsbier (5.5%),
Ottersheimer Bärenbräu Schwarzbier (5.6%),
Ottersheimer Bärenbräu Weizenbock (6.5%)

Microbrewery which has long had plans for a
tap but, as yet, doesn't have one. Beer is
available from the brewery in litre bottles
Mon–Fri 10.00–20.00 and Sat 10.00–16.00.
Buses Nos. 589 and 591 run between Landau
and Bellheim via Ottersheim.
DB Bellheim 5.5km, Landau Hbf 8km

PIRMASENS 889

Kuchems Brauhaus

Brauhaus am Schloßplatz GmbH
Hauptstraße 13, 66953 Pirmasens
T 06331 21 38 94   **F** 06331 21 38 95
www.kuchems-brauhaus.de
Owner: Wolfgang Kuchem   Founded: 02.10.2001
REGULAR BEERS:
Kuchems Hell
Kuchems Dunkel
SEASONAL BEERS:
Kuchems Sommerweizen (summer), **Kuchems Winterweizen** (winter), **Kuchems Bock** (spring)

Attached to a shopping centre, this glass-fronted brewpub is actually between Schloßplatz and Schloßstraße, opposite St. Priminus church. They also have a large beer garden in the Neuffer park.

🍺 **Kuchems Brauhaus**
Hauptstraße 13, 66953 Pirmasens
Mon–Sat 09.00–24.00, Sun & hols 11.00–24.00
DB Pirmasens Hbf 950m

Park

Park-Brauerei AG
Zweibrückerstraße 2–4, 66953 Pirmasens
T 06331 80 50   **F** 06331 80 52 20
www.parkbrauerei.de
Owner: Actris AG   Founded: 1888
Output: 350,000hl
REGULAR BEERS:
Park Leicht (2.9%)
Park Pils (4.8%)
Park Primus (4.8%)
Park Export (5.2%)
SEASONAL BEERS:
Park Schwarzbock (6.9%), **Park Pirminator** (6.9%)
VALENTINS WEISSBIER:
Valentins Premium Hefeweissbier (5.3%)

Large brewery north of the town centre, owned by Actris since 2004. Park merged with Bellheimer in 1995 but the two still brew at their old sites. Park Platz hosts regular live rock.

🍺 **Park Platz**
Zweibrückerstraße 1–3, 66953 Pirmasens
T 06331 126 26   **F** 06331 22 99 45
Daily from 19.00   DB Pirmasens Hbf 650m

RANSBACH-BAUMBACH 890

Fohr

Brauerei Gebrüder Fohr oHG
An der Brauerei, 56235 Ransbach-Baumbach
T 02623 30 21   **F** 02623 805 21
www.fohr.de
Owners: Dirk & Dr. Franz Fohr
Founded: 1676
Availability: c.250 pubs
REGULAR BEERS:
Fohr Pils (4.5%)
Fohr Jubiläums-Pils (4.5%)

Pils brewery on the western edge of town. They don't have a tap but recommend Hotel Eisbach. Buses Nos. 130 & 462 run from Montabaur station but may not be much use if you want to drink at the Hotel.

🍺 **Hotel Eisbach**
Schulstraße 2, 56235 Ransbach-Baumbach
T 02623 88 13 30   **F** 02623 881 33 98
Daily 18.00–23.00; rooms available
DB Montabaur 10km

REHBORN 891

Rehborner Hof-Brauhaus

Obergasse 11, 55592 Rehborn
T 06753 96 24 79
E mmtriebel@onlinehome.de
Owner: Michael Triebel
Founded: 2003
REGULAR BEERS:
Rehborner Hof-Brauhaus Obergärig
Rehborner Hof-Brauhaus Pils
Rehborner Hof-Brauhaus Weizen
Rehborner Hof-Brauhaus Märzen
SEASONAL BEERS:
Rehborner Hof-Brauhaus Maibock,
Rehborner Hof-Brauhaus Fastnachtsbock,
Rehborner Hof-Brauhaus Weihnachtsbock

Microbrewery in the centre of the village. There's no tap at the moment but they're usually open Mon–Fri 17.00–20.00 and Sat 11.00–19.00 if you want to buy the beers. Bus No. 260 runs from Staudernheim station.
DB Staudernheim 7km

SCHÖNBORN   892

Hof Schauferts

Gasthausbrauerei Hof Schauferts
Schaufertshof, Schaufertstraße, 56370 Schönborn
T 06486 62 08   **F** 06486 90 28 68
www.schauferts.de
Owner: Oliver Luzius   Founded: 2004
REGULAR BEER:
Hof Schauferts Märzen

This small brewery isn't actually in Schönborn
itself but on a farm just over a kilometre west of
the village. Bus No. 588 runs to Schönborn from
the station in Diez on weekdays but there are no
services back after the pub opens.

🍺 **Hof Schauferts**
Schaufertshof, Schaufertstraße, 56370 Schönborn
Closed Mon & Tue; Wed–Thu from 17.00
DB Diez 11km

SPEYER   893

Domhof

Hausbrauerei im Domhof GmbH & Co. KG
Große Himmelsgasse 6, 67346 Speyer
T 06232 674 40   **F** 06232 712 71
www.domhof.de
Founded: 1988   Output: 4,000hl
REGULAR BEERS:
Domhof Hell
Domhof Dunkel
Domhof Weizen
SEASONAL BEERS:
Domhof Maibock, Domhof Nikolausbock

On the western side of the city centre, this
brewpub is barely 100m from Speyer's historic
cathedral, a UNESCO World Heritage site. The
brewery has a courtyard hotel around the corner.
Bus No. 565 from the station saves the walk but
not much time.

🍺 **Domhof**
Große Himmelsgasse 6, 67346 Speyer
Mon–Thu 10.00–24.00, Fri 11.00–01.00,
Sat 10.00–01.00, Sun 10.00–24.00; rooms
available
DB Speyer Hbf 1.3km

ST. SEVERINSBERG
(Kasbach-Ohlenberg)   894

Steffens

Privat-Brauerei Franz Steffens KG
St. Severinsberg, Kasbachtalstraße, 53547
Kasbach-Ohlenberg/St. Severinsberg
T 02644 560 00   **F** 02644 56 00 96
www.brauerei-steffens.de
Founded: 1866   Output: 50,000hl
REGULAR BEERS:
Steffens Alt (4.9%)
Steffens Steffi (4.9%)
Steffens Kräusen (4.9%)
Steffens Pilsener (5%)
Steffens Casbacher Braunbier (5.2%)
SEASONAL BEER:
Steffens Festbier (5.2%)

Family-run brewery in a wooded valley just off
the Rhein, north of Linz. There's a station for the
brewery on the local tourist railway which runs
on Sundays and holidays from April to October.
At other times take bus No.135 to Kasbach and
walk the last kilometre to the pub.

🍺 **Steffens Brauereischänke**
St. Severinsberg, Kasbachtalstraße, 53547
Kasbach-Ohlenberg/St. Severinsberg
T 02644 98 07 80   **F** 02644 60 18 76
Nov–Apr: closed Mon; Tue–Sun from 11.00
May–Oct: daily from 11.00
DB Linz (Rhein) 3.5km

TRIER   895

Kraft-Bräu

Olewigerstraße 135, 54295 Trier-Olewig
T 0651 360 60   **F** 0651 36 06 33
www.blesius-garten.de
Owner: Hans Werner Kraft   Founded: 1998
Output: 1,200hl   Availability: 1 pub
REGULAR BEERS:
Kraft-Bräu Hell
Kraft-Bräu Dunkel
Kraft-Bräu Weizen
SEASONAL BEERS:
**Kraft-Bräu Maibock, Kraft-Bräu
Weihnachtsbock**

The Kraft family installed a small brewery in their
hotel in the eastern suburb of Olewig in 1998.

To get there take bus No. 6 from Balduinstraße, near the Hauptbahnhof, to Auf der Ayl.

🍺 Blesius Garten

Olewigerstraße 135, 54295 Trier-Olewig
Sun–Thu 11.30–01.00, Fri & Sat 11.30–02.00;
rooms available
DB Trier Hbf 2.6km

WINDESHEIM   896

Guldenbacher

Guldenbacher Brauhaus Nahetal
Riemenschneider Straße 6, 55452 Windesheim
T 01511 535 9014 (mobile)
www.guldenbacher.de
Owners: A. Dietrich & M. Jovy   Founded: 2003
Output: 700hl   Availability: 4 pubs
REGULAR BEERS:
Guldenbacher Weissbier Hefe-Hell (4.8%)
Guldenbacher Spezial
Guldenbacher Pilsener (5.2%)
SEASONAL BEERS:
Guldenbacher Maibock (6.5%, Apr–Jun),
Guldenbacher Bockbier (6.5%, Nov–Dec)

Microbrewery in the centre of the village. They
have no regular outlets in Windesheim except
Fuchsbau (below) in winter. Oddly, two pubs
in Ahrweiler, just over 100km to the north-west,
sell the beers: Alter Weinbau and Pumpe,
both in Adenbachhutstraße. There's a brewery
festival over the last weekend in August.
DB Bad Kreuznach 10km

Präsidenten Pils

Präsidenten Pils GmbH & Co. Brauerei
Kreuznacher Straße 4, 55452 Windesheim
T 06707 107 10   **F** 06707 10 71 28
www.praesidenten.de
Owner: Hans Erich Fuchs   Founded: 1873
Output: 25,000hl
REGULAR BEERS:
Präsidenten Alt (4.7%)
Präsidenten Premium-Pils (4.7%)
Präsidenten Export (4.7%)

Family-run brewery that changed its name from
Brauerei Fuchs to that of its principal product
in 1989. The tap opposite serves Guldenbacher
Bock in winter. Bus No. 240 from Bad Kreuznach
stops nearby (not Sundays).

🍺 Fuchsbau

Kreuznacher Straße 9, 55452 Windesheim
T 06707 96 12 32   **F** 06707 91 55 33
Closed Mon; Tue–Sun 11.00–14.00 & from 17.00
DB Bad Kreuznach 10km

WINNWEILER   897

Bischoff

Privatbrauerei Bischoff GmbH & Co. KG
An den Hopfengärten 6, 67722 Winnweiler
T 06302 91 20   **F** 06302 91 21 20
www.bischoff-bier.de
Founded: 1866   Output: 120,000hl
REGULAR BEERS:
Bischoff Fritz Walter Bier (4.7%)
Bischoff Premium Pilsener (4.7%)
Bischoff Pils (4.8%)
Christian Bischoff Kellerbier (5%)
Bischoff Export (5.2%)
Bischoff Falkensteiner Ur-Weisse (5.2%)
Bischoff Falkensteiner Ur-Schwarze (5.2%)
Bischoff Falkensteiner Weizen (5.2%)
Bischoff Donnersberger (5.2%)
SEASONAL BEER:
Bischoff Doppelbock (7.5%)

Large brewery east of the station, now owned
by the fifth generation of the Bischoff family.
The tap is in the centre of Windesheim. They
also own Brauhaus am Markt in Kaiserslautern
and Brauhaus zur Post in Frankenthal.

🍺 Hauswirtschaft Bischoff

Marktplatz 6, 67722 Winnweiler
T 06302 20 17
Closed Mon; Tue–Sun 12.00–24.00
DB Winnweiler 400m

WORMS   898

Hagenbräu

Hagenbräu Rheincafe Betriebs GmbH
Am Rhein 3, 67547 Worms
T 06241 92 11 00   **F** 06241 921 10 33
www.hagenbraeu.de
Owner: Uwe Thudium   Founded: 1995
Output: 1,400hl   Availability: 1 pub
REGULAR BEERS:
Wormser Hell (4,8%)

Wormser Dunkel (5%)
Wormser Weizen (5.3%)
SEASONAL BEERS:
Wormser Maibock (7%),
Wormser Nikolausbock (7%)

Riverside brewpub near the Nibelungenbrücke. They close for around six weeks from New Years

Day. We warn you it's not much quicker, but if you want to avoid the walk from the Hauptbahnhof, take bus No. 410 to Rheinpromenade.

Hagenbräu
Am Rhein 3, 67547 Worms
Closed Mon; Tue–Sun 08.30–23.00
DB Worms Hbf 1.6km

Maximilians Brauwiesen, Niederlahnstein. The Rhein is behind the photographer.

Saarland

By FAR THE SMALLEST of the non-city states, Saarland has been the subject of much dispute over the years, alternating between French and German control. It almost became independent in the 1950s but rejoined the Federal Republic of Germany on 1 January 1957. Although renowned for its heavy industry, particularly coal and steel, this aspect of Saar life has long been in decline and you're likely to see more industrial buildings derelict than working. Indeed, the giant ironworks Völklinger Hütte are now a UNESCO world heritage site. Most industry was (and still is) concentrated in the Dillingen–Neunkirchen–Saarbrücken triangle.

Like neighbouring Rheinland-Pfalz, Saarland has some lovely scenery, particularly the area around the Saar valley, perfectly suited to walking and cycling holidays. It's far less touristy, however, partly the result of its industrial reputation, partly due to a lack of more obvious tourist attractions.

The brewing scene is dominated by the giant Karlsberg brewery, responsible for more than 95% of all production in Saarland. Happily, there are still two small independents and ten modern brewpubs to interest the beer lover.

Transport: Public transport in the state is excellent, buses in particular being more frequent than in many other parts of the country. The day DB ticket also covers Rheinland-Pfalz and costs €23 for up to five people travelling together.

BESSERINGEN (Merzig)   899

Ponter
Brückenstraße 36, 66663 Merzig-Besseringen
T/F 06861 27 42   www.ponter-hausbrauerei.de
Owner: Jürgen Uder   Founded: 2002
REGULAR BEERS:
Ponter Hell (5%)
Ponter Schwarzer Abt (5%)

Small brewpub between Besseringen station and the river Saar. They've got quite an unusual brew kettle which sits in one corner of the bar.

Ponter
Brückenstraße 36, 66663 Merzig-Besseringen
Closed Mon; Tue–Fri from 16.00, Sat from 15.00, Sun 09.45–13.00 & from 17.00
DB Besseringen 100m

EIWEILER (Heusweiler)   900

Grosswald
Grosswald Brauerei Bauer GmbH & Co. KG
Grosswaldstraße 130, 66265 Heusweiler-Eiweler
T 06806 60 70   **F** 06806 607 77
www.grosswald.de
Owner: Alexander Kleber   Founded: 1860
Output: 50,000hl
REGULAR BEERS:
Grosswald Pilsener (4.7%)
Grosswald Hofgut Pils (4.9%)
Grosswald Export (4.9%)
Grosswald Landbier (5.1%)
Grosswald Zwickel (5.1%)
Grosswald Urweizen (5.3%)
Grosswald Urweizen Dunkel (5.3%)
SEASONAL BEER:
Grosswald Festtrunk (5.5%)

This family-run brewery is just north of the village, on the road to Eppelborn. They don't have a tap. Bus No. R9 runs between Saarbrücken Hbf and Lebach but stops in the centre of Eiweiler, the best part of 2km from the brewery.

DB Lebach 6km, Saarbrücken Hbf 19km

HOMBURG 901

Homburger Brauhaus

Homburger Brauhaus Karl-Heinz Wiernz GmbH
Talstraße 38d, 66424 Homburg
T 06841 24 66   **F** 06841 648 08
www.homburger-brauhaus.de
Owner: Karl-Heinz Wierz   Founded: 1990
Output: 1,050hl   Availability: 1 pub
REGULAR BEERS:
Wirtsbräu Hell (4.8%)
Wirtsbräu Dunkel (4.8%)
SEASONAL BEERS:
Wirtsbräu Champagner-Hefeweizen (5%),
Wirtsbräu Märzen (5%), **Wirtsbräu Bockbier** (6%)

Modern brewpub on the first floor of the Saarpfalz-Center, a small shopping centre in the centre of town. Has live music once a month.

🍺 **Homburger Brauhaus**
Talstraße 38d, 66424 Homburg
Closed Mon; Tue–Sat 09.00–24.00,
Sun 17.00–24.00
DB Homburg (Saar) Hbf 750m

Karlsberg

Karlsberg Brauerei GmbH & Co. KG
Karlsbergstraße 62, 66424 Homburg
T 06841 10 50   **F** 06841 10 52 69
www.karlsberg.de
Founded: 1878   Output: 3,000,000hl
REGULAR BEERS:
Karlsberg Ur-Pils Light (2.8%)
Karlsberg Blondes (4.8%)
Karlsberg Alt (4.8%)
Karlsberg Pils (4.8%)
Karlsberg UrPils (4.8%)
Karlsberg UrMild (4.8%)
Karlsberg Karlsbräu (4.8%)
Karlsberg Feingold (5%)
Karlsberg Export (5.4%)
Karlsberger Hof (5.4%)
SEASONAL BEER:
Karlsberg Bock (6.5%, winter)

Enormous brewery on the western side of Homburg, between Talstraße and Karlsberg-straße. They also own Königsbacher and the considerably smaller Merziger Brauhaus but don't have a tap of their own.

DB Homburg (Saar) Hbf 900m

KÖRPRICH (Nalbach) 902

Körpricher Landbräu

Bahnhofstraße 40, 66809 Nalbach-Körprich
T 06838 14 47   **F** 06838 98 49 69
www.landbrauerei.de
Owner: Gaby Kriebs-Schwarz
Founded: 1996
Availability: 1 pub
REGULAR BEERS:
Körpricher Hell
Körpricher Dunkel
SEASONAL BEERS:
Körpricher Weizen (summer), **Körpricher Alt** (winter), **Körpricher Haferbier** (winter), **Körpricher Dinkelbier** (winter), **Körpricher Märzen** (Mar), **Körpricher Michaelsbier** (Oct), **Körpricher Maibock** (May), **Körpricher Nikolausbock** (Christmas)

Single-storey brewpub on the southern side of the valley, close to the old station. Bus No. R5 runs between Saarlouis and Lebach via Dillingen and Körprich.

🍺 **Körpricher Landbräu**
Bahnhofstraße 40, 66809 Nalbach-Körprich
Closed Mon (& Tue after hols); Tue–Sat from 17.00,
Sun & hols from 15.00
DB Lebach 6km, Dillingen (Saar) 11km

LOSHEIM am See 903

Hochwälder

Hochwälder Braugasthaus GmbH
Zum Stausee 190, 66679 Losheim am See
T 06872 50 57 72   **F** 06872 50 57 73
www.hochwaelder-brauhaus.de
Founded: 2001   Output: 1,200hl
Availability: 1 pub
REGULAR BEERS:
Hochwälder Hell (4.8%)
Hochwälder Donatus Dunkel (5.4%)

Right: *Frauenkirche Church, Dresden*

SEASONAL BEERS:

Hochwälder Weizen, Hochwälder Festbier, Hochwälder Maibock, Hochwälder Weihnachtsbock

Modern brewpub at the eastern corner of Losheim reservoir, north of the town itself. Bus No. R1 runs daily from Merzig station, supplemented occasionally by other routes.

📍 **Hochwälder**

Zum Stausee 190, 66679 Losheim am See
Daily 11.00–01.00   DB Merzig (Saar) 13km

MERZIG · 904

Saarfürst

Saarfürst Merziger Brauhaus GmbH
Gottfried von Cramm Weg, 66663 Merzig
T 06861 79 16 35   **F** 06861 79 16 56
www.merziger-brauhaus.de
Owner: Karlsberg, Homburg   Founded: 2000
Output: 1,200hl   Availability: 1 pub
REGULAR BEERS:
Saarfürst Hell (4.8%)
Saarfürst Dunkel (4.8%)
Saarfürst Weizen (4.8%)
SEASONAL BEERS:
Saarfürst Maibock, Saarfürst Weihnachtsbock

Named after the original Saarfürst brewery which was closed by Karlsberg in 1987, this large brewpub is located in Merzig's marina, on the opposite side of the Saar to the station and town.

📍 **Saarfürst**

Gottfried von Cramm Weg, 66663 Merzig
Mon–Sat from 11.00, Sun & hols from 10.00
DB Merzig (Saar) 1.2km

METTLACH · 905

Abtei-Bräu

Mettlacher Abtei-Bräu GmbH
Bahnhofstraße 32, 66693 Mettlach
T 06864 932 32   **F** 06864 932 35
www.abtei-brauerei.de
Owners: K. Fell, W. Fell, M. Schorn & U. Schorn
Founded: 1997   Output: 2,000hl
Availability: 1 pub
REGULAR BEER:
Abtei Bräu (4.8%)

SEASONAL BEERS:

Sondersud Vital (3.4%), **Josef Sud Hefeweizen Dunkel** (5.1%), **Blonde Hexe Hefeweizen Hell** (5.3%), **Kloster Bier, Bock** (6.2%, Nov & Dec)

Large modern brewpub just north of the station. It's named after the nearby abbey which is now home to Villeroy & Boch. The pub closes for the whole of January. Mettlach is famous for the *Saarschleife*, the loop of the river Saar that almost completely encircles the town.

📍 **Abtei-Bräu**

Bahnhofstraße 32, 66693 Mettlach
Closed Mon; Tue–Sun 11.00–01.00
DB Mettlach 200m

NEUNKIRCHEN · 906

Stumm's Brauhaus

Turm Gastro GmbH – Stumm's Brauhaus
Saarbrücker Straße 16, 66538 Neunkirchen
T 06821 17 91 45   **F** 06821 17 91 43
www.stumms-brauhaus.de
Founded: 1997   Availability: 1 pub
REGULAR BEERS:
Stumm's Hell (4.8%)
Stumm's Dunkel (5.1%)
SEASONAL BEERS:
Stumm's Weizen (summer), **Stumm's Märzen** (spring), **Stumm's Maibock** (May), **Stumm's Herbstbräu** (autumn), **Stumm's Bock** (winter)

This brewpub in part of a former steelworks was formerly known as Neunkircher Brauhaus. It was re-named in October 2003 when it re-opened following six months out of use.

📍 **Stumm's Brauhaus**

Saarbrücker Straße 16, 66538 Neunkirchen
Sun–Thu 11.00–24.00, Fri & Sat 11.00–01.00
DB Neunkirchen (Saar) Hbf 1km

SAARBRÜCKEN · 907

Bruch

Brauerei G. A. Bruch, Scheidter Straße 24–42, 66123 Saarbrücken-St. Johann
T 0681 93 63 60   **F** 0681 390 47 36
www.brauerei-bruch.de
Owner: Thomas Bruch   Founded: 1702
Output: 30,000hl

REGULAR BEERS:
Bruch Landbier (4.8%)
Bruch Zwickel (4.8%)
Bruch's No.1 Pilsener (4.8%)
Bruch Spezial (4.8%)
SEASONAL BEER:
Bruch Festbock (6.8%)

Fairly small brewery on the western side of Saarbrücken, owned by the Bruch family for more than 300 years. The tap in the city centre is attached to the Stiefelbräu brewpub, which they also own.

🍺 Zum Stiefel

St. Johanner Markt, 66111 Saarbrücken-St. Johann
T 0681 312 46
Closed Sun; Mon–Sat 11.45–14.15 & 17.30–24.00
DB Saarbrücken Hbf 1km

Stiefel Bräu

Stiefel Gastronomie GmbH – Stiefel Bräu
Am Stiefel 2, 66111 Saarbrücken-St. Johann
T 0681 93 64 50   **E** derstiefel@t-online.de
Owner: Thomas Bruch   Founded: 1990
Output: 1,800hl
REGULAR BEERS:
Stiefel Hell (4.5%)
Stiefel Dunkel (4.5%)
SEASONAL BEERS:
Stiefel Weizen (4.8%), **Stiefel Märzen** (4.8%),
Stiefel Festbier (4.8%), **Stiefel Bockbier** (6.3%)

'Boot Brew' is the original home of the Bruch brewery. This city-centre brewpub, owned by Bruch, is next door to their tap.

🍺 Stiefelbräu

Am Stiefel 2, 66111 Saarbrücken-St. Johann
Mon–Fri 11.30–01.00, Sat 11.00–01.00,
Sun 16.00–01.00
Tram No. S1 Johanneskirche 350m
DB Saarbrücken Hbf 1km

SCHMELZ 908

Schmelzer Brauhaus

Schmelzer Brauhaus Betriebs GmbH
Am Erzweg 12, 66839 Schmelz-Bettingen
T 06887 88 91 09   **F** 06887 88 91 19
www.schmelzer-brauhaus.de
Owners: the Quinten family

Founded: 01.09.2000   Output: 500hl
Availability: 2 pubs
REGULAR BEERS:
Erzbräu Hell (SW 11.5%)
Erzbräu Dunkel (SW 12.5%)
Erzbräu Weizen (SW 13.5%)
SEASONAL BEER:
Erzbräu Märzen (SW 15%)

Modern brewpub east of the centre, on an industrial estate just off the B268, the main road to Lebach. Several bus routes run from Lebach station – get off at Industriegebiet.

🍺 Schmelzer Brauhaus

Am Erzweg 12, 66839 Schmelz-Bettingen
Daily 11.00–24.00
DB Lebach 5km

ST. WENDEL 909

St. Wendeler Brauereihaus

Balduinstraße 43, 66606 St. Wendel
T 06851 93 99 66   **F** 06851 93 99 67
www.brauereihaus.de
Founded: 2003
REGULAR BEERS:
Wendels Hell
Wendels Dunkel

A small brewery was installed in the bar of this 200-year-old pub east of the pedestrianised town centre during 2003.

🍺 St. Wendeler Brauereihaus

Balduinstraße 43, 66606 St. Wendel
Mon 11.00–15.00, Tue–Fri 11.00–15.00 &
17.00–01.00, Sat 17.00–01.00, Sun 11.00–15.00
& 17.00–24.00
DB St. Wendel 700m

Sachsen (Saxony)

THE MOST HEAVILY POPULATED state of the former East Germany, Sachsen derives it's name from the former inhabitants of what is today Schleswig-Holstein who migrated to the area during the Middle Ages. Its people pride themselves on being from the area in which the modern German language originated.

Although northern parts are largely flat or gently undulating, the Erzgebirge mountain range runs through much of the south and includes some of the east's most stunning landscape. It's to this part of the state that many tourists flock, drawn in the winter by the ski resorts that are dotted along the Czech border. The area is also famous for its wooden Christmas decorations. Its eastern and north-eastern part, known as Sächsische Schweiz (Saxon Switzerland) or Elbsandsteingebirge (Elbe limestone mountains), features some spectacular rock formations.

The best known city in Sachsen is the capital, Dresden. Renowned both as a cultural centre and the home of some fabulous architecture, Dresden was also the scene of one of the most controversial bombing raids of the Second World War. Sachsen's second city, Leipzig, is covered in more detail in our pub guide (see pp **000**).

Just under half the breweries here survive from the communist era and earlier. The 30 or so brewpubs that have sprung up in the last 15 years are largely concentrated in the Erzgebirge mountains and the larger cities.

Transport: The region has suffered badly from railway closures since 1990, though many of the surviving lines have been upgraded. Bus services are generally good and several large towns and cities have excellent tram systems. The DB day ticket for Sachsen currently costs €24 for up to five people and can also be used in Sachsen-Anhalt and Thüringen. As ever, it's not valid until 09.00 on weekdays and may not be used on certain services – be sure to check.

AUE   910

Lotters Wirtschaft

Am Altmarkt 1, 08280 Aue
T 03771 59 20   **F** 03771 231 73
www.hotel-blauerengel.de
Owner: Tilo Unger   Founded: 2001
Output: 200hl
REGULAR BEERS:
Lotters Weizen (4.7%)
Lotters Hell (5%)
Lotters Dunkel (5%)
SEASONAL BEERS:
Lotters Rauchbier (5.5%, Sep), **Lotters Märzen** (5.7%, Mar), **Lotters Maibock** (6%, May)

Small brewery and pub in the rather grand Blauer Engel hotel on Aue's main square. Room rates drop significantly at weekends.

🍺 **Lotters Wirtschaft**
Am Altmarkt 1, 08280 Aue
Mon–Sat 10.00–24.00, Sun 15.00–24.00; rooms available
DB Aue (Sachsen) 800m

BAUTZEN   911

Altstadtbrauhaus

Altstadtbrauhaus zu Bautzen
Schloßstraße 3, 02625 Bautzen
T/F 03591 48 09 12
www.altstadt-brauhaus.de
Owners: Thomas Frenzel & Kai Otte
Founded: 01.03.2003
REGULAR BEERS:
Altstadtbrauhaus Hell
Altstadtbrauhaus Dunkel
Altstadtbrauhaus Hefeweizen

Altstadtbrauhaus Märzen, Altstadtbrauhaus Weihnachtsbier, Altstadtbrauhaus Maibock

On the northern edge of Bautzen's medieval centre, this small brewpub's brewing equipment is a little out of the ordinary.

Altstadtbrauhaus

Schloßstraße 3, 02625 Bautzen
Daily 12.00–24.00 (from 11.00 in summer)
DB Bautzen 1.3km

Bautzener

Bautzener Brauerei GmbH
Thomas-Mann-Straße 7, 02625 Bautzen
T 03591 46 06   **F** 03591 46 08
www.bautzener-brauhaus.de
Owners: Dr. Horst & Karsten Hermann
Founded: 30.12.1996   Output: 3,000hl
Availability: c.50 pubs
REGULAR BEERS:
Bautzener Original (4.9%)
Bautzener Kräusen (4.9%)
Bautzener Kupfer (5%)
Bautzener Schwarzes (5%)

Set back from the street, this microbrewery and tap east of the town centre has revived the name of Bautzen's last large brewery, opened in 1847 and closed in 1991. Parts of the old brewery's coppers survive as decoration. They brew occasional special beers but nothing regular.

Bautzener Brauhaus

Thomas-Mann-Straße 7a, 02625 Bautzen
T 03591 49 14 56   **F** 03591 403 72
Mon–Fri from 17.00, Sat, Sun & hols from 11.00
DB Bautzen 1km

BERGGIESSHÜBEL
(Bad Gottleuba)   912

Weltenbummler

Brauhaus Weltenbummler Gaststätte & Pension
Sebastian-Kneipp-Straße 6,
01816 Bad Gottleuba-Berggießhübel
T/F 035023 609 99
Owner: Armand Thiele   Founded: 1999
Output: 100hl   Availability: 1 pub
REGULAR BEERS:
Weltenbummler Pils
Weltenbummler Dunkel

Weltenbummler Rotes
Weltenbummler Honig
SEASONAL BEERS:
Kirsch, Hanf, Kräuter, Bock

Pub and pension alongside the river Gottleuba, in the Sächsische Schweiz region. The tiny brewery is used to brew some refreshingly adventurous beers; a *Weltenbummler* is a globetrotter. Buses Nos. 216 and 219 run daily from Pirna.

Weltenbummler

Sebastian-Kneipp-Straße 6,
01816 Bad Gottleuba-Berggießhübel
Closed Mon; Tue–Fri from 17.00,
Sat & Sun from 11.30; rooms available
DB Pirna 11km

CHEMNITZ   913

Braustolz

Am Feldschlößchen 18, 09116 Chemnitz-Kappel
T 0371 366 80   **F** 0371 366 81 00
www.braustolz.de
Owner: Brau Holding International
Founded: 1868   Output: 160,000hl
REGULAR BEERS:
Braustolz Lager (4.5%)
Braustolz Black Art (4.9%)
Braustolz Pils (4.9%)
Braustolz Kappler Braumeister (4.9%)
Braustolz Landbier (5.2%)
Braustolz Spezial (5.4%)
Braustolz Bock Dunkel (6.5%)
SEASONAL BEER:
Braustolz Kappler Festbier (5.4%, Dec)

Known as Feldschlößchen until the early 1990s, this large brewery stands on the opposite side of the tracks to the tram museum, next to the stop at Am Feldschlößchen. No tap, but the beers can be found all over Chemnitz (which was re-named Karl-Marx-Stadt during DDR times).
Tram No. 1 Am Feldschlößchen 20m
DB Chemnitz-Schönau 1.1km, Hbf 4km

Friedrichs Brauhaus

Ermafa-Passage, Reichstraße 58–60,
09112 Chemnitz-Kaßberg
T 0371 31 70 74
Owner: Michael Friedrich   Founded: 1997
Output: 500hl   Availability: 2 pubs

REGULAR BEERS:
Friedrichs Pils
Friedrichs Braun
Friedrichs Schwarz

The address for this modern brewpub is a little misleading as it's actually just off Hartmann-straße, near Am Schlossteich bus stop (No. 23 from the Hbf). Friedrichs also supplies the Sudhaus (which we think Michael Friedrich owns), about 800m to the north on Schloßplatz. They also own the new Karls Brauhaus.

📍 Friedrichs Brauhaus
Ermafa-Passage, Reichstraße 58–60,
09112 Chemnitz-Kaßberg
Daily from 17.00
DB Chemnitz Hbf 1.8km

Karls Brauhaus

Brückenstraße 17, 09111 Chemnitz-Zentrum
T 0371 909 38 80
www.karls-brauhaus.de
Owner: Michael Friedrich   Founded: 09.12.2005
REGULAR BEERS:
Karls Braunbier
Karls Pils

Brand-new brewpub in the Stadthalle concert hall, owned by Michael Friedrich of nearby Friedrichs Brauhaus. Several bus routes stop outside.

📍 Karls Brauhaus
Brückenstraße 17, 09111 Chemnitz-Zentrum
Mon–Sat from 11.00, Sun from 10.00
Tram Straße der Nationen 200m
DB Chemnitz Hbf 800m

Reichenbrander

Brauerei Reichenbrand GmbH & Co. KG
Zwickauer Straße 478,
09117 Chemnitz-Reichenbrand
T 0371 85 02 14   F 0371 85 34 77
www.brauerei-bergt.de
Owner: Joachim & Matthias Bergt
Founded: 1874   Output: 25,000hl
Availability: 100 pubs
REGULAR BEERS:
Reichenbrander Unser Helles (4.2%)
Reichenbrander Classic Pilsner (4.8%)
Reichenbrander Dunkelbier (4.8%)
Reichenbrander Kellerbier (4.8%)
Reichenbrander Premium (5.5%)

SEASONAL BEER:
Reichenbrander Bockbier (6.5%)

Formerly called Brauerei Bergt, Reichenbrand is in the western suburb of the same name, formerly a village in its own right. The tap is in front of the brewery – several bus routes stop outside.

📍 Bräu-Stübl
Zwickauer Straße 478,
09117 Chemnitz-Reichenbrand
T 0371 85 80 41   Daily 11.00–24.00
DB Chemnitz-Siegmar 700m

Turm Brauhaus

Neumarkt 2, 09111 Chemnitz-Zentrum
T 0371 909 50 95   F 0371 909 50 96
www.turmbrauhaus.de
Founded: 25.06.2004
REGULAR BEERS:
Chemnitzer Turmbräu Hell
Chemnitzer Turmbräu Kupfer

Another recent opening, Turmbräu is on the Neumarkt, in the heart of Chemnitz. We've received no word that they brew seasonals.

📍 Turm Brauhaus
Neumarkt 2, 09111 Chemnitz-Zentrum
Sun–Thu 10.00–01.00, Fri & Sat 10.00–03.00
Tram Roter Turm 150m, Zentrale 150m
DB Chemnitz Hbf 1km

COPITZ *(Pirna)*   914

Brauhaus Pirna

Brauhaus Pirna – Zum Giesser
Basteistraße 60, 01796 Pirna-Copitz
T 03501 46 46 46   F 03501 46 46 47
www.brauhaus-pirna.de
Owner: the Schnees family   Founded: 1998
Output: 1,000hl   Availability: 4 pubs
REGULAR BEERS:
Pirnauer Bastei Pils (4.6%)
Pirnauer Giesser Dunkel (4.6%)
SEASONAL BEERS:
Pirnauer 1. Sächsisches Rauchbier (4.6%),
Pirnauer Bastei Bock (6.2%)

Large brewpub in north-eastern Copitz, close to an industrial estate. The beers are sold in a few other pubs locally. Bus route M from the main station at Pirna stops virtually outside the door.

📌 Zum Giesser
Basteistraße 60, 01796 Pirna-Copitz
Daily 11.00–24.00
DB Pirna-Copitz Nord 750m, Pirna 2.7km

DÖBELN 915

Döbelner Brauhaus

Obermarkt 1, 04720 Döbeln
T 03431 71 00 95   **F** 03431 71 00 96
Owners: Christian Hönsch & Michael Köhler
Founded: 1997   Output: 300hl
Availability: 1 pub

REGULAR BEERS:
Döbelner Brauhaus Pils (4.8%)
Döbelner Brauhaus Dunkel (4.9%)

SEASONAL BEER:
Döbelner Bock (5.5%)

Small brewpub in the town hall. Döbeln is known as the *Stiefelstadt* (boot town) and they've got a giant boot to prove it. Take a bus from the Hauptbahnhof to the bus station if you'd rather not walk.

📌 Döbelner Brauhaus
Obermarkt 1, 04720 Döbeln
Daily from 11.00
DB Döbeln Ost 700m, Döbeln Hbf 2.1km

DRESDEN 916

Feldschlößchen

Brauerei Feldschlößchen AG
Cunnersdorfer Straße 25,
01189 Dresden/Coschütz-Gittersee
T 0351 408 30   **F** 0351 408 37 22
www.feldschloesschen.de/dd
Owner: Carlsberg Breweries, Denmark
Founded: 1858   Output: 1,800,000hl

FELDSCHLÖSSCHEN BEERS:
Feldschlößchen Diät Pilsner (4.9%)
Feldschlößchen Pilsner Premium (4.9%)
Feldschlößchen Export (5.1%)

SEASONAL BEER:
Feldschlößchen Urbock (7%)

DRESDNER FELSENKELLER BEERS:
Dresdner Felsenkeller Pilsner (4.8%),
Dresdner Felsenkeller Urhell (5.2%),
Dresdner Felsenkeller Spezial (5.4%)

OTHER BEERS:
Coschützer Pils (4.8%); **Schwarzer Steiger** (4.8%)

Now owned by Carlsberg, this massive brewery moved to the southern suburbs, next to the A17, in 1981. The tap is in part of the original brewery, west of the main station.

📌 Feldschlößchen-Stammhaus
Budapester Straße 32, 01069 Dresden/
Südvorstadt-West
T 0351 471 88 55   **F** 0351 471 88 93
Daily 11.00–01.00
Tram Budapester Straße 500m
DB Dresden Hbf 1.1m

Neustädter Hausbrauerei

Schönbrunnstraße 1, 01097 Dresden-Neustadt
T 0351 799 37 74   www.obergaerig.de
Owner: Christian Schwingenheuer
Founded: 01.03.2002   Output: 200hl
Availability: 11 pubs

REGULAR BEERS:
Neustädter Elbhang Rot (4.9%)
Neustädter Neustadt Hell (5%)
Neustädter Hecht Alt (5%)
Neustädter Lenins Hanf (5.4%)

SEASONAL BEER:
Wilder Mann Bock (7%, Sep–Apr)

FOR GRÜNZEUG BLUMENHANDLUNG:
Grünzeug Bier (4.9%)

This microbrewery near Neustadt station is one of only two in Germany that also makes cider (we think). Lenins Hanf is a hemp beer (motto: "don't smoke, just drink"), and the Grünzeug (greenery) beer is brewed for a florists. Zum Bautzner Tor opens at 10.00 on the first Wednesday of each month for a brewing seminar.

📌 Zum Bautzner Tor
Hoyerswerdaer Straße 37,
01099 Dresden–Neustadt
T 0351 803 82 02
Daily from 14.00
Tram Bautzner/Rothenburger Straße 50m
DB Dresden-Neustadt 900m, Hbf 3.2km

Waldschlösschen

Brauhaus am Waldschlösschen Rank & Büttig
Am Brauhaus 8b, 01099 Dresden-Radeberger
Vorstadt
T 0351 652 39 00   **F** 0351 652 39 04

www.waldschloesschen.de
Owners: Uwe Büttig & Thoralf Rank
Founded: 1997   Output: 3,000hl
REGULAR BEERS:
Waldschlösschen Hefe (5%)
Waldschlösschen Original Hell (5.3%)
Waldschlösschen Zwickelbier (5.3%)
Waldschlösschen Dunkel (5.5%)
SEASONAL BEERS:
Waldschlösschen Oktoberfestbier (Oct),
Waldschlösschen Faschingsbier (Nov),
Waldschlösschen Weihnachtsbier (Christmas),
Waldschlösschen Maibock (May)

Large brewpub just north of the river Elbe, in part of the former Waldschlösschen brewery which closed in 1981 when all brewing in the city moved to the new Feldschlößchen plant. The daily live music is mostly from the house grand piano.

Waldschlösschen
Am Brauhaus 8b, 01099 Dresden-Radeberger Vorstadt
Daily 11.00–01.00
No. 11 Waldschlößchen 200m
DB Dresden-Neustadt 2.9km, Hbf 5km

Watzke
Hausbräu im Ballhaus Watzke GmbH
Kötschenbroder Straße 1, 01139 Dresden/
Pieschen-Süd
T 0351 85 29 20   F 0351 852 92 22
www.watzke.de
Owner: Rudi Vogel   Founded: 1996
Output: 2,700hl   Availability: 2 pubs
REGULAR BEER:
Watzke Pils (5%)
Watzke Altpieschener Spezial (5.2%)
SEASONAL BEERS:
Watzke Rauchbier (4.9%, Nov), **Watzke Weizen** (5.1%, Jul), **Watzke Landbier** (5.2%, Sep), **Watzke Neujahrsbier** (5.3%, Jan), **Watzke Urhell** (5.3%, Aug), **Watzke Märzen** (5.4%, Mar), **Watzke Oktoberbier** (5.4%, Oct), **Watzke Weihnachtsbier** (5.4%, Dec), **Watzke Porterbier** (6.3%), **Watzke Dunkler Doppelbock** (7.3%, Feb)

Grand brewpub in a former ballroom overlooking the Elbe, owned by Karlsruhe brewpub baron Rudi Vogel. They now have a second outlet in the city centre. We suspect there may be other seasonal beers.

Watzke
Kötschenbroder Straße 1, 01139 Dresden/
Pieschen-Süd
Daily 11.00–24.00
Altpieschen 150m
DB Dresden-Pieschen 850m, Hbf 5km

Brauereiausschank am Goldenen Reiter
Hauptstraße 1, 01097 Dresden-Innere Vorstadt
T 0351 810 68 20   F 0351 810 68 34
Daily 09.00–24.00
Nos. 4 & 9 Goldener Reiter 50m
DB Dresden-Neustadt 1km, Hbf 2.2km

EHRENFRIEDERSDORF   917

Specht
Privatbrauerei Specht GbR
Thomas-Mann-Straße 17,
09427 Ehrenfriedersdorf
T/F 037341 22 29
www.privatbrauerei-specht.de
Owner: Gerd Specht   Founded: 1844
Output: 8,000hl
REGULAR BEERS:
Specht Pilsner (4.8%)
Specht Greifensteinquell Landbier (4.8%)
Specht Export (5%)
Specht Spezial (5%)
Schwarzer Specht (6.1%)
SEASONAL BEER:
Specht Bockbier (6.1%, Sep–Apr)

One of comparatively few breweries to remain private during the DDR period, this small brewery is at the southern end of the village. The *Specht* (woodpecker) of the owner's name features on the labels. They don't have a tap. Bus No. 210 runs from Chemnitz to Annaberg-Buchholz via Ehrenfriedersdorf and Schönefeld-Wiesa.
DB Schönefeld-Wiesa 6km

EIBAU   918

Münch-Bräu
Münch-Bräu Eibau GmbH
Neueibauer Straße 9, 02739 Eibau
T 03586 781 40   F 03586 78 14 18
www.eibauer.de

Owners: the Münch family   Founded: 1810
Output: 100,000hl   Availability: c.300 pubs
REGULAR BEERS:
Eibauer Helles Landbier (4.1%)
Eibauer Lausitzer Dunkel (4.2%)
Eibauer Schwarzbier (4.5%)
Eibauer Pilsner (4.8%)
SEASONAL BEERS:
Eibauer St. Marienthal Klosterbier (5.3%),
Eibauer Dunkler Bock (6.4%, Oct–Jan)

Large brewery in Eibau, a few miles from the
Czech border. The St. Marienthal Klosterbier is
brewed to a recipe of the St. Marienthal Cister-
cian convent brewery which closed in 1920. The
Spitzbergbaude tap is on the Spitzberg hill near
Oderwitz, 3km south-east of Eibau.

🍺 Spitzbergbaude

Spitzbergstraße 6, 02791 Oderwitz
T 035842 279 90   **F** 035842 292 11
Nov–Apr: closed Thu; Fri–Wed 11.00–02.00.
May–Oct: daily 11.00–02.00
DB Oberoderwitz 1.2km

EINSIEDEL (Chemnitz)   919

Einsiedler

Einsiedler Brauhaus GmbH
Einsiedler-Hauptstraße 144,
09123 Chemnitz-Einsiedel
T 037209 66 10   **F** 037209 661 39
www.einsiedler.de
Owners: Frank Kapp & Hans-Dieter Oermann
Founded: 1885   Output: 329,000hl
Availability: c.500 pubs
REGULAR BEERS:
Einsiedler Weißbier Hefetrüb (4.7%)
Einsiedler Weißbier Dunkel (4.7%)
Einsiedler Schwarzbier St. Peter (4.9%)
Einsiedler Privat Pils (4.9%)
Einsiedler Jubiläums-Pils (4.9%)
Einsiedler Landbier (5%)
Einsiedler Heller Bock (6.5%)
Einsiedler Doppel-Bock (7.5%)
SEASONAL BEER:
Einsiedler Mai-Bock (6.5%, May)

Large regional brewery at the southern tip of
the village. Officially a suburb of Chemnitz, we
listed Einsiedel separately because it's such a
distance away. The tap is a couple of kilometres
to the north-east – buses Nos. 206 and 207 from
Chemnitz Hbf. stop outside.

🍺 Goldener Hahn

Zschopauer Straße 565, 09128 Chemnitz/
Kleinolbersdorf-Altenhain
T 0371 77 23 38
Closed Mon & Tue; Wed–Sun 08.00–20.00
DB Einsiedel 2.3km, Chemnitz Hbf 9km

ERLABRUNN   920

Kunos Braugasthaus

Schulstraße 8, 08349 Erlabrunn
T 03773 88 05 43   **F** 03773 88 05 42
www.hotel-alte-schleiferei.de
Founded: 2001
REGULAR BEERS:
Kunobräu Pils
Kunobräu Dunkel
Kunobräu Schwarzbier
SEASONAL BEER:
Kunobräu Bock

Bar and brewery in the 4-star Alte Schleiferei
hotel (the Old Grinding Shop). Erlabrunn is a
small village in the attractive Vogtland national
park whose peaks reach up to 1,200m above
sea level.

🍺 Kunos Braugasthaus

Schulstraße 8, 08349 Erlabrunn
Daily 11.00–24.00; rooms available
DB Erlabrunn (Erzgebirge) 600m

ERLBACH (Vogtland)   921

Erlbacher Brauhaus

Klingenthaler Straße 12, 08265 Erlbach
T 037422 63 84   **F** 037422 468 80
www.brauhaus-erlbach.de
Owner: Hans Geilert   Founded: 10.04.1999
Output: 500hl   Availability: 1 pub
REGULAR BEERS:
Erlbacher Zwickel Hell (5%)
Erlbacher Schwarze Seele (5%)
SEASONAL BEER:
Erlbacher Bock (7%)

The original Erlbach brewery, dating from 1563,
closed in 1974. Its current incarnation opened
in the spring of 1999, with the brewing
equipment in the bar. *Schwarze Seele* means
black soul. If you are using public transport at
least one change of bus will be necessary.

🍺 Erlbacher Brauhaus

Klingenthaler Straße 12, 08265 Erlbach
Closed Wed; Mon, Tue & Thu–Sat 14.00–22.00,
Sun 12.00–22.00
DB Siebenbrunn 6km, Adorf (Vogtland) 9km

FREIBERG   922

Freiberger

Freiberger Brauhaus AG
Am Fürstenwald, 09599 Freiberg
T 03731 36 30   **F** 03731 36 32 91
www.freiberger-bier.de
Owner: Actris AG   Founded: 1850
Output: 800,000hl
REGULAR BEERS:
Freiberger Premium-Pils (4.9%)
Freibergisch Diät Pils (4.9%)
Freibergisch Schwarzes Bergbier (4.9%)
Freibergisch Export Spezial (5.5%)
Freibergisch Jubiläums-Festbier (5.8%)
Freibergisch Bock Dunkel (6.7%)

Very large brewery which moved to its current
site on the north-eastern outskirts of Freiberg in
1996. The tap is at the former site of the brewery,
on the southern edge of the town centre.

🍺 Brauhof

Körnerstraße 2, 09599 Freiberg
T 03731 353 00   **F** 03731 35 30 22
Closed Sun; Mon–Sat 11.00–24.00; rooms
available   DB Freiberg (Sachsen) 750m

GEISING   923

Ratskeller

Hauptstraße 31, 01778 Geising
T 035056 38 00   **F** 035056 380 20
www.ratskeller-geising.de
Owner: Sven Knauthe   Founded: 2002
REGULAR BEERS:
Bergamts-Dunkel
Bergamts-Pils
SEASONAL BEERS:
**Bergamts-Sommer-Pils, Bergamts-Kumpel-
Pils, Bergamts-Hefeweizen, Bergamts-Xmas,
Bergamts-Bock**

Not the town-hall brewpub you might expect
from the 'Ratskeller' name, but a half-timbered

inn that's also seen use as private housing and
at one time included a butcher's shop. The small
brewery is a recent addition.

🍺 Ratskeller

Hauptstraße 31, 01778 Geising
Daily 11.30–22.00; rooms available
DB Geising 350m

GERSDORF   924

Glückauf

Glückauf-Brauerei GmbH Gersdorf
Hauptstraße 176, 09355 Gersdorf
T 037203 91 00   **F** 037203 42 31
www.glueckaufbiere.de
Owner: Innstadt, Passau & Ottakringer, Wien
Founded: 1880   Output: 50,000hl
Availability: c.150 pubs
REGULAR BEERS:
Glückauf Edelpils (4.8%)
Glückauf Kräusen (4.9%)
Glückauf Pilsener (4.9%)
Glückauf Edel (4.9%)
Glückauf Deputat (4.9%)
Glückauf Schwarzes (5.1%)
Glückauf Karl May Jubiläums-Pils (5.2%)
SEASONAL BEER:
Glückauf Bock Dunkel (5.9%, winter)

The brewery is on the main road through the
village and has its tap next door. Bus No.116 runs
between Hohenstein-Ernstthal and Oelsnitz via
Gersdorf. *Glückauf!* is a miners' good-luck
greeting. Karl May was a famous 19th-century
Saxon writer of Wild West stories that are still
extremely popular all over Germany today.

🍺 Grünes Tal

Hauptstraße 178, 09355 Gersdorf
T 037203 45 02
Closed Thu; Mon–Wed 10.00–14.00 & from
17.00, Fri–Sun from 11.00; rooms available
DB Hohenstein-Ernstthal 5km, Mitteloelsnitz 5km

GLAUCHAU   925

Sommerlust

Vereinsheim und Hausbrauerei Sommerlust
Oststraße 39, 08371 Glauchau
T 03763 55 65

www.glauchauer-bier.de
Owner: Bernd Biedermann   Founded: 2000
REGULAR BEERS:
Glauchauer Schwarzbier Spezial
Glauchauer Weizen

Small brewpub on the southern side of the town. We think it's the meeting place for a number of local clubs and societies. Note the restricted opening hours.

🍺 **Sommerlust**
Oststraße 39, 08371 Glauchau
Closed Thu & Sat; Mon & Wed 15.30–20.00, Tue 15.30–22.00, Fri 15.30–23.00, Sun 09.30–13.00 & 16.00–19.00
DB Glauchau (Sachsen) 2km

GÖRLITZ   926

Fritz Bräu

Elisabethstraße 41, 02826 Görlitz
T 03581 480 80   F 03581 48 08 11
www.bon-apart.de
Founded: 2002   Availability: 2 pubs
REGULAR BEER
Fritz-Pilsener (4.8%)
Fritz-Dunkel (5.2%)
Fritz-Export (5.2%)

Small brewery in the restaurant of the 4-star Hotel Bon Apart in the centre of Görlitz. We believe they brew seasonal beers but don't think they supply anywhere else. Görlitz is hoping to become European cultural capital in 2010, and the magnificent park at Bad Muskau nearby, straddling the German–Polish border, is a UNESCO World Heritage site.

🍺 **Bon Apart**
Elisabethstraße 41, 02826 Görlitz
Closed Mon; Tue–Sun 11.30–14.00 & from 17.00; rooms available
Tram Demianiplatz 150m   DB Görlitz 1km

Landskron

Landskron Brauerei Görlitz GmbH
An der Landskronbrauerei 116, 02826 Görlitz
T 03581 46 50   F 03581 46 51 52
www.landskron.de
Owner: Carlsberg Breweries, Denmark
Founded: 1869   Output: 200,000hl

REGULAR BEERS:
Landskron Pupen-Schultzes Schwarzes (3.9%)
Landskron Hell (4.7%)
Landskron Lausitzer Kindl (4.8%)
Landskron Premium Pilsener (4.8%)
Landskron Weizen (5.2%)
Landskron Ein Schlesier (5.2%)
SEASONAL BEERS:
Landskron Winterhopfen (5.3%, winter),
Landskron Maibock (6.2%. Mar–Jun),
Landskron Goldbock (6.2%, Sep–Jan)

Regional brewery just 150m from the Polish border. They used to have a brewpub in Cottbus but that closed in 2004. We're not aware of any tap but the beers are easy to find. The peculiarly named Pupen-Schultzes Schwarzes, which translates as Farting Schultze's black beer, hails from the time when people collected their beer in jugs and bottles from the horse-cart or lorry. Occasionally the beer went flat and leading to obvious results – and an unusual name. Bizarrely, the brewery was used in the recent remake of "Around the World in 80 Days" – for scenes set in New York!
Tram No. 3 Goethestraße 750m
DB Görlitz 1.2km

Obermühle

Brauhaus Obermühle Görlitz
An der Obermühle 5, 02826 Görlitz
T 03581 87 98 32
E brauhaus-obermuehle@gmx.de
Owner: Susanne Daubner
Founded: 2001
Output: 150hl
Availability: 1 pub
REGULAR BEERS:
Obermühle Deutsches Pilsner Hell (4.9%)
Obermühle Deutsches Pilsner Dunkel (4.9%)
Obermühle Märzen (4.9%)

Pension, pub and brewery on the banks of the Lausitzer Neiße river, north-east of the railway bridge into Poland. It's even closer to the Polish border than Landskron (approximately 75m). Buses Nos. B or N to Emmerichstraße shorten the walk.

🍺 **Obermühle**
An der Obermühle 5, 02826 Görlitz
Daily from 12.00; rooms available
DB Görlitz 1.5km

GROSSRÖHRSDORF 927

Böhmisch Brauhaus

Böhmisch Brauhaus GmbH & Co. KG
Bahnhofstraße 11, 01900 Großröhrsdorf
T 035952 40 30   **F** 035952 403 30
Founded: 1887   Output: 25,000hl
REGULAR BEERS:
Böhmisch Brauhaus Edel Sünde (4.6%)
Böhmisch Brauhaus Pilsner Premium (4.9%)
SEASONAL BEER:
Böhmisch Brauhaus Bock (6.5%)

The Bohemian Brewhouse is just south of
Großröhrsdorf station. They don't have a tap
but the beers are available in a few local pubs.
DB Großröhrsdorf 200m

GROSSRÜCKERSWALDE 928

Weißer Hirsch

Brauerei Uhlemann & Uhlemann GbR
Marienberger Straße 72, 09518
Großrückerswalde
T 03735 647 76   **F** 03735 647 70
www.brauereigasthof-weisser-hirsch.de
Owner: Andreas Uhlemann   Founded: 2001
REGULAR BEERS:
Hirschbräu Pils
Hirschbräu Schwarzbier
SEASONAL BEERS:
Hirschbräu Festbier, Hirschbräu Bock

The White Stag brewpub is on the main road
through the village. Bus No. 490 runs from
Annaberg-Buchholz bus station, conveniently
situated on the opposite side of town to the
three railway stations.

🍺 **Weißer Hirsch**
Marienberger Str. 72, 09518 Großrückerswalde
Closed Mon; Tue–Thu & Sun 11.00–22.00,
Fri & Sat 11.00–23.00
DB Annaberg-Buchholz Unterer Bf. 11km

*We intend to post regular updates to the
Guide at* **www.german-breweries.com**
*If you find anything you think we should
be told about we can be contacted at*
GermanBreweries@aol.com.

GRÜNBACH 929

Bayerischer Hof

Muldenberger Straße 19, 08223 Grünbach
T 03745 78 97 60   **F** 03745 7897 69 28
www.bayerischerhof-gruenbach.de
Owner: Ines Apfelstädt   Founded: 1998
Output: 150hl   Availability: 1 pub
REGULAR BEERS:
Bayerischer Hof Hell
Bayerischer Hof Dunkel
SEASONAL BEERS:
**Bayerischer Hof Weihnachtsbier, Bayerischer
Hof Maibock, Bayerischer Hof Herbstbock**

Hotel and brewpub on the main road through
Grünbach, a village at the western end of the
Erzgebirge mountains.

🍺 **Bayerischer Hof**
Muldenberger Straße 19, 08223 Grünbach
Closed Tue; Mon & Wed–Fri 11.00–15.00 &
18.00–22.00, Sat, Sun & hols 11.00–22.00;
rooms available
DB Grünbach 800m

HARTSMANNSDORF 930

Hartmannsdorfer Brauhaus

Chemnitzer Straße 5, 09232 Hartmannsdorf
T 03722 719 10   **F** 03722 71 91 91
www.mittweidaer-loewenbraeu.de
Owner: Mittweidaer Löwenbräu GmbH
Founded: 1887   Output: 80,000hl
REGULAR BEERS:
Hartmannsdorfer Hell (4.6%)
Hartmannsdorfer Pils (5%)
FOR MITTWEIDAER LÖWENBRÄU:
Mittweidaer Löwenbräu Pils (4.9%),
Mittweidaer Löwenbräu Black Lion (5.4%),
Mittweidaer Löwenbräu Export (5.5%)

Modern brewery built in 1996 to replace both
the existing Hartmannsdorf brewery and that of
Mittweida Löwenbräu, who own it. Buses Nos.
652 and 657 operate from Burgstädt station.

🍺 **Braugut**
Chemnitzer Straße 2, 09232 Hartmannsdorf
T 03722 63 13 10
Daily from 11.00; rooms available
DB Burgstädt 4km

KROSTITZ 931

Krostitzer

Krostitzer Brauerei GmbH
Brauerei Sraße 12–14, 04509 Krostitz
T 034295 77 60 **F** 034295 776 66
www.ur-krostitzer.de
Owner: Oetker Gruppe AG   Founded: 1534
Output: 370,000hl   Availability: c.2,500 pubs
REGULAR BEERS:
Ur-Krostitzer Schwedenquell Pils (4.8%)
Ur-Krostitzer Schwarzes (4.9%)
Ur-Krostitzer Feinherbes Pilsner (5%)

Large regional brewery whose Schwarzbier is widely available but easily confused with the similarly named Köstritzer. Several bus routes run from Krestitz, the No. 196 going through to Leipzig Hauptbahnhof.

Krostitz
Brauerei Sraße 2, 04509 Krostitz
T 034295 723 24
Closed Thu; Fri–Wed 11.30–14.00 & from 18.00
DB Krensitz 3.5km, Leipzig Hbf 15km

LEIPZIG 932

Bauer

Familienbrauerei Ernst Bauer KG
Täubchenweg 5–7, 04103 Leipzig/Zentrum-Ost
T 0341 688 46 76 **F** 0341 688 19 30
www.bauer-bier.de
Founded: 1881   Output: 30,000hl
REGULAR BEERS:
Bauer Bier Hell (4.6%)
Bauer's Schwarzes Bier (4.9%)
Bauer Bier Pils (5%)
Bauer's Kellerbier (5%)
SEASONAL BEER:
Bauer Bier Bock (6.1%)
FOR W. GOEDECKE & CO., BURGLIEBENAU:
Goedecke's Döllnitzer Ritterguts-Gose (3.9%)

Small, family-run brewery, just down the street from the Grassi Museum. There are plans to open a tap at the brewery which should make the beers much easier to find.
Johannisplatz 400m
DB Leipzig Hbf 1.3km

Bayerischer Bahnhof

Gasthaus & Gosebrauerei Bayerischer Bahnhof
Bayerischer Platz 1, 04103 Leipzig/Zentrum-Südost   **T** 0341 124 57 60 **F** 0341 124 57 70
www.bayerischer-bahnhof.de
Owner: Thomas Schneider   Founded: 2000
Output: 1,500hl   Availability: 4 pubs
REGULAR BEERS:
Original Leipziger Gose (4.6%)
Schaffner Pils (5%)
Kuppler Weißbier (5.2%)
Heizer Schwarzbier (5.3%)
SEASONAL BEER:
Prellbock (6.7%)

Brewpub in the former Bayerischer Bahnhof. Although known primarily for its Gose, several other beers are also brewed, mostly railway-themed. A *Prellbock* is a buffer stop, the *Schaffner* is the ticket collector, the *Kuppler* the coupler and the *Heizer* the stoker.

Bayerischer Bahnhof
Bayerischer Platz 1, 04103 Leipzig/Zentrum-Südost   Daily 11.00 – 01.00
DB Bayerischerplatz 100m, Leipzig Hbf 1.8km

Kaiser Napoleon

Prager Straße 233, 04289 Leipzig-Probstheida
T 0341 86 91 10 **F** 0341 869 11 19
www.kaisernapoleon.de   Founded: 1997
REGULAR BEERS:
Napoleon Bonaparte Pils (4.7%)
Napoleon Kanonier Schwarzbier (5.1%)
SEASONAL BEERS:
Dragoner Altbier (4.6%, Jun), **Kürassier Hefeweizen** (5.2%), **Helena Hanfbier** (5,6%), **Husar Haferbier** (5.7%), **Musketier Märzen** (5.7%, Mar), **Sapeur Maibock** (6.5%, May), **Grenadier Weizenbock** (6.5%, Dec), **1813 Doppelbock** (7%, Oct)

Historic pub & brewery in the south-western suburb of Probstheida. Although still open when the Guide visited in May 2005 it's possible they may have since closed as the phone, fax and website no longer work.

Kaiser Napoleon
Prager Straße 233, 04289 Leipzig-Probstheida
Mon–Thu 17.00–24.00, Fri–Sun 11.00–14.00 & 17.00–24.00
Nos. 2 & 15 Prager/Russenstraße 50m
DB Leipzig Hbf 5km

Reudnitzer

Leipziger Brauhaus zu Reudnitz GmbH & Co. KG
Mühlstraße 13, 04317 Leipzig/Reudnitz-Thonberg
T 0341 267 10   **F** 0341 267 11 75
www.reudnitzer.de
Owner: Oetker Gruppe AG   Founded: 1862
Output: 900,000hl   Availability: c.700 pubs
REGULAR BEERS:
Reudnitzer Diät (3.9%)
Reudnitzer Pilsner (5%)
Reudnitzer Naturtrüb (5%)
Reudnitzer Schwarz (5.1%)
Reudnitzer Export (5.4%)
SEASONAL BEERS:
Reudnitzer Festbier (5.6%), **Reudnitzer
Weihnachtsbier** (5.6%), **Reudnitzer Ur-Bock
Hell** (6.9%)
FOR BRAUEREI STERNBURG, LEIPZIG:
Sternburg Pilsener (4.9%), **Sternburg
Schwarzbier** (4.9%), **Sternburg Export** (5.2%)

Very large regional brewery west of the city
centre with the tap on the street behind.
Sternburg beers have been brewed here since
the brewery in Lützschena (now a suburb of
Leipzig) closed. The Naturtrüb is only available
in a few pubs.

🍺 **Hopfenspeicher**
Oststraße 38, 04317 Leipzig/Reudnitz-Thonberg
T 0341 124 88 98   **F** 0341 2252 97 90
Mon–Fri 15.00–24.00, Sat 11.00–03.00,
Sun 11.00–23.00
🚋 No. 4 Riebeck-/Oststraße 250m
🚆 Leipzig-Hbf 2km

Thomaskirche

Brauerei an der Thomaskirche
Thomaskirchhof 3–5, 04109 Leipzig-Zentrum
T 0341 212 61 10   **F** 0341 212 61 20
www.brauerei-thomaskirche.de
Owner: Lazzaretti GbR   Founded: 1998
Output: 2,000hl   Availability: 1 pub
REGULAR BEERS:
Thomaskirche Spezial Schwarzbier (5%)
Thomaskirche Pilsener (5.2%)
SEASONAL BEERS:
Thomaskirche Hefeweizen Hell (5.6%),
Thomaskirche Hefeweizen Dunkel (5.6%),
Thomaskirche Weihnachtsbier (5.7%),
Thomaskirche Märzen (5.8%), **Thomaskirche
Bockbier** (6.5%), **Thomaskirche Lipsiator** (7.3%)

Modern brewpub virtually next door to the
slightly better known church of the same name.
We've seen the Spezial Schwarzbier wrongly
reported as two other beers (Spezial and Dunkel).

🍺 **Thomaskirche**
Thomaskirchhof 3–5, 04109 Leipzig-Zentrum
Daily 11.00–24.00
🚋 No. 9 Thomaskirche 100m
🚆 Leipzig Hbf 850m

LIESKE (Oßling) 933

Bergschlösschen

Missionshof Lieske – Brauerei zum
Bergschlösschen
Hauptstraße 30, 01920 Oßling-Lieske
T 035792 57 10   **F** 035792 571 12
www.missionshof-lieske.de
Founded: 1997   Output: 2,000hl
REGULAR BEERS:
Bergschlösschen Zwickel
Bergschlösschen Dunkel
Bergschlösschen Pilsner
SEASONAL BEER:
Bergschlösschen Bock (spring & autumn)

Missionshof Lieske is a centre for people with
learning difficulties that includes a microbrewery among its many enterprises. The tap is in the
village of Weißig, a mile west of Lieske. In fine
weather the pub closes and their beer garden
opens. The last bus out of Weißig leaves before
opening.

🍺 **Gasthof Weißig**
Dorfstraße 9, 01920 Oßling-Weißig
T 035792 503 53
Closed Mon–Wed; Thu–Sat from 18.00,
Sun & hols from 10.00
🚆 Kamenz 10km, Hoyerswerda 16km

LÖBAU 934

Bergquell

Bergquell Brauerei Löbau GmbH
Weststraße 7, 02708 Löbau
T 03585 474 70   **F** 03585 47 47 19
www.bergquell-loebau.de
Owner: Steffen Dittmar   Founded: 1846
Output: 112,000hl   Availability: c.150 pubs

REGULAR BEERS:
Löbauer Bergquell Lausitzer Porter (4.4%)
Löbauer Bergquell Pilsner (4.7%)
Bergquell Lausitzer Mühlen-Pils (4.7%)
Löbauer Bergquell Goldener Reiter (4.7%)
Löbauer Bergquell Gold (5.1%)
Bergquell Lausitzer Hefeweizen (5.1%)
SEASONAL BEERS:
Löbauer Bergquell Festbier (5.1%),
Löbauer Bergquell Maibock (7%),
Löbauer Bergquell Lausitzer Berg-Bock (7%),
Löbauer Bergquell Lausitzer Strong Porter (7.5%)

Small regional brewery on the western outskirts of town. They also produce Kirsch-Porter and Porter-Punsch which are not included as they're mixed drinks. The tap overlooks the railway at the west end of the station.

Hotel Stadt Löbau
Elisenstraße 1, 02708 Löbau
T 03585 86 18 30   F 03585 86 80 26
Closed Mon; Tue–Sun 09.00–24.00;
rooms available
DB Löbau (Sachsen) 450m

MEISSEN   935

Schwerter
Schwerter Brauerei Wohlers KG
Ziegelstraße 6, 01662 Meißen
T 03521 73 25 13   F 03521 73 25 12
www.schwerter-brauerei.de
Owners: Andreas Girbig & Elke Wohlers
Founded: 1460
Output: 15,000hl
Availability: 80 pubs
REGULAR BEERS:
Meissner Schwerter Privat Pils (4.9%)
Meissner Schwerter Red Lager (4.9%)
Meissner Schwerter St. Afra Dunkel (4.9%)
Meissner Schwerter German Porter (6.5%)

Although founded in 1460, Schwerter moved to the current site on the eastern edge of Meißen as recently as 1997. They also produce draught beer for three unknown breweries. Bus No. 411 stops outside. Meißen, is of course, the home of the world-famous Meissener Porzellan, and the porcelain factury's emblem are two crossed swords, or *Schwerter*.

Zum Schwerter Bräu
Ziegelstraße 6, 01662 Meißen
T 03521 73 14 43   F 03521 73 14 44
Mon–Fri 07.00–15.00 & from 17.00;
Sat & Sun from 11.00
DB Meißen 2.5km

OBERSCHEIBE
(Scheibenberg)   936

Fiedler
Privatbrauerei Christian Fiedler
Silberstraße 28, 09481 Scheibenberg-Oberscheibe
T 037349 82 49   F 037349 61 01
www.brauerei-fiedler.de
Owner: Christian Fiedler   Founded: 1813
Output: 13,000hl
REGULAR BEERS:
Fiedler Pilsener (4.7%)
Fiedler Orgelpfeifen Bräu Landbier (4.7%)
Fiedler Magisterbräu Dunkel (4.7%)
Fiedler Export (4.9%)
SEASONAL BEERS:
Fiedler Festbier (5.5%),
Fiedler Abrahams-Bock Hell (6.1%),
Fiedler Bockbier Dunkel (6.1%)

The Fiedler family retained ownership of this small brewery throughout the DDR period. Production has doubled in the last ten years but they're still without a tap. Bus No. 415 runs between Annaberg-Buchholz and Aue via Oberscheibe.
DB Schwarzenberg (Erzgebirge) 10km, Annaberg-Buchholz Unterer Bf 11km

OLBERNHAU   937

Olbernhau
Privatbrauerei Olbernhau
Blumenauer Straße 25, 09526 Olbernhau
T 037360 76 70   F 037360 767 18
E stadtbrauerei-olbernhau@t-online.de
Owner: Gunther Tippmann   Founded: 1896
Output: 10,000hl
REGULAR BEERS:
Olbernhauer Böhmisch (2.8%)
Erzgebirgs-Premium Pils (4.9%)
Olbernhauer Export (5.2%)

Erzgebirgisches Weihnachtsfestbier (5.6%),
Bock Bier Dunkel (6%),
Stülpner-Bräu Starkbier (6.5%)

Small brewery, sometimes still known as Stadtbrauerei Olbernhau. The railway to Olbernhau
has recently re-opened which makes life easier
if you'd like to look for the beers in the town.
They are sold in the Altes Brauhaus in Steinbach,
25km south-west of Olbernhau. This is sometimes quoted as brewing but we're not sure it
ever has, despite the small coppers.
DB Olbernhau 800m

OSTRITZ — 938

Ostritz

Brauhaus Ostritz
Brauhausstraße 3, 02899 Ostritz
T 035823 791 71   **F** 035823 777 61
www.brauhaus-ostritz.de
Owners: A. & B. Junge, F. Liebchen
Founded: 2001
Output: 60hl
Availability: 1 pub
REGULAR BEERS:
Ostritzer Pilsner (4.8%)
Ostritzer Dunkel (4.8%)
SEASONAL BEER:
Ostritzer Bock (6.8%)

Pub in the centre of Ostritz, with a bowling alley
and a very small brewery. The town's railway
station is now in Poland but all trains between
Görlitz and Zittau stop there. The border crossing
is a footbridge which is only open Nov–Mar
08.00–18.00 and until 20.00 at other times.
You will need your passport.

🍺 **Ostritz**
Brauhausstraße 3, 02899 Ostritz
Mon–Fri 11.00–24.00, Sat & Sun 10.00–24.00
DB Krzewina Zgorzelecka 700m

PENIG — 939

Peniger

Peniger Spezialitätenbrauerei
Lutherplatz 2, 09322 Penig
T 037381 803 70   **F** 037381 803 58

Owner: Maximilian Hösl   Founded: 1706
Output: 12,000hl
REGULAR BEERS:
Peniger Pilsner Premium (4.8%)
Peniger Goldsiegel Spezial (5.2%)
SEASONAL BEERS:
Peniger Weihnachtstraum Spezial (5.2%),
Peniger Edel-Bock (6.5%)

This small brewery has the same owner as
Luckenwalder Spezialitätenbrauerei and
Gardelegen Spezialitätenbrauerei. The former
has similarly named beers to Peniger and we
wouldn't be entirely surprised if all were
brewed here. There's no tap that we're aware of.
DB Penig 800m

PLAUEN — 940

Sternquell

Sternquell-Brauerei GmbH
Dobenaustraße 83, 08523 Plauen
T 03741 21 10   **F** 03741 21 12 16
www.sternquell.de
Owner: Brau Holding International, München
Founded: 1857
Output: 480,000hl
Availability: c.2,000 pubs
REGULAR BEERS:
Stern Gold (4.3%)
Sternquell Diät Pils (4.9%)
Sternquell Pils (4.9%)
Sternquell Dunkel (5.3%)
Sternquell Premium Pils (5.4%)
SEASONAL BEERS:
Sternquell Sommerbier (3.6%, summer),
Sternquell Weihnachtsbier (5.8%, Christmas),
Sternquell Bockbier (6.5%, Nov–Mar)

Large regional brewery acquired by Kulmbach
in 1990 and now under the control of Brau
Holding International. The tap is on the edge of
the Stadtpark, west of Oberer Bahnhof. If you
find yourself at Unterer Bahnhof you're probably
best taking tram No. 2 to the upper station and
walking from there, or getting a taxi.

🍺 **Tennera**
Tennera 20, 08525 Plauen
T 03741 22 67 85   **F** 03741 14 70 10
Daily 11.00–22.00
DB Plauen Oberer Bf 1km, Unterer Bf 2.7km

RADEBERG   941

Radeberger

Radeberger Exportbierbrauerei GmbH
Dresdner Straße 2, 01454 Radeburg
T 03528 45 40   **F** 03528 45 43 21
www.radeberger.de
Owner: Oetker Gruppe AG   Founded: 1872
Output: 2,000,000hl
REGULAR BEERS:
Radeberger Pilsner (4.8%)
FOR KAISERHOF, RADEBERG:
Radeberger Zwickel (4.8%)

Sachsen's largest brewery, their Pilsner is
available throughout the country. An unfiltered
version is available only at the tap.

🍺 **Kaiserhof**
Hauptstraße 62, 01454 Radeberg
T 03528 409 70   **F** 03528 40 97 50
Daily from 11.00; rooms available
DB Radeberg 600m

RECHENBERG
(Rechenberg-Bienenmühle)   942

Rechenberger

Privatbrauerei Traditionsbrauerei Meyer OHG
An der Schanze 3, 09623 Rechenberg-
Bienenmühle/Rechenberg
T 037327 12 08   **F** 037327 16 62
www.rechenberger.com
Owners: Andreas & Thomas Meyer
Founded: 1558   Output: 15,000hl
Availability: c.300 pubs
REGULAR BEERS:
Rechenberger Lager (5%)
Rechenberger Pilsener (5%)
Rechenberger Dunkel (5%)
SEASONAL BEERS:
Rechenberger Festbier (5%),
Rechenberger Bockbier (6.5%)

Modern brewery in the small village of Rechenberg. The current buildings, completed in 1995,
stand alongside the old brewery which re-opened
in 2002 as a museum. Tours start Tue–Fri 11.00
& 14.00 and Sat/Sun 11.00, 13.00 & 15.00.

🍺 **Schalander im Brauereimuseum**
An der Schanze 3, 09623 Rechenberg-
Bienenmühle/Rechenberg

T 037327 880 15
Closed Mon; Tue–Sun from 11.00
DB Rechenberg 700m

RIESA   943

Hammer-Bräu

Hammer-Bräu – Brauhaus im Riesenhügel
Bahnhofstraße 42, 01587 Riesa
T 03525 53 09 30   **F** 03525 53 09 39
www.hammerbraeu.de
Owner: Magnet Riesa GmbH   Founded: 1999
Output: 1,000hl   Availability: 1 pub
REGULAR BEERS:
Hammer-Bräu Pils
Hammer-Bräu Marzen

Modern brewpub in the grounds of the Mercure
hotel. It's housed in a bizarre artificial hill that's
also home to a North American restaurant. We
believe they brew numerous seasonal beers
but don't have any details.

🍺 **Hammer-Bräu**
Bahnhofstraße 42, 01587 Riesa
Closed Wed; Mon & Sun 11.00–01.00, Tue & Thu
17.00–01.00, Fri 17.00–02.00, Sat 11.00–02.00
DB Riesa 600m

SCHWARZKOLLM
(Hoyerswerda)   944

Braustube Schwarzkollm

Dorfstraße 72, 02977 Hoyerswerda-
Schwarzkollm
T 035722 915 52
Owner: Ralf Müller   Founded: 1999
REGULAR BEERS:
Schwarzkollm Hell
Schwarzkollm Dunkel

Pub on the main road through the village. We're
not entirely certain if the brewery is here or
elsewhere in the vicinity. Be warned that the
telephone number no longer works and we can't
find another, so they may no longer be open.

🍺 **Braustube Schwarzkollm**
Dorfstraße 72, 02977 Hoyerswerda-
Schwarzkollm
Closed Tue & Wed; Thu–Mon from 17.00
DB Schwarzkollm 1km

TORGAU   945

Torgauer

Neues Torgauer Brauhaus GmbH
Naundorfer Straße 7, 04860 Torgau
Founded: 1865
REGULAR BEERS:
Torgauer Hell (4.7%)
Torgauer Premium Pilsner (4.9%)
Torgauer Landbier (5.5%)
SEASONAL BEERS:
Torgauer Weihnachtsbier (5.7%), **Torgauer
Maibock** (6.5%), **Torgauer Landbock** (6.5%)

Large brewery next to the railway.
They asked not to be included.
DB Torgau 350m

TREUEN   946

Blechschmidt

Privatbrauerei Karl Blechschmidt
Straße der Jugend 33, 08233 Treuen
T/F 037468 28 67
Owner: Arndt Blechschmidt   Founded: 1483
Output: 2,000hl
REGULAR BEERS:
Treuener Schwarzbier
Treuener Pilsner
Treuener Spezial
SEASONAL BEER:
Treuener Bock

One of the smallest breweries to survive the
DDR era, Blechschmidt remained in private
hands throughout. We don't think they have a
tap but there is a drinks market at the brewery.
DB Treuen 1.4km

WACHAU   947

Schiller

Hausbrauerei Schiller
Teichstraße 43b, 01454 Wachau
T 03528 44 21 08   www.bierscheune.com
Owner: Hagen Schiller   Founded: 2005
REGULAR BEERS:
Wachauer Landbier Hell (4.9%)
Wachauer Landbier Dunkel (4.9%)
Wachauer Festbier Schwarz (5.7%)

Microbrewery which started operations in
March 2005. They currently supply one local pub
regularly and the brewery is open for direct sales
on Friday afternoons and Saturday mornings.
Bus No. 317 runs from Radeberg on weekdays.

🍺 **Ebgericht**
Hauptstraße 55, 01454 Wachau
T 03528 448 20   **F** 03528 44 82 11
Mon–Thu 11.00–23.00, Fri & Sat 11.00–24.00,
Sun 11.00–22.00; rooms available
DB Radeberg 6km

WEESENSTEIN (Müglitztal) 948

Weesensteiner Schlossbräu

Am Schloßberg 1, 01809 Müglitztal-Weesenstein
T 035027 420 04   **F** 035027 420 05
www.schlossbrauerei-weesenstein.de
Owner: Ulrich Betsch   Founded: 08.08.1999
Output: 500hl
REGULAR BEER:
Weesensteiner Original
SEASONAL BEERS:
Weesensteiner Pils,
Weesensteiner Weizen,
Weesensteiner Bock

In 1999 brewing resumed in Weesenstein
castle after a brief pause of 135 years. All the
necessary brewing ingredients are brought in
by Gambrinus the 2nd and Walhalla the 3rd –
the brewery's two donkeys. Tragically, the
previous pair were killed in the floods of 2002.

🍺 **Weesensteiner Schlossbräu**
Am Schloßberg 1, 01809 Müglitztal-Weesenstein
Closed Mon; Tue–Fri 18.00–24.00 (from 12.00
May–Oct), Sat & Sun 11.00–24.00
DB Weesenstein 700m

WERNESGRÜN (Steinberg)   949

Wernesgrüner

Wernesgrüner Brauerei GmbH
Bergstraße 4, 08237 Steinberg-Wernesgrün
T 037462 610   **F** 037462 297 99
www.wernesgruener.de
Owner: Bitburger Getränkegruppe
Founded: 1436   Output: 565,000hl
Availability: c.10,000 pubs

REGULAR BEERS:
Wernesgrüner Pils Legende (4.9%)

Sachsen's oldest brewery, Wernesgrüner nowadays produce just Pils. Bus No. T64 from Rodewisch bus station stops outside but doesn't run at the weekend.

Brauschenke
Bergstraße 2, 08237 Steinberg-Wernesgrün
T 037462 613 11   **F** 037462 613 10
Daily from 11.00   DB Rodewisch 7km

WITTICHENAU 950

Stadtbrauerei

Stadtbrauerei Wittichenau E. Glaab GmbH
Haschkestraße 33, 02997 Wittichenau
T 035725 75 10   **F** 035725 751 51
www.wittichenauer.de
Owners: L. Willert, G. Glaab & E. Glaab
Founded: 1885   Output: 20,000hl
Availability: 180 pubs
REGULAR BEERS:
Wittichenauer Gold (4.4%)
Wittichenauer Premium Pils (5%)
Lausitzer Premium Pils (5%)
SEASONAL BEER:
Wittichenauer Bock (6%)
FOR KLOSTERBRAUEREI ST. MARIENSTERN:
St. Marienstern Klosterbräu Dunkel (5%),
St. Marienstern Klosterbräu Spezial (5%)

Small brewery in the centre of the village, with the tap a few hundred metres away on the road towards Hoske. Several bus routes run from Hoyerswerda but the weekend service is poor.

Zur Kegelbahn
Hosker Straße 25, 02997 Wittichenau
T 035725 714 81
Mon–Sat 11.00–14.00 & 17.30–24.00,
Sun 10.30–24.00   DB Hoyerswerda 6km

ZITTAU 951

Zittauer Bürgerbräu

Zittauer Bürgerbräu GmbH & Co. Productions KG
Innere Weberstraße 6, 02763 Zittau
T 03583 70 69 35   **F** 03583 70 69 36
www.zittauer-buergerbraeu.de
Owners: Ulrich Helmdach & Sebastian Stampfl

Founded: 1993
REGULAR BEERS:
Zittauer Bürgerbräu (4.9%)
Zittauer Schwarzbier (5.1%)
SEASONAL BEER:
Royal Gründerbier

Microbrewery in the centre of Zittau. The tap in the town's Wienaupark closed at the end of 2005 and we don't know of any other regular outlets for the beers.
DB Zittau 850m

ZWICKAU 952

Brauhaus Zwickau

Gaststätte Brauhaus Zwickau GmbH
Peter-Breuer-Straße 14, 08056 Zwickau-Innenstadt
T 0375 303 20 32   **F** 0375 303 20 33
www.brauhaus-zwickau.de
Owner: Andre Stockmann   Founded: 2001
Output: 1,400hl   Availability: 2 pubs
REGULAR BEERS:
Priesterhell (5.5%)
Priesterdunkel (5.5%)
Priesterhefe (5.5%)
SEASONAL BEERS:
Priesterrauch (6%), **Priesterbock** (6%)

City-centre brewpub in the shadow of the cathedral, housed in what is reputedly one of Sachsen's oldest buildings. Seasonal beers are brewed in addition to the regular three.

Brauhaus Zwickau
Peter-Breuer-Straße 14, 08056 Zwickau-Innenstadt
Daily 10.00–02.00; rooms available
Tram Georgenplatz 450m
DB Zwickau (Sachsen) Hbf 1.4km

Mauritius

Mauritius Brauerei Zwickau GmbH
Talstraße 2, 08066 Zwickau-Eckersbach
T 0375 494 90   **F** 0375 494 93 33
www.mauritius-brauerei.de
Founded: 1859
Output: 380,000hl   Availability: c. 230 pubs
REGULAR BEERS:
Mauritius Zwickauer Pilsener (4.9%)
Mauritius Zwickauer Schwarzes Gold (4.9%)

Mauritius Zwickauer Urtyp (5.5%)
Mauritius Zwickauer Bock Dunkel (7.1%)

Large brewery just over the river from the city centre. Briefly owned by InBev, they're now independent following a management buyout in November 2005. There's no tap but tram No.1 from the Hauptbahnhof stops outside if you'd like a closer look.

🚋 Nos. 1 & 3 Brauerei 20m
Ⓓ🅱 Zwickau (Sachsen) Hbf 2km

ZWÖNITZ   953

Zwönitz

Brauerei und Gasthof Zwönitz
Grünhainer Straße 15, 08297 Zwönitz
T 037754 599 05   **F** 037754 599 06

www.brauerei-zwoenitz.de
Owner: Frieder Naumann   Founded: 1997
Output: 800hl
REGULAR BEERS:
Zwönitzer Dunkel
Zwönitzer Nachtwächter Schwarzbier
Zwönitzer Pilsner
SEASONAL BEER:
Zwönitzer Ziegenbock (winter)

Brewpub on the opposite side of the town to the station. They have a fairly substantial bottling plant and we suspect the beers are sold else-where. A *Nachtwächter* is a night watchman, and a *Ziegenbock* a billy goat.

🍺 Zwönitz
Grünhainer Straße 15, 08297 Zwönitz
Daily 11.00–14.00 & 17.00–21.00; rooms
available   Ⓓ🅱 Zwönitz 1.5km

The railway station at Mittenwald is dwarfed by the 2,385 metre high Karwendel mountain.

Sachsen-Anhalt
(Saxony-Anhalt)

CREATED IN 1990 following re-unification, Sachsen-Anhalt lies between the two other Saxon states. It is a largely agricultural region, albeit with some pockets of heavy industry. The administrative centre is Magdeburg, one of two state capitals not to feature a brewery (the other is Wiesbaden).

Although not that high on many tourists' agendas, there are many worthwhile attractions here. The south-west contains part of the lovely Harz Mountains, together with the superbly preserved medieval towns of Quedlinburg and Wernigerode. Further east are the two Lutheran towns, Eisleben and Wittenberg.

Like several other parts of east Germany, the brewing scene suffered badly following re-unification, with just four breweries surviving from the communist era. The majority of the entries on these pages are brewpubs that have sprung up in the intervening years, largely in the more touristy towns and cities.

Transport: If you're using public transport you should have little difficulty reaching the majority of pubs and breweries in Sachsen-Anhalt. The state's day rail-rover can also be used in Sachsen and Thüringen but is subject to the usual time restrictions. Up to five people can travel for €24 a day but, as usual, you are advised to ascertain exactly which services it's valid on.

COLBITZ 954

Colbitzer Heidebrauerei

Brauereistraße 1, 39326 Colbitz
T 039207 880   F 039207 881 50
www.colbitzer-heidebrauerei.de
Owner: Christian August   Founded: 1872
Output: 35,000hl
REGULAR BEERS:
Colbitzer Heide-Pils (4.8%)
Colbitzer Ritter-Premium (4.8%)
Colbitzer Heide-Schwarzbier (4.8%)
Colbitzer Heide-Bock (6.8%)

Named after the heath which covers several hundred square miles north of Colbitz, this small brewery stands just off the main road through the village, the B189. Bus No. 606 runs from Wolmirstedt station on weekdays and there's a scheduled taxi service at other times with limited seating.

Zum Heidequell
Brauereistraße 1, 39326 Colbitz
T 039207 807 09
Closed Mon; Tue–Sun 11.00–14.30 & from 17.30
DB Wolmirstedt 8km

DESSAU 955

Zum Alten Dessauer

Lange Gasse 16, 06844 Dessau-Innenstadt
T 0340 220 59 09   F 0340 850 72 38
www.alter-dessauer.de
Founded: 11.11.2001
REGULAR BEERS:
Alter Dessauer Zwickelbier (4.9%)
Alter Dessauer Original (4.9%)
Alter Dessauer Edles Pils (4.9%)

*: Lüdde, Quedlinburg. Revived brewery
e Unesco World Heritage town.*

Brewpub in what we believe is part of the former Schade brewery, closed as long ago as 1952. They brew several seasonal beers during the course of the year.

🍺 Zum Alten Dessauer
Lange Gasse 16, 06844 Dessau-Innenstadt
Daily 11.00–24.00
🚋 Hauptpost 370m   DB Dessau Hbf 1km

FREYBURG   956

Burgmühle
Brauhaus Burgmühle Freyburg GmbH
Mühlstraße 10, 06632 Freyburg
T 034464 610 88   **F** 034664 610 90
www.brauhaus-burgmuehle.de
Founded: 1998
REGULAR BEERS:
Burgenländisch Hell
Burgenländisch Dunkel
SEASONAL BEERS:
Burgenländisch Festbier,
Burgenländisch Maibock,
Burgenländisch Bockbier

Brewpub in a former mill on the Unstrut river, beneath Neuenburg castle. Neither the phone nor fax numbers currently work, and although we believe they were still open in summer 2005 that may no longer be the case. Don't say you weren't warned...

🍺 Zur Schwemme
Mühlstraße 10, 06632 Freyburg
Winter: closed Tue; Mon & Wed–Sat 11.00–24.00; Sun 11.00–18.00
Summer: Mon–Sat 11.00–24.00; Sun 11.00–18.00
DB Freyburg (Unstrut) 500m

GARDELEGEN   957

Garley
Garley Spezialitäten-Brauerei GmbH
Sandstraße 58–60, 39638 Gardelegen
T 03907 722 00   **F** 03907 72 20 40
www.garley.de
Owner: Maximilian Hösl   Founded: 1314
Output: 50,000hl
REGULAR BEERS:
Bismarck Pilsner Premium (4.8%)

Garley Diät-Pilsner (4.9%)
Garley Pilsner Premium (4.9%)
Garley Jubiläums Pilsner (4.9%)
Garley Premium Spezial-Export (5.1%)
Garley Schwarzer Reiter (5.2%)
SEASONAL BEERS:
Altmärker Narrenbräu (5.2%),
Altmärker Weihnacht Festbier (5.2%),
Bock Premium (6.5%)
FOR BERGSCHLOSS, SALZWEDEL:
Soltmann Pilsner Premium (5.1%),
Soltmann Doppel-Bock (8.5%)
FOR ZITTAUER BRAUEREI, ZITTAU:
Elch Pils (4.9%)

Eastern Germany's oldest brewery, Garley is one of three owned by Maximilian Hösl, all of which are known as *Spezialitäten-Brauerei* (speciality brewery). The tap is a couple of streets away.

🍺 Bräustübl
Rudolf-Breitscheid-Straße 14, 39638 Gardelegen
T 03907 20 44
Closed Tue; Wed–Mon 16.00–24.00
DB Gardelegen 1.4km

HALBERSTADT   958

Heine Bräu
Große Ringstraße 10, 38820 Halberstadt
T 03941 314 00   **F** 03941 315 00
www.hotel-heine.de
Founded: 14.07.1999
REGULAR BEERS:
Heine Bräu Edelpils (4.9%)
Heine Bräu Schwarzer Friedrich (5%)
SEASONAL BEERS:
Heine Bräu Hell (4.9%),
Heine Bräu Urtyp (4.9%),
Heine Bräu Hefeweizen,
Heine Bräu Maibock,
Heine Bräu Oktoberbock

Upmarket brewpub at the rear of the 4-star Hotel Villa Heine, a short walk from Halberstadt station. We think they brewed for Brauhaus Goslar for a short time.

🍺 Heine Bräu
Große Ringstraße 10, 38820 Halberstadt
Daily from 12.00; rooms available
DB Halberstadt 300m

HALLE 959

Hallesches Brauhaus

Hallesche Spezialitätenbrauerei Kühler Brunnen
Große Nikolaistraße 2, 06108 Halle-Mitte
T 0345 21 25 70   F 0945 212 57 11
www.hallesches-brauhaus.de
Founded: 2005   Output: 1,200hl
Availability: 1 pub
REGULAR BEERS:
Hallsch (4.8%)
Albrecht Dunkel (5.4%)
Schönitz Pilsener (5.4%)
SEASONAL BEER:
Weihnachtsbock (6.9%)

This city-centre brewpub is just north of the
Marktplatz. They've so far brewed just one
seasonal beer but we anticipate others.

🏠 **Hallesches Brauhaus**
Große Nikolaistraße 2, 06108 Halle-Mitte
Daily from 11.00
🚋 Marktplatz 200m   DB Halle (Saale) Hbf 1.6km

Zum Schad

Gasthausbrauerei zum Schad GmbH
Reilstraße 10, 06114 Halle-Nord
T 0345 523 03 66   F 0345 523 20 79
www.zum-schad.de
Founded: 1992
Output: 1,000hl   Availability: 1 pub
REGULAR BEERS:
Schad Dunkel (4.8%)
Schad Pils (4.9%)
Schad Weizen (5.1%)
SEASONAL BEERS:
Schad Sommerzwickel (3.2%),
Schad Rauchbier (5.6%),
Schad Märzen (6.1%),
Schad Festbier (6.1%),
Schad Bock (6.4%),
Schad Nikolator (7.3%)

Halle's first modern brewpub is in the north of
the city, close to the tram stops at Reileck. We
think there may be other seasonal beers.

🏠 **Zum Schad**
Reilstraße 10, 06114 Halle-Nord
Daily 08.00–24.00
🚋 Reileck 100m   DB Halle (Saale) Hbf 2.8km

HELFTA
(Lutherstadt Eisleben) 960

Kloster Helfta

Brauhaus An der Klosterpforte
Lindenstraße 34, 06295 Lutherstadt Eisleben-
Helfta
T 03475 714 40   F 03475 714 41 00
www.klosterpforte.com
Founded: 2002
REGULAR BEERS:
Kloster Helfta Bräu Hell
Kloster Helfta Bräu Dunkel

Brewpub in the grounds of Helfta convent, once
again home to nuns after an absence of more
than 450 years. The address is a little misleading as the main entrance is off Hallesche Straße.
Several bus routes run from Lutherstadt
Eisleben station.

🏠 **Kloster Helfta**
Lindenstraße 34, 06295 Lutherstadt Eisleben-
Helfta
Daily 07.00–23.00; roms available
DB Lutherstadt Eisleben 2.4km

KÖTHEN 961

Köthener Brauhaus

Brauhaus Köthen GmbH
Holzmarkt 6, 06366 Köthen
T 03496 309 94 90   F 03496 309 94 91
www.koethener-brauhaus.de
Founded: 27.06.2003
REGULAR BEERS:
Köthener Zwickelbier
Köthener Premium Pils

Small brewery in the 400-year-old Altdeutscher
Hof, in the centre of Köthen. The half-timbered
pub is on the Holzmarkt but the brewery's official
address is around the corner, at Lachsfang 1–3.
Not to be confused with the Köthener Brauerei
whose beers we suspect are brewed by
Pfungstädter.

🏠 **Altdeutscher Hof**
Holzmarkt 6, 06366 Köthen
Daily 11.00–24.00; rooms available
DB Köthen 1km

LANDSBERG 962

Landsberger

Brauerei Landsberg GmbH
Bahnhofstraße 33, 06188 Landsberg
T 034602 403 33   **F** 034602 40 33 20
www.landsberger.de
Owners: Christoph & Heidemarie Thormann
Founded: 1997
REGULAR BEERS:
Landsberger Premium Pils (4.9%)
Landsberger Low-Carb (5%)
Landsberger Schwarzes (5%)
Landsberger Export-Bier (5.3%)
SEASONAL BEERS:
Hallisches (4.5%), **Delitzscher Peter und Paul Festbier** (5.6%), **Landsberger Goitzsche-Bräu** (5.6%), **Saline-Bräu** (5.6%), **Zeitzer Grottenbräu** (5.6%), **Aschersleber Festbier** (5.6%), **Landsberger Mai-Bock** (7.2%), **Landsberger Heller Ur-Bock** (7.2%), **Landsberger Bock-Bier** (7.2%)

Microbrewery in a purpose-built building between the station and the town centre. They supply numerous pubs and drinks markets in the region.

🍺 **Ratskeller**
Markt 1, 06188 Landsberg
T 034602 204 32
Closed Mon; Tue–Sun from 11.00
DB Landsberg (bei Halle/Saale) 1km

LUTHERSTADT EISLEBEN 963

Reformator

Brauhaus zum Reformator
Friedensstraße 12, 06295 Lutherstadt Eisleben
T 03475 68 05 11   **F** 03475 68 02 54
www.brauhaus-reformator.de
Founded: 1995
Output: 1,000hl   Availability: 2 pubs
REGULAR BEERS:
Reformator Herren-Pils (4.9%)
Reformator Alt Eisleber Dunkel (5.9%)
SEASONAL BEERS:
Reformator Hell (4.9%), **Reformator St. Martin Festbier** (5.2%), **Reformator Kupfer Märzen** (5.8%), **Reformator Bock** (6.5%)

Brewpub south of the town centre, close to the railway. We have a sneaking suspicion they

may no longer brew but are quite prepared to be proved wrong. Lutherstadt was added to the town's name in recognition of Martin Luther, who was born and died here.

🍺 **Reformator**
Friedensstraße 12, 06295 Lutherstadt Eisleben
Mon–Thu 12.00–24.00, Fri & Sat 12.00–01.00, Sun 12.00–23.00
DB Lutherstadt Eisleben 650m

LUTHERSTADT WITTENBERG 964

Brauhaus Wittenberg

Markt 6, 06886 Lutherstadt Wittenberg
T 03491 43 31 30   **F** 03491 43 31 31
www.brauhaus-wittenberg.de
Founded: 1999
REGULAR BEERS:
Wittenberger Pilsener
Wittenberger Kuckucksbier
SEASONAL BEERS:
Wittenberger Lager,
Wittenberger Weizen,
Wittenberger Bock

On the market square, opposite the Rathaus, this brewpub is in one of Lutherstadt Wittenberg's oldest buildings. They also hold beer seminars and smoke their own fish. It was in this town that Martin Luther started the Reformation in 1517.

🍺 **Brauhaus Wittenberg**
Markt 6, 06886 Lutherstadt Wittenberg
Daily 11.00–23.00; rooms available
DB Lutherstadt Wittenberg-Elbtor 300m, Lutherstadt Wittenberg 1.4km

NEUENDORF (Altmark) 965

Demmert-Bräu

Hauptstraße 10, 38486 Neuendorf
T 03909 423 24   **F** 03909 45 32
www.demmert-brauerei.de
Owner: Wolfgang Demmert   Founded: 1997
Output: 2,500hl
REGULAR BEERS:
Demmert Altmärkisches Landbier
Demmert Ökoland Hell
Demmert Ökoland Dunkel

Demmert Pils
Demmert Export
SEASONAL BEER:
Demmert Doppelbock

Originally a dairy, this brewery in the village of Neuendorf was owned by Wolfgang Demmert's father until it closed in 1953 when he was expelled to the west. Public transport options are severely limited by the pub's opening hours but may improve if the railway line to Klötze re-opens. The Ökoland beers are brewed from organic ingredients.

🍺 **Demmert**
Hauptstraße 10, 38486 Neuendorf
T 03909 45 33
Closed Mon & Tue; Wed–Fri 17.00–23.00,
Sat & Sun 11.00–23.00; rooms available
DB Salzwedel 25km, Gardelegen 27km

QUEDLINBURG 966

Lüdde

Blasiistraße 14, 06484 Quedlinburg
T 03946 70 52 06   **F** 03946 32 51
www.hotel-brauhaus-luedde.de
Owner: Christin Clair   Founded: 1992
Output: 1,000hl   Availability: 1 pub
REGULAR BEERS:
Lüdde Bräu Pilsener (4.9%)
Lüdde Bräu Knuttenforz Schwarzbier (4.9%)
SEASONAL BEERS:
Lüdde Bräu Weizen, Lüdde Bräu Bock

The original Lüdde brewery closed in 1966, this revival being in the style of a modern brewpub, albeit in far more historic surroundings than most. In addition to the above beers they also brew Pubarschknall, a Braunbier with an alcohol content of just 0.8% whose name charmingly translates as 'fart-arse-bang'.

🍺 **Lüdde**
Blasiistraße 14, 06484 Quedlinburg
T 03946 70 52 06   **F** 03946 32 51
Mon–Sat 11.00–24.00, Sun 11.00–22.00; rooms available
DB Quedlinburg 1.1km

SCHOLLENE 967

Mühlenbergbrauerei

August-Bebel-Straße 13, 14715 Schollene
T 039389 963 49   **F** 039389 961 60
www.gasthofbrauerei.de
Founded: 2002
REGULAR BEERS:
Schollener Schwarzbier
Schollener Pils
SEASONAL BEER:
Schollener Maibock, Schollener Schollator

Small brewpub on the main road through the village, a few hundred metres from the river Havel which in this area marks the border with Brandenburg. Although you can get to Schollene by bus on weekdays, you can't get back after the pub opens.

🍺 **Mühlenbergbrauerei**
August-Bebel-Straße 13, 14715 Schollene
Closed Wed; Mon, Tue & Thu–Sat from 15.00,
Sun & hols from 10.00
DB Rathenow 16km

WERNIGERODE 968

Hasseröder

Hasseröder Brauerei GmbH
Auerhahnring 1, 38855 Wernigerode
T 03943 93 60   **F** 03943 63 21 40
www.hasseroeder.de
Owner: InBev   Founded: 1848
Output: 2,350,000hl
REGULAR BEERS:
Hasseröder Premium Pils (4.8%)
Hasseröder Premium Export (5.5%)

Currently eastern Germany's largest brewery, Hasseröder moved to their present site on the western outskirts of town in 1997. The original brewery was in the suburb of Hasserode. We don't think they have a tap but finding the beers won't prove difficult.
DB Wernigerode-Elmowerk 2km,
    Wernigerode 3.8km

WIPPRA 969

Museumsbrauerei

Museums- und Traditionsbrauerei Wippra/Harz
Fleckstraße 4, 06543 Wippra
T 034775 202 05   **F** 034775 210 29
www.wippraer-bier.de   Founded: 1480
Owners: Dirk & Dr. Norbert Gehring
Output: 1,500hl   Availability: 20 pubs

REGULAR BEERS:
Original Wippraer Schwarzbier
Original Wippraer Pils

SEASONAL BEER:
Original Wippraer Festbier

Half-timbered brewery that has remained
virtually unchanged for over a century.
They seemingly have problems with others
marketing fake Wippraer beer. The tap is
just around the corner.

Deutsches Haus
Bahnhofstraße 45, 06543 Wippra
T 034775 20284
Closed Mon; Tue–Sun 10.00–23.00
DB Wippra 600m

Schleswig-Holstein

GERMANY'S NORTHERN MOST STATE occupies the southern part of the Jutland peninsula. To the north is Denmark, which controlled much of the region for centuries – the majority of what constitutes modern Schleswig-Holstein did not become part of Germany until 1864. Danish remains an official language here, as do Friesian and Low German.

Overwhelmingly flat, the state relies heavily on the sea and land for income. The largest ports are Kiel and Lübeck, both on the Baltic coast. This sandy coastline is punctured by long bays and water inlets, the longest of which reaches the city of Schleswig. On the western side, the North Sea coastline and its mudflats form the Nationalpark Schleswig-Holsteinisches Wattenmeer, at 450 kilometres the largest mudflat landscape of the world. Off the coast, there are strings of islands, boasting an impressive landscape of sand dunes and exposed steep cliffs.

Just two of Schleswig-Holstein's ten breweries are more than 20 years old, with Flensburger beers being the most widely available. The newcomers are spread throughout the state and most appear to have settled in for the long haul.

Transport: Those looking to visit the region shouldn't have any problems reaching the breweries by public transport – all bar one are in towns on the DB network. The day ticket for the region costs €27 for up to five people and is also valid in Hamburg and Mecklenburg-Vorpommern. As usual it's valid until 03.00 the following day and can't be used until 09.00 on weekdays.

EUTIN   970

Brauhaus Eutin
Markt 11, 23701 Eutin
T 04521 76 67 77   F 04521 84 91 75
www.brauhaus-eutin.de
Owner: Marcus Gutzeit   Founded: 1989
REGULAR BEERS:
St. Michaelis Bräu Pils (4.8%)
St. Michaelis Bräu Rothbier (5%)
St. Michaelis Bräu Tafelbier (5.5%)
SEASONAL BEERS:
St. Michaelis Bräu Maibock (6.5%),
St. Michaelis Bräu Weihnachtsbock (6.5%)

Market square brewpub which returned Eutin to the brewing map after an absence of 75 years.

🍎 **Brauhaus Eutin**
Markt 11, 23701 Eutin
Winter: closed Tue; Wed–Mon 11.00–23.00.
Summer: daily 11.00–23.00   DB Eutin 500m

FLENSBURG   971

Flensburger
Flensburger Brauerei Emil Petersen GmbH & Co.
Munketoft 12, 24937 Flensburg-Sandberg
T 0461 86 30   F 0461 86 33 00
www.flensburger.de
Founded: 1888   Output: 550,000hl
REGULAR BEERS:
Flensburger Gold (4.8%)
Flensburger Dunkel (4.8%)
Flensburger Pilsener (4.8%)
Flensburger Weizen (5.1%)
SEASONAL BEER:
Flensburger Winterbock (7%)
FOR RÖTGER FELDMANN, BORDESHOLM:
Bölkstoff (4.8%)

Large regional brewery whose beers can be found throughout the state and beyond. Unusually for a brewery of their size, Flensburger will brew small quantities of beer to order. The Flensburger Pilsener is popularly known as Flens. Bölkstoff is the favourite beer of a popular cartoon character called Werner (German answer to Homer's Duff?).
DB Flensburg 700m

Hansens

Erste Flensberger Gasthausbrauerei GmbH
Schiffbrücke 16, 24939 Flensburg-Altstadt
T 0461 222 10   F 0461 242 44
www.hansens-brauerei.de
Owners: Franz-Dieter Weiß   Founded: 1990
Output: 1,500hl   Availability: 1 pub
REGULAR BEERS:
Hansens Pilsener (5.1%)
Hansens Schwarzbier (5.1%)
SEASONAL BEERS:
Hansens Alt, Hansens Märzen, Hansens Festbier, Hansens Bock

Germany's most northerly brewery. Hansens moved to their current location overlooking the harbour in 2000, having outgrown their previous home on the Nordermarkt.

🍺 **Hansens**
Schiffbrücke 16, 24939 Flensburg-Altstadt
Mon–Fri from 16.30; Sat & Sun from 11.30
DB Flensburg 2.1km

HUSUM   972

Husums Brauhaus

Neustadt 60–64, 25813 Husum
T 04841 896 60   F 04841 819 33
www.husums-brauhaus.de   Founded: 1991
REGULAR BEERS:
Husumer Pilsner (5.2%)
Husumer Dunkel (5.4%)
Husumer Weizen (5.6%)
SEASONAL BEERS:
Husumer Märzenbier (5.4%), **Husumer Festbier** (5.8%), **Husumer Maibock** (6.8%), **Husumer Winterbock** (7.8%)

This modern brewpub is in part of the 4-star Theodor Storm Hotel, north of Husum's inner harbour. We wouldn't be surprised if the beers were sold elsewhere.

🍺 **Husums Brauhaus**
Neustadt 60–64, 25813 Husum
Winter: closed Sun; Mon–Sat from 17.00.
Summer: daily from 15.00; rooms available
DB Husum 1km

KIEL   973

Kieler

Kieler-Brauerei am Alten Markt GmbH
Alter Markt 9, 24103 Kiel-Altstadt
T 0431 90 62 90   F 0431 906 29 15
www.kieler-brauerei.de
Owner: Manfred Werner   Founded: 1988
REGULAR BEER:
Kieler Bier (4.8%)
SEASONAL BEERS:
Kieler Schwarzbier (4.8%), **Kieler Grafenbräu** (4.9%), **Kieler Bock** (6.6%), **Kieler Herbstbock** (7%)

Brewpub in the centre of the old city, close to the embarkation points for the Baltic ferries. To avoid the walk from the station, catch a bus to Eggerstedtstraße.

🍺 **Kieler**
Alter Markt 9, 24103 Kiel-Altstadt
Mon–Sat from 10.00, Sun from 12.00
DB Kiel Hbf 1.1km

LÜBECK   974

Brauberger

Traditionsbrauerei Brauberger zu Lübeck
Alfstraße 36, 23552 Lübeck-Innenstadt
T 0451 714 44   F 0451 741 16
www.brauberger.com
Owner: Thomas Rosenhahn   Founded: 1988
Output: 1,000hl   Availability: 1 pub
REGULAR BEER:
Brauberger Zwickelbier (4.8%)

On the western side of Lübeck's old city, close to the river Trave, Brauberger's cellar dates from 1225. Unusually for a new-wave brewpub, the beer is gravity dispensed from wooden barrels.

🍺 **Brauberger**
Alfstraße 36, 23552 Lübeck-Innenstadt
Closed Sun; Mon–Fri 17.00–24.00, Sat 18.00–01.00
DB Lübeck Hbf 900m

Right: *Klüver's Brauhaus, Neustadt in Holstein. Perhaps unsurprisingly, fish features on the menu*

MARNE 975

Dithmarscher

Dithmarscher Brauerei K. Hintz GmbH & Co. KG
Oesterstraße 18, 25709 Marne
T 04851 96 20   **F** 04851 962 22
www.dithmarscher.de
Owners: Karl-Friedrich & Wolf-Dieter Hintz
Founded: 1899   Output: 140,000hl
REGULAR BEERS:
Dithmarscher Pils (4.8%)
Dithmarscher Dunkel (4.9%)
Dithmarscher Urtyp (4.9%)

Large brewery named after the surrounding
marsh. No tap. In summer you can get to Marne
along the closed railway from St. Michaelisdonn
on sail or pedal-powered trolleys. For the less
adventurous, bus No. 10a runs Mon–Sat.
DB St. Michaelisdonn 8km

NEUSTADT in Holstein 976

Klüver's Brauhaus

Schiffbrücke 2–4, 23730 Neustadt in Holstein
T 04561 71 48 11   **F** 04561 71 49 22
www.kluevers-brauhaus.de
Owner: Olaf Klüver   Founded: 23.04.2004
REGULAR BEERS:
Klüver's Dunkel
Klüver's Pils
Klüver's Hefeweizen
SEASONAL BEER:
Klüver's Doppelbock

Quayside brewpub on the town-side of Neustadt's
harbour. Olaf Klüver also has a fish smokery in
Niendorf, its products featuring on the pub menu.

🍺 **Klüver's Brauhaus**
Schiffbrücke 2–4, 23730 Neustadt in Holstein
Daily 10.00–24.00
DB Neustadt (Holstein) 600m

RICKLING 977

Ricklinger Landbrauerei

Ricklinger Landbrauerei 'Zur Alten Forsterei'
Grüner Weg 1, 24635 Rickling
T 04328 13 14   **F** 04328 17 01 72

www.ricklinger-landbrauerei.de
Owners: Kerstin Lämmer   Founded: 1997
REGULAR BEERS:
Ricklinger Pils (4.8%)
Ricklinger Dunkel (5%)
Ricklinger Stout (5%)
Ricklinger Märzen (5.5%)
SEASONAL BEERS:
Ricklinger Rauchbier (5%), **Ricklinger Maibock**
(6.5%), **Ricklinger Weihnachtsbock** (7%),
Ricklinger Porter (10%)

Microbrewery and pub at the northern end of
the village. The railway to Rickling has recently
re-opened which makes getting here a lot
easier, though it's a fair walk from the station.

🍺 **Zur Alten Försterei**
Grüner Weg 1, 24635 Rickling
Closed Wed; Mon, Tue, Thu & Fri 16.00–22.00
(11.00–24.00 in summer), Sat, Sun & hols
10.00–24.00
DB Rickling 2.2km

SCHLESWIG 978

Asgaard

Asgaard Brauerei Schleswig
Königstraße 27, 24837 Schleswig-Altstadt
T 04621 292 06   **F** 04621 216 55
www.asgaard.de
Owner: Ronald T. Carius   Founded: 1994
Output: 3,500hl   Availability: 10 pubs
REGULAR BEERS:
Asgaard Das Göttliche (4.8%)
Asgaard Bio Premium Pils (4.8%)
Asgaard Nordisches Weizen (5%)
SEASONAL BEERS:
Asgaard Maibock (6.8%), **Asgaard Nikolator**
(6.8%)
FOR RITTERLADEN, HAMMERSBACH:
Wikingerbräu Honigbier (5.8%)

Viking-themed microbrewery which uses
coppers dating from 1889. Several bus routes
run from the station to the town centre.

🍺 **Brauerei Scheswig**
Königstraße 27, 24837 Schleswig-Altstadt
Oct–Apr: closed Sun & Mon; Tue–Fri 17.00–
24.00, Sat 11.00–02.00
May–Sep: Sun–Fri 17.00–24.00, Sat 11.00–02.00
DB Schleswig 2.6km

Thüringen
(Thuringia)

WITH THE EXCEPTION OF BERLIN, Thüringen is the smallest of the eastern German states, but it can claim to be one of the most interesting. Created in 1920 from a number of much smaller regions, the state was abolished in 1952, along with all other DDR states. Re-unification led to its re-emergence in 1990.

The capital is Erfurt, one of a number of beautifully preserved medieval towns that grace Thüringen. Others include Eisenach, Gotha, Mühlhausen and Weimar, all of which are cities of great cultural and historical interest. Weimar is perhaps the best known outside the country – Goethe, Schiller, Liszt and Nietzsche all lived and worked here, and the city was also the birthplace of the Weimar Republic. In the south-west of the state lies the Thüringer Wald – a beautiful densely forested mountain region with a number of peaks just under 1,000 metres.

Thüringen's brewing scene is more balanced than that of other eastern states, with the majority of breweries dating from the 19th century or earlier and new breweries having opened at the rate of roughly one a year since 1990. The only brewery whose products can easily be found outside Thüringen is Köstritzer.

Transport: Public transport, particularly rail, is generally better than elsewhere in the east, although some areas have relatively poor weekend bus services. A DB Thüringen day ticket will currently set you back €24 but can be used by up to five people and is also valid in Sachsen and Sachsen-Anhalt. The usual time restrictions apply on weekdays.

ALTENBURG   979

Altenburger

Altenburger Brauerei GmbH
Brauereistraße 20, 04600 Altenburg
T 03447 312 90   F 03447 31 29 19
www.brauerei–altenburg.de
Owner: Leikeim, Altenkunstadt   Founded: 1871
Output: 150,000hl
REGULAR BEERS:
Altenburger Lager (4.9%)
Altenburger Schwarze (4.9%)
Altenburger Premium (4.9%)
SEASONAL BEER:
Altenburger Festbier (6%)

Regional brewery to the north of the historic railway station and town centre. They don't have a public tap but the Sudhaus-Stube opens for groups.
DB Altenburg Hbf 700m

APOLDA   980

Vereinsbrauerei

Vereinsbrauerei Apolda GmbH
Topfmarkt 14, 99510 Apolda
T 03644 848 40   F 03644 84 84 88
www.vereinsbrauerei–apolda.de
Founded: 1887
Output: 118,000hl   Availability: c.200 pubs
REGULAR BEERS:
Apoldaer Glocken-Hell (4.5%)
Apoldaer Glocken-Pils (4.8%)
Apoldaer Diät Pils (4.8%)
Apoldaer Premium Pils (4.8%)
Apoldaer Gambrinus Pilsner (4.9%)
Apoldaer Pils Spezial Domi (5%)
Apoldaer Urtyp (5%),

Apoldaer 1806 Jubiläumsbier (5%),
Apoldaer Export (5.2%).
Apoldaer Festbock (6.5%).

Founded in 1887 when two local brewers merged, the Club Brewery is in the town centre, close to Apolda's small castle. They've listed the 4-star Hotel am Schloß as their tap.

🍴 Am Schloß

Jenaer Straße 2, 99510 Apolda
T 03644 58 00   **F** 03644 58 01 00
Mon–Fri 11.00–22.30, Sat & Sun 10.30–22.30; rooms available
DB Apolda 1.3km

ARNSTADT   981

Hopfengrund

Hopfengrund 1, 99310 Arnstadt
T 03628 607 90
Owner: Jürgen Gerber   Founded: 2004
REGULAR BEERS:
Hopfengrund Helles Pils
Hopfengrund Dunkles Pils

Microbrewery attached to a pension on the southern tip of the town, at the edge of the forest. There's no pub on site but we understand they usually open on Friday and Saturday for direct sales. The Stadtbrauerei is around half a mile due north.
DB Arnstadt-Süd 1.4km, Hbf 2.6km

Stadtbrauerei

Hotelpark Stadtbrauerei Arnstadt
Brauhausstraße 1–3, 99310 Arnstadt
T 03628 60 74 00   **F** 03628 60 74 44
www.arnstadt-stadtbrauerei.de
Owner: Kultur & Stadtbrauerei Betriebsgesellschaft mbH   Founded: 1997
Output: 1,000hl   Availability: 1 pub
REGULAR BEERS:
Arnstädter Urstoff Hell (5.1%)
Arnstädter Urtyp Dunkel (5.1%)
Arnstädter Urweizen (5.1%)
SEASONAL BEER:
Arnstädter Urbock (7.1%)

Hotel and brewpub in the former Felsenkeller brewery which closed in 1992. They open rather early but we're not sure if beer is served from the start.

🍴 Brauhaus Gaststätte

Brauhausstraße 1–3, 99310 Arnstadt
T 03628 60 75 90
Daily 06.00–01.00; rooms available
DB Arnstadt-Süd 500m, Hbf 1.9km

BAD KÖSTRITZ   982

Köstritzer

Köstritzer Schwarzbierbrauerei GmbH
Heinrich-Schütz-Straße 16, 07586 Bad Köstritz
T 036605 830   **F** 036605 22 22
www.koestritzer.de
Owner: Bitburger Getränkegruppe
Founded: 1543   Output: 879,000hl
REGULAR BEERS:
Köstritzer Schwarzbier (4.8%)
Köstritzer Edel Pils (4.8%)
Köstritzer Diät Pils (5%)

Germany's biggest Schwarzbier producer. They don't have a tap but their main product can be found all over the country and beyond.
DB Bad Köstritz 1.3km

DINGSLEBEN   983

Metzler

Privatbrauerei Metzler GmbH & Co. KG
An der Klinge 1, 98646 Dingsleben
T 036873 28 40   **F** 036873 284 84
www.dingslebenerbrauerei.de
Owner: Ulrich Metzler   Founded: 1895
Output: 40,000hl   Availability: 220 pubs
REGULAR BEERS:
Dingslebener Edel-Pils (4.9%)
Dingslebener Edel-Pils Premium (4.9%)
Dingslebener Diät-Pils (4.9%)
Dingslebener Landbier (4.9%)
Dingslebener Weißbier (5.4%)
Dingslebener Lava Schwarzbier (6%)
Dingslebener Bock (6.4%)

Independent brewery on the western edge of the village. Their tap re-opened recently following a number of years out of use. Bus No. 222 runs from Hilburghausen on weekdays.

🍴 Metzler

Ortstraße 27, 98646 Dingsleben
T 036873 687 65

Closed Tue; Mon & Wed–Fri 10.00–14.00 &
17.00–24.00, Sat & Sun 11.00–24.00
DB Hildburghausen 11km

EISENACH   984

Eisenacher

Eisenacher Brauerei GmbH
Wartburgallee 25a, 99817 Eisenach
T 03691 238 00   **F** 03691 78 48 25
www.eisenacherbrauerei.de
Owner: Braugold, Erfurt   Founded: 1828
Output: 36,000hl   Availability: c.300 pubs
REGULAR BEERS:
Eisenacher Schwarzer Drachen (4.9%)
Eisenacher Wartburg Pils (4.9%)
Eisenacher Rennsteig Spezial (4.9%)
Eisenacher Wartburg Export (5.2%)
SEASONAL BEER:
Eisenacher Bock (6.5%)

This small regional brewery backs onto the
Stadtpark, south-west of the main station. The
tap is a fairly large hotel just across the street.
Wartburg is the Eisenach castle-fortress that
offered refuge to the excommunicated Martin
Luther in 1521. Rennsteig is Thuringia's most
famous long-distance rambling trail.

🍺 Glockenhof
Grimmelgasse 4, 99817 Eisenach
T 03691 23 40   **F** 03691 23 41 31
Daily 11.00–24.00; rooms available
DB Eisenach 850m

ERFURT   985

Braugold

Braugold Brauerei Riebeck GmbH & Co. KG
Schillerstraße 7, 99096 Erfurt-Löbervorstadt
T 0361 399 00   **F** 0361 399 02 17
www.braugold.de
Founded: 1888   Output: 250,000hl
REGULAR BEERS:
Braugold Hell (4.8%)
Braugold Spezial Pilsner (4.9%)
Braugold 1888 (5.1%)
Erfurter Angerbräu Premium Pils (5.2%)
SEASONAL BEER:
Braugold Bock (6.5%)

Large brewery on the southern side of the
Hauptbahnhof, west of the Stadtpark. There's
no tap that we're aware of but the beers are
widely available locally. They also own the
Eisenacher brewery.
Tram Nos. 4 & 5 Kaffeetrichter 100m
DB Erfurt Hbf 600m

Erfurter Brauhaus

Anger 21, 99084 Erfurt-Altstadt
T 0361 562 58 27   **F** 0361 566 98 34
Owner: Christoph Beyer   Founded: 1997
Output: 2,500hl
REGULAR BEERS:
Erfurter Brauhaus Pils (4.8%)
Erfurter Brauhaus Schwarzes (4.8%)
Erfurter Brauhaus Weizen (5%)

Large brewpub close to Erfurt's main tram
interchange, through which all routes pass.
As well as the three regular beers, a number of
seasonals are also produced.

🍺 Erfurter Brauhaus
Anger 21, 99084 Erfurt-Altstadt
Mon–Sat 11.00–24.00, Sun 11.00–22.00
Tram Anger 120m   DB Erfurt Hbf 550m

Zum Goldenen Schwan

Michaelisstraße 9, 99084 Erfurt-Altstadt
T 0361 262 37 42   **F** 0361 262 37 44
www.zum-goldenen-schwan.de
Owners: the Geiger family   Founded: 2003
REGULAR BEER:
Zum Goldenen Schwan Hausbier (4.8%)

The Golden Swan is a small restaurant just north
of the Rathaus. The tiny brewery was installed
in 2003. They own another restaurant nearby
and the recently revived Felsenkeller in Weimar,
but we think their sole beer is only sold here.

🍺 Zum Goldenen Schwan
Michaelisstraße 9, 99084 Erfurt-Altstadt
Daily 11.00–24.00
Tram Fischmarkt/Rathaus 150m
DB Erfurt Hbf 1km

Haus zur Pfauen

Hausbrauerei Neumann
Marbacher Gasse 12–13, 99084 Erfurt-Altstadt
T 0361 211 11 00   **F** 0361 211 52 09

www.haus-zur-pfauen.de
Owner: Günther Neumann   Founded: 1996
Output: 120hl   Availability: 1 pub
REGULAR BEERS:
Pfauenbräu Hell
Erfurter Schluntz Dunkel

Restaurant and pension north of the cathedral
that resumed brewing in 1996, 287 years after
beer had last been produced in the house. The
two beers are brewed to ancient recipes. They
also have a glazier's workshop.

🍺 **Haus zur Pfauen**
Marbacher Gasse 12–13, 99084 Erfurt-Altstadt
T 0361 643 80 99   **F** 0361 60 11 73
Daily 10.30–24.00; rooms available
Tram Nos. 3 & 6 Webergasse/Andreaskirche 100m
DB Erfurt Hbf 1.5km

Waldhaus

Rhodaer Chaussee 12, 99094 Erfurt-Rhoda
T 0361 345 93 20   **F** 0361 345 22 68
www.waldhaus-erfurt.de
Owner: Lazzaretti, Renner, Baldi
Founded: 1994   Output: 1,750hl
Availability: 1 pub
REGULAR BEERS:
Waldhaus Pils (5%)
Waldhaus Stockdunkel (5%)
SEASONAL BEERS:
Waldhaus Rauchbier (4.8%), **Waldhaus Red**
(5%), **Waldhaus Marone** (5.3%, Jan), **Waldhaus
Weizen-Hell** (5.5%, Apr–Sep), **Waldhaus
Weizen-Dunkel** (5.5%, Oct–Mar), **Waldhaus
Überraschungsbier** (Jul), **Waldhaus
Weihnachtsbier** (5.5%, Dec), **Waldhaus
Bockbier Dunkel** (6.5%, Oct), **Waldhaus
Weizenbock-Hell** (6.6%), **Waldhaus
Thüringator** (7.8%, Feb).

Despite being in Erfurt, this is a rural brewpub
on the southern edge of the Steigerwald. They
have what must be one of the largest beer
gardens outside Bayern. Bus No. 60 from the
Hauptbahnhof stops outside. Two of the three
owners also have an interest in Leipzig's
Thomaskirche brewery.

🍺 **Waldhaus**
Rhodaer Chaussee 12, 99094 Erfurt-Rhoda
Daily 11.00–24.00
Tram No. 4 Thüringenhalle 3.2km
DB Erfurt-Bischleben 2.3km, Hbf 5km

Waldkasino

Waldkasino Erfurter Brauereigaststätte
Am Waldkasino 2, 99096 Erfurt-Löbervorstadt
T 0361 345 66 77   **F** 0361 345 65 52
www.waldkasino.de
Owner: Salvatore Sauna   Founded: 2000
Output: 1,000hl   Availability: 1 pub
REGULAR BEERS:
Steigerwald Schwarz (4.6%)
Steigerwald Pils (4.8%)
Steigerwald Weizen (5%)
SEASONAL BEERS:
Steigerwald Märzen (5.1%), **Steigerwald Bock-
Dunkel** (6.8%), **Steigerwald Doppelbock** (7.8%)

Brewpub on the opposite side of the
Steigerwald to the Waldhaus. The beer garden
has fine views across the city. Buses stop virtually outside the door on the way out of Erfurt,
but those going back into the city depart lower
down the hill.

🍺 **Waldkasino**
Am Waldkasino 2, 99096 Erfurt-Löbervorstadt
Daily 10.00–01.00
Tram No. 4 Thüringenhalle 650m
DB Erfurt Hbf 2.3km

GIERSTÄDT   986

Zum Goldenen Lamm

Kleine Gasse 1, 99100 Gierstädt
T 036206 232 48   **F** 036206 185 90
Founded: 2004
REGULAR BEERS:
Lamm Bräu Helles Landbier
Lamm Bräu Dunkles

The Golden Lamb is a small brewery, pub and
pension in the centre of the village. Buses run
from both Erfurt (No. 112) and Gotha (No. 892,
weekdays only) to Döllstadt via Gierstädt, but
the weekend service is limited.

🍺 **Zum Goldenen Lamm**
Kleine Gasse 1, 99100 Gierstädt
Closed Mon & Tue; Wed–Sun 11.00–15.00 &
18.00–24.00
DB Döllstadt 5km, Erfurt Hbf 20km

GOTHA 987

Gotha

Brauerei Gotha, Zweigniederlassung der
Oettinger Brauerei GmbH
Leinastraße 50, 99867 Gotha
T 03621 46 70 **F** 03621 46 72 12
www.oettinger-bier.de
Owner: Oettinger Gruppe   Founded: 1830
Output: 1,800,000hl
REGULAR BEERS:
Thüringer Premium Pils (4.7%)
St. Gothardus Pils (4.9%)
St. Gothardus Spezial (5.6%)
St. Gothardus Bock (6.5%)
FOR OETTINGER, OETTINGEN:
Original Oettinger Leicht (2.8%), **Original
Oettinger Leichte Weiße** (2.8%), **Original
Oettinger Vollbier Hell** (4.7%), **Original
Oettinger Pils** (4.7%), **Original Oettinger Alt**
(4.9%), **Original Oettinger Gold** (4.9%),
Original Oettinger Schwarzbier (4.9%),
Original Oettinger Hefeweißbier (4.9%),
Original Oettinger Dunkles Weißbier (4.9%),
Original Oettinger Kristall Weizen (4.9%),
Original Oettinger Export (5.4%), **Original
Oettinger Urtyp** (5.6%)
SEASONAL BEER:
Winterbier (5.6%)
FOR STUTZHÄUSER, LUISENTHAL:
Stutzhäuser Pils

The largest of Oettinger's subsidiaries, Brauerei
Gotha produces the full range Oettinger beers
as required, like the others. They've given us
the Stutzhäuser brewery museum and pub in
Luisenthal (20km south of Gotha) as their tap.

🍺 Stutzhäuser Brauereimuseum
Karl-Marx-Straße 8, 99885 Luisenthal
T 036257 402 16 **F** 036257 317 96
Closed Mon; Tue–Sun 11.00–24.00; rooms
available
DB Luisenthal (Thüringen) 1.5km

König-Sahl

Brühl 5–7, 99867 Gotha
T 03621 85 25 06 **F** 03621 22 68 41
Owner: Stefan Oelsner   Founded: 1997
REGULAR BEERS:
König-Sahl Pils
König-Sahl Schwarzbier

SEASONAL BEERS:
**König-Sahl Weizen, König-Sahl Märzen,
König-Sahl Bock**

This brewpub is just off the Hauptmarkt, close
to Gotha's historic town hall. We've had our
doubts about its brewing status but have been
assured that it still produces its own beer.

🍺 König-Sahl
Brühl 5–7, 99867 Gotha
Mon–Thu 11.00–14.30 & 18.00–23.00, Fri & Sat
11.00–14.30 & 18.00–01.00, Sun 11.00–14.30
Tram Bertha-von-Suttner-Platz 100m
DB Gotha 1.9km, Gotha Ost 2.3km

GREIZ 988

Göltzschtal

Brauhaus bei der Göltzsch GmbH
Feldschlößchenstraße 4, 07973 Greiz
T 03661 68 99 58 **F** 03661 68 99 60
www.brauhaus-bei-der-goeltzsch.de
Founded: 1876   Output: 8,000hl
REGULAR BEERS:
Göltzschtal Pils (4.9%)
Göltzschtal Premium Pils (4.9%)
Göltzschtal Dunkel (5.2%)

Small brewery on the western side of town,
about a kilometre beyond the Vereinsbrauerei.
Bus No. 6 stops at the swimming pool nearby
but the service is poor. An alternative is the
number No. 1 to Warthalle.

🍺 Feldschlößchen
Feldschlößchenstraße 4, 07973 Greiz
T/F 03661 3304
Closed Tue; Wed–Sat & Mon 16.00–23.00,
Sun & hols 11.00–21.00
DB Greiz 3.2km

Vereinsbrauerei

Vereinsbrauerei Greiz GmbH
Lindenstraße 60, 07973 Greiz
T 03661 61 00 **F** 03661 61 02 26
www.greizer.de
Owner: the Wagner family   Founded: 1872
Output: 50,000hl   Availability: c.200 pubs
REGULAR BEERS:
Greizer Zwickl (4.6%)
Greizer Urbräu (4.8%)

Greizer Diät-Pils (4.9%)
Greizer Schloß Pils (4.9%)
SEASONAL BEER:
Greizer Bock (6.7%)

By far the larger of Greiz's two breweries. The owning family also control Rosenbrauerei Pößneck and Ehringsdorfer. The tap is more or less opposite. Take bus No. 6 or 7 to Schmidt-straße if you don't want to walk from the station.

🍎 **Grüne Linde**
Grüne Linde 2, 07973 Greiz
T/F 03661 43 17 90
Closed Wed; Mon, Tue & Thu–Sat 11.00–22.00, Sun 11.00–14.30 & 17.30–22.00
DB Greiz 1.8km

HESSBERG (Veilsdorf)　　989

Hessberger

Hessberger Brauerei und Mineralbrunnen GmbH
Brauereistraße 43, 98669 Veilsdorf-Heßberg
T 03685 793 80　**F** 03685 79 38 16
www.hessberger-brauerei.de
Owner: Peter Werg　　Founded: 1860
REGULAR BEERS:
Tannen Bräu Hessberger Pils (4.9%)
Tannen Bräu Diät-Pilsener (5.2%)
Tannen Bräu Spezial (5.4%)

Independent brewery that we suspect produces a greater volume of soft drinks then beer. There's no official tap but several bus routes run through the village on weekdays if you'd like to look for a pub that sells the beers.
DB Veilsdorf 3km, Hildburghausen 4.2km

JENA　　990

Papiermühle

Hotel und Brau-Gasthof Papiermühle
Erfurter Straße 102, 07743 Jena
T 03641 459898　**F** 03641 459845
www.jenaer-bier.de
Owners: the Kanz family　　Founded: 1996
Output: 1,000hl　Availability: 1 pub
REGULAR BEERS:
Jenaer Deutsche Pils (4.5%)
Jenaer Burschenpils (4.5%)
Jenaer Premium Dunkel (5.2%)

Jenaer Schellenbier Bock Dunkel (5.8%)
Alt Jenaer Bock Hell (5.8%)
SEASONAL BEERS:
Jenaer Maibock (5.8%),
Jenaer Weihnachtsbock (5.8%)

Brewpub on the western outskirts of Jena, the town made famous for its glass and as home of the Zeiss optics company. Despite the name (paper mill), they haven't made paper here since 1868. Unusually, they regularly brew two bocks, albeit of lower than normal strength. Take bus No. 16 or 18 to Mühltal.

🍎 **Papiermühle**
Erfurter Straße 102, 07743 Jena
Daily 11.30–24.00; rooms available
DB Jena-West 2.5km, Jena-Paradies 2.6km

Talschänke

Gasthausbrauerei Talschänke
Pennickental 44, 07749 Jena-Wöllnitz
T 03641 33 43 21
Owner: Kai Hoppe　　Founded: 1997
REGULAR BEER:
Wöllnitzer Weißbier

Effectively still a village, the south-eastern suburb of Wöllnitz is home to this brewpub, producer of just one beer. Various buses run to the stop around 500m from the pub.

🍎 **Talschänke**
Pennickental 44, 07749 Jena-Wöllnitz
Mon–Fri 12.00–24.00, Sat & Sun 11.00–24.00
DB Jena-Paradies 3km, Jena-West 3km

JÜCHSEN　　991

Zur Goldenen Henne

Witte 6, 98631 Jüchsen　　**T/F** 036947 512 29
www.brauerei-juechsen.de
Owner: Reizlein Gastronomie Betriebs GmbH
Founded: 1890　　Output: 2,000hl
REGULAR BEER:
Jüchsener Pilsener
SEASONAL BEER:
Jüchsener Bock

Traditional brewery of a kind that's rarely seen outside Franconia (admittedly it's only 10km outside). Bus No. 404 runs from Meiningen via Untermaßfeld to The Golden Hen on weekdays.

Zur Kleinen Brauerei

Queinfelder Straße 6a, 98631 Jüchsen
T 036947 509 01   **F** 036947 509 03
Daily from 12.00; rooms available
DB Untermaßfeld 10km, Meiningen 15km

KALTENNORDHEIM — 992

Rhönbrauerei Dittmar

Fuldaer Straße 6, 36452 Kaltennordheim
T 036966 834 90   **F** 036966 83 49 33
www.rhoenbrauerei.de
Owner: Friedrich Dittmar   Founded: 1875
Output: 30,000hl
REGULAR BEERS:
Rhöner Land Premium (4.5%)
Rhöner Pils (4.5%)
Rhöner Pummpils Hefetrüb (4.5%)
Rhöner Edel Export (4.8%)
Rhöner Spezial Export (4.8%)
Rhöner Urtyp Dunkel (4.9%)
Rhöner Weisse (4.9%)
Rhöner Schwarze Hefeweizen (4.9%)
Rhöner Weizen Kristall (4.9%)
Rhöner Feuertaufe (5.3%)
SEASONAL BEERS:
Rhöner Weihnachtsbier (4.8%, Christmas),
Rhöner Bock Hell (6%, winter)

Family-run brewery in a small town at the heart of the Rhön nature reserve. The tap is on the main road through the village. Public transport options are limited if you want to visit the pub, but it is possible to get back to Bad Sulzungen by bus on weekdays.

Zur Brauerei

Altenbrunnenstraße 1, 36452 Kaltennordheim
T 036966 835 45
Daily from 17.00
DB Meiningen 23km, Bad Sulzingen 28km

MEININGEN — 993

Meininger

Meininger Privatbrauerei GmbH
Am Bielstein 3, 98617 Meiningen
T 03693 45 31 20   **F** 03693 45 31 30
www.meininger-privatbrauerei.de
Owner: Klaus Weydringer   Founded: 1841

Output: 80,000hl   Availability: 150 pubs
REGULAR BEERS:
Meininger Black Jack (4.4%)
Meininger Gold Urhell (4.7%)
Meininger Landsbergbräu Export (4.7%)
Meininger Frisches Pilsener (5%)
Meininger Hefeweizen (5.3%)
Meininger Heller Bock (6.3%)
SEASONAL BEERS:
Meininger Maibock (6.3%),
Meininger Winterbock (6.3%)
FOR THURINGIA BRAUEREI, MÜHLHAUSEN:
Thuringia Braumeister (4.7%),
Thuringia Export (5.2%)

Brewery and tap north of the town centre, on the opposite side of the valley to the railway station. Other members of the Weyringer family own Klosterbrauerei Münnerstadt and Rother Bräu.

Zur Sudpfanne

Am Bielstein 3, 98617 Meiningen
T 03693 45 31 40
Mon & Tue 11.00–14.30, Wed–Sun 11.00–14.30 & from 18.00
DB Meiningen 1km

MÜHLHAUSEN — 994

Zum Löwen

Mühlhauser Brauhaus Zum Löwen
Kornmarkt 3, 99974 Mühlhausen
T 03601 47 10   **F** 03601 47 12 22
www.brauhaus-zum-loewen.de
Founded: 1992
Output: 1,600hl   Availability: 1 pub
REGULAR BEERS:
Zum Löwen Apotheker Dunkel
Zum Löwen Mühlhäuser Pils
SEASONAL BEER:
Zum Löwen Weihnachtsbock

Half-timbered brewpub within the town walls, close to the Rathaus. Mühlhausen has a particularly attractive medieval centre. The Lion is owned by the Willinger Brauhaus.

Zum Löwen

Kornmarkt 3, 99974 Mühlhausen
Sun–Thu 07.00–01.00, Fri & Sat 07.00–03.00; rooms available
DB Mühlhausen (Thüringen) 1.2km

PÖSSNECK 995

Rosenbrauerei

Rosenbrauerei Pößneck GmbH
Dr.-Wilhelm-Külz-Straße 41, 07381 Pößneck
T 03647 410 90   **F** 03647 410 93 51
www.rosenbrauerei.de
Owners: the Wagner family   Founded: 1866
Output: 65,000hl   Availability: c. 500 pubs
REGULAR BEERS:
Rosen Pils (4.8%)
Rosen Schwarze Rose (4.9%)
Rosen Spezial Pils (4.9%)
SEASONAL BEER:
Rosen Bock (6.5%)

The Rose brewery is on the western side of
town, just below Pößneck's upper station.
There's no tap that we're aware of. The Wagner
family have acquired both Vereinsbrauerei
Greiz and Ehringsdorfer (Weimar) within the
last five years.
DB Pößneck-Oberer Bahnhof 500m,
Pößneck-Unterer Bahnhof 1.7km

SAALFELD 996

Saalfelder

Bürgerliches Brauhaus Saalfeld GmbH
Pößnecker Straße 55, 07318 Saalfeld
T 03671 673 60   **F** 03671 67 36 40
www.brauhaus-saalfeld.de
Owner: Max Gramelsberger   Founded: 1892
Output: 25,000hl
REGULAR BEERS:
Saalfelder Dunkel (4.8%)
Saalfelder Pilsner (4.8%)
Saalfelder Grotten Pils (4.8%)
Saalfelder Premium Pilsner (4.8%)
Saalfelder Gaudi Weizen (5.4%)
Ur-Saalfelder (5.6%)
Saalfelder Jubiläumsbier (5.6%)
SEASONAL BEER:
Saalfelder Bockbier (6.5%)

Small brewery north of the station, close to
Saalfeld's engine sheds. We don't believe they
have a tap but the beers are widely available
about the town.
DB Saalfeld (Saale) 400m

SCHWARZBACH 997

Schloßbrauerei

Schloßbrauerei Schwarzbach GmbH
Zur Schleuse 1, 98673 Auengrund-Schwarzbach
T 036878 27 60   **F** 036878 276 20
www.schlossbrauerei-schwarzbach.de
Owners: Christel & Oliver Nowak
Founded: 1400   Output: 20,000hl
Availability: c.100 pubs
REGULAR BEERS:
Schwarzbacher Hopfenperle Pils (5%)
Schwarzbacher Raubritter Dunkel (5%)
Schwarzbacher Sonnen-Weisse (5%)
SEASONAL BEERS:
Schwarzbacher Narrenkrug (5.6%), **Schwarz-
bacher Weihnachtsbier** (5.6%, Christmas),
Schwarzbacher Sonnengold Bock (7%)

Small village brewery with family connections
to Sonnenbräu in Lichtenberg. For a closer look,
take bus 207 from Hildburghausen on weekdays.

🍺 **Zur Eisenbahn**
Bahnhofstr. 40, 98673 Auengrund-Schwarzbach
T 036878 614 01   **F** 036878 607 65
Closed Thu; Fri & Mon–Wed 11.00–13.30 &
16.00–22.00, Sat & Sun 11.00–13.30 & 15.00–
22.00; rooms available
DB Hildburghausen 12km

SINGEN (Thüringen) 998

Museums-Brauerei Schmitt

Brauereiweg 1, 99326 Ilmtal-Singen
T 03629 80 25 56
Owner: Uwe Obstfelder   Founded: 1875
Output: 750hl   Availability: 3 pubs
REGULAR BEER:
Singer Bier (4.8%)

How it used to be. The brewing equipment in
this small brewery largely dates from the 19th
century, including the steam engine that is still
used to power everything. There's a beer garden
at the brewery that opens in fine weather (hours
unknown) and a tap nearby in the centre of the
village.

🍺 **Biergarten an der Brauerei**
Brauereiweg 1, 99326 Ilmtal-Singen

Nov–Easter: closed. Easter–Oct: daily in fine weather
DB Singen (Thüringen) 1km

🍺 Zum Singer Berg
Zum Anger 17, 99326 Ilmtal-Singen
T/F 03629 80 22 44
Winter: closed Mon & Tue; Wed–Sun from 11.00.
Summer: closed Mon; Tue–Sun from 11.00
DB Singen (Thüringen) 1km

SONNEBERG   999

Gessner
Privatbrauerei Gessner GmbH & Co.
Am Lindenbach 27, 96515 Sonneberg-Malmerz
T 03675 407 90   **F** 03675 40 79 40
www.privatbrauerei-gessner.de
Owners: Manuela & Otto Schäfer
Founded: 1622   Output: 90,000hl
REGULAR BEERS:
Gessner Premium Pils (4.9%)
Gessner Alt-Sumbarcher Dunkel (5.2%)
SEASONAL BEERS:
Gessner Festbier (5.4%),
Gessner Dunkler Bock (6.8%)

Gessner's brewery was originally in Steinach, 10km to the north. The move to the current premises in the eastern suburb of Malmerz came in 1997. We don't think they have a tap.
DB Sonneberg (Thüringen)-Ost 1.8km

STEINACH   1000

Ankerbräu
Dr.-Max-Volk-Straße 7, 96523 Steinach
T 036762 283 16   **F** 036762 281 40
Owner: Heinz Greiner-Wohlleben
Founded: 1736   Output: 2,500hl
REGULAR BEERS:
Steinacher Anker Pils (5%)
Steinacher Ankerla Dunkel (5.2%)
SEASONAL BEER:
Steinacher Bock

Ankerbräu moved into the former Gessner brewery shortly after the latter upped and left for Sonneberg in 1997. The tap remains at the former brewery. Fortunately for those without a car, the railway to Steinach re-opened recently.

🍺 Ankerbräu
Steinbächlein 6a, 96523 Steinach
T 036762 312 51   **F** 036762 312 52
Closed Mon; Tue 17.00–22.00, Wed–Sat 11.30–24.00, Sun 11.30–21.00; rooms available
DB Steinach (Thüringen) 350m

VACHDORF   1001

Öko-Markt
Öko Markt Werratal GmbH & Co. KG
Riethweg 239, 98617 Vachdorf
T 036949 29 70   **F** 036949 297 21
www.oekomarkt-vachdorf.de
Founded: 2000
REGULAR BEERS:
Öko-Markt Hell
Öko-Markt Dunkel

The Öko-Markt Werratal is a modern complex on the outskirts of Vachdorf, with an organic butchers, bakery and brewery. The two regular beers are, we think, joined by occasional seasonals.

🍺 Öko-Markt
Riethweg 239, 98617 Vachdorf
Mon–Wed 17.00–22.00, Thu–Sat 11.30–14.30 & 17.00–22.00, Sun 11.30–22.00; rooms available
DB Vachdorf 750m

WATZDORF
(Bad Blankenburg)   1002

Watzdorfer
Watzdorfer Traditions- und Spezialitätenbrauerei
Watzdorf 14, 07422 Bad Blankenburg-Watzdorf
T 036741 61 60   **F** 036741 616 16
www.watzdorfer.de
Owners: Olaf Hoffmann & Dr. Gerhard Rögner
Founded: 1411   Output: 25,000hl
REGULAR BEERS:
Watzdorfer Burg Pils (4.8%)
Watzdorfer Schwarzbier (4.8%)
Watzdorfer Burg Export (5%)
SEASONAL BEERS:
Watzdorfer Burg Bock Hell (7%, spring),
Watzdorfer Burg Bock Dunkel (7%, winter)

Small brewery in the hamlet of Watzdorf. The tap only opens for brewery visits so you're probably best advised to look for the beers in Bad Blankenburg. If you're determind to visit Watzdorf, bus No. 15 runs up the valley.

DB Quittelsdorf 2km, Bad Blankenburg 3km

WEIMAR 1003

Ehringsdorfer

Brauerei Weimar-Ehringsdorf
Hainweg 13, 99425 Weimar-Ehringsdorf
T 03643 87 60 **F** 03643 876 15
www.ehringsdorfer.de
Owner: the Wagner family Founded: 14.05.2003
Output: 10,000hl
REGULAR BEERS:
Ehringsdorfer Urbräu (4.8%)
Weimarer Pilsener (4.9%)

This small brewery was originally founded in 1840 but ceased brewing in 1995. It was bought and re-opened by the Wagner family who also own Rosenbrauerei Pößneck and Vereinsbrauerei Greiz. They don't yet have a tap. Take bus No. 1 from the main station to Am Anger if you want to see the brewery.

DB Oberweimar 1.5km, Weimar 4.5km

Felsenkeller

Gasthausbrauerei Felsenkeller Weimar
Humboldtstraße 37, 99425 Weimar
T 03643 41 47 41 **F** 03643 41 47 42
www.felsenkeller-weimar.de
Owners: the Geiger family Founded: 1990
Output: 1,000hl Availability: 5 pubs
REGULAR BEERS:
Deinhardt Hell
Deinhardt Dunkel
SEASONAL BEERS:
Deinhardt Honigbräu, Deinhardt Bockbier

This brewpub in the south of the city was re-opened by the owners of Erfurt's Zum Goldenen Schwan in August 2005, following a couple of years out of use. There was an earlier brewery on the site which closed in 1963. Take bus No. 6 from the main station to Wilhelm-Külz-Straße.

🍺 **Felsenkeller**
Humboldtstraße 37, 99425 Weimar
Closed Mon; Tue–Sat 11.00–24.00,
Sun 11.00–22.00
DB Weimar Berkaer 1.2km, Weimar 2.2km

WEISSENSEE 1004

Weißenseer Ratsbräu

Ratsbrauerei Weißensee GmbH
Marktplatz 26, 99631 Weißensee
T 036374 369 70 **F** 036374 369 75
Owner: Klaus Müller Founded: 2000
Output: 250hl
Availability: 5 pubs
REGULAR BEERS:
Weißenseer Ratsbräu Hell (5%)
Weißenseer Ratsbräu Dunkel (5%)
Weißenseer Ratsbräu Bock (6.5%)

Small brewpub in the former stables of Weißensee's 15th-century town hall. The beer is brewed to the town's own Reinheitsgebot which dates from 1434 – eighty-two years earlier than the better-known version.

🍺 **Ratsbrauerei**
Marktplatz 26, 99631 Weißensee
Closed Mon; Tue–Thu 18.00–23.00, Fri 18.00–24.00, Sat 14.00–24.00, Sun 14.00–22.00
DB Weißensee (Thüringen) 1.5km

WORBIS (Leinefelde) 1005

Neunspringe

Brauerei Neunspringe Worbis GmbH
Neunspringer Straße 4, 37339 Leinefelde-Worbis
T 036074 97 90 **F** 036074 979 44
www.brauerei-neunspringe.de
Founded: 1867 Output: 25,000hl
REGULAR BEERS:
Neunspringer Pilsner (4.9%)
Neunspringer Premium Pilsner (4.9%)
Neunspringer Schwarzbier (5.2%)
SEASONAL BEERS:
Neunspringer Winter-Schwarzbier (5.2%),
Neunspringer Dunkler Bock (7.2%, Oct–Dec)

This small brewery is named after the Nine Springs scattered around the brewery's land. The tap is only open for brewery visits but there are local pubs that sell the beers – take bus Nos. 1 or 26 from Leinefelde to look for one.

DB Leinefelde 5km

Breweries location maps

Germany

SCHLESWIG-HOLSTEIN

MECKLENBURG-VORPOMMERN

● HAMBURG

NIEDERSACHSEN

● BERLIN

BRANDENBURG

SACHSEN-ANHALT

NORDRHEIN-WESTFALEN

● LEIPZIG

● DÜSSELDORF

SACHSEN

● KÖLN

THÜRINGEN

HESSEN

● FRANKFURT

RHEINLAND-PFALZ

● BAMBERG

● NÜRNBERG

SAARLAND

● KARLSRUHE

BAYERN

● STUTTGART

BADEN-WÜRTTEMBERG

● AUGSBURG

● MÜNCHEN

0 km   100

Baden-Württemberg

Bayern (north)

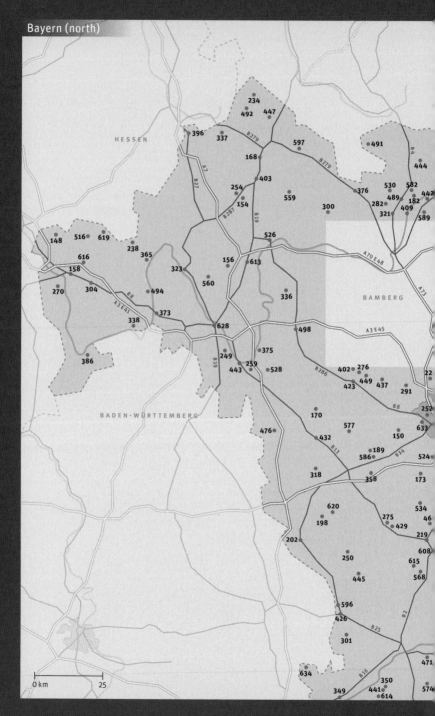

HESSEN

234
492 447

396 337
597 491
B 279
168 444
B 4
B 279
403
254 559 376 530 582 442
154 300 489 182
526 282 409
321 589

148 516 619
238 365 A 70 E 48
616 156 613 BAMBERG
158 323
560 336 A 73
270 304 494
A 3 E 41 498 A 3 E 45
338 373
628
386 375
B 19 249 528 402 276 22
443 259 449 437 291
B 286 423 B 8
170 252
577 633
476 432 150
B 13 189 524
586 B 14
318 358 173
620 534
198 275 46
429 219
202 608
250 615
445 568
596
426 B 25
301 B 2 471
634 B 16 350 574
349 441 614

0 km   25

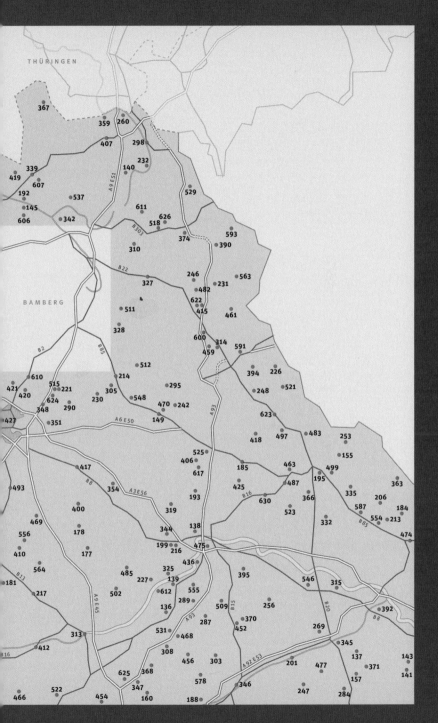

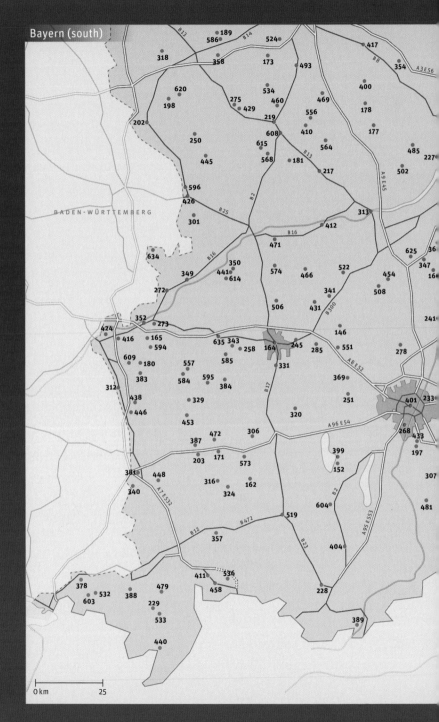

Bayern (south)

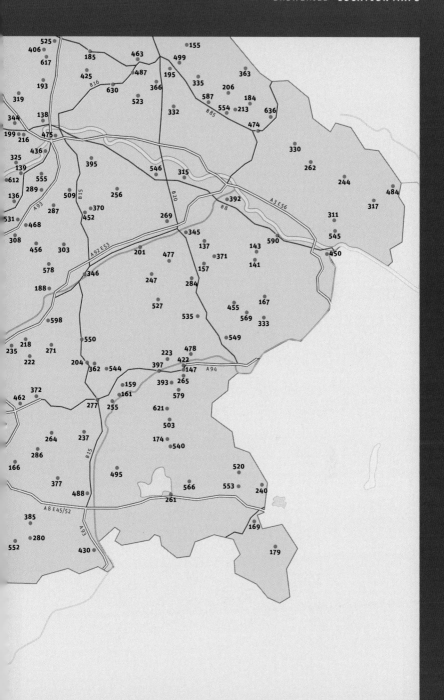

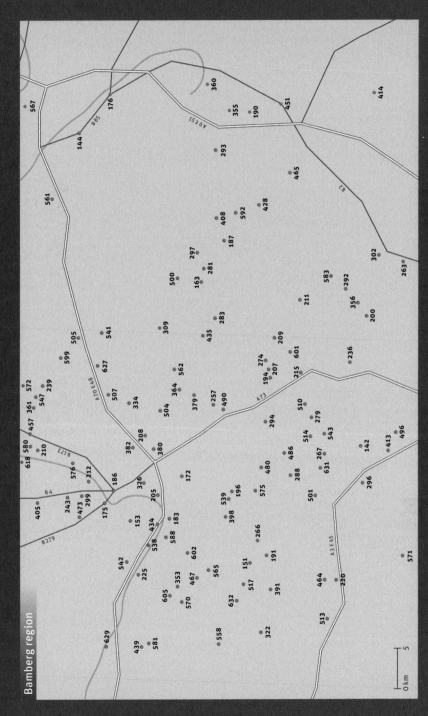

Bamberg region

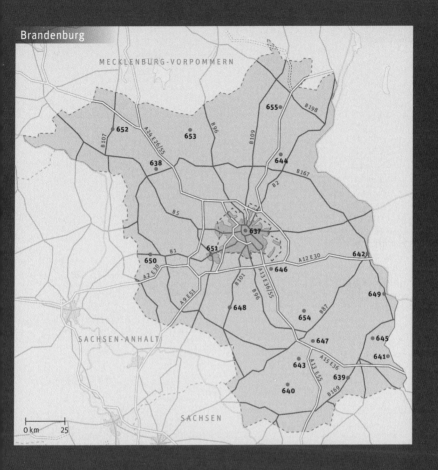

Brandenburg

MECKLENBURG-VORPOMMERN

655

B 198

652

B 107

A 24 E 26/55

653

B 96

B 109

638

644

B 167

B 2

B 5

637

651

650

B 1

646

A 12 E 30

642

A 2 E 30

B 101

A 13 E 36/55

B 96

649

A 9 E 51

648

654

B 87

SACHSEN-ANHALT

647

645

643

A 15 E 36

641

A 13 E 55

639

640

B 169

0 km   25

SACHSEN

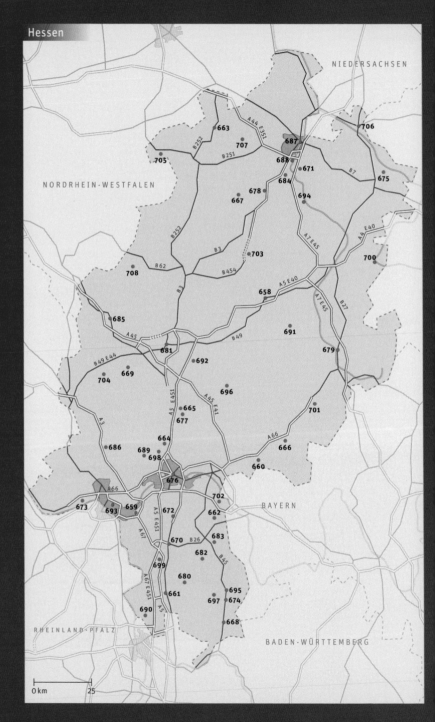

Hessen

NIEDERSACHSEN

NORDRHEIN-WESTFALEN

BAYERN

RHEINLAND-PFALZ

BADEN-WÜRTTEMBERG

0 km   25

Mecklenburg-Vorpommern

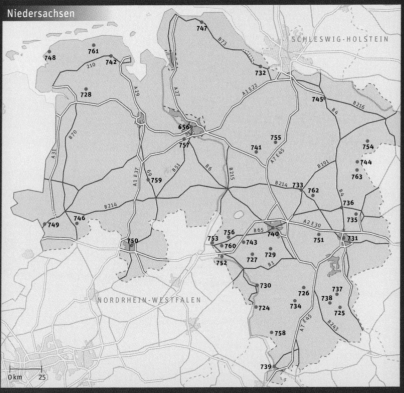

Niedersachsen

Nordrhein-Westfalen

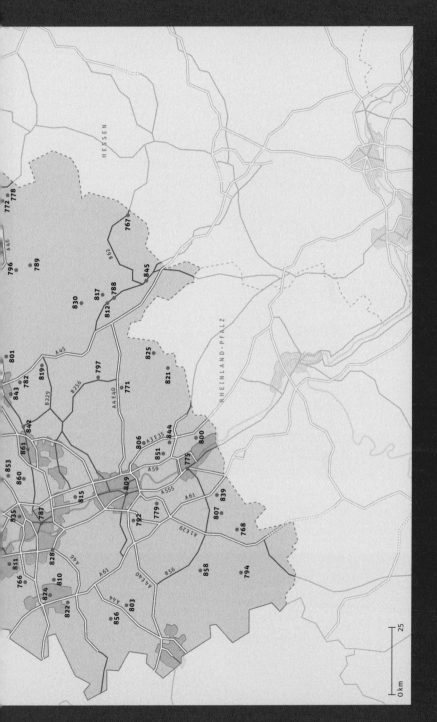

Rheinland-Pfalz and Saarland

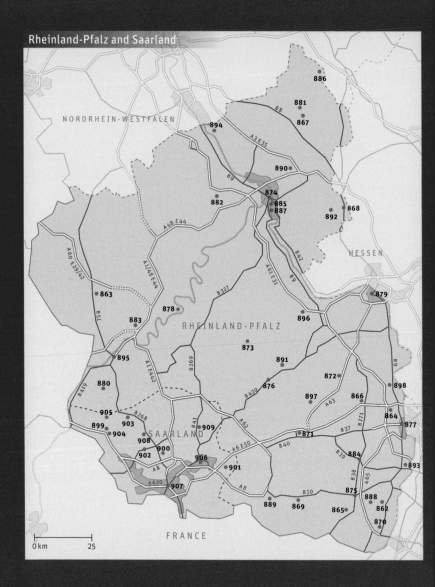

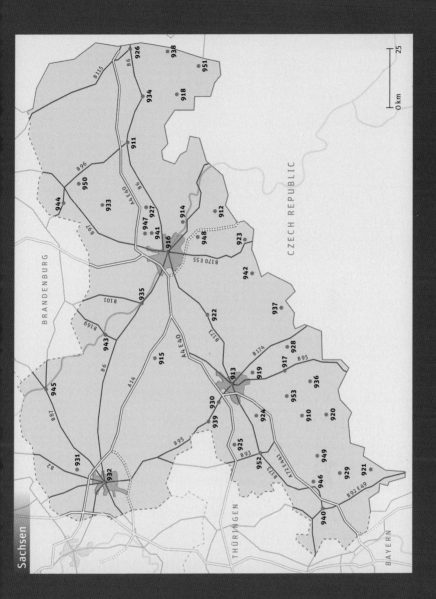

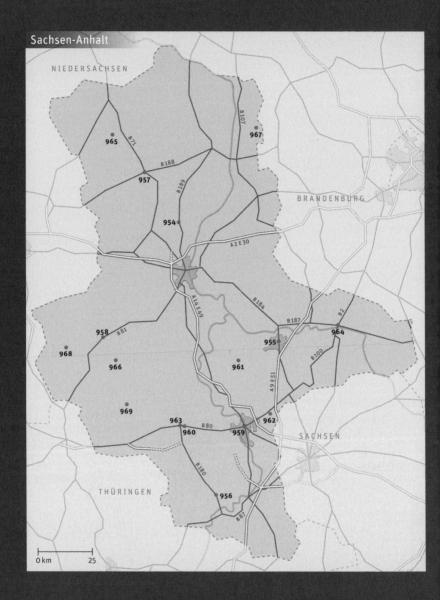

Sachsen-Anhalt

NIEDERSACHSEN

BRANDENBURG

SACHSEN

THÜRINGEN

965
967
957
954
958
968
966
969
955
964
961
963
960
959
962
956

B 107
B 71
B 188
B 189
A 2 E 30
A 14 E 49
B 184
B 187
B 2
B 81
B 100
A 9 E 51
B 80
B 180
B 87

0 km   25

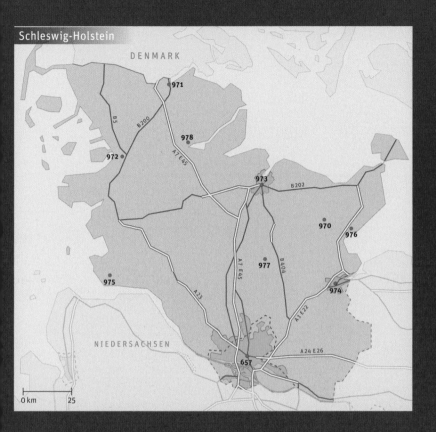

Schleswig-Holstein

DENMARK

971

B5
B200

978

972

A7 E45

973
B202

970
976

A7 E45
B404
977

975
A23

974

A1 E22

A24 E26

657

0 km
25

NIEDERSACHSEN

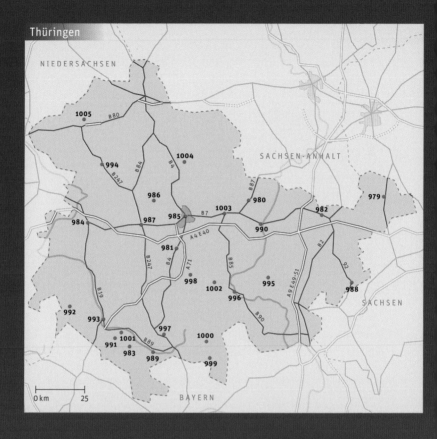

Thüringen

NIEDERSACHSEN

SACHSEN-ANHALT

SACHSEN

BAYERN

0 km   25

The Pubs

Drinking in a German pub

MOST TRADITIONAL German pubs (*Gasthof/ Gaststätte/Wirtschaft)* are very comfortable, the epitome of what Germans call *Gemütlichkeit* (cosy friendliness). There are usually a number of different rooms, often featuring scrubbed wooden tables and wood-panelling, although it's not unusual to visit a half-timbered 500-year old pub that feels new inside, such has been the extent of unsympathetic refurbishments. There's not normally a distinction between public and saloon bar, but some rooms may be set aside for drinking, others for eating, and there are usually private function rooms. Many have a *Stammtisch* – a table set aside for regulars, a club or employees of a particular company. This may not be too obvious at first glance but is usually close to the bar and is likely to have an ornate lamp-shade, ashtray or sign with *Stammtisch* written on it. Don't sit at one unless invited to do so – you may find a regular sitting in your lap! Old-fashioned bars may have a skittles alley downstairs; modern ones are more likely to feature a bowling alley.

A *Kneipe* is a basic bar, in many ways quite similar to a British boozer. This is the sort of place you go for a beer and a chat with your mates, for a quick drink, or just to read the paper. Many only open during the evening but they are likely to stay open later than other places in town. Kneipes tend to be much livelier than more traditional pubs, often featuring fruit machines and juke boxes, darts and pool. As elsewhere, Irish and American bars have invaded the scene, and drinking foreign beers (of whatever quality) and beer cocktails is apparently considered cool. During special festivities, such as the Oktoberfest or Carnival, you may find yourself befriended by the locals, whether you speak German or not. You may even find yourself singing and dancing, voluntarily or otherwise...

There is as yet no smoking ban in German pubs although there is a general move in that direction. Some now have a non-smoking area but these are in the minority. Children are generally allowed into pubs in the company of adults. They can visit on their own and drink beer from age 16, spirits from 18.

At most pubs you will be served at the table, although in a *Kneipe* you may be asked by the landlord/lady to collect your beer from the bar to save him/her the effort of walking to your table twice. In some larger pubs waiters will walk around with freshly poured beers and just leave them at the tables they pass unless you tell them not to. If you drink Pils, you'll need to be patient – a 'proper' Pils takes at least seven minutes to pour. The waiters/ waitresses often wear special regional or local uniforms – in Düsseldorf and Köln, for example, they are called *Köbes* and wear blue aprons; in Munich the waitresses may be wearing *Dirndls* and sometimes carry as many as five 1-litre glasses of beer in each hand!

Generally you are not expected to pay on the spot, although you may have to at particularly busy times. Instead, the waiter will usually mark your *Deckel* (beermat) with a line for every standard drink, the main draft beer they are selling, and with the price for anything different such as non-alcoholic drinks or schnapps. You pay when you leave and your beermat is destroyed. If you're standing at the bar, your beermat may be marked with your name and kept behind the bar. Make sure you have some change when you visit the toilet, too – in many cities the larger pubs will have someone sitting there to charge you.

Augsburg

www2.augsburg.de

BAVARIA's third-largest city and one of the most attractive towns in Germany, Augsburg was founded by Emperor Augustus in 15BC and remained one of the most influential cities in central Europe for many centuries. The city lost some of its pre-eminence after the Thirty Years' War, but even today it still retains economic and cultural importance. Highlights include the Gothic cathedral, the bishops' residence, the Fuggerei (a medieval social housing project), the town hall (Rathaus) as well as shops and Renaissance and Baroque buildings in Maximilianstraße.

For the beer tourist Augsburg boasts six breweries. Although the majority of pubs only sell beer from within the city boundaries, some of the larger regional brewers do also have a presence.

Transport: www.avv-augsburg.de
The main railway station is on the western edge of the city. There's a small tram network centred on Königsplatz. None of the pubs listed are more than a few minutes walk from a tram stop.

Bauerntanz (1)

Bauerntanzgässchen 1,
86150 Augsburg-Innenstadt
T 0821 15 36 44   **F** 0821 373 38
Daily 11.00–23.30; food until 22.00
Tram Nos. 1 & 2 Moritzplatz 200m
DB Augsburg Hbf 1.2km

Tucked away in the network of lanes below Maximilianstraße, the 'Peasants' Dance' is one of the city's oldest pubs, dating from 1572. Until 1918 it had its own brewery, but these days the beers come from Hasen. The interior is furnished in a fairly typical rustic Bavarian style, with red-tiled floors, pine furniture and panelling. Although this is more of a restaurant than a bar, with tablecloths on the tables, they don't mind if you've come just for a beer. In warm weather you can sit outside and relax next to the quiet street.

DRAUGHT: **Hasen-Bräu Urhell, Pilsener**
BOTTLED: **Hasen-Bräu Weißer Hase**

Charly Bräu (2)

Ulmer Straße 43, 86154 Augsburg-Oberhausen
T 0821 42 63 46   **E** info_charly-braeu@web.de
www.charly-braeu.de
Fri & Sat 11.00–01.00, Sun–Thu 11.00–24.00
Tram No. 2 Oberhausen Bahnhof 20m
DB Augsburg-Oberhausen 150m

Street-corner brewpub on the square outside Oberhausen station. The brewing coppers are in a prominent raised position against one wall, with the fermenting and lager tanks in the cellar below. Seating is on three floors, the ground-floor Brauereistube being the only room that's always open. There are plenty of cosy nooks and crannies in which to hide away. Old photos adorn the walls, with one corner devoted to strongmen sporting barbells. Note also the banknotes from the days of hyperinflation. The menu features a number of dishes cooked with beer. In summer there's seating in the square, with beer served outside from a wooden hut.

DRAUGHT: **Charly Bräu Kellerbier, Weisse, Oberhauser-Dunkel, Primus (seasonal)**

Drei Königinnen (3)

Meister-Veits-Gässchen 32,
86152 Augsburg-Innenstadt
T 0821 15 84 05
Closed Mon; Tue–Sun 18.00–01.00;
food until 23.00

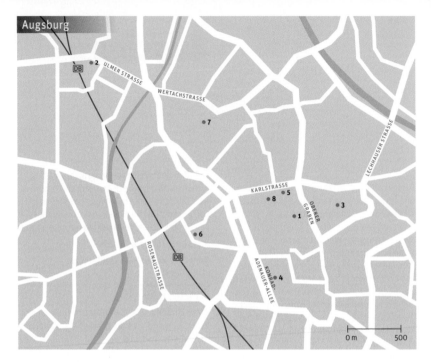

Augsburg

Tram	No. 1 Jakobsplatz 250m
DB	Augsburg Hbf 1.6km

Street-corner brewery tap of Augusta-Bräu, with a surprisingly modern interior, despite the dark wooden seats and panelling. At the rear of the 'Three Queens' is an enclosed beer garden shaded by four chestnut trees. Opposite the pub is the Fuggerei, the world's first social housing project, built in the early part of the 16th century. It still serves its original purpose, tenancy being open only to pensioners and those on low incomes.

DRAUGHT: **Augusta Urhell, Kellerbier, Schwarzbier, Hefe-Weizen, seasonals**

BOTTLED: **Augusta Leicht, Pils, Privat, Edelquell Märzen, Hunnen-Bock**

Goldene Gans (4)

Weite Gasse 11, 86150 Augsburg-Innenstadt
T 0821 51 22 66 **E** brauerei@goldene-gans.de
www.Goldene-Gans.de
Closed Sun & hols; Mon–Sat 11.30–14.00 & 18.00–24.00; food 11.30–14.00 & 18.00–22.00
Tram Nos. 3 & 4 Theodor-Heuss-Platz 280m
DB Augsburg Hbf 1.2km

The tap of the brewery which brewed next door until 1998. Through the windows you can see a thick layer of dust on the coppers in the brewhouse. We think the beers are now brewed by Hasen, a stone's throw away. The pub interior has been modernised and the emphasis is on food as much as beer. At the rear is a pleasant beer garden shaded by trained ivy. The food is rather more eclectic than usual for German pubs and includes curries. There are apparently plans to resume brewing, possibly as a brewpub on a different site.

DRAUGHT: **Goldene Gans 1346 Urhell**

BOTTLED: **Goldene Gans Leichte Weisse, Karolinen Weisse; Scheyern Kloster Dunkles Export, Dunkles Weizen, Tucher Pilsener**

König von Flandern (5)

Karolinenstraße 12, 86150 Augsburg-Innenstadt
T 0821 15 8 050 **E** info@koenigvonflandern.de
www.koenigvonflandern.de
Sun & hols 17.00–01.00,
Mon–Sat 11.00–01.00; food until 00.30
Tram Nos. 1 & 2 Rathausplatz 100m
DB Augsburg Hbf 1.2km

Brewpub in the cellar of the old Augsburg bath houses, just up the street from the town hall. The entrance is via stairs in the middle of a bookshop. There was a brewery on this site in the 16th century. The King of Flanders' main restaurant, split into four distinct areas, is laid out around the bottom of the stairs. The brewing kettles are to the left as you enter and beyond these is a further room that's mainly used when busy. Bread is freshly baked at the pub every day and you'll be offered it in a basket when you order a drink.

DRAUGHT: **Drei-Heller-Bier Hell, Dunkel, Alligator**

Riegele (6)

Viktoriastraße 4, 86150 Augsburg-Innenstadt
T 0821 50 90 00   **F** 0821 51 77 46
www.riegele.de
Sun 11.00–14.00, Mon–Sat 11.00–14.00 &
17.00–22.00; rooms available
DB Augsburg Hbf 130m

An upmarket hotel and restaurant opposite the main station, the Riegele also happens to be the tap of Augsburg's largest brewery, although they don't shout that fact from the rooftops. There are four main rooms, three of which are occupied by the fairly formal restaurant, while the Bräustüble is a little bit more relaxed. At the rear, next to the car park, is a small terrace garden with half a dozen tables. More foody than beery – our Belgian expert reported difficulty when he just wanted a beer, but the Guide has encountered no such problems.

DRAUGHT: **Riegele Augsburger Herren Pils, Commerzienrat Riegele Privat**

BOTTLED: **Riegele Leichte Weisse, Feines Urhell, Aechtes Dunkel, Sebastian Riegele's Weisse, Alte Weisse, Speziator Doppelbock**

Thorbräu (7)

Wertachbrucker-Tor-Straße 9,
86152 Augsburg-Zentrum
T 0821 346 35 57   **E** info@thorbraeu.de
www.thorbraeu-stueberl.de
Closed Mon; Sat 18.00–24.00,
Sun & Tue–Fri 11.00–14.00 & 18.00–24.00
Tram No. 2 Senkelbach 170m
DB Augsburg Hbf 1.5km

Thorbräu's tap is attached to the brewery, in the shadow of the Wertachbrucker Gate. There are four recently refurbished rooms, three of which have a traditional interior with tiled floors, wooden tables and seats. The fourth, at the rear, is more modern and features a glass roof. Beyond this you'll find the brewery yard, with tables and chairs in summer. From here you can look into the Sudhaus at the brewing coppers. There's a larger, better beer garden across the street, on the other side of the tower. Thorbräu's Dunkel is advertised as Schwarzbier and served in unusual, partially glazed earthenware mugs. Good food.

DRAUGHT: **Thorbräu Hefe-Weizen, Augsburger Altstadt Weiße, Maximilian's Kellerbier, Dunkel**

BOTTLED: **Thorbräu Leichte Weisse, Hell, Celtic Bier, Portator**

Weißer Hase (8)

Annastraße/Unter dem Bogen 4,
86150 Augsburg-Innenstadt
T 0821 51 85 08
Daily 10.00–22.00
Tram Nos. 1 & 2 Rathausplatz 150m
DB Augsburg Hbf 1km

Two-roomed pub on a pedestrianised street in the old town, close to the town hall. Downstairs is the Bräustüble, upstairs a restaurant, both decked out in pale pine. In summer there's some pleasant seating under the trees on the street outside. In addition to Hasen's own beers, the White Hare also sells three of those they currently brew for Klosterbrauerei Scheyern. As the Guide closed for press this old brewery was due to resume brewing, so it remains to be seen whether their beers will be sold here in the future.

DRAUGHT: **Hasen-Bräu Pilsener, Weißer Hase, Extra**

BOTTLED: **Hasen-Bräu Leichte Weiße; Scheyern Kloster Dunkles Export, Dunkles Weizen, Doppelbock Dunkel**

Bamberg

www.stadt.bamberg.de
www.bamberg.info

BAMBERG, around 60km north of Nürnberg and straddling the banks of the river Regnitz and Main–Donau canal, is one of Europe's most beautiful cities. Boasting several thousand Baroque, Renaissance and medieval buildings, it was declared a UNESCO World Heritage site in 1993. The heart of the old town, beneath the 13th-century cathedral, is a cluster of narrow, winding streets that lead towards the old town hall. This magnificent pile stands on a sandbank in the middle of the Regnitz, supposedly built there because the bishop wouldn't give the townsfolk any land elsewhere. Between river and canal you'll find the university as well as the modern city centre – although most of the buildings here would be considered old anywhere else. Suffice to say there are dozens of worthwhile attractions and numerous shops to explore.

Beer has a long tradition in Bamberg – the first licence to brew was granted in 1122, and the Bamberg Reinheitsgebot, stipulating the strict use of only hop, malt and water in brewing, predated the Bavarian law by 26 years. In 1817 the town was home to 65 breweries – not bad for a population of only 20,000. Only six of those breweries have survived today: Fässla, Greifenklau, Heller, Klosterbräu, Mahr and Spezial. Since then, Keesmann first opened its doors in 1867, followed by Maisel in 1894. Kaiserdom (or Bürgerbräu brewery, as it was known then) was based in the village of Gaustadt which didn't become part of Bamberg until the 1970s. In recent years these breweries have been joined by Robesbierre and Ambräusianum to give a current total of 11 breweries, an exceptional number for only 70,000 Bambergers. If the ratio of breweries to people of 1817 were to be matched, however, room would have to be found for another 216! For those interested in the history of Bamberg's breweries, *Bamberg – die wahre Hauptstadt des Bieres* (Bamberg – The true beer capital) by Christian Fiedler is a good source of information.

Transport: If you arrive at the railway station on the east side of the city, it is only around 1.5km to the centre, and the walk can be pleasantly broken by a stop at either Fässla or Spezial. There are usually plenty of taxis available and several bus services run to the central bus station (ZOB). Hotels may be hard to find at peak periods so book well in advance.

Abseits (1)

Pödeldorfer Straße 39, 96052 Bamberg
T 0951 30 34 22
www.abseits-bamberg.de
Daily 09.00–01.00; food until 23.30
DB Bamberg 1.1km

Free house in a largely residential area east of the station. One large, split-level room, with a small beer garden at the rear. The beer range changes monthly but usually includes the four draught beers listed below, plus one or two others. 'Offside', which calls itself Bamberg's oldest student café, usually offers around 30 bottled beers, many from southern Bavaria. The Bamberger Hofbräu brewery, a few hundred metres farther down the street, closed in 1977 (the tap near the old town hall is still open).

DRAUGHT: **Andechser Dunkel; Grasser Huppendorfer Vollbier; Keesmann Bamberger Herren Pils; Zehendner Mönchsambacher Lagerbier; guest beers**

BOTTLED: **around 30 beers**

---

ft: *Ambräusianum, Bamberg. The latest addition the city's already crowded brewing scene.*

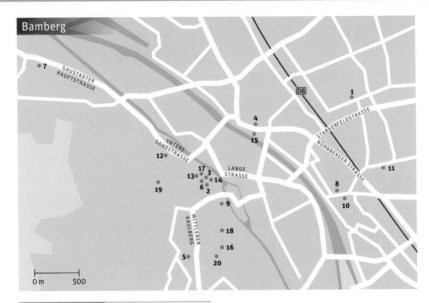

Bamberg

Alt-Ringlein (2)

Dominikanerstraße 9, 96049 Bamberg
T 0951 953 20　　**E** info@alt-ringlein.com
www.alt-ringlein.de
Daily 09.00–01.00; rooms available
DB Bamberg 1.6km

Hotel and restaurant on the tourist trail below the cathedral. This was the former home of the Ringlein brewery which closed in 1957, although we believe in latter years they brewed at Oberer Stephansberg 45 (the brewery chimney can be seen from the Spezial Keller). The dark wood-panelled restaurant is divided by a large *Kachel-ofen* (tiled stove). Outside, there's a pleasant terrace that gets extremely busy in fine weather. One remnant of the brewery is Ringlas Helles, supposedly brewed to an old recipe but according to John Conen (in his excellent guide) it's just Mahr's Hell re-badged. We'll let you decide.

DRAUGHT: **Ringlas Helles; Mahr's Ungespundet; Heller Aecht Schlenkerla Rauchbier-Märzen or Spezial Rauchbier Lager**

Ambräusianum (3)

Dominikanerstraße 10, 96049 Bamberg
T 0951 509 02 62　　**E** info@ambraeusianum.de
www.ambraeusianum.de
Mon–Sat 11.00–23.00, Sun 11.00–22.00
DB Bamberg 1.6km

This brewpub, a couple of doors along from Schlenkerla, is Bamberg's latest attraction. Originally part of a monastery, then a restaurant for many years, it opened as a brewpub in August 2004, a week after the Guide had spent six nights in the Alt-Ringlein opposite! Essentially a single room, there are several distinct drinking areas off the central corridor, with the bar to the right and the gleaming coppers opposite. Currently brews three beers all year round, with Doppelbock appearing in May and December.

DRAUGHT: **Ambräusianum Hell, Dunkel, Weizen; Heller Aecht Schlenkerla Rauchbier Märzen**

Fässla (4)

Obere Königstraße 1921, 96052 Bamberg
T 0951 265 16　　**E** info@faessla.de
www.faessla.de
Sun 08.30–13.00, Mon–Sat 08.30–23.00;
food Mon–Sat 11.00–14.00 & 18.00–21.00;
rooms available
DB Bamberg 700m

Bustling pub, possibly the liveliest of Bamberg's brewery taps and frequently host to some very noisy card schools. Extensively refurbished in the late 1980s following acquisition by the Kalb family, Fässla (The Little Barrel) still retains its traditional style. The entrance leads into the Schwemme, with a small courtyard and the brewery beyond. To the right the bar and adjoining room feature wood panelling and chairs carved with the brewery motif. The bedrooms upstairs are reputed to be some of the best value in the city and are often booked up months in advance.

DRAUGHT: **Fässla Lagerbier, Gold-Pils**

BOTTLED: **Fässla Weizla-Hell, Weizla-Dunkel, Zwergla, Bambergator (seasonal)**

Greifenklau (5)

Laurenziplatz 20, 96049 Bamberg
T 0951 532 19   **E** brauerei@greifenklau.de
www.greifenklau.de
Closed Mon; Sun & hols 09.30–14.00,
Tue–Sat 09.00–23.30; food Tue–Sat 11.30–21.30
DB Bamberg 2.6km

The smallest of Bamberg's established breweries, Greifenklau is located on the Kaulberg in Laurenziplatz, just off the main road west out of town. Numerous bus routes run past if you don't fancy the climb. The main, wood-panelled bar is on the left as you enter, and there's a room for the overflow to the right. At the rear is the beer garden, function room and brewery. The garden has a great view of the Altenburg and its castle. Laurenzikirchweih festival is celebrated on the second weekend in August, Bockbier arrives in mid-November, and the annual holiday is during early November.

DRAUGHT: **Greifenklau Lagerbier, Weizen**

BOTTLED: **Greifenklau Pils**

Kachelofen (6)

Obere Sandstraße 1, 96049 Bamberg
T 0951 571 72   **E** info@zumkachelofen.de
www.zumkachelofen.de
Daily 10.00–01.00; food until 23.00
DB Bamberg 1.6km

Small pub that's actually located on Katzenberg, a short street that runs up towards the cathedral, opposite Alt-Ringlein and Ambräusianum. It takes its name from the large tiled stove, a typical feature of Franconian pubs. The main room contains around half a dozen tables, and there's a lovely little snug behind the bar. The front terrace is very popular in summer. Most of the beers come from the St. Georgen brewery in nearby Buttenheim.

DRAUGHT: **Heller Aecht Schlenkerla Rauchbier; St. Georgen Bräu Pilsener, Keller Bier**

BOTTLED: **St. Georgen Bräu Weiß-Bier**

Kaiserdom (7)

Gaustadter Hauptstraße 26,
96049 Bamberg-Gaustadt
T 0951 96 51 40   **E** info@kaiserdom.de
www.kaiserdom.de
Mon 18.00–22.00, Tue–Sun 11.00–14.00 &
17.00–22.00; rooms available
DB Bamberg 3.8km

Recently refurbished tap and hotel in the northern suburb of Gaustadt, not long ago a village in its own right. The brewery is on Breitäckerstraße, up the hill on the left just before you reach the pub. The large building next door is the brewery's old maltings. The interior displays far less character than most other pubs in town, and despite its official status as Kaiserdom's brewery tap, you get the impression they're more interested in food than beer here. It's worth a visit all the same, particularly as Röckeleins Kellerbier is still available, though given the closure of the Röckeleinskeller, it may not be so for much longer.

DRAUGHT: **Kaiserdom Pilsener, Meranier Schwarzbier, Weizenland Weissbier Hefetrüb, Röckeleins Kellerbier**

Keesmann (8)

Wunderburg 5, 96050 Bamberg
T 0951 981 98 10   **F** 0951 981 98 14
Closed Sun; Mon–Fri 09.00–23.00,
Sat 09.00–15.00
DB Bamberg 1.6km

Keesmann's tap, in Bamberg's south-eastern suburb of Wunderburg, stands in front of the brewery. The bar is to the left up a few steps and features light wooden panelling, although tobacco smoke is doing its bit to darken this. If at first glance the pub appears full, check around the corner to the right where a couple of tables are hidden from view. At the rear is a courtyard for summer drinking, and a further room to the left that opens when the bar is busy.

DRAUGHT: **Keesmann Bamberger Herren Pils, Sternla, seasonals**

BOTTLED: **Keesmann Hell, Weissbier**

Klosterbräu (9)

Obere Mühlbrücke 1–3, 96049 Bamberg
T 0951 522 65   **E** mail@klosterbraeu.de
www.klosterbraeu.de
Sat, Sun & hols 10.00–23.00, Mon–Fri 10.30–
23.00; food 11.30–14.00 & 17.00–22.00
[DB] Bamberg 1.8km

Tucked away at the foot of the Stephansberg,
down a short alley close to the river, this is the
tap of Bamberg's oldest surviving brewery. The
pub itself only re-opened in 1988 following many
years out of use. There are four rooms, with only
two normally open to the public. Of these, the
small Braunbier-Stübla on the left as you enter is
particularly atmospheric. In summer you can sit
outside on the terrace, next to the cobbled street.

DRAUGHT: **Klosterbräu Schwärzla, Bamberger
Gold Pils, Braunbier, seasonals**

BOTTLED: **Klosterbräu Braun's Weisse**

Klosterbräu, by three years, Bamberg's oldest brewery.

Mahr's-Bräu (10)

Wunderburg 10, 96050 Bamberg
T 0951 915 17 19   **E** info@mahrs.de
www.mahrs-braeu.de
Daily 09.00–23.00   [DB] Bamberg 1.6km

Across the street from Keesmann, this 'Mahr's
bar' is one of Bamberg's most authentic pubs.
The tap room, on the right as you enter, is a
classic, with low beams, varnished wood, a
Kachelofen (tiled stove) and copper-topped bar.

There are two further rooms, and in the evening
stand-up drinkers crowd the corridor. Out front
is a beer garden, shaded by chestnut trees.
Next door you'll find the brewery and office/shop.
Mahr's Ungespundet (known locally as 'U') is
generally only available on draught in the
evening. No food at lunchtime.

GRAVITY: **Mahr's-Bräu Hell, Ungespundet,
seasonals**

BOTTLED: **Mahr's-Bräu Leicht, Pilsner, Weisse**

Maisel-Keller (11)

Moosstraße 32, 96050 Bamberg
T 0951 149 75
E maisel-braeu-bamberg@t-online.de
www.maisel-braeu-bamberg.de
Sat 10.00–02.00, Sun–Fri 10.00–01.00
[DB] Bamberg 1.6km

Maisel's small tap is just along from the brewery,
a short walk from Keesmann and Mahr's. The
interior has been refurbished in a modern style
– all light, varnished pine, but it includes some
brewery memorabilia and is cosier than many
other pubs in town. In the pleasant beer garden,
sheltered from the road by a thick hedge,
barbecues are a regular summer feature. Stays
open later than the city's other brewery taps.

DRAUGHT: **Maisel Bamberger Hell, Kellerbier,
Pils, seasonals**

BOTTLED: **Maisel Bamberger Leichtes,
Domreiter Pils, Premium Lager, Eine Bamberger
Weisse Dunkel, Eine Bamberger Weisse**

Pelikan (12)

Untere Sandstraße 45, 96049 Bamberg
T 0951 60 34 10
Fri 17.00–02.00, Sat 17.00–03.00,
Sun–Thu 17.00–01.00; food until 24.00
[DB] Bamberg 1.8km

This lively bar is five minutes walk from the
heart of the old town. The single room is on
several levels, with the bar to the right as you
enter. Unusually for a Kneipe, most of the light
comes from candles, most of the noise from
conversation. The beer range may vary slightly,
but expect to find most of the beers listed below.
Of particular note are those from the very small
Hausbräu Stegaurach and Winkler breweries.
The former consider this their tap.

DRAUGHT: **Grasser Huppendorfer Vollbier; Jever Pilsener; Zirndorfer Landbier**

BOTTLED: **Hausbräu Stegaurach Lager; Heller Aecht Schlenkerla Rauchbier-Märzen; Keesmann Bamberger Herren Pils; Winkler (Melkendorf) Fränkisches Lagerbier; Zehendner Mönchsambacher Weizenbier; Zirndorfer Landweizen**

Pizzini (13)

Obere Sandstraße 17, 96049 Bamberg
T 0951 563 89
Closed Sun; Mon–Sat 20.00–02.00
DB Bamberg 1.7km

Across the street from Stilbruch (see below), Weinstube Pizzini is the ideal venue if you fancy a break from the bustle and noise that characterises many of the city's pubs. High-backed settles, dark-wooden panelling, velvet curtains, numerous paintings, subdued lighting and eclectic music help create a very relaxed atmosphere. The landlady has been here for over 40 years. We sincerely hope nothing changes when she eventually retires.

DRAUGHT: **Andechser Dunkel; Fässla Gold-Pils; Spezial Rauchbier Lager**

BOTTLED: **Fässla Lagerbier, Weizla-Hell, Weizla-Dunkel; Schneider Weisse Original**

Schlenkerla (14)

Dominikanerstraße 6, 96049 Bamberg
T 0951 560 60   **F** 0951 54 01
www.schlenkerla.de
Closed Tue; Wed–Mon 09.30–23.30;
food 12.00–22.00   DB Bamberg 1.6km

Bamberg's most famous pub, seemingly visited by every tourist in town. The left-hand side is a half-timbered building with sagging beams and window boxes, featuring on many a postcard. Inside this part is the Altes Local, Schlenkerla's main room and bar. This is next to the main corridor in which locals congregate for a quick drink and to buy their take-outs. To the right are three other rooms which usually open only at busy times. The beer has been brewed half a mile away, on Oberer Stephansberg, since 1936.

GRAVITY: **Heller Aecht Schlenkerla Rauchbier-Märzen, seasonals**

BOTTLED: **Heller Schlenkerla Rauchweizen**

Spezial (15)

Obere Königstraße 10, 96052 Bamberg
T 0951 243 04   **F** 0951 263 30
Sat 09.00–14.00, Sun–Fri 09.00–23.00;
rooms available
DB Bamberg 700m

Opposite the Fässla, Spezial is another picture-postcard pub, half-timbered and featuring three rooms that don't appear to have changed much in centuries. The main bar is a classic of its kind, with long tables shared by different groups of guests. The other two rooms are smaller, one wood-panelled and used as an overflow, the other more homely but usually used only by local groups. The small brewery with its even smaller maltings is at the rear. Sadly, we believe the wooden barrels on the bar are now fakes. Spezial closes for their annual holiday during the first week of September.

DRAUGHT: **Spezial Rauchbier Lager, Ungespundet, seasonals**

BOTTLED: **Spezial Rauchbier Weissbier, Rauchbier Märzen**

Spezial-Keller (16)

Sternwartstraße, 96049 Bamberg
T 0951 548 87   **F** 0951 548 62
Closed Mon; Tue–Sat 15.00–23.00,
Sun & hols 10.00–23.00; food until 21.00
DB Bamberg 2.5km

The official address is Oberer Stephansberg 47, but there's been no access via that entrance for years. Instead, turn left at the Heller brewery, then either follow Sternwartstraße round, or (in fine weather) cut up to the Keller via the path that runs behind the brewery. The building looks a little like a chalet but inside it's typical of the traditional pubs in town. Pleasant as the inside undoubtedly is, it's the garden that attracts most visitors, and this can get ve ry busy on warm evenings. There's a decent view of the cathedral and Michaelsberg.

GRAVITY: **Spezial Rauchbier Lager**

BOTTLED: **Spezial Rauchbier Weissbier, Ungespundet, Rauchbier Märzen**

Stilbruch (17)

Obere Sandstraße 18, 96049 Bamberg
T 0951 243 04   E stefan@stilbruch-bamberg.de
www.stilbruch-bamberg.de
Sun from 11.00, Mon–Sat from 19.00
DB Bamberg 1.7km

Until 1915 this was the Grüner Wald brewery, but a fire ended almost 300 years of brewing. The single room is usually very busy, particularly when hosting one of the frequent live events, for which admission may be charged. Hübner-Bräu (Steinfeld) Vollbier is usually available on Sundays, but is described as Landbier. On our last visit they changed the barrel twice during the 90 minutes we were there! The food is good value but the choice is fairly limited except on Sundays when the menu expands.

GRAVITY: **Hübner-Bräu Vollbier** (Sunday only)

DRAUGHT: **Keesmann Bamberger Herren Pils; Mahr's-Bräu Ungespundet; Zirndorfer Landbier**

BOTTLED: **Erdinger Weißbier; Heller Aecht Schlenkerla Rauchbier Märzen; Jever Pilsener; Klosterbräu Schwärzla; Spezial Rauchbier Lager; Schneider Weisse; Tucher Kristall Weizen**

Stöhrenkeller (18)

Oberer Stephansberg 11, 96049 Bamberg
T 0951 302 07 88
Closed Sun; Mon–Fri 19.00–01.00,
Sat 19.00–02.00
DB Bamberg 2.2km

This small, single-roomed pub, a few doors down from the Heller brewery, is the former beer cellar of Brauerei Baltsenwirt which closed as long ago as 1893. The modern interior is in traditional style, if that makes any sense. Those of a curious disposition are advised not to investigate the suspended lighting too closely! The two regular draught beers are occasionally joined by a guest, and if you're very lucky, you could find something from Robesbierre here. May not open until 20.00 in fine weather.

DRAUGHT: **Keesmann Bamberger Herren Pils; Sonne (Bischberg) Urtyp Hell**

BOTTLED: **Heller Schlenkerla Rauchbier Märzen; Keesmann Hell; Mager Dunkel; Zehendner Mönchsambacher Weizenbier**

Torschuster (19)

Obere Karolinenstraße 10, 96049 Bamberg
T 0951 509 92 55
Daily 18.00–02.00
DB Bamberg 2.1km

Between the cathedral and Michaelsberg, just below Jakobsplatz, this former disco opened in its current guise in August 2005. A contender for the smallest pub in Bamberg, there are seats for around only 12 people and virtually no standing room. The walls are covered in brewery enamels, and a brewery mirror may soon be added. Free of any tie, although limited by the small size, owner Thomas Grube is dedicated to showcasing the best beers the city has to offer. May open later than advertised and the beer range is likely to vary.

DRAUGHT: **Keesmann Bamberger Herren Pils; Mahr's-Bräu Ungespundet**

BOTTLED: **Aecht Schlenkerla Rauchbier Märzen; Keesmann Weissbier; Klosterbräu Schwärzla; Spezial Rauchbier Lager**

Wilde-Rose-Keller (20)

Oberer Stephansberg 49, 96049 Bamberg
T 0951 57691   E info@wilde-rose-keller.de
www.wilde-rose-keller.de
Oct–Apr: closed. Summer in fine weather: Sat, Sun & hols 15.00–23.00, Mon–Fri 16.00–23.00
DB Bamberg 2.5km

Large self-service beer garden at the top of the Stephansberg, above the former Lagerhaus of the Wilde Rose brewery (on Kesslerstraße), now the home of Brauhaus Robesbierre. There's one kiosk for beer from the wood, another for Weißbier and other drinks, plus a Gaststätte serving snacks and housing a small distillery. Around 70 trees and a pavillion provide shade from the sun. They wouldn't tell the Guide who brews the house beers, although we suspect Maisel. Incidentally, the large brick building on the right as you near the top of the hill used to be the Löwenbräu brewery which ceased brewing in 1988, its beers being brewed by Kaiserdom until official closure in 1993.

GRAVITY: **Aecht Schlenkerla Rauchbier Märzen; Keesmann Bamberger Herren Pils; Wilde Rose Kellerbier, Wilde Rose Pils**

DRAUGHT: **Maisel Eine Bamberger Weisse**

---

t: The Cathedral, Bamberg.

Berlin

www.berlin.de

As in the rest of the former DDR, breweries in East Berlin were hit hard after the fall of the Wall. Today only two remain from the days before reunification, Bürgerbräu and Schultheiss, the latter still brewing Berlin's main contribution to the beer world, the sour but refreshing Berliner Weisse. The only large brewery in the former West Berlin is Kindl but that is expected to have closed by the time you read this. Conversely, modern brewpubs have flourished, with a dozen dotted over both halves of the formerly divided city.

Transport: **www.bvg.de**

The public transport system in Berlin is divided into three zones (A, B & C). The Guide recommends you invest in a day ticket (Tageskarte). This is valid on all BVG (Berliner Verkehrsbetriebe) ferries, buses, trams and underground trains plus the S-Bahn network. It costs €5.60 for two zones or €6.00 for all three, and is valid until 03.00 the following day. All Berlin pubs in the Guide are within zones A and B. For groups of three to five people, group tickets (Gruppentageskarte) are available for €14.00 and €15.00, respectively. Day tickets are not valid on DB mainline trains (RB, RE, IC, ICE, IR, etc.).

CHARLOTTENBURG

Luisen-Bräu (1)

Luisenplatz 1, 10585 Berlin
T 030 341 93 88   **E** info@luisenbraeu.com
www.luisenbraeu.com
Fri & Sat 09.00–02.00, Sun–Thu 09.00–01.00; food from 11.00 (breakfast from 09.00)
Ⓤ No.7 Richard-Wagner-Platz 600m
DB Ⓢ Charlottenburg 1.7km

Walk up Kaiser-Friedrich-Straße (if arriving by train) or Otto-Suhr-Allee (if taking the underground) to the busy crossroads of those two streets at the south-west corner of Charlottenburg Palace. Here, on the ground floor of a modern three-storey building, you'll find one of the older new-wave brewpubs. The long, wood-panelled bar houses the copper brew kettles and a canteen-style kitchen. There are seats on the front terrace in fine weather. The three house beers are available all-year round.

DRAUGHT: **Luisen-Bräu Hell, Dunkel, Weizen**

FRIEDRICHSHAGEN

Bräustübl (2)

Müggelseedamm 164, 12587 Berlin
T 030 645 57 16   **E** info@braeustuebl.de
www.braeustuebl.de
Closed Mon; Tue-Sat 12.00–24.00,
Sun 11.00–24.00
Tram Nos. 60 & 61 Müggelseedamm/
Bölschestraße 100m
Ⓢ S3 Friedrichshagen 1.2km

Take the S-Bahn to Friedrichshagen, then either walk down Bölschestraße or take the tram to this lovely old tap in front of the Bürgerbräu brewery. The five rooms include a ballroom, a winter garden and a gorgeous old taproom with varnished root-wood arches and recessed tables. To the front is a wood-decked beer garden shaded by a few old chestnut trees. Very good food served all day.

DRAUGHT: **Berliner Bürgerbräu Premium Pils, Bernauer Schwarzbier, Rotkehlchen, Maibock** (spring), **Dunkler Bock** (winter)

BOTTLED: **Hofmark Premium Weisse, Dunkle Weisse, Kristallweizen**

---

ft: *Brandenburg Gate, Berlin.*

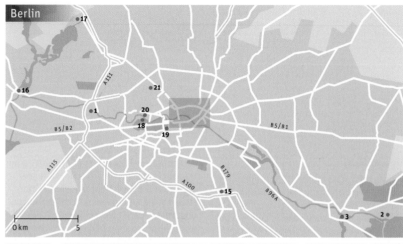

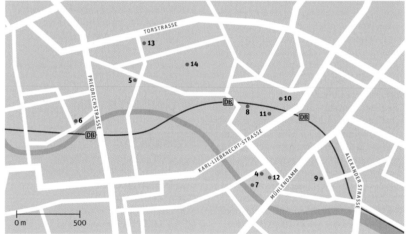

KÖPENICK

Schloßplatzbrauerei (3)

Astrid Rubbert
Schloßplatz, 12555 Berlin-Köpenick
T 0176 24 39 95 68 (mobile)
Daily 12.00–23.00
🚋 Schlossplatz Köpenick 50m,
    Rathaus Köpenick 80m
Ⓢ S3 Köpenick 1.5km

Six tram routes call at the Schlossplatz and
Rathaus, with services running one-way anti-
clockwise around the historic town centre.

Routes include Nos. 60 and 61, which makes
this an easy place to visit in conjunction with the
Bürgerbräu Bräustübl (see above). This very
unusual brewpub in Köpenick's main square is a
tiny, glass-sided building seating just 20 people,
but accommodating significantly larger numbers
in fine weather when tables are set up outside.
The small brewery is just inside the entrance
and currently brews two unfiltered beers,
supplemented by a number of seasonal Bocks.
The 'cellar' is a large refrigerated unit next to
the brewing equipment. One of a kind!

DRAUGHT: **Schloßplatzbrauerei Hell, Kupfer,
seasonals.**

Alt-Berliner Weißbierstube (4)

Rathausstraße 21, 10178 Berlin
T 030 242 44 54 **F** 030 24 71 98 24
Daily 11.00–24.00
Tram M4, M5 & M6 Spandauer Straße/
Marienkirche 250m
U S DB Alexanderplatz 600m

South of Alexanderplatz, among a row of bars
and restaurants near the Rotes Rathaus (Red
Town Hall), this re-creation of an old-Berlin pub
evokes the spirit of a bygone age. Seats feature
leather upholstery and varnished wood, light
fittings are highly polished, the walls covered
in old photographs. As you would expect,
Berliner Weisse is the drink here, with both
Kindl and Schultheiss available either unadult-
erated or in one of the many different beer
cocktails. Good, local dishes. Zum Nußbaum
and Georgbræu are close by (see below).

DRAUGHT: **Schultheiss Lager Schwarz,
Pilsener, Berliner Pilsener**

BOTTLED: **Erdinger Weißbier, Weißbier Dunkel,
Weißbier Kristallklar; Berliner Kindl Weisse;
Schultheiss Original Berliner Weisse; Aecht
Patzenhofer Premium Pilsner**

Aufsturz (5)

Oranienburger Straße 67, 10117 Berlin
T 030 28 04 74 07 **F** 030 28 04 78 09
www.aufsturz.de
Daily 12.00–02.00
S S1 & S2 Oranienburger Straße 50m
U S DB Friedrichstraße 800m

Fashionable but basic bar outside Oranienburger
Straße S-Bahn station. For some inexplicable
reason, the sole draught beer is Heineken.
Fortunately, they also offer around 100 mostly
German bottled beers. On arriving you'll be
handed a menu that lists beers by style rather
than origin (some appear in more than one
category). If there's nothing here that tickles
your fancy, this is the wrong book for you! The
basement club regularly features live music.

DRAUGHT: **Heineken**

BOTTLED: **Too many to list!**

Berliner Republik (6)

Schiffbauerdamm 8, 10117 Berlin
T 030 30 87 22 93
E info@die-berliner-republik.de
www.die-berliner-republik.de
Daily 11.30–04.00 (from 10.00 in summer)
U S DB Friedrichstraße 150m

Single-roomed pub with a fairly modern interior,
on the opposite side of the river from Friedrichstraße station, to the north of the railway. The
quickest way to get here is via the steps at the
west end of the S-Bahn platforms which lead to
a footbridge (built under the railway bridge)
over the river Spree. There's an island bar, and
dotted around the room are screens displaying
the current prices for the beer on sale. From
19.00 each evening prices fluctuate according
to demand on the Brokers Bier Börse (Brokers
Beer Exchange), some beers reaching astronom-
ical levels before commonsense prevails and
the price crashes again. Gimicky to say the least,
but if Pils from national breweries rocks your
boat, this is the place for you.

DRAUGHT: **Berliner Kindl Jubiläums Pilsener;
Berliner Pilsener; Binding Lager; Bitburger
Premium Pils; DAB Pilsener; Diebels Alt;
Fürstenberg Premium Pilsener; Jever Pilsener;
König Pilsener; Köstritzer Schwarzbier; Paulaner
Premium Pils, Hefeweißbier; Potsdamer Rex Pils;
Radeberger Pilsener; Zunft Kölsch**

BOTTLED: **Paulaner Hefeweißbier Dunkel,
Hefeweißbier Kristallklar; Schultheiss Original
Berliner Weisse**

Georgbræu (7)

Spreeufer 4, 10178 Berlin
T 030 242 42 44 **E** info@georgbraeu.de
www.georgbraeu.de
Apr–Dec: daily from 10.00. Jan–Mar:
daily from 12.00
Tram Nos. M4, M5 & M6 Spandauer Straße/
Marienkirche 400m
U S DB Alexanderplatz 700m

On the river Spree at the edge of the
Nikolaiviertel, close to the Palast der Republik
(the former DDR showcase cultural centre,
likely to be demolished in the near future), this
brewpub is, not surprisingly, very popular with
tourists. The Georgbræu's half-dozen rooms
together seat nearly 400. In fine weather a

similar number can be accommodated outside on the large terrace and watch the procession of tourist boats pass by. From the bar you can observe the brewmaster at work. Georg Pils is only available here. Food is served all day and an English menu is available.

DRAUGHT: **Georg Pils Hell, Pils Dunkel**

Lemke (8)

S-Bahnbogen 143, Dircksenstraße, 10178 Berlin
T 030 24 72 87 27   **E** info@brauerei-lemke.de
www.brauerei-lemke.de
Daily from 12.00
Ⓢ Hackescher Markt 100m
ⓊⓈ DB Alexanderplatz 500m

From Hackescher Markt station, walk below the north side of the S-Bahn towards Alexanderplatz and you'll soon find this pub in one of the railway arches. Opposite the bar is the compact brewery and to the rear is a small conservatory and beer garden. The extensive menu includes nine different types of sausage. There are usually four house beers on draught and these may include some very unusual styles for Germany, the brewer being most adventurous for this part of the world. More than 40 different beers have been brewed over the years!

DRAUGHT: **Lemke Original, Pilsner, seasonals**

Zur Letzten Instanz (9)

Waisenstraße 14–16, 10179 Berlin-Mitte
T 030 242 55 28   **E** Post@ZurLetztenInstanz.de
www.zurletzteninstanz.de
Mon–Sat 12.00–01.00, Sun 12.00–23.00
Ⓤ U2 Klosterstraße 100m
ⓊⓈ DB Alexanderplatz 650m

Built in 1621, this pleasant pub sits in a quiet street in a residential part of Berlin. Look for the church in between either of the entrances to Klosterstraße U-Bahn station – Zur Letzten Instanz is behind it. Since 1945 'The Final Judgement' has been widely accepted to be Berlin's oldest pub. The bar features wood-panelling and a magnificent old majolica-tiled stove that incorporates a bench. Two further ground-floor rooms are on different levels, the lower room housing a spiral staircase. The pub has hosted some illustrious guests over the years, including, it is said, Napoleon.

DRAUGHT: **Schultheiss Lager Schwarz, Pilsener, Berliner Pilsener**

BOTTLED: **Scherdel Helle Weisse, Dunkle Weisse, Kristall Weizen; Schultheiss Original Berliner Weisse**

Marcus-Bräu (10)

Münzstraße 1–3, 10178 Berlin
T 030 247 69 85   **E** marcus-braeu@gmx.de
www.brau-dein-bier.de
Mon–Fri 11.00–03.00, Sat & Sun 16.00–03.00
ⓊⓈ DB Alexanderplatz 250m

A short walk from Alexanderplatz station and both Brauhaus Mitte and Lemke, this very small brewpub is known variously as Brauhaus Alexanderplatz, Marcus-Bräu or Microbrauerei Barkowsky. The tiny brew-plant is actually built into the bar! One of at least half a dozen brewpubs claiming to be the smallest in Germany, we're not even sure it's the smallest in Berlin since the Schloßplatzbrauerei opened. Unusually, the home-brewed Pils is available both filtered and unfiltered. The limited menu includes Flammkuchen (Germany's answer to pizza) as a speciality. Note also the late closing time.

DRAUGHT: **Marcus-Bräu Pils, Preußen Dunkel, seasonals**

Mitte (11)

Karl-Liebknecht-Straße 13, 10178 Berlin
T 030 30 87 89 89   **F** 030 30 87 89 88
Daily 11.00–24.00
ⓊⓈ DB Alexanderplatz 150m

Recently renamed from Leopolds Brauhaus following takeover by the owner of nearby Lemke, this modern brewpub is on the first floor of the Berlin Carré shopping centre. Exit Alexanderplatz station from the south-west corner and cross Karl-Liebknecht-Straße. The pub is directly ahead, up a flight of stairs. The semi-circular bar features the brewery and there are a couple of other drinking areas and an outside balcony which overlooks the S-Bahn. The menu includes both local and Bavarian specialities at reasonable prices.

DRAUGHT: **Brauhaus Pils, Dunkel, Hefeweizen Hell, seasonal beers**

Zum Nußbaum (12)

Am Nußbaum 3, 10178 Berlin
T 030 242 30 95
Daily 12.00–02.00
[Tram] M4, M5 & M6 Spandauer Straße/
Marienkirche 300m
[U] [S] [DB] Alexanderplatz 600m

The original Walnut Tree, located in Alt-Cölln,
was the oldest pub in Berlin (dating from 1571),
before it was destroyed in an air raid during
1943. It was rebuilt here in 1986 to the original
design at the heart of the Nikolaiviertel,
opposite the Nikolaikirche. Inside, the tiny bar
has room for just one table. The other two rooms
manage around eight tables between them.
Outside, the comparatively gigantic beer garden
has seven tables and seating for 30. Good, local
menu.

DRAUGHT: **Berliner Kindl Jubiläums Pilsener,
Potsdamer Rex Pils, Märkischer Landmann-
Schwarzbier**

BOTTLED: **Berliner Kindl Weisse; Schöfferhofer
Hefeweizen, Dunkles Hefeweizen,
Kristallweizen**

*Zum Nussbaum, Berlin. Despite appearances to the contrary,
this pub is barely twenty years old. The original 'Nut Tree' was
destroyed during a wartime air raid.*

Schwarzwaldstuben (13)

Tucholskystraße 48, 10117 Berlin
T 030 2809 8084
E mail@schwarzwaldstuben-berlin.de
www.schwarzwaldstuben-berlin.de
Daily 09.00–24.00; food from 10.00
[S] S1 & S2 Oranienburger Straße 350m

This modern interpretation of a Black Forest pub
is on the corner of Linienstraße and Tucholskystraße. One long, narrow room with a copper-
fronted bar, reproduction tiled stove and walls
adorned with hunting trophies. The draught
beers come from two of Baden-Württemberg's
larger breweries, with bottled beers from these
and a few other well-known brewers. Unusually,
they also sell St. Louis Kriek from the Van Honse-
brouck brewery in Belgium. The draught wheat
beer alternates between Eichbaum and Rothaus.

DRAUGHT: **Eichbaum Ureich Pils, Hefe-Weizen;
Rothaus Pils, Hefe Weizen**

BOTTLED: **Astra Pils; Augustiner-Bräu Edelstoff;
Eichbaum Dunkles Weizen, Kristall-Weizen;
Jever Pilsener; Rothaus Tannenzäpfle, Hefe
Weizen Zäpfle, Eiszäpfle**

Sophie'n Eck (14)

Große Hamburger Straße 37, 10115 Berlin
T 030 282 21 09   **E** info@sophieneck-berlin.de
www.sophieneck-berlin.de
Daily from 12.00;
food until 24.00 (Fri & Sat until 01.00)
[Tram] Nos. M1 & M6 Monbijouplatz 350m
[S] Hackescher Markt 600m
[S] S1 & S2 Oranienburger Straße 600m

From Hackescher Markt, walk up Oranienburger
Straße then turn left into Große Hamburger
Straße. This prominent pub is on the corner of
Sophienstraße, hence the name. Over the years
it's been a laundry, stables, bakery, undertakers
and café, and was only converted into a pub as
recently as 1986, featuring an above-average
interior for a modern pub, with dark wood and
old enamel signs dominating. Sophie's Corner
stocks a decent range of beer styles and the
kitchen is open late, offering a menu with
several vegetarian options.

DRAUGHT: **Jever Pilsener; Schlösser Alt;
Schultheiss Lager-Schwarz, Berliner Pilsener;
Sion Kölsch**

BOTTLED: **Erdinger Weißbier, Weißbier Dunkel,
Weißbier Kristallklar; Schultheiss Original
Berliner Weisse**

NEUKÖLLN

Brauhaus in Rixdorf (15)

Glasower Straße 27, 12051 Berlin
T 030 626 88 80   E info@brauhaus-rixdorf.de
www.brauhaus-in-rixdorf.de
Closed Mon; Tue-Sat 12.00–01.00,
Sun 10.00–23.00
Ⓢ Hermannstraße 600m

Long-established brewpub, actually located
between Delbrückstraße and Glasower Straße
and accessible from both. From Hermannstraße
station head south along the street of the same
name and turn left into Delbrückstraße. After
about 150m you'll find the pub on your left
through a car park. Outside there's a large,
pleasant beer garden with its own bar. The pub,
formerly a house, has several rooms with a
slightly rustic atmosphere. The brewery is
tucked away at the rear. Food is served all day
and includes local specialities.

DRAUGHT: **Rixdorfer Hell, Dunkel, seasonals;
guest beer**

BOTTLED: **Paulaner Hefeweißbier Dunkel,
Hefeweißbier, Hefeweißbier Kristallklar**

SPANDAU

Brauhaus in Spandau (16)

Neuendorfer Straße 1, 13585 Berlin
T 030 353 90 70
E brauhaus-spandau@t-online.de
www.brauhaus-spandau.de
Fri & Sat 11.00–01.00, Sun 10.00–24.00,
Mon 16.00–24.00, Tue–Thu 11.00–24.00;
rooms available
Ⓤ U7 Altstadt Spandau 200m
Ⓢ DB Spandau 900m

Originally the laundry of Spandau Barracks, this
imposing brewpub is set on the northern edge
of Spandau's old town. From Altstadt Spandau
U-Bahn station turn right into Carl-Schurz-Straße
and cross the dual carriageway. Carry straight
on over the river bridge and look for the large
brick building with tower and chimney. Inside,
the brewing kettles take centre stage on a raised
platform at the heart of the main bar which is
overlooked by the large drinking area on the

first-floor gallery. Beer garden at the rear.
Rooms available.

DRAUGHT: **Spandauer Havelbräu Hell, seasonals**

TEGEL

Alter Fritz (17)

Karolinenstraße 12, 13507 Berlin
T 030 433 50 10
E mail@restaurant-alter-fritz.de
www.restaurant-alter-fritz.de
Mon–Thu 16.00–01.00, Fri 16.00–02.00,
Sat 11.00–02.00, Sun 11.00–01.00
Ⓤ U6 Alt-Tegel 1km   Ⓢ S25 Tegel 1.4km

Named for Frederick the Great's nickname, this
sprawling inn to the north of Tegel has the look
and feel of a country pub – not surprising perhaps,
given that it's on the edge of the Tegeler Forest.

*Alter Fritz, Berlin. On the edge of the Tegeler Forest,
parts of this brewpub reputedly date from the 15th century.*

Claims to be the oldest pub in Berlin, with parts
dating back to at least 1410, although Zur Letzten
Instanz (see above) is generally accepted to hold
that record. As you enter you'll see the brewery
to your left, and the bar on the right. Beyond are
several other rooms, while the beer garden at
the rear unusually features a large pond. If you
don't fancy the walk from either station, take
buses 124, 133 or 222 from Tegel U-Bahnhof to
Heiligenseestraße/Ruppiner Chaussee – they
stop almost outside the door. Good food.

DRAUGHT: **Alter Fritz Kupfer, Messing, seasonals**

TIERGARTEN

Brewbaker (18)

S-Bahnbogen 415, Flensburger Straße,
10557 Berlin
T 030 39 90 51 56   **E** info@brewbaker.de
www.brewbaker.de
Mon–Sat 10.00–23.00, Sun 12.00–20.00
Ⓢ Bellevue 100m

Exit Bellevue station on the north side, turn left
and cross the road. Brewbaker is on the left, in
the fifth arch of the railway viaduct. Opened in
February 2005, the first brew was delayed due to
problems with the floor. Happily, this difficulty
has been overcome and the first of many beers
appeared during the summer. The enthusiastic
young owner plans to brew up to 48 different
beers a year! Apart from traditional German and
international styles, these are to include new
beers such as Pumpkin Ale, Potato Stout and
Ginger Honey Dream. A single brick-walled bar
houses both the stainless steel brewing equipment and kitchen. There's a small beer garden
to the rear and a few seats at the front for sunny
days. Very good food. The in-house bakery still
hadn't opened at the time of writing.

DRAUGHT: **Brewbaker Pils, Weizen, seasonals;
Jahns Pilsener; Andechs Dunkel, Hefeweizen**

Lindenbräu (19)

Sony Center, Bellevuestraße 3–5, 10785 Berlin
T 030 25 75 12 80   **E** info@lindenbraeu-berlin.de
www.lindenbraeu-berlin.de
Fri & Sat 11.00–02.30, Sun–Thu 11.00–01.00;
food 11.00–23.00
Ⓤ Ⓢ Potsdamer Platz 200m

At the heart of the undeniably impressive Sony
Center – just follow the signs from Potsdamer
Platz station. Lindenbräu is spread over three
floors and features the world's only sterling
silver brewing kettle – although it's unclear what
benefit this bestows on the beer! Take sunglasses
if you don't want to damage your eyes when
looking at it. Outside, below the Center's awe-
inspiring roof, are the beer garden and terrace,
open for business in all weather. Best visited at
night, although finding one of the 800-odd seats
empty can be surprisingly difficult. Just one
house-brewed beer, the others coming from
parent company Hofbräuhaus Traunstein.

DRAUGHT: **Lindenbräu Hofbräu Weiße;
Hofbräuhaus Traunstein Fürsten Pils, 1612er
Zwicklbier, Altbairisch Dunkel**

Paulaner's im Spreebogen (20)

Alt Moabit 98, 10559 Berlin
T 030 399 43 32   **F** 030 32 30 40 11
Mon–Sat 11.00–24.00, Sun 11.00–23.00
Ⓤ U9 Turmstraße 300m   Ⓢ Bellevue 600m

Located between Alt Moabit and the river, close
to the Interior Ministry. From Bellevue station,
turn right into Bartningallee, cross the river,
then turn left and follow the riverside path for a
couple of hundred metres. Paulaner's is on the
right among several other restaurants on the
ground-floor platform of a former dairy. Outside
there's a large seating area to the front and a
smaller terrace to the rear. Inside the style is
München beer hall, all dark wood and scrubbed
tables with Bavarian beer and food (and portions)
to match – as you'd expect of this Munich brewery.

DRAUGHT: **Paulaner Original Münchner Hell,
Premium Pils, Original Münchner Dunkel,
Hefeweißbier**

BOTTLED: **Paulaner Hefeweißbier Dunkel,
Hefeweißbier Kristallklar**

WEDDING

Eschenbräu (21)

Triftstraße 67, 13353 Berlin
T 030 462 68 37   **E** info@eschenbraeu.de
www.eschenbraeu.de
Mon–Fri from 17.00, Sat & Sun from 19.00
Ⓤ U6 Wedding 500m   Ⓢ Wedding 600m

From the Wedding stations walk north up
Müllerstraße and turn left into Triftstraße –
Eschenbräu is on the left, tucked away behind
some flats opposite Genter Straße. This recent
addition to the Berlin brewing scene has the feel
of a British micro-brewery. The brewery itself is
at ground level, visible through large plate-glass
windows. Underneath, in a converted cellar,
is the small and cosy Braukeller. Outside, the
surprisingly pleasant beer garden is dominated
by a large oak tree. No food, but they do have a
pretzel oven.

DRAUGHT: **Eschenbräu Pils, Dunkles, Weizen,
seasonals**

Düsseldorf

www.duesseldorf.de

The state capital of North-Rhine Westfalia, which is one in the eye for arch-rival Köln. The heart of the city is the Altstadt, on the eastern bank of the Rhine. Largely destroyed during World War II, only few buildings survived. What you see today is mostly the result of reconstruction in the 1940s and 1950s, which has mostly been sympathetic to the past. As well as being a major financial and industrial centre, Düsseldorf is the hub of the German fashion industry. Those with money to burn should consider a visit to Königsallee, locally known as Kö. If your tastes are a little more culture-oriented, there is plenty to interest art and theatre lovers. The Kunstsammlung Nordrhein-Westfalen (art gallery) is an obvious place to start.

In the beer world, Düsseldorf is famous for just one thing – Altbier. Four breweries in the city still brew the stuff – Füchschen, Schlüssel, Schumacher and Uerige. All are essentially large brewpubs that happen to supply other outlets. In addition there's Johann Albrecht, a modern brewpub in the north-western suburb of Niederkassel. What were until recently by far the largest two breweries in the city now brew their beers elsewhere. Frankenheim moved to new premises on the outskirts of Neuss in 1991, and Schlösser Alt is now brewed at Brinkhoff's brewery in Dortmund.

Transport: www.rheinbahn.de
The Hauptbahnhof is around a mile south-east of the old town, home to the majority of pubs in the Guide. The local tram network is a combination of ordinary street trams and high-floor inter-urban trams billed as U-Bahn. The latter run to nearby cities and are hidden underground in the city centre.

---

t: Füchschen, Düsseldorf. Brewery and tap. The small office next the bar is known as the 'Bleichstuhl'. Note the blue-aproned bes', traditional waiters of Köln and Düsseldorf pubs.

Alter Bahnhof (1)

Belsenplatz 2, 40545 Düsseldorf-Oberkassel
T 0211 58 33 55 64
Mon–Thu 11.00–02.00, Fri & Sat 11.00–24.00, Sun & hols 10.00–24.00
U Belsenplatz 30m   **DB** Düsseldorf Hbf 4km

With luck the Old Station should be brewing again by the time you read this entry. Gatzweilers Brauhaus ceased brewing in 2003, but all that's changed since then is the pub's name. The brewing equipment is still fully functional and the owners plan to resume brewing but currently lack the funds to employ a brewer. The striking yellow-bricked pub was formerly a railway station but the trains are long gone. To get here, catch one of several U-Bahn routes from the city centre – they stop outside.

DRAUGHT: **Krombacher Pils; Maisel's Weisse Original; Rhenania Alt**

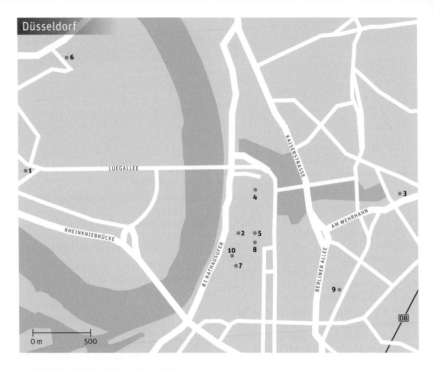

Düsseldorf

Alter Bahnhof, Düsseldorf. A former railway station, this pub brewed for a number of years but the still operative equipment is currently dormant (see photo on previous page).

Diebels Fasskeller (2)

Bolkerstraße 14–16, 40213 Düsseldorf-Altstadt
T 0211 32 50 85 **E** stieffenhofera@diebels.de
www.diebelsfasskeller.de
Fri & Sat 11.00–03.00, Sun–Thu 11.00–01.00;
food until 23.00 (Fri & Sat until 22.00)
Ⓤ Heinrich-Heine-Allee 300m
DB Düsseldorf Hbf 1.7km

Just down the street from the Schlüssel and the Goldener Kessel is Diebel's Barrel Cellar, the Düsseldorf showcase of a growing number of similarly named pubs around the country. One large room with a central bar and a combination of low and high tables and chairs, plus seating on the pedestrianised street out front in dry weather. It's a sobering (?!) thought that Diebels produces 40 times as much Alt as Düsseldorf's four traditional breweries combined.

GRAVITY: **Diebels Premium Altbier**

DRAUGHT: **Diebels Pils**

BOTTLED: **Becks Gold; Franziskaner Weissbier**

Frankenheim (3)

Wielandstraße 14–16,
40211 Düsseldorf-Stadtmitte
T 0211 35 14 47   **E** info@frankenheim.de
www.frankenheim.de
Sun–Thu 10.30–24.00, Fri & Sat 10.30–01.00
🚋 Pempelforter Straße 50m
DB Düsseldorf Hbf 1.2km

Frankenheim's original brewery tap, the beer was brewed behind the pub until a new, much larger brewery opened in Holzheim near Neuss in 1991. The brewery offices are still next door. The large, multi-roomed pub in traditional style features a semi-circular bar which dispenses Alt from the barrel. In summer you can drink outside in the rear courtyard next to the old brewery. The toilet invites you to 'recycle correctly'…

GRAVITY: **Frankenheim Alt**

Füchschen (4)

Ratinger Straße 28, 40213 Düsseldorf-Altstadt
T 0211 86 79 60   **E** mail@fuechschen.de
www.fuechschen.de
Fri & Sat 09.00–01.00, Sun–Thu 09.00–24.00; food from 11.30 (breakfast from 09.00)
U Heinrich-Heine-Allee 350m
DB Düsseldorf Hbf 1.8km

Traditional brewery and tap on the northern edge of the old town, the 'Little Fox' was destroyed during World War II. The current building is a fairly modern red-brick effort. Inside things are more traditional, the bar area with its *Beichtstuhl* (confessional) and congregation of noisy drinkers being particularly atmospheric. The restaurant alongside is plain but comfortable, the conservatory at the rear pleasant and airy. There's also a little snug behind the bar and seating on the pavement outside in summer. Traditional Düsseldorf dishes are served.

GRAVITY: **Füchschen Alt, Weihnachtsbier**
BOTTLED: **Silberfüchschen-Weizen**

Goldener Kessel (5)

Bolkerstraße 44, 40213 Düsseldorf-Altstadt
T 0211 32 60 07
E info@brauerei-schumacher.de
www.schumacher-alt.de   Daily 10.00–24.00
U Heinrich-Heine-Allee 150m
DB Düsseldorf Hbf 1.6km

Schumacher's main Altstadt outlet, on the pedestrianised Bolkerstraße. A former brewery, as with many other pubs in the Guide the 'Golden Kettle' was destroyed during World War II. Photographs on the walls show the pub in its original guise. Its current incarnation is similar in style to most of the city's brewery taps, with several rooms radiating from the central kitchen. The beer is served from wooden barrels. Turn up on the third Thursday of March, September or November if you wish to try Latzenbier.

GRAVITY: **Schumacher Jung, Alt**

Johann Albrecht (6)

Niederkasseler Straße 104,
40547 Düsseldorf-Niederkassel
T 0211 57 01 29
E info@brauhaus-joh-albrecht.de
www.brauhaus-joh-albrecht.de
Daily 12.00–01.00; food until 22.30
U Belsenplatz 1.3km
DB Düsseldorf Hbf 4.7km

One of a chain of six brewpubs across the country, this place comes as something of a surprise after the bars in the city centre as it has far more of a country pub character than you would expect to find in Düsseldorf. Next door is the Schmittmann distillery – Johann Albrecht acts as the tap for their products. The interior consists of a rustic bar with unusual beer fonts and a conservatory which also houses the brewery. Take bus 833 from Belsenplatz to Heinsbergstraße. The Gold is filtered Messing.

DRAUGHT: **Johann Albrecht Messing, Gold, Kupfer, seasonals**

Johann Albrecht, Düsseldorf. Attractive pub next to a small distillery in the north-western suburb of Niederkassel.

Schiffchen (7)

Hafenstraße 5, 40213 Düsseldorf-Altstadt
T 0211 13 24 21
E info.schiffchen@stockheim.de
www.brauerei-zum-schiffchen.de
Closed Sun; Mon–Sat 11.30–24.00
U Heinrich-Heine-Allee 450m
DB Düsseldorf Hbf 1.6km

Dating from 1628, although completely rebuilt after wartime damage, Brauerei Zum Schiffchen is Düsseldorf's oldest pub. The name, The Little Ship Brewery, is slightly misleading as they stopped brewing here in 1975, one of six breweries in the city to close between 1974-76. It still retains its beerhall atmosphere, although it's a little more restrained than some. One of the rooms features an unusual curved roof in the manner of an old sailing ship, a model of which is suspended from the ceiling. There's outdoor drinking across the street in summer.

DRAUGHT: **Frankenheim Alt, Stauder Pils**

BOTTLED: **Andechser Weissbier Hefetrüb**

Schlüssel (8)

Bolkerstraße 41–47, 40213 Düsseldorf-Altstadt
Fri & Sat 10.00–01.00, Sun–Thu 10.00–24.00
T 0211 828 95 50   **E** info@zumschluessel.de
www.zumschluessel.de
U Heinrich-Heine-Allee 150m
DB Düsseldorf Hbf 1.6km

If you don't know much German, one look at the sign hanging outside the Schlüssel should be enough to translate the name. Like most buildings in the city centre this is a post-war reconstruction, refurbished in the late 1980s. The front part of the pub houses the taproom and bar, the rear is more foody, with the brewery visible through windows on the left-hand side. If you don't mind standing, there are high tables on the street in summer. The Goldener Kessel is across the street.

GRAVITY: **Original Schlüssel Alt**

Schumacher Stammhaus (9)

Oststraße 123, 40210 Düsseldorf-Stadtmitte
T 0211 32 60 04
E info@brauerei-schumacher.de
www.schumacher-alt.de
Sun–Thu 10.00–24.00, Fri & Sat 10.00–01.00
U Oststraße 150m   **DB** Düsseldorf Hbf 600m

The only one of Düsseldorf's four traditional breweries outside the old town, Schumacher Stammhaus is comparatively close to the Hauptbahnhof. With more rooms than most pubs in the city, there's something here to suit most tastes, from the basic taproom to more ornate wood-panelled rooms with some stained glass through to full-blown dining rooms. As in Schumacher's Altstadt pub, Latzenbier is only sold on the third Thursday of March, September and November.

GRAVITY: **Schumacher Jung, Alt**

Uerige (10)

Bergerstraße 1, 40213 Düsseldorf-Altstadt
T 0211 86 69 90   **E** info@uerige.de
www.uerige.de
Daily 10.00–24.00
U Heinrich-Heine-Allee 300m
DB Düsseldorf Hbf 1.7km

In the heart of the old town, this bustling pub with its brewery to the rear is possibly the most popular of all the city's brewpubs, though we're sure many would argue otherwise. The street outside is thronged with drinkers in the evening, the multi-roomed interior equally busy through-out much of the day, although some rooms only open for parties or when the pub is especially busy. The Alt is drawn from frequently changed wooden barrels, the wheatbeer bottled only. Uerige Sticke is available on the third Tuesday of January and October.

GRAVITY: **Ueriger Alt**

BOTTLED: **Ueriger Weizen**

Frankfurt-am-Main

www.frankfurt.de

FRANKFURT is situated on the banks of the Main river, in the state of Hessen, right in the heart of Germany and Europe. It's Germany's financial and commercial capital, wielding great power and influence worldwide. The cityscape is dominated by some of Germany's highest skyscrapers, a fact that led to the nickname 'Mainhattan'. Many government organisations and bank headquarters are based here, and the giant trade fairs, such as the Frankfurt Bookfair, attract some 12 million visitors every year.

However, there are also some excellent museums and galleries, there's great shopping in Zeil, and beautiful countryside is all around.

The local speciality is Apfelwein (cider) rather than beer, best enjoyed in the old town or the Sachsenhausen district. And, as everywhere in Germany, Bavarian breweries have advanced into this part of the country. There are some gems though, not just in Frankfurt, but also in the wider Rhein-Main area. Frankfurt is not generally known as a tourist destination. Be warned that most of the pubs featured here are well outside the city centre.

Transport: **www.vgf-ffm.de**
Thanks to its central location, Frankfurt is a vital crossroads of air, road and rail connections. The airport is tied in to Cologne and Düsseldorf by ICE, as well as to Frankfurt Hauptbahnhof. Frankfurt-Hahn, alas, served by Ryanair, is beyond Mainz and Bingen, and only reached by special shuttle bus... The city itself has a system of U-Bahn and tram lines, and buses.

Alt-Oberurseler Brauhaus (1)

Ackergasse 13, 61440 Oberursel
T 06171 543 70   **F** 06171 569 00
Mon–Sat 9.00–24.00, Sun 10.00–23.00
🇺 U3 Portstraße 500m
🇸 Oberursel (Taunus) 800m

Another out-of-Frankfurt place, but actually on the U-Bahn system, this rustic brewpub is located in Oberursel old town. In the main room you can see, smell, hear and taste the beer being made in the brew kettles, which are in operation during opening hours. There's seating for around 190 people, plus a vaulted beer cellar accommodating a further 110 at long tables and in intimate niches. Further rooms can be hired for weddings and private functions, and in summer the large beer garden is open. Breakfast, including a large 'Bayer-Frühstück' is served every day and good regional food, including home-made charcuteries are also on the menu. The beer fan can choose from three home brews: all-year-round there are Pils and Vetter 33, the latter supposedly the 'the world's strongest beer' (SW at least 33%). The third beer is one of 16 different seasonal specialities. They also have a distillery, and guests can watch them make beer schnapps.

DRAUGHT: **Alt-Oberursel Brauhaus-Pils, Vetter 33 plus seasonals such as Dunkel, Altbier, Bockbier, Hefeweizen, Maibock, St. Ursula Doppelbock, Märzen, Rauchbier and others**

Bier-Hannes (2)

Hanauer Landstraße 568,
60386 Frankfurt-Fechenheim
T 069 41 28 90   **E** bier-hannes@gmx.de
www.bier-hannes.de
Closed Sun & hols; Mon–Sat 16.00–24.00
🄳🄱 Frankfurt-Mainkur 250m

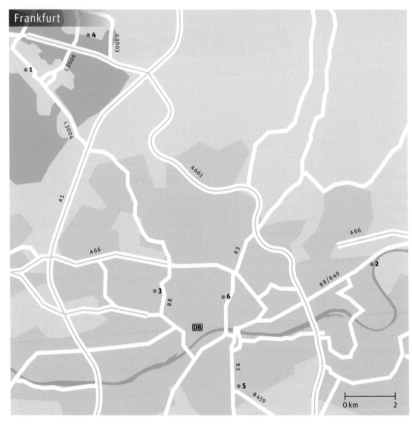

Traditional brewpub in eastern Frankfurt, with a pleasant beer garden open in summer (both of which seat around 60). Bier-Hannes on draught. Food consists of hearty country-fare, with traditional German dishes, some made with beer. There are separate function rooms, and space for a marquee for up to 200 in the brewery courtyard, and guided brewery tours are available on reservation.

DRAUGHT: **Bier-Hannes Export Dunkel, Bier-Hannes Pils, Bier-Hannes Hefeweizen** plus seasonals such as **Krollebock** (Dec–Jan), **Märzen, Maibock**

Doctor Flotte (3)

Gräfstraße 87, 60487 Frankfurt-Bockenheim
T 069 70 45 95   **F** 069 97 78 34 63
www.doctor-flotte.com
Daily 6.00–2.00

U U4, U6, U7 Bockenheimer Warte 20m
DB Frankfurt Hbf 2km

Traditional Frankfurt pub with seating for 70, rustic and comfortable. Very centrally located at the uni, in an attractive turn-of-the-century house next to the Bockenheimer Warte, a medieval tower. Known as 'Frankfurt's last great pub', it was recently renovated by the new owners in traditional style, but without the chintz – there's lots of wood, old photographs and bric-a-brac. Local food plus schnitzel and steaks are on the menu. Beers come from a number of breweries in both draught and bottled varieties.

DRAUGHT: **Binding Römer Pils, Binding Export; Andechser Klosterbräu dunkel; Kutscher Alt; Tucher Hefeweizen; Flensburger Pils**

BOTTLED: **Schöfferhofer Weizen Hell; Schöfferhofer Weizen Kristall**

Graf Zeppelin (4)
(Bad Homburger Brauhaus)

Zeppelinstraße 10, 61352 Bad Homburg
T 06172 28 86 62   **E** brauhaus@worldonline.de
www.badhomburger-brauhaus.de
Mon–Fri 11.00–24.00, Sat 11.00–1.00,
Sun 11.00–23.00
Ⓢ S5 Bad Homburg 1.3km

Not strictly Frankfurt, but not that far out and
easy to reach on S-Bahn, this brewpub and inn,
farm and riding stables, all form part of the
historic Kronenhof, which originally supplied
the nearby Homburg palace. The pub has room
for about 200, with separate function rooms for
20 to 200, as well as a beer garden for 300 in
summer. Home-cooked regional specialities
are served, and the beer is brewed using barley
grown on the Kronenhof farm, with some
success. In August 2004, Kronenhof beer was
the first beer to be awarded the seal of quality
'Geprüfte Qualität – Hessen' (assured quality –
Hessen), certifying the entire production
process, from the field to the glass. They even
generate their own electricity here, from home-
grown rapeseed oil. The Kronenhof also runs
year-round beer seminars.

DRAUGHT: **Kronenhof hell und dunkel;** seasonals
such as **Dinkel-Bier** (spring), **Bernstein Weizen**
(summer), **Quattro-Bier** (a 4-grain beer; autumn),
Mai-Bock and Nikolaus-Bock

Sachsenhäuser Warte (5)

Darmstädter Landstraße 279,
60598 Frankfurt-Sachsenhausen
T 069 68 27 16
E gabriele.heimann@sachsenhaeuser-warte.de
www.sachsenhaeuserwarte.de
Daily 11.30–1.00
🚌 Nos. 30, 36   DB Frankfurt-Süd 1.8km

Two-room pub, the oldest tap of the Binding
brewery a few metres up the road, within the
historic walls of the Sachsenhäuser Warte,
dating from 1767. Sensitively renovated to
preserve the original character and incorporate
some of the old stone walls. Apart from the
typical Apfelwein and local and international
wines, there are of course Binding beers, with
the Sachsenhäuser Warte served unfiltered in a
krug. Regional and international food is available, and in summer you can sit in the attractive
courtyard (seating for about 250). The beer
garden is opened with live music each year.

GRAVITY: **Sachsenhäuser Warte Naturtrüb**

DRAUGHT: **Binding Römer Pilsener Spezial,**
Schöfferhofer Hefeweizen, Krusovice
Schwarzbier, Grenadier Kölsch plus seasonals
such as **Märzen, Bockbier, Festtagsbier**

BOTTLED: **Schöfferhofer Kristall Weizen,**
Schöfferhofer Hefeweizen Dunkel, Clausthaler
Extra Herb, Binding Kraftmalz, Kutscher Alt

Zu den Zwölf Apostel (6)

Rosenberger Straße 1,
60313 Frankfurt-Innenstadt
T 069 28 86 68   **E** info@12apostel.net
www.12apostel.net
Daily 11.30–1.00
Ⓤ Ⓢ Konstablerwache 300m
DB Frankfurt Hbf 2.2km

'Frankfurt's first house brewery', the Twelve
Apostles is a pub on three floors, with room for
about 180. On the ground floor is a cosy pub
with dark wood panelling and warm colours.
The bar is decorated with beer jugs and *Bembels*,
the typical grey stoneware apple-wine jugs. On
the first floor is a rustic beer 'cellar', separated
into distinct areas by fine stone arches, with a
long bar framed by brick walls. In summer you
can drink your beer on the terrace. The brewery
makes a light and a dark Pils, both hoppy and
naturally cloudy. The extensive menu features
local and international dishes, mainly from
Croatia, with good-value lunchtime set meals
during the week.

DRAUGHT: **Zwölf Apostel Bräu Hell, Zwölf**
Apostel Bräu Dunkel plus seasonals such as
Bockbier, Festbier, Jubiläumsbräu

Hamburg

www.hamburg.de

The Free Hanseatic City of Hamburg is Germany's second largest city (pop. around 1.7 million) as well as one of the city states. In economic terms, it is the capital of northern Germany, and its port, more than 800 years old, is the ninth largest container port in the world. Apart from the river Elbe and access to the North Sea, Hamburg also boasts the Alster, a vast inland lake right in the heart of the city, and is home to 2302 bridges, more than Venice and Amsterdam combined. Worldwide trade has made Hamburg one of the most cosmopolitan cities in Germany, and the harbour has brought with it the development of the Reeperbahn area, one of the most (in)famous red-light districts in the world.

Visitors to Hamburg should not miss a harbour trip to explore the historic dock area. The town hall with its green copper dome is worth seeing, and so is the Baroque Michaeliskirche, nicknamed 'Michel', which is Hamburg's emblem. There are excellent restaurants and very fashionable shops to explore. The city is also the home of newspaper, magazine and internet publishing.

In late medieval times Hamburg was known as the 'Hanseatic brewery'. No fewer than 457 breweries were based in the city at the time, small enterprises without exception, and beer was the No. 1 export – especially to Denmark and the Netherlands! Beer in Hamburg was first red, then white and only later amber in colour. The breweries were all huddled close together, mostly near canals because they needed water and in the district around the Katharinenkirche, St. Katharine being the patron saint of the breweries. The history is still evident today in street names such as Hopfengasse, Brauerknecht-straße and Hopfenmarkt. Unfortunately, brewing here has declined. By 1890 only 32 breweries remained – still a proud number compared with today's three brewpubs and sole large-scale brewer. All the traditional brewers such as Elbschloß, St. Pauli or Bavaria Brauerei have disappeared. Lüneburg, some 60km from Hamburg, has northern Germany's only brewery museum.

Transport: www.hvv.de
Hamburg has a U-Bahn system and three S-Bahn lines. It is also an important crossroads for national and European railway lines, and boasts five international railway stations.

Anno 1905 (1)

Schank- und Speisewirtschaft Anno 1905
Holstenplatz 17, 22765 Hamburg
T 040 439 25 35   **E** HDralle@t-online.de
www.anno1905.de
Closed Mon; Tue–Fri & Sun from 17.00,
Sat 12.00–14.30 & from 17.00; food until 22.00
Ⓢ S31, S11 or S21 Holstenstraße 120m

Right opposite the Holsten brewery, the 'Anno' opened in 1905 as the name implies. After 'modernisation' in the 1950s and 1960s, the pub was restored to its former glory in the 1980s. It now features the original bar, shelving, large mirrors, cast-iron columns and a magnificent ancient cash register as well as a cosy fireplace corner. Food is traditional Hamburg fare, with Labskaus a speciality (corned beef with beetroot, rollmop, gherkin and fried egg!)

DRAUGHT: **Holsten Pilsener; Jever Pils; Duckstein Obergärig Dunkel; Schneider Hefeweizen Hell**

BOTTLED: **Schneider Hefeweizen dunkel, Schneider Kristallweizen**

Franziskaner (2)

Colonnaden/Große Theaterstraße 9,
20354 Hamburg

left: Museum harbour Övelgönne Port Hamburg.

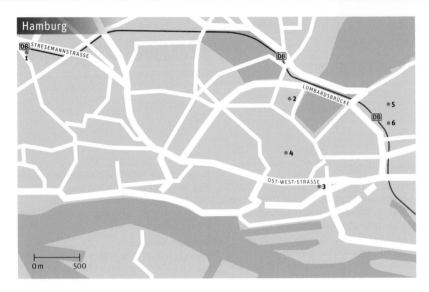

Hamburg

0 m   500

T 040 34 57 56
E info@restaurant-franziskaner.de
Daily 11.30–24.00
U U1 Stephansplatz 300m
DB Hamburg-Dammtor 600m

This traditional pub, a rustic, Bavarian-style inn
with room for 200 guests on two floors, opened
some 45 years ago. The friendly landlord and
his efficient staff serve up good Bavarian beers
and hearty meals. Located right in the heart of
the city, near Jungfernstieg and the State Opera
House, this place is always popular.

DRAUGHT: **Franziskaner Hefe Hell, Franziskaner
Hefe Dunkel**

BOTTLED: **Löwenbräu Original, Premium Pils**

Gröninger (3)

Willy-Brand-Straße 47 (road until recently
known as Ost-West-Straße), 20457 Hamburg
T 040 33 13 81   **E** info@groeninger-hamburg.de
www.groeninger-hamburg.de
Closed Sun & hols; Mon–Fri from 11.00,
Sat from 17.00
U U1 Messberg 200m
DB Hamburg Hbf 1.1km

Hamburg's oldest brewpub – and one of only
three private breweries still in existence today
– housed in a beautifully restored century-old
building. The Braukeller is in the large, rustic

vaulted cellars where guests can watch the
brewers create the house brew in the gleaming
copper brew kettles. Pass the scrubbed wooden
tables and barrels around which you can sit, and
you'll reach the house bakery where delicious
Gröninger beer bread is baked. A few steps
further along is the Gröninger Gasthaus, at
Zippelhaus 4, with its traditional copper lamps
and wooden tables. You can enjoy a meal or snack
with your beer and bread at both the Braukeller
or the Gasthaus. There's always a good atmosphere, and you can grill their home-made
sausages or steaks at your own table. Stairs at
the rear of the cellar bar lead to Brauhaus
Hanseat, Gröninger's more modern subsidiary,
although they're not always open and you may
have to walk around the block if the stairs are
closed.

DRAUGHT: **Gröninger Pils, Hanseaten Weisse**

Joh. Albrecht (4)

Adolphsbrücke 7, 20457 Hamburg
T 040 36 77 40
E hamburg@brauhaus-joh-albrecht.de
www.brauhaus-joh-albrecht.de
Daily from 11.00;
food 11.30–23.30 (Sun until 22.00)
DB Jungfernstieg 350m, Hamburg Hbf 1.3km

One of six Joh. Albrechts nationwide, this one is
located near one of the many bridges, not far from

the Rathaus. As you enter, your eyes immediately alight on the large copper brew kettles where the brewmaster creates his beer specialities according to traditional artisan methods. All the beers are unfiltered. The brewhouse, with seating for 240, has a great atmosphere. Try to get a window-seat, with views over the Fleet, one of Hamburg's numerous waterways. The décor is rustic wooden, and hearty food, including children's and vegetarian choices, snacks and Sunday brunches are also served.

GRAVITY: **Albrechts Messing, Albrechts Kupfer** plus seasonals **Maibock, Weizen, Nickelbier**

MAX & Consorten (5)

Spadenteich 6, 20099 Hamburg
T 040 24 56 17
Daily from 10.00
DB Hamburg Hbf 200m

Close to the Hauptbahnhof in the trendy district of St. George this pub is very popular with young and middle-aged people. Nearly 30 years old and reminiscent of student bars, it may well be noisy but it's always cheerful. There's seating for 160, plus additional space in a side-street in good weather for a further 90. On draught is the typical Hamburg Ratsherrn Pilsener which may not be brewed for much longer – drink it while you can! Food is available until midnight at the weekend.

DRAUGHT: **Ratsherrn Premium Pilsener, Jever, Ducksteiner**

Paulaner's Miraculum (6)

Kirchenallee 45, 20099 Hamburg
T 040 24 82 47 67   **F** 040 24 82 47 99
Daily 11.30–1.00
DB Hamburg Hbf 130m

Very centrally located in Kirchenallee, near Hauptbahnhof, this Bavarian pub is popular with locals and visitors alike. Tasty Bavarian beers, very popular in northern Germany have been served at the Paulaner (no one ever says 'Paulaner's Miraculum!) by friendly staff since 1998. There's also a good-value lunch menu during the week.

DRAUGHT: **Paulaner Pils, Lager, Dunkel, Hefeweizen**

Museum harbour Övelgönne Port Hamburg.

Karlsruhe

One of the youngest cities in Germany, Karlsruhe was conceived in 1715 by the margrave of Baden, Karl-Wilhelm von Baden-Durlach. The city radiates like a fan from the palace he had built. It was in this palace that he decided to spend his final years in peace, a fact recalled in the city's name, 'Karl's rest'. Today Karl rests in the small pyramid on the Marktplatz.

Aside from the palace and a couple of museums, there's not a great deal to divert the ordinary tourist. For the beer lover, however, Karlsruhe is a lot more interesting and currently home to seven breweries. An eighth closed in summer 2005, the short-lived Fischer-Bräu which had only started in May 2004.

Transport: www.kvv.de
The city has an excellent tram system which is connected to the main rail network. The local S-Bahn trams/trains run directly from the streets of Karlsruhe to places as far away as Freudenstadt and Heilbronn, although readers are warned that there are no toilets on these services!

Alte Schmiede (1)

Ochsentorstraße 4, 76227 Karlsruhe-Durlach
T 0721 49 32 51
E info@alte-schmiede-durlach.de
www.alte-schmiede-durlach.de
Sat from 17.30, Sun–Fri 11.30–14.00 & from 17.30
Tram Nos. 1 & 8 Schlossplatz 100m
DB Karlsruhe-Durlach 950m

Cosy little pub and restaurant just off Durlach's main street. There are three rooms, with exposed timber on both the walls and ceilings. A former blacksmith's, as students of German will have surmised from the name (The Old Smithy), many of the tools of that trade adorn the walls. The small bar with its snug is best if you just want a drink. The restaurant serves high-quality food and booking is advisable. Turmberg Bräu is brewed by Schlossbrauerei zu Schmieheim and available only here and in the Letsche Bacchus wine and tapas bar on the next street. Oddly, it's not advertised on the menu.

DRAUGHT: **Hoepfner Goldköpfle; König Pilsener; Köstritzer Schwarzbier; guest beer**

BOTTLED: **Hoepfner Hefe-Weizen, Keller-Weizen; Türmberg Bräu Pilsener Naturtrüb**

Badisch Brauhaus (2)

Stephanienstraße 38–40,
76133 Karlsruhe/Innenstadt-West
T 0721 14 47 00   **F** 0721 144441
www.badisch-brauhaus.de
Daily 11.30–01.00; rooms available
Tram Europaplatz 300m   DB Karlsruhe Hbf 2.2km

Welcome to one of the world's whackiest breweries! The front looks like any other hotel/bar and gives few hints as to the oddities within. These include a fish pond and a slide. That's right, a slide. From the bar to the lower

ft: *Hoepfner, Karlsruhe. Hoepfner's gothic tap*
th *the brewery behind.*

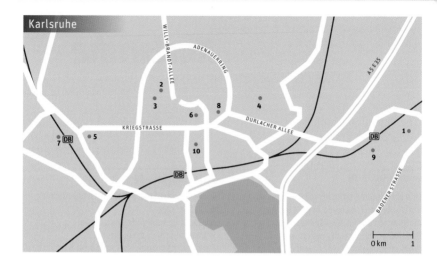

Karlsruhe

basement (which houses the brewing kettles) you can avoid the effort of walking down a few flights of stairs by availing yourself of a tubular slide, although we advise larger readers to give it a miss! In addition, the interior design looks as though it was done by Lawrence Llewellyn-Bowen on acid. Unbelievably, the rear of the pub is even more eccentric. One of a kind.

DRAUGHT: **Badisch Hell, Dunkel, seasonals**

Bierakademie (3)

Douglasstr. 10, 76133 Karlsruhe/Innenstadt-West
T 0721 273 02
www.bierakademie-karlsruhe.de
Fri 13.00–03.00, Sat 18.00–03.00,
Sun–Thu 13.00–01.00
Tram Europaplatz 200m   DB Karlsruhe Hbf 2.1km

Street-corner, L-shaped bar within sight of the Badisch Brauhaus. The narrow island bar is squeezed in down one side of the pub, with plenty of stools for those who wish to sit here. On the other side of the pub, a few tables stand on a raised floor. Exposed wooden beams, bare floorboards and white walls are the extent of the decor. A few brewery mirrors and signs hang from the walls and ceiling. The ten regular draught beers are occasionally joined by a guest.

DRAUGHT: **Andechser Doppelbock Dunkel; Bitburger Premium Pils; Dom Kölsch; Frankenheim Alt; Hoepfner Pilsner; Jever Pilsener;**

Köstritzer Schwarzbier; Paulaner Hefeweißbier, Münchner Urtyp; Rothaus Pils; guest beer

BOTTLED: **Erdinger Weißbier; Flensburger Pils; Rothaus Hefe Weizen; Schneider Aventinus**

Hoepfner Burghof (4)

Haid-und-Neu-Str. 18, 76131 Karlsruhe-Oststadt
T 0721 618 34 00   **E** info@hoepfner-burghof.de
www.hoepfner-burghof.de
Daily from 11.00; food Mon–Fri 11.30–21.00,
Sat 11.30–14.30 & 18.00–21.00; rooms available
Tram Nos. 4 & 5 Karl-Wilhelm-Platz 250m,
Nos. 4, 5 & 8 Hauptfriedhof 300m
DB Karlsruhe Hbf 3km

Next door to the magnificent turreted castle, sorry, brewery. The architecture here is not quite on the same scale, but is nonetheless impressive. You enter through modern sliding doors but inside things are firmly traditional. The bar sweeps around to the left, the seating either divided by snob screens or solid wrought-ironwork embellished by the brewery's logo. To the right is a restaurant and at the rear the festival hall. Some of the walls feature large murals. At the opposite end of the brewery is a beer garden which is open 11.00–23.00 in fine weather. We believe the Kommerzienrat is Goldköpfle re-badged.

DRAUGHT: **Hoepfner Pilsner, Hefe-Weizen, Kräusen, Kommerzienrat, Porter, seasonals**
BOTTLED: **Hoepfner Keller-Weizen, Edel-Weizen**

Kühler Krug (5)

Wilhelm-Baur-Str. 3a, 76135 Karlsruhe-Weststadt
T 0721 831 64 16
E restaurant-kuehler-krug@t-online.de
www.brauhaus-kuehler-krug.com
Fri & Sat 11.00–01.00, Sun 10.00–23.00, Mon–
Thu 11.00–24.00; food Mon–Sat 11.30–23.00,
Sun 10.30–22.00; rooms available
No. 4 Kühler Krug 150m
Karlsruhe West 700m, Hbf 3km

The Cool Tankard is a large, sprawling, single-
storeyed brewpub in a park on the western side
of the city, alongside the river Alb. There are five
rooms, including a conservatory and a couple of
rooms that are available for hire. The brewing
kettles are on a pedestal in the main restaurant,
the bar next door to the right. Two sides of the
pub are adjoined by a terrace, a third by the large
beer garden. As in many brewpubs, the lager
tanks are downstairs, next door to the toilets.
From here it's a 15-minute stroll to the Moninger
brewery and tap.

DRAUGHT: **Kühler Krug Zwickel Pils, Dunkel,
Weizen, seasonals**

Litfaß (6)

Kreuzstraße 10, 76133 Karlsruhe/Innenstadt-Ost
T 0721 69 34 87
Daily 10.00–01.00
Karlsruhe Marktplatz 100m
Karlsruhe Hbf 1.9km

Single-roomed, street-corner pub just off the
Marktplatz. There's an island bar around which
the locals sit, plus tables and chairs on a raised
platform along three walls. Nicely appointed,
with good wooden furniture and some exposed
stonework. A number of wood carvings are
built into the bar and hang on the walls. In fine
weather there's plenty of seating on the little
square outside. Popular with all ages and very
busy at lunchtime, when you may struggle to
find a seat. They have a sister pub next door
called Litfaßle.

DRAUGHT: **Hoepfner Pilsner, Hefe-Weizen,
Kräusen, Export, seasonals**

BOTTLED: **Hoepfner Keller-Weizen,
Edel-Weizen**

Moninger (7)

Zeppelinstraße 17, 76185 Karlsruhe-Grünwinkel
T 0721 921 22 13
www.moninger.de
Sat & Sun 10.00–24.00, Mon–Fri 11.00–24.00
Tram Nos. 2 & S2 Eckenerstraße 500m
DB Karlsruhe West 500m, Hbf 4km

Recently refurbished tap at the side of the brewery, now Moninger's showcase pub following the closure of Zum Moninger in the city centre. The full range of regular Moninger beers is available, joined by all four seasonals at the appropriate times of the year. The bar has some interesting old brewery photographs and other paraphernalia. There are a couple of further rooms to the right and a beer garden at the rear between pub and brewery, complete with artificial beach! Food is available, though we think they close the kitchen during the afternoon. If you don't fancy the walk from either tram or train, buses 60 and 62 run here from Entenfang.

DRAUGHT: **Moninger Zwickel, Pilsener, Hefe-Weizen, Urtrübes Helles, Export, seasonals**

BOTTLED: **Moninger Dunkles Weizen, Kristall-Weizen, Alt-Badisch Dunkel**

Vogelbräu (8)

Kapellenstr. 50, 76131 Karlsruhe/Innenstadt-Ost
T 0721 37 75 71   **E** karlsruhe@vogelbraeu.de
www.vogelbraeu.de
Daily 10.00–01.00
Tram Durlacher Tor 250m
Tram No. 3 Mendelssohnplatz 350m
DB Karlsruhe Hbf 2.3km

Rudi Vogel's first brewpub recently celebrated its 20th anniversary. The split-level bar is quite austere and more modern than most of its kind. Expansion over the years has seen rooms added behind the brewery and across the corridor. There's a decent beer garden at the rear. *Vogel* is German for bird and the walls in the bar are covered in cartoons featuring various feathered creatures in humanoid form. Although only one beer is brewed regularly there is an impressive list of seasonals, one of which should be available at all times. There's also a thriving trade in take-home beer.

DRAUGHT: **Vogelbräu Pils, seasonals**

Vogel Hausbräu (9)

Amalienbadstraße 16, 76227 Karlsruhe-Durlach
T 0721 81 96 80   **E** durlach@vogelbraeu.de
www.vogelbraeu.de
Fri & Sat 10.00–01.00, Sun–Thu 10.00–24.00;
food until 23.00 (Fri & Sat 24.00)
Tram No. 1 Friedrichschule 300m
DB Karlsruhe-Durlach 600m

Modern brewpub attached to the Blauer Reiter hotel, the most recent addition to the Vogel empire. The entrance to the pub is actually around the corner on Kanzlerstraße. The square bar has a partition on two sides and beyond this you'll find that rarest of things in a German bar – a no-smoking section. There are some decent paintings of Durlach on the walls. Large floor-to-ceiling windows provide plenty of daylight. The brewery itself is in a three-storey glass-fronted tower across the passage at the rear. Alongside is the cobbled beer garden.

DRAUGHT: **Vogelbräu Pils, seasonals**

Wolfbräu (10)

Werderstraße 51, 76137 Karlsruhe-Südstadt
T 0721 354 57 70   **E** info@wolfbraeu.de
www.wolfbraeu.de
Daily 11.00–01.00; food 11.30–14.30 & 17.30–23.30
Tram No. 3 Werderstraße 200m
DB Karlsruhe Hbf 1.3km

Street-corner tap on Werderplatz attached to the brewery. Head straight on as you enter – the left-hand door leads to a café. The single room features some imaginative seating, an unusual beer-bottle light shade and what can only be described as a carved tree. Brewery-related posters and paintings hang from the walls, many featuring cartoon wolves. All bar one of Wolfbräu's beers are available. The food tends towards pizza and pasta.

DRAUGHT: **Wolf Pils, Kräusen Pils, Export, Hefe-Weizen**

BOTTLED: **Wölfle Pils, Schwarz, Hefeweizen Dunkel, Indianer Bock**

Köln (Cologne)

www.koeln.de

Probably best known to the outside world for its magnificent Gothic cathedral, a vast structure next to the Hauptbahnhof that took over 600 years to complete, Köln has much to offer the tourist. Founded by the Romans some 2,000 years ago as Colonia Claudia Ara Agrippinensis, the city has evolved to become one of the largest and most important in the country. The old town is south of the cathedral, a network of streets and squares around the Groß St. Martin church, largely built on the site of the Roman settlement. The modern city centre west of this is one of the best places to shop in Germany, or so we're told.

Each year, over the six days before Ash Wednesday, the city lets its hair down with a huge carnival. It begins on the Thursday, *Weiberfastnacht,* when the women of Köln rule the town and can essentially do whatever they want. A series of events over the next few days culminates in a grand parade on *Rosenmontag* (Rose Monday), attracting about a million spectators despite the often perishing weather, by which time most of the population are seriously smashed.

For the beer tourist, Köln means one thing – Kölsch. A pale, top-fermented beer, Kölsch is brewed exclusively in the city and surrounding area. In the late 1980s there were still around 20 breweries, more than anywhere else in the world at the time, but in the last decade or so a number have either been taken over or merged to form the Kölner Verbund Brauereien. Eight Kölsch brands are currently produced at the brewery in Mülheim, on the right bank of the Rhine. We hope this worrying trend stops soon, but given the acquisitive nature of parent company Oetker, this seems unlikely. Nevertheless, there are still 12 independent breweries, including several new starters.

Transport: www.vrsinfo.de
The city's U-Bahn is in reality a tram network that runs underground in some parts of the city. Ⓤ signifies an underground tram station, Ⓣ a surface tram stop.

Bierhaus en d'r Salzgass (1)

Salzgasse 5–7, 50667 Köln/Altstadt-Nord
T 0221 800 19 00 **F** 0221 800 19 01
www.bierhaus-salzgass.de
Daily from 12.00
Ⓣ Heumarkt 200m Ⓤ Ⓓ Ⓑ Köln Hbf 750m

Formerly Brauhaus zur Täsch, brewing ended in 1907 and it ceased to be a pub in the 1970s. Re-opened in its current guise in 2003, possibly in retaliation to nearby Pfaffen's decision to stop selling Päffgen and start its own brewery. The main bar is deceptively large and appears to have been at least four rooms in a previous life. There's an upstairs restaurant overlooking the bar itself and a small beer garden to the rear.

GRAVITY: **Päffgen Kölsch**

Biermuseum (2)

Buttermarkt 39, 50667 Köln/Altstadt-Nord
T 0221 257 78 02 **F** 0221 250 86 73
Daily 14.00–03.00
Ⓣ Heumarkt 350m Ⓤ Ⓓ Ⓑ Köln Hbf 600m

Basic bar between Fischmarkt and Heumarkt, attracting mainly tourists. The extensive range of beers (over 50) includes many from outside Germany, the bottled beers include Hövels Bitterbier and a Berliner Weisse, though whether it's Kindl or Schultheiss is not clear. The number of draught bocks is unusually high. We don't think they do food, but plenty of others round here do.

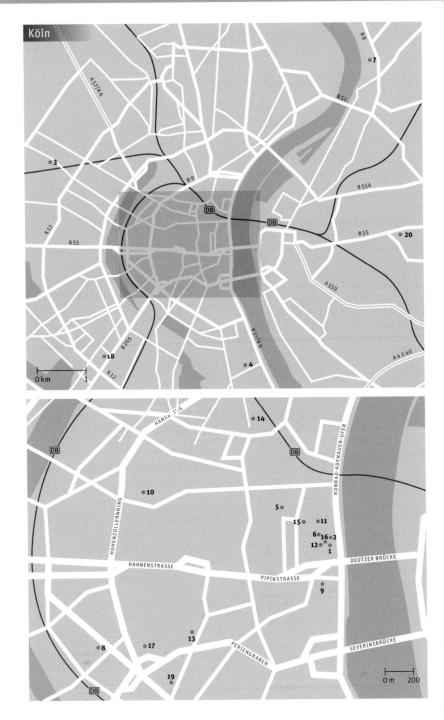

DRAUGHT: **Bitburger Pils; Becks; Diebels Alt; Einbecker Ur-Bock Hell, Maibock** (May)**; Heller Aecht Schlenkerla Rauchbier; Jever Pilsener; Königs Pilsener; Krombacher Pils; Kulmbacher Doppelbock, Eisbock; Sion Kölsch; Warsteiner Premium**

BOTTLED: **various**

Braustelle (3)

Christianstraße 2, 50825 Köln-Ehrenfeld
T 0221 285 69 32   **www.braustelle.com**
Closed Sun; Mon–Sat 18.00–01.00
Ⓤ Leyendeckerstraße 100m
ⒹⒷ Köln-Ehrenfeld 900m

Small street-corner brewpub, the most recent and smallest addition to Köln's brewing scene. It's refreshingly basic inside, featuring bare wooden floorboards and furniture. The small, uncomplicated brewery is in one corner, a collection of wheat-beer glasses lines one of the walls and, er … that's it. (*Braustelle*, or brewing site, is a pun: *Baustelle*, without the R, means building site!) The beer range does vary from that listed on the website – Ehrenfelder Alt apparently now being a regular beer and additional seasonals do appear, some quite adventurous. On our last visit we were more than a little surprised to find Hibiscusbier, made from … you guessed it! On Wednesday evenings you can watch – or help with – the brewing process.

DRAUGHT: **Helios Kölsch, Weizen, Ehrenfelder Alt, seasonals**

Dom (4)

Alteburger Straße 157, 50968 Köln-Bayenthal
T 0221 934 78 10   **E** info@dombrauhaus.com
www.dom-brauhaus.com
Daily 11.00–24.00; food until 22.30
🚊 No. 16, Schönhauser Straße 400m
Ⓤ ⒹⒷ Köln Hbf 3.5km

Until 2001 this was Küpper's brewery and tap. Following their move to join the rest of the Brau and Brunnen clan at Kölner Brauerei-Verband, Dom moved the short distance from their old home on Tacitusstraße. The large brewery occupies both sides of Alteburger Straße, the two parts being connected by a pipeline and a bridge. The tap is all you'd expect – wood panelling, tiled floors and scrubbed pine-topped tables. There's also a large, walled beer garden,

the entrance to which is on Schönhauser Straße. This features a former brewing kettle that has been converted into a fountain. Oh, and there's a brewery museum as well.

GRAVITY: **Dom Kölsch, Kölner Wieß**

Früh am Dom (5)

Am Hof 12–14, 50667 Köln/Altstadt-Nord
T 0221 261 32 11   **F** 0221 261 32 99
www.frueh.de
Daily 08.00–01.00; food 08.30–24.00
Ⓤ ⒹⒷ Köln-Hbf 400m

Close to the cathedral, as indicated by the name, Früh's showcase outlet (and the former home of the brewery) is probably the best-known and most-visited pub in the city. When the Guide first came in 1991 we found a much smaller pub than you'll see today, new restaurants and bars having opened upstairs, downstairs and alongside the main body of the *Brauhaus* over the last 15 years. Grab a spot in the taproom and watch the countless glasses of Kölsch disappearing to all corners of the building.

GRAVITY: **Früh Kölsch**

Gaffel-Haus (6)

Alter Markt 20–22, 50667 Köln/Altstadt-Nord
T 0221 257 76 92   **E** info@gaffel-haus.de
www.gaffel-haus.de   Daily 11.00–01.00
🚊 Heumarkt 250m   ⒹⒷ Köln Hbf 600m

Gaffel's tap is at the bottom end of the Alter Markt. The bar is on the left as you enter, with a small raised seating area to the right. There's a larger restaurant to the rear plus a smaller one upstairs that we've never seen open. In summer, tables occupy a large part of the square in front. Sadly, the Kölsch is from a fount, not the barrel. Food is served all day.

DRAUGHT: **Gaffel Kölsch**

BOTTLED: **Gaffel 1396**

Gilden (7)

Clevischer Ring 121, 51063 Köln-Mülheim
T 0221 640 63 39   **F** 0221 640 63 71
www.gilden.de
Daily 11.00–01.00
🚊 No. 4 Von-Sparr-Straße 600m
Ⓤ ⒹⒷ Köln-Hbf 6km

Opened in 2002, this may or may not be the official Gilden tap, but for purists it's a lot closer to the brewery than the city-centre Ausschank. The interior is similar in style to many modern brewpubs and still has a 'just out of the box' feel to it. There's a beer garden on one side of the pub, and the Hotel Park Consul on the other. A long way from the centre, on the western side of the busy Clevischer Ring which, frankly, is a bit of a bugger to cross, some may feel this pub is not worth the effort.

GRAVITY: **Gilden Kölsch**
DRAUGHT: **Jever Pils; Kölner Wieß; Warsteiner Premium Verum**

Hellers Brauhaus (8)

Roonstraße 33, 50674 Köln-Neustadt
T 0221 24 25 45   **E** info@hellers-brauhaus.de
www.hellers-brauhaus.de
Closed Sun & hols; Mon–Thu 18.00–01.00,
Fri & Sat 18.00–03.00; food until 23.00
Tram Zülpicher Platz 200m   DB Köln-Süd 450m

The modern brick front gives way to four rooms with both tiled and wooden floors and the usual dark wooden chairs and scrubbed tables. The rear restaurant has an unusual amount of greenery, however. The bar features a small (disused) still and some brewing paraphernalia. The two seasonal beers (No. 33 and Euro Bock) are available for much of the year as they're normally bottled.

DRAUGHT: **Hellers Kölsch, Wiess**
BOTTLED: **seasonals**

Malzmühle (9)

Heumarkt 6, 50667 Köln-Nord/Altstadt
T 0221 21 01 17   **E** info@muehlenkoelsch.de
www.muehlen-koelsch.de
Mon–Sat 10.00–24.00, Sun 11.00–23.00;
food 11.30–23.00 (22.00 Sun)
Tram Heumarkt 70m   U DB Hbf 950m

One of the most popular pubs in Cologne, the Malt Mill counted Bill Clinton among its guests. The address is slightly misleading as the bottom end of Heumarkt has now been bisected by tramlines and roads – the pub is south of the tram stop. You enter through one of two revolving doors, the left one leading to the main bar/restaurant, the right (usually locked) leads to more of a drinker's den. The Schänke is at the

head of these two rooms. Wood-panelling abounds – very little appears to have changed in the last 50 years. Always busy.

GRAVITY: **Mühlen Kölsch**

Päffgen (10)

64-66 Friesenstraße, 50670 Köln/Altstadt-Nord
T 0221 257 77 65   **E** brauereipaeffgen@aol.com
www.paeffgen-koelsch.de
Closed Mon; Tue–Sun 10.00–24.00
U Friesenplatz 150m   U DB Hbf 1.2km

Don't be put-off by the austere 1950s facade – inside you'll find one of Köln's more traditional brewpubs, complete with *Beichtstuhl* (confessional) and *Thekenschaf* (the 'bar sheep', keeping order!). The main corridor houses the bar and leads to the rear yard/beer garden. Here you can relax whilst marvelling at the source of the Kölsch you're drinking through windows beyond. Back inside, the main restaurant is on the right and there are a couple of smaller rooms to the left of the corridor. The windows feature some interesting stained glass and you won't be surprised to learn the beer comes from the wood.

GRAVITY: **Päffgen Kölsch**

Peters (11)

Mühlengasse 1, 50667 Köln/Altstadt-Nord
T 0221 257 39 50   **E** info@peters-brauhaus.de
www.peters-brauhaus.de
Daily 11.00–00.30; food 11.30–24.00
Tram Heumarkt 350m   U DB Köln Hbf 500m

The home of Brauhaus zum Kranz until 1898, and from 1994 until 2004 the tap of Peters & Bambeck brewery (of Monheim). Sadly, the brewery succumbed to the wallet of the Oetker group in 2004 and the beer is now brewed at the Kölner Brauerei-Verbund plant in Köln-Mülheim. The pub, however, hasn't changed a bit. Murals adorn many walls and there's a lovely glass roof in the Braustube.

GRAVITY: **Peters Kölsch**

Pfaffen (12)

Heumarkt 62, 50667 Köln-Innenstadt
T 0221 257 77 65   **F** 0221 257 99 47
www.max-paeffgen.de
Closed Mon; Tue–Sun 12.00–24.00
Tram Heumarkt 150m   U DB Köln Hbf 700m

At the top end of Heumarkt, until 2001 this was called Altstadt Päffgen and was Päffgen's old-town pub. Following a dispute pub owner Max Päffgen decided to start his own brewery, and this lies around 20km south-east of Köln near the hamlet of Kellershohn, between Rösrath and Lohmar. The interior is one of the nicest in the city, and features some lovely woodwork and glass. The beer is served direct from wooden barrels and as far as we're aware is only available in this pub.

GRAVITY: **Pfaffen**

Reissdorf (13)

Kleiner Griechenmarkt 40,
50676 Köln/Altstadt-Süd
T 0221 21 92 54   **F** 0221 21 92 55
www.brauhaus-reissdorf.de
Daily from 16.00
[U] Poststraße 200m   [DB] Köln-Süd 800m

Despite the brewery having been around for over a century, Reissdorf's official tap opened as recently as 1992. The building is a modern brick affair and far removed from what you'd expect of a Köln brewery tap. Inside, things aren't too bad with many of the usual features, although it's in need of a bit of aging. Disappointingly, the Kölsch is served from an obviously fake barrel.

DRAUGHT: **Reissdorf Kölsch**

Schreckenskammer (14)

Ursulagartenstraße 11–15,
50668 Köln/Altstadt-Nord
T 0221 13 25 81
www.schreckenskammer.com
Closed Sun & hols and three weeks in July;
Mon–Fri 11.00–13.45 & 16.30–22.30,
Sat 11.00–14.00; food 12.00–13.45 & 17.00–21.30
[U] [DB] Köln-Hansaring 400m
[U] [DB] Köln Hbf 600m

Destroyed during 1943, The Horror Chamber remained closed for 17 years before re-opening in August 1960, albeit without the brewery that previously graced the premises (we believe the Kölsch is brewed by Dom). Opposite the Ursula church, the rooms are in typical Brauhaus style but, unlike most, this place is traditional enough to have sawdust on the floor. The barrels are raised from the cellar by pulley.

GRAVITY: **Schreckenskammer Kölsch**

Sion (15)

Unter Taschenmacher 5, 50667 Köln/Altstadt-Nord
T 0221 257 85 40   **E** info@brauhaus-sion.de
www.brauhaus-sion.de
Fri & Sat 10.00–01.00, Sun–Thu 10.00–00.30;
food 11.30–24.00
[Tram] Heumarkt 400m   [U] [DB] Köln Hbf 450m

Large, rambling pub between the cathedral and Alter Markt. At the entrance is a taproom with several tables, the main body of the restaurant being to the right and rear of this. There's been no brewery on site since 1942 when the pub was destroyed. It re-opened in 1951 but Sion Kölsch was brewed by Früh and Malzmühle until 1978 when production moved to the Hubertus brewery in the western suburb of Müngersdorf. Since 1993 it's been brewed in the former Bergische Löwen Brauerei, now the all-consuming Kölner Brauerei-Verband.

DRAUGHT: **Sion Kölsch**

Sünner im Walfisch (16)

Salzgasse 13, 50667 Köln-Altstadt Nord
T 0221 257 78 79   **F** 0221 257 78 09
www.walfisch.net
Mon–Thu 17.00–01.00, Fri 12.00–02.00,
Sat & Sun 11.00–02.00
[Tram] Heumarkt 200m   [U] [DB] Köln Hbf 750m

Sünner's city tap since 1996, until 1889 this was a brewery in its own right (Zum Kirchenbrau-haus). The interior is typical of a traditional Köln pub; multi-roomed with wood-panelling, wooden floors, scrubbed tables, etc. Like an increasing number of local bars, The Whale has started selling Kölsch in 3- or 5-litre 'towers'. The menu includes all you would expect. Annual holiday first two weeks in August.

GRAVITY: **Sünner Kölsch**
BOTTLED: **Sünner Hefeweizen**

Töller (17)

Weyerstraße 96, 50676 Köln/Altstadt-Süd
T 0221 258 93 16   www.haus-toeller.de
Closed Sun & hols; Mon–Sat 17.00–00.30; food 17.30–22.30

🚊 Barbarossaplatz 200m   DB Köln-Süd 500m

Pleasant old pub, not far from Barbarossaplatz. We think it brewed, briefly, in the late 19th century (if it didn't, it would have been almost unique!), but the pub's own website only mentions a distillery here around this time. The interior is airier than in some pubs in the city, but rather than updating the owners believe in restoring. Under a previous owner in the 20th century, regulars included many celebrities such as chancellor Adenauer, filmmaker Fassbinder and artist Buys. All food is freshly prepared; horse-lovers beware the Rheinischer Sauerbraten!

GRAVITY: **Sion Kölsch**

Unkelbach (18)

Luxemburger Straße 260, 50937 Köln-Klettenberg
T 0221 41 41 84   **E** info@hausunkelbach.de
www.hausunkelbach.de
Mon–Fri 16.00–24.00, Sat & Sun 11.00–01.00

🚊 Nos. 18 & 19 Sülzburgstraße 5m
DB Köln-Süd 1.5km

The original Haus Unkelbach, opened over 75 years ago in Weyerstraße, was destroyed in World War II as was the second one, in the neighbouring building! Third time lucky, and Unkelbach opened in its present location as a typically Cologne-style brewpub. The current landlord, the first owner's grandson, took over in 2000 and turned this pub into a Cologne legend. The pub really comes into its own during carnival – and on 11th November, the

official opening of the carnival season! – when queues of thirsty celebrators stretch around the block. There's a bar room at the front, a restaurant area through the back, a party room upstairs and an asphalted beer garden for 220 outside. The kitchen serves local specialities. The decor is nothing special, but it's the unique atmosphere that makes this a worthwhile trip into the suburbs.

GRAVITY: **Reissdorf Kölsch**

Weißbräu zu Köln (19)

Am Weidenbach 24, 50676 Köln/Altstadt-Süd
T 0221 23 18 23   **E** info@weiss-braeu.de
Daily 11.00–01.00

🚊 Eifelstraße 150m 🚊 Barbarossaplatz 250m
DB Köln-Süd 500m

This atmospheric street-corner brewpub is one of several formerly owned by Hofbräuhaus Traunstein and the only one to brew anything other than wheat beer. The interior is divided into various rooms and drinking areas, and stretches over two floors. The brewery is in the nose of the building, next to the main entrance. Amongst the bric-a-brac is a rowing boat suspended above the bar.

DRAUGHT: **Weiss Bräu Lecker Kölsch, Hefeweizen, Pantaleons Schwarze**

Zechengarten (20)

Kalker Hauptstraße 262-268, 51103 Köln-Kalk
T 0221 98 79 90   **F** 0221 87 83 81
www.zechengarten.de
Closed Oct–Mar. Apr–Sep: Fri from 16.00, Sat from 13.00, Sun from 11.00, Mon–Thu from 16.00

🚇 Nos. 1 & 9 Kalk Kapelle 200m
🚇 DB Köln Hbf 4.5km

This small, well-tended beer garden, alongside Sünner's attractive two-tone brick brewery, only opens in fine weather during spring and summer. The name translates as 'mine garden', a reminder of the mine that stood on this spot before the brewery came along. Food is served, including a giant 850g pork chop, but the menu is limited. If you find the garden closed, Sünner's Bier & Kornhaus, outside Kalk Kapelle U-Bahn station at Kalker Hauptstraße 218, is open from 09.00 to 01.00 daily.

GRAVITY: **Sünner Kölsch**
BOTTLED: **Sünner Hefeweizen**

Leipzig

www.leipzig.de

SAXONY's second city, Leipzig has long been a major cultural centre. Wagner was born in the city, Bach and Mendelssohn both lived and died here. Goethe studied at the university, his favourite watering hole featuring in a scene from Faust. The Opera House is home to Germany's second oldest opera, and the Gewandhaus hosts the world-famous orchestra of the same name. The German National Library was established in Leipzig in 1912. More recently, the Velvet Revolution of 1989 (which eventually led to the fall of the Berlin Wall) began at Leipzig's Nikolaikirche, and with demonstrations held outside the Stasi headquarters (now a museum). Several dozen trade fairs attracting more than a million visitors annually are held in purpose-built fairgrounds to the south of the city centre. Consequently, accommodation in the city may be hard to find.

On the beer front, Leipzig is home to five breweries – the large Reudnitzer and comparatively small Bauer, plus three modern brewpubs. The jewel in Leipzig's beery crown, however, is Gose. Once again available after years of extinction, this unique style (ingredients include coriander and salt) is now brewed by both Bauer (for W. Goedecke & Co.) and Gosebrauerei Bayerischer Bahnhof.

Transport: www.lvb.de
Leipzig's central station boasts the largest terminus building in the world – 26 platforms under one roof. Outside is the main tram station, from where you can catch a tram to most parts of the city.

Bayerischer Bahnhof (1)

Bayerischer Platz 1, 04103 Leipzig
T 0341 124 57 60
E info@bayerischer-bahnhof.de
www.bayerischer-bahnhof.de
Daily 11.00–01.00
🚋 Nos. 2, 9 & 16 Bayerischerplatz 100m
DB Leipzig Hbf 1.8km

Large, ornate brewpub in the former 'Bavarian Station' – however, you can no longer arrive by train as the station closed in 2001. Trains should return (underground) in 2009 with the opening of the City-Tunnel. Today, several tram routes pass by, the tram stop being 100m or so north of the pub (easily found – just look for the four white arches). Gose is the speciality here, but more conventional beers are available. Rooms of differing size and character lead off the main bar, which houses the brewery. Good Saxon food is served all day. There's a large self-service beer garden from April to October.

DRAUGHT: **Bayerischer Bahnhof Leipziger Gose, Schaffner Pils, Kuppler Weißbier, Heizer Schwarzbier, Prellbock** (seasonal)

BOTTLED: **Bayerischer Bahnhof Leipziger Gose**

Gohliser Wirtschaft (2)

Gohliser Straße 20, 04105 Leipzig
T 0341 564 40 33   E wirtschaft@gohliser.de
www.gohliser.de
Daily 11.00–01.00
🚋 No. 12 Fritz-Seger-Straße 200m
DB Leipzig Hbf 1.5km

If you arrive by tram, follow the lines back towards the city centre and the pub is on your left. A cosy bar with a summer terrace; limited snack menu plus one or two daily specials. The former tap of Brauerei Gohlis, taken over by

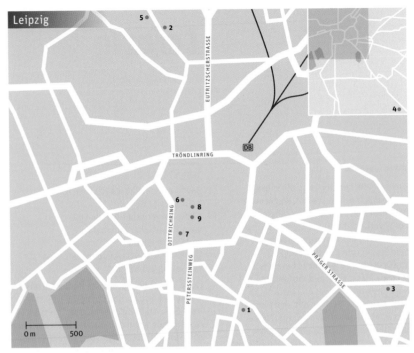

Sachsenbräu (now Reudnitz) in 1958. The rear bar is for televised sport, except on the last Tuesday of the month when Gohliser hosts live theatre performances. We believe the house beers are brewed by Hartmannsdorfer Brauhaus.

DRAUGHT: **Gohliser Bräu, Schwarzer Gohliser, Gohliser Böckchen; Früh Kölsch; Radeberger Pilsener; Schneider Weiße**

Hopfenspeicher (3)

Oststraße 38, 04317 Leipzig
T 0341 124 88 98 **F** 0341 22 52 97 90
Mon–Fri 15.00–24.00, Sat 11.00–03.00,
Sun 11.00–23.00
🚋 No. 4 Riebeck-/Oststraße 250m
DB Leipzig-Hbf 2km

This recently refurbished tap is at the rear of the Reudnitzer brewery, in a rather austere suburb south-east of the centre. There's a choice of routes if you come by tram, with a stop at either end of the street. The main bar is up a few steps off the central passage. Above this is a bowling alley and bar with pool and darts. Outside, the beer garden backs onto one of the brewery's

storage yards – the pub's name means Hop Store. One of the few outlets for Reudnitzer Naturtrüb, served in ceramic mugs.

DRAUGHT: **Reudnitzer Pilsner, Naturtrüb, Schwarzbier**

BOTTLED: **Erdinger Champ, Weißbier, Weißbier Dunkel, Reudnitzer Ur-Bock Hell**

Kaiser Napoleon (4)

Prager Straße 233, 04289 Leipzig
T 0341 86 91 10 **F** 0341 869 11 19
Mon–Thu 17.00–24.00,
Fri, Sat & Sun 11.00–14.00 & 17.00–24.00
🚋 Nos. 2 & 15 Prager/Russenstraße 50m
DB Leipzig Hbf 5km

Take a tram (they stop outside) to this historic pub in the leafy suburb of Probstheida. Napoleon and King Murat of Naples reputedly met here during 'The Battle of Nations' in October 1813, the largest battle of the Napoleonic Wars, which ended in defeat for the Petit Général. The building was largely destroyed during World War II. The cool, vaulted bar has housed a brewery since 1997. The food menu has an international flavour, with the emphasis on French cuisine. Seasonal brews include very rare hemp and oat beers. Although still open when the Guide visited in May 2005 it's possible they may have since closed as the phone, fax and website no longer work.

DRAUGHT: **Napoleon Bonaparte Pils, Kanonier Schwarzbier, seasonal beers; Köstritzer Schwarzbier**

Ohne Bedenken (5)

Menckestraße 5/Poetenweg 6, 04155 Leipzig
T 0341 566 23 60   **E** info@gosenschenke.de
www.gosenschenke.de
Sat 12.00–01.00, Sun 12.00–24.00,
Mon–Fri 17.00–01.00 (from 12.00 in summer)
Tram No. 12 Fritz-Seger-Straße 50m
DB Leipzig Hbf 1800m

A short walk from the tram stop, the vast beer garden is on Poetenweg and the pub behind it, on Menckestraße; you can reach one from the other.

Re-opened as a pub in the mid 1980s, Ohne Bedenken (Without Hesitation) was the first place to resume selling Gose 20 years after the last original Gosebrauerei closed, and for many years it remained the only place in the world where this unusual style was available. A lovely wood-panelled bar and a couple of smaller rooms. There should be many more places like this. On summer weekdays the beer garden opens earlier than the pub.

DRAUGHT: **Goedecke's Döllnitzer Ritterguts-Gose; Bayerischer Bahnhof Leipziger Gose; Bauer's Schwarzes Bier; Reudnitzer Pilsner; Ur-Krostitzer Feinherbes Pilsner**

Paulaner Restaurants (6)

Klostergasse 3–5, 04109 Leipzig
T 0341 211 31 15
E info-PaulanerLeipzig@t-online.de
www.paulaner-leipzig.de

Look for these four arches if you're going to the Bayerischer Bahnhof – they're part of the old station.

Daily 11.00–01.00
🚋 No. 9 Thomaskirche 100m
🚆 Leipzig Hbf 800m

This slightly refined complex of restaurants and bars, at the edge of the old town, less than 100m north of the Thomaskirche church and brewpub, and within easy walking distance of the station, came back under the Munich brewery's control in 1990 having been nationalised in 1948. After extensive refurbishment it re-opened in 1992 and offers a taste of Bavaria in central Leipzig. Both Saxon and Bavarian dishes served all day.

DRAUGHT: **Paulaner Original Münchner Hell, Premium Pils, Original Münchner Dunkel, Hefeweißbier**

BOTTLED: **Paulaner Diät Pils, Hefeweiß. Dunkel, Hefeweißbier Kristallklar**

Ratskeller (7)

Lotterstraße 1, 04109 Leipzig
T 0341 123 45 67   **E** info@ratskeller-leipzig.de
www.ratskeller-leipzig.de
Mon–Sat 11.00–23.00, Sun & hols 11.00–15.00
🚋 Nos. 2, 8 or 9 Neues Rathaus 150m
🚆 Leipzig Hbf 1.3km

Many German towns make intelligent use of the space underneath their town halls, and Leipzig is no exception. Located on the southern edge of the city centre, in the cellars of the New Town Hall, this large pub celebrated its centenary in 2004. The focal point is the Reudnitzer Ratsbierkeller, a large wood-panelled room featuring a vaulted ceiling and a four-metre-high chair. There are six other rooms of differing sizes and characters, altogether seating some 700 people. The above-average menu features some vegetarian options. Another outlet for the comparatively rare Reudnitzer Naturtrüb.

DRAUGHT: **Reudnitzer Pilsner, Naturtrüb, Schwarzbier; Jever Pilsener**

BOTTLED: **Reudnitzer Pilsner, Schwarzbier; Erdinger Weißbier, Weißbier Dunkel**

The opening hours of German pubs, particularly those in less populous areas, can and do change from year to year. If you find times different to those we've listed, please let us know at **GermanBreweries@aol.com.**

Thomaskirche (8)

Thomaskirchhof 3–5, 04109 Leipzig
T 0341 212 61 10
E info@brauerei-thomaskirche.de
www.brauhaus-thomaskirche.de
Daily 11.00–24.00
🚋 No. 9 Thomaskirche 100m
🚆 Leipzig Hbf 850m

To find this place, look up Thomasgasse on the map, or search for the Thomas Church – the brewpub is within spitting distance. Decorated in the traditional Saxon/Bavarian/Italian style, this modern pub seats around 300. In fine weather the large terrace at the front enables you to admire the church and observe passing tourists while enjoying your beer. Extensive menu, mainly Italian, available all day.

DRAUGHT: **Thomaskirche Pils, Spezial Dunkel, seasonal beers**

Thüringer Hof (9)

Burgstraße 19, 04109 Leipzig
T 0341 994 49 99
E reservierung@thueringer-hof.de
www.thueringer-hof.de
Daily 11.00–24.00
🚋 No. 9 Thomaskirche 250m,
　　Wilhelm-Leuschner-Platz 300m
🚆 Leipzig Hbf 1km

Roughly half-way between the new and old town halls. Originally built in 1454, this was once one of Germany's largest pubs, comprising 17 rooms and seating more than 1,200 people. It was completely destroyed in 1943 and only a small part has been rebuilt. The current incarnation dates from 1996 – hard to believe at first glance, the reconstruction has been so sympathetic. The main restaurant is the vaulted Luthersaal, which feels smaller than it is, due to the numerous pillars. There's also a small atrium to the rear. The menu features various Thuringian specialities.

DRAUGHT: **Würzburger Hofbräu Premium-Pilsner, Schwarzbier; Julius Echter Hefe-Weißbier Hell**

BOTTLED: **Julius Echter-Weißbier Dunkel, Echter Kristallweizen**

München *(Munich)*

www.muenchen.de

Top of the list for many tourists, München is the capital of Bayern (Bavaria) and the largest city in the state. Stereotypically synonymous with the Oktoberfest, that world-famous two-week orgy of binge-drinking, there is much besides to entertain the visitor. Suffice to say, the heart of the city is the Marienplatz and many of München's historic buildings and museums, as well as most shops, are within walking distance from here. Farther out, the Englischer Garten is a vast park north-east of the centre, the Theriesenwiese, where the Oktoberfest takes place is to the south-west and the Olympiapark is on the north-western edge of the city.

In the beer world München is one of the most renowned cities on the planet. At the forefront of the bottom-fermenting revolution, some of the first golden 'lager' beers were brewed here, and many breweries still label their beers *Münchner Art* (Munich style). There are nine breweries within the city limits. Five are huge – Augustiner, Hofbräu, Löwenbräu, Paulaner and Spaten-Franziskaner. The other four are all brewpubs: the long-established Forschungsbrauerei, the more modern Paulaner Bräuhaus and Unionsbräu, and the new Bavaria-Bräu. A tenth, Hacker-Pschorr, is owned by Brau Holding International, but all beers are now brewed by Paulaner.

Transport: www.mvv-muenchen.de
The majority of visitors will arrive at the Hauptbahnhof, even those who fly. This is the hub of München's excellent public transport system which comprises S-Bahn, U-Bahn, tram and bus services. The network is divided into four zones, all the pubs listed (with the exception of Airbräu) being in the inner zone. Day tickets for the one zone cost €4.50 for one person, or €8.00 for up to five adults. All four zones (including the airport) will set you back €9.00 for one adult, or €16.00 for up to five. Make sure you validate your ticket using one of the machines at the entrances to platforms or on board buses and trams.

Airbräu (1)

München Airport Center, Terminalstraße Mitte 18, 85356 München-Flughafen
T 089 97 59 31 01   **F** 089 97 59 31 06
www.airbraeu.de   Daily 10.00–01.00
U S Flughafen München Terminal 50m

Now, this isn't strictly München. In fact, Airbräu, as the name suggests, is one of the world's few airport breweries and based at Munich Airport. The single-storey pub above the S-Bahn station features a large bar and kitchen, with the gleaming brewing kettles at one end of the room. Under a high glass roof is an all-weather beer garden with seating for several hundred. Amazingly, the beer is just €2 for half a litre, making it possibly the best-value bar at any international airport. They also have a pub air-side in terminal 2.

DRAUGHT: **Airbräu Flieger-Quell, Kumulus Weißbier, seasonals**

Altes Hackerhaus (2)

Sendlinger Straße 14,
80331 München/Altstadt-Lehel
T 089 260 50 26   **E** hackerhaus@aol.com
www.hackerhaus.de
Daily 09.00–23.00
U S Marienplatz 200m
U S DB München Hbf 1km

Cosy pub south of Marienplatz, the original home of the Hacker brewery. Full of brewery memorabilia, with photographs, posters,

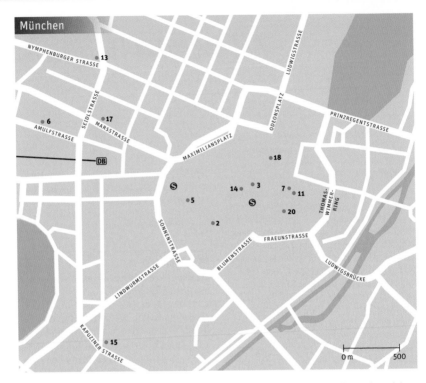

enamels, krugs, bottles and barrels seemingly occupying every available space. Around half a dozen separate rooms and drinking areas make up the pub, most fitted in old oak and pine. Towards the rear is a pleasant courtyard with a retractable roof that makes it all-weather. The pub may be a little twee for some tastes, though in our experience it's usually pretty busy and you may struggle to find a table at meal times.

DRAUGHT: **Hacker-Pschorr Münchner Hell, Braumeister Pils, Münchner Dunkel, Dunkle-Weisse, Hefe Weisse**

BOTTLED: **Hacker-Pschorr Leichte Weisse, Anno 1417 Kellerbier, Sternweisse, Hubertus Bock, Animator; Paulaner Diät Pils**

Andechser am Dom (3)

Weinstraße 7a, 80333 München/Altstadt-Lehel
T 089 29 84 81 **E** info@andechser-am-dom.de
www.andechseramdom.de
Daily 10.00–23.00; food until 22.30
Ⓤ Ⓢ Marienplatz 180m
Ⓤ Ⓢ DB München Hbf 1.1km

The address is a little misleading – the pub is actually opposite the cathedral, on the corner of Frauenplatz and Filserbräugasse. The restaurant has some very nice wood panelling featuring miniature cloistered windows as well as impressive ceiling paintings. On a smaller scale is a nice portrait of three monks enjoying a beer. Alongside the restaurant is an arcade with a large stand-up drinking area, and there's further seating outside in the summer. One of only two pubs to serve the Dunkel Naturtrüb on draught – the other is the brewery tap at Andechs monastery, 30km south-west of the city.

DRAUGHT: **Andechser Hell, Weißbier Hell, Weißbier Dunkel, Dunkel Naturtrüb, Doppelbock Dunkel**

BOTTLED: **Sanwald Hefeweizen Leicht**

Augustiner Bräustuben (4)

Landsberger Straße 19, 80339 München-Schwanthalerhöhe
T 089 50 70 47
E augustinerbraustuben@t-online.de

www.augustiner-braeustuben.de
Daily 10.00–24.00
[Tram] Nos. 18 & 19 Holzapfelstraße 70m
Ⓢ Hackerbrücke 450m
Ⓤ Ⓢ [DB] München Hbf 1km

Augustiner Bräustuben, next door to the brewery, opened as recently as 1995. There are two rooms. To the left a small wood-panelled Stüble in traditional style. To the right, in a former stable block, is the main room which houses both kitchen and bar. Seating here consists of large table and benches along one side, plus central tables perched on old barrels. In the middle, next to the toilets, is a window through which you can admire Augustiner's remaining equine population, now mainly used to pull the Oktoberfest dray. The pub is frequently very busy and is often used by workers from the brewery on their breaks.

DRAUGHT: **Augustiner-Bräu Pils, Lagerbier Hell, Dunkel, Edelstoff, seasonals**

BOTTLED: **Augustiner-Bräu Weissbier**

Augustiner Großgaststätte (5)

Neuhauser Straße 27,
80331 München/Altstadt-Lehel
T 089 23 18 32 57
E mail@augustiner-restaurant.com
www.augustiner-restaurant.com
Daily 10.00–24.00
Ⓤ Ⓢ Karlsplatz 200m
Ⓤ Ⓢ ⅅⅉ München Hbf 700m

Augustiner's showcase pub and restaurant, on the main pedestrianised street between Hauptbahnhof and Marienplatz. The brewery was here for more than 500 years, before moving to its present site in 1885. Of the half a dozen rooms on the ground floor, the restaurant is by far the largest and most ornate, in original Art-Nouveau style, aimed firmly towards diners rather than the casual drinker. Beyond this is a rather lovely Italianate garden, adorned by frescoes, an arcade and a fountain. To the left of the restaurant are rooms in more traditional beerhall style with scrubbed tables and long benches. During summer there's extensive seating out front. Food is served all day.

DRAUGHT: **Augustiner-Bräu Dunkel, Edelstoff**

BOTTLED: **Augustiner-Bräu Pils, Weissbier**

Augustiner-Keller (6)

Arnulfstraße 52, 80335 München-Maxvorstadt
T 089 59 43 93   **E** buero@augustinerkeller.de
www.augustinerkeller.de   Daily 10.00–01.00
ⓣ Hopfenstraße 100m
Ⓤ Ⓢ ⅅⅉ München Hbf 500m

Augustiner-Keller, a few hundred metres east of the Hauptbahnhof, on the north side of the railway, is justifiably one of the most popular beer gardens in the city. Under dozens of mature trees are seats for 5,000 people, but on hot summer days you may still struggle to find one empty. There are several bars dispensing Edelstoff from large, frequently changed

wooden barrels, plus various food stalls, including a grilled mackerel stand. Overlooking all this is the Keller itself, a large pub with several rooms, a couple of which were converted from former ice-houses. Food is available all day.

GRAVITY: **Augustiner-Bräu Edelstoff**

DRAUGHT: **Augustiner-Bräu Dunkel, seasonals**

BOTTLED: **Augustiner-Bräu Pils, Weissbier; Prinzregent Luitpold Weissbier Light, Dunkel**

Ayingers am Platzl (7)

Am Platzl 1a, 80331 München/Altstadt-Lehel
T 089 23 70 36 66   E info@platzl.de
www.ayinger.de
Daily 11.00–01.00; food until 23.00
U S Marienplatz 350m, DB München Hbf 1.6km

Opposite the Hofbräuhaus, Ayingers am Platzl, the brewery's main München outlet, opened in 2000. Completely different in style to the traditional München beerhalls, it's embellished throughout with modern two-toned wooden inlays and panelling and leather seating. Apparently affiliated with the Platzl Hotel, they appear to be tailored towards the business traveller as much as the casual drinker.

DRAUGHT: **Ayinger Hell, Liebhard's Kellerbier, Premium Pils, Altbairisch Dunkel, Bräu Weisse, Ur-Weisse, seasonals**

BOTTLED: **Ayinger Leichte Bräu-Weisse, Celebrator Doppelbock**

Forschungsbrauerei (8)

Unterhachinger Straße 76,
81737 München-Altperlach
T 089 670 11 69   www.forschungsbrauerei.de
Closed Mon & mid-Oct–Mar;
Sun & hols 10.00–22.00, Mon–Sat 11.00–23.00
DB München-Perlach 700m

The Experimental Brewery was founded in 1930, the pub following in 1936, so the public could try the outstanding beer for themselves. It still serves its original purpose, however, so the pub shuts in October and the owners concentrate on research during the winter, re-opening for a three-week binge from around the third weekend in March. The brewery and pub are housed in a plain, single-storey building with the brewing kettles in a raised tower to the right,

visible through large windows. Inside are several rooms of various sizes, by far the cosiest of which is the small wood-panelled bar. Outside is a decent-sized beer garden with privacy from the road provided by a large hedge. The menu consists of snacks plus one or two hot meals. If you want to drink the beer in quantities smaller than a litre, come before 16.00.

DRAUGHT: **Pilsissimus, St. Jakobus Blonder Bock**

Hirschgarten (9)

Hirschgartenalle 1, 80639 München-Neuhausen
T 089 17 25 91   E restaurant@hirschgarten.de
www.hirschgarten.de/biergarten.html
Daily 09.00–24.00
Tram Nos. 16 & 17 Kriemhildenstraße 550m
DB München-Laim 1.1km

The largest beer garden in the world sits on the edge of the royal park of the same name, next to an enclosure full of deer (the Bambi kind, aaah...), with the odd goat thrown in for good measure. The garden is truly enormous, with 8,000 seats, five bars from which the Edelstoff and others are dispensed from 200-litre wooden barrels, plus various food shacks. It is also one of the last places in Bayern that requires drinkers to select and wash their own glasses, these being stored in numerous wooden cabinets (they should be washed both before and after use). When the weather's not so good customers make use of the substantial pub at the edge of the garden which is open all year round.

DRAUGHT: **Augustiner-Bräu Pils, Lagerbier Hell, Edelstoff; Kaltenberg König Ludwig Dunkel; Prinzregent Luitpold Weissbier Light, Hell, Dunkel; Tegernseer Spezial**

BOTTLED: **Augustiner-Bräu Heller Bock (spring), Maximator (winter); Spaten Diät Pils; Tegernseer Leicht**

Hofbräukeller (10)

Innere Wiener Straße 19,
81667 München/Au-Haidhausen
T 089 459 92 50   E info@hofbraeukeller.de
www.hofbraeukeller.de
Daily 09.00–24.00
Tram No. 18 Wiener Platz 20m
U U4 & U5 Max-Weber-Platz 350m
U S DB München Hbf 2km

t: The ornate Italianate beer garden at the
of the Augustiner Großgaststätte, München.

Large, pale-green pub, on the corner of Wiener Platz. Until the late 1980s the brewery was alongside. The ground floor is home to three large rooms in typical München beerhall style, while upstairs you'll find a couple of banqueting halls. The cellar holds a dance hall and club. At the rear is a large beer garden, most of which is self-service (if your table hasn't got a tablecloth, you need to get your own beer!). The full range of Hofbräu beers is usually available, along with decent Bavarian food.

DRAUGHT: **Hofbräu Original, Kellerbier, Münchner Kindl Weissbier, Dunkel, seasonals**

BOTTLED: **Hofbräu Weissbier Light, Schwarze-Weisse, Kristall Weisse**

Hofbräuhaus (11)

Am Platzl 9, 80331 München/Altstadt-Lehel
T 089 290 13 60   **E** hbteam@hofbraeuhaus.de
www.hofbraeuhaus.de   Daily 10.00–23.30
Ⓤ Ⓢ Marienplatz 350m
Ⓤ Ⓢ ⒹⒷ München Hbf 1.6km

Probably the most famous pub in the world. One of those places you have to visit once, if only to see the horrified looks on the faces of many of the tourists when presented with a litre of beer for the first time. There are, however, a surprising number of locals among the throng, many of them in traditional Bavarian dress, plus a dozen or so thriving *Stammtischs* (tables reserved for regulars). The main hall or Schwemme is usually bouncing, often to the accompaniment of an oompah band, with the courtyard beer garden only slightly quieter. Upstairs you'll find the slightly more refined Bräustüberl and large festival hall where many of the tourists on organised trips go to watch Bavarian theatre. The name (Court Brew House) is purely historical, brewing having ended here in 1896.

DRAUGHT: **Hofbräu Original, Münchner Kindl Weissbier, Dunkel**

Leiberheim (12)

Nixenweg 9, 81739 München-Waldperlach
T 089 430 00 00   **E** info@leiberheim.de
www.leiberheim.de
Closed Mon (Tue after hols);
Sun & hols 10.00–01.00, Mon–Sat 16.00–01.00
(from 10.30 in fine weather)
Ⓢ Neubiberg 1.2km

Just inside the south-eastern boundary of the city (you pass the sign on the way from the station), deep in leafy suburbia. Leiberheim, the former holiday home for the Bavarian King's Infantry Regiment, consists of a fairly large semi-rural pub and a large self-service beer garden with seating for 2,500. The pub comprises a large hall with a stage for regular live performances. The beer garden, one of the city's best, also has an impressive play area for kids. Food is available but you can bring your own to eat in the beer garden if you wish. A good place to try Erharting beers in the absence of a brewery tap.

DRAUGHT: **Erharting Pils, Dunkel, Dunkle Ritter-Weisse, Hefe-Weisse, Export Hell, seasonals**

BOTTLED: **Erharting Leichte Weisse, Maisel's Edelhopfen Diät-Pilsener**

Löwenbräukeller (13)

Nymphenburger Straße 2,
80335 München-Maxvorstadt
T 089 52 60 21   **F** 089 52 89 33
www.loewenbraeukeller.com
Daily 10.00–24.00
Ⓤ U1 & U7 Stiglmaierplatz 20m
ⒹⒷ München Hbf 750m

Outside Stiglmaierplatz U-Bahn station, next to the brewery, the Löwenbräukeller is an impressive pub by any standards. The main entrance is beneath a large tower. Inside are around a dozen rooms of differing sizes and degrees of grandeur. Opened in 1883 at a cost of over 400,000 Marks, roughly €4,000,000 in today's money, it could at one time seat more than 8,000 people. A bombing raid in late 1944 destroyed much of the building and when it re-opened in 1950, capacity was halved. Between the pub and the main road is a large, self-service beer garden that gets very busy on warm evenings.

DRAUGHT: **Löwenbräu Original, Löwen Weisse, Dunkel, Triumphator**

BOTTLED: **Löwenbräu Premium-Pils, Kristallweizen, Schwarze Weisse**

Nürnberger Bratwurst Glöckl (14)

Frauenplatz 9, 80331 München-Altstadt-Lehel
T 089 291 94 50   **E** info@bratwurst-gloeckl.de
www.bratwurst-gloeckl.de

Closed Sun; Mon–Sat 10.00–24.00
U S Marienplatz 200m
U S DB München Hbf 1km

This lovely little pub opposite the cathedral is a München institution. Dimly-lit, and with dark wood panelling everywhere, this is a very atmospheric place. It takes its name from Nürnberg's speciality sausages, particularly good examples of which are cooked here over an open fire and served on pewter plates. Try them with the local wholegrain mustard. The Augustiner Hell is served direct from a wooden barrel perched on the bar at the back of the pub. In warm weather you can sit outside on the pavement terrace in the shadow of the Frauenkirche.

GRAVITY: **Augustiner-Bräu Lagerbier Hell**

DRAUGHT: **Kaltenberg König Ludwig Dunkel; Tucher Hefe Weizen Hell**

BOTTLED: **Augustiner-Bräu Edelstoff**

Paulaner Bräuhaus (15)

Kapuzinerplatz 5, 80337 München/
Ludwigsvorstadt-Isarvorstadt
T 089 544 61 10   **E** mail@paulanerbraeuhaus.de
www.paulanerbraeuhaus.de
Daily 09.00–01.00
U U3 & U6 Goetheplatz 200m
U S DB München Hbf 1.2km

Until 1927, this was the home of Thomasbräu. Brewing ceased following the merger with Paulaner but resumed in 1989 after extensive refurbishment. The large, very grand building occupies one side of Kapuzinerplatz. The main restaurant and bar, with its ornate marble pillars form a V-shape at the point of which lies the brewery. At the rear are a couple of other rooms, one of which has a small library. Beyond is the beer garden, also accessible directly from the street. Good food is served all day. Confusingly, the house-brewed wheatbeer has the same alcohol content and a very similar name to that brewed by the parent brewery, but we promise you it's different. Bus No. 58 runs here from the Hauptbahnhof.

DRAUGHT: **Paulaner Bräuhaus Thomas Zwickl, Hefe-Weißbier Naturtrüb, seasonals; Paulaner Pils, Original Münchner Dunkel**

BOTTLED: **Paulaner Hefeweißbier Leicht**

Paulaner am Nockherberg (16)

Hochstraße 77, 81541 München/Au-Haidhausen
T 089 459 91 30   **E** info@nockherberg.com
www.nockerberg.com
Daily 10.00–01.00
Tram Ostfriedhof 300m   U Kolumbusplatz 500m
DB München Hbf 2.5km

Next door to the brewery, the Paulaner tap is a massive complex that includes a beer garden, festival hall, Bierkeller and restaurant, with seating for almost 6,000 people in total. What you see today is all new, the old buildings having been destroyed in a catastrophic fire on the night of 27 November 1999. It took almost four years to rebuild, finally re-opening in 2003 under a new name. It was formerly known as the Salvator Keller, the name now being applied just to the *Bierkeller*. The main bar has four large copper tanks from which we assume much of the beer originates. When the beer garden is open the Hell is dispensed from wooden barrels. This is the only place where Paulaner Nockherberger Kellerbier is available. Food served all day.

DRAUGHT: **Paulaner Original Münchner Hell, Original Münchner Dunkel, Nockherberger, Hefeweißbier Dunkel, Hefeweißbier, Salvator, seasonals**

BOTTLED: **Paulaner Hefeweißbier Leicht, Original Münchner Leicht, Diät Pils, Premium Pils, Roggen**

Spaten Braustüberl (17)

Marsstraße 16, 80335 München-Maxvorstadt
T/F 089 54 50 71 41
Closed Sun; Mon–Sat 10.00–01.00
U S DB München Hbf 350m

A couple of streets north of the Hauptbahnhof you'll find Spaten's brewery tap. The brewery itself is a few hundred metres down the street on the same side as the pub. Small by München beerhall standards, the single wood-panelled room features wooden floorboards, pine-topped tables and chairs carved with the brewery logo. Numerous old brewery photographs are mounted on the walls. Although advertised as opening all day we have found it closed during the afternoon.

DRAUGHT: **Spaten Pils, Münchner Hell**

BOTTLED: **Franziskaner Hefe-Weissbier Leicht, Hell, Dunkel; Löwenbräu Dunkel, Triumphator**

Spatenhaus (18)

Residenzstraße 12,
80335 München/Altstadt-Lehel
T 089 290 70 60
E spatenhaus@kuffler-gastronomie.de
Daily 09.30–23.30
▭ No. 19 Nationaltheater 100m
Ⓤ Ⓢ Marienplatz 350m
Ⓤ Ⓢ ▣ München Hbf 1.4km

Opposite the Nationaltheater. In warm weather you can sit outside on the pavement overlooking Max-Josef-Platz. The front of Spatenhaus features some unusual copper canopies and other embellishments. Inside, wood is the dominant building material, every room including wooden furniture and panelling, with those upstairs featuring Baroque styling and conceived as dining rather than drinking rooms. Downstairs the main bar is furnished in bare pine, a pleasant change from the very dark wood that dominates most beerhalls. Traditional Bavarian cooking.

DRAUGHT: **Franziskaner Hefe-Weissbier Hell, Dunkel; Löwenbräu Dunkel; Spaten Pils, Münchner Hell**

BOTTLED: **Franziskaner Hefe-Weissbier Leicht; Löwenbräu Triumphator; Spaten Diät Pils**

Unionsbräu (19)

Einsteinstraße 42,
81675 München/Au-Haidhausen
T 089 47 76 77   **E** info@unionsbraeu.de
www.unionsbraeu.de
Sun 10.00–16.00, Mon–Sat 11.00–01.00;
food Mon-Sat 11.00–24.00
Ⓤ U4 & U5 Max-Weber-Platz 20m
Ⓤ Ⓢ ▣ München Hbf 2km

Brewing started here in 1869 but stopped in 1930, a few years after Löwenbräu had taken over. Fast-forward 60 years and house-brewed beer returned following the installation of a brewery in the cellar bar. The two regular beers are occasionally joined by Unimator Doppelbock.

Leave the U-Bahn station, using the exit farthest from the city centre and you'll find yourself outside the pub entrance. To the left and up a few steps is the restaurant, which is more upmarket in feel than most brewpubs. Downstairs is the cellar bar, which opens at 16.00 Mon–Sat. At the rear is a small beer garden.

DRAUGHT: **Unionsbräu Hell, Dunkel, seasonals**

BOTTLED: **Löwenbräu Premium Pils; Franziskaner Hefe-Weissbier Hell, Dunkel, Kristallklar**

Weisses Bräuhaus (20)

Tal 7, 80331 München/Altstadt-Lehel
T 089 290 13 80
E info@weisses-brauhaus.de
www.weisses-brauhaus.de
Daily from 07.00
Ⓤ Ⓢ Marienplatz 200m
Ⓤ Ⓢ ▣ München Hbf 1.5km

Until its relocation to Kelheim in 1944 this was the site of the Schneider brewery, and they still consider it their tap. Its previous name was Maderbräu, a fact that's still reflected in the name of the street that runs alongside. There are two large, wood-panelled rooms on the ground floor, the front one housing the bar and boasting some lovely stained-glass windows, a couple of which feature products of the brewery. Photos on the wall provide a poignant reminder of how it all used to be. Upstairs are more rooms to cope with the overflow from below, and in warmer weather further seating is provided on the pavement at the front. The Karmeliten beers are advertised as Donau Pils and Bräu Girgl Dunkel.

DRAUGHT: **Karmeliten Kloster Pils, Dunkel; Schneider Weizen-Hell, Weisse Original; Tegernseer Hell**

BOTTLED: **Schneider Weisse Leicht Weisse, Weizen-Hell, Weisse Kristall, Weisse Original, Aventinus, Aventinus Weizen-Eisbock**

Nürnberg *(Nuremberg)*

www.nuernberg.de

THE CAPITAL OF FRANKEN *(Franconia)*, outside Germany Nürnberg is still tainted by its strong associations with the Nazi era and the rallies that were staged here, together with the post-war trials. It deserves to be better known as a beautiful city and home to countless medieval buildings, both in their original state and painstakingly reconstructed since the 1950s. The old city is surrounded by a massive wall, several miles in circumference. The river Pegnitz runs through the centre, dividing the city from east to west. On the Kaiserburg in the north-eastern corner, and visible from much of the city, stands the 12th-century castle. Other attractions include the German National Museum and National Transport Museum, both within walking distance of the Hauptbahnhof. In the run-up to Christmas there is a massive market in the Hauptmarkt, where you can buy, among other things, the wooden toys and tree decorations typical of Nuremberg and surroundings. The market attracts tens of thousands of visitors daily.

Perhaps surprisingly given the number of breweries in nearby towns, Nürnberg currently has only four, and one of these is effectively a hobby brewery. The other three are Altstadthof and Barfüßer, both modern brewpubs, and the very large Tucher, who may move all production to nearby Fürth. Despite the relative paucity of breweries, the city's pubs sell a large array of beers from outside town and, unusually, there are a number of freehouses.

Transport: www.vgn.de
The Hauptbahnhof, on the southern edge of the city wall, is the hub of the tram and U-Bahn systems. They are of only limited use if you intend to visit the old town, as there are just two U-Bahn stations and no tram stops within the wall.

Andechser im Deutschen Kaiser (1)

Königstraße 55, 90402 Nürnberg-Lorenz
T 0911 236 98 44
E info@deutscher-kaiser-hotel.de
www.deutscher-kaiser-hotel.de/german/ restaurant.htm
Daily 11.00–24.00; food until 23.00; rooms available
U U1 & U11 Lorenzkirche 200m
DB Nürnberg Hbf 400m

One of a growing chain of Andechs showpubs in major Bavarian cities, this one is in the bar of the Deutscher Kaiser Hotel, opposite Barfüßer (below). The brewery's entire range of beers is usually available on draught. The long, narrow bar is furnished in typical beer-hall style, with wood prominent and a nice vaulted ceiling, although it could do with a bit of aging. There's limited seating outside in the summer months.

DRAUGHT: **Andechser Dunkel, Hell, Weißbier Hell, Weißbier Dunkel, Spezial Hell, Bergbock Hell, Doppelbock Dunkel**

Barfüßer (2)

Hallplatz 2, 90402 Nürnberg-Lorenz
T 0911 20 42 42   **E** info@barfuesser-brauhaus.de
www.barfuesser-brauhaus.de
Daily 11.00–01.00
U U1 & U11 Lorenzkirche 200m
DB Nürnberg Hbf 400m

Subterranean brewpub near the Hauptbahnhof, the first of the Barfüßer (meaning barefoot) chain; the others are in Heilbronn, Ulm and Neu-Ulm. One very large, vaulted bar, with old British pub signs suspended from the ceiling, plus a couple of smaller rooms for hire. The brewing equipment is prominent on the right, opposite the bar and kitchen. In fine weather there's a large terrace at the front on Königstraße

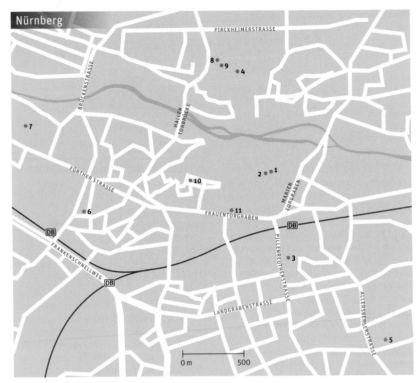

Nürnberg

where you'll also find the pub's main entrance, despite the address.

DRAUGHT: **Barfüßer Blonde, Schwarze; Tucher Hefe Weizen Hell**

Café Express (3)

Bulmann Straße 4, 90459 Nürnberg-Südstadt
T 0911 43 51 36
www.cafe-express.de
Mon–Fri 11.00–01.00, Sat 12.00–01.00,
Sun 15.00–01.00
DB Nürnberg Hbf 350m

Modern café-bar south of the Hauptbahnhof – exit the station from the western subway near platform 22. The single L-shaped room features a bright yellow bar and patio doors that open onto the street in summer. The beer range generally includes those listed below, with the draught beers changing occasionally and additional bottles appearing regularly. The locals play darts on a proper board. Frequent live music.

DRAUGHT: **Fässla Lagerbier; Keesmann**

Bamberger Herren Pils; Krug-Bräu Dunkel; Meister Vollbier; Wagner Ungespundetes Lagerbier

BOTTLED: **Fässla Weizla-Hell, Weizla Dunkel, Zwergla; Jever Pils; Maisel's Weisse Light, Weisse Kristall; Riedenburger Weisse; Spalter Premium Pils**

Hütt'n (4)

Burgstraße 19, 90403 Nürnberg-Lorenz
T 0911 201 98 81
E huettn@Nuernberg.Bayern-Online.de
Mon–Fri 16.00–24.00, Sat 11.30–00.30,
Sun 11.30–22.30
Tram No. 4 Tiergärtnertor 400m
DB Nürnberg Hbf 1.3km

Cosy street-corner pub in the old town, a couple of minutes walk from Schlenkerla Schranke and Schwarzer Bauer. Free of any tie, Hütt'n offers two constantly changing draught beers and around 15 bottled beers, mostly from small Franconian breweries. From reports received, the bottled beers below seem likely to be regulars with others as guests. We're not sure who brews the Bernreuther Kellerbier but suspect it may be Pyraser. They also stock a range of Franconian wines and serve food.

DRAUGHT: range varies

BOTTLED: Bernreuther Kellerbier; Fischer Rauchbier; Gutmann Hefeweizen, Dunkles Hefeweizen; Heller Aecht Schlenkerla Rauchbier Märzen; Neder Schwarze Anna; Penning Hetzelsdorfer Fränkisches Vollbier; Pyraser Landbier Export Hell; Spalter Premium Pils; guest beers

Landbierparadies (Wodanstraße) (5)

Wodanstraße 15, 90461 Nürnberg-Südstadt
T 0911 46 88 82   E info@landbierparadies.com
www.landbierparadies.com/wirtshaeuser/
    wodanstrasse/index.htm
Mon–Thu 17.30–01.00, Fri 14.00–01.00,
Sat 12.00–01.00, Sun & hols 10.00–01.00
Tram Nos. 7 & 9 Wodanstraße 120m
DB Nürnberg Hbf 1.5km

The Country Beer Paradise originated in 1986 as a drinks market specialising in beers from Franconia's small country brewers. In 1994 the company opened this pub on the corner of Brunhildstraße. Since then, two more have opened in Nürnberg, along with franchised pubs in both Nürnberg and Fürth. The premise is simple – one draught beer from the wood and at least 15 bottled beers are available at all times. Although the bottled beers generally include those below, the draught beer changes constantly. The pub itself is on two levels and furnished in a very basic style, not that this is likely to put off the average beer nut.

GRAVITY: guest beer

BOTTLED: Drummer Dunkles Vollbier, Först Goldener Löwe Altfränkisches Lager; Gentner-Bräu Minnesänger-Pils; Held Bräu Hell; Hofmann Hofmannstropfen Dunkel; Krug-Bräu Dunkel; Meister Vollbier; Neder Schwarze Anna; Penning Hetzelsdorfer Fränkisches Vollbier; Pfister Weißbier; Reichold Lagerbier; Ritter-Bier Schwarzer Ritter Hefe-Dunkel; Sauer Gunzendorfer Schlückla Rauchbier; Schroll Nankendorfer Landbier; Sonnen Bräu Eber-Weisse; guest beers

Landbierparadies (Rothenburger Str.) (6)

Rothenburger Str 26, 90443 Nürnberg-Gostenhof
T 0911 287 86 73   E info@landbierparadies.com
www.landbierparadies.com/wirtshaeuser/
    rothenburgerstrasse/index.htm
Mon–Sat 17.30–01.00, Sun & hols 10.00–01.00
U Plärrer 500m
DB Nürnberg-Gostenhof 300m, Hbf 1.8km

The second of the Landbierparadies pubs, this branch opened in 1996. The other two Nürnberg pubs are at Galvinstraße 10 and Sterzinger Straße 4, with the Fürth franchise at Friedrich-Ebert-Straße 100. All have the same opening hours except Sterzinger Straße which opens at 11.00 on Sundays. Slightly cosier than the Wodanstraße branch, though to be honest that's no great achievement.

GRAVITY: guest beer

BOTTLED: as at Wodanstraße (see above).

Lederer Kulturbrauerei (7)

Sielstraße 12, 90429 Nürnberg-Gostenhof
T 0911 801 00   E info@lederer.de   www.l-kb.de
Fri & Sat 10.00–01.00, Sun–Thu 10.00–24.00
U U1 & U11 Bärenschanz 150m
DB Nürnberg Hbf 2.6km

Next door to the former brewery, this pub is a shrine to all things Lederer with a steam engine and four brewing coppers the most notable of the countless artifacts. On a previous jaunt we were told by staff that the coppers are occasionally used for their intended purpose, which seemed unlikely given their size and lack of other equipment. Indeed, on our last visit it was confirmed that all beer is brewed in Fürth. This pub does, however, have the largest beer garden in town, with seating for over 1,000.

DRAUGHT: Kroko Spezial Kellerbier, Lederer Premium Pils, Tucher Weizen Hell

BOTTLED: Tucher Hefe Weizen Leicht, Hefe Weizen Dunkel

Schlenkerla Schranke (8)

Beim Tiergärtnertor 3, 90403 Nürnberg-Sebald
T 0911 22 54 74
E Schlenkerla@Nuernberg.Bayern-Online.de
Closed Sun; Mon–Sat 11.00–23.00
Tram No. 4 Tiergärtnertor 200m
DB Nürnberg Hbf 1.4km

This small pub, dating from 1500, stands below the Tiergärtnertor, close to the castle and across the street from Albrecht Dürer's house. Capacity increases substantially in fine weather when around 50 tables appear outside. They have their own butchers and serve the finest Nürnberger Rostbratwurst the Guide has encountered. The five regular draught beers are occasionally supplemented by a guest.

DRAUGHT: **Bub Leinburger Dunkel; Erdinger Weißbier; Heller Aecht Schlenkerla Rauchbier Märzen; König Pilsener; Tucher Original Urbräu**

BOTTLED: **Bub Leinburger Hell, Dunkel; Erdinger Weißbier Leicht, Kristallklar, Dunkel, Pikantus Dunkler Weizenbock; Tucher Bajuvator**

Schwarzer Bauer (9)

Bergstraße 19, 90403 Nürnberg-Sebald
T 0911 22 72 17   www.altstadthof.de
Daily 11.00–01.00
No. 4 Tiergärtnertor 250m
Nürnberg Hbf 1.4km

Hausbrauerei Altstadthof was the first of the new-wave breweries to open in Germany back in 1984. It was originally owned by Neumarkter Lammsbräu but we believe it's now independent. The brewery, together with a small distillery plus a couple of other bars, stands behind the pub. The Black Farmer is a small, single-roomed bar with seating for around 30 people. Food is available, although the menu is comparatively limited. Schlenkerla Schranke is a few doors up the hill.

DRAUGHT: **Altstadthof Helles, Schwarze, Weisse, Rothbier, seasonals**

Steichele (10)

Knorrstraße 2–8, 90402 Nürnberg-Lorenz
T 0911 20 22 80   **E** info@steichele.de
www.steichele.de
Mon–Sat 10.30–24.00, Sun & hols 11.00–15.00
U1 & U11 Weißer Turm 150m
Nürnberg Hbf 1km

Hotel, restaurant and wine bar in the south-western part of the old town. Wine is favoured over beer, but there are nevertheless a couple of interesting beers available. The rambling restaurant has several different rooms, one or two featuring some lovely wood panelling.

Good food is served and is appreciated by the mostly mature clientele. The small Weinstube next to the hotel entrance opens at 10.00 Monday to Saturday.

DRAUGHT: **Lindenbräu Vollbier Dunkel; Tucher Pilsener, Hefe Weizen Hell**

BOTTLED: **Neumarkter Lammsbräu Dinkel; Tucher Hefe Weizen Leicht**

Tucher-Bräu am Opernhaus (11)

Am Kartäusertor 1, 90402 Nürnberg-Lorenz
T 0911 20 46 49
E leitner@tucherbraeuamopernhaus.de
www.tucherbraeuamopernhaus.de
Daily 11.00–24.00
U2 & U21 Opernhaus 30m
Nürnberg Hbf 500m

Possibly not the official tap, but it'll do. This characterful pub stands alongside the city wall opposite the Opera House, between the German National Museum and the German Transport Museum. Full of bric-a-brac, it's seemingly Christmas all year round. There's one main room with an annex to the side, and a beer garden at the rear which overlooks the old-town's dry moat. The menu includes some Balkan specialities.

DRAUGHT: **Tucher Pilsener, Urfränkisch Dunkel, Hefe Weizen Hell, Übersee Export, seasonals**

BOTTLED: **Tucher Hefe Weizen Leicht, Hefe Weizen Dunkel, Kristall Weizen**

Stuttgart

www.stuttgart.de
www.cannstatter-volksfest.de

THE HOME OF Daimler, Mercedes-Benz and Porsche, you could be forgiven for expecting Stuttgart to look a little like Dagenham, but nothing could be further from the truth. Nestled in a valley between steep hills covered in forests and vineyards, this is a surprisingly green city. Granted, the centre is a bit of a concrete jungle, a combination of modern pedestrianised streets, subways and busy dual carriageways, but many parts are a delight. Among the attractions are the Schlossgarten, Schlossplatz, Schillerplatz and the Staatsgallerie, which houses many of the nation's finest paintings. Like München, the city has a massive knees-up in late September/early October, Stuttgart's being the Cannstatter Volksfest, known locally as the Cannstatter Wasen. The 2006 event runs from 23 September to 8 October.

The local brewing scene is dominated by two giants – Dinkelacker Schwaben-Bräu and Stuttgarter Hofbräu. Oddly, the beers from the latter are comparatively rare in pubs and most commonly found in foreign restaurants and snack bars. Stuttgart is well represented by modern brewpubs and six can now be found scattered around the city.

Transport: www.vvs.de
As in most German cities there's an excellent public transport system centred on the Hauptbahnhof (north-east of the city centre). During the Cannstatter Volksfest a special U-Bahn route (U11) runs anti-clockwise through the city centre direct to the festival site in Bad Cannstatt.

Bierakademie (1)

Johannesstraße 95, 70176 Stuttgart-West
T 0711 997 92 61
Fri & Sat 10.00–03.00, Sun–Thu 10.00–02.00
[U] U2 Hölderlinplatz 10m **[DB]** Stuttgart Hbf 2km

Sports bar alongside the northern terminus of U2. Darts and pool are played and the TV usually shows live sport. The three rooms feature wooden floorboards and furniture, the one at the rear housing the pool table. A couple of old barrels are perched above the bar. One of the few pubs – as opposed to snackbars or Chinese restaurants – in the city to stock Stuttgarter Hofbräu beers. Basic, and the focus is inevitably on sport as much as beer, but it's friendly enough.

DRAUGHT: **Sanwald Hefeweizen; Stuttgarter Hofbräu Pilsner**

BOTTLED: **Becks; Diebels Premium Altbier; Paulaner Hefeweißbier; Rothaus Tannenzäpfle, Hefe Weizen; Sanwald Weizen Dunkel, Kristallweizen; Stuttgarter Hofbräu Herrenpils; Warsteiner Premium Verum**

Biergarten im Schloßgarten (2)

Cannstatter Straße 18, 70173 Stuttgart-Mitte
T 0711 226 12 74
E info@biergarten-schlossgarten.de
www.biergarten-schlossgarten.de
Closed in wet weather; daily 10.30–01.00; food until 00.30
[DB] Stuttgart Hbf 400m

Conveniently situated near the Hauptbahnhof (use the side exit near platform 16, enter the park by the bus station and follow the path north), this large beer garden is similar to many in München, albeit with far fewer trees and not a grilled food stall in sight. There are seats for around 1,500, those on the station side of the main bar and

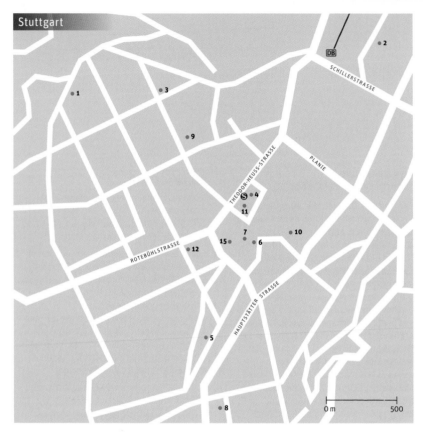

Stuttgart

kitchen being much more comfortable than you'll usually find in this sort of establishment. The beer comes from Eichbaum, the state's largest brewery. Service is canteen style, with a €2 deposit on glasses.

DRAUGHT: **Eichbaum Schwarzbier, Hefe-Weizen, Dunkles Weizen, Export**

BOTTLED: **Eichbaum Kristall Weizen**

Bierhaus West (3)

Seidenstraße 40, 70174 Stuttgart
T 0711 29 59 17   **F** 0711 226 49 99
www.bierhaus-west.de
Closed Sun; Mon–Sat 11.00–01.00
U U2 Rosenbergstraße/Seidenstraße 20m
DB Stuttgart Hbf 1.4km

Comfortable, street-corner pub close to the Bosch Areal centre. The beer range is unadventurous but well kept. The central bar has a mazy layout of high tables for stand-up drinking. Beyond is a small, wood-panelled restaurant that is better designed and cosier than most. The food is good and they score points simply for having proper pots of mustard rather than the usual sachets. The U-Bahn stop is in the middle of the street outside. Mash is only a few minutes walk away.

DRAUGHT: **Bitburger Premium Pils; Diebels Premium Altbier; Dom Kölsch; Erdinger Weißbier; König Pilsener; Schwäben-Bräu Urtyp Export; Warsteiner Premium Verum**

BOTTLED: **Erdinger Weißbier Kristallklar, Dunkel, Pikantus Dunkler Weizenbock**

Calwer-Eck-Bräu (4)

Calwer Straße 31, 70173 Stuttgart-Mitte
T 0711 22 24 94 40   **E** info@calwereck.de

498

www.calwereck.de
Mon–Thu 09.00–01.00, Fri 09.00–02.00, Sat 10.00–02.00, Sun 10.00–01.00, hols 17.00–01.00
🅄 Rotebühlplatz 100m
🅳🅱 Stadtmitte 150m, Stuttgart Hbf 1.2km

Climb the marble staircase off Calwer Straße to reach this first-floor brewpub. Essentially a single room, the pub is divided into several distinct areas and features some quite intricate woodwork. In the centre is a partially enclosed booth with four tables and some nice stained glass. Around the edge of the room, next to windows overlooking both Calwer and Lange Straße, are raised tables with bench seating. There are a couple of smaller, cosier nooks and further seating around the bar. The wooden-clad brewing vessels are behind glass to the right as you enter, between the bar and kitchen.

DRAUGHT: **Calwer Eck Helles Hefeweizen, Naturtrübes Pils, Braumeisterbier, seasonals**

Dinkelacker (5)

Tübinger Straße 48, 70178 Stuttgart-Süd
T 0711 60 37 97   **E** dinkelacker@ds-ag.de
www.dinkelacker.de
Closed Sun & hols; Mon–Sat 11.30–24.00; food 11.30–14.15 & 17.30–21.45
🅄 U1 & U14 Österreicher Platz 400m
🅳🅱 Stuttgart Hbf 2km

The Dinkelacker tap is in front of the brewery, on the western side of the city close to Marienplatz. The brick-fronted building, dating from the latter half of the 20th century, has unusual angled windows with stained-glass. The main restaurant is on the right as you enter, a little more up-market than some, with cloths on the tables. Beers from three of the four labels brewed next door are available but for some unknown reason there are none from Schwaben-Bräu.

DRAUGHT: **Cluss Kellerpils; Dinkelacker CD Pils, Privat, seasonals; Sanwald Hefeweizen**

BOTTLED: **Sanwald Hefeweizen Leicht, Weizen Dunkel, Kristallweizen; Diebels Alt**

Hacienda (6)

Tübinger Straße 8, 70178 Stuttgart-Süd
T 0711 29 59 49   **E** tue-8@t-online.de
www.tue8.de/hacienda/
Daily 17.00–03.00

🅄 Rotebühlplatz 250m
🅳🅱 Stadtmitte 400m, Stuttgart Hbf 1.4km

Cellar bar and restaurant specialising in Mexican food. The brewing kettles are directly ahead as you enter, in the centre of the room opposite the peninsular bar. Most of the seating is to the left but there are some tables on the far side of the bar. As you might expect, there is a strong Mexican theme throughout which is strangely at odds with the gleaming coppers. They occasionally have live music and other performances. Finally, a health warning: many sources no longer list Hacienda (or Tü8) as a brewery. However, the brewing kettles are still plumbed and wired in, have the stains you would expect to find on regularly used equipment, and three separate members of staff told us they still brew. We believe them. We believe everything we are told. You have been warned!

DRAUGHT: **Tü 8 Pils, Hefeweizen**

Ketterer (7)

Marienstraße 3, 70178 Stuttgart-Mitte
T 0711 29 75 51   **E** ketterer-stuttgart@t-online.de
www.ketterer-stuttgart.de
Closed Sun; Mon–Sat 11.00–23.30
🅄 Rotebühlplatz 150m
🅳🅱 Stadtmitte 300m, Stuttgart Hbf 1.4km

Next to the (Best Western) hotel of the same name, this is the main Stuttgart outlet for Pforzheim's largest brewery. At the front are a dozen or so tables, generally used by those who just wish to drink. Beyond these the pub opens out into the main restaurant, a surprisingly grand affair. To the left, seven large windows light up the room, albeit somewhat dimmed by the hotel next door. The walls display a number of large paintings with scenes from around the globe. At the far end is a low-ceilinged Stüble. Ketterer also have a jazz hall which has live music Thu–Sat from 19.30.

DRAUGHT: **Ketterer Pilsener, Gold Privat Export, Sebastian Hefe-Weissbier, seasonals**

BOTTLED: **Ketterer Sebastian Dunkel Weizen; Thurn und Taxis Kristallweizen**

Lehen (8)

Lehenstraße 13, 70180 Stuttgart-Süd
T 0711 640 72 91

Fri & Sat 17.00–02.00, Sun–Thu 17.00–01.00;
food 18.00–22.30

🇺 U1 & U14 Marienplatz 300m
DB Stuttgart Hbf 2.6km

This basic, street-corner bar, reminiscent of a
northern England town pub, is situated in a
residential area close to the Marienplatz. Entry
is via a porch which leads into the bar itself, by
far the largest of the three rooms. There are
wooden floors throughout, together with wood
panelling that has been painted in a two-tone
colour scheme. The windows, large, arched
affairs, are particularly pleasing to the eye.
The walls are decorated with paintings and
photographs. Of the two smaller rooms, one is a
pool room while the other holds a small library
and television. A rare example of a city pub
that's so far resisted modernisation. We hope it
continues to do so.

DRAUGHT: **Dinkelacker CD Pils, Privat; Sanwald
Hefeweizen**

BOTTLED: **Diebels Alt; Dinkelacker Märzen;
Sanwald Hefeweizen Leicht, Weizen Dunkel,
Kristallweizen**

Mash (9)

Forststraße 7, 70174 Stuttgart-Mitte
T 0711 120 93 30   **E** mail@mash-stuttgart.de
www.mash-stuttgart.de
Fri 11.30–04.00, Sat 17.00–03.00,
Sun–Thu 11.30–01.00; food until 23.00
🇺 Berliner Platz 250m
DB Stuttgart Hbf 1.5km

Über-modern brewpub in the middle of the
Bosch Areal centre. The right-hand side of the
long main room has a bar at either end with the
kitchen in between. Behind the two bars stand
the lager tanks. To the left of the entrance you
get into a smaller, semi-circular room furnished
with upholstered block seating. There's further
seating outside under the high glass roof.
During the day Mash is food oriented and
comparatively quiet. At night things liven up
considerably, often helped along by a DJ, and
there may be an admission charge. Not the sort
of place you would expect to brew.

DRAUGHT: **Mash One, Hefe.**
BOTTLED: **Mash Silver**

Mathäser (10)

Geißstraße 12, 70173 Stuttgart-Mitte
T 0711 24 23 97
Closed Sun; Mon–Thu 10.30–24.00, Fri & Sat
10.30–01.00; food 11.00–15.00 & 17.00–24.00
🇺 Rathaus 250m   DB Stuttgart Hbf 1.3km

At the heart of the tiny area near the town hall
that constitutes Stuttgart's old town. The name
may be familiar to those who visited München
before the Millennium – it's the same you could
see on the old Löwenbräu beer hall near the
Hauptbahnhof, which has since been converted
into a shopping centre. Externally, Mathäser is
a rather grand-looking pub, with seating on the
little pedestrian square at the front. Internally,
the bar on the ground floor is surprisingly small
and cosy, with only a few tables plus stools
ranged around the bar. There is a restaurant on
the first floor. The styling is more Bavarian than
Schwabian, hardly surprising given the
brewery who owns it.

DRAUGHT: **Löwenbräu Original, Premium-Pils,
Dunkel, Märzen, Triumphator; Franziskaner
Hefe-Weissbier Hell**

BOTTLED: **Franziskaner Hefe-Weissbier Dunkel,
Kristallklar**

Paulaner (11)

Calwer Straße 45, 70173 Stuttgart-Mitte
T 0711 22 41 50   **E** info@zumpaulaner.de
www.hotel-sautter.de/paulaner/index.php
Daily 11.00–23.00
🇺 Rotebühlplatz 50m
DB Stadtmitte 100m, Stuttgart Hbf 1.3km

At the end of Calwer Straße, opposite Rotebühlplatz U-Bahn station, this is one of a chain of
Paulaner showcase pubs nationwide. Virtually
the full range of Paulaner beers is available,
along with typical Bavarian dishes. The cosy,
wood-panelled restaurant has a bar and in one
corner an unusual white *Kachelofen* (tiled stove),
plus a dozen or so tables. There's a further room
upstairs that opens at busy times. In front of the
pub is a small square which doubles as a beer
garden in warm weather, although the fountain
may at times dampen your clothes if not your
spirits.

DRAUGHT: **Paulaner Premium Pils, Hefeweißbier
Dunkel, Hefeweißbier, Original Münchner Urtyp,
Salvator; Hacker-Pschörr Anno 1417 Kellerbier**

BOTTLED: **Paulaner Original Münchner Dunkel, Roggen, Hefeweißbier Kristallklar, Original Münchner Märzen**

Sanwald (12)

Siberburgerstraße 157, 70178 Stuttgart-West
T 0711 61 08 63
Sat 16.00–24.00, Sun–Fri 11.00–24.00
DB Feuersee 150m, Stuttgart Hbf 1.6km

The Sanwald brewery was taken over by Dinkelacker in 1977 but their tap west of the city centre is still going strong. Several rooms lead off the central bar, with wood-panelling a feature throughout. They appear to be very proud of Sanwald beers here and the casual visitor could be forgiven for thinking there's still a brewery given the amount of breweriana on display. The kitchen produces a good range of local dishes.

DRAUGHT: **Dinkelacker CD Pils, Privat, Sanwald Hefeweizen**

BOTTLED: **Sanwald Weizen Dunkel, Kristallweizen**

Schlampazius (13)

Wagenburgstraße 147, 70186 Stuttgart-Ost
T 0711 46 57 75   **E** post@schlampazius.de
www.schlampazius.de
Daily 15.00–01.00
U U4 Ostendplatz 500m
DB Stuttgart Hbf 2.2km

If you like classic rock (think Black Sabbath, Janis Joplin, Frank Zappa) and a very laid back atmosphere, this is the pub for you. There are three rooms, the central one's the bar into which you enter. The walls are covered in old music posters and promos. You get the distinct impression that were one removed, the wall underneath would be a much brighter hue than that around it. The bar, plastered in old cuttings and photographs, is crowned by a very old coffin which we sincerely hope is not second-hand. The owner of the bar is Spanish, but has lived in Stuttgart since 1973. Incidentally: the Stevie from Cardiff mentioned behind the bar is no relation to the Guide!

DRAUGHT: **Dinkelacker Privat; Diebels Alt**

BOTTLED: **Dinkelacker CD Pils, Märzen; Sanwald Hefeweizen, Weizen Dunkel, Kristallweizen; Schwäben-Bräu Das Schwarze**

Schloßturm (14)

SI-Erlebnis-Centrum, Plieninger Straße 100, 70567 Stuttgart-Möhringen
T 0711 721 20 06   **F** 0711 721 29 50
www.si-centrum.de/de/gastronomie/
Mon 16.00–24.00, Tue–Fri 16.00–01.00, Sat 12.00–02.00, Sun 11.00–24.00
U U3 Sälzacker (SI-Centrum) 250m
DB Stuttgart Hbf 8km

Despite the name, neither a castle nor a tower are in sight at this subterranean brewpub. It's located in a modern entertainment complex that includes a couple of large theatres and can be surprisingly hard for the first-time visitor to find (it's below the Palladium Theatre). Inside it has one large room, with the bar to the left and the main body of the restaurant on the right, in front of the brewing coppers. There's also a large seating area outside in the passage. Unusually, you're supposed to wait and be seated, although this doesn't apply if you just want a drink at the bar, where a couple of dozen cow-hide stools await your backside. Very popular with theatre-goers.

DRAUGHT: **Schloßturm Pils, seasonals; Maisel's Weisse Original**

BOTTLED: **Maisel's Weisse Kristall, Dunkel**

Sophie's (15)

Marienstraße 28, 70178 Stuttgart-Mitte
T 0711 61 09 62   **E** info@sophies-brauhaus.de
www.sophies-brauhaus.de
Sun 10.30–24.00, Mon–Sat 16.00–01.00
(Sep–May from 11.00)
U Rotebühlplatz 200m
DB Stadtmitte 300m, Stuttgart Hbf 1.4km

Despite the address, the entrance to this first-floor brewpub is actually off Sophienstraße. The large island bar is directly ahead as you enter, with most of the seating to the left and beyond the bar. On the right are the comparatively large brewing kettles, together with a few more tables and a colourful glass ceiling. The beer range has recently been expanded to include three regular beers and may occasionally include a seasonal brew. Food is served all day. Unusually, the pub opens later on summer weekdays than during the rest of the year.

DRAUGHT: **Sophie's Hausbräu, Schwarz, Hefeweissbier**

Wichtel (16)

Stuttgarter Straße 21, 70469 Stuttgart-Feuerbach
T 0711 82 05 16 90 **E** info@wichtel.de
www.wichtel.de
Fri & Sat 11.00–01.00, Sun–Thu 11.00–24.00
DB Stuttgart-Feuerbach 400m

Located in an old red-brick building of industrial origin, set back from Stuttgarter Straße behind its own beer garden. The brewing kettles are in the middle of the ground-floor bar, within touching distance of the high stools and tables that surround them. They are overlooked by a first-floor gallery which only opens when the pub is busy, and above all of this towers an old gantry crane. Wichtel (Gnome) has a small play area for young children complete with toys and, judging by the water bowl inside the entrance, dogs are welcome too. Food consists mostly of Flammkuchen, but they also do salads and a few more substantial specials.

DRAUGHT: **Wichtel Pils, Dunkles Hefeweizen, seasonals**

Useful words and phrases

MANY GERMANS, particularly younger people, speak good English. More still have a basic understanding. However, a fair proportion of the population speak little or no English at all, particularly among the over-50s and those from the former DDR (who learned Russian instead).

Understandably, many people will not volunteer the fact that they speak some English, so please try a few words of German. A little effort goes a long way and you'll find people far more willing to help if you at least try to, however badly.

There are many excellent English–German phrasebooks available and most guidebooks include some everyday phrases. The Guide can't pretend to better any of these, so what follows is a list of words and phrases that will be of particular use to the beer tourist, as well as a few other essentials.

Ordering beer

A beer, please – *Ein Bier, bitte*
A draught beer, please – *Ein Fassbier, bitte*
A pale beer, please – *Ein Helles, bitte*
A dark beer, please – *Ein Dunkles, bitte*
A wheat beer, please – *Ein Weizenbier, bitte*
Another beer, please – *Noch ein Bier, bitte*
Bottled, please – *In der Flasche, bitte*
Do you have any seasonal beers? – *Haben Sie saisonale Biere?*
Do you sell beer to take-away? – *Verkaufen Sie Bier zum Mitnehmen?*
Draught, please – *Vom Fass, bitte*
What draught beers do you have? – *Welche Fassbiere haben Sie?*
What bottled beers do you have? – *Welche Flaschenbiere haben Sie?*
What beer do you recommend? – *Welches Bier empfehlen Sie?*

Beer descriptions

aroma – *Aroma*
beer types – *Biersorten*
bitter – *bitter*
bottom-fermented beer – *untergäriges Bier*
cloudy – *trüb*
dark – *dunkel*

dry – *trocken*
filtered – *filtriert; klar; kristallklar*
fruity – *fruchtig*
full-bodied – *vollmundig*
gassy – *kohlensäurehaltig; viel Kohlensäure*
head – *Schaum*
hoppy – *hopfig; nach Hopfen*
malty – *malzig; nach Malz*
nutty – *nussartig*
pale – *hell*
sediment – *Bodensatz*
sour – *sauer*
sparkling – *prickelnd; sprudelnd*
spicy – *würzig*
strong – *kräftig; stark*
sweet – *süß*
taste – *Geschmack*
thin – *schwach*
top-fermented beer – *obergäriges Bier*
unfiltered – *naturtrüb; mit Hefe*

Beware!

alkoholfrei – non-alcoholic (less than 0.5%)
Alsterwasser – shandy
Banana-Weizen – wheat beer mixed with banana syrup
Biermischgetränke – beer mixed with another drink

Cola-Weizen/Colabier/Diesel – wheat beer mixed with cola
Leichtbier – low alcohol beer (usually 2.9%)
Radler – shandy
Russ – wheat beer shandy

Names for beer mixer drinks vary considerably from one region or locality to the next.

Vessels and measures

barrel – *Fass*
bottle – *Flasche*
bottle top – *Kronenkorken*
case – *Kasten*
flip-top bottle – *Bügelflasche*
glass – *Glas*
jug – *Pitcher/Pitcher-Krug*
label – *Etikett*
mug – *Bierseidel, Krug*
wooden barrel – *Holzfass*
0.2l – *null (Komma) zwei*
0.25l – *ein Viertel*
0.3l – *null (Komma) drei*
0.33l – *ein Drittel*
0.4l – *null (Komma) vier*
0.5l – *eine halbe; null (Komma) fünf*
1l – *eine Maß*

Types of pub

bar – *Ausschank; Kneipe; Lokal; Schänke; Wirtschaft*
brewery tap – *Brauerei-Ausschank; -Gasthof; -Gaststätte*
brewpub – *Hausbrauerei*
inn – *Gasthof; Gaststube; Gastwirtschaft; Schänke*
night bar – *Kneipe; Bar; Nachtclub*
pub – *Kneipe; Wirtschaft; Lokal; Gasthaus; Wirtshaus*
restaurant – *Gaststätte; Restaurant*

In the pub

bar (counter) – *Schanktisch; Theke; Tresen*
beer garden – *Biergarten*
beer mat – *(Bier)deckel*
beer tap – *Zapfhahn*
bench – *Bank*

cellar – *Keller*
chair – *Sitz; Stuhl*
closing day – *Ruhetag*
closing time – *Sperrstunde*
kitchen – *Küche*
landlady – *Wirtin*
landlord – *Wirt*
no smoking – *Rauchen verboten; Nichtraucher*
opening times – *Öffnungszeiten*
regulars – *Stammgäste*
regulars' table – *Stammtisch*
room – *Gastraum; -stube; -zimmer*
snug – *kleines Nebenzimmer*
stool – *Schemel*
table – *Tisch*
terrace – *Terrasse*
toilet (male/female) – *WC/Toilette (Herren/ Damen)*
Do you have a closing day? – *Haben Sie einen Ruhetag?*
I'd like to pay – *Ich möchte zahlen/bezahlen*
We'd like to pay (separately / together) – *Wir möchten (getrennt / zusammen) bezahlen*
What time do you open? – *Um wieviel Uhr / wann machen Sie auf?*
What time do you close? – *Um wieviel Uhr / wann schließen Sie?*
Where are the toilets? – *Wo ist die Toilette?*

In the brewery

barrelling plant – *Fassabfüllerei*
barley – *Gerste*
boil – *kochen*
bottling plant – *Abfüllanlage*
brew – *brauen*
brew kettle – *Braukessel; Sudpfanne*
brewer – *Bierbrauer; Braumeister*
brewery tour – *Brauereiführung*
brewhouse – *Sudhaus*
conditioning – *Konditionierung*
distillery – *Brennerei*
fermenting tank – *Gärtank*
filter – *Filter*
grain – *Korn*
grist – *Schrot*
hops – *Hopfen*
liquor – *Brauwasser*
malt – *Malz*
mash – *Maische*
mash tun – *Maischbottich*
master brewer – *Braumeister*

output (volume) – *Ausstoß*
refrigeration – *Kühlung*
steep – *weichen*
sterile – *steril*
storage tank – *Lagertank*
tap – *Hahn; Spund*
wheat – *Weizen*
wort – *Würze*
yeast – *Hefe*
Do you still brew beer here? – *Wird in Ihrer Brauerei noch Bier gebraut?*

On the menu

Abendessen – evening meal
Ananas – pineapple
Apfel – apple
Apfelsine – orange
Aprikose – apricot
Aubergine – aubergine
Banane – banana
Birne – pear
Blumenkohl – cauliflower
Blutwurst – black pudding
Bockwurst – boiled sausage
Bohnen – beans
-braten – roast ...
Bratkartoffeln – sautéed potatoes
Bratwurst – grilled or fried sausage
Brot – bread
Brötchen – bread roll
Brotzeit – snacks (Bavarian)
-brust – breast of ...
Champignons – button mushrooms
Ei – egg
Eis – ice, ice-cream
Eisbein – pigs' trotters
Ente – duck
Erbsen – peas
Erdbeeren – strawberries
-filet – fillet ...
Fisch – fish
Flammkuchen – flat, pizza-like food (Alsace)
Forelle – trout
Frikadellen – meat rissole
Fritten – chips
Frühstück – breakfast
Gans – goose
Garnelen – prawns
gebacken – baked
gebraten – fried, roasted
gefüllt – stuffed

gegrillt – grilled
gekocht – boiled
Gemüse – vegetables
geräuchert – smoked
Grapefruit – grapefruit
grüner Salat – green salad
Gulasch – goulash (beef stew)
Hähnchen – chicken
Hase – hare
Hauptgericht – main course
Hausfrauenart – traditional style
hausgemacht – home-made
Hering – herring
Herz – heart
Himbeeren – raspberries
Hirsch – stag
Honig – honey
Jäger- – in a mushroom and cream sauce
Kalb – veal
Kaninchen – rabbit
Karotten – carrots
Karpfen – carp
Kartoffeln – potatoes
Kirschen – cherries
Kloß – dumpling
Knoblauch – garlic
Knödel – dumpling (Bavaria)
Kohl – cabbage
Kraut – cabbage (Bavaria)
Kuchen – cake, gâteau
Kürbis – pumpkin
Kutteln – tripe
Lachs – salmon
Lamm – lamb
Lauch – leeks
Leber – liver
Leberkäse – meatloaf
Limone – lime
Linsen – lentils
Matjesfilet – herring fillets
Meerrettich – horseradish
Melone – melon
Mittagessen – lunch
Möhren – carrots
Muscheln – mussels
Nachspeise – dessert
Nieren – kidneys
Nudeln – noodles
Nuss – nut
Obst – fruit
Oliven – olives
Orange – orange
Pampelmuse – grapefruit

Pfannkuchen – pancake
Pfeffer – pepper
Pfifferlinge – chanterelle mushrooms
Pfirsich – peach
Pflaume – plum
Pilze – mushrooms
Pommes – chips
Preiselbeeren – cranberries
Puter – turkey
Rahm – cream
Reh – venison
Reis – rice
Rettich – radish
Rind – beef
Rosenkohl – brussels sprouts
Rösti – potato rosti
Rotkohl – red cabbage
Sahne – cream
Salat – lettuce, salad
Salz – salt
Salzkartoffeln – boiled potatoes
Sauerbraten – pickled beef pot roast (Rhineland)
Sauerkraut – sauerkraut
Schinken (gekochter) – ham
Schinken (roher) – smoked ham, similar to
    Parma ham
Schnitzel – escalope
Schwein – pork
Schweinshaxe – roast pork knuckle
Semmel – bread roll (Bavaria)
Semmelknödel – bread dumpling
Senf – mustard
Soße / Sauce – gravy
Spanferkel – suckling pig
Spargel – asparagus
Spätzle – egg noodles (Suabia)
Speck – bacon
Spiegelei – fried egg
Spinat – spinach
Sülze – brawn
Suppe – soup
Thunfisch – tuna
Tomate – tomato
Trauben – grapes
Truthahn – turkey
Vorspeisen – starters
Weißwurst – boiled veal sausage (Bavaria)
Wiener Schnitzel – breaded veal escalope
Wildschwein – wild boar
Wurst – sausage; cold meats
Zigeuner- – with peppers, onion & tomato sauce
Zitrone – lemon
Zwiebel – onion

Ordering food

fork – *eine Gabel*
knife – *ein Messer*
medium – *mittel*
rare – *blutig*
spoon – *einen Löffel*
well done – *gut durchgebraten*
take-away – *zum Mitnehmen*
Can I have it with...? – *Kann ich es mit ... haben?*
Can I have it without...– *Kann ich es ohne ...
    haben?*
Can I have the menu, please?– *Kann ich bitte die
    Speisekarte haben?*
Do you have any vegetarian options?– *Haben
    Sie etwas für Vegetarier?*
I'd like... – *Ich hätte gern ... ; Ich möchte ...*
Is the kitchen open? – *Ist die Küche offen?*
The bill, please – *Die Rechnung, bitte.*
What do you recommend?– *Was empfehlen Sie?*
What time does the kitchen open?– *Um wieviel
    Uhr / wann macht die Küche auf?*
What time does the kitchen open?– *Um wieviel
    Uhr/ wann schließt die Küche?*

Drinks

beer – *Bier*
coffee – *Kaffee*
dry (wine) – *trocken*
fizzy drink – *Limonade / Limo*
gin – *Gin*
juice – *Saft*
lemonade – *Zitronenlimonade*
mineral water (sparkling) – *Mineralwasser
    (mit Kohlensäure); Sprudel*
milk – *Milch*
schnapps – *Schnaps*
sweet (wine) – *lieblich*
tea – *Tee*
vodka – *Wodka*
water – *Wasser*
whisky – *Whisky*
wine (red / white / rosé) – *Wein (Rotwein/
    Weißwein/Rosé)*

Greetings and farewells

bye – *Tschüss; Auf Wiedersehen*
good morning – *Guten Morgen*
good day – *Guten Tag*

good evening – *Guten Abend*
good night – *Gute Nacht*
goodbye – *Auf Wiedersehen*
hello – *Hallo*
see you again – *Auf Wiedersehen*
see you soon – *Bis bald*

Civilities

excuse me – *Entschuldigung*
I'm sorry – *Es tut mir Leid*
please – *bitte (- schön; – sehr)*
thank you (-very much) – *danke (- schön; – sehr)*
you're welcome – *bitte sehr*

Travelling around

Airport – *Flughafen*
arrivals – *Ankunft*
departures – *Abfahrt*
Do we have to change? – *Müssen wir umsteigen?*
Does the train stop at...? – *Hält der Zug in ...?*
How do I get to...? – *Wie komme ich nach ...?*
How far is it to...? – *Wie weit ist es bis ...?*
How much is it? – *Was kostet es?*
I want to go to... – *Ich möchte nach ... fahren.*
I'd like a single ticket to... – *Ich möchte eine einfache Fahrkarte nach ...*
I'd like a return ticket to... – *Ich möchte eine Rückfahrkarte nach ...*
I'd like a day ticket...– *Ich möchte eine Tageskarte*
Is this the train to...? – *Ist das der Zug nach ...?*
Please get me a taxi – *Besorgen Sie mir bitte ein Taxi.*
Please stop here – *Halten Sie hier, bitte.*
Take me to... – *Bringen Sie mich zu(m) / nach ...*
ticket machine – *Fahrkartenautomat*
ticket office – *Fahrkartenschalter*
travel centre – *Reisezentrum*
When is the last train to...? – *Wann fährt der letzte Zug nach ...?*
When is the next train to...? – *Wann fährt der nächste Zug nach ...?*
Where can I get a taxi? – *Wo finde ich ein Taxi?*
Where's the nearest bus stop? – *Wo ist die nächste Bushaltestelle?*
Where's the main bus station? – *Wo ist der Hauptbusbahnhof?*
Where's the main railway station? – *Wo ist der Hauptbahnhof?*

Where's the nearest tram stop? – *Wo ist die nächste Straßenbahnhaltestelle?*
Where's the nearest underground stop? – *Wo ist die nächste U-Bahnstation?*
Which bus goes to...? – *Welcher Bus fährt nach ...?*
Which platform does the train to... leave from? – *Auf welchem Gleis fährt der Zug nach ... ab?*
Will you tell me where to get off for...? – *Können Sie mir bitte sagen, wo ich für ... aussteigen muss?*

At the hotel

Can I reserve a room? – *Kann ich ein Zimmer ... reservieren?*
...for next Tuesday – *für nächsten Dienstag*
Do you have a room free? – *Haben Sie ein Zimmer frei?*
For... nights – *Für ... Nächte*
Here's the confirmation – *Hier ist die Bestätigung.*
How much does it cost (per night)? – *Wieviel kostet es (pro Nacht)?*
I'd like a... – *Ich möchte ein ...*
...single room – *Einzelzimmer*
...double room – *Doppelzimmer*
...triple room – *Dreibettzimmer*
...twin room – *Zimmer mit zwei Betten*
Is breakfast included? – *Ist Frühstück inbegriffen?*
Is there air-conditioning? – *Gibt es eine Klimaanlage?*
I've a reservation – *Ich habe reservieren lassen.*
My name is... – *Ich heiße*
One night only – *Nur eine Nacht*
We'd like a room... – *Wir möchten ein Zimmer...*
...with a bath – *mit Bad*
...with a shower – *mit Dusche*
...with a toilet – *mit Toilette*
...with a view – *mit Aussicht*
We've reserved three rooms – *Wir haben drei Zimmer reservieren lassen.*
What time is breakfast? – *Um wieviel Uhr / wann ist Frühstück?*
Where's the breakfast room? – *Wo ist das Frühstückszimmer?*

Days, dates, months and seasons

yesterday – *gestern*
today – *heute*
tomorrow – *morgen*
Monday – *Montag*

Tuesday – *Dienstag*
Wednesday – *Mittwoch*
Thursday – *Donnerstag*
Friday – *Freitag*
Saturday – *Samstag / Sonnabend*
Sunday – *Sonntag*
1st – *erste*
2nd – *zweite*
3rd – *dritte*
4th – *vierte*
bank/public holiday – *Feiertag*
New Year – *Neujahr*
Lent – *Fastenzeit*
Easter – *Ostern*
Whitsun – *Pfingsten*
Christmas – *Weihnachten*
January – *Januar*
February – *Februar*
March – *März*
April – *April*
May – *Mai*
June – *Juni*
July – *Juli*
August – *August*
September – *September*
October – *Oktober*
November – *November*
December – *Dezember*
spring – *Frühling; Frühjahr*
summer – *Sommer*
autumn – *Herbst*
winter – *Winter*

Numbers

0 – *null*
1 – *eins*
2 – *zwei*
3 – *drei*
4 – *vier*
5 – *fünf*
6 – *sechs*
7 – *sieben*
8 – *acht*
9 – *neun*
10 – *zehn*
11 – *elf*
12 – *zwölf*
13 – *dreizehn*
14 – *vierzehn*
15 – *fünfzehn*
16 – *sechzehn*
17 – *siebzehn*
18 – *achtzehn*
19 – *neunzehn*
20 – *zwanzig*
21 – *einundzwanzig*
22 – *zweiundzwanzig*
30 – *dreißig*
40 – *vierzig*
50 – *fünfzig*
60 – *sechzig*
70 – *siebzig*
80 – *achtzig*
90 – *neunzig*
100 – *einhundert*
101 – *hunderteins*
102 – *hundertzwei*
110 – *hundertzehn*
1,000 – *eintausend*
1,000,000 – *eine Million*

Language problems

Do you speak English? – *Sprechen Sie English?*
Does anyone here speak English? – *Spricht hier jemand English?*
I don't understand – *Ich verstehe nicht.*
I'm sorry, I don't speak German – *Es tut mir Leid, ich spreche kein Deutsch.*
My German's not very good – *Mein Deutsch ist nicht sehr gut.*
Please repeat, slowly – *Bitte wiederholen Sie das, langsam.*

Emergencies

Call a doctor! – *Rufen Sie einen Arzt!*
Call the police! – *Rufen Sie die Polizei!*
chemist – *Apotheke*
dentist – *Zahnarzt*
doctor – *Arzt*
Help! – *Hilfe!*
hospital – *Krankenhaus*
I'm lost (on foot/by car) – *Ich habe mich verlaufen/verfahren.*
I've been robbed! – *Ich bin bestohlen worden!*
police – *Polizei*
Thief! – *Dieb!*

Brewing groups

UNTIL COMPARATIVELY recently most large German breweries were independent and there was little or no foreign ownership. Those halcyon days have disappeared and around 70 per cent of beer is now produced in breweries controlled by the seven corporations listed below. It remains to be seen how many of these breweries survive – at least two of them may already have closed by the time you read this.

Actris

Käfertaler Straße 170, 68167 Mannheim-Wohlgelegen   T 0621 337 00   F 0621 337 03 06
www.actris-ag.de
Approximate output: 3,000,000hl
BREWERIES:
Bellheimer, Bellheim
Eichbaum, Mannheim
Freiberger, Freiberg
Park, Pirmasens

Essentially Eichbaum's corporate arm, Actris was formed in 2001. They took over the Bellheimer and Park breweries in 2004, Eichbaum having acquired Freiberger soon after re-unification. We believe they also own Mammut of Sangerhausen but have no idea where their beers are brewed.

Bitburger Getränkegruppe

Bitburger Getränke Verwaltungsgesellschaft mbH
Römermauer 3, 54634 Bitburg
T 06561 140   F 06561 14 22 89
www.bitburger.de
Approximate output: 9,500,000hl
BREWERIES:
Bitburger, Bitburg
König, Duisburg
Köstritzer, Bad Köstritz
Licher, Lich
Wernesgrüner, Wernesgrün

Already Rheinland-Pfalz's largest brewer by far, Bitburger bought Köstritzer and Wernesgrüner in the early 1990s, with König and Licher being added to the portfolio in July 2004 following a joint take-over of the Holsten Group with Carlsberg.

Brau Holding International

Owners: Heineken International (49.9%), Schörghuber Unternehmensgruppe (50.1%)
Denninger Straße 165, 81904 München-Bogenhausen   T 089 92 38 03   F 089 923 86 03
www.schoerghuber-unternehmensgruppe.de
Approximate output: 11,000,000hl
BREWERIES:
Auerbräu, Rosenheim (P)
Bavaria-Bräu, München (P)
Braustolz, Chemnitz (K)
Fürstenberg, Donaueschingen (K)
Fürstliches Brauhaus, Regensburg (P)
Hoepfner, Karlsruhe (K)
Kulmbacher, Kulmbach (K)
Lohrer, Lohr (K)
Paulaner Bräuhaus, München (P)
Paulaner/Hacker-Pschorr, München (P)
Scherdel, Hof (K)
Sternquell, Plauen (K)
Würzburger Hofbräu, Würzburg (K)

Formed in 2001 by the Dutch brewer Heineken and Bayerische Brau Holding (owned by Schörghuber of München). The latter already controlled the Kulmbacher (K) and Paulaner (P) brewing groups which are often still listed as owning the above breweries. In the last five years Fürstenberg, Hoepfner, Lohrer and Würzberger Hofbräu have all been taken over. They also have a 45 per cent stake in Karlsberg of Homburg.

Carlsberg Breweries

100 Ny Carlsberg Vej, DK–1760 Copenhagen, Denmark   T +45 3327 3300   F +45 3327 4701

www.carlsberg.com
Approximate output: 9,000,000hl (Germany)
BREWERIES:
Feldschlößchen, Braunschweig
Feldschlößchen, Dresden
Holsten, Hamburg
Landskron, Görlitz
Lübzer, Lübz

Carlsberg's first foray into the German brewing industry occurred in 1988 when they bought the Hannen brewery in Mönchengladbach. That was sold on to Oettinger in 2003 but the following year they and Bitburger took over the seven breweries of the Holsten Group. König and Licher are controlled by Bitburger but the other five remain in Carlsberg's hands. Rumours abound that up to three of these may soon close.

InBev

Brouwerijplein 1, B–3000 Leuven, Belgium
T +32 1627 6111 **F** +32 1650 6111 www.inbev.com
Approximate output: 15,000,000hl (Germany)
BREWERIES:
Beck/Haake-Beck, Bremen
Diebels, Issum
Dinkelacker–Schwaben-Bräu, Stuttgart
Gilde, Hannover
Hasseröder, Wernigerode
Hofbrauhaus, Berchtesgaden
Hofbrauhaus Wolters, Braunschweig
Löwenbräu, München
Spaten–Franziskaner-Bräu, München

The world's largest brewing company, InBev was formed in 2004 when Belgian giant Interbrew merged with the South American colossus AmBev. Interbrew first entered the German market in 2001 when they bought Diebels, swiftly followed by Beck/Haake-Beck. The following year Gilde and its subsidiaries Hasseröder and Hofbrauhaus Wolters followed suit. 2003 saw the acquisition of the remainder and for a short time Interbrew was Germany's largest brewing group, although they've since been overtaken by Oetker.

Oetker Gruppe

Dr. August Oetker KG, Lutterstraße 14, 33617 Bielefeld **T** 0521 15 50 **F** 0521 155 29 95
www.oetkergruppe.de
Approximate output: 19,000,000hl
BREWERIES:

Allgäuer Brauhaus, Leuterschach (RG)
Binding, Frankfurt (RG)
Brinkhoff, Dortmund (BB)
DAB, Dortmunder (RG)
Erbacher, Erbach (RG)
Hasen-Bräu, Augsburg (BB)
Hövels, Dortmund (RG)
Jever, Jever (BB)
Kindl, Berlin (RG)
Kölner Verbund, Köln (BB)
Krostitzer, Krostitz (RG)
Radeberger, Radeberg (RG)
Reudnitzer, Leipzig (BB)
Rostocker, Rostock (BB
Schultheiss, Berlin (BB)
Stuttgarter Hofbräu, Stuttgart (RG)
Tucher, Fürth (BB)
Tucher, Nürnberg (BB)
Zirndorfer, Zirndorf (BB)

The Oetker Group has its roots in the food industry, having risen from its origins as the inventor of baking powder. They became Germany's largest brewing group early in 2004, following their take-over of Brau und Brunnen (BB). Oetker already owned the Radeberger Gruppe (RG), until 2002 known as the Binding Gruppe. The two subsidiaries are still usually quoted as the owners of the breweries above.

Oettinger Gruppe

Owners: the Kollmar family, Brauhausstraße 8, 86732 Oettingen **T** 09082 7080 **F** 09082 70810
Approximate output: 4,000,000hl
BREWERIES:
Dessow, Dessow
Forstquell, Fürnheim
Gotha, Gotha
Mönchengladbach, Mönchengladbach
Oettingen, Oettingen
Schweriner Schloßbrauerei, Schwerin

Still owned by the Kollmar family, Oettinger expanded into eastern Germany following re-unification, buying Dessow, Gotha and Schweriner Schloßbrauerei. Hannen's former brewery in Mönchengladbach was bought from Carlsberg in 2003. All four of these breweries brew the full range of Oettinger beers as and when required. To their credit, each bottle is labelled with the brewery of origin. The smallest brewery in the group is the Forstquell brewpub, sometimes used to train Oettinger's brewers.

Beers of unknown origin

WE'D LIKE TO BE able to tell you where every beer in Germany is brewed, but unfortunately we can't. Over the years we've come across a number of beers brewed for drinks companies, former breweries, supermarket chains etc. The breweries that produce these beers and those that commission them are often extremely reluctant to divulge their origin, sometimes to a degree that would put several national security agencies to shame.

What follows is a list of companies whose beers have so far eluded all our efforts to establish their source. There are doubtless many others we're not aware of. If you've any concrete information where these beers are brewed or know of any others we haven't listed, please don't hesitate to contact GermanBreweries@aol.com

Angermann

Angermann Markenvertrieb GmbH
Marktplatz 3, 95326 Kulmbach
T 09221 80 46 11
KNOWN BEERS:
Angermann Hell (4.9%)
Angermann Pils (4.9%)
Angermann Hefe-Weissbier (5.1%)
Angermann Hefe-Weissbier Dunkel (5.1%)
Angermann Weissbier Kristall (5.1%)

We suspect these beers are either brewed by Kaiserdom or Kulmbacher but, to be honest, they could come from just about anywhere.

Bavaria-St. Pauli

Hamburg
KNOWN BEERS:
Elbschloss Pilsener (4.8%)
Ratsherrn Pilsener (4.8%)
Dübelsbrücker Dunkel (4.9%)

When Holsten closed the Bavaria-St. Pauli brewery on Hopfenstraße in 2001, their best known beers, Astra and Duckstein, moved to new homes at Holsten and Feldschlößchen (Braunschweig). The above beers are still being brewed but we don't know where.

Bayernbräu

Bayernbräu Fränkische Saale GmbH
97616 Bad Neustadt
KNOWN BEERS:
Falkenfelser Premium Hell (4.9%)
Falkenfelser Premium Pilsener (5%)
Falkenfelser Weißbier Hell (5.2%)
Falkenfelser Premium Export (5.5%)

We can't trace a contact address for Bayernbräu and have no idea where their beers might be brewed.

Bürgerbräu

Bürgerbräu Bamberg GmbH
KNOWN BEERS:
Bürgerbräu Bamberg Urtyp Hell (4.7%)
Bürgerbräu Bamberg Pils (5%)
Bürgerbräu Bamberg Export (5.2%)

A former name of the Kaiserdom brewery, it's widely assumed Bürgerbräu Bamberg beers are brewed by them, but they don't own up to it.

Burkarth

Marktplatz 4, 63916 Amorbach
T 09373 48 63
www.brauerei-burkarth.de

KNOWN BEERS:
Burkarth Export (4.8%)
Burkarth Pils (5.3%)

Despite Burkarth's website stating these beers are brewed by Distelhäuser, the latter deny all knowledge. It's possible they may simply be re-badged.

🍺 Burkarth

Marktplatz 4, 63916 Amorbach
Closed Mon; Tue from 17.00,
Wed–Sun 11.00–14.00 & from 17.00
DB Amorbach 270m

Euler

Privatbrauerei Gebrüder Euler GmbH & Co. KG
Garbenheimer Straße 20, 35578 Wetzlar
T 06441 948 10   **F** 06441 94 81 30
KNOWN BEERS:
Euler Hell
Euler Landpils
Euler Wetzlarer Dom-Pilsener

The Euler brewery closed in 2001, and there have long been plans to convert it into a brewpub, but nothing has yet come to fruition. In the meantime, the above beers are contract-brewed somewhere in Hessen.

Falk

Weizenbierbrauerei Hans Falk KG
92224 Amberg
KNOWN BEERS:
Bauer Hefe-Weizen (5.3%)
Falk Dunkles Weizen (5.3%)

Falk stopped brewing in 1989 but we think the beers are still brewed in Amberg. Bruckmüller is our prime suspect.

Förster & Brecke

Förster & Brecke Getränke GmbH
31785 Hameln
KNOWN BEERS:
Gutsherren Pils (4.8%)
Gutsherren Export (5%)

Until 1985, a brewery in its own right, Förster & Brecke now have the above beers brewed else-where – our money's on Brauerei Allersheim.

Frankenthaler

Frankenthaler Brauhaus GmbH
Johann-Klein-Straße 22, 67227 Frankenthal
T 06233 87 40   **F** 06233 211 88
KNOWN BEERS:
Germania Pilsener (4.8%)
Steininger Pils (4.8%)
Germania Hefe Weizen (5%)
Karfürst Carl Theodor Weizenbier Hell (5%)
Germania Export (5.1%)

Frankenthaler, owned by Actris, no longer brew themselves. The beers almost certainly originate from one of the company's three breweries in the region.

Fränky

Fränky Getränkemarkt AG
Geisseestraße 41, 90439 Nürnberg
T 0911 65 65 60   **F** 0911 65 65 62 00
www.fraenky-getraenke.de
KNOWN BEERS:
Fränky Landbier Hell (4.8%)
Fränky Premium Pils (4.9%)
Fränky Hefeweizen Hell (5.1%)

Fränky own 15 drinks markets in the Nürnberg area and have the above beers contract-brewed by an unknown brewery.

Germania

Germania Brauerei F. Dieninghoff GmbH
Borkstraße 11, 48163 Münster
Germania Edel Pils (4.9%)
Germania Alt (4.9%)

Münster's Germania brewery last brewed in 1987 but still has a couple of beers produced elsewhere.

GSM

Gastro Service Mittelsachsen GmbH
Am Fürstenwald, 09599 Freiberg
T 03731 36 30   **F** 03731 36 31 09
KNOWN BEERS:
Meister Bräu Pilsner (4.9%)
Meister Bräu Export (5.4%)

We believe GSM is owned by Actris and strongly suspect Meister Bräu beers are brewed by Freiberger, not least because they share the same address…

Hike

97342 Marktsteft
KNOWN BEERS:
Steigerwald Pils (4.9%)
Steigerwald Export (5.1%)
Haderlump Bockbier (6.2%)

We know nothing about the company these beers are brewed for and can't even trace an address.

Hörl

Getränke Hörl
Pindharter Straße 22, 85290 Geisenfeld-Gaden
T 08452 20 48
KNOWN BEERS:
Geisenfelder Ur Hell (4.8%)
Geisenfelder Weizen Hell (5.3%)

Hörl is a drinks market in the village of Gaden, just east of Geisenfeld. We've no idea who brews their two beers.

Hubauer

Hubauer Getränke & Logistik GmbH & Co. KG
Lochhamer Schlag 3, 82166 Gräfelfing
T 089 89 81 80
www.hubauer.de
KNOWN BEERS:
Eine Bayern Halbe Urhell (4.7%)
Eine Bayern Halbe Pils (4.8%)
Eine Bayern Halbe Export (5.1%)
Eine Bayern Halbe Hefeweisse (5.3%)

Hubauer is a drinks wholesaler based in Gräfelfing, south-west of München.

Jodlbauer

Dietrich-Bonhoeffer-Straße 27,
94113 Tiefenbach
T 08509 912 00   **F** 08509 91 20 50
www.jodlbauer-weizen.de
KNOWN BEERS:
Jodlbauer Leichte-Weisse (2.6%)
Jodlbauer Helle-Weisse (5.3%)
Jodlbauer Zwickl-Weisse (5.3%)
Jodlbauer Josefi-Dunkel (5.3%)
Jodlbauer Spektakulator (6%)

The Yodelling Farmer no longer brew themselves and we've been unable to find out where their beers originate. The website has a list of all outlets.

Katharinen

Katharina-von-Bora GbR
Am Doktorteich 6, 04808 Wurzen
T/F 03425 81 59 81
www.katharinenbier.com
KNOWN BEERS:
Katharinen Hell (4.9%)
Katharinen Bier Original (4.9%)
Katharinenbier Premium (5.4%)
Katharinenbier Schwarzbier (5.6%)

These beers are named after Katharina von Bora, the wife of Martin Luther. We think they may be brewed in either Bayreuth or Herborn.

Klausner

Klausner Getränke- und Vertriebs GmbH
Einsiedler Hauptstraße 136,
09123 Chemnitz-Einsiedel
T 037209 68 50
KNOWN BEERS:
Klausner Export (4.8%)
Klausner Pils (5%)

We're not certain who brews Klausner's two beers but given they're next to the Einsiedler brewery it wouldn't come as any great surprise to learn it was them.

Köthener

Köthener Brauerei GmbH
Gnetscher Straße 10, 06366 Köthen
T 03496 41 14 11   **F** 03496 41 14 29
www.koethener-brauerei.de
KNOWN BEERS:
Köthener Spezial Pils (4.9%)
Hubertus 1861 Premium Pilsener (4.9%)
Hubertus J. S. Bach Jubiläumsbier (4.9%)
Hubertus Schwarzbier (5.3%)
Köthener Export (5.3%)
KuKaKö-stlich Karnevalsbier (5.3%)
Hubertus Bock (6.9%)

We think Köthener last brewed for themselves in 1992. They moved out of the old brewery to new premises on the outskirts of town in 2003.

Kronenbrauerei Wahl

Kronenbrauerei Rudolf Wahl KG
Prof-Bamannstraße 20, 89423 Gundelfingen
T 09073 73 58   **F** 09073 38 74

KNOWN BEERS:
Cannabia (5%)
The 4 Elements (5%)

Kronenbrauerei Wahl last brewed in Gundelfingen during 2003 and we believe the beers may now originate from Switzerland.

Linden-Bräu

Nürnberger Straße 46,
90559 Burgthann-Oberferrieden
T 09183 95 07 70   **T** 09183 95 07 71
KNOWN BEERS:
Linden-Bräu Vollbier (4.8%)
Linden-Bräu Bock (7.5%)

This small brewery ceased to produce its own beer in 2001 and we believe the tap closed at the same time.

Lindenbrauerei

Unna
KNOWN BEERS:
Gutsherren Pils (4.8%)
Spinola Pilsener (4.8%)
Urfels Alt (4.8%)
Waldschloss Alt (4.8%)
Waldschloss Pils (4.8%)
Lindenbrauerei Golden Pils (4.9%)
Berg Quell (5%)
Gutsherren Landbier (5%)

Unna's original Lindenbrauerei closed in 1979 but a number of beers are still brewed under its name, we suspect by one of Oetker's Dortmund breweries. Not to be confused with the current Lindenbrauerei which is a brewpub in part of the former brewery.

Löwenbrauerei

Löwenbrauerei Trier J. Mendgen GmbH & Co.
Olweiger Straße 7, 54295 Trier
T 0651 97 01 40   **F** 0651 970 14 21
KNOWN BEERS:
Löwenbrauerei Edelpils (4.7%)

We think Löwenbrauerei's sole beer may be brewed by Karlsberg in Homburg. The brewery used to have a tap at Bergstraße 47 but we understand that's now closed.

Lüneburger Kronen-Brauerei

Gebrüder-Heyn-Straße 8, 21337 Lüneburg
T 04131 89 90   **F** 04131 89 94 24
KNOWN BEERS:
Lüneburger Kronen Dunkel (4.8%)
Lüneburger Pilsener (4.8%)
Moravia Pils (4.8%)

Sometimes known as the Moravia Brauhaus, Lüneburger Kronen-Brauerei moved from their old town-centre site (now a pub and museum – see below) to a new brewery on the eastern outskirts in 1985. We believe the beers are now brewed by one of Carlsberg's breweries.

🍺 **Krone**
Heiligengeiststraße 39, 21335 Lüneburg-Altstadt
T 04131 71 32 00   **F** 04131 418 61
Mon–Sat from 08.00, Sun from 10.00
DB Lüneburg 900m

Mammut

Juri-Gagarin-Straße 33, 06526 Sangerhausen
T 03464 62 70   **F** 03464 627 30
www.mammut-brauerei.de
KNOWN BEERS:
Mammut Giant Gold (4.8%)
Mammut Ur-Pils (4.8%)
Mammut Black (4.9%)
Mammut Export (5.5%)
Mammut Ur-Bock (6.9%)

Henninger of Frankfurt bought the former VEB Brauerei Sangerhausen in 1991 and changed the name to Mammut. We don't think they've brewed there for a number of years and are sure the above beers originate from one of the four Actris breweries.

Maxxum

Getränkelogistik Maxxum GmbH
Westpreußenerstraße 38, 47809 Krefeld-Linn
T 02151 1570 18 19
KNOWN BEERS:
Oscar Maxxum Alt (4.8%)
Oscar Maxxum Pils (4.9%)
Oscar Maxxum Export (5%)

We believe Krefeld drinks company Maxxum has three beers brewed by Iserlohner but have been unable to confirm our suspicions.

Penzkofer

Getränke Penzkofer
Freibachstraße 1, 93458 Eschlkam
T 09948 940 60   **F** 09948 94 06 11
KNOWN BEERS:
Waldschmidt Hell (4.8%)
Waldschmidt Weissbier (5.3%)

Family-owned drinks market in the outskirts of Eschlkam that has the two beers brewed locally.

Rittmayer

Willersdorf 108, 91352 Hallerndorf-Willersdorf
T 09195 947 30   **F** 09195 947 31 50
www.rittmayer.com
Rittmayer Hausbräu (4.9%)

Rittmayer stopped brewing their own beer in 2003 and now have it contract-brewed. If you want to visit, take bus No. 265 from Eggolsheim station, but be warned you'll probably have to return to Forchheim.

🍺 **Rittmayer**

Willersdorf 108, 91352 Hallerndorf-Willersdorf
Closed Mon; Tue 17.00–23.00, Wed–Sun 11.30–14.30 & 17.00–23.00; rooms available
DB Eggolsheim 7km

Sachsengold

Sachsengold Getränke Vertriebsgesellschaft
08412 Werdau
KNOWN BEERS:
Sachsengold Spezial Hell (4.6%)
Sachsengold Pilsner (4.8%)
Sachsengold Landbier (4.9%)

We can find out very little about this drinks company and aren't even sure if they're based in Werdau or Zwickau. Don't ask us who brews their three beers.

Sachsenschlösser

Elbtal Getränke GmbH
Müglitztalstraße 76, 01809 Müglitztal-Mühlbach
T 035027 55 66   **F** 035027 55 15
KNOWN BEERS:
Sachsenschlösser Dunkel (5%)
Sachsenschlösser Pils (5%)
Sachsenschlösser Export (5.5%)

We're not sure if these beers are brewed for Elbtal or Sachsenschlösser GbR and have only a rough idea where they may originate.

Salch

Brauerei Salch GmbH
Rote-Kreuz-Straße 8, 97762 Hammelburg
T 09732 22 66   **F** 09732 78 32 49
KNOWN BEERS:
Hammelburger Hell
Hammelburger Pils
Hammelburger Altstadtbier Dunkel
Hammelburger Märzen
Hammelburger Weihnachtsbier

Salch was bought by Hochstiftliches Brauhaus in 1997 and stopped brewing soon after. We think their beers are either brewed in Fulda or Motten.

Schloss Bräu

Schloßstraße 16, 93491 Stamsried
T 09466 232   **F** 09466 13 29
KNOWN BEERS:
Herzog Wilhelm Hell (4.9%)
Herzog Wilhelm Pilsener (4.9%)
Herzog Wilhelm Export (5.2%)

These beers haven't been brewed in Stamsried for 15 years. The only clue to their origin we have is that Dimpfl of Furth im Wald does the bottling.

Schmitt Bräu

Oberend 19, 96110 Scheßlitz
T 09542 563   **F** 09542 73 14
KNOWN BEERS:
Schmitt Bräu Hausbrauerart Bier (4.8%)
Schmitt Bräu Jura Hell (4.9%)
Schmitt Bräu Edel Pils (4.9%)
Schmitt Bräu Export (5.1%)

No longer brewing themselves, Schmitt Bräu beers are now rumoured to originate from Bayreuth. Scheßlitz still has two working brewpubs and can be reached by bus No. 8224 from Bamberg.

🍺 **Schmitt Bräu**

Oberend 19, 96110 Scheßlitz
Closed Sat & Sun; Mon–Fri from 16.00
DB Bamberg 14km

Steinbräu

Getränkehandel Bär
Industriestraße 5, 63755 Alzenau
T 06023 79 47
KNOWN BEERS:
Steinbräu Export (5.3%)

Steinbräu Festbier (5.3%)

The original Stein brewery closed in 1973 but the name was revived by a local drinks company in 2001. The beers are reputedly brewed by the Erbacher Brauhaus but they deny this.

Sudmeister & Fruchtgut

Dilo Getränke Center Lobitz GmbH
Gahlensche Straße 95, 44809 Bochum-Hamme
T 0234 95 27 40
KNOWN BEERS:
Brauer Pilsener (4.6%),
Sudmeister Pilsener (5%),
Sudmeister Hefe-Weißbier (5%),
Sudmeister Schwarzbier (5.2%).

Sudmeister & Fruchtgut appears to be a trading name of the Dilo Getränke Center. We have no idea where the four beers are brewed.

Treiber

Rheintorstraße 25, 67071 Ludwigshafen-Notwende
T 0621 67 20 41   **F** 0621 67 20 42
KNOWN BEERS:
Treiber Pils (4.9%)
Treiber Export (5.3%)

Treiber stopped brewing sometime around 1990. We understand the beers may currently be brewed by Pfungstädter but have been unable to confirm this.

Trinklogistik

Trinklogistik GmbH, Getränkegroßhandel
Trarbacher Straße 38, 47259 Duisburg-Huckingen
KNOWN BEERS:
Traugott Simon Alt (4.8%)
Traugott Simon Pils (4.8%)
Traugott Simon Kellerbier 1798 (4.8%)
Traugott Simon Landbier 1798 (4.8%)
Traugott Simon Pilsener 1798 (4.8%)
Traugott Simon Mölmsch 1798 (4.8%)
Traugott Simon Urtyp (4.9%)
Traugott Simon Export (5.1%)
Traugott Simon Schwarzbier (5.2%)
Traugott Simon Dunkel (5.3%)
Traugott Simon Weizenbier Hefetrüb (5.3%)
Traugott Simon Weizenbier Dunkel (5.3%)
Traugott Simon Weizenbier Kristall (5.3%)

Traugott Simon Weizen 1798 (5.4%)
Traugott Simon Winterbier (5.6%)
Traugott Simon Weihnachtsbier (5.6%)
Traugott Simon Heller Bock 1798 (7.2%)

Somewhere there's a brewery doing very well out of their contract with Duisburg's Trinklogistik. Unfortunately, we don't know who it is.

Waldschmidt

Privatbrauerei Waldschmidt GmbH & Co. KG
Pfannenstielsgasse 17, 35578 Wetzlar
T 06441 420 69
KNOWN BEERS:
Waldschmidt Pils (4.8%)
Waldschmidt Export (5.2%)

Like Euler, Wetzlar's other recently closed brewery, Waldschmidt beers are currently brewed elsewhere. The last time the coppers at their town centre brewery were used was during 1996.

Winkels

Winkels Getränke Logistik GmbH
Auerstraße 70, 76227 Karlsruhe
T 0721 949 60   **F** 0721 949 61 09
www.winkels.de
KNOWN BEERS:
Markgrafenbräu Pilsener (4.7%)
Markgrafenbräu Export (5.1%)

Large drinks wholesaler based in Karlsruhe whose above two beers are contract-brewed. We have no idea where.

Wüllner

Schlossbrunnen Wüllner GmbH
39444 Hecklingen-Gänsefurth
T 03925 927 10   **F** 03925 92 71 19
www.gaensefurther.de
KNOWN BEERS:
Wüllner's Braumeister Gold (4.9%)
Wüllner's Braumeister Landbier (4.9%)
Wüllner's Braumeister Pilsener (4.9%)
Wüllner's Zwergen Bräu Pilsener (4.9%)
Wüllner's Braumeister Schwarzbier (5.1%)
Wüllner's Braumeister Export (5.2%)
Wüllner's Braumeister Weissbier (5.2%)

Mineral water and soft drinks producer in the hamlet of Gänsefurth, just north of Hecklingen.

References

THE FOLLOWING (mostly German-language) books have proved useful over the last 15 years, many covering some of the breweries in the Guide in far more detail than we ever could.

Bierkultur & Gastlichkeit. Memmelsdorf: Geschäftsstelle Privater Braugasthöfe, 2005. – Free pamphlet published annually by a group of more than 50 independent brewpubs. Each entry also includes a brief description in English. Copies can be picked up in the member pubs. They also have a website (in English, German and Italian): www.braugasthoefe.de

Brauerei-Adressbuch. Nürnberg: Verlag Hans Carl, 23rd edition, 2004. – The German brewing industry's pocket bible containing the addresses of (almost) all breweries, maltings, equipment suppliers, etc. It's published every other September.

BRAUN, Boris. *Brauns Brauerei Atlas (Band 1).* Nürnberg: Verlag Hans Carl, 2003. – Comprehensive guide to the breweries of Mittelfranken and southern parts of Oberfranken (roughly, all Franconian breweries south of Bamberg). There is a photograph for each of the 135 entries.

BRAUN, Boris. *Brauns Brauerei Atlas (Band 2).* Nürnberg: Verlag Hans Carl, 2004. – Covering the parts of Franconia the first part didn't reach, Boris Braun's second book features 158 breweries across Unterfranken and northern Oberfranken.

CONEN, John Leslie. *Bamberg and Franconia: Germany's Brewing Heartland.* John Conen, 2003. – Our first trip to Bamberg (for beer) was inspired by John Conen's short guide to the area, published in 1991. This considerably expanded version concentrates on Bamberg but also includes other notable towns and villages in the region, together with a short menu guide and other tips.

HAWTHORNE, Larry. *The Beer Drinker's Guide to Munich.* Hemet, CA: Freizeit Publishers, 5th edition, 2005. – An American's guide to the better pubs of Munich, with the emphasis on Bierkellers. There are maps and detailed instructions on how to get to each of the 57 places that are featured.

JACKSON, Michael. *Michael Jackson's Pocket Beer Book.* London: Mitchell Beazley, 3rd edition, 1991. – Although not exclusively a German guide (it covers the whole world), back in 1991 this was the only source we were aware of that covered breweries outside Franconia.

KOEPKE, Harald. *Brauereiführer Baden-Württemberg.* Stuttgart: Media Kontor, 2003. – Essentially a printed version of the Bierschrank website (www.bierschrank.de), featuring virtually all the breweries in Baden-Württemberg, together with their beers and taps.

KOEPKE, Harald. *Brauereiführer Hessen, Rheinland-Pfalz & Saarland.* Stuttgart: Media Kontor, 2005. – The third in Harald Koepke's expanding series (a fourth covering Franconia should now be available). Like the one covering eastern Germany's southern states, only around two-thirds of breweries feature.

KOEPKE, Harald. *Brauereiführer Sachsen, Thüringen & Sachsen-Anhalt.* Stuttgart: Media Kontor, 2004. – Not just a brewery guide, this useful book also includes beer-related recipes and tourist tips. For some reason, only around two-thirds of the region's breweries feature.

LEES, Graham. *Good Beer Guide to Munich and Bavaria* (CAMRA Guide). St Albans: Verulam Publishing, 1994. – If you've any doubt just how much the brewing scene has changed over the last couple of decades, read Graham Lees' excellent guide and check how many of the featured breweries have closed!

MACK, Stefan. *(Die neue) Fränkische Brauereikarte*. Nürnberg: Verlag Stefan Mack, 1997. – It was probably this book more than any other that led to the creation of the Good Beer Guide Germany. More than 60 of the 330 breweries included have since stopped brewing. If you think that's bad, the first edition in 1990 featured 379!

SCHIEDER, Harald, and FORSTER, Ralph. *Bierführer Niederbayern*. Regensburg: MZ Buchverlag, 2000. – The follow-up to Schneider & Forster's Oberpfälz guide (see below) was one covering the Niederbayern region. Like its predecessor, breweries that have their beers contract-brewed are also included

SCHIEDER, Harald, and FORSTER, Ralph. *Oberpfälzer Bierführer*. Regensburg: MZ Buchverlag, 1999. – Excellent guide to the breweries of the Oberpfalz region of Bayern (the area between Unterfranken and the Czech border), with tasting notes for many of the beers.

Beer and brewery websites

There are many things in life that would be far more difficult, if not impossible, were it not for the invention of the internet. This Guide is one of them.

www.beerguide.de – Despite the German address, this is an English-language guide covering the four south-western states. The brewery listings are a little out of date but the separate pub guides are very good.

www.beerme.com – Probably the most comprehensive brewery website in the world. Its owner aims to include every brewery on the planet and has entries for more than 9,000 breweies, both open and recently closed.

www.bier1.de – Beer tasters' website featuring notes on more than 3,000 predominantly German beers, although most other countries are covered.

www.bierregion-franken.info – This frequently updated site lists all currently open Franconian breweries and includes a few pages in English, although the rest of the site should pose few problems for the monoglot.

www.bierschrank.de – The website of the Baden-Württembergischer Brauerbund (Baden-Württemberg Brewers' Alliance). Almost all of the state's breweries and beers are listed.

www.biertest-online.de – Biertest-Online is run by a group of friends from Hannover and features tasting notes on more than 5,000 beers from around the world.

www.brauer-bund.de – The German Brewers' Alliance website. There are also dozens of pages featuring brewing tips, beers styles, recipes, how to serve beer, etc. It also includes enough beer and brewing statistics to keep any obsessive happy.

www.braugasthoefe.com – As mentioned on the previous page, this is the online version of Bierkultur & Gastlichkeit and includes all the breweries featured in that publication with the added bonus of English pages throughout.

www.germanbeerguide.co.uk – The best source of information on where to find German beer in Britain, with county-by-county listings of all known outlets.

www.german-breweries.com – Originally intended to be an online version of this Guide, when we eventually get round to setting this website up we hope to feature updates to the brewery and pub listings.

www.franconiabeerguide.com – American-run website concentrating on Franconian breweries. Based on Bierregion-Franken (above), every functioning brewery is listed, often with visitor reports.

www.klausehm.de – Indispensable if you're after information on closed breweries. Klaus Ehm is a beer label collector whose site lists around 25,000 German breweries, some of which closed almost two hundred years ago – Köln alone has 400 listings!

www.newbreweries.fsnet.co.uk – The best source of information for new wave brewpubs and micro-breweries. Paul Harrop aims to include every brewery to open in Austria, the Czech Republic, Denmark, Germany, Slovenia and Switzerland since 1984. The site is updated roughly five times a year.

www.ratebeer.com – American-based website that features tastings of thousands of beers worldwide with the emphasis on North American brews.

www.xs4all.nl/~patto1ro/index.htm – Extensive website run by Ron Pattinson, an Englishman (possibly from Yorkshire) who now lives in Amsterdam. It covers much of Europe but there are large sections devoted to Germany, featuring both pub and brewery guides.

Directory of places

Perhaps a little more comprehensive than may be strictly necessary, this directory includes every brewery (or suspected brewery) that we had reason to investigate over the last five years. Many were found to have stopped brewing but all have been included here in order that you are spared the many wild-goose chases we've had to endure. Where we know the year brewing ceased this has been included in brackets, as has any brewery known to brew the beers on contract. The basic rule is this: if a name's printed in bold we think the brewery is still functioning and have included it in the Guide – if it's not, it's not.

A

Aalen *B-W* Aalener Löwenbrauerei, Grünbaum, Köpf, Löwenbrauerei Wasseralfingen
Abbach *Bay* see: Bad Abbach
Abensberg *Bay* Hofbräu, Kuchlbauer, Ottenbräu
Abstgmünd *B-W* see: Untergröningen
Adelsdorf *Bay* see: Aisch, Neuhaus (Adelsdorf)
Adldorf *Bay* Graf Arco
Adlersberg *Bay* Proßlbräu
Affecking *Bay* Frischeisen
Ahlbeck *M-V* Ahlbecker Kellerbräu
Ahorn *B-W* see: Schillingstadt
Ahornberg *Bay* Ahornberger
Ahorntal *Bay* see: Hintergereuth, Oberailsfeld
Aichach *Bay* see: Oberbernbach
Aidenbach *Bay* Brauhaus Aidenbach
Aisch *Bay* Rittmayer
Aldersbach *Bay* Aldersbach
Aldingen *B-W* Rosenbrauerei (1997)
Alerheim *Bay* Scheible-Bräu (1999, brewed by Fürst Wallerstein, Wallerstein?)
Alfeld *Nie* Ratsbrauhaus (2005, brewed by Ratsbrauhaus, Hann. Münden)
Alfershausen *Bay* Jura (1996)
Allersheim *Bay* Allersheim
Almdorf *S-H* Krog (2000)
Alpirsbach *B-W* Klosterbräu
Alsfeld *Hes* Alsfeld
Alt-Haßloch *Hes* Rüsselsheimer Brauhaus
Alt Reddevitz *M-V* Kliesow's Reuse
Alt-Walsum *N-W* Walsumer Brauhaus Urfels
Altdorf *Bay* Brauhaus Altdorf (1998, brewed by Glossner, Neumarkt)
Altdrossenfeld *Bay* Schnupp
Altenau *Nie* Kolberg
Altenburg *Thü* Altenburger
Altendorf *Bay* Götz (1986)

Altenhaßlau *Hes* Brauhaus Linsengericht
Altenkunstadt *Bay* Leikeim
Altenmarkt *Bay* see: Baumburg
Altenmünster *Bay* Kronenbrauerei (2003, brewed by Allgäuer, Leuterschach)
Altenrüthen *N-W* Altenrüthener
Altmannstein *Bay* see: Sandersdorf
Altomünster *Bay* Kapplerbräu, Maierbräu
Altötting *Bay* Hell-Bräu. See also: Graming, Neuötting
Altusried *Bay* Postbrauerei (1976)
Alzenau *Bay* Brezel-Bräu, Steinbräu (1973, contract-brewed)
Amberg *Bay* Brauhaus (1990, brewed by Kummert, Amberg), Bruckmüller, Falk (1989, contract-brewed), Jordan-Bräu (1997), Kummert, Malteser (1993, brewed by Dinkelacher-Schwaben, Stuttgart), Schiessel (1994, brewed by Winkler), Schloderer, Sudhang, Wingershof (1989), Winkler. See also: Raigering
Amerdingen *Bay* Adlerbrauerei Reitschuster (1998)
Ammerndorf *Bay* Dorn-Bräu
Amorbach *Bay* Burkarth (1985, contract-brewed), Odenwaldbräu (1994)
Ampferbach *Bay* Hermann, Max-Bräu (brewed by Zehendner, Mönchsambach)
Andechs *Bay* Klosterbrauerei
Anrath *N-W* Schmitz-Mönk
Ansbach *Bay* Hofbräuhaus (2002), Hürnerbräu (1994)
Apolda *Thü* Vereinsbrauerei
Appendorf *Bay* Fößel-Mazour
Arnhausen *Bay* Wittelsbacher Turm-Bräu
Arnschwang *Bay* Mühlbauer
Arnstadt *Thü* Felsenkeller (1992), Hopfengrund, Stadtbrauerei
Arnstein *Bay* Bender
Arnstorf *Bay* Schloßbrauerei. See also: Mariakirchen
Arolsen *Hes* see: Bad Arolsen

Artern *Thü* Barbarossa (1993)
Aschaffenburg *Bay* Heylands (merged with Eder in 2001, brewed in Großostheim), Schlappeseppel (1979, brewed by Eder & Heylands, Großostheim), Schwindbräu
Aschau am Inn *Bay* Ametsbichler
Au (Hallertau) *Bay* Schloßbrauerei
Au am Inn *Bay* Kloster-Bräu
Aue *Sach* Lotters Wirtschaft
Auerbach *Hes* Burggraf-Bräu
Aufkirch *Bay* Kaltentaler Brauhaus
Aufseß *Bay* Rothenbach. See also: Heckenhof, Hochstahl, Sachsendorf
Augsburg *Bay* Augusta, Bürgerbräu (1997, brewed by Hasen, Augsburg), Charly Bräu, Goldene Gans (1998, brewed by Hasen, Augsburg), Hasen-Bräu, König von Flandern, Riegele, Thorbräu
Auingen *B-W see:* Münsingen-Auingen
Aulendorf *B-W* Ritterkeller/Zum Rad (does not brew)
Aurich *Nie* Brauhaus Aurich (1996)
Autenried *Bay* Schloßbrauerei
Aying *Bay* Ayinger

B

Baar *Bay see:* Unterbaar
Babenhausen *Hes* Michelsbräu
Bad Abbach *Bay* Zirngibl (1996). See also: Oberndorf
Bad Arolsen *Hes* Hofbrauhaus
Bad Birnbach *Bay* Graf Arco
Bad Blankenburg *Thü* see: Watzdorf
Bad Endorf *Bay* Weißbräuhaus (2002)
Bad Gandersheim *Nie* Ratsbrauhaus
Bad Gottleuba *Sach* see: Berggießhübel
Bad Herrenalb *B-W* Mönchs Klosterbräu (1998)
Bad Homburg *Hes* Graf Zeppelin
Bad Kissingen *Bay* see: Arnhausen, Garitz
Bad Königshofen *Bay* Büttnerbräu (1993)
Bad Köstritz *Thü* Köstritzer
Bad Laasphe *N-W* Bosch
Bad Meinberg *N-W see:* Horn
Bad Mergentheim *B-W see:* Herbsthausen
Bad Münder *Nie* Kornhus
Bad Münstereifel *N-W* Kleines Eifeler Brauhaus
Bad Nauheim *Hes* Schluckebier
Bad Neustadt (Saale) *Bay* Bayernbräu (contract-brewed), Karmeliter-Bräu
Bad Orb *Hes* Kärrners
Bad Rappenau *B-W* Häffner
Bad Reichenhall *Bay* Bürgerbräu
Bad Rodach *Bay* see: Roßfeld
Bad Saulgau *B-W* Bilgram (depot for Memminger)
Bad Schussenried *B-W* Schussenrieder
Bad Staffelstein *Bay* Bärenbräu (1998), Brütting (1995), Meixner, Staffelberg (1998). See also: Frauendorf, Loffeld, Nedensdorf, Stublang, Uetzing, Vierzehnheiligen, Wiesen (Bad Staffelstein), Zilgendorf
Bad Tölz *Bay* Grüner Bräu (2001)
Bad Urach *B-W* Olpp (1995), Quenzer Bräu (2001), Schäfer-Bräu

Bad Waldsee *B-W* Steinacher Hausbräu
Bad Wildungen *Hes* Bad Wildunger Brauhaus
Bad Windsheim *Bay* Bürgerbräu, Döbler, Freilandmuseum
Bad Wörishofen *Bay* Löwenbräu
Bagband *Nie* Ostfriesen-Bräu
Bahlen *M-V* Electro-Bräu
Baienfurt *B-W* Löwenbrauerei Rittler (1971, brewed by Leibinger, Ravensburg?)
Baisingen *B-W* Löwenbrauerei
Baldenberg *N-W* Baldenberger Brauhaus (2004)
Balingen *B-W* Adlerbrauerei (1993)
Ballenberg *B-W* Spall
Bamberg *Bay* Ambräusianum, Bürgerbräu (contract-brewed), Fässla, Greifenklau, Heller, Kaiserdom, Keesmann, Klosterbräu, Löwenbräu (1988), Mahr's, Maisel, Robesbierre, Spezial
Barmen *N-W see:* Wuppertal-Barmen
Barntrup *N-W see:* Sonneborn
Barthelmesaurach *Bay* Gundel
Baumbach *R-P see:* Ransbach-Baumbach
Baumburg *Bay* Klosterbrauerei Dietl
Baunach *Bay* Sippel
Baunatal *Hes see:* Knallhütte
Bautzen *Sach* Altstadtbrauhaus, Bautzener Brauhaus
Bayreuth *Bay* Bayreuther Bierbrauerei (brewed by Maisel, Bayreuth), Becher Bräu, Beck'n Bräu (does not brew), Bürgerbräu, Glenk, Götschel-Bräu (2001), Maisel, Schaller-Bräu (1978), Schinner (now called, Bürgerbräu)
Beckum *N-W* Stiefel-Jürgens
Bedburg *N-W* Schopen (brewed by Sünner, Köln)
Beerfelden *Hes* Felsenkeller
Beilngries *Bay* Schattenhofer Bräu
Belgern *Sach* Zur Alten Brauerei
Bellheim *R-P* Bellheimer
Bennigsen *Nie* Bennexer Brauhaus
Bensheim-Auerbach *Hes see:* Auerbach
Beratzhausen *Bay* Englbräu (1994)
Berching *Bay* Schuller, Winkler. See also: Plankstetten
Berchtesgaden *Bay* Hofbrauhaus
Berg (Ehingen) *B-W* Zimmermann
Berg (Kressbronn) *B-W* Max & Moritz
Berg (Oberfranken) *Bay* see: Gottsmannsgrün
Bergen *Bay* see: Thalmannsfeld
Berggießhübel *Sach* Weltenbummler
Bergneustadt *N-W* see: Baldenberg
Berlin *Ber* Alter Fritz, Aschinger (2000), Bärenquell (1994, brewed by Preussen Pils, Pritzwalk), Bier-Company (2003, brewed by Brauerei Falken, Schaffhausen, Swaitzerland), Braams (2003, re-opened in 2005 as Südstern), Brewbaker, Bürgerbräu, Eschenbräu, Georgbræu, Kindl, Lemkes Spezialitätenbrauerei, Lindenbräu, Leopold's (now Brauhaus Mitte), Luisen-Bräu, Marcus-Bräu, Mitte, Reich-Bräu (later Aschinger), Brauhaus in Rixdorf, Schloßplatzbrauerei, Schoppe Bräu, Schultheiss, Südstern, Brauhaus in Spandau

Bernhausen *B-W* **Schwanen-Bräu**
Bernkastel-Kues *R-P* see: **Machern**
Bessenbach *Bay* see: **Hohenwart**
Besseringen *Saar* **Ponter**
Bettingen *Saar* see: **Schmelz**
Biberach (Baden) *B-W* Jehle (1997, brewed by
    Kronenbrauerei, Offenburg)
Biberach (Heilbronn) *B-W* **Kronenbrauerei**
Biberach (Riß) *B-W* Biber-Bräu (2004), **Grüner Baum,**
    Haberhäusle (1991). See also: **Ummendorf**
Biberach (Roggenburg) *Bay* **Schmid**
Bielefeld *N-W* **Johann Albrecht**
Bielstein *N-W* **Erzquell**
Bienenmühle *Sach* see: **Rechenberg**
Bieswang *Bay* **Hirschbräu Wurm**
Bietigheim-Bissingen *B-W* Brauhaus Michel (2003)
Bigge *N-W* Alter-Bahnhof (2000), **Josefsbräu**
Bindlach *Bay* Hochbräu Theta (does not brew),
    Schoberth (1998)
Bingen (Hohenzollern) *B-W* Engelbrauerei (1974),
    Lammbräu (2001)
Birkach am Forst *Bay* **Eller**
Birnbach *Bay* see: **Bad Birnbach**
Bischberg *Bay* **Sonne**
Bischofsheim *Bay* see: **Kreuzberg**
Bischofswiesen *Bay* Brennerbräu (1999)
Bissingen *B-W* see: **Bietigheim-Bissingen**
Bitburg *R-P* **Bitburger**
Blaichach *Bay* see: **Ettensberg**
Blankenburg *Thü* see: **Bad Blankenburg**
Bobingen *Bay* Kirch Bräu (1995)
Böbingen *R-P* Heidhof (2003)
Böblingen *B-W* **Schönbuch Bräu**
Böbrach *Bay* see: **Eck**
Bocholt *N-W* **Bocholter Brauhaus,** Hirschbrauerei (1986)
Bochum *N-W* **Fiege,** Mappenbräu, Sudmeister &
    Fruchtgut (contract-brewed), **Tauffenbach**
Bockhorn *Bay* see: **Grünbach**
Bodenkirchen *Bay* Brauhaus Bodenkirchen (1996)
Bodenmais *Bay* **Adam-Bräu**
Bodenwerder *Nie* **Münchhausen**
Bodenwöhr *Bay* **Jacob**
Böhringen *B-W* **Hirschbrauerei Schilling**
Boizenburg *M-V* see: Bahlen
Bonn *N-W* **Bönnsch, Brauhaus am Ennert,** Kurfürsten-
    Bräu. See also: **Niederholtorf**
Bonstetten *Bay* Schaller (1998)
Bopfingen *B-W* Kronenbrauerei Karl (1982)
Bopfingen-Oberdorf *B-W* see: Bopfingen, **Oberdorf**
Borbeck *N-W* see: **Essen**
Borgfeld *Bre* see: **Bremen**
Bornstedt *Bra* see: **Potsdam**
Bösingen *B-W* see: **Herrenzimmern**
Bottrop *N-W* **Bottich.** See also: **Kirchhellen**
Braam-Ostwennemar *N-W* **Brauhof Wilshaus**
Brachstadt *Bay* Guldene Sonne (has never brewed)
Brakel *N-W* see: **Rheder**
Brandenburg *Bra* see: **Plaue**

Braunfels *Hes* Brau-und-Artfactory (will be at the old
    Euler brewery in Wetzlar), **Obermühle,**
    Schlossbrauerei (brewed by Bärenbräu, Herborn)
Bräunlingen *B-W* **Löwenbrauerei**
Braunschweig *Nie* **Feldschlößchen, Hofbrauhaus
    Wolters, Zum Löwen,** Mummebrauerei (Maltbeer
    only), **Schadt's**
Breidenbach *Hes* see: **Wolzhausen**
Breitengüßbach *Bay* **Hümmer**
Breitenlesau *Bay* **Krug-Bräu**
Breitenworbis *Thü* Heiner Bräu (2001)
Breitscheid *R-P* see: Hochscheid
Bremen *Bre* **Beck / Haake-Beck, Borgfelder Landhaus,**
    St. Magnus Bräu (hobby brewers), St. Pauli
    (brewed by Beck for export only), **Schüttinger**
Bremerhaven *Bre* Koggen Bräu (2005)
Bretten *B-W* **Michaeli Bräu**
Brielhof *B-W* **Domänen Bräu**
Bruchhausen *N-W* **Hofbrauerei**
Bruchsal *B-W* **Wallhall.** See also: **Untergrombach**
Bruckberg (Landshut) *Bay* **Wimmer**
Bruckberg (Mittelfranken) *Bay* Dietz, **Dorn-Bräu**
Bruckmühl *Bay* Franzl-Bräu (1996). See also:
    Heufeldmühle
Brühl *N-W* **Bischoff'sche,** Giesler (1998, brewed by
    Dom, Köln)
Büchenbach *Bay* **Herold**
Buchenrod *Bay* Kommunbrauerei
Bückeburg *Nie* see: **Röcke**
Burbach *N-W* Brauhaus zu Burbach (1996), Gut Höhne
    (beer brewed by Rainer, Welz)
Burgau *Bay* Lammbrauerei (1992)
Burgebrach *Bay* Schwan. See also: **Ampferbach,
    Grasmannsdorf, Mönchsambach,** Unterneuses
Burghaslach *Bay* Finster (1989)
Burghausen *Bay* Weißbierbrauerei Auer (1999).
    See also: Raitenhaslach
Burgkunstadt *Bay* **Gick-Bräu, Günther-Bräu, Hellmuth**
Burglengenfeld *Bay* **Birkenseer**
Burgsteinfurt *N-W* see: **Steinfurt**
Burgthann *Bay* see: Oberferrieden
Burgwindheim *Bay* Löwenbräu (1994). See also: **Kappel**
Buschbell *N-W* see: **Hücheln**
Buttenheim *Bay* **Löwenbräu, St. Georgen Bräu.**
    See also: **Dreuschendorf, Gunzendorf**
Buttenwiesen *Bay* see: **Lauterbach, Oberthürheim**
Buxtehude *Nie* **Buxtehuder Brauhaus**

C

Cannewitz *Sach* Cannewitz (2000)
Castrop-Rauxel *N-W* **Rütershoff**
Celle *Nie* **Betz,** Kruse Bräu (2002)
Cham *Bay* see: **Chammünster, Loifling,** Thierlstein
Chammünster *Bay* **Hintereder**
Chemnitz *Sach* Brau & Boegen/Gambrinus (2002),
    Braustolz, Friedrichs, Karls, Reichenbrander,
    Sudhaus (2001, brewed by Friedrichs, Chemnitz),
    Turm. See also: **Einsiedel**

Chorin *Bra* see: **Golzow**
Clausthal-Zellerfeld *Nie* Städtische (1984)
Clenze *Nie* see: **Satkau**
Coburg *Bay* Exportbierbrauerei Sturm (2001),
   Hofbrauhaus (1982), Scheidmantel (2001)
Coesfeld *N-W* Stephanus
Colbitz *S-A* Heidebrauerei
Colditz *Sach* Colditz (1995)
Copitz *Sach* Brauhaus-Pirna
Cottbus *Bra* Landskron Brauhaus (2004)
Crailsheim *B-W* Engel-Bräu
Creußen *Bay* see: **Lindenhardt**

D

Dachau *Bay* Schloßberg (2000)
Dahl *N-W* Vormann
Dahlen *Sach* Löwenbrauerei (1993)
Dargun *M-V* Darguner
Darmstadt *Hes* Darmstädter, Grohe, Ratskeller
Debring *Bay* Müller
Deisenhofen *Bay* Weißbräu
Delbrück-Sudhagen *N-W* Antpöhler Landbier (re-
   badged Pott's beers)
Dellmensingen *B-W* Adlerbrauerei
Dentlein am Forst *Bay* Hauf-Bräu
Dessau *S-A* Dessau (1995), **Zum Alten Dessauer**
Dessow (Mark) *Bra* Dessow
Detmold *N-W* Strate, Sudhaus
Deuerling *Bay* Goss
Dietmannsweiler *Bay* Schörebräu
Dietzhof *Bay* Alt
Dillenburg *Hes* Kronenbrauerei Haubach (1985, brewed
   by Giessener Brauhaus, Gießen)
Dillingen (Donau) *Bay* Dillinger Brauhaus (1999)
Dingolfing *Bay* Wasserburger
Dingsleben *Thü* Metzler
**Dinkelsbühl *Bay* Brauhaus Dinkelsbühl (1981), Hauf,
   Weib's Brauhaus**
Dirlewang *Bay* Hirsch
Dischingen *B-W* see: **Dunstelkingen**
Distelhausen *B-W* Distelhäuser
Ditzingen *B-W* Wichtel
Döbeln *Sach* Döbelner Brauhaus
Donaueschingen *B-W* Fürstenberg
Dorfen *Bay* Bachmeyer
Dörfleins *Bay* Eichhorn
Dormagen *N-W* Garde (2001, brewed by Gaffel (Porz),
   Köln)
Dormitz *Bay* Frölich (1995)
Dörnhagen *Hes* Fuldabrücker Landbrauerei
Dorsten *N-W* see: **Wulfen**
Dortmund *N-W* Best of Pütt (2000), **Brinkoff, DAB,**
   (Brewed by DAB, Dortmund), **Hövels,** Krone am Markt/
   Wenkers (2000), Kronen (1997, brewed by DAB,
   Dortmund), Ritter (now called Brinkhoff), Stifts (1996,
   brewed by DAB, Dortmund), Thier (1992, brewed by
   DAB, Dortmund), Union (1995, merged with Ritter)
Drachselried *Bay* Falterbräu, Schlossbräu
Drebkau *Bra* Kirchers

Drehna *Bra* see: **Fürstlich Drehna**
**Dresden *Sach* Feldschlößchen, Neustädter,
   Waldschlösschen, Watzke**
Dreuschendorf *Bay* Meusel-Bräu
Drosendorf *Bay* Göller
Drügendorf *Bay* Goldener Löwe, Kohlmann (1990)
Dudweiler *Saar* Sudhaus (2005)
Duisburg *N-W* König, Brauhaus Schacht 4/8,
   Trinklogistik (contract-brewed), **Webster.** See also:
   Alt-Walsum, Röttgersbach
Dunningen *B-W* Wehle
Dunstelkingen *B-W* Härtsfelder
Durchholz *N-W* Wolfs-Bier
Durlach *B-W* see: **Karlsruhe**
Dürmentingen *B-W* see: **Hailtingen**
Dürren *B-W* Farny
**Düsseldorf *N-W* Frankenheim (now brewed in Neuss),
   Füchschen,** Gatzweiler Brauerei (1999),
   Gatzweilers Brauhaus (no longer brews),
   Hirschbrauerei (1975, now brewed by Brinkhoff,
   Dortmund), **Johann Albrecht,** Schlösser (2003, now
   brewed by Brinkhoff, Dortmund), **Schlüssel,
   Schumacher, Uerige.** See also: **Neuss**

E

Ebelsbach *Bay* Klosterbräu (2002), Krug (1996)
Eben *Bay* Apostelbräu (brewed in Austria?)
Ebensfeld *Bay* Schwanenbräu. See also: **Pferdsfeld,
   Unterneuses**
Ebermannstadt *Bay* Schwanenbräu, Sonnenbräu
Ebing *Bay* Schwanen-Bräu
Eck *Bay* Ecker Bräu
Edelsfeld *Bay* Heldrich
Edermünde *Hes* see: **Haldorf**
Egelsbach *Hes* Schuhbeck's
Eggenfelden *Bay* see: **Spanberg**
Eggenstein-Leopoldshafen *B-W* see: **Leopoldshafen**
Eggolsheim *Bay* Schwarzes Kreuz. See also:
   Drügendorf, Weigelshofen
Egloffstein *Bay* see: Hundshaupten
**Ehingen (Donau) *B-W* Rößle, Schwanenbrauerei,
   Schwert.** See also: **Berg (Ehingen), Rißtissen**
Ehrenfriedersdorf *Sach* Specht
Ehringsdorf *Thü* see: **Weimar**
Eibau *Sach* Münch-Bräu
Eichen *N-W* Eichener
Eichendorf *Bay* see: **Adldorf**
Eichhofen *Bay* Schlossbrauerei
Eichstätt *Bay* Hofmühl
Einbeck *Nie* Einbecker
Einsiedel *Sach* Einsiedler, Klausner (contract-brewed)
Eisenach *Thü* Clemensbräu, **Eisenacher**
Eisenberg *Bay* see: **Speiden**
Eisleben *S-A* see: **Lutherstadt Eisleben**
Eislingen *B-W* Adlerbrauerei (1971)
Eitting *Bay* Eittinger Fischerbräu
Eiweiler *Saar* Grosswald
Elberfeld *N-W* see: **Wuppertal-Elberfeld**
Ellingen *Bay* Fürstliches Brauhaus

Ellwangen (Jagst) *B-W* **Rotochsen**
Ellzee *Bay* see: Stoffenried
Elsendorf (Niederbayern) *Bay* see: **Horneck**
Elsendorf (Schlüsselfeld) *Bay* **Sternbräu**
Eltmann (Main) *Bay* Lamm-Bräu (2005). See also:
    Eschenbach, Lembach, Roßstadt, Weisbrunn
Eltville (Rhein) *Hes* **Kleines Eltviller Brauhaus**
Elzach *B-W* **Löwenbrauerei Dold**
Endorf *Bay* see: Bad Endorf
Engelsberg *Bay* see: **Wiesmühl**
Enzenreuth *Bay* **Enzensteiner**
Enzklösterle *B-W* see: **Poppeltal**
Eppingen *B-W* **Palmbräu**
Erbach (Donau) *B-W* see: **Dellmensingen**
Erbach (Odenwald) *Hes* **Erbacher**
Erding *Bay* **Erdinger Weißbräu,** Fischer's
    Stiftungsbräu (1998)
Erfurt *Thü* Braugold, Erfurter Brauhaus, Goldenen
    Schwan, Pfauen, Waldhaus, Waldkasino
Ergenzingen *B-W* **Hirschbrauerei, Ochsen**
Erharting *Bay* **Erharting**
Erlabrunn *Sach* **Kunos Braugasthaus**
Erlangen *Bay* **Kitzmann, Steinbach Bräu**
Erlau *Bay* Kießling (1996)
Erlbach (Vogtland) *Sach* **Erlbacher Brauhaus**
Erwitte *N-W* see: **Schmerlecke**
Eschenbach *Bay* **Wagner-Bräu**
Eschlkam *Bay* Penzkofer (unknown brewer)
Eschwege *Hes* **Klosterbrauerei**
Eslarn *Bay* Bauriedl, Kommunbrauerei, Schlaffer (1998)
Eslohe *N-W* **Esloher Brauhaus**
Espelkamp *N-W* **Brauhaus Espelkamp**
Essen *N-W* **Borbecker Dampfbier-Brauerei,** Graf Beust
    (2002), **Rüttenscheider, Stauder, Stern** (brewed by
    Stauder, Essen)
Essing *Bay* **Kleines Brauhaus im Altmühltal**
Essingen *B-W* Sonnenbrauerei (1990)
Esslingen *B-W* **Schwanen**
Ettal *Bay* **Klosterbrauerei**
Ettensberg *Bay* **Klier-Bräu**
Ettlingen *B-W* **Vogel**
Etzelwang *Bay* **Pürner**
Eurasburg *Bay* see: Hergertswiesen
Euskirchen *N-W* see: Kirchheim
Eutin *S-H* **Brauhaus Eutin**

F

Falkenberg *Bay* **Kommunbrauerei**
Fallersleben *Nie* **Altes Brauhaus**
Fattigau *Bay* **Schloßbrauerei Stelzer**
Feldkirchen *Bay* **Flieger Bräu**
Fichtelbrunn *Bay* Fichtelbrunn/Pöhlmann/Rahm (1996)
Filderstadt *B-W* see: **Bernhausen**
Finsterwalde *Bra* **Radigk's, Sieben Brunnen**
Fintel *Nie* Eurostrand
Fladungen *Bay* **Gemeindebrauhaus**
Flein *B-W* **Reiners Rosine**
Flensburg *S-H* **Flensburger, Hansens**
Flözlingen *B-W* **Hirschbrauerei**

Flughafen-München *Bay* **Airbräu**
Forchheim *Bay* Brauhaus Forchheim (1994),
    Eichhorn, Hebendanz, Greif, Neder
Forst *Bra* **Worrich's Pub**
Forsting *Bay* **Gut Forsting**
Förtschendorf *Bay* Leiner (1997)
Frammersbach *Bay* **Waldschloss**
Frankenthal *R-P* **Brauhaus zur Post,** Frankenthaler
    (contract-brewed)
Frankfurt (Main) *Hes* **Bier Hannes, Binding,**
    Henninger (2002, merged with Binding),
    Hermannsbräu (1990), **Wäldches, Zwölf Apostel**
Frankfurt (Oder) *Bra* **Frankfurter Brauhaus,**
    Oderspeicher (2003)
Frauenalb *B-W* **König von Preußen**
Frauenaurach *Bay* Nachtbräu (hobby brewers)
Frauendorf *Bay* **Hetzel**
Frechen *N-W* **Hüchelner Urstoff,** Metzmacher (1994,
    brewed by Dom, Köln)
Freiberg *Sach* **Freiberger,** GSM (contract-brewed)
Freiburg *B-W* **Ganter, Hausbrauerei Feierling,**
    Inselbrauerei Feierling (1981), **Kleines Freiburger
    Brauhaus, Martin's-Bräu**
Freilassing *Bay* **Weißbräu**
Freising *Bay* **Bräuhaus Freising, Hofbrauhaus,**
    Weihenstephan, Zahn-Bräu. See also: **Flughafen-
    München**
Frensdorf *Bay* Messingschlager (1978). See also:
    Herrnsdorf, Reundorf, Untergreuth
Freudenberg *Bay* **Märkl**
Freudeneck *Bay* **Fischer**
Freudenstadt *Bay* **Turm-Bräu**
Freyburg *S-A* **Burgmühle**
Freyung *Bay* **Lang-Bräu**
Fridolfing *Bay* Stadlerbräu (1987)
Friedberg (Augsburg) *Bay* **Herzog Ludwig**
Friedberg (Hessen) *Hes* **Friedberger Brauhaus**
Friedenfels *Bay* **Schloßbrauerei**
Friedrichsfeld *B-W* see: Mannheim
Friedrichshafen *B-W* Lukullum Bräu (has never
    brewed – beers are from Leibinger re-badged)
Friesen *Bay* Brütting (2002)
Fritzlar *Hes* **Brauhaus 18·80**
Frontenhausen *Bay* Renkl, Röhrl
Fuchsberg *Bay* **Schloßbrauerei**
Fuchsstadt *Bay* **Wolf**
Fulda *Hes* **Hochstift, Wiesenmühle**
Fuldabrück *Hes* see: Dörnhagen
Fürnheim *Bay* **Forstquell**
Fürstenfeldbruck *Bay* **Kaltenberg**
Fürstlich Drehna *Bra* **Schloßbrauerei**
Fürth *Bay* Humbser (1972, brewed by Tucher, Fürth),
    Patrizier Bräu (1998, brewery now called Tucher),
    Tucher
Furth (Landshut) *Bay* Klosterbrauerei (2000)
Furth im Wald *Bay* **Dimpfl Bräu, Hofer,** Späth (2001,
    brewed by Mühlbauer, Arnschwang)
Füssen *Bay* Bräuhaus Füssen (2002)

G

Gaden *Bay* Hörl (contract-brewed)
Gadernheim *Hes* Lautertaler Hausbrauerei
Gaggenau *B-W* Christoph-Bräu
Gaildorf *B-W* Häberlen
Gamertingen *B-W* see: Kettenacker
Gandersheim *Nie* see: Bad Gandersheim
Gangkofen *B-W* see: Seemannshausen
Gänsefurth *S-A* Wüllner (contract-brewed)
Gardelegen *S-A* Garley
Garitz *Bay* Stärker
Gars am Inn *Bay* Baumer
Geiselhöring *Bay* Erl
Geisenfeld *Bay* see: Gaden
Geisfeld *Bay* Griess, Krug
Geising *Sach* Ratskeller
Geislingen (Steige) *B-W* Adlerbrauerei Götz, Glocke
  (1999), Kaiser
Gelsenkirchen *N-W* Hibernia
Geltendorf *Bay* see: Kaltenberg
Gemünd *N-W* Gemünder
Geretsried *Bay* Sudhaus (2004)
Gerolfingen *Bay* Rötter (1997, brewed by Koepf, Aalen)
Gerolzhofen *Bay* Weinig (2001)
Gersdorf *Sach* Glückauf
Gessertshausen *Bay* Schimpfle
Giengen (Brenz) *B-W* Lamm (1991), Schlüsselbräu,
  Schwanenbrauerei (1981)
Gierstädt *Thü* Zum Goldenen Lamm
Gießen *Hes* Alt-Giessen, Giessener Brauhaus
Gifhorn *Nie* Gifhorner Brauhaus
Gladbeck *N-W* Brauhaus Gladbeck
Glauchau *Sach* Sommerlust
Glonn *Bay* see: Herrmannsdorf
Gnodstadt *Bay* Düll
Göcklingen *R-P* Göcklinger Hausbräu
Göggingen (Augsburg) *Bay* see: Augsburg
Göggingen (Krauchenwies) *B-W* Adler (1997)
Göhren *M-V* Rügener Brauhaus (2003)
Golßen *Bra* Gleich (maltbeer only)
Golzow *Bra* Uckermärker
Gommern *S-A* Burgbräu (2003)
Göppingen *B-W* Staufen Bräu (1995)
Görlitz *Bra* Fritz Bräu, Dreibeiniger Hund (2003),
  Landskron, Obermühle
Goslar *Nie* Brauhaus Goslar/Gils Bräu (1995),
  Brauhaus Goslar (second brewery). See also:
  Hahnenklee, Oker
Gotha *Thü* Gotha, König-Sahl
Göttingen *Nie* Göttingener Brauhaus (brewed by
  Einbecker, Einbeck)
Gottsmannsgrün *Bay* von Koch'sche
Graben-Neudorf *B-W* Oasen-Bräu
Grabenstätt *Bay* Chiemseebräu
Grabow *M-V* Rose (1998)
Gräfelfing *Bay* Doemens (brewing school), Hubauer
  (contract-brewed)
Grafenau *Bay* Bucher Bräu
Gräfenberg *Bay* Friedmann, Lindenbräu

Grafenhausen *B-W* see: Rothaus
Grafing *Bay* Grandauer (2001, merged with Wildbräu),
  Wildbräu-Grandauer
Graming *Bay* Graminger-Weissbräu
Grasmannsdorf *Bay* Kaiser
Greifswald *M-V* Alten Fritz (brewed by Stralsunder,
  Stralsund)
Greiz *Thü* Göltzschtal, Vereinsbrauerei
Greuth *Bay* Fischer
Grevenstein *N-W* Veltins
Grimmelthal *Thü* see: Vachdorf
Gronau *N-W* Dinkel-Lager (2004)
Gröningen *B-W* Wacker (1999)
Groß-Bieberau *Hes* Biberland, Schönberger (1999)
Groß-Umstadt *Hes* Umstädter Brauhaus
Großefehn *N-W* Feyen (maltbeer only). See also:
  Bagband
Großheirath *Bay* see: Buchenrod, Rossach
Großhesselohe *Bay* Isarbräu
Großköllnbach *Bay* Egerer
Großostheim *Bay* Eder & Heylands
Großröhrsdorf *Sach* Böhmisch Brauhaus
Großrückerswalde *Sach* Weißer Hirsch
Gruibingen *B-W* Lammbrauerei Hilsenbeck
Grünbach (Bockhorn) *Bay* Schloßbrauerei
Grünbach (Vogtland) *Sach* Bayerische Hof
Grundfeld *Bay* see: Vierzehnheiligen
Grünstadt *Sach* Hausbrauerei Grünstadt
Grünwettersbach *B-W* Green Corner (2001)
Gummersbach *N-W* Brauhaus Gummersbach
Gundelfingen *Bay* Bucher Kronenbrauerei Wahl
  (2003, contract-brewed)
Günthersbühl *Bay* Wohlfart (hobby brewery)
Günz *Bay* Laupheimer (1997)
Günzburg *Bay* Hirschbrauerei (1995), Münz (1999,
  brewed by Postbräu, Thannhausen Radbrauerie
  Bucher)
Günzburg *Bay* Radbrauerei Bucher
Gunzendorf *Bay* Sauer
Gunzenhausen *Bay* Brauhaus Gunzenhausen (1998),
  Leuchtturm. See also: Oberasbach
Gutenstetten *Bay* Windsheimer. See also: Pahres
Gütersloh *N-W* Demuth im Domhof, Gütersloher
  Brauhaus

H

Haag (Oberbayern) *Bay* Hofbrauhaus (1972/1999),
  Unertl Weissbräu
Hachenberg *R-P* Westerwald
Hacklberg *Bay* see: Passau
Hadmersleben *S-A* Klosterbrauerei (1991)
Hagen *N-W* Altes Pfingsten Brauhaus, Andreas
  (brewed by DAB, Dortmund). See also: Dahl,
  Selbecke
Hahnenklee *Nie* Paul-Lincke-Treff
Hahnstätten *R-P* Nassauische
Haigerloch *B-W* Schloßbrauerei Zöhrlaut
Hailtingen *B-W* Adlerbrauerei
Haimhausen *Bay* Schloßbrauerei

Halberstadt *S-A* Harzbrauerei Reich, **Heine Bräu**
Haldorf *Hes* **Edermünder Brauscheune**
Halfing *Bay* see: **Rothmoos**
Halle *S-A* **Hallesches Brauhaus, Zum Schad**
Hallerndorf *Bay* **Lieberth, Rittmayer.** See also: **Schlammersdorf, Schnaid, Stiebarlimbach,** Willersdorf
Hallstadt *Bay* see: **Dörfleins**
Haltern *N-W* **Peters Bauernstube**
Hamburg *Ham* Bavaria St. Pauli (2001, brewed elsewhere), Bierernst/Gravensteiner (2001), **Elbschloß, Gröninger, Hanseat,** Harburger Engelbräu (2001), **Holsten, Johann Albrecht,** Johann Matz (2000), Luitbräu (1994)
Hameln *Nie* Förster & Brecker (1985, contract-brewed)
Hamm *N-W* Henin Gasthausbrauerei (1993), Klosterbrauerei (1977), Isenbeck (1990, brewed by Paderborner). See also: **Braam-Ostwennemar**
Hammelburg *Bay* Salch (1997, contract-brewed)
Hammersbach *Hes* Ritterladen (brewed by Asgaard, Schleswig)
Hamminkeln *N-W* Feldschlößchen (maltbeer only)
Hann. Münden *Nie* **Ratsbrauhaus**
Hannover *Nie* **Ernst August, Gilde, Herrenhäuser,** Hof-Brau-Haus (2004), Roneburg (2002), Wülfel (1991)
Hannoversch Münden *Nie* See: **Hann.Münden**
Harsewinkel *N-W* see: **Marienfeld**
Hartmannsdorf *Sach* **Hartmannsdorfer**
Haselbach *Bay* Schloßbrauerei (2002)
Haspe *N-W* see: Hagen
Haßfurt *Bay* Hiernickel (2000)
Haßloch *Hes* see: **Alt-Haßloch**
Hausen (Kelheim) *Bay* see: **Herrnwahlthann**
Hausen (Rhön) *Bay* see: **Roth (Hausen)**
Hausham *Bay* **Brauhaus Hausham**
Hauzenberg *Bay* see: Eben
Havixbeck *N-W* see: **Poppenbeck**
Hechingen *B-W* see: **Brielhof**
Heckenhof *Bay* **Kathi-Bräu**
Hecklingen *S-A* see: Gänsefurth
Heideck *Bay* Lindwurmbräu (2001)
Heidelberg *B-W* **Heidelberger, Kulturbrauerei, Vetter,** Vetter Neuenheim (2005)
Heidenheim *B-W* see: **Oggenhausen**
Heilbronn *B-W* **Barfüßer,** Cluss (1995, brewed by Dinkelacker-Schwaben, Stuttgart). See also: **Biberach (Heilbronn)**
Heilgersdorf *Bay* **Scharpf**
Heiligenstadt *Bay* **Aichinger.** See also: **Oberleinleiter**
Heilmfurt *Bay* **Bücher**
Heimenkirch *Bay* see: **Meckatz**
Heisterbacherrott *N-W* **Alte Bürgerstube**
Helfta *S-A* **Kloster Helfta**
Helmsdorf *B-W* see: **Immenstaad**
Hemau *Bay* Donhauser (1997). See also: Neukirchen
Hemsbach *B-W* Zehntscheuer (1999)
Herbertingen *B-W* see: **Hundersingen**
Herborn *Hes* **Bärenbräu**
Herbsthausen *B-W* **Herbsthäuser**

Herford *N-W* see: **Sundern**
Hergertswiesen *Bay* **Koller**
Heringsdorf *M-V* **Usedomer Brauhaus**
Herrenalb *B-W* see: Bad Herrenalb
Herrenzimmern *B-W* **Sonne**
Herreth *Bay* Stirnweiß (2001)
Herrieden *Bay* Brauhaus Herrieden (2000)
Herrmannsdorf *Bay* **Schweinsbräu**
Herrngiersdorf *Bay* **Schlossbrauerei**
Herrnsdorf *Bay* **Barnikel**
Herrnwahlthann *Bay* **Stanglbräu**
Herrsching *Bay* see: **Mühlfeld**
Hersbrück *Bay* **Bürgerbräu**
Herzogau *Bay* Schloßbrauerei (1998)
Herzogenaurach *Bay* **Heller,** Polster Bräu (1971)
Heßberg *Thü* **Hessberger**
Hettingen *B-W* see: Inneringen
Hetzelsdorf *Bay* **Penning**
Heubach *B-W* **Heubacher**
Heufeldmühle *Bay* Starkmeth
Heusweiler *Saar* see: **Eiweiler**
Hiddenhausen *N-W* see: **Sundern**
Hildesheim *Nie* Brauhaus Hildesheim (2002)
Hintergreuth *Bay* **Stöckel**
Hinterweidenthal *R-P* **Brauhaus Ehrstein**
Hirschaid *Bay* **Krauss.** See also: Friesen, **Röbersdorf**
Hirschau *Bay* **Schloßbrauerei Dorfner**
Hochdorf *B-W* **Hochdorfer Kronenbrauerei**
Hochscheid *R-P* Lindauer Hausbräu (2004)
Höchstadt (Aisch) *Bay* **Blauer Löwe, Brauhaus Höchstadt.** See also: **Greuth, Zentbechhofen**
Höchstadt (Donau) *Bay* Kronenbrauerei (1972)
Hochstahl *Bay* **Reichold**
Hof *Bay* **Bürgerbräu,** Deininger Kronenbräu (1995), **Falter, Meinel-Bräu, Scherdel, Zeltbräu**
Höfen *Bay* **Goldenen Adler**
Hoffnungsthal *N-W* Bergisches Landbier (2003)
Hofheim (Unterfranken) *Bay* **Raab**
Hohenaltheim *Bay* **Bauer's**
Hohenlimburg *N-W* Paulshof
Hohenschwärz *Bay* **Hofmann**
Hohenstein *B-W* see: **Ödenwaldstetten**
Hohenthann *Bay* **Schloßbrauerei**
Hohenwart *Bay* **Hohe-Wart-Bräu**
Holnstein *Bay* **Schloßbrauerei**
Holzhausen *Bay* **Holzhausener Landbrauerei**
Holzheim *Bay* see: **Neuhausen**
Holzheim *N-W* see: **Neuss**
Holzkirchen *Bay* Genossenschaftsbrauerei (1995), **Holzkirchner Oberbräu**
Holzminden *Nie* see: **Allersheim**
Homburg *Saar* **Homburger Brauhaus, Karlsberg**
Horb am Main *Bay* Gampert-Bräu (1999)
Hörde *N-W* see: Dortmund
Horn-Bad Meinberg *N-W* **Brauhaus Horn**
Hornberg *B-W* **Ketterer,** Kronenbrauerei (1985)
Horneck *Bay* **Horneck**
Hörvelsingen *B-W* **Pflugbrauerei Gnann**
Höxter *N-W* see: **Ottbergen**

Hoyerswerda *Sach* see: **Schwarzkollm**
Hücheln *N-W* see: **Frechen**
Hüllhorst *N-W* see: **Reineberg**
Hummelthal *Bay* see: Weiglathal
Hundersingen *B-W* **Adlerbrauerei**
Hundshaupten *Bay* Pöhlmann (1994)
Hünzingen *Nie* **Schnuckenbräu**
Huppendorf *Bay* **Grasser**
Husum *S-H* **Husums Brauhaus**
Hütten *Bay* **Hütten**
Hutthurm *Bay* **Hutthurm**

I

Ichenhausen *Bay* see: **Autenried**
Idstein *Hes* **Alte Feuerwache**
Igling *Bay* see: **Holzhausen**
Illerberg *Bay* Kronbräu (1985)
Illertissen *Bay* **Schloßbrauerei**
Ilmtal *Thü* see: **Singen**
Ilshofen *B-W* Goldochsenbrauerei
Immenstaad *B-W* Schloßbrauerei Helmsdorf (1999)
Indersdorf *Bay* see: Markt Indersdorf
Ingolstadt *Bay* **Herrnbräu, Ingobräu, Nordbräu,**
    Ringseer Quartlbräu (2001), **1516 Westparkbräu**
Inneringen *B-W* Sonnenbräu Maier
Innstadt *Bay* see: **Passau**
Irlbach *Bay* **Schloßbrauerei**
Irschenrieth *Bay* **Hösl**
Irsee *Bay* **Irseer Klosterbräu**
Isen *Bay* Schnellinger (1982)
Iserlohn *N-W* **Iserlohn**
Isny *B-W* **Stolz**
Issum *N-W* **Diebels**
Ittersbach *B-W* Michelbräu (2003)
Itzgrund *Bay* see: Herreth, **Kaltenbrunn,** Mürsbach

J

Jandelsbrunn *Bay* **Lang**
Jänschwalde *Bra* see: **Kolonie**
Jena *Thü* **Papiermühle,** Städtische Brauerei (1997),
    Talschänke
Jengen *Bay* see: *Ummenhofen*
Jettenbach *Bay* Jettenbach (2001, brewed by
    Hofbrauhaus, Freising)
Jever *Nie* Altstadtbrauerei/Marienbräu (2003), **Jever**
Jochsberg *Bay* **Reindler**
Jockgrim *R-P* **Froschbräu**
Jüchsen *Thü* **Zur Goldenen Henne**
Jülich *N-W* **Herzogen Brauhaus**
Junkersdorf *Bay* Kommunbrauhaus (hobby brewery)

K

Kaan-Marienborn *N-W* see: **Siegen**
Kaiserslautern *R-P* **Bayerische Brauerei, Brauhaus am**
    Markt
Kalkar *N-W* **Kalkarer Mühle**
Kalletal *N-W* Landgasthaus Waterloo (has never brewed)
Kallmünz *Bay* **Zum Goldenen Löwen**
Kaltenberg *Bay* **Schloßbrauerei**

Kaltenbrunn *Bay* **Schleicher**
Kaltennordheim *Bay* **Rhönbrauerei Dittmar**
Kaltental *Bay* see: **Aufkirch**
Kamenz *Sach* Sachsenquell
Kammerstein *Bay* see: **Barthelmesaurach**
Kamp-Lintfort *N-W* **Zunft Bräu**
Kandel *R-P* Brauhaus Schalander
Kappel *Bay* **Ibel**
Karlsbad *B-W* see: Ittersbach
Karlsruhe *B-W* **Badisch Brauhaus,** Fischer Bräu (2005),
    Hoepfner, Kühler Krug, Moninger, Vogelbräu, Vogel
    Hausbräu, Winkels (contract-brewed), **Wolf.** See
    also: Grünwettersbach
Karlstadt am Main *Bay* **Brauhaus im Wurzgrund**
Kasbach-Ohlenberg *R-P* see: **St. Severinsberg**
Kasendorf *Bay* Magnus-Bräu (1994)
Kassel *Hes* Binding Braustätte Kassel/Herkules/
    Schöfferhofer (2000), Kasselaner Brauhaus (2005),
    Kleines Schweinchen, Martini, Schalander Bräu
    (1997). See also: Obervellmar
Kastel *Hes* see: **Mainz-Kastel**
Kaufbeuren *Bay* **Aktienbrauerei,** Rosenbrauerei
    (1997), Zoigl (brewed by Rittmayer, Aisch)
Kelheim *Bay* **Aukofer-Bräu,** Ehrnthaller (1993),
    Schneider. See also: **Affecting, Weltenburg**
Kellershohn *N-W* **Zum Pfaffen**
Kellmünz *Bay* Brauhaus Kellmünz (1993)
Kemmern *Bay* **Wagner Bräu**
Kemnath *Bay* **Klosterbrauerei**
Kempten *Bay* Allgäuer Brauhaus (2005, brewery
    moved to Leuterschach)
Kenzingen *B-W* **Hirschen**
Kettenacker *B-W* Löwenbrauerei (1995)
Kiedrich *Hes* Waldmühle (brewed by Kleines Eltviller
    Brauhaus, Eltville)
Kiel *S-H* **Kieler**
Kippenheim *B-W* see: **Schmieheim**
Kirchenrohrbach *Bay* Schwarzfischer (1983)
Kirchenthumbach *Bay* **Heberbräu**
Kirchheim (Euskirchen) *N-W* **Steinbach**
Kirchheim (Schwaben) *Bay* **Lechler**
Kirchheim (Teck) *B-W* **Stiftsscheuer**
Kirchheimbolanden *R-P* **Brauhaus am Turm**
Kirchhellen *N-W* **Brauhaus am Ring**
Kirchhundem *N-W* see: Varste
Kirn *R-P* **Kirner**
Kißlegg *B-W* see: **Dürren**
Kitzingen *Bay* Bürgerbräu (1998)
Klasberg *N-W* see: **Kellershohn**
Klingenbrunn *Bay* **Klingenbrunn**
Knallhütte *Hes* **Hütt-Brauerei Bettenhauser**
Koblenz *R-P* Kloster-Brauerei (1986), **Königsbacher,**
    Sewenig's Brauhaus (2002)
Köln *N-W* **Braustelle, Dom, Früh, Gaffel (Altstadt),**
    Gaffel (Porz), Gilden (brewed by Kölner Verbund,
    Köln), **Heller, Kölner Verbund Brauereien,** Küppers
    (2001 (now Dom), brewed by Kölner Verbund),
    Malzmühle, Päffgen, Reissdorf, Richmodis (now
    called Gaffel (Porz)), Römer (brewed by Kölner

Verbund, Köln), Sester (1993, brewed by Kölner
Verbund, Köln), Sion (1942, brewed by Kölner
Verbund, Köln), **Sünner, Weißbräu**
Kolonie *Bra* **Zur Linde**
Königs Wusterhausen *Bra* **Kavalierhäuser**
Königsbronn *B-W* Klosterbrauerei (1990)
Königsbrunn *Bay* **Charivari-Bräu**
Königsee *Thü* Königsee (1995)
Königseggwald *Bay* **Königsegger Walderbräu**
Königsfeld *Bay* see: **Huppendorf**
Königswinter *N-W* see: **Heisterbacherrott**
Konradsreuth *Bay* see: **Ahornberg**
Konstanz *B-W* **Johann Albrecht, Ruppaner**
Konzell *Bay* **Klett-Bräu**
Körprich *Saar* **Körpricher Landbräu**
Korschenbroich *N-W* **Bolten**
Kösching *Bay* Amberger (1996)
Kößlarn *Bay* **Weißbräu**
Köthen *S-A* Köthener Brauerei (1992, contract-brewed),
  Köthener Brauhaus
Köttensdorf *Bay* **Hoh**
Kötzting *Bay* **Kolbeck**
Krautheim *Bay* **Düll**
Krefeld *N-W* **Gleumes**, Maxxum (contract-brewed),
  Rhenania (2001, brewed by Eichener, Eichen)
Kressbronn *B-W* see: **Berg (Kressbronn)**
Kreuzau *N-W* Röhr (1998)
Kreuzberg *Bay* **Klosterbrauerei**
Kreuztal *N-W* see: **Eichen, Krombach, Littfeld**
Kreuzwertheim *Bay* **Spessart**
Krombach *N-W* **Krombacher**
Kronach *Bay* **Kaiserhof**
Kronberg *Hes* **Kronberger Brauhaus**
Kronburg *Bay* **Kronburger**
Krostitz *Sach* **Krostitzer**
Krummenhagen *M-V* **Rumpelstilz**
Küdinghoven *N-W* see: **Bonn**
Kühbach *Bay* **Kühbach**
Kuhlemühle *N-W* **Warburger**
Kühlungsborn *M-P* **Ostsee Brauhaus**
Kulmbach *Bay* Angermann (contract-brewed),
  Bayerisches Brauereimuseum, EKU (1996, brewed by
  Kulmbacher), **Kommunbräu, Kulmbacher**, Mönchs-
  hofbräu (1999, brewed by Kulmbacher), Reichelbräu
  (now called Kulmbacher), Sandlerbräu (1982)
Kusel *R-P* Emrich
Kutzenhausen *Bay* **Rapp**

L
Laaber *Bay* **Plank**
Laatzen *Nie* see: Hannover
Lahnstein *R-P* See: **Niederlahnstein, Oberlahnstein**
Lampertheim *Hes* **Alte Kelter**
Landau (Isar) *Bay* **Krieger**
Landau (Pfalz) *R-P* **Landauer Brauhof**
Landsberg *S-A* **Landsberger**
Landshut *Bay* **Landshuter Brauhaus**, Reichardt-Bräu
  (1987), **Wittmann**
Langenau *B-W* see: **Hörvelsingen**

Langenberg *N-W* **Hohenfelder**
Langenfeld *N-W* **Lohmann**
Langensteinbach *B-W* see: **Ittersbach**
Larsbach *Bay* **Lampl-Bräu**
Lauenau *Nie* **Rupp-Bräu**
Lauenstein *Bay* Burgbräu (1987, brewed by Jahns
  Bräu, Ludwigsstadt)
Lauf *Bay* Dreykorn, Brauhaus Lauf (1993), **Simon**. See
  also: Günthersbühl, **Neunhof**
Lauffen *B-W* s' Dächle-Bräu
Lauingen *Bay* **Hirschbrauerei Schwarz**
Laupheim *B-W* **Kronenbrauerei**, Rössle (2002)
Lauter *Bay* see: **Appendorf**
Lauterbach (Buttenwiesen) *Bay* **Lauterbach**
Lauterbach (Hessen) *Hes* **Lauterbacher Burgbrauerei**
Lauterecken *R-P* **Lauterecker Brauhaus**
Lautertal *Hes* see: **Gadernheim**
Lehesten *Thü* Lehesten (1991, brewed by Jahns Bräu,
  Ludwigsstadt)
Leimen *B-W* **Bergbrauerei**
Leinburg *Bay* **Bub**
Leinefelde *Thü* see: **Worbis**
Leipheim *Bay* **Hirschbräu Gaissmaier**
Leipzig *Sach* **Bauer, Bayerischer Bahnhof, Kaiser
  Napoleon, Reudnitzer,** Sternburg (1991, brewed by
  Reudnitzer, Leipzig), **Thomaskirche**
Lembach *Bay* **Thein**
Lemgo *N-W* see: **Lütte**
Lengenfeld *Bay* **Winkler Bräu**
Lenggries *Bay* Schloßbrauerei Hohenburg (1975)
Lengloh *Bay* see: **Schalchen**
Lennestadt *N-W* see: **Meggen**
Lenzkirch *B-W* **Rogg**
Leonberg B-W **Brauhaus Sacher**
Leonberg *B-W* Schwarzer Adler (1998)
Leopoldshafen *B-W* **Andreasbräu**
Lerchenfeld *Bay* see: **Freising**
Leups *Bay* **Gradl**
Leutenbach *Bay* **Drummer**. See also: **Dietzhof**
Leuterschach *Bay* **Allgäuer Brauhaus**
Leutershausen *Bay* see: **Jochsberg**
Leutkirch im Allgäu *Bay* **Härle**
Leverkusen *N-W* Ganser (2001, brewed by Dom, Köln)
Lich *Hes* **Licher**
Lichtenau *Bay* **Hauff-Bräu**
Lichtenberg *Bay* **Sonnenbräu**
Lichtenfels *Bay* Brauwirt (1993), Wicklespeter (1992).
  See also: **Oberwallstadt**
Lieske *Sach* **Bergschlösschen**
Limburg *Hes* Busch (1985), Max-Bräu
Lindau *Bay* Inselbrauerei (1973), Steig (1992)
Lindenhardt *Bay* **Kürzdörfer**
Linnich *N-W* see: **Welz**
Linsengericht *Hes* see: **Altenhaßlau**
Linz (Rhein) *R-P* see: **St. Severinsbräu**
Lippstadt *N-W* **Lippstädter,** Weissenburger (1989,
  brewed by Paderborner, Paderborn)
Lisberg *Bay* see: **Trabelsdorf**
Littfeld *N-W* **Ilsen-Bräu**

Litzendorf *Bay* see: **Lohndorf, Melkendorf, Schammelsdorf, Tiefenellern**
Löbau *Sach* **Bergquell**
Lobenstein *Thü* Oberländische Dampfbierbrauerei (1993)
Loffeld *Bay* **Staffelberg-Bräu**
Loh *Bay* **Bräu z' Loh**
Lohberg *Bay* **Späth-Bräu**
Lohmar *N-W* see: **Kellershohn**
Löhnberg *Hes* see: Niedershausen
Lohndorf *Bay* **Hölzlein, Reh**
Lohr am Main *Bay* **Lohrer Bier**
Loifling *Bay* **Hofmark**
Lonnerstadt *Bay* **Hausmann** (2003)
Lörrach *B-W* **Brauereigesellschaft** (2004), **Kulturbrauhaus, Lasser**
Losheim am See *Saar* **Hochwälder**
Lübbecke *N-W* **Barre**
Lübbenau *Bra* **Babben**
Lübeck *S-A* **Brauberger**, Lübsch/Ratskeller
Lüben *Nie* **Tennenbräu**
Lübz *S-A* **Lübzer**
Luckenwalde *Bra* **Luckenwalder**
Lüdenscheid *N-W* **Schillerbad**
Ludwigsburg *B-W* **Rossknecht, Sudhaus**
Ludwigshafen *R-P* **Bürgerbräu** (1990), **Mayer-Bräu**, Pfalz-Bräu/Treiber (1990, contract-brewed), **Weißes Häus'l**
Ludwigsstadt *Bay* **Jahn's Bräu**
Lüneburg *Nie* Kronen-Brauerei (2001, contract-brewed), **Mälzer, Nolte**
Lünne *Nie* **Landhaus**
Lutherstadt Eisleben *S-A* **Reformator**. See also: Helfta
Lutherstadt Wittenberg *S-A* **Wittenberg**
Lütschena *Sach* see: Leipzig
Lütte *N-W* **Lütter Krug**

M
Machern *R-P* **Kloster Machern**
Mainburg *Bay* Kopp-Bräu (2000), **Ziegler Bräu**. See also: Sandelshausen
Mainz *R-P* Aktien-Bierbrauerei (1982), **Eisgrub-Bräu**, Zur Sonne (1992)
Mainz-Kastel *Hes* **Brauhaus Castel**
Maisach *Bay* **Maisach**
Malgersdorf *Bay* see: **Heilmfurt**
Mallersdorf *Bay* **Klosterbrauerei**. See also: Oberlindhart, **Pfaffenberg**
Mallersdorf-Pfaffenberg *Bay* see: **Mallersdorf**, Oberlindhart, **Pfaffenberg**
Malmerz *Thü* see: **Sonneberg**
Malsch *B-W* **Alter Bahnhof**
Malsfeld *Hes* **Hessisches Löwenbier**
Mannebach *Saar* **Mannebacher Brauhaus**
Mannheim *B-W* **Eichbaum**, Brauerei Habereckl (1990), Hausbrauerei zum Habereckl (1993), Hofbräu/ Schwäblerei
Marbach *B-W* **Salzscheuer**
Marburg *Hes* Spezialitäten Brauerei (2004)

Mariabrunn *Bay* Schloßbrauerei (2001)
Mariakirchen *Bay* **Schlossbräu**
Marienfeld *N-W* Heinerbräu (2001)
Marienstatt *R-P* **Marienstatter Brauhaus**
Markt Indersdorf *Bay* Klosterbrauerei (2002)
Markt Schwaben *Bay* **Schweiger**, Widmann (2003)
Markt Werneck *Bay* see: **Werneck**
Marktbreit *Bay* see: **Gnodstadt**
Marktheidenfeld *Bay* **Martinsbräu**
Marktleuthen *Bay* Goldschadt (1980)
Marktoberdorf *Bay* see: **Leuterschach**
Marktredwitz *Bay* **Nothhaft**
Marktsteft *Bay* Hike (contract-brewed), **Kesselring**
Marktzeuln *Bay* see: Horb am Main
Marne *S-H* **Dithmarscher**
Maroldsweisach *Bay* **Hartleb**
Marsberg *N-W* see: **Westheim**
Marxzell *B-W* see: **Frauenalb**
Mauel *N-W* **Maueler Hofbräu**
Maxlrain *Bay* **Schloßbrauerei**
Mayen *R-P* Löwen
Meckatz *Bay* **Meckatzer Löwenbräu**
Meckesheim *B-W* **Mall**
Meggen *N-W* Brauhaus Landtag Meggen (1993)
Meiningen *Thü* **Meininger**
Meisenheim *R-P* Bonnet (1982)
Meißen *Sach* **Schwerter Brauerei Wohlers**
Melkendorf *Bay* **Winkler**
Memmelsdorf *Bay* **Drei Kronen, Höhn**, Leicht (1999). See also: Drosendorf, Merkendorf
Memmingen *Bay* **Memminger**
Mendig *R-P* **Vulkan**
Mennrath *N-W* **Brauhaus zum Stephanus**
Merkendorf *Bay* **Hummel, Wagner**
Merzig *Saar* **Saarfürst**. See also: **Besseringen**
Meschede *N-W* see: **Grevenstein**
Mespelbrunn *Bay* see: **Hohenwart**
Meßhofen *Bay* **Kolb**
Meßstetten *B-W* **Lindenbrauerei**
Mettlach *Saar* **Abtei-Bräu**
Mettmann *N-W* see: Burbach
Michelbach *B-W* **Adlerbrauerei Schmetzer**
Michelsneukirchen *Bay* see: **Schrötting**
Michelstadt *Hes* **Dörr, Rathausbräu**
Mickhausen *Bay* **Schloßbrauerei**
Middelhagen *M-V* **Zur Linde**. See also: **Alt Reddevitz**
Miesbach *Bay* **Hopf**
Miltenberg *Bay* **Faust, Kalt-Loch-Bräu**
Mindelheim *Bay* **Lindenbrauerei**
Mintraching *Bay* see: **Moosham**
Missen *Bay* **Schäffler**
Missen-Wilhams *Bay* see: **Missen**
Mistelgau *Bay* see: Obernsees
Mittenwald *Bay* **Mittenwald**
Mitterteich *Bay* **Hösl, Kommunbrauerei**
Mittweida *Sach* Löwenbräu (1993, now brewed by Hartmannsdorfer, Hartmannsdorf)
Mitwitz *Bay* see: **Neundorf**
Moers *N-W* **Moerser Brauhaus**

Mögglingen *B-W* Adlerbrauerei
Möhringen (Stuttgart) *B-W* see: **Stuttgart**
Möhringen (Tuttlingen) *B-W* Kronenbrauerei (1998), Link (1994)
Mönchengladbach *N-W* Mönchengladbach. See also: *Mennrath*
Mönchsambach *Bay* Zehendner
Mönchsdeggingen *Bay* Kronenbräu Finkler (1988)
Monheim *N-W* Peters & Bambeck (2004, brewed by Kölner Brauer Verbund, Köln)
Monschau *N-W* Felsenkeller (1997, brewed by Rainer, Welz)
Moos (Plattling) *Bay* Arcobräu
Moos (Tüßling) *Bay* Bräu im Moos
Moosbach (Oberpfalz) *Bay* Scheuerer
Moosbeuren *B-W* Adlerbräu (2002), **Kreuz**
Moosburg *Bay* Drei Rosen Bräu (2001)
Moosham *Bay* Gutsbrauerei Meyringer
Morsbach *N-W* Knoorz-Bräu
Mosbach *B-W* Mosbacher Brauhaus
Mossautal *Hes* see: **Ober-Mossau**
Mössingen *B-W* Fischer's Brauhaus
Motten *Bay* Hochstiftliches Brauhaus
Mudersbach *R-P* see: **Niederschelderhütte**
Muggendorf *Bay* Wehrfritz (1990)
Müglitztal *Sach* see: Mühlfeld, **Weesenstein**
Mühlacker *B-W* Michelbräu (2003)
Mühlbühl *Bay* Mauth-Bräu (1997)
Mühldorf *Bay* Unertl
Mühlendorf *Bay* Mühlenbräu
Mühlfeld *Bay* Mühlfelder Brauhaus
Mühlfeld *Sach* Sachsenschlösser (contract-brewed)
Mühlhausen (Bayern) *Bay* Bender
Mühlhausen (Thüringen) *Thü* Zum Löwen, Thüringer Brauhaus (2001), Thüringia (1994, brewed by Meininger, Meiningen)
Mülheim an der Rühr *N-W* Aspera (maltbeer only), Berg, **Mühlheimer Brauhaus**
Münchberg *Bay* Bischoff-Bräu (1992)
München *Bay* Augustiner, Bavaria-Bräu, Das Kleine Brauhaus (1995), **Forschungs-Brauerei**, Hacker-Pschorr (1997, now brewed by Paulaner / Hacker-Pschorr, München), Hofbräuhaus, Löwenbräu, Paulaner / Hacker-Pschorr, Paulaner Bräuhaus, Spaten-Franziskaner, Unionsbräu. See also: Flughafen-München
Münchsteinach *Bay* Loscher
Münnerstadt *Bay* Kloster-Brauerei
Münsingen-Auingen *B-W* Waldrast (1998)
Münster *N-W* Germania (1987, contract-brewed), **Pinkus Müller**
Murnau *Bay* Griesbräu, **Karg**
Mürsbach (Itzgrund) *Bay* Feiler (2002)
Mürsbach (Rattelsdorf) *Bay* Sonnen-Bräu
Mutlangen *B-W* Stegmaier (1997)

N

Naabeck *Bay* Schloßbrauerei
Nagel *Bay* see: Mühlbühl

Nagold *B-W* Anker, Gambrinus (1993). See also: Hochdorf
Naila *Bay* Bürgerbräu
Nalbach *Saar* see: **Körprich**
Nankendorf *Bay* Schroll
Nassau *R-P* Löwenbrauerei
Nattheim *B-W* Nattheimer
Naurath *R-P* Zils-Bräu
Neckarsulm *B-W* Neckarsulmer Brauhaus
Nedensdorf *Bay* Reblitz
Nemsdorf *Bay* Zwieseltaler Jägerklause (2005)
Nennslingen *Bay* Ritter St. Georgen
Nersingen *Bay* Seybold (1983)
Nesselwang *Bay* Bärenbräu (2002), **Postbrauerei**
Neubrandenburg *M-V* Alten Schlachthof, Nordbräu (1990)
Neuburg (Donau) *Bay* Juliusbräu, Neuhofbräu (2001)
Neudrossenfeld *Bay* Hölzel-Bräu (1991). See also: Altdrossenfeld
Neuendorf (Altmark) *S-A* Demmert-Bräu
Neuhaus (Aisch) *Bay* Löwenbräu, Schmidt-Bräu (1996)
Neuhaus (Oste) *Nie* Alt Neuhaus
Neuhaus (Pegnitz) *Bay* Falkenloch (1999), Kaiser-Bräu, Kommunbrauerei (1999)
Neuhaus (Windischeschenbach) *Bay* Kommunbrauerei
Neuhausen *Bay* Bärenbräu
Neukirchen (Bogen) *Bay* see: Obermühlbach
Neukirchen (Hemau) *Bay* St. Georg (1996)
Neukirchen (Sulzbach-Rosenberg) *Bay* see: Fichtelbrunn, Holnstein
Neuler *B-W* Ladenburger
Neumarkt (Oberpfalz) *Bay* Gansbräu, Glossner, Lammsbräu
Neunburg vorm Wald *Bay* Frankbräu (1997), **Weißes Brauhaus**
Neundorf *Bay* Franken Bräu
Neunhof *Bay* Wiethaler
Neunkirchen (Brand) *Bay* Polsterbräu (2003), **Vasold & Schmitt**
Neunkirchen (Saar) *Saar* Stumm's Brauhaus
Neunkirchen (Sand) *Bay* see: Wolfshöhe
Neuötting *Bay* Müllerbräu
Neureichenau *Bay* see: **Riedelsbach**
Neusäß *Bay* see: Täferting
Neuss *N-W* Frankenheim
Neustadt (Aisch) *Bay* Brauhaus Neustadt (1998), Kohlenmühle
Neustadt (Coburg) *Bay* Geussen-Bräu (2002), Werner-Bräu (1993)
Neustadt (Donau) *Bay* Neumeyer (1999)
Neustadt (Holstein) *S-H* Klüver's Brauhaus
Neustadt (Saale) *Bay* see: Bad Neudtadt
Neustadt (Weinstraße) *R-P* Neustadter
Neustadt (Wiedenau) *R-P* Bavaria Bräugasthof (1999)
Neustetten *B-W* see: Remmingsheim
Neutraubling *Bay* Zippel
Neu-Ulm *Bay* Barfüßer, Max'l Bräu (2000), **Schlössle**
Neuzelle *Bra* Klosterbrauerei

Nidda *Hes* **Marktbräu**
Nideggen *N-W* see: **Wollersheim**
Niederholtorf *N-W* Dreizehn-Linden (2004)
Niederlahnstein *R-P* **Maximilians Brauwiesen**
Niedermendig *Saar* see: **Mendig**
Niedermurach *Bay* Pröls (1997)
Niederrieden *Bay* Ruhland (1999)
Niederschelderhütte *R-P* **Erzquell**
Niedershausen *Hes* Waldschlößchen
Niedervellmar *Hes* see: Obervellmar
Nittenau *Bay* **Brauhaus Nittenau**
Nittendorf *Bay* see: **Eichhofen**
Norddeich *Nie* **Diekster Bräu**
Norden *Nie* see: **Norddeich**
Nordhausen *Thü* Roland Bräu (1998)
Nordhorn *Nie* **Grafschafter Brauhaus**
Nördlingen *Bay* **Ankerbräu**
Nörten-Hardenberg *Nie* Wiederholts (1991, now brewed
by Martini, Kassel)
Nürnberg *Bay* **Altstadthof, Barfüßer,** Fränky (contract-
brewed), Lederer (brewed by Tucher, Fürth),
Lederer Kulturbrauerei (brewed by Tucher, Fürth),
Tucher, Weizenbierglasmuseum, Zeltner (1974)
Nürtingen *B-W* **Schlachthof Bräu**
Nußdorf am Inn *Bay* Inntalbräu (2003)

O

Oberailsfeld *Bay* **Held-Bräu**
Oberasbach *Bay* **Schorschbräu**
Oberaudorf *Bay* **Alpenrose, Bals**
Oberaurach *Bay* see: **Oberschleichach, Trossenfurt &**
Unterschleichach
Oberbauerschaft *N-W* see: **Reineberg**
Oberbernbach *Bay* **Berabecka Boandl-Bräu**
Oberdachstetten *Bay* **Haag**
Oberdischingen *Bay* Bräumaier
Oberdorf *B-W* **Schwind**
Oberferrieden *Bay* Linden-Bräu (2001, contract-brewed)
Obergriesbach *Bay* Schloßbrauerei (1994)
Oberhaching *Bay* **Stadlbräu.** See also: *Deisenhofen*
Oberhaid *Bay* **Wagner.** See also: **Staffelbach,** Unterhaid
Oberhausen *N-W* *Oberhausener Brauhaus (2001),*
Zeche Jacobi
Oberkassel *N-W* see: **Düsseldorf**
Oberkonnersreuth *Bay* see: Bayreuth
Oberkotzau *Bay* see: **Fattigau**
Oberlahnstein *R-P* Hof Aspich (2001), **St. Martin**
Oberleinleiter *Bay* **Ott**
Oberlindhart *Bay* Rossmann (hobby brewery)
Obermassfeld-Grimmelthal *Thü* see: **Vachdorf**
Ober-Mossau *Hes* **Schmucker**
Obermühlbach *Bay* Edbauer (1989)
Oberndorf *B-W* Oberndorfer (2004)
Oberndorf *Bay* **Berghammer**
Obernkirchen *Nie* see: **Vehlen**
Obernsees *Bay* Maisel-Altbräu (1982)
Oberreichenbach *Bay* **Geyer**
Oberroth *Bay* **Reitinger**
Oberscheibe *Sach* **Fiedler**

Oberscheinfeld *Bay* Rückel (2001)
Oberschleichach *Bay* **Zenglein**
Oberstadion *B-W* see: **Moosbeuren**
Oberstdorf *Bay* **Dampfbierbrauerei**
Obertaufkirchen *Bay* see: **Stierberg**
Oberthürheim *Bay* **Bio-Bräu**
Oberuckersee *Bra* see: **Warnitz**
Oberursel *Hes* **Alt-Oberurseler Brauhaus**
Oberveischede *N-W* **Müller**
Obervellmar *Hes* Pill's (2003)
Oberwallenstedt *Bay* **Wichert**
Oberwarmensteinach *Bay* see: **Hütten**
Oberwohlsbach *Bay* Lauterburgbräu (1997)
Oberzell *Bay* see: **Zell**
Ochsenfurt *Bay* **Kauzen-Bräu, Oechsner.** See also:
Tückelhausen
Odelzhausen *Bay* see: **Taxa**
Ödenwaldstetten *B-W* **Speidel's Brauerei'le**
Oelde *N-W* **Pott's**
Oelsnitz (Vogtland) *Sach* Brauhaus Oelsnitz
Oeslau *Bay* **Grosch**
Oettingen *Bay* **Oettinger**
Offenburg *B-W* **Kronenbrauerei,** Mundinger (1992),
Wagner-Bräu (1994, brewed by Kronenbrauerei,
Offenburg)
Offenhausen *Bay* see: **Neu-Ulm**
Oggenhausen *B-W* **Königsbräu**
Oggersheim *R-P* see: **Ludwigshafen**
Ohlenberg *R-P* see: **St. Severinsberg**
Oker *Nie* Gosebrauhaus Goslar (2004)
Olbernhau *Sach* **Olbernhau**
Oldenburg *Nie* Hengelbräu (1998), Ziegelhof (2003)
Olpe *N-W* see: **Oberveischede**
Olsberg *N-W* see: **Bigge, Bruchhausen**
Ortenburg *Bay* see: **Söldenau**
Oschersleben *S-A* Germania (1995)
Osnabrück *Nie* **Rampendahl**
Oßling *Sach* see: **Lieske**
Osterberg *Bay* **Deil**
Osterode am Harz *Nie* Ratskeller (2004)
Ostheim (Rhön) *Bay* **Peter, Streck**
Ostritz *Sach* **Brauhaus Ostritz**
Ostwennemar *N-W* see: **Braam-Ostwennemar**
Ottbergen *N-W* **Meierhof**
Ottensoos *Bay* Kronen-Bräu (2001)
Ottersheim *R-P* **Bärenbräu**
Ottobeuren *Bay* Benediktinerbrauerei (1970), Hirschbräu
(1997), **Kleines Brauhaus am Kloster,** Otto Bräu (2002)
Ottweiler *Saar* Ottweiler (1982)

P

Paderborn *N-W* **Paderborner**
Pahres *Bay* **Hofmann**
Palling *Bay* Füchsbuchler (1996)
Panschwitz *Sach* Klosterbrauerei St. Marienstern
(1972, brewed by Stadtbrauerei, Wittichenau)
Pappenheim *Bay* see: **Bieswang**
Parsberg *Bay* Hirschenhof
Passau *Bay* **Andorfer, Hacklberg, Innstadt,**

Löwenbrauerei, Peschl
Pegnitz *Bay* Jura-Bräu, Brauer-Vereinigung. See also:
   Büchenbach, Leups
Peine *Nie* Härke
Peißenberg *Bay* Plötz (1992)
Penig *Sach* Peniger
Penzberg *Bay* Penzberger Brauhaus (2004)
Petersaurach *Bay* see: **Vestenberg**
Pettendorf *Bay* see: **Adlersberg**
Petting *Bay* see: **Schönram**
Pfaffenberg *Bay* Stöttner. See also: Mallersdorf,
   Oberlindhart
Pfaffenhausen *Bay* Storchenbräu
Pfaffenhofen (Ilm) *Bay* Müllerbräu, Urbanus
Pfaffing *Bay* see: **Forsting**
Pfarrkirchen *Bay* Gässlbräu, Weizenbierbräuerei
   Steiner (1999)
Pfarrweisach *Bay* see: Junkersdorf
Pfeffenhausen *Bay* Pöllinger, Reder (1994)
Pferdsfeld *Bay* Leicht
Pforzheim *B-W* Bayerisches Brauhaus,
   Hopfenschlingel, Ketterer
Pfronten-Ried *Bay* Falkenstein
Pfuhl *Bay* see: Neu-Ulm
Pfungstadt *Hes* Pfungstädter
Philippsthal *Hes* see: **Röhrigshof**
Pieschen *Sach* see: **Dresden**
Pilsting *Bay* see: **Großköllnbach**
Pirk *Bay* Pirker Brauhaus
Pirmasens *R-P* Kuchems Brauhaus, Park
Pirna *Sach* see: **Copitz**
Plankstadt *B-W* Welde-Bräu
Plankstetten *Bay* Benediktinerabtei. (1959, brewed
   by Riedenburger, Riedenburg)
Plaue *Bra* Kneipe Pur
Plauen *Sach* Sternquell
Pleinfeld *Bay* Kleines Pleinfelder Brauhaus
Plettenberg *N-W* Eichen-Bräu
Plochingen *B-W* Waldhorn (1995)
Plößberg *Bay* Riedl
Poing *Bay* Liebhart's Bräuhaus
Pommersfelden *Bay* see: Sambach
Poppeltal *B-W* Poppel-Mühle
Poppenbeck *N-W* Klute's
Poppenhausen *Bay* Werner (2003, brewed by
   Würzburger Hofbräu, Würzburg)
Pörnbach *Bay* Hallertau (2002, brewed by
   Hofbrauhaus, Freising)
Porz *N-W* see: Köln
Pösing *Bay* Drexler
Possenfelden *Bay* Scheubel
Pößneck *Thü* Rosenbrauerei
Potsdam *Bra* Braumanufaktur, Kindl Braustätte
   Potsdam (2002), Hofbrauerei Krongut Bornstedt,
   Meierei
Pottenstein *Bay* Hufeisen, Mager, Wagner-Bräu
   (1996, brewed by St. Georgen, Buttenheim)
Pöttmes *Bay* Schloßbrauerei
Pressing *Bay* see: **Förtschendorf**

Pretzfeld *Bay* see: **Hetzelsdorf, Unterzaunsbach**
Priesendorf *Bay* Schrüfer
Pritzwalk *Bra* Preussen Pils
Pullach *Bay* see: **Großhesselohe**
Pürkwang *Bay* Metzgerbräu
Püttlingen *Saar* Brauhaus am Burgplatz (2004)
Pyras *Bay* Pyraser

Q
Quedlinburg *S-A* Lüdde

R
Radeberg *Sach* Radeberger
Radebeul *Sach* Brauhaus Radebeul (2003)
Raigering *Bay* Sterk
Rain *Bay* Brauhaus Rain (1994), **Kleinbrauerei,**
   Ratsbrauerei zum Bäuml
Raitenhaslach *Bay* Klosterbrauerei (2003)
Rammingen *Bay* Häpfenbräu
Ransbach-Baumbach *Rhein* Fohr
Rastatt *B-W* Franz, Hofbräuhaus Hatz, Hopfenschlingel
Rathenow *Bra* Rathenow (1997)
Ratingen *N-W* Ratinger Brauhaus
Rattelsdorf *Bay* see: **Ebing, Freudeneck, Höfen,**
   Mürsbach
Rauhenebrach *Bay* see: **Theinheim**
Ravensburg *B-W* Bürgerbräu (2001), **Leibinger**
Ravenstein *B-W* see: **Ballenberg**
Rechenberg *Sach* Rechenberger
Rechenberg-Bienenmühle *Sach* see: **Rechenberg**
Reckendorf *Bay* Schroll, Schloßbrauerei
Recklinghausen *N-W* Boente
Regen *Bay* Falter
Regensburg *Bay* Bischofshof, Fürstliches Brauhaus,
   Johann Albrecht, Kneitinger, Spitalbrauerei, Thurn
   & Taxis (1997, brewed by Paulaner/Hacker-Pschorr,
   München)
Rehborn *R-P* Hof-Brauhaus
Rehling *Bay* see: **Scherneck**
Reichelshofen *Bay* Landwehr-Bräu
Reichenberg *Bay* see: **Fuchsstadt**
Reichenbrand *Sach* see: **Chemnitz**
Reichertsheim *Bay* Rampl-Bräu (1996)
Reineberg *N-W* Niedermeiers Hof
Reisbach (Vils) *Bay* Lang
Reischach *Bay* Berger
Remmingsheim *B-W* Kronenbrauerei Schimpf
Renchen *Bay* see: **Ulm (Renchen)**
Rendsburg *S-H* Provianthaus (2000)
Rettenberg *Bay* Engelbräu, Zötler
Reundorf *Bay* Müller
Reutberg *Bay* Klosterbrauerei
Reuth (bei Erbendorf) *Bay* Schloßbrauerei
Rhan *Bay* Rhanerbräu
Rheder *N-W* Schloßbrauerei
Rheinbach *N-W* Brauhaus Rheinbach
Rheinsberg *Bra* Zum Alten Brauhaus
Rhoda *Thü* see: **Erfurt**
Rickling *S-H* Ricklinger Landbrauerei

Ried *Bay* see: **Pfronten-Ried**
Riedbach *B-W* **Franken Bräu**
Riedelsbach *Bay* **Sitter-Bräu**
Riedenburg *Bay* **Riedenburger, Riemhofer**
Riedlingen *B-W* see: **Zwiefaltendorf**
Riegel *B-W* **Elchbräu,** Riegeler (brewed by Fürstenburg, Donaueschingen)
Ries *Bay* see: **Passau**
Riesa *Sach* **Hammer-Bräu**
Rietheim-Weilheim *B-W* see: **Weilheim (Württemberg)**
Rinteln *Nie* **Hartinger**
Rißtissen *B-W* **Adler**
Röbersdorf *Bay* **Weber**
Röcke *Nie* **Klüsker Waldbräu**
Rodach *Bay* see: **Bad Rodach**
Rödental *Bay* see: **Oeslau**
Roding *Bay* **Brantl, Greiner**
Roggenburg *Bay* see: **Biberach (Roggenburg), Meßhofen**
Rohr *Bay* see: Nemsdorf
Rohrenfels *Bay* **Schneiderbräu** (1995)
Röhrigshof *Hes* **Brauhaus Extra**
Röhrmoos *Bay* see: **Mariabrunn**
Römerstein *B-W* see: Böhringen
Rosenberg *Bay* see: **Sulzbach-Rosenberg**
Rosenfeld *B-W* **Lehner**
Rosenheim *Bay* **Auerbräu, Flötzinger,** Weißbräu Bierbichler (1996, brewed by Flötzinger, Rosenheim)
Rösrath *N-W* see: Hoffnungsthal
Rossach *Bay* **Kommunbrauerei**
Roßdorf am Forst *Bay* **Sauer**
Roßfeld *Bay* **Gemeinschaftsbrauerei**
Roßstadt *Bay* Weiss Rössl (2001, brewed by Kaiser, Neuhaus)
Rostock *M-V* Alten Fritz (brewed by Stralsunder, Stralsund), **Rostocker, Trotzenburg**
Roth (Hausen) *Bay* **Rother Bräu**
Roth (Mittelfranken) *Bay* **Stadtbrauerei,** Valentin Bräu (1993)
Rothaus *B-W* **Rothaus**
Rothenburg *Bay* Brauhaus Rothenburg (1975)
Rothenfels *Bay* **Bayer Bräu**
Rothmoos *Bay* **Schmiedbräu**
Röttenbach *Bay* **Sauer**
Rottenburg (Neckar) *B-W* Schützenbrauerei (2001). See also: **Baisingen, Ergenzingen**
Röttgersbach *N-W* **Mattlerhof**
Rotthalmünster *Bay* Jodlbauer (moved to Tiefenbach, contract-brewed)
Rottweil *B-W* Pflug-Bräu (1995)
Rötz *Bay* **Genossenschaftsbrauerei**
Rötz *Bay* Reichelbräu/ Thamer (1981)
Rüdenhausen *Bay* **Wolf**
Rüdesheim *Hes* Rüdesheimer Brauhaus (2001)
Rügland *Bay* see: **Unternbibert**
Rülzheim *R-P* Brauhaus Rülzheim (2004)
Runding *Bay* **Schloßbrauerei**
Rüsselsheim *Hes* see: **Alt-Haßloch**
Rüthen *N-W* see: **Altenrüthen**

S
Saal *Bay* see: **Waltershausen**
Saalfeld *Thü* **Saalfelder**
Saarbrücken *Saar* **Bruch,** Neufang (2002), **Stiefel Bräu.** See also: Dudweiler
Sachsendorf *Bay* **Stadter**
Sachsenkam *Bay* see: **Reutberg**
Sailauf *Bay* see: **Weyberhöfe**
Salzweg *Bay* see: **Straßkirchen**
Sambach *Bay* **Hennemann**
Salzwedel *S-A* Bergschloss (1992, brewed by Garley, Gardelegen)
Sandelzhausen *Bay* Schloßbrauerei Wimmer (1986)
Sandersdorf *Bay* **Schloßbrauerei de Bassus**
Sangerhausen *S-A* Mammut (contract-brewed)
Sankt Augustin *N-W* Sankt Augustiner Brauhaus (2005)
Sankt Wolfgang *Bay* Bauer/St. Wolfgang
Satkau *Nie* **Wendland Bräu**
Sattelpeilnstein *Bay* Schloßbrauerei Schauer (1994)
Saulgau *B-W* see: Bad Saulgau
Schalchen *Bay* **Weissbräu Schwendl**
Schallstadt-Wolfenweiler *B-W* see: **Wolfenweiler**
Schammelsdorf *Bay* **Knoblach**
Schaufertshof *R-P* see: **Schönborn**
Schederndorf *Bay* **Will**
Scheer *B-W* Götz (1989)
Schefflenz *B-W* see: **Unterschefflenz**
Scheibenberg *Sach* see: **Oberscheibe**
Scherneck *Bay* **Schloßbrauerei**
Scheßlitz *Bay* **Drei Kronen,** Schmitt (2001, contract-brewed), **Senger.** See also: **Köttensdorf, Straßgeich, Würgau**
Scheyern *Bay* **Klosterbrauerei**
Schierling *Bay* **Spezial-Brauerei**
Schillingstadt *B-W* **Dörzbacher**
Schlammersdorf (Hallerndorf) *Bay* **Witzgall**
Schlammersdorf (Oberpfalz) *Bay* **Püttner**
Schleiden *N-W* see: **Gemünd**
Schlepzig *Bra* **Spreewälder**
Schleswig *S-H* **Asgaard**
Schlicht *Bay* **Winkler-Bräu**
Schlitz *Hes* Auerhahn-Bräu (1998, brewed by Lauterbacher, Lauterbach)
Schlüchtern *Hes* **Brauhaus Schlüchtern**
Schlüsselfeld *Bay* **Adler-Bräu, Stern-Bräu** Scheubel. See also: **Elsendorf, Possenfelden**
Schmelz *Saar* **Schmelzer Brauhaus**
Schmerlecke *N-W* **Braumühle**
Schmiedefeld *Thü* Rennsteig (1997)
Schmieheim *B-W* **Schloßbrauerei**
Schnaid *Bay* **Friedel**
Schnaittach *Bay* **Kanone, Schaffer-Bräu.** See also: Enzenreuth
Schollene *S-A* **Mühlenbergbrauerei**
Schöllkrippen *Bay* **Barbarossa**
Schönborn *R-P* **Hof Schauferts**
Schönbrunn (Steigerwald) *Bay* **Bähr, Wernsdörfer.** See also: **Zettmannsdorf**
Schönbrunn (Wunsiedel) *Bay* **Lang-Bräu**

Schongau *Bay* Schongauer Brauhaus
Schönram *Bay* Schönram
Schönsee *Bay* Haberl
Schönthal *Bay* Klosterbrauerei (2000). See also: Rhan
Schorndorf *B-W* Kesselhaus, Löwenbrauerei (1985)
Schrobenhausen *Bay* Gritschenbräu
Schrötting *Bay* Schröttinger
Schrozberg *B-W* see: Riedbach, Spielbach
Schwabach *Bay* Leitner, Lösel (1991), Weller-Bräu (1994)
Schwaben *Bay* see: Markt Schwaben
Schwäbisch Gmünd *B-W* Engelbrauerei (2001)
Schwäbisch Hall *B-W* Haller Löwenbräu, Sudhaus
Schwalmstadt *Hes* see: Treysa
Schwalmtal *N-W* Schloßbrauerei Leven
Schwandorf *Bay* Arcobräu (1982), Schmidt-Bräu. See also: Naabeck, Wiefelsdorf
Schwarzbach *Thü* Schloßbrauerei
Schwarzenfeld *Bay* Bauer/Bierbauer (2003/2005)
Schwarzkollm *Hes* Braustube
Schwedt (Oder) *Bra* Turmbräu (2005)
Schweinfurt *Bay* Brauhaus Schweinfurt, *Bay* Roth, Tabasco (not currently brewing)
Schwelm *N-W* Schwelm
Schwenningen *B-W* Bärenbrauerei (1975, brewed by Fürstenberg, Donaueschingen). See also: Villingen
Schwerin *M-V* Schweriner Schloßbrauerei, Zum Stadtkrug
Schwetzingen *B-W* Brauhaus zum Ritter
Schwindheim *Bay* see: Aschaffenburg
Sebnitz *Sach* Hirschbrauerei (2001)
Seebad Ahlbeck *M-V* see: Ahlbeck
Seebad Heringsdorf *M-V* see: Heringsdorf
Seehausen *Bra* see: Warnitz
Seemannshausen *Bay* Klosterbräu
Seesen *Nie* Felskeller
Seinsheim *Bay* Seinsheimer Kellerbräu
Selb *Bay* Bürgerbräu (2001), Ploss, Rauh & Ploß (1991)
Selbecke *N-W* Mackinger Bräu
Seligenstadt *Hes* Glaabsbräu, Kleines Brauhaus
Seßlach *Bay* Kommunbrauhaus. See also: Heilgersdorf
Siegburg *N-W* Siegburger Brauhaus
Siegen *N-W* Irle
Siegenburg *Bay* Schmidmayer-Bräu
Sigmaringen *B-W* Zoller-Hof
Simmerberg (Allgäu) *Bay* Aktienbrauerei, Bräustatt und Taferne (has never brewed). See also: Weiler
Simmozheim *B-W* Mönchswasen
Sindelfingen *B-W* Lammbrauerei (2005)
Singen (Thüringen) *Thü* Museums-Brauerei Schmitt
Sinsheim *B-W* see: Steinsfurt
Soest *N-W* Brauhaus Zwiebel
Söflingen *B-W* see: Ulm (Donau)
Söhnstetten *B-W* Hirsch
Söldenau *Bay* Schloßbrauerei (1996)
Soltau *Nie* Johann Albrecht
Sonneberg *Thü* Gessner
Sonneborn *N-W* Röhr Bräu
Sonthofen *Bay* Hirschbräu

Spabrücken *R-P* Topferbräu (has never brewed)
Spalt *Bay* Stadtbrauerei
Spanberg *Bay* Brunner-Bräu
Speiden *Bay* Kössel-Bräu
Speyer *R-P* Domhof
Spiegelau *Bay* see: Klingenbrunn
Spielbach *B-W* Gold Ochsen
Springe *Nie* see: Bennigsen
St. Georgen *B-W* Klimperkasten
St. Ingbert *Saar* Becker (1993)
St. Severinsberg *R-P* Steffens
St. Wendel *Saar* Brauereihaus
Stadelhofen *Bay* see: Schederndorf, Steinfeld
Stadthagen *Nie* Schaumburger
Stadtsteinach *Bay* Schübel
Staffelbach *Bay* Hertlein
Staffelstein *Bay* see: Bad Staffelstein
Stamsried *Bay* Schloss Bräu (1991, contract-brewed)
Stegaurach *Bay* Hausbräu. See also: Debring, Mühlendorf
Stein (Traun) *Bay* Schlossbrauerei
Steinach (Baden) *B-W* Kälble (1995), Mellert
Steinach (Thüringen) *Thü* Anker Bräu, Gessner (1997, now in Sonneberg)
Steinbach (Erzgebirge) *Sach* Altes Brauhaus
Steinberg *Sach* see: Wernesgrün
Steinfeld *Bay* Hübner-Bräu
Steinfurt *N-W* Rolinck
Steinhagen *M-V* see: Krummenhagen
Steinheim *B-W* see: Söhnstetten
Steinhude am Meer *Nie* Heidemann
Steinsfeld *Bay* see: Reichelshofen
Steinsfurt *B-W* Jupiter
Stettfeld *Bay* Adler Bräu
Stiebarlimbach *Bay* Roppelt
Stierberg *Bay* Stierberg
Stralsund *M-V* Stralsunder
Straßgeich *Bay* Drei Kronen (1991/2003)
Straßkirchen *Bay* Gutsbräu
Straubing *Bay* Karmeliten, Röhrl
Streithausen *R-P* see: Marienstatt
Strullendorf *Bay* see: Geisfeld, Roßdorf am Forst
Stübig *Bay* Merklein (1978)
Stublang *Bay* Dinkel, Hennemann
Stuhr *N-W* Stuhrer Mühle
Stuttgart *B-W* Calwer-Ecke, Dinkelacker-Schwäben, Mash, Sanwald (1980, brewed by Dinkelacker-Schwaben, Stuttgart), Schloßturm, Sophie's Brauhaus, Stuttgarter Hofbräu, Tü 8, Wichtel
Sudhagen *N-W* see: Delbrück-Sudhagen
Sulzbach-Rosenberg *Bay* Bayerischer Hof (1996), Fuchsbeck, Sperber-Bräu
Sundern *N-W* Herforder
Suttrop *N-W* Suttroper Brauhof

T

Tacherting *Bay* see: Schalchen
Täferting *Bay* Brauhaus Schmid (1989)
Tann *Bay* Weideneder

Tapfheim *Bay* see: Brachstadt
Tauberbischofsheim *B-W* see: **Distelhausen**
Taufkirchen *Bay* Brauereigenossenschaft
Taxa *Bay* Schloßbrauerei Odelzhausen
Tegernsee *Bay* Herzoglich Brauhaus
Teisendorf *Bay* Weininger
Teisnach *Bay* Ettl-Bräu
Tettnang *B-W* Krone. See also: **Dietmannsweiler**
Teugn *Bay* Dantscher
Teunz *Bay* see: **Fuchsberg**
Thalmannsfeld *Bay* Felsenbräu
Thalmässing *Bay* see: **Pyras**
Thannhausen *Bay* Postbräu
Theinheim *Bay* Bayer
Theres *Bay* see: Untertheres
Thierhaupten *Bay* see: **Unterbaar**
Thierlstein *Bay* Sauer (1988)
Thierstein *Bay* Mocker (2002)
Thurnau *Bay* Thurnauer Schloßbräu
Thundorf *Bay* Gemeindebrauhaus
Thüngen *Bay* Burgbrauerei
Tiefenbach *Bay* Jodlbauer (contract-brewed). See also: **Haselbach**
Tiefenellern *Bay* Hönig
Tirschenreuth *Bay* Schels
Titting *Bay* Gutmann
Torgau *Sach* Brauhaus Torgau
Trabelsdorf *Bay* Beck, Schloßbrauerei (1999)
Train *Bay* Schloßbrauerei (1992)
Traitsching *Bay* see: **Loifling**, Sattelpeilnstein
Traunstein *Bay* Hofbräuhaus, Maximiliansbräu, Schnitzlbaumer, Weissbräu (1997), Wochinger-Bräu
Trebgast *Bay* Haberstumpf
Treuchtlingen *Bay* Schäff. See also: **Wettelsheim**
Treuen *Sach* Blechschmidt
Treysa *Hes* Schwalm Bräu
Trier *R-P* Kraft-Bräu, Löwenbrauerei (1993, contract-brewed)
Triftern *Bay* Weißbierbrauerei Bauer
Trochtelfingen *B-W* Albquell Bräuhaus
Troisdorf *N-W* Stadtbrauerei
Trossenfurt *Bay* Roppelt
Trunstadt *Bay* see: Viereth, Weiher
Tübingen *B-W* Neckarmüller
Tückelhausen *Bay* Heil (1980, brewed by Würzburger Hofbräu, Würzburg)
Tuntenhausen *Bay* see: **Maxlrain**
Tüßling *Bay* see: **Moos**
Tuttlingen *B-W* Pfauen (1996). See also: Möhringen, **Wurmlingen**

U

Ueckermünde *M-V* Brauhaus Ueckermünde
Uelfeld *Bay* Prechtel, Zwanzger
Uetzing *Bay* Dinkel
Uffenheim *Bay* Geuder'sche (1992)
Uhingen *B-W* Gerber Bräu
Ulm (Donau) *B-W* Barfüßer, Drei Kannen (1944), **Gold Ochsen, Kronenbrauerei Söflingen**, Ulmer Münster

(2001, brewed by Memminger, Memmingen)
Ulm (Renchen) *B-W* Bauhöfer
Ummendorf *B-W* Bräuhaus Ummendorf
Ummenhofen *Bay* Rössle-Bräu
Unna *N-W* Lindenbrauerei (1979, contract-brewed), Lindenbrauerei (new brewery)
Unterbaar *Bay* Schloßbrauerei
Untergreuth *Bay* Büttner
Untergrombach *B-W* Bundschuh-Bräu
Untergröningen *B-W* Lammbrauerei
Unterhaid *Bay* Gambrinusbräu
Unterkotzau *Bay* see: **Hof**
Unterleiterbach *Bay* Hennemann, Mahkorn (1995)
Unternbibert *Bay* Reuter
Unterneuhausen *Bay* Weinzierl
Unterneukirchen *Bay* Leidmann
Unterneuses (Burgebrach) *Bay* Post (1998)
Unterneuses (Ebensfeld) *Bay* Martin
Unterschefflenz *B-W* Egolf
Unterschleichach *Bay* Löwenbräu Neeb
Untersiemau *Bay* Murmann. See also: **Birkach am Forst**
Untertheres *Bay* Lammbräu (2003)
Unterzaunsbach *Bay* Meister
Ursberg *Bay* Klosterbräuhaus
Ursensollen *Bay* see: Zant
Uslar *Nie* Bergbräu
Ustersbach *Bay* Ustersbacher
Uttenweiler *B-W* Sauter

V

Vach *Bay* Dorn-Bräu (1997)
Vachdorf *Thü* Öko-Markt
Valley *Bay* Arco-Valley (brewed by Graf Arco, Adldorf)
Varste *N-W* Brau-Optimal (does not brew, see Selbecke)
Vechta *Nie* Stierbräu
Vehlen *Nie* Meierhöfer
Veilsdorf *Thü* see: **Heßberg**
Velbert *N-W* Velberter Brauhaus
Velburg *Bay* see: **Lengenfeld**
Velden (Vils) *Bay* Stammler (2000)
Vellmar *Hes* see: **Obervellmar**
Vestenberg *Bay* Löwenbräu
Viechtach *Bay* Gesellschaftsbrauerei, Greinerbräu (2001)
Vielank *M-P* Vielanker Brauhaus
Viereth *Bay* Mainlust. See also: **Weiher**
Viereth-Trunstadt *Bay* see: **Viereth, Weiher**
Vierzehnheiligen *Bay* Trunk
Villingen *B-W* Fortuna (1980), Jankes Bierhaus (1995), Romäus (1995). See also: Schwenningen
Vilsbiburg *Bay* Aktienbrauerei (2001)
Vilseck *Bay* see: **Schlicht**
Vilshofen *Bay* Wolferstetter
Vochem *N-W* see: **Brühl**
Vohburg *Bay* Antoni-Bräu (2000)
Vohenstrauß *Bay* Behringer, Würschinger (1997)
Vöhringen *Bay* see: **Illerberg**
Volkach *Bay* see: **Krautheim**
Volkmarsen *Hes* Alte Phönix (2004)

Voßheide *N-W* see: **Lütte**
Vreden *N-W* **Vredener Brauhaus**

W
Wachau *Sach* **Schiller**
Wächtersbach *Hes* Fürstliche Brauerei (1999; brewed by Würzburger Hofbräu, Würzburg)
Waibstadt *B-W* **Adler-Brauerei**
Waischenfeld *Bay* Heckel. See also: **Breitenlesau, Nankendorf**
Waldbronn *Bay* **Lindenbräu**
Walderbach *Bay* see: Kirchenrohrbach
Waldershof *Bay* Waldershofer Brauhaus (brewed by Strössner, Ahornberg)
Waldhaus *B-W* **Waldhaus**
Waldheim *Sach* Richzenhain (1999)
Waldkirch *B-W* **Hirschenbrauerei**, Mutschler (2000)
Waldmünchen *Bay* Hammerbräu (1991). See also: Herzogau
Waldsassen *Bay* **Ziegler**
Waldshut *B-W* see: Waldhaus
Waldstetten *Bay* **Goldener Engel**
Walkertshofen *Bay* **Schorer**
Wallerstein *Bay* **Fürst Wallerstein**
Wallhausen *B-W* Bräuninger (1993). See also: **Michelbach**
Walsrode *Nie* see: **Hünzingen**
Walsum *N-W* see: **Alt-Walsum**
Waltershausen *Bay* **Lang**
Wangen *B-W* see: **Dürren**
Warburg *N-W* see: **Kuhlemühle**
Warmensteinach *Bay* Trassl-Bräu (2003, brewed by Hösl, Mittertech). See also: **Hütten**
Warnitz *Bra* **Burgwall-Bräu**
Warstein *N-W* **Warsteiner**. See also: **Suttrop**
Wartenberg *Bay* **Reiter-Bräu**
Wasseralfingen *B-W* see: **Aalen**
Wasserburg *Bay* Brauwirt (1990), Fletzinger (1995)
Wassertrüdingen *Bay* see: **Fürnheim**
Wattendorf *Bay* **Dremel, Hübner**
Watzdorf *Thü* **Watzdorfer**
Weesenstein *Sach* **Weesensteiner Schlossbräu**
Wehlen *R-P* see: **Machern**
Weiden (Oberpfalz) *Bay* **Bräuwirt**, Bürgerbräu (1982), **Gambrinus**, Iblacker (2001)
Weigelshofen *Bay* **Pfister**
Weiglathal *Bay* Übelhack
Weihenstephan *Bay* see: **Freising**
Weiher *Bay* **Kundmüller**
Weihmichl *Bay* see: **Unterneuhausen**
Weilburg *Hes* **Helbig**
Weiler (Allgäu) *Bay* **Post**. See also: **Simmerberg**
Weiler-Simmerberg *Bay* see: **Simmerberg, Weiler**
Weilheim (Oberbayern) *Bay* Bräuwastl (1989), **Dachsbräu**
Weilheim (Waldshut) *B-W* see: Waldhaus
Weilheim (Württemberg) *B-W* **Lammbrauerei**
Weimar *Thü* **Ehringsdorfer, Felsenkeller,** Zum Paulaner (2000)

Weinheim *B-W* Brauhaus Stadl (2003), **Woinemer**
Weisbrunn *Bay* **Bräutigam**
Weismain *Bay* Obendorfer (1997), **Püls Bräu**
Weißenbrunn *Bay* Brauhaus Weißenbrunn (1992), **Gampertbräu**
Weißenburg *Bay* **Schneider, Sigwart**
Weißenfels *S-A* Felsbräu (1999)
Weißenhorn *Bay* **Hasenbrauerei**
Weißenohe *Bay* **Klosterbrauerei**
Weißensee *Thü* **Weißenseer Ratsbräu**
Weißenstadt *Bay* **Michael**
Weißenthurm *R-P* Nette (brewed by Königsbacher, Koblenz), Schultheis (2004)
Weitnau *Bay* Weitnau (1986, brewed by Memminger, Memmingen)
Weltenburg *Bay* **Klosterbrauerei**
Welz *N-W* **Rainer**
Werdau *Sach* Sachsengold (contract-brewed)
Werdum *Nie* **Küsten-Brauerei**
Werneck *Bay* **Wernecker**
Wernesgrün *Sach* **Wernesgrüner**
Wernigerode *S-A* **Hasseröder**
Wertingen *Bay* **Schwanen-Bräu**
Westerheim *Bay* see: Günz
Westheim *N-W* **Westheimer**
Wettelsheim *Bay* **Strauß**
Wettringen *N-W* Wettringer Brauhaus (2003)
Wetzlar *Hes* Euler (2001, contract-brewed), Waldschmidt (1996, contract-brewed)
Weyberhöfe *Bay* **Weyberbräu**
Weyhausen *Hes* Brauhaus Weyhausen
Wiedergeltingen *Bay* Landbrauerei Ritter (1999)
Wiefelsdorf *Bay* **Plank**
Wiehl *N-W* see: **Bielstein**
Wienhausen *Nie* **Mühlengrund**
Wiernsheim *Bay* **Adler Bräu**
Wiesbaden *Hes* Rathsbräu (2001, brewed by Eltviller, Eltville)
Wiesen (Bad Staffelstein) *Bay* **Hellmuth, Thomann**
Wiesen (Unterfranken) *Bay* **Bürgerliches Brauhaus**
Wiesensteig *B-W* **Zum Lamm**
Wiesenttal *Bay* see: Muggendorf, Wüstenstein
Wieseth *Bay* **Fischer**
Wiesmühl *Bay* **Wieser**
Wildenberg *Bay* see: **Pürkwang**
Wilhams *Bay* see: **Missen-Wilhams**
Wilhermsdorf *Bay* Wilhermsdorfer Brauhaus (1993)
Willersdorf *Bay* Rittmayer (2003, contract-brewed)
Willich *N-W* see: **Anrath**
Willingen *Hes* **Rössel Bräu, Willinger Brauhaus**
Windeck *N-W* see: **Mauel**
Windelsbach *Bay* Markgrafenbräu (1989)
Windesheim *R-P* **Guldenbacher, Präsidenten Pils**
Windischeschenbach *Bay* **Kommunbrauerei, Würth.** See also: **Neuhaus (Windischeschenbach)**
Winklarn *Bay* **Betz**
Winnweiler *R-P* **Bischoff**
Winterlingen *B-W* Lehner-Bräu (1991)
Wippra *S-A* **Museumsbrauerei**

Wismar *M-V* Brauhaus am Lohberg
Witten *N-W* see: **Durchholz**
Wittenberg *S-A* see: **Lutherstadt Wittenberg**
Wittichenau *Sach* Stadtbrauerei
Wittingen *Nie* **Wittinger.** See also: **Lüben**
Witzenhasuen *Hes* **Schinkel's Brauhaus**
Wolfenweiler *B-W* **Mooswald Heimbräu**
Wolfhagen *Hes* **Alte Brauerei**
Wolfsburg *Nie* see: **Fallersleben**
Wolfshöhe *Bay* **Wolfshöher**
Wollersheim *N-W* **Cramer**
Wöllnitz *Thü* see: **Jena**
Wolnzach *Bay* **Bürgerbräu,** Wolnzacher Brauhaus
    (1993). See also: **Larsbach**
Wolzhausen *Hes* **Thome**
Worbis *Thü* **Neunspringe**
Wörlitz *S-A* Wörlitz
Worms *R-P* **Hagenbräu**
Wulfen *N-W* **Metzler,** Rose
Wülfrath *R-P* **Alt Wulfrath**
Wunsiedel *Bay* **Hönicka-Bräu.** See also: **Schönbrunn**
Wunstorf *Nie* see: Steinhude am Meer
Wuppertal-Barmen *N-W* Bremme, **Wuppertaler**
    Brauhaus, Wicküler (1993, brewed by Brinkhoff,
    Dortmund)
Wuppertal-Elberfeld *N-W* Janke's Bierhaus (1994)
Würgau *Bay* **Hartmann**
Wurmlingen *B-W* **Hirsch-Brauerei Honer**
Würzburg *Bay* **Brauhaus, Würzburger Hofbräu**

Wurzen *Sach* Katharinen (contract-brewed)
Wüstenstein *Bay* Schoberth/Lehneis (1969)
Wüstmark *M-V* see: **Schwerin**

Z

Zant *Bay* Gaisbauer (hobby brewery)
Zapfendorf *Bay* Drei Kronen (2002). see:
    Unterleiterbach
Zeil (Main) *Bay* **Göller**
Zell *Bay* **Schloßbrauerei Schwarzfischer**
Zellerfeld *Nie* see: Clausthal-Zellerfeld
Zentbechhofen *Bay* **Friedel**
Zenting *Bay* Kamm (1990)
Zettmannsdorf *Bay* **Seelmann**
Zeutern *B-W* Met Brauhaus (2000)
Zilgendorf *Bay* Gick (1998)
Zimmern *B-W* see: **Flözlingen**
Zirndorf *Bay* **Zirndorf**
Zittau *Sach* **Bürgerbräu,** Zittauer (1992, brewed by
    Garley, Gardelegen)
Zöschingen *Bay* **Behnle Bräu**
Zusmarshausen *Bay* **Schwarzbräu**
Zuzenhausen *B-W* **Adler Bräu**
Zwickau *Sach* **Brauhaus Zwickau, Mauritius**
Zwiefalten *B-W* **Klosterbräu**
Zwiefaltendorf *B-W* **Blank**
Zwiesel *Bay* **Dampfbierbrauerei,** Janka-Bräu (2004)
Zwönitz *Sach* **Zwönitz**

Directory of beers and breweries

Due to the sheer number of entries, this directory has been devised to enable you to find a beer or brewery without the aid of page numbers. We list the name of every active brewery and each beer (except generic names) in **bold** print followed by the producer and/or place in *italics*, together with the state (abbreviated in brackets). Names shared by more than one brewery or beer have the producers listed in order of place name.

The following beer styles and common names have not been included here unless they form part of a distinctive name: Alt(-bier), Bock(-bier), Diät, Doppelbock, Dunkel/Dunkle/Dunkles, Edel/Edles *(noble)*, Erntebier *(harvest beer)*, Export, Fastenbier *(Lent beer)*, Festbier, Frühlingsbier *(spring beer)*, Gold, Hefe(-trüb/-weizen/-weissbier, etc.), Hell/Helle/Helles, Herbstbier *(autumn-beer)*, Jubiläum(-sbier) *(anniversary beer)*, Keller(-bier), Kölsch, Kristall(-weizen), Lager, Landbier, Leicht, Light, Märzen, Maibock, Naturtrüb *(naturally cloudy)*, Oktoberfestbier, Original, Osterbier *(Easter beer)*, Pils/Pilsner/Pilsener, Premium, Schankbier, Schwarz(-bier), Spezial *(special)*, Starkbier, Ur- *(original)*, Urtyp *(original type)*, Vollbier, Weihnachtsbier *(Christmas beer)*, Weiss/Weissbier/Weisse/Weizen(-bock), Winterbier, Zwickl/Zwickel(-bier).

A

Aalener *Aalener Löwenbrauerei, Aalen (B-W)*
Aascher Hausbier *Rittmayer, Aisch (Bay)*
Abrahams Bock Hell *Fiedler, Oberscheibe (Sach)*
Absolvinator *Meinel-Bräu, Hof (Bay)*
Abt Andreas Traditionstrunk *Hösl, Mitterteich (Bay)*
Abt Knauer Bock *Püls Bräu, Weismain (Bay)*
Abtei Bräu *Mettlach (Saar)*
Achinger *Heiligenstadt (Bay)*
Adam Bräu *Bodenmais (Bay)*
Adam Riese Urtrunk *Ebensfelder, Ebensfeld (Bay)*
Adamator *Adam-Bräu, Bodenmais (Bay)*
Adler *Adlerbrauerei, Dellmensingen (B-W);*
    Adlerbrauerei Götz, Geislingen (B-W);
    Adlerbrauerei, Hundersingen (B-W); Adler, Rißtissen
    (B-W); Adler-Brauerei, Waibstadt (B-W)
Adlerbräu *Adlerbrauerei Rupf, Hailtingen (B-W);*
    Schlüsselfeld (Bay); Stettfeld (Bay); Wiernsheim (B-W);
    Zuzenhausen (B-W)
Adlerbrauerei *Dellmensingen (B-W); Geislingen (B-W);*
    Hailtingen (B-W); Hundersingen (B-W); Michelbach
    (B-W); Mögglingen (B-W); Rißtissen (B-W);
    Waibstadt (B-W)
Adlersberger *Prößlbräu, Adlersberg (Bay)*
Adventsbier *Schlossbrauerei, Stein (Bay)*
Aecht Fränkisches Landbier *Raab, Hofheim (Bay)*
Aecht Patzenhofer *Schultheiss, Hohenschönhausen (Ber)*
Aecht Schlenkerla Rauchbier *Heller, Bamberg (Bay)*
Aecht's Haberstumpf *Haberstumpf, Trebgast (Bay)*
Aechtes Dunkel *Riegele, Augsburg (Bay)*
Aegidi *Schlossbräu, Drachselried (Bay)*
Aegidius *Schlossbräu, Drachselried (Bay)*
Ahlbecker Kellerbräu *Ahlbeck (M-V)*

Ahnengold *Schloßbrauerei, Holnstein (Bay)*
Ahnentrunk *Schloßbrauerei, Holnstein (Bay)*
Ahornberger *Ahornberg (Bay)*
Aiblinger Schwarzbier *Schloßbrauerei, Maxlrain (Bay)*
Aidenbach *Aidenbach (Bay)*
Airbräu *Flughafen-München (Bay)*
Aischgründer *Windsheimer, Gutenstetten (Bay);*
    Löwenbräu, Neuhaus (Bay)
Aitermoser *Falter, Hof (Bay)*
Aktien *Maisel, Bayreuth (Bay)*
Aktienbrauerei *Kaufbeuren (Bay); Simmerberg (Bay)*
Aktionator *Bürgerbräu, Wolnzach (Bay)*
Albfels Pilsener *Heubacher, Heubach (B-W)*
Albquell Bräuhaus *Trochtelfingen (B-W)*
Albrecht Dunkel *Hallesches Brauhaus, Halle (S-A)*
Albrecht Dürer Pils *Tucher, Fürth (Bay)*
Albweizen *Bürgerbräu, Hersbruck (Bay)*
Aldersbach *Aldersbach (Bay)*
Ale *Stierbräu, Vechta (Nie)*
Alex Rolinck *Rolinck, Steinfurt (N-W)*
Alexanderplatz *Microbrauerei Barkowsky, Mitte (Ber)*
Alexator *Schwanenbräu, Burgebrach (Bay)*
Allersheim *Allersheim (Nie)*
Allgäu Weisse Leicht *Post, Weiler (Bay)*
Allgäuer Brauhaus *Leuterschach (Bay)*
Allgäuer Jagdbier *Allgäuer, Leuterschach (Bay)*
Allgäuer Landbier *Postbrauerei, Nesselwang (Bay)*
Allgäuer Öko-Bier *Hirschbräu, Sonthofen (Bay)*
Alligator *König von Flandern, Augsburg (Bay);*
    Hofmühl, Eichstätt (Bay)
Aloisius *Nothhaft, Marktredwitz (Bay);*
    Klosterbräuhaus, Ursberg (Bay)

Aloysius *Kuchlbauer, Abensberg (Bay)*
Alpenrose *Oberaudorf (Bay)*
Alpha-Bier *Brauhaus Schweinfurt, Schweinfurt (Bay)*
Alpirsbacher *Alpirsbacher Klosterbräu, Alpirsbach (B-W)*
Alpkönig *Memminger, Memmingen (Bay)*
Alsfeld *Alsfeld (Hes)*
Alt *Dietzhof (Bay)*
Alt Amberger *Winkler, Amberg (Bay)*
Alt aus Dahl *Vormann, Dahl (N-W)*
Alt Badisch Dunkel *Moninger, Karlsruhe (B-W)*
Alt Bairisch Dunkel *Schweiger, Markt Schwaben (Bay)*
Alt Bayrisch Dunkel *Bucher Bräu, Grafenau (Bay)*
Alt Berchinger Dunkel *Winkler, Berching (Bay)*
Alt Eisleber Dunkel *Reformator, Lutherstadt Eisleben (S-A)*
Alt Fränkisch *Kauzen-Bräu, Ochsenfurt (Bay)*
Alt Fränkisches *Held, Oberailsfeld (Bay); Werner, Poppenhausen (Bay); Adler Bräu, Stettfeld (Bay)*
Alt Giessen *Gießen (Hes)*
Alt Irlbacher *Schloßbrauerei, Irlbach (Bay)*
Alt Jenaer Bock Hell *Papiermühle, Jena (Thü)*
Alt Kemptener *Allgäuer Brauhaus, Leuterschach (Bay)*
Alt Meckesheimer Dunkel *Mall, Meckesheim (B-W)*
Alt Meierhof Dunkel *Meierhof, Ottbergen (N-W)*
Alt Moosbacher Kellerbier *Scheuerer, Moosbach (Bay)*
Alt Münchner Weisse *Bavaria-Bräu, München (Bay)*
Alt Nailaer Dunkel *Bürgerbräu, Naila (Bay)*
Alt Neuhaus *Neuhaus (Nie)*
Alt Pahreser Dunkel *Hofmann, Pahres (Bay)*
Alt Pott's Landbier *Pott's, Oelde (N-W)*
Alt Reuther *Schloßbrauerei, Reuth (Bay)*
Alt Schwäbisch Dunkel *Ladenburger, Neuler (B-W)*
Alt Schwoihier Dunkel *Schwind, Aschaffenburg (Bay)*
Alt Straubinger Schwarzbier *Röhrl, Straubing (Bay)*
Alt Sumbarcher Dunkel *Gessner, Sonneberg (Thü)*
Alt Viechtacher *Gesellschaftsbrauerei, Viechtach (Bay)*
Alt Waldecker Dunkel *Hofbrauhaus, Bad Arolsen (Hes)*
Alt Windsheimer Kiliani *Bürgerbräu, Bad Windsheim (Bay)*
Alt Wülfrath *Wülfrath (N-W)*
Altbadisch *Fürstlich Fürstenbergische, Donaueschingen (B-W)*
Altbairisch *Aying, Aying (Bay); Hofbräu, Traunstein (Bay)*
Altbairisches Hefe-Weißbier *Peschl, Passau (Bay)*
Altbayerisch *Jacob, Bodenwöhr (Bay); Egerer, Großköllbach (Bay); Bärenbräu, Nesselwang (Bay); Müllerbräu, Neuötting (Bay); Gritschenbräu, Schrobenhausen (Bay); Ustersbacher, Ustersbach (Bay)*
Altbayerisches *Weißes Brauhaus, Neunburg (Bay); Riemhofer, Riedenburg (Bay)*
Altbayrisch *Kummert, Amberg (Bay); Müllerbräu, Pfaffenhofen (Bay); Urban, Pfaffenhofen (Bay); Schönram, Schönram (Bay)*
Altböhmisches Schwarzbier *Rossknecht, Ludwigsburg (B-W)*
Altdeutsch Dunkel *Helbig, Weilburg (Hes)*
Altdeutsches *Postbräu, Thannhausen (Bay)*
Altdorfer *Glossner-Bräu, Neumarkt (Bay)*
Alte Brauerei Wolfhagen *Wolfhagen (Hes)*

Alte Braukunst Dunkles Weizen *Greiner, Roding (Bay)*
Alte Bürgerstube *Heisterbacherrott (N-W)*
Alte Dürrener Weiße *Edelweissbrauerei, Dürren (B-W)*
Alte Feuerwache *Idstein (Hes)*
Alte Kelter *Lampertheim (Hes)*
Alte Klosterbrauerei *Trunk, Vierzehnheiligen (Bay)*
Alte Liebe *Kuchlbauer, Abensberg (Bay)*
Alte Weisse *Hasen, Augsburg (Bay); Riegele, Augsburg (Bay)*
Altenauer *Kolberg, Altenau (Nie)*
Altenburger *Altenburg (Thü)*
Altenmünster *Allgäuer Brauhaus, Leuterschach (Bay)*
Altenrüthener *Altenrüthen (N-W)*
Alter Bahnhof *Malsch (B-W)*
Alter Dessauer *Zum Alten Dessauer, Dessau (S-A)*
Alter Fritz *Brauhaus Alter Fritz, Tegel (Ber)*
Alter Schachthof *Zum Alten Schlachthof Neubrandenburg (M-V)*
Alter Schwede *Eschenbräu, Wedding (Ber)*
Alterlanger Dunkel *Steinbach Bräu, Erlangen (Bay)*
Altes *Wolfshöher, Wolfshöhe (Bay)*
Altes Brauhaus *Zum Alten Brauhaus, Rheinsberg (Bra)*
Altes Brauhaus zu Fallersleben *Fallersleben (Nie)*
Altes Sudhaus Dunkel *Heubacher, Heubach (B-W)*
Altfranken Braunbier *Bürgerbräu, Bayreuth (Bay)*
Altfranken Markator *Bürgerbräu, Bayreuth (Bay)*
Altfranken Urstoff *Bürgerbräu, Bayreuth (Bay)*
Altfränkisch *Schnupp, Altdrossenfeld (Bay); Herbsthäuser, Herbsthausen (B-W); Brauer-Vereinigung, Pegnitz (Bay); Pyraser, Pyras (Bay); Würzburger Hofbräu, Würzburg (Bay)*
Altfränkische *Klosterbrauerei, Weißenohe (Bay)*
Altfränkisches *Hümmer, Breitengüßbach (Bay); Först, Drügendorf (Bay); Brauhaus 18·80, Fritzlar (Hes); Bürgerliches Brauhaus, Wiesen (Bay)*
Alto Dunkel *Maierbräu, Altomünster (Bay)*
Altmärker *Garley, Gardelegen (S-A)*
Altmärkisches Landbier *Demmert, Neuendorf (S-A)*
Altmühltaler *Schäff, Treuchtlingen (Bay)*
Altomünsterer Weisse *Kapplerbräu, Altomünster (Bay)*
Altöttinger *Hell-Bräu, Altötting (Bay)*
Altpieschener Spezial *Watzke, Dresden (Sach)*
Altstadt *Thorbräu, Augsburg (Bay); Döbler, Bad Windsheim (Bay); Münchhausen Brauhaus, Bodenwerder (Nie); Barre, Lübbecke (N-W); Sollinger Bergbrauerei, Uslar (Nie)*
Altstadtbier Dunkel *Salch, Hammelburg (Bay, unknown brewer)*
Altstadtbrauhaus *Bautzen (Sach); Schwerin (M-V)*
Altstadthof *Nürnberg (Bay)*
Altweizen *Schloßbrauerei, Grünbach (Bay)*
Alzthaler *Leidmann, Unterneukirchen (Bay)*
Amber *Brauhaus Wallhall, Bruchsal (B-W)*
Amber Ale *Lemke's Spezialitätenbrauerei, Mitte (Ber)*
Amberger *Winkler, Amberg (Bay)*
Ambräusianum *Bamberg (Bay)*
Ambrosiator *Kloster-Bräu, Au (Bay)*
Ametsbichler *Aschau am Inn (Bay)*
Ammerndorfer *Dorn-Bräu, Ammerndorf (Bay)*

An der Klosterpforte *Helfta (S-A)*
An der Thomaskirche *Leipzig (Sach)*
Andechser *Klosterbrauerei, Andechs (Bay)*
Andorfer *Passau (Bay)*
Andreas Pils *DAB, Dortmund (N-W)*
Andreasbock *Sauer, Gunzendorf (Bay)*
Andreasbräu *Leopoldshafen (B-W)*
Angele Pils *Bräuhaus Ummendorf, Ummendorf (B-W)*
Angerbräu Premium Pils *Braugold, Erfurt (Thü)*
Angermann *Kulmbach (Bay, unknown brewer)*
Angerwirts Weizen *Pyraser, Pyras (Bay)*
Animator *Hacker-Pschorr, München (Bay);*
Anker *Nagold (B-W); Nördlingen (Bay); Ochsenfurt (Bay);*
    Greiner, Roding (Bay); Ankerbräu, Steinach (Thü)
Ankerbräu *Steinach (Thü)*
Ankerla Dunkel *Ankerbräu, Steinach (Thü)*
Anna Weisse *Neder, Forchheim (Bay)*
Annaberg Festbier *Sperber-Bräu, Sulzbach-Rosenberg*
    (Bay)
Annafestbier *Löwenbräu, Buttenheim (Bay); St.*
    Georgen Bräu, Buttenheim (Bay); Greif, Forchheim
    (Bay); Wolfshöher, Wolfshöhe (Bay)
Anno 25 Hefe-Weisse *Aktienbrauerei, Kaufbeuren (Bay)*
Anno 1050 *Klosterbrauerei, Weltenburg (Bay)*
Anno 1308 Kellerbier *Aktienbrauerei, Kaufbeuren (Bay)*
Anno 1402 *Pöllinger, Pfeffenhausen (Bay)*
Anno 1417 Kellerbier *Hacker-Pschorr, München (Bay)*
Anno 1516 Landbier *Aktienbrauerei, Kaufbeuren (Bay)*
Anno 1518 Lager Hell *Aktienbrauerei, Kaufbeuren (Bay)*
Anno 1605er Weisse *Oberbräu, Holzkirchen (Bay)*
Anno 1650 Zwickel *Schloßbrauerei, Autenried (Bay)*
Anno 1651 *Lauterbach, Lauterbach (Bay)*
Anno 1792 *Eder & Heylands, Großostheim (Bay)*
Anno 1885 Weissbier *Aktienbrauerei, Kaufbeuren (Bay)*
Anno 1900 *Jura-Bräu, Pegnitz (Bay)*
Anno 2000 *Schloßbrauerei, Unterbaar (Bay)*
Anti-Aging Bier *Klosterbrauerei, Neuzelle (Bra)*
Antonator *Brauhaus Schweinfurt, Schweinfurt (Bay);*
    Kössel-Bräu, Speiden (Bay)
Antonius *Stanglbräu, Herrnwahlthann (Bay); Nothhaft,*
    Marktredwitz (Bay)
Antonius-Sartor-Starkbier *Hohe-Wart, Hohenwart (Bay)*
Apoldaer *Vereinsbrauerei, Apolda (Thü)*
Apostel-Bräu *Eichbaum, Mannheim (B-W)*
Apostulator *Eichbaum, Mannheim (B-W)*
Apotheker Dunkel *Zum Löwen, Mühlhausen (Thü)*
Arber *Falterbräu, Drachselried (Bay)*
Arcobräu *Gräfliche Brauhaus, Moos (Bay)*
Arcolator *Gräfliche Brauerei Arco Valley, Adldorf (Bay)*
Arnschwanger *Mühlbauer, Arnschwang (Bay)*
Arnstädter *Stadtbrauerei, Arnstadt (Thü)*
Arnsteiner *Bender, Arnstein (Bay)*
Arnstorf *Schloßbrauerei, Arnstorf (Bay)*
Arolsen *Hofbrauhaus Arolsen, Bad Arolsen (Hes)*
Arolser Pils *Hofbrauhaus Arolsen, Bad Arolsen (Hes)*
Aroma Pils *Schillerbad, Lüdenscheid (N-W)*
Ärwin's Weizen Gold *Schacht 4/8, Duisburg (N-W);*
    Hibernia, Gelsenkirchen (N-W); Mühlheimer Brauhaus,
    Mühlheim (N-W); Zeche Jacobi, Oberhausen (N-W)

AS Weisse *Karmeliten, Straubing (Bay)*
Asam Bock *Klosterbrauerei, Weltenburg (Bay)*
Aschauer *Ametsbichler, Aschau am Inn (Bay)*
Aschersleber Festbier *Landsberger, Landsberger (S-A)*
Asgaard *Schleswig (S-H)*
Astra *Holsten, Altona (Ham)*
Au Hallertau *Schloßbrauerei, Au (Bay)*
Auer *Schloßbrauerei, Au (Bay)*
Auerbräu *Rosenheim (Bay)*
Auerhahn *Lauterbacher Burgbrauerei, Lauterbach (Hes)*
Aufsesser *Rothenbach, Aufseß (Bay)*
Augsburger *Riegele, Augsburg (Bay); Thorbräu,*
    Augsburg (Bay)
August *Hannover (Nie)*
Augusta *Augsburg (Bay)*
Augustiner *München (Bay)*
Aukofer *Kelheim (Bay)*
Aurator *Löwenbräu Neeb, Unterschleichach (Bay)*
Autenrieder *Schloßbrauerei, Autenried (Bay)*
Aventinus *Schneider, Kelheim (Bay)*
Aviator *Airbräu, Flughafen-München (Bay)*
Awetator *Weideneder, Tann (Bay)*
Ayinger *Aying (Bay)*

B

Babben *Lübbenau (Bra)*
Bächla Leicht *Hebendanz, Forchheim (Bay)*
Bachmayer *Dorfen (Bay)*
Bad Homburger Brauhaus *Bad Homburg (Hes)*
Bad Wildunger Brauhaus *Bad Wildungen (Bay)*
Bad Wörishofer Löwenbräu *Bad Wörishofen (Bay)*
Badebier *Klosterbrauerei, Neuzelle (Bra)*
Badisch Brauhaus *Karlsruhe (B-W)*
Badisch Weizen *Ganter, Freiburg (B-W)*
Badische Staatsbrauerei *Rothaus (B-W)*
Bagbander Bockbier *Ostfriesen-Bräu, Bagband (Nie)*
Bähr *Schönbrunn (Bay)*
Baisinger *Baisinger Löwenbrauerei, Baisingen (B-W)*
Bajuvator *Tucher Bräu, Fürth & Nürnberg (Bay)*
Bajuwaren Dunkel *Auerbräu, Rosenheim (Bay)*
Bals *Weißbierbrauerei, Oberaudorf (Bay)*
Balthasar Neumann *Wernecker, Werneck (Bay)*
Bambergator *Fässla, Bamberg (Bay)*
Bamberger *Keesmann, Bamberg (Bay); Klosterbräu,*
    Bamberg (Bay); Maisel, Bamberg (Bay)
Bär Bier *Michael, Weißenstadt (Bay)*
Barbara Bock *Kronenbrauerei, Hochdorf (B-W)*
Barbarossa *Schöllkrippen (Bay)*
Bären *Mühlbauer, Arnschwang (Bay); Fürstenberg,*
    Donaueschingen (B-W); Bärenbräu, Herborn (Hes);
    Bärenbräu, Neuhausen (Bay)
Bärenbräu *Herborn (Hes); Neuhausen (Bay);*
    Ottersheim (R-P)
Bärenpils *Berliner Kindl, Neukölln (Ber)*
Bärenquell Pilsener *Preussen Pils, Pritzwalk (Bra)*
Bärenstark *Bucher Bräu, Grafenau (Bay)*
Bärentrunk *Winkler, Berching (Bay)*
Barfüßer *Heilbronn (B-W); Neu-Ulm (Bay); Nürnberg*
    (Bay); Ulm (B-W);

Barkowsky *Mitte (Ber)*
Barley Wine *Lemke's Spezialitätenbrauerei, Mitte (Ber)*
Barnikel *Herrnsdorf (Bay)*
Barock Dunkel *Klosterbrauerei, Weltenburg (Bay)*
Barock Hell *Bischofshof, Regensburg (Bay)*
Baron Augustus *Schloßbrauerei, Sandersdorf (Bay)*
Baron Dominicus *Schloßbrauerei, Sandersdorf (Bay)*
Baron Ferdinand *Schloßbrauerei, Sandersdorf (Bay)*
Baron Maximilian *Schloßbrauerei, Sandersdorf (Bay)*
Baron Tassilo *Schloßbrauerei, Sandersdorf (Bay)*
Baronator *Schloßbrauerei, Reuth (Bay)*
Baroness Weisse *Schloßbrauerei, Holnstein (Bay)*
Barons Urhell *Schloßbrauerei, Holnstein (Bay)*
Barre *Lübbecke (N-W)*
Bartelsteiner Weisse *Adlerbrauerei, Geislingen (B-W)*
Bartholomäus *Brinkhoff, Dortmund (N-W)*
Bartmann's Kölsch *Hüchelner Urstoff, Frechen (N-W)*
Bastei *Pirna, Copitz (Sach)*
Bauer *Falk, Amberg (Bay, unknown brewer); Leipzig (Sach); Weißbierbrauerei, Triftern (Bay)*
Bauer's *Hohenaltheim (Bay); Bauer, Leipzig (Sach)*
Bauernbier *Held, Oberailsfeld (Bay); Brauhaus Preussen Pils, Pritzwalk (Bra); Neeb, Unterschleichach (Bay)*
Bauhöfer *Ulm (B-W)*
Baumburger *Klosterbrauerei Dietl, Baumburg (Bay)*
Baumer *Gars (Bay)*
Bäuml *Rain (Bay)*
Baupils *Oasen-Bräu, Graben-Neudorf (B-W)*
Bauriedl *Eslarn (Bay)*
Bautzener *Alstadtbrauhaus, Bautzen (Sach)*
Bauweizen *Oasen-Bräu, Graben-Neudorf (B-W)*
Bavaria *Eder & Heylands, Großostheim (Bay)*
Bavaria Bräu *München (Bay)*
Bavaria St. Pauli *Hamburg (Ham, now brewed elsewhere)*
Bavariator *Müllerbräu, Pfaffenhofen (Bay)*
Bayer *Rothenfels (Bay); Theinheim (Bay)*
Bayerator *Bayer, Rothenfels (Bay)*
Bayerisch *Hebendanz, Forchheim (Bay); Zötler, Rettenberg (Bay); Wieninger, Teisendorf (Bay); Ustersbacher, Ustersbach (Bay); Eschenbräu, Wedding (Ber); Wernecker, Werneck (Bay)*
Bayerische Museumsbrauerei *Kulmbach (Bay)*
Bayerische Staatsbrauerei Weihenstephan *Freising (Bay)*
Bayerischer Bahnhof *Leipzig (Sach)*
Bayerischer Haisl *Lauterbach, Lauterbach (Bay)*
Bayerischer Hof *Grünbach (Sach)*
Bayerisches *Sonnenbräu, Lichtenberg (Bay)*
Bayerisches Brauhaus *Pforzheim (B-W)*
Bayernbräu *Bad Neustadt (Bay, unknown brewer)*
Bayerwald *Hutthurm (Bay)*
Bayreuther Bierbrauerei *Maisel, Bayreuth (Bay)*
Bayrisch *Altöttinger Hell-Bräu, Altötting (Bay); Kummert, Amberg (Bay); Hauf, Dinkelsbühl (Bay); Wildbräu-Grandauer, Grafing (Bay); Brauhaus Hausham, Hausham (Bay); Zeltbräu, Hof (Bay); Hutthurmer Bayerwald, Hutthurm (Bay); Allgäuer Brauhaus, Leuterschach (Bay); Neckarsulmer,*

Neckarsulm *(B-W); Bärenbräu, Nesselwang (Bay); Storchenbräu, Pfaffenhausen (Bay)*
Becher *Bayreuth (Bay)*
Beck *Bremen (Bre); Trabelsdorf (Bay)*
Beck/Haake-Beck *Bremen (Bre)*
Beck'n Bier *Herold, Büchenbach (Bay)*
Beck's *Beck, Bremen (Bre)*
Becker *Gaffel, Köln (N-W)*
Beerfelder *Felsenkeller, Beerfelden (Hes)*
Behnle Bräu *Zöschingen (Bay)*
Behringer *Vohenstrauß (Bay)*
Bei der Göltzsch *Greiz (Thü)*
Bekenner-Bock *Betz, Celle (Nie)*
Bellheimer *Bellheim (R-P)*
Bender *Arnstein (Bay); Mühlhausen (Bay)*
Benedikt Dunkel *Vasold & Schmitt, Neunkirchen (Bay)*
Benedikt XVI *Lang-Bräu, Schönbrunn (Bay)*
Benediktinerabtei *Riedenburger, Riedenburg (Bay)*
Bennexator *Bennexer Brauhaus, Bennigsen (Nie)*
Bennexer Brauhaus *Bennigsen (Nie)*
Benno Scharl Weizen *Schloßbrauerei, Grünbach (Bay)*
Berabecka Boandl-Bräu *Oberbernbach (Bay)*
Berchinger *Winkler, Berching (Bay)*
Berchtesgaden *Hofbrauhaus, Berchtesgaden (Bay)*
Berg *Berg Brauerei Ulrich Zimmermann, Berg (B-W)*
Berg Gold Export *Mittenwald, Mittenwald (Bay)*
Berg Quell *Lindenbrauerei, Unna (N-W, unknown brewer)*
Bergamts *Ratskeller, Geising (Sach)*
Bergbier *Freiberger, Freiberg (Sach)*
Bergbock *Klosterbrauerei, Andechs (Bay)*
Bergbräu *Uslar (Nie)*
Bergbrauerei *Leimen (B-W)*
Berger *Reischach (Bay)*
Berggeist *Graminger-Weissbräu, Graming (Bay)*
Berghammer *Oberndorf (Bay)*
Bergkirchweihbier *Kitzmann, Erlangen (Bay); Steinbach Bräu, Erlangen (Bay)*
Bergkristall *Schussenrieder, Bad Schussenried (B-W); Gesellschaftsbrauerei, Viechtach (Bay)*
Bergquell *Löbau (Sach)*
Bergschlösschen *Lieske (Sach)*
Bergt-Bräu *Reichenbrand, Reichenbrand (Sach)*
Berliner Bürgerbräu *Friedrichshagen (Ber)*
Berliner Kindl *Neukölln (Ber)*
Berliner Pilsener *Schultheiss, Hohenschönhausen (Ber)*
Berliner Schultheiss *Hohenschönhausen (Ber)*
Berliner Weisse *Schultheiss, Hohenschönhausen (Ber); Kindl, Neukölln (Ber)*
Bernauer Schwarzbier *Bürgerbräu, Friedrichshagen (Ber)*
Bernhardus Bock *Schnitzlbaumer, Traunstein (Bay)*
Bernstein *Kommunbräu, Kulmbach (Bay); Lütter Krug, Lütte (N-W); Moerser, Moers (N-W); Schloßbrauerei, Scherneck (Bay); Schwelm, Schwelm (N-W); Stralsunder, Stralsund (M-V); Reuter, Unternbibert (Bay)*
Bertl's Pils *Dantscher, Teugn (Bay)*
Bertold Bock *Moninger, Karlsruhe (B-W)*
Bettenhauser *Hütt-Brauerei, Knallhütte (Hes)*

Betz *Winklarn (Bay); Celle (Nie)*
Biberacher *Schmid, Biberach (Bay)*
Biberland *Groß-Bieberau (Hes)*
Bielstein *Erzquell, Bielstein (N-W)*
Bier Hannes *Frankfurt (Hes)*
Bier Strolch *Lauterbacher Burgbrauerei, Lauterbach (Hes)*
Bierappel *Lammbrauerei, Untergröningen (B-W)*
Bierbichler Weißbier *Flötzinger, Rosenheim (Bay)*
Bierbrauerei zum Lamm *Wiesensteig (B-W)*
Bierchen *Nattheimer, Nattheim (B-W)*
Bierkutscher *Egerer, Großköllbach (Bay)*
Binding *Frankfurt (Hes)*
Bio Bräu *Oberthürheim (Bay)*
Bio Dinkel Weisse *Unertl, Mühldorf (Bay)*
Bio Gold *Schloßbrauerei Stelzer, Fattigau (Bay); Glossner-Bräu, Neumarkt (Bay)*
Bio Hell *Aktienbrauerei, Simmerberg (Bay)*
Bio Pils *Braumanufaktur, Potsdam (Bra)*
Bio Premium Pils *Schleswig, Schleswig (S-H)*
Bio Weizen *Meierhof, Ottbergen (N-W)*
Biolandbier *Landgasthof zur Linde, Middelhagen (M-V)*
Birkenseer *Burglengenfeld (Bay)*
Birnbacher Schwarzbier *Gräfl. Arco, Bad Birnbach (Bay)*
Bischoff *Bischoff'sche, Brühl (N-W); Winnweiler (R-P)*
Bischoff'sche *Brühl (N-W)*
Bischofshof *Regensburg (Bay)*
Bismark Pilsner Premium *Garley, Gardelegen (S-A)*
Bitburger *Bitburg (R-P)*
Bitterbier *Hövels, Dortmund (N-W); Kneipe Pur, Plaue (Bra)*
Black Art *Braustolz, Chemnitz (Sach)*
Black & Dry *Mayer, Ludwigshafen (R-P)*
Black Jack *Meininger, Meiningen (Thü)*
Black Lager *Schweiger, Markt Schwaben (Bay)*
Black Lion *Hartmannsdorfer, Hartmannsdorf (Sach)*
Blank *Zwiefaltendorf (B-W)*
Blaubändele *Stolz, Isny (B-W)*
Blauer Löwe *Höchstadt (Bay)*
Blaustöpsel *Heldrich, Edelsfeld (Bay)*
Blauweisse *Röhrl, Straubing (Bay)*
Blechschmidt *Treuen (Sach)*
Blobb-Bier *Winkler, Lengenfeld (Bay)*
Blond *Webster, Duisburg (N-W); Westparkbräu, Ingolstadt (Bay); Iserlohn, Iserlohn (N-W); Schweiger, Markt Schwaben (Bay); Mattlerhof, Röttgersbach (N-W)*
Blonde *Barfüßer, Heilbronn (B-W); Abtei-Bräu, Mettlach (Saar); Barfüßer, Neu-Ulm (Bay); Barfüßer, Nürnberg (Bay); Sitter-Bräu, Riedelsbach (Bay); Barfüßer, Ulm (B-W)*
Blonder Bock *Forschungsbrauerei, München (Bay)*
Blondes *Karlsberg, Homburg (Saar)*
Boandl-Bräu *Oberbernbach (Bay)*
Böbracher Pils *Ecker-Bräu, Eck (Bay)*
Bocholter Brauhaus *Bocholt (N-W)*
Böckl *Püttner, Schlammersdorf (Bay)*
Böckla *Drei Kronen, Memmelsdorf (Bay)*
Böckle *Königsegger Walderbräu, Königseggwald (B-W); Clemens Härle, Leutkirch (B-W); Lohrer Bier, Lohr*

(Bay); Haller Löwenbräu, Schwäbisch Hall (B-W); Zoller-Hof, Sigmaringen (B-W); Fürst Wallerstein Brauhaus, Wallerstein (Bay)
Bockser *Müllerbräu, Neuötting (Bay)*
Bodenmaiser Dunkel *Adam-Bräu, Bodenmais (Bay)*
Bodenwöhrer Weissbier *Jacob, Bodenwöhr (Bay)*
Boente *Recklinghausen (N-W)*
Böheim *Brauer-Vereinigung, Pegnitz (Bay)*
Böhmisch *Olbernhau, Olbernhau (Sach)*
Böhmisches Brauhaus *Grossröhrsdorf (Sach)*
Böhms Böhmisches *Ziegler, Waldsassen (Bay)*
Bölkstoff *Flensburger, Flensburg (S-H)*
Bolten *Korschenbroich (N-W)*
Bombastic *Schimpfle, Gessertshausen (Bay)*
Bonaparte Pils *Kaiser Napoleon, Leipzig (Sach)*
Bonifatius *Brauhaus 18·80, Fritzlar (Hes)*
Bönnsch *Bonn (N-W)*
Bonsai Weißbier *Weissbräu Schwendl, Schalchen (Bay)*
Borbecker Dampfbierbrauerei *Essen (N-W)*
Borgfelder *Bremen (Bre)*
Bornstedter Büffel *Hofbrauerei, Potsdam (Bra)*
Bornsteiner *Hofbrauerei, Bruchhausen (N-W)*
Bosch *Bad Laasphe (N-W)*
Bottich *Bottrop (N-W)*
Brandenburger *Brauhaus Preussen Pils, Pritzwalk (Bra)*
Brantl *Roding (Bay)*
Bräu im Moos *Moos (Bay)*
Bräu Josef *Albquell Bräuhaus, Trochtelfingen (B-W)*
Bräu 'z Loh *Loh (Bay)*
Brauberger *Lübeck (S-H)*
Brauer Pilsener *Sudmeister & Fruchtgut, Bochum, (N-W, unknown brewer)*
Brauer Vereinigung *Pegnitz (Bay)*
Brauer Weisse *Der Hausbrauer Dietz, Bruckberg (B-W)*
Bräufaß *Wieninger, Teisendorf (Bay)*
Braugasthaus Mühlengrund *Wienhausen (Nie)*
Braugasthof Falkenstein *Pfronten-Ried (Bay)*
Braugold *Erfurt (Thü)*
Brauhaus *Weißes Brauhaus, Neunburg (Bay); Schweinfurt, Schweinfurt (Bay); Würzburg (Bay)*
Brauherren Premium Pils *Einbecker, Einbeck (Nie)*
Brauhof Wilshaus *Braam-Ostwennemaar (N-W)*
Braumanufaktur *Potsdam (Bra)*
Braumeister *Brauhaus Aidenbach, Aidenbach (Bay); Bürgerbräu, Bad Reichenhall (Bay); Zimmermann, Berg (B-W); Braustolz, Chemnitz (Sach); Wüllner, Gänsefurth (S-A, unknown brewer); Horneck, Horneck (Bay); Meininger, Meiningen (Thü); Hacker-Pschorr, München (Bay); Bürgerbräu, Naila (Bay); Calwer-Eck-Bräu, Stuttgart (B-W)*
Braumühle *Schmerlecke (N-W)*
Braun's Weisse *Klosterbräu, Bamberg (Bay)*
Braunbier *Bosch, Bad Laasphe (N-W); Klosterbräu, Bamberg (Bay); Bürgerbräu, Bayreuth (Bay); Friedrich's, Chemnitz (Sach); Webster, Duisburg (N-W); Hald, Dunstelkingen (B-W); Steinbach, Erlangen (Bay); Vogel, Ettlingen (B-W); Neder, Forchheim (Bay); Brauhaus 18·80, Fritzlar (Hes); Chiemseebräu, Grabenstätt (Bay); Vogelbräu, Karlsruhe (B-W);*

Vogel Hausbräu, Karlsruhe (B-W); Emsländer, Lünne (Nie); Maximilians Brauwiesen, Niederlahnstein (R-P); Grafschafter, Nordhorn (Nie); Kneipe Pur, Plaue (Bra); Hof-Brauhaus Bornstedt, Potsdam (Bra); Lüdde, Quedlinburg (S-A); Mattlerhof, Röttgersbach (N-W); Steffens, St. Severinsberg (R-P); Gutsbräu, Straßkirchen (Bay)

Braune Weisse *Felsenbräu, Thalmannsfeld (Bay)*
Brauner Schlawiner *Obermühle, Braunfels (Hes)*
Braunfelser Pils *Bärenbräu, Herborn (Hes)*
Bräunlinger *Löwenbrauerei, Bräunlingen (B-W)*
Bräustatt *Aktienbrauerei, Simmerberg (Bay)*
Braustelle *Köln (N-W)*
Braustoff *Maximiliansbräu, Traunstein (Bay)*
Braustolz *Chemnitz (Sach)*
Braustüb'l *Darmstädter, Darmstadt (Hes)*
Bräutigam *Weisbrunn (Bay)*
Brauwiesen *Maximilians, Niederlahnstein (R-P)*
Bräuwirt *Weiden (Bay)*
Brehm's *Adlerbrauerei, Dellmensingen (B-W)*
Brenzkofer-Dunkel *Zoller-Hof, Sigmaringen (B-W)*
Brewbaker *Tiergarten (Ber)*
Brezel-Bräu *Alzenau (Bay)*
Brezenbier *Kommunbräu, Kumbach (Bay)*
Brinkhoff *Dortmund (N-W)*
Brotzeitbier *Lauterbach, Lauterbach (Bay)*
Brotzeitseidla *Göller, Zeil (Bay)*
Bruch *Saarbrücken (Saar)*
Bruchhausen *Hofbrauerei, Bruchhausen (N-W)*
Bruckberger *Dorn-Bräu, Bruckberg (Bay); Wimmer, Bruckberg (Bay)*
Bruckmüller *Amberg (Bay)*
Bruder Straubinger Edelhell *Röhrl, Straubing (Bay)*
Bruder Tak *Obermühle, Braunfels (Hes)*
Brunator *Brunner-Bräu, Spanberg (Bay)*
Brunnenbier *Lammbrauerei, Gruibingen (B-W)*
Brunner Bräu *Spanberg (Bay)*
Bub *Leinburg (Bay)*
Büble Bier *Allgäuer Brauhaus, Leuterschach (Bay)*
Bucher *Grafenau (Bay); Gundelfingen (Bay); Günzburg (Bay)*
Büchner *Heilmfurt (Bay)*
Buddyvator *Alt Wülfrath, Wülfrath (N-W)*
Büffel *Hofbrauerei, Potsdam (Bra)*
Bügel *Allersheim, Allersheim (Nie); Erl, Geiselhöring (Bay); Stuttgarter Hofbräu, Stuttgart (B-W)*
Bundschuh-Bräu *Untergrombach (B-W)*
Bure Bier *Kleines Herzogliches Brauhaus, Jülich (N-W)*
Burg *Watzdorfer, Watzdorf (Thü)*
Burgbräu *Johns-Bräu, Ludwigsstadt (Bay);*
Burgbrauerei *Lauterbach (Hes); Thüngen (Bay)*
Burgenländisch *Burgmühle, Freyburg (S-A)*
Bürger Bräu *Bürgerbräu, Hof (Bay)*
Bürger Kölsch *Gaffel (Porz), Köln (N-W)*
Bürgerbräu *Hasen, Augsburg (Bay); Bad Reichenhall (Bay); Bad Windsheim (Bay); Bamberg (Bay), unknown brewer); Bayreuth (Bay); Friedrichshagen (Ber); Hersbruck (Bay); Hof (Bay); Naila (Bay); Wolnzach (Bay); Zittau (Sach)*

Bürgerfestbier *Leitner, Schwabach (Bay)*
Bürgerliches Brauhaus *Saalfeld (Thü); Wiesen (Bay)*
Bürgermeisterbräu *Altes Brauhaus, Fallersleben (Nie)*
Burgfest Bier *Pyraser, Pyras (Bay)*
Burggraf Bräu *Auerbach (Hes)*
Burggraf Dunkel *Lang-Bräu, Schönbrunn (Bay)*
Burgherren Pils *Streck-Bräu, Ostheim (Bay)*
Burglengenfelder *Birkenseer, Burglengenfeld (Bay)*
Burgmühle *Freyburg (S-A)*
Burgwall Bräu *Warnitz (Bra)*
Burkarth *Amorbach (B-W, unknown brewer)*
Burschenpils *Papiermühle, Jena (Thü)*
Bussen Kindle Pilsner *Adlerbrauerei, Hailtingen (B-W)*
Bütten Alt *Lauterbacher Burgbrauerei, Lauterbach (Hes)*
Büttner *Untergreuth (Bay)*
Buxtehuder *Buxtehude (Nie)*

C

Cääner Blondes *Irle, Siegen (N-W)*
Calwer Eck Bräu *Stuttgart (B-W)*
Cambonator *Allgäuer Brauhaus, Leuterschach (Bay)*
Cannabia *Kronenbrauerei Wahl, Gundelfingen (Bay, unknown brewer)*
Cannabis Club *Klosterbrauerei, Weißenohe (Bay)*
Capitulare *Greif, Forchheim (Bay)*
Carl Daniel Mayer *Mayer Bräu, Ludwigshafen (R-P)*
Carl Theodor *Frankenthaler, Frankenthal (R-P, unknown brewer)*
Carl Wittmann Dunkel *Wittmann, Landshut (Bay)*
Carlsberg *Mönchengladbach, Mönchengladbach (N-W)*
Carnevale *Kaiser, Geislingen (B-W)*
Carolus der Starke *Binding, Frankfurt (Hes)*
Carry's Monatsbier *Schwanen-Bräu, Wertingen (Bay)*
Casbacher Braunbier *Steffens, St. Severinsberg (R-P)*
Castel *Mainz-Kastel (Hes)*
Castelator *Castel, Mainz-Kastel (Hes)*
Castroper *Brauhaus Rütershoff, Castrop-Rauxel (N-W)*
Cave Gladium *Dimpfl, Furth im Wald (Bay)*
CD Pils *Dinkelacker-Schwaben-Bräu, Stuttgart (B-W)*
Celebrator *Aying, Aying (Bay); Kärrners, Bad Orb (Hes)*
Celler *Betz, Celle (Nie)*
Celtic Bier *Thorbräu, Augsburg (Bay)*
Celtic Stout *Grafschafter, Nordhorn (Nie)*
Champ *Erdinger Weißbräu, Erding (Bay)*
Champagnerbier *Lemke's Spezialitätenbrauerei, Mitte (Ber)*
Charivari-Bräu *Königsbrunn (Bay)*
Charly Bräu *Augsburg (Bay)*
Chemnitzer Turmbräu *Turm, Chemnitz (Sach)*
Chiemseebräu *Grabenstätt (Bay)*
Chiemseer *Maximiliansbräu, Traunstein (Bay)*
Chorherren Bock *Klosterbrauerei Dietl, Baumburg (Bay)*
Chorherrn-Pils *Kloster-Bräu, Au (Bay)*
Choriner *Uckermärker, Golzow (Bra)*
Christian Bischoff Kellerbier *Bischoff, Winnweiler (R-P)*
Christkindl *Riegele, Augsburg (Bay); Arcobräu Gräfliches Brauhaus, Moos (Bay)*
Christkindlesmarkt Bier *Tucher, Fürth & Nürnberg (Bay)*
Christoph Bräu *Gaggenau (B-W)*

Christopherus *Hald, Dunstelkingen (B-W)*
Christoph's *Jahns-Bräu, Ludwigsstadt (Bay)*
Clarissen Alt *Hövels, Dortmund (N-W)*
Classic *Reichenbrander, Chemnitz (Sach); Bachmayer, Dorfen (Bay); DAB, Dortmund (N-W); Eschweger Klosterbrauerei, Eschwege (Hes); Uckermärker, Golzow (Bra); Meinel-Bräu, Hof (Bay); Jahns-Bräu, Ludwigsstadt (Bay); Memminger, Memmingen (Bay); Scheuerer, Moosbach (Bay); Fürst Wallerstein Brauhaus, Wallerstein (Bay); Klosterbrauerei, Weißenohe (Bay); Würzburger Hofbräu, Würzburg (Bay)*
Classix Dunkles *Bärenbräu, Herborn (Hes)*
Clemens Spezial *Clemens Härle, Leutkirch (B-W)*
Closter Zell *Klosterbrauerei, Neuzelle (Bra)*
Cluss *Dinkelacker-Schwaben-Bräu, Stuttgart (B-W)*
Colbitzer *Heidebrauerei, Colbitz (S-A)*
Cölner Hofbräu P. J. Früh *Köln (N-W)*
Commerzienrat Riegele Privat *Riegele, Augsburg (Bay)*
Conrad *Adler-Bräu, Wiernsheim (B-W)*
Conrator *Adler-Bräu, Wiernsheim (B-W)*
Cool Pils *Flözinger-Bräu, Rosenheim (Bay)*
Coronator *Ratskeller, Darmstadt (Hes); Arcobräu Gräfliches Brauhaus, Moos (Bay); Krone, Tettnang (B-W)*
Coschützer Pils *Feldschlößchen, Dresden (Sach)*
Cramer *Wollersheim (N-W)*
Crailsheimer *Engel-Bräu, Crailsheim (B-W)*
Cronemeyers *Alt Neuhaus, Neuhaus (Nie)*
Curator *Klosterbrauerei, Ettal (Bay)*

D

d'Inn'Staade *Innstadt, Passau (Bay)*
D Pils *Brinkhoff, Dortmund (N-W)*
DAB *Dortmund (N-W)*
Dachsbräu *Weilheim (Bay)*
Dachsenfranz *Adler-Bräu, Zuzenhausen (B-W)*
Dahler Urbräu *Vormann, Dahl (N-W)*
Dampfbier *Maisel, Bayreuth (Bay); Borbecker Dampfbier-Brauerei, Essen (N-W); Dampfbierbrauerei, Oberstdorf (Bay); Schloßbrauerei, Rheder (N-W); Dampfbierhaus Rössel Bräu, Willingen (Hes); Erste Dampfbierbrauerei, Zwiesel (Bay)*
Dampfbierbrauerei *Essen (N-W); Oberstdorf (Bay); Zwiesel (Bay)*
Dampfbierhaus Rössel Bräu *Willingen (Hes)*
Dampfsud Dunkel *Bürgerbräu, Hersbruck (Bay)*
Dantscher *Teugn (Bay)*
Darguner *Dargun (M-V)*
Dark *Meinel-Bräu, Hof (Bay); Friesisches Bräuhaus, Jever (Nie); Lauterbacher Burgbrauerei, Lauterbach (Hes); Paderborner, Paderborn (N-W)*
Darmstädter *Darmstadt (Hes)*
Das Alt *Brinkhoff, Fortmund (N-W)*
Das Bockbier *Fischer, Wieseth (Bay)*
Das Echte Märzen *Dinkelacker-Schwaben, Stuttgart (B-W)*
Das Elefant *Krug, Geisfeld (Bay)*
Das Göttliche *Schleswig, Schleswig (S-H)*
Das Helle *Krug, Geisfeld (Bay); Dinkelacker-Schwaben-Bräu, Stuttgart (B-W); Fischer, Wieseth (Bay)*

Das Kleine Brauhaus *Kleines Pleinfelder, Pleinfeld (Bay)*
Das Landbier *Fischer, Wieseth (Bay)*
Das Leichte *Faust, Miltenberg (Bay)*
Das Pils *Fischer, Wieseth (Bay)*
Das Schlappeseppel *Eder & Heyland, Großostheim (Bay)*
Das Schwarze *von Koch'sche, Gottsmannsgrün (Bay); Dinkelacker-Schwaben, Stuttgart (B-W)*
Das Schwarze Schaf *Krug, Geisfeld (Bay)*
Das Spezial *Fischer, Wieseth (Bay)*
Das Weizen *Dinkelacker-Schwaben-Bräu, Stuttgart (B-W)*
de Bassus *Schloßbrauerei, Sandersdorf (Bay)*
Deflorator *Kommunbräu, Kumbach (Bay)*
Deil *Osterberg (Bay)*
Deinhardt *Felsenkeller, Weimer (Thü)*
Deisenhofener Weissbräu *Weißbräu, Deisenhofen (Bay)*
Delirium *Kommunbräu, Kumbach (Bay)*
Delitzscher Festbier *Landsberger, Landsberger (S-A)*
Dellmensinger *Adlerbrauerei, Dellmensingen (B-W)*
Demmert *Neuendorf (S-A)*
Denninghoff's *Giessener Brauhaus, Gießen (Hes)*
Dentleiner *Hauf-Bräu, Dentlein (Bay)*
Deputat *Glückauf, Gersdorf (Sach)*
Der Bräu im Tü 8 *Stuttgart (B-W)*
Der Hausbrauer Dietz *Bruckberg (B-W)*
Der Jubilar *Wasserburger, Dingolfing (Bay)*
Der Leichte Bär *Mühlbauer, Arnschwang (Bay)*
Der Leichte Hirsch *Hirschbräu, Sonthofen (Bay)*
Der Postillion *Postbrauerei, Nesselwang (Bay)*
Dessauer *Zum Alten Dessauer, Dessau (S-A)*
Dessow *Dessow (Bra)*
Detmolder *Strate, Detmold (N-W)*
Deutsches Pils *Papiermühle, Jena (Thü)*
Deutsches Pilsner *Obermühle, Görlitz (Sach)*
Deutschhof *Schwind, Oberdorf (B-W)*
Die Leichte Jura *Plank, Wiefelsdorf (Bay)*
Die Leichtere *Weißbierbrauerei Hopf, Miesbach (Bay)*
Die Schwarze Kuni Weizenbock *Simon, Lauf (Bay)*
Diebels *Issum (N-W)*
Diekster Bräu *Norddeich (Nie)*
Dietl *Klosterbrauerei, Baumburg (Bay)*
Dietz *Der Hausbrauer Dietz, Bruckberg (B-W)*
Dimpfl Bräu Strauß *Furth im Wald (Bay)*
Dingslebener *Metzler, Dingsleben (Thü)*
Dinkel *Stublang (Bay); Uetzing (Bay)*
Dinkelacker *Dinkelacker-Schwaben-Bräu, Stuttgart (B-W)*
Dinkelator *Hauf, Dinkelsbühl (Bay)*
Dinkelbier *Bad Homburger, Bad Homburg (Hes); Körpricher Landbräu, Körprich (Saar); Landhaus, Lünne (Nie); Nattheimer, Nattheim (B-W); Lammsbräu, Neumarkt (Bay); Riedenburger Brauhaus, Riedenburg (Bay); Michael, Weißenstadt (Bay)*
Diplom Pils *Waldhaus, Waldhaus (B-W)*
Distelhäuser *Distelhäuser, Distelhausen (B-W)*
Dithmarscher *Marne (S-H)*
Dittmar *Kaltennordheim (Thü)*
Döbelner Brauhaus *Döbeln (Sach)*
Döbler *Bad Windsheim (Bay); Freilandmuseum, Bad Windsheim (Bay)*
Dold *Löwenbrauerei Dold, Elzach (B-W)*

Döllnitzer Ritterguts Gose *Bauer, Leipzig (Sach)*
Dom *Köln (N-W); Euler, Wetzlar (Hes, unknown brewer)*
Domänen Bräu *Brielhof (B-W)*
Domhof *Speyer (R-P)*
Domi *Vereinsbrauerei, Apolda (Thü)*
Domreiter Pils *Maisel, Bamberg (Bay)*
Donator *Brauhaus 18-80, Fritzlar (Hes)*
Donatus Dunkel *Hochwälder, Losheim (Saar)*
Donauthaler *Ingobräu, Ingolstadt (Bay)*
Donnerbock *Schorschbräu, Oberasbach (Bay)*
Donnersberger *Bischoff, Winnweiler (R-P)*
Donnerweizen *Schorschbräu, Oberasbach (Bay)*
Doppel Hirsch *Hirschbräu, Sonthofen (Bay)*
Doppel Hopfen Pils *Schloßbrauerei, Fattigau (Bay)*
Doppel Ritter *Erharting, Erharting (Bay)*
Dorfbräu Export *Lammbrauerei, Gruibingen (B-W)*
Dorfner *Schloßbrauerei, Hirschau (Bay)*
Dorn Bräu *Ammerndorf (Bay); Bruckberg (Bay)*
Dörr *Michelstadt (Hes)*
Dörzbacher *Schillingstadt (B-W)*
Dortmunder Aktien Brauerei *Dortmund (N-W)*
Dortmunder Hansa *DAB, Dortmund (N-W)*
Dortmunder Kronen *DAB, Dortmund (N-W)*
Dortmunder Stifts *DAB, Dortmund (N-W)*
Dortmunder Thier *DAB, Dortmund (N-W)*
Dortmunder Union *Brinkhoff, Dortmund (N-W)*
Drachen Weisse *Mühlbauer, Arnschwang (Bay)*
Drachenblut *Mühlbauer, Arnschwang (Bay); Griesbräu, Murnau (Bay)*
Drachselrieder Schlossbräu *Drachselried (Bay)*
Dragoner Altbier *Kaiser Napoleon, Leipzig (Sach)*
Drei Heller Bier *König von Flandern, Augsburg (Bay)*
Drei Kronen *Memmelsdorf (Bay); Scheßlitz (Bay)*
Drei Wappen Weiße *Hofer, Furth im Wald (Bay)*
Dreifürsten-Pils *Fischer's, Mössingen (B-W)*
Dreikorn *Brauhaus Wallhall, Bruchsal (B-W); Mannebacher Brauhaus, Mannebach (R-P)*
Dremel *Wattendorf (Bay)*
Dresdner Felsenkeller *Feldschlößchen, Dresden (Sach)*
Drexler *Pösing (Bay)*
Dreykorn *Lauf (Bay)*
Drummer *Leutenbach (Bay)*
Dry *Paderborner, Paderborn (N-W)*
Dübelsbrücker *Bavaria St. Pauli (Ham, brewed elsewhere)*
Duckstein *Feldschlößchen, Braunschweig (Nie)*
Düll *Gnodstadt (Bay); Krautheim (Bay)*
Dult Bier *Wittmann, Landshut (Bay)*
Dult Märzen *Altöttinger Hell-Bräu, Altötting (Bay)*
Dultfestbier *Hacklberg, Passau (Bay)*
Dunkle Wolke *Glossner-Bräu, Neumarkt (Bay)*
Dunkler Hirsch *Hirschbräu, Sonthofen (Bay)*
Dunkles Goldblondchen *Steinbach Bräu, Erlangen (Bay)*
Dunkles Salonbier *Borbecker Dampfbier, Essen (N-W)*

E

Eber Weizen *Ebermannstadt (Bay)*
Eberhards Bock *Aalener Löwenbrauerei, Aalen (B-W)*
Ebriosus *Weizenbierglasmuseum, Nürnberg (Bay)*

Ecco Pilsner *Schloßbrauerei, Au (Bay)*
Echt Meierhof Landbier-Hell *Meierhof, Ottbergen (N-W)*
Echt Veldensteiner Landbier *Kaiser, Neuhaus (Bay)*
Echte Altomünsterer *Kapplerbräu, Altomünster (Bay)*
Echtes *Hösl, Irchenrieth (Bay)*
Ecke *Stuttgart (B-W)*
Ecker Bräu *Eck (Bay)*
Edel Gold *Meusel-Bräu, Dreuschendorf (Bay)*
Edel Herb *Schaumburger, Stadthagen (Nie)*
Edel Ross *Rößle, Ehingen (B-W)*
Edel Sünde *Böhmisches, Grossröhrsdorf (Sach)*
Edel Tropfen *Ankerbräu, Nördlingen (Bay)*
Edel Trunk *Schroll, Reckendorf (Bay)*
Edel Weisse *Stadtbrauerei Roth, Roth (Bay)*
Edelbitter *Adlerbrauerei, Dellmensingen (B-W)*
Edelherb Premium Pils *Kulmbacher, Kulmbach (Bay)*
Edelhirsch *Hirschbräu, Sonthofen (Bay)*
Edelhopfen Diät Pilsener *Maisel, Bayreuth (Bay)*
Edelquell *Schwindbräu, Aschaffenburg (Bay); Augusta, Augsburg (Bay)*
Edelstoff *Augustiner-Bräu, München (Bay); Schloßbrauerei Schwarzfischer, Zell (Bay)*
Edelsud *Innstadt, Passau (Bay)*
Edeltrunk *Hofbrauhaus, Freising (Bay)*
Edeltyp *Zwiefalter Klosterbräu, Zwiefaltendorf (B-W)*
Edelweiss *Edelweissbrauerei, Dürren (B-W)*
Edelweissbrauerei *Dürren (B-W)*
Edelweiße *Schübel, Stadtsteinach (Bay)*
Eder & Heylands *Großostheim (Bay)*
Eder's *Eder & Heylands, Großostheim (Bay)*
Edermünder Brauscheune *Haldorf (Hes)*
Egerer *Großköllbach (Bay)*
Egerthaler Leicht *Michael, Weißenstadt (Bay)*
Egolf *Schefflenz (B-W)*
Ehrenfelder Alt *Braustelle, Köln (N-W)*
Ehringsdorfer Urbräu *Weimar-Ehringsdorf, Weimar (Thü)*
Ehrstein *Hinterweidenthal (R-P)*
Eibauer *Münch-Bräu, Eibau (Sach)*
Eichator *Schlossbrauerei, Eichhofen (Bay)*
Eichbaum *Mannheim (B-W)*
Eichener *Eichen (N-W)*
Eichhofener *Schlossbrauerei, Eichhofen (Bay)*
Eichhorn *Dörfleins (Bay); Forchheim (Bay)*
Eierberg Urstoff *Hellmuth, Wiesen (Bay)*
Eifel Böckchen *Gemünder, Gemünd (N-W)*
Eifel Manna *Eifeler-Brauhaus, Bad Münstereifel (N-W)*
Eifeler Brauhaus *Bad Münstereifel (N-W)*
Eifeler Landbier *Gemünder, Gemünd (N-W)*
Ein Schlesier Export *Landskron Brauerei, Görlitz (Sach)*
Einbecker *Einbeck (Nie)*
Eine Bamberger Weisse *Maisel, Bamberg (Bay)*
Eine Bayern Halbe *Hubauer, Gräfelfing (Bay, unknown brewer)*
Einkorn Edelbier *Riedenburger, Riedenburg (Bay)*
Einsiedler *Einsiedel (Sach)*
Eisbock *König von Preußen, Frauenalb (B-W); Nordbräu, Ingolstadt (Bay); Schneider, Kelheim (Bay); Kulmbacher, Kulmbach (Bay); Lauterbach, Lauterbach (Bay); Hopf, Miesbach (Bay); Lemke's*

Spezialitätenbrauerei, Mitte (Ber); Kronenbrauerei, Ulm (B-W)
Eisenacher *Eisenach (Thü)*
Eisgrüb Bräu *Mainz (R-P)*
Eisleber Dunkel *Reformator, Lutherstadt Eisleben (S-A)*
Eispils *Stierberg, Stierberg (Bay)*
Eiszäpfle *Badische Staatsbrauerei, Rothaus (B-W)*
Eittinger *Fischerbräu, Eitting (Bay)*
EKU *Kulmbacher, Kulmbach (Bay)*
Elbhang Rot *Neustädter, Dresden (Sach)*
Elbeschloss *Bavaria St. Pauli (Ham, brewed elsewhere)*
Elchbier *Brauhaus Schweinfurt, Schweinfurt (Bay)*
Elchbräu *Riegel (B-W)*
Elch Pils *Garley, Gardelegen (S-A)*
Elefant *Krug, Geisfeld (Bay)*
Eller *Birkach (Bay)*
Ellertaler *Reh, Löhndorf (Bay)*
Ellingen *Ellingen (Bay)*
Eltviller *Kleines Eltviller Brauhaus, Eltville (Hes)*
Elzacher *Löwenbrauerei Dold, Elzach (B-W)*
Emmerbier *Riedenburger, Riedenburg (Bay); Leidmann, Unterneukirchen (Bay)*
Emsländer *Landhaus, Lünne (Nie)*
Engel *Engel-Bräu, Crailsheim (B-W); Hald, Dunstelkingen (B-W)*
Engelbräu *Crailsheim (B-W); Rettenberg (Bay)*
Engele Pils *Engel-Bräu, Crailsheim (B-W)*
Engelhardt Pilsener *Schultheiss, Hohenschönhausen (Ber)*
Engelsbräu *Bad Wildunger, Bad Wildungen (Bay)*
Ennert *Bonn (N-W)*
Enzensteiner *Enzenreuth (Bay)*
Equator *Kronenbrauerei, Laupheim (B-W)*
Erbacher *Erbach (Hes)*
Erbpils *Lauterbacher Burgbrauerei, Lauterbach (Hes)*
Erbschänk 1550 *Hartmann, Würgau (Bay)*
Erdinger *Erdinger Weißbräu, Erding (Bay)*
Eremitentrunk *Mühlenbräu, Mühlendorf (Bay)*
Erfurter Angerbräu Premium Pils *Braugold, Erfurt (Thü)*
Erfurter Brauhaus *Erfurt (Thü)*
Erfurter Schluntz *Haus zur Pfauen, Erfurt (Thü)*
Ergolator *Wittmann, Landshut (Bay)*
Erharting *Erharting (Bay)*
Erl *Geiselhöring (Bay)*
Erlanger Urbock *Kitzmann, Erlangen (Bay)*
Erlbacher *Erlbach (Sach)*
Erlebnisbrauerei *Bad Schussenried (B-W)*
Erlkönig *Erl, Geiselhöring (Bay)*
Ernst August *Hannover (Nie)*
Erotik Bier *Lang-Bräu, Schönbrunn (Bay)*
Erste Dampfbierbrauerei Zwiesel *Zwiesel (Bay)*
Erste Laufamholzer *Weizenbierglasmuseum, Nürnberg (Bay)*
Erste Rintelner Lokalitätenbrauerei *Rinteln (Nie)*
Erstes Forchheimer Braunbier *Neder, Forchheim (Bay)*
Erstes Forchheimer Leicht *Eichhorn, Forchheim (Bay)*
Erstes Forchheimer Weizen *Hebendanz, Forchheim (Bay)*
Erstes Laufer Weißbier *Simon, Lauf (Bay)*

Erstes Sächsiches Rauchbier *Pirna, Copitz (Sach)*
Erzbräu *Schmelzer, Schmelz (Saar)*
Erzgebirgisches Weihnacht *Olbernhau, Olbernhau (Sach)*
Erzgebirgs Premium Pils *Olbernhau, Olbernhau (Sach)*
Erzquell *Bielstein (N-W); Niederschelderhütte (R-P)*
Eschenbacher *Wagner-Bräu, Eschenbach (Bay)*
Eschenbräu *Wedding (Ber)*
Eschweger *Klosterbrauerei, Eschwege (Hes)*
Eslarner *Bauriedl, Eslarn (Bay); Kommunbrauerei, Eslarn (Bay)*
Esloher Brauhaus *Eslohe (N-W)*
Espelkamp *Espelkamp (N-W)*
Essel Bräu *Esloher Brauhaus, Eslohe (N-W)*
Ettaler *Klosterbrauerei, Ettal (Bay)*
Ettensberger *Klier Bräu, Ettensberg (Bay)*
Ettl *Ettl-Bräu, Teisnach (Bay)*
Etzelwanger *Pürner, Etzelwang (Bay)*
Eucharius Märzen *Klosterbrauerei, Weißenohe (Bay)*
Euler *Wetzlar (Hes, unknown brewer)*
Euro Pils *Marcus-Bräu, Mitte (Ber)*
Eurobock *Hellers, Köln (N-W)*
Eutin *Eutin (S-H)*
Ex *Hofmann, Pahres (Bay); Hacklberg, Passau (Bay)*
Excellent *Hochstiftliches Brauhaus Fulda, Fulda (Hes)*
Exclusiv *Bavaria-St. Pauli, St. Pauli (Ham, brewed elsewhere); Ladenburger, Neuler (B-W); Riemhofer, Riedenburg (Bay); Zwiefalter Klosterbräu, Zwiefaltendorf (B-W)*
Export Privat *Nassauische, Hahnstätten (R-P)*
Export 2000 *Betz, Celle (Nie)*
Exportbierbrauerei *Bayreuth (Bay); Radeberg (Sach)*
Exquisit *Adlerbrauerei Götz, Geislingen (B-W); Kronenbrauerei, Offenburg (B-W); Schwarzbräu, Zusmarshausen (Bay)*
Extra *Hasen-Bräu, Augsburg (Bay); Röhrigshof (Hes)*
Extra Hell *Erl, Geiselhöring (Bay)*
Extra Mild *Krombacher, Krombach (N-W); Pfungstädter, Pfungstadt (Hes)*
Extra Schwarz *Innstadt, Passau (Bay)*
Exzellent *Schloßbrauerei, Irlbach (Bay)*

F

Fahnenschwinger *Dampfbierbrauerei, Zwiesel (Bay)*
Fairlight *Krombacher, Krombach (N-W)*
Falk *Amberg (Bay, unknown brewer)*
Falkenberger *Kommunbrauerei, Falkenberg (Bay)*
Falkenfelser *Bayernbräu, Bad Neustadt (Bay, unknown brewer)*
Falkenstein *Pfronten-Ried (Bay)*
Falkensteiner *Jahns-Bräu, Ludwigsstadt (Bay); Bischoff, Winnweiler (R-P)*
Fallersleber Schloßbräu *Fallersleben (Nie)*
Falter *Regen (Bay); Hof (Bay)*
Falterbräu *Drachselried (Bay)*
Fanfaren Weiße *Schlossbrauerei, Herrngiersdorf (Bay)*
Farny *Edelweissbrauerei, Dürren (B-W)*
Faschings Weiße *Schweinsbräu, Hermannsdorf (Bay)*
Faschingsbier *Waldschlößchen, Dresden (Sach);*

Steinbach, Erlangen (Bay); Wiesenmühle, Fulda (Hes);
Lindenbräu, Mindelheim (Bay)
Fasnetbier Fürstlich Fürstenbergische Brauerei,
Donaueschingen (B-W)
Fasnets Fläschle Hochdorfer, Hochdorf (B-W)
Fasnetsbier Kronenbrauerei Schimpf, Remmingsheim
(B-W)
Fässla Bamberg (Bay)
Fattigau Schloßbrauerei, Fattigau (Bay)
Faust Miltenberg (Bay)
Feder Weizen Wieninger, Teisendorf (Bay)
Feiderleichte Weisse Pyraser, Pyras (Bay)
Feierling Freiburg (B-W)
Fein Herb Altöttinger Hell-Bräu, Altötting (Bay)
Fein & Leicht Meusel-Bräu, Dreuschendorf (Bay)
Feine Weisse Clemens Härle, Leutkirch (B-W)
Feines Export Bucher, Gundelfingen (Bay)
Feines Helles Schwarzbräu, Zusmarshausen (Bay)
Feines Urhell Riegele, Augsburg (Bay)
Feingold Karlsberg, Homburg (Saar)
Feinherb Maisel, Bamberg (Bay); Püls Bräu, Weismain
(Bay)
Feinherbs Pilsner Krostitzer, Krostitz (Sach)
Feinmild Kulmbacher, Kulmbach (Bay)
Feldschlößchen Braunschweig (Nie); Dresden (Sach)
Felsator Felsenbräu, Thalmannsfeld (Bay)
Felsen Pils Felsenkeller, Beerfelden (Hes); Fürstenberg,
Donaueschingen (B-W)
Felsen Quell Fürst Wallerstein, Wallerstein (Bay)
Felsen Weisse Hartmann, Würgau (Bay)
Felsenbräu Thalmannsfeld (Bay)
Felsenkeller Beerfelden (Hes); Feldschlößchen,
Dresden (Sach); Heforder, Sundern (N-W); Weimar
(Thü); Rainer, Welz (N-W); Hartmann, Würgau (Bay)
Felsenquell Pils Rainer, Welz (N-W)
Felsentrunk Wasserburger, Dingolfing (Bay); Felsenbräu,
Thalmannsfeld (Bay); Hartmann, Würgau (Bay)
Feschtbier Fischer's Brauhaus, Mössingen (B-W)
Fest Engel Hald, Dunstelkingen (B-W)
Festbier 1580 Kalt-Loch-Bräu, Miltenberg (Bay)
Festliches Moosbacher Scheuerer, Moosbach (Bay)
Festtags Weisse Mahr, Bamberg (Bay)
Feuerfest Edel-Bier Treuchtlingen (Bay)
Feuerio Tropfen Eichbaum, Mannheim (B-W)
Feuertaufe Rhönbrauerei, Kaltennordheim (Thü)
Fichtelgebirgs Lang-Bräu, Schönbrunn (Bay)
Fichten Zäpfla Bürgerbräu, Naila (Bay)
Fidelis Weizen Zoller-Hof, Sigmaringen (B-W)
Fiedler Oberscheibe (Sach)
Fiege Moritz Fiege, Bochum (N-W)
Filstal Pils Adlerbrauerei Götz, Geislingen (B-W)
Fips Weizen Arcobräu Gräfliches Brauhaus, Moos (Bay)
First Lady Engel-Bräu, Crailsheim (B-W)
First Premium Pils Brinkhoff, Dortmund (N-W)
Fischer Freudeneck (Bay); Greuth (Bay); Wieseth (Bay)
Fischer Weisse Fischerbräu, Eitting (Bay)
Fischer's Mössingen (B-W)
Fischerbräu Eitting (Bay)
Fit Weisse Bucher, Gundelfingen (Bay)

Flattermann Lager Walderbräu, Königseggwald (B-W)
Flensburger Flensburg (S-H)
Flieger Fliegerbräu, Feldkirchen (Bay)
Flieger Quell Airbräu, Flughafen-München (Bay)
Fliegerbräu Feldkirchen (Bay)
Flight Memminger, Memmingen (Bay)
Flinderer Spezialbier Brauer-Vereinigung, Pegnitz (Bay)
Flindererbier Jura-Bräu, Pegnitz (Bay)
Florian Trunk Schübel, Stadtsteinach (Bay)
Florinator Franken Bräu, Riedbach (B-W)
Flößer Hell Brauhaus Pforzheim, Pforzheim (B-W)
Flözinger Bräu Rosenheim (Bay)
Flözlinger Hirschbrauerei, Flözlingen (B-W)
Fohr Ransbach-Baumbach (R-P)
Forchheimer Leicht Eichhorn, Forchheim (Bay)
Förderstoff Post, Weiler (Bay)
Forschungsbrauerei München (Bay)
Först Drügendorf (Bay)
Forst Pils Hauf-Bräu, Dentlein (Bay)
Förster Gampertbräu, Weissenbrunn (Bay)
Förster & Brecker Hameln, (Nie, unknown brewer)
Forstmeister Pils Schönbuch-Bräu, Böblingen (B-W)
Forstquell Fürnheim (Bay)
Fößel-Mazour Appendorf (Bay)
Frammersbacher Waldschloss, Frammersbach (Bay)
Franken Bräu Neundorf (Bay); Riedbach (Bay)
Franken Gold Brauhaus Schweinfurt, Schweinfurt (Bay)
Frankenheim Neuss (N-W)
Frankenländer Hauff-Bräu, Lichtenau (Bay)
Frankfurter Frankfurt (Bra)
Fränkische Weihnacht Kesselring, Marktsteft (Bay)
Fränkischer Land Bock Wernecker, Werneck (Bay)
Fränkisches Festtagsbier Döbler, Bad Windsheim (Bay)
Fränkisches Freilandmuseum Bad Windsheim (Bay)
Fränkisches Kellerbier Michael, Weißenstadt (Bay)
Fränkisches Lagerbier Winkler, Melkendorf (Bay)
Fränkisches Landbier Schwanen-Bräu, Ebensfeld (Bay);
Raab, Hofheim (Bay); Kalt-Loch-Bräu, Miltenberg (Bay)
Fränkisches Vollbier Penning, Hetzelsdorf (Bay);
Vasold & Schmitt, Neunkirchen (Bay)
Fränky Nürnberg (Bay, unknown brewer)
Franz Rastatt (B-W)
Franz Josef Jubelbier Allgäuer, Leuterschach (Bay)
Franz Xaver Unertl Unertl, Mühldorf (Bay)
Franziskaner Spaten-Franziskaner-Bräu, München (Bay)
Frauenstein Betz, Winklarn (Bay)
Freiberger Freiberg (Sach)
Freibergisch Freiberger, Freiberg (Sach)
Freibeuter Hanseatische Brauerei, Rostock (M-V)
Freiburger Ganter, Freiburg (B-W); Kleines Freiburger
Brauhaus, Freiburg (B-W)
Freigraf DAB, Dortmund (N-W)
Freiheitsbier Dunkel Franz, Rastatt (B-W)
Freiherrn Pils Aldersbach, Aldersbach (Bay)
Freilandmuseum Bad Windsheim (Bay); Fladungen (Bay)
Freilassinger Weißbräu, Freilassing (Bay)
Freising Freising (Bay)
Freisinger Hofbrauhaus, Freising (Bay)
Freisinger Bräuhaus Freising, Freising (Bay)

Freudenberger *Märkl, Freudenberg (Bay)*
Freyungs Weisse *Göller, Zeil (Bay)*
Friedberger Brauhaus *Friedberg (Hes)*
Friedel *Schnaid (Bay); Zentbechhofen (Bay)*
Friedenfelser *Schloßbrauerei, Friedenfels (Bay); Scheuerer, Moosbach (Bay)*
Friedensreiter Bräu *Rolinck, Steinfurt (N-W)*
Friedmann *Gräfenberg (Bay)*
Friedrich Hauf 1901 Bayerisch *Hauf, Dinkelsbühl (Bay)*
Friedrichs *Chemnitz (Sach)*
Friesisches Bräuhaus zu Jever *Jever (Nie)*
Frischeisen *Affecking (Bay)*
Frisches Pilsener *Meininger, Meiningen (Thü)*
Fritz *Görlitz (Sach)*
Fritz Walter Bier *Bischoff, Winnweiler (R-P)*
Froschbräu *Jockgrim (R-P)*
Froscher Bock *Steinbach Bräu, Erlangen (Bay)*
Fröschl *Froschbräu, Jockgrim (R-P)*
Früh *Köln (N-W)*
Frühjahrsbier *Reiners Rosine, Flein (B-W)*
Frühlings Bote *Postbrauerei, Nesselwang (Bay*
Frühlingserwachen *Braustelle, Köln (N-W)*
FS *Flözinger-Bräu, Rosenheim (Bay)*
Fuchsbeck *Sulzbach-Rosenberg (Bay)*
Füchsen *Düsseldorf (N-W)*
Füchserl *Hösl, Irchenrieth (Bay)*
Fuchsstadter *Wolf, Fuchstadt (Bay)*
Fuhrmann's Weisse *Waldschloss, Frammersbach (Bay)*
Fuhrmannstrunk *Grosch, Oeslau (Bay)*
Fulda Excellent *Hochstiftliches Brauhaus, Fulda (Hes)*
Fuldabrücker Landbrauerei *Dörnhagen (Hes)*
Fun Hefeweizen *Waldhaus, Waldhaus (B-W)*
Fünf Komma 2 *Leibinger, Ravensburg (B-W)*
Fünfzehn Plus *Am Sudhang, Amberg (Bay)*
Fürst Carl *Fürstliches Brauhaus, Ellingen (Bay)*
Fürst Lynar *Schloßbrauerei, Fürstliche Drehna (Bra)*
Fürst Wallerstein Brauhaus *Wallerstein (Bay)*
Fürst Ysenburg *Würzburger Hofbräu, Würzburg (Bay)*
Fürstabt *Allgäuer Brauhaus, Leuterschach (Bay)*
Fürsten *St. Martin, Oberlahnstein (R-P); Zoller-Hof, Sigmaringen (B-W); Hofbräuhaus, Traunstein (Bay); Fürst Wallerstein Brauhaus, Wallerstein (Bay); Würzburger Hofbräu, Würzburg (Bay)*
Fürsten Quell *Hofbräuhaus, Traunstein (Bay)*
Fürstenberg *Donaueschingen (B-W)*
Fürstengold *Paulaner, München (Bay)*
Fürstlich Fürstenbergische *Donaueschingen (B-W)*
Fürstliche Drehna *Schloßbrauerei, Fürstliche Drehna (Bra)*
Fürstliches Brauhaus *Ellingen (Bay); Regensburg (Bay)*
Further Drachen Weisse *Mühlbauer, Arnschwang (Bay)*
Further Ritterschaft *Dimpfl Bräu, Furth im Wald (Bay)*
Füssener *Schloßbrauerei, Fürstenfeldbrück (Bay)*

G

Gaffel *Köln (N-W)*
Gaildorfer *Häberlen, Gaildorf (B-W)*
Gaissmaier *Leipheim (Bay);*
Gambrinus *Vereinsbrauerei, Apolda (Thü); Dorn-Bräu,*

Bruckberg (Bay); Eisgrub-Bräu, Mainz (R-P); Weiden (Bay)
Gampertbräu *Weissenbrunn (Bay)*
Gams Bier *Holzkirchner Oberbräu, Holzkirchen (Bay)*
Gans Bier *Martinsbräu, Marktheidenfeld (Bay)*
Gansbräu *Neumarkt (Bay)*
Ganser Kölsch *Dom, Köln (N-W)*
Ganter *Freiburg (B-W)*
Garley *Spezialitäten Brauerei, Gardelegen (S-A)*
Garde Kölsch *Gaffel (Porz), Köln (N-W)*
Gartenweizen *Brauereimuseum, Kulmbach (Bay)*
Gassenhauer *Zeltbräu, Hof (Bay)*
Gassewoiza *Salzscheuer, Marbach (B-W)*
Gässlbräu *Pfarrkirchen (Bay)*
Gastro Weiße *Hofbräuhaus, Traunstein (Bay)*
Gatz Altbier *Mönchengladbach, Mönchengladbach (N-W)*
Gäuboden Landbier *Röhrl, Straubing (Bay)*
Gäubodenfestbier *Schloßbrauerei, Irlbach (Bay)*
Gaudi Weizen *Bürgerliches Brauhaus, Saalfeld (Thü)*
Gaugraf Silach *Memminger, Memmingen (Bay)*
Gebremstes Weizen *Riemhofer, Riedenburg (Bay)*
Geburtstag Bier *Postbrauerei, Nesselwang (Bay)*
Geheimbier *Vogel Hausbräu, Ettlingen (B-W); Vogelbräu, Karlsruhe (B-W); Vogel Hausbräu, Karlsruhe (B-W)*
Geiler Bock *Ziegler, Waldsassen (Bay)*
Geisenfelder *Hörl, Gaden (Bay, unknown brewer)*
Geising *Ratskeller, Geising (Sach)*
Geißler *Weizenbierglasmuseum, Nürnberg (Bay)*
Geißplosator *Weizenbierglasmuseum, Nürnberg (Bay)*
Geisterbräu *Nittenau, Nittenau (Bay)*
Geistertrunk *Bauriedl, Eslarn (Bay)*
Gemeindebrauhaus *Thundorf (Bay)*
Gemeinschaftsbrauerei *Roßfeld (Bay)*
Gemünder *Gemünd (N-W)*
Genossenschafts *Genossenschaftsbrauerei, Rötz (Bay)*
Genossenschaftsbrauerei Rötz *Rötz (Bay)*
Georg Bader *Lauterbach, Lauterbach (Bay)*
Georg Pils *Georgbräu, Mitte(Ber)*
Georgbräu *Mitte (Ber)*
Georgi *Gutsbrauerei Meyringer, Moosham (Bay)*
Georgi Sud *Ritter St. Georgen, Nennslingen (Bay)*
Georgius *Bocholter Brauhaus, Bocholt (N-W)*
Gerber Bräu *Uhingen (B-W)*
German Porter *Schwerter Brauerei Wohlers, Meißen (Sach)*
Germanen Trunk *Lammbrauerei, Weilheim (B-W)*
Germania *Frankenthaler, Frankenthal (R-P, unknown brewer); Münster (N-W, unknown brewer)*
Geroldsecker *Schloßbrauerei, Schmieheim (B-W)*
Gerolfinger *Köpf, Aalen (B-W)*
Gesellschaftsbrauerei *Viechtach (Bay)*
Gessner *Sonneberg (Thü)*
Geyer *Oberreichenbach (Bay)*
Giant Gold *Mammut, Sangerhausen (S-A, unknown brewer)*
Gick Bräu *Burgkunstadt (Bay)*
Giengener *Schlüsselbräu, Giengen (B-W)*
Giesler Kölsch *Dom, Köln (N-W)*
Giessener *Gießen (Hes)*

Giesser *Pirna, Copitz (Sach)*
Gifhorner Brauhaus *Gifhorn (Nie)*
Gig *Mahr's, Bamberg (Bay)*
Gilde *Hannover (Nie)*
Gilden Kölsch *Kölner Verbund Brauereien, Köln (N-W)*
Gillamoosbier *Ottenbräu, Abensberg (Bay)*
Girgl *Karmeliten, Straubing (Bay)*
Glaabsbräu *Seligenstadt (Hes)*
Gladbeck *Gladbeck (N-W)*
Glauchauer *Sommerlust, Glauchau (Sach)*
Glenk *Exportbierbrauerei Richard Glenk, Bayreuth (Bay)*
Gleumes *Krefeld (N-W)*
Glocken *Vereinsbrauerei, Apolda (Thü)*
Glöckl *Glossner, Neumarkt (Bay)*
Glossner *Neumarkt (Bay)*
Glückauf *Gersdorf (Sach)*
Glühbier *Winkler, Lengenfeld (Bay)*
Glühtrunk *Nordbräu, Ingolstadt (Bay)*
Gnann *Pflugbrauerei, Hörvelsingen (B-W)*
Göcklinger Hausbräu *Göcklingen (R-P)*
Goedecke's Döllnitzer Ritterguts *Bauer, Leipzig (Sach)*
Gogolori *Freising, Freising (Bay)*
Goissbock *Bierbrauerei zum Lamm, Wiesensteig (B-W)*
Goitzsche Bräu *Landsberg, Landsberg (S-A)*
Gold Engel *Hald, Dunstelkingen (B-W)*
Gold Ochsen *Spielbach (B-W); Ulm (B-W)*
Gold Privat Export *Ketterer, Pforzheim (B-W)*
Gold Specht *Spessart, Kreuzwertheim (Bay)*
Gold Weisse *Gold Ochsen, Ulm (B-W)*
Goldblondchen Weizen *Steinbach Bräu, Erlangen (Bay)*
Golden *Leitner, Schwabach (Bay)*
Golden Lager *Alsfeld, Alsfeld (Hes)*
Golden Pils *Lindenbrauerei, Unna (N-W, unknown brewer)*
Golden Premium *Pfungstädter, Pfungstadt (Hes)*
Goldene Gans *Hasen-Bräu, Augsburg (Bay)*
Goldene Henne *Jüchsen (Thü)*
Goldener Adler *Zum Goldenen Adler, Höfen (Bay)*
Goldener Engel *Waldstetten (Bay)*
Goldener Löwe *Först, Drügendorf (Bay); Kallmünz (Bay)*
Goldener Reiter *Bergquell, Löbau (Sach)*
Goldener Schwan *Erfurt (Thü)*
Goldenes Lamm *Gierstädt (Thü)*
Goldenes Land *Leidmann, Unterneukirchen (Bay)*
Goldköpfle *Hoepfner, Karlsruhe (B-W)*
Goldner Hirsch *Hirschbrauerei, Böhringen (B-W)*
Goldrausch *Ankerbräu, Nördlingen (Bay)*
Goldsiegel *Spezialitäten Brauerei, Luckenwalde (Bra); Peniger Spezialitätenbrauerei, Penig (Sach)*
Goldstadt *Brauhaus Pforzheim, Pforzheim (B-W)*
Göller *Drosendorf (Bay); Zeil (Bay)*
Göltzsch *Greiz (Thü)*
Göltzschtal *Göltzsch, Greiz (Thü)*
Görchla *Höhn, Memmelsdorf (Bay)*
Gose *Goslar, Goslar (Nie); Bauer, Leipzig (Sach); Gosebrauerei Bayerischer Bahnhof, Leipzig (Sach)*
Gosebrauerei Bayerischer Bahnhof *Leipzig (Sach)*
Goslar *Goslar (Nie)*
Goss *Deuerling (Bay)*

Gotha *Gotha (Thü)*
Göttinger *Einbecker, Einbeck (Nie)*
Göttliche *Schleswig, Schleswig (S-H)*
Gottmannsgrüner *von Koch'sche, Gottsmannsgrün (Bay)*
Götz *Adlerbrauerei Götz, Geislingen (B-W)*
Gourmet Bier *Hutthurmer Bayerwald, Hutthurm (Bay)*
Gourmet Weisse *Unertl, Mühldorf (Bay)*
Gradl *Leups (Bay)*
Graf Arco *Graf Arco, Adldorf (Bay); Graf Arco, Bad Birnbach (Bay); Arcobräu, Moos (Bay)*
Graf Bray Klassik *Schloßbrauerei, Irlbach (Bay)*
Graf Gebhard *Sperber-Bräu, Sulzbach-Rosenberg (Bay)*
Graf Ignaz *Hofbrauhaus, Freising (Bay)*
Graf Stolberg Dunkel *Westheimer, Westheim (N-W)*
Graf Toerring *Hofbrauhaus, Freising (Bay)*
Graf Zeppelin *Bad Homburg (Hes)*
Grafen Hell *Gräfliche Brauerei Arco Valley, Adldorf (Bay)*
Grafen Pils *Bender, Mühlhausen (Bay)*
Grafenauer Säumer-Festbier *Bucher, Grafenau (Bay)*
Gräfenberger *Lindenbräu, Gräfenberg (Bay)*
Gräfenbräu *Kieler, Kiel (S-H)*
Grafentrunk *Gräfliche Brauerei Arco Valley, Adldorf (Bay)*
Gräflich zu Stolberg'sche Brauerei *Westheim (N-W)*
Gräfliche Brauerei Arco Valley *Adldorf (Bay); Bad Birnbach (Bay)*
Gräfliches Brauhaus *Moos (Bay)*
Grafschafter *Nordhorn (Nie)*
Graminger Weissbräu *Graming (Bay)*
Grandauer *Wildbräu-Grandauer, Grafing (Bay)*
Grasser *Huppendorf (Bay)*
Greif *Forchheim (Bay)*
Greifenklau *Bamberg (Bay)*
Greifensteinquell *Specht, Ehrenfriedersdorf (Sach)*
Greiner *Roding (Bay)*
Greizer *Vereinsbrauerei, Greiz (Thü)*
Grenadier Weizenbock *Kaiser Napoleon, Leipzig (Sach)*
Grenzfähnlein Festbier *Hofer, Furth im Wald (Bay)*
Grenzquell Pilsener *Bavaria-St. Pauli, St. Pauli (Ham)*
Griesbräu *Murnau (Bay)*
Griess *Geisfeld (Bay)*
Grimms *Hütt-Brauerei, Knallhütte (Hes)*
Gritschenbräu *Schrobenhausen (Bay)*
Grohe *Darmstadt (Hes)*
Gröninger *Meßberg (Ham)*
Grosch *Oeslau (Bay)*
Grosswald *Eiweiler (Saar)*
Grotten Pils *Bürgerliches Brauhaus, Saalfeld (Thü)*
Grottenbräu *Landsberg, Landsberg (S-A)*
Gruben Gold Zwickl *Schacht 4/8, Duisburg (N-W); Hibernia, Gelsenkirchen (N-W); Mühlheimer Brauhaus, Mühlheim (N-W); Zeche Jacobi, Oberhausen (N-W)*
Gruibinger *Lammbrauerei Hilsenbeck, Gruibingen (B-W)*
Grünbacher *Schloßbrauerei, Grünbach (Bay)*
Grünbaum *Aalen (B-W)*
Günder Hell *Moritz Fiege, Bochum (N-W)*
Gründerbier *Zittauer Bürgerbräu, Zittau (Sach)*
Grüner Baum *Biberach (B-W)*
Grünstadt *Grünstadt (R-P)*

Grünten *Engelbräu, Rettenberg (Bay)*
Grünzeug Bier *Neustädter Hausbrauerei, Dresden (Sach)*
Grüß de Gott Alois *Kaiser, Geislingen (B-W)*
GSM *Freiberg (Sach, unknown brewer)*
Guidobald *Wieninger, Teisendorf (Bay)*
Gulden Classic *Memminger, Memmingen (Bay)*
Guldenbacher *Windesheim (R-P)*
Gummersbach *Gummersbach (N-W)*
Gundel *Barthelmsaurach (Bay)*
Gundelfinger Sud *Bucher, Gundelfingen (Bay)*
Günther-Bräu *Burgkunstadt (Bay)*
Günzburger *Radbrauerei Bucher, Günzburg (Bay)*
Gunzendorfer *Sauer, Gunzendorf (Bay)*
Güßbacher Urtyp *Hümmer, Breitengüßbach (Bay)*
Gut Forsting *Forsting (Bay)*
Gut Höhne *Rainer, Welz (N-W)*
Gut Mergenthauer *Lauterbacher, Lauterbach (Bay)*
Gütersloher *Gütersloh (N-W)*
Gutmann *Titting (Bay)*
Guts und Brauereigenossenschaft *Taufkirchen (Bay)*
Gutsbräu *Straßkirchen (Bay)*
Gutsbrauerei Meyringer *Moosham (Bay)*
Gutsherren *Förster & Brecker, Hameln (Nie, unknown brewer); Lindenbrauerei, Unna (N-W, unknown brewer)*
Gutsherrn Pils *Pyraser, Pyras (Bay)*
Gutshof Weizen *Adlerbrauerei Götz, Geislingen (B-W)*
Guttensteiner Halbe *Genossenschaftsbrauerei, Rötz (Bay)*

H

Haag *Oberdachstetten (Bay)*
Haake Beck *Bremen (Bre)*
Haalgeist *Haller Löwenbräu, Schwäbisch Hall (B-W)*
Haaß *Schwalm Bräu, Treysa (Hes)*
Habereckl Feuerio Tropfen *Eichbaum, Mannheim (B-W)*
Haberl *Schönsee (Bay)*
Häberlen *Gaildorf (B-W)*
Haberstumpf *Trebgast (Bay)*
Hachenburger *Westerwald, Hachenburg (R-P)*
Hacker Pschorr *Paulaner Hacker-Pschorr, München (Bay)*
Hacklberg *Passau (Bay)*
Haderlump *Hike, Marktsteft (Bay, unknown brewer)*
Hadmar Export *Plank, Laaber (Bay)*
Haferbier *Adlerbrauerei, Dellmensingen (B-W); Enzensteiner, Enzenreuth (Bay); Körpricher Landbräu, Körprich (Saar); Kaiser Napoleon, Leipzig (Sach)*
Haffner *Bergbräu, Uslar (Nie)*
Häffner Bräu *Bad Rappenau (B-W)*
Hagenbräu *Worms (R-P)*
Hahnenkleer Edelbräu *Paul-Lincke, Hahnenklee (Nie)*
Haidhausen *Unionsbräu-Haidhausen, München (Bay)*
Haimhauser *Schloßbrauerei, Haimhausen (Bay)*
Halali Edelbock *Mayer Bräu, Ludwigshafen (R-P)*
Halbdunkel *Hirschbrauerei, Flözlingen (B-W)*
Halbe *Steinacher Hausbräu, Bad Waldsee (B-W)*
Halbe M *Murmann, Untersiemau (Bay);*
Hald *Dunstelkingen (B-W)*
Haller Löwenbräu *Schwäbisch Hall (B-W)*
Hallerndorfer *Rittmayer, Hallerndorf (Bay)*
Hallertau *Schloßbrauerei, Au (Bay)*

Hallertauer Hopfentrunk *Horneck, Horneck (Bay)*
Hallesches Brauhaus *Halle (S-A)*
Hallgrafen Bock *Bürgerbräu, Bad Reichenhall (Bay)*
Hallisches *Landsberger, Landsberger (S-A)*
Halloween Bier *Vogel Hausbräu, Ettlingen (B-W); Vogelbräu, Karlsruhe (B-W); Vogel Hausbräu, Karlsruhe (B-W); Alt Oberurseler, Oberursel (Hes); Leitner, Schwabach (Bay)*
Hallsch *Hallesches Brauhaus, Halle (S-A)*
Halter *Kronenbrauerei Halter, Biberach (B-W)*
Hammelburger *Salch, Hammelburg (Bay, unknown brewer)*
Hammer Bräu *Riesa (Sach)*
Hammer Pils *Jacob, Bodenwöhr (Bay)*
Hanfbier *Weltenbummler, Berggießhübel (Sach); Neustädter, Dresden (Sach); Kaiser Napoleon, Leipzig (Sach)*
Hanfinger Urtrunk *Stanglbräu, Herrnwahlthann (Bay)*
Hannen *Mönchengladbach, Mönchengladbach (N-W)*
Hanöversch *Brauhaus Ernst August, Hannover (Nie)*
Hansa *DAB, Dortmund (N-W)*
Hansa Kölsch *Kölner Verbund Brauereien, Köln (N-W)*
Hanse Porter *Stralsunder, Stralsund (M-V)*
Hanseat *Meßberg (Ham)*
Hanseaten Weisse *Hanseat, Meßberg (Ham)*
Hanseatische Brauerei *Rostock (M-V)*
Hansebräu *Hanseatische Brauerei, Rostock (M-V)*
Hansens *Flensburg (S-H)*
Häpfenbräu *Rammingen (Bay)*
Härke *Peine (Nie)*
Härle *Clemens Härle, Leutkirch (B-W)*
Harrods 1849 Lager *Hofmark, Loifling (Bay)*
Hartinger *Rinteln (Nie)*
Hartleb *Maroldswiesach (Bay)*
Hartmann *Würgau (Bay)*
Hartmannsdorfer *Hartmannsdorf (Sach)*
Härtsfelder *Hald, Dunstelkingen (B-W)*
Harzer Urstoff *Kolberg, Altenau (Nie)*
Haselaner *Brauhaus Linsengericht, Altenhaßlau (Hes)*
Hasen Bräu *Augsburg (Bay)*
Hasenbrauerei *Weißenhorn (Bay)*
Hasseröder *Wernigerode (S-A)*
Haßlocher *Kleines Rüsselsheimer, Alt Haßloch (Hes)*
Hattorfer Rauchbier *Brauhaus Extra, Röhrigshof (Hes)*
Hatz *Hofbräuhaus Hatz, Rastatt (B-W)*
Haubach *Giessener Brauhaus, Gießen (Hes)*
Hauf *Dinkelsbühl (Bay)*
Hauf Bräu *Dentlein (Bay)*
Hauff *Lichtenau (Bay)*
Hauptmann von Köpenick *Bürgerbräu, Friedrichshagen (Ber)*
Haus zur Pfauen Erfurt (Thü)
Hausbräu *Rittmayer, Aisch (Bay); Bad Waldsee (B-W); Wagner-Bräu, Eschenbach (Bay); Göcklingen (R-P); Sudhaus, Ludwigsburg (B-W); Löwenbräu, Neuhaus (Bay); Stegaurach (Bay); Rittmayer, Willersdorf (Bay, unknown brewer); Zwanzger, Uehlfeld (Bay)*
Hausbrauerart *Grasser, Huppendorf (Bay); Schmitt, Scheßlitz (Bay, unknown brewer)*

Hausbrauerbier *Brauhaus Höchstadt, Höchstadt (Bay); Gemeinschaftsbrauerei, Roßfeld (Bay); Scheubel, Schlüsselfeld (Bay); Kommunbrauhaus, Seßlach (Bay); Sophie's, Stuttgart (B-W); Gemeindebrauhaus, Thundorf (Bay); Roppelt, Trossenfurt (Bay); Murmann, Untersiemau (Bay); Göller, Zeil (Bay)*
Hausham *Hausham (Bay)*
Haustrunk *Schongauer Brauhaus, Schongau (Bay)*
Havelbräu *Brauhaus in Spandau, Spandau (Ber)*
HB *Hofbräuhaus, Traunstein (Bay)*
Hebendanz *Forchheim (Bay)*
Heberbräu *Kirchenthumbach (Bay)*
Hecht Alt *Neustädter, Dresden (Sach)*
Heckel *Waischenfeld (Bay)*
Heide *Heidebrauerei, Colbitz (S-A)*
Heidebrauerei *Colbitz (S-A)*
Heidelberger *Heidelberg (B-W)*
Heil *Hofbräu, Würzburg (Bay)*
Heilmfurter *Büchner, Heilmfurt (Bay)*
Heimbräu *Wolfenweiler (B-W)*
Heimer Leicht *Müllerbräu, Pfaffenhofen (Bay)*
Heine Bräu *Halberstadt (S-A)*
Heiner Weisse *Zeltbräu, Hof (Bay)*
Heinerle *Fischer's, Mössingen (B-W)*
Heinz vom Stein *Schlossbrauerei, Stein (Bay)*
Heizer *Gosebrauerei Bayerischer Bahnhof, Leipzig (Sach)*
Helbig *Weilburg (Hes)*
Held Bräu *Oberailsfeld (Bay)*
Heldrich *Edelsfeld (Bay)*
Helena Hanfbier *Kaiser Napoleon, Leipzig (Sach)*
Helfta *An der Klosterpforte, Helfta (S-A)*
Helios *Braustelle, Köln (N-W)*
Hell Bräu *Altötting (Bay)*
Helle Wolke *Glossner-Bräu, Neumarkt (Bay)*
Heller *Bamberg (Bay); Herzogenaurach (Bay)*
Hellers *Köln (N-W)*
Helles Gold *Paulaner, München (Bay)*
Hellmuth *Burgkunstadt (Bay); Wiesen (Bay)*
Helyator *Lang, Jandelsbrunn (Bay)*
Hemelinger *Haake Beck, Bremen (Bre)*
Hennemann *Sambach (Bay); Stublang (Bay); Unterleiterbach (Bay)*
Henninger *Binding, Frankfurt (Hes)*
Henrici Bock *Schloßbrauerei, Reckendorf (Bay)*
Henry *Bergbräu, Uslar (Nie)*
Herb *Schimpfle, Gessertshausen (Bay)*
Herb Pils *Uckermärker, Golzow (Bra)*
Herborner *Bärenbräu, Herborn (Hes)*
Herbsthäuser *Herbsthausen (B-W)*
Herforder *Felsenkeller Herford, Sundern (N-W)*
Herminator *Ziegler Bräu, Mainburg (Bay)*
Herold *Büchenbach (Bay)*
Herrmann *Ampferbach (Bay)*
Herren Pils *Riegele, Augsburg (Bay); Keesmann, Bamberg (Bay); Schloßbrauerei, Fürstliche Drehna (Bra); Zum Reformator, Lutherstadt Eisleben (S-A); Anker, Nagold (B-W)*
Herrenhausen *Hannover (Nie)*
Herrenhäuser *Herrenhausen, Hannover (Nie)*

Herrenpils *Memminger, Memmingen (Bay); Stuttgarter Hofbräu, Stuttgart (B-W)*
Herrmannsdorfer Schweinsbräu *Hermannsdorf (Bay)*
Herrn Pils *Herrnbräu, Ingolstadt (Bay)*
Herrnbräu *Ingolstadt (Bay)*
Herrngiersdorf *Schlossbrauerei, Herrngiersdorf (Bay)*
Herrntrunk *Herrnbräu, Ingolstadt (Bay)*
Hersbrucker *Bürgerbräu, Hersbruck (Bay)*
Hertlein *Staffelbach (Bay)*
Herzog *Bender, Arnstein (Bay)*
Herzog Christian August *Sperber, Sulzbach-Rosenberg (Bay)*
Herzog Ludwig *Friedberg (Bay)*
Herzog von Franken *Burgbrauerei, Thüngen (Bay)*
Herzog Wilhelm *Schloss Bräu, Stamsried (Bay, unknown brewer)*
Herzogen Brauhaus *Jülich (N-W)*
Herzogen Bure *Herzogen Brauhaus, Jülich (N-W)*
Herzogenauracher Bock *Bürgerbräu, Hersbruck (Bay)*
Herzoglich Bayerisches Brauhaus *Tegernsee (Bay)*
Herzogliches Brauhaus *Jülich (N-W)*
Hessberger *Heßberg (Thü)*
Hess'isches Landbier *Fuldabrücker, Dörnhagen (Hes)*
Hessisches Löwenbier *Malsfeld (Hes)*
Hetzel *Frauendorf (Bay)*
Hetzelsdorfer *Penning, Hetzelsdorf (Bay)*
Heubacher *Heubacher, Heubach (B-W)*
Hexator *Michelsbräu, Babenhausen (Hes)*
Hexe *Michelsbräu, Babenhausen (Hes)*
Hexe Hefeweizen *Abtei-Bräu, Mettlach (Saar)*
Hexenbier *Kommunbräu, Kumbach (Bay); Lammbrauerei, Untergröningen (B-W)*
Hexenstoff *Schloderer, Amberg (Bay);*
Hexensud *Bauhöfer, Ulm (B-W)*
Heyland's *Eder & Heylands, Großostheim (Bay)*
Hibernator *Schacht 4/8, Duisburg (N-W); Hibernia, Gelsenkirchen (N-W); Mühlheimer Brauhaus, Mühlheim (N-W); Zeche Jacobi, Oberhausen (N-W)*
Hibernia *Gelsenkirchen (N-W)*
Hibiscusbier *Braustelle, Köln (N-W)*
Hieronymus *Münchhausen, Bodenwerder (Nie); Schloßbrauerei, Schmieheim (B-W)*
Highlander *Binding, Frankfurt (Hes)*
Hike *Marktsteft (Bay, unknown brewer)*
Hilsenbeck *Lammbrauerei, Gruibingen (B-W)*
Hintereder *Chammünster (Bay)*
Hirsch *Dirlewang (Bay); Memminger, Memmingen (Bay); Söhnstetten (B-W); Hirschbräu, Sonthofen (Bay); Honer, Wurmlingen (B-W)*
Hirschbräu *Wurm, Bieswang (Bay); Zum Hirsch, Dirlewang (Bay); Hirschbrauerei, Ergenzingen (B-W); Hirschbrauerei, Flözlingen (B-W); Weißer Hirsch, Großrückerswalde (Sach); Leipheim (Bay); Höss, Sonthofen (Bay);*
Hirschbrauerei *Böhringen (B-W); Ergenzingen (B-W); Flözlingen (B-W); Lauingen (Bay)*
Hirschen *Kenzingen (B-W)*
Hirschen Bräu *Hirschenbrauerei, Waldkirch (B-W)*
Hirschen Trunk *Kraus, Hirschaid (Bay)*

Hirschen's *Winkler, Lengenfeld (Bay)*
Hirschenbrauerei *Waldkirch (B-W)*
Hochdorfer *Kronenbrauerei, Hochdorf (B-W)*
Hochfürst Pilsener *Hacklberg, Passau (Bay)*
Höchstadt *Höchstadt (Bay)*
Hochstift *Hochstiftliches Brauhaus, Fulda (Hes)*
Hochstiftliches Brauhaus *Fulda (Hes); Motten (Bay)*
Hochwälder *Losheim (Saar)*
Hochzeits *Schloderer, Amberg (Bay); Landshuter, Landshut (Bay)*
Hoepfner *Karlsruhe (B-W)*
Hof Brauhaus *Rehborn (R-P)*
Hof Schauferts *Schönborn (R-P)*
Hofatius *Zeltbräu, Hof (Bay)*
Hofbier *Lauterbach, Lauterbach (Bay)*
Hofbräu *Abensberg (Bay); Früh, Köln (N-W); Mauel (N-W); Stuttgart (B-W); Hofbräuhaus, Traunstein (Bay); Würzburg (Bay)*
Hofbräu Weiße *Lindenbräu, Tiergarten (Ber)*
Hofbrauerei *Bruchhausen (N-W)*
Hofbrauhaus *Bad Arolsen (Hes); Berchtesgaden (Bay); Braunschweig (Nie); Freising (Bay); Potsdam (Bra);*
Hofbräuhaus *München (Bay); Rastatt (B-W); Traunstein (Bay)*
Hofer *Furth im Wald (Bay)*
Hofer Hell *Zeltbräu, Hof (Bay)*
Hofgut Pils *Grosswald, Eiweiler (Saar)*
Hofgutsbier *Edelweissbrauerei, Dürren (B-W)*
Hofmann *Hohenschwärz (Bay); Pahres (Bay)*
Hofmannstropfen *Hofmann, Hohenschwärz (Bay)*
Hofmark *Loifling (Bay)*
Hofmühl *Eichstätt (Bay)*
Höglwörther Maifestbier *Wieninger, Teisendorf (Bay)*
Hoh *Köttensdorf (Bay)*
Hohe Wart Bräu *Hohenwart (Bay)*
Hohenfelder *Langenberg (N-W)*
Hohenthanner *Schloßbrauerei, Hohenthann (Bay)*
Höhlentrunk *St. Georgen, Buttenheim (Bay)*
Höhn *Memmelsdorf (Bay)*
Holledauer *Schloßbrauerei, Au (Bay)*
Holledauer Florian *Siegenburger, Siegenburg (Bay)*
Holnsteiner *Schloßbrauerei, Holnstein (Bay)*
Holsten *Altona (Ham)*
Holunderblütenbier *Christoph-Bräu, Gaggenau (B-W)*
Holzar Bier *Hirschbräu, Sonthofen (Bay)*
Holzhacker Weisse *Schloßbrauerei, Hohenthann (Bay)*
Holzhausener *Holzhausen (Bay)*
Holzkirchner Oberbräu *Holzkirchen (Bay)*
Hölzlein *Löhndorf (Bay)*
Homburger *Homburg (Saar)*
Honer *Hirsch-Brauerei Honer, Wurmlingen (B-W)*
Honey Sun *Marcus-Bräu, Mitte (Ber)*
Hönicka *Wunsiedel (Bay)*
Hönickator *Hönicka, Wunsiedel (Bay)*
Honig *Tiefenellern (Bay)*
Honigbier *Weltenbummler, Berggießhübel (Sach); Kneipe Pur, Plaue (Bra); Asgaard, Schleswig (S-H); Barbarossa, Schöllkrippen (Bay); Felsenkeller, Weimar (Thü); Alt Wülfrath, Wülfrath (N-W)*

Honorator *Ingobräu, Ingolstadt (Bay)*
Hopf *Weißbierbrauerei Hopf, Miesbach (Bay)*
Hopfazupfa Weisse *Ziegler Bräu, Mainburg (Bay)*
Hopfen Gold Pils *Staffelberg-Bräu, Loffeld (Bay)*
Hopfen Herbes *Würzburger Hofbräu, Würzburg (Bay)*
Hopfen Leicht *Heubacher, Heubach (B-W); Hochdorfer Kronenbrauerei, Hochdorf (B-W); Stadtbrauerei Spalt, Spalt (Bay)*
Hopfen Medium *Lang-Bräu, Schönbrunn (Bay)*
Hopfen Perle *Stolz, Isny (B-W)*
Hopfen Stoff *Brauhaus Pfaffenhofen, Pfaffenhofen (Bay)*
Hopfenblume *Eschenbräu, Wedding (Ber)*
Hopfenbock *Neckarsulmer, Neckarsulm (B-W)*
Hopfengarten *Glossner-Bräu, Neumarkt (Bay)*
Hopfengold *Schloßbrauerei, Au (Bay); Hofmann, Pahres (Bay)*
Hopfenland Pils *Müllerbräu, Pfaffenhofen (Bay)*
Hopfenperle Pils *Sonnenbräu, Lichtenberg (Bay); Schloßbrauerei, Schwarzbach (Thü)*
Hopfenflücker Pils *Pyraser, Pyras (Bay)*
Hopfenschlingel *Pforzheim (B-W); Rastatt (B-W)*
Hopfentrunk *Horneck, Horneck (Bay)*
Hopfenzupferbier *Lampl-Bräu, Larsbach (Bay); Klosterbrauerei, Scheyern (Bay)*
Hörl *Gaden (Bay, unknown brewer)*
Hopfig Herb *Allgäuer Brauhaus, Leuterschach (Bay)*
Horneck *Horneck (Bay)*
Horst Hell *Schönbuch-Bräu, Böblingen (B-W)*
Hösl *Irchenrieth (Bay); Mitterteich (Bay)*
Höss *Sonthofen (Bay)*
Hövel's Hausbrauerei *Dortmund (N-W)*
Hövel's Original Bitterbier *Hövel's, Dortmund (N-W)*
Höxterbier *Meierhof, Ottbergen (N-W)*
Hubauer *Gräfelfing (Bay, unknown brewer)*
Huber Weisses *Hofbrauhaus, Freising (Bay)*
Hubertus *Köthener Brauerei, Köthen (S-A, unknown brewer); Paulaner Hacker-Pschorr, München (Bay)*
Hübner *Steinfeld (Bay); Wattendorf (Bay)*
Hüchelner Urstoff *Frechen (N-W)*
Hufeisen *Pottenstein (Bay)*
Hugo's Spezial *Fridolin Mall, Meckesheim (B-W)*
Humbser *Tucher, Fürth (Bay)*
Hummel *Merkendorf (Bay)*
Hümmer *Breitengüßbach (Bay)*
Humorator *Hacklberg, Passau (Bay)*
Humpis Original *Edelweissbrauerei, Dürren (B-W)*
Hunnen Bock *Augusta, Augsburg (Bay)*
Huppendorfer *Grasser, Huppendorf (Bay)*
Husar Haferbier *Kaiser Napoleon, Leipzig (Sach)*
Husaren Trunk *Schloßbrauerei, Rheder (N-W)*
Hussitten Weiße *Weißes Brauhaus, Neunburg (Bay)*
Husumer *Husums Brauhaus, Husum (S-H)*
Husums Brauhaus *Husum (S-H)*
Hütt *Knallhütte (Hes)*
Hütten *Hütten (Bay)*
Hutthurmer Bayerwald *Hutthurm (Bay)*

I

Ibel *Kappel (Bay)*
Ice *Weißbierbrauerei Hopf, Miesbach (Bay); Ankerbräu, Nördlingen (Bay)*
Ice Cap *Giessener Brauhaus, Gießen (Hes)*
Icebeer *Herrenhausen, Hannover (Nie)*
Illertissen *Schloßbrauerei, Illertissen (Bay)*
Ilmthaler Leichte Weiße *Müllerbräu, Pfaffenhofen (Bay)*
Ilsen Bräu *Ludger's Kleine Brauerei, Littfeld (N-W)*
Impulsator *Wieninger, Teisendorf (Bay)*
In *Herrnbräu, Ingolstadt (Bay)*
Ingobräu *Ingolstadt (Bay)*
Insel Weisse Dunkel *Feierling, Freiburg (B-W)*
Indianer Bock *Wolf, Karlsruhe (B-W)*
Innstadt *Passau (Bay)*
Inselhopf *Feierling, Freiburg (B-W)*
Irchenriether *Hösl, Irschenrieth (Bay)*
Irish Black *Woinemer, Weilheim (B-W)*
Irlbacher *Schloßbrauerei, Irlbach (Bay)*
Irle *Siegen (N-W)*
Irseer *Klosterbräu, Irsee (Bay)*
Isarbräu *Großhesselohe (Bay)*
Isartaler Leichtes Weiße *Krieger, Landau (Bay)*
Isartaler Stationsweizen *Isarbräu, Großhesselohe (Bay)*
Isenbeck *Paderborner, Paderborn (N-W)*
Iserlohn *Iserlohn (N-W)*
Isnyer Hopfen Perle *Stolz, Isny (B-W)*
Itzgrunder Landbier *Schleicher, Kaltenbrunn (Bay)*

J

J.S. Bach *Köthener Brauerei, Köthen (S-A, unknown brewer)*
Jacob *Bodenwöhr (Bay)*
Jacobator *Jacob, Bodenwöhr (Bay)*
Jacobi Pils *Maierbräu, Altomünster (Bay)*
Jacobi Weißbier *Hacklberg, Passau (Bay)*
Jacobinus *Eschweger Klosterbrauerei, Eschwege (Hes)*
Jacobus Export Dunkel *Schmidt-Bräu, Schwandorf (Bay)*
Jadwiga *Schlossbrauerei, Herrngiersdorf (Bay)*
Jagahalbe *Wildbräu-Grandauer, Grafing (Bay)*
Jagdbier *Allgäuer Brauhaus, Leuterschach (Bay)*
Jagdherren Pils *Hofbräu, Würzburg (Bay)*
Jäger Dunkel *Mittenwald, Mittenwald (Bay)*
Jägerbier *Hofbrauhaus, Freising (Bay)*
Jahns Bräu *Ludwigsstadt (Bay)*
Jahrgangsbier *Ulrich Zimmermann, Berg (B-W); Adler, Zuzenhausen (B-W)*
Jahrhundert *Hofbrauhaus, Berchtesgaden (Bay)*
Jahrhundertbier *Aying, Aying (Bay); Beck, Trabelsdorf (Bay)*
Jahrtausend Bock *Mall, Meckesheim (B-W); Müllerbräu, Neuötting (Bay)*
Jahrtausend Sud *Maierbräu, Altomünster (Bay)*
Jahrtausend Weisse *Lauterbach, Lauterbach (Bay)*
Jakober Kirchweih Festbier *Augusta, Augsburg (Bay)*
Jandelsbrunner *Lang, Jandelsbrunn (Bay)*
Jännerbock *Wiesenmühle, Fulda (Hes)*
Jehle *Kronenbrauerei, Offenburg (B-W)*
Jehu Pils *Krone, Tettnang (B-W)*

Jenaer *Papiermühle, Jena (Thü)*
Jet A-1 *Airbräu, Flughafen-München (Bay)*
Jever *Friesisches Brauhaus zu Jever, Jever (Nie)*
Jo Püt *Püttner, Schlammersdorf (Bay)*
Jockgrim *Froschbräu, Jockgrim (R-P)*
Jodlbauer *Tiefenbach (Bay, unknown brewer)*
Joe's Lagerbier *Zötler, Rettenberg (Bay)*
Johann Albrecht *Bielefeld (N-W); Düsseldorf (N-W); Konstanz (B-W); Meßberg (Ham); Regensburg (Bay); Soltau (Nie)*
Johann Auer Dunkle-Weiße *Auerbräu, Rosenheim (Bay)*
Johann Friedrich *Irle, Siegen (N-W)*
Johannes Dunkel *Hirschbrauerei, Böhringen (B-W)*
Jonges Naturtrübe Alt *Brinkhoff, Dortmund (N-W)*
Josef Groll Pils *Wolferstetter, Vilshofen (Bay)*
Josef Schneider's *Kleines Brauhaus, Essing (Bay)*
Josef Sud *Abtei-Bräu, Mettlach (Saar)*
Josefator *Schwindbräu, Aschaffenburg (Bay); Bachmayer, Dorfen (Bay)*
Josefi Bier *Kühbach, Kübach (Bay)*
Josefi Bock *Winkler, Berching (Bay); Lang-Bräu, Freyung (Bay); Grasser, Huppendorf (Bay); Wurzgrund, Karlstadt (Bay); Mittenwald, Mittenwald (Bay); Klosterbrauerei, Reutberg (Bay); Flözinger-Bräu, Rosenheim (Bay)*
Josefsbock *Scussenrieder, Bas Schussenried (B-W)*
Josefsbräu *Bigge (N-W)*
Josephi Bier *Pyraser, Pyras (Bay)*
Josephi Bock *Keesmann, Bamberg (Bay); Fürstliches Brauhaus, Ellingen (Bay)*
Josephi Weizen *Wieser, Wiesmühl (Bay)*
Jubelbier *Hoepfner, Karlsruhe (B-W)*
Jubel Export *Greif, Forchheim (Bay)*
Jubel Weisse Altfränkisch *Pyraser, Pyras (Bay)*
Jubeltrunk Altfränkisch *Pyraser, Pyras (Bay)*
Jubilar *Wasserburger, Dingolfing (Bay)*
Jubilate *Pinkus Müller, Münster (N-W)*
Jubilator *Spessart, Kreuzwertheim (Bay); Schloßbrauerei, Maxlrain (Bay)*
Jubiläum Ex *Welde-Bräu, Plankstadt (B-W)*
Jubiläums Erlanger *Kitzmann, Erlangen (Bay)*
Jubiläums Mumme *Brauhaus am Lohberg, Wismar (M-V)*
Jüchsener *Zur Goldenen Henne, Jüchsen (Thü)*
Julius Echter *Würzburger Hofbräu, Würzburg (Bay)*
Juliusbräu *Neuburg (Bay)*
Jupiator *Jupiter, Steinsfurt (B-W)*
Jupiter *Steinsfurt (B-W)*
Jung *Schumacher, Düsseldorf (N-W)*
Junker Leicht & Frisch *Kaiser, Geislingen (B-W)*
Jura *Pegnitz (Bay); Plank, Wiefelsdorf (Bay)*
Jura Gold *Kaiser-Bräu, Neuhaus (Bay)*
Jura Hell *Schmitt, Scheßlitz (Bay, unknown brewer)*
Justus Weizen *Pfungstädter, Pfungstadt (Hes)*
Juwel *Bucher, Gundelfingen (Bay)*

K

KaDeWe Pilsner *Bürgerbräu, Friedrichshagen (Ber)*
Kaiser *Geislingen (B-W); Grasmannsdorf (Bay); Neuhaus (Bay)*

Kaiser Heinrich *Mahr's Bräu, Bamberg (Bay)*
Kaiser Klee Gold *Brauhaus Goslar, Goslar (Nie)*
Kaiser Maximilian *Aktienbrauerei, Kaufbeuren (Bay)*
Kaiser Napoleon *Leipzig (Sach)*
Kaiser Pilsener *Binding, Frankfurt (Hes)*
Kaiserdom *Bamberg (Bay)*
Kaiserhof *Kronach (Bay)*
Kaiserritter *Schloßbrauerei, Mickhausen (Bay)*
Kaitersberg *Kolbeck, Kötzting (Bay)*
Kalkarer Mühle *Kalkar (N-W)*
Kallmünzer *Zum Goldenen Löwen, Kallmünz (Bay)*
Kalomator *Kalt-Loch-Bräu, Miltenberg (Bay)*
Kalt Loch Bräu *Miltenberg (Bay)*
Kaltenberg *Schloßbrauerei, Fürstenfeldbrück (Bay); Schloßbrauerei, Kaltenberg (Bay)*
Kaltenbrunner Vollbier *Schleicher, Kaltenbrunn (Bay)*
Kaltentaler Brauhaus *Aufkirch (Bay)*
Kanone *Schnaittach (Bay)*
Kanonier Schwarzbier *Kaiser Napoleon, Leipzig (Sach)*
Kantine *Kulturbrauhaus, Lörrach (B-W)*
Kappl Weisse *Ziegler, Waldsassen (Bay)*
Kappler *Braustolz, Chemnitz (Sach)*
Kapplerbräu *Altomünster (Bay)*
Kapuziner *Kulmbacher, Kulmbach (Bay)*
Kapuziner Doppelbock *Innstadt, Passau (Bay)*
Karg *Murnau (Bay)*
Karl May Jubiläums Pils *Glückauf, Gersdorf (Sach)*
Karls Brauhaus *Chemnitz (Sach)*
Karlsberg *Homburg (Saar)*
Karlsberger Hof *Karlsberg, Homburg (Saar)*
Karlsbräu *Karlsberg, Homburg (Saar)*
Karmeliten *Straubing (Bay)*
Karmeliter *Bad Neustadt (Bay)*
Karolinen Weisse *Hasen-Bräu, Augsburg (Bay)*
Karpfen Gold *Klosterbrauerei, Kemnath (Bay)*
Karpfen Weisse *Löwenbräu, Neuhaus (Bay)*
Karpfentrunk *Schloßbrauerei, Friedenfels (Bay)*
Kärrners *Bad Orb (Hes)*
Karschter *Wurzgrund, Karlstadt (Bay)*
Kartäuser *Memminger, Memmingen (Bay)*
Karthäuserbräu *Bischoff'sche Brauerei, Brühl (N-W)*
Karwendel Hell *Mittenwald, Mittenwald (Bay)*
Kasseler Premium Pils *Martini, Kassel (Hes)*
Kastanienbier *Christoph-Bräu, Gaggenau (B-W)*
Katharinen *Wurzen (Sach, unknown brewer)*
Kathi Bräu *Heckenhof (Bay)*
Kathrein Bock *Grasser, Huppendorf (Bay)*
Kaufbeurer Hell *Aktienbrauerei, Kaufbeuren (Bay)*
Kauzen *Ochsenfurt (Bay)*
Kavalierhäuser Schloß K.W. *Königs Wusterhausen (Bra)*
Keesmann *Bamberg (Bay)*
Kelheimer Festbier *Aukofer-Bräu, Kelheim (Bay)*
Keller Gold *Jahns-Bräu, Ludwigsstadt (Bay)*
Keller Pils *Schwarzbräu, Zusmarshausen (Bay)*
Kellerberg *Köpf, Aalen (B-W); Brauhaus Höchstadt, Höchstadt (Bay)*
Kellerbräu *Ahlbecker Kellerbräu, Ahlbeck (M-V); Klimperkasten, St. Georgen (B-W)*
Kellergold *Hofmühl, Eichstätt (Bay)*

Kellerkrönla *Haberstumpf, Trebgast (Bay)*
Kellermeister *Bergbrauerei, Leimen (B-W)*
Kellertrunk *Meusel-Bräu, Dreuschendorf (Bay); Püls Bräu, Weismain (Bay)*
Keltisches Emmerbier *Leidmann, Unterneukirchen (Bay)*
Kemnath *Klosterbrauerei, Kemnath (Bay)*
Kenzinger *Hirschen, Kenzingen (B-W)*
Kerwa-Bier *Rittmayer, Aisch (Bay); Kommunbräu, Kulmbach (Bay)*
Kesselhaus *Schorndorf (B-W)*
Kesselring *Marksteft (Bay)*
Ketterer *Hornberg (B-W); Pforzheim (B-W)*
Keiler Weißbier *Lohrer Bier, Lohr (Bay)*
Kieler *Kiel (S-H)*
Kiliani *Bürgerbräu, Bad Windsheim (Bay)*
Kindl *Berliner Kindl, Neukölln (Ber)*
Kindl Weissbier *Hofbräuhaus, München (Bay)*
King *Königsbräu, Oggenhausen (B-W)*
Kini Bier *Schlossbräu, Drachselried (Bay)*
Kirchdunkel *Brauhaus am Ring, Kirchhellen (N-W)*
Kirchers *Drebkau (Bra)*
Kirchhell *Brauhaus am Ring, Kirchhellen (N-W)*
Kirchweihbier *Augusta, Augsburg (Bay); Heller, Herzogenaurach (Bay); Mühlenbräu, Mühlendorf (Bay); Postbrauerei, Nesselwang (Bay); Landwehr, Reichelshofen (Bay); Schweinfurt, Schweinfurt (Bay)*
Kirchweihstoff *Ritter St. Georgen, Nennslingen (Bay)*
Kirner *Kirn (R-P)*
Kirsch *Weltenbummler, Berggießhübel (Sach)*
Kirta *Graminger-Weissbräu, Graming (Bay)*
Kirta Bier *Bräu z 'Loh, Loh (Bay)*
Kirta Halbe *Aying, Aying (Bay)*
Kirtabier Märzen *Schloßbrauerei, Maxlrain (Bay)*
Kitzmann *Erlangen (Bay)*
Klassik *Schloßbrauerei, Irlbach (Bay); Landshuter Brauhaus, Landshut (Bay)*
Klassik 1554 *Neder, Forchheim (Bay)*
Klausator *Memminger, Memmingen (Bay)*
Klausner *Einsiedel (Sach, unknown brewer)*
Kleinbrauerei Rain *Rain (Bay)*
Kleine Brauhaus *Kleines Pleinfelder, Pleinfeld (Bay)*
Kleiner Mönch *Klosterbräu, Alpirsbach (B-W)*
Kleines Blondes *Kleines Brauhaus, Essing (Bay)*
Kleines Brauhaus *Seligenstadt (Hes)*
Kleines Brauhaus am Kloster *Ottobeuren (Bay)*
Kleines Brauhaus im Altmühltal *Essing (Bay)*
Kleines Eifeler-Brauhaus *Bad Münstereifel (N-W)*
Kleines Eltviller Brauhaus *Eltville (Hes)*
Kleines Freburger Brauhaus *Freiburg (B-W)*
Kleines Pleinfelder Brauhaus *Pleinfeld (Bay)*
Kleines Rüsselsheimer Brauhaus *Alt Haßloch (Hes)*
Kleines Schweinchen *Kassel (Hes)*
Klett Bräu *Konzell (Bay)*
KLGB Bier *Mahr's Bräu, Bamberg (Bay)*
Klier Bräu *Ettensberg (Bay)*
Kliesow's Reuse *Alt Reddevitz (M-V)*
Klimperkasten *St. Georgen (B-W)*
Klingenbrunn *Klingenbrunn (Bay)*
Klingenbrunner *Klingenbrunn, Klingenbrunn (Bay)*

Kloster *Aldersbach, Aldersbach (Bay); Au (Bay); Hasen-Bräu, Augsburg (Bay); Klosterbrauerei, Baumburg (Bay); Münchhausen, Bodenwerder (Nie); Eschweger Klosterbrauerei, Eschwege (Hes); Klosterbrauerei, Ettal (Bay); Irseer Klosterbräu, Irsee (Bay); Klosterbrauerei, Kemnath (Bay); Machern (R-P); Klosterbrauerei, Münnerstadt (Bay); Kleines Brauhaus, Ottobeuren (Bay); Klosterbrauerei, Reutberg (Bay); Karmeliten, Straubing (Bay); Kronenbrauerei Söflingen, Ulm (B-W); Klosterbrauerei, Weißenohe (Bay); Klosterbrauerei, Weltenburg (Bay); Zwiefalter Klosterbräu, Zwiefaltendorf (B-W)*
Kloster Au *Kloster-Bräu, Au (Bay)*
Kloster Helfta *Helfta (S-A)*
Kloster Machern *Machern (R-P)*
Kloster Seeon Ur-Dunkel *Schlossbrauerei, Stein (Bay)*
Klosterbier *Münch-Bräu, Eibau (Sach); Peters Bauern-stube, Haltern (N-W); Klosterbrauerei, Kreuzberg (Bay); Abtei-Bräu, Mettlach (Saar); Klosterbrauerei, Scheyern (Bay); Klosterbrauerei, Weißenohe (Bay)*
Klosterbräu *Alpirsbach (B-W); Bamberg (Bay); Darguner, Dargun (M-V); Klosterbrauerei, Eschwege (Hes); Irsee (Bay); Mallersdorf (Bay); Marienstatter, Marienstatt (R-P); Klosterbrauerei, Neuzelle (Bra); Seemannshausen; Stadtbrauerei, Wittichenau (Sach); Zwiefaltendorf (B-W)*
Klosterbrauerei *Andechs (Bay); Baumburg (Bay); Eschwege (Hes); Ettal (Bay); Kemnath (Bay); Kreuzberg (Bay); Mallersdorf (Bay); Münnerstadt (Bay); Neuzelle (Bra); Reutberg (Bay); Scheyern (Bay); Weißenohe (Bay); Weltenburg (Bay)*
Klosterbräuhaus *Ursberg (Bay)*
Klosterbraunbier *Hald, Dunstelkingen (B-W)*
Klosterdunkel *Irseer Klosterbräu, Irsee (Bay)*
Klostergold *Kloster-Bräu, Au (Bay)*
Klosterhell *Aldersbach, Aldersbach (Bay)*
Klosterhof Dunkel *Hauf-Bräu, Dentlein (Bay)*
Klösterl Weisse *Aukofer-Bräu, Kelheim (Bay)*
Klosterpforte *Helfta (S-A)*
Klosterpils *Prosslbräu, Adlersberg (Bay)*
Klostersud *Klosterbrauerei, Weißenohe (Bay)*
Klosterweizen *Winkler-Bräu, Schlicht (Bay)*
Klusker Waldbräu *Röcke (Nie)*
Klute *Poppenbeck (N-W)*
Klüver's *Neustadt (S-H)*
Knallhütte Schwarzes Gold *Hütt, Knallhütte (Hes)*
Knappentrunk *Bruckmüller, Amberg (Bay)*
Kneipe Pur *Plaue (Bra)*
Kneitinger *Regensburg (Bay)*
Knoblach *Schammelsdorf (Bay)*
Knoblachbräu *Kneipe Pur, Plaue (Bra)*
Knoorz Bräu *Morsbach (N-W)*
Knuttenforz Schwarzbier *Lüdde, Quedlinburg (S-A)*
Kocherreiter Pils *Lammbrauerei, Untergröningen (B-W)*
Kohlenmühle *Neustadt an der Aisch (Bay)*
Köhler's Bräu *Ratsbrauhaus, Bad Gandersheim (Nie); Ratsbrauhaus, Hann. Münden (Nie)*
Koksbock *Kohlenmühle, Neustadt an der Aisch (Bay)*
Kolb *Meßhofen (Bay)*

Kolbeck *Kötzting (Bay)*
Kolberg *Altenau (Nie)*
Koller *Hergertswiesen (Bay)*
Koller's Klassik *Landshuter Brauhaus, Landshut (Bay)*
Kölner Verbund Brauereien *Köln (N-W)*
Kölner Wieß *Kölner Verbund Brauereien, Köln (N-W)*
Kommunbier *Kommunbrauerei, Eslarn (Bay)*
Kommunbräu *Kumbach (Bay)*
Kommunbrauerei *Eslarn (Bay); Falkenberg (Bay); Mitterteich (Bay); Neuhaus (Bay); Rossach (Bay); Windischeschenbach (Bay)*
Kommunbrauhaus *Seßlach (Bay)*
König *Duisburg (N-W)*
König Ludwig Dunkel *Schloßbrauerei, Kaltenberg (Bay)*
König Sahl *Gotha (Thü)*
König von Flandern *Augsburg (Bay)*
König von Preußen *Frauenalb (B-W)*
König Wenzel *Schlossbrauerei, Hirschau (Bay)*
König Wilhelm Helles *Egerer, Großköllbach (Bay)*
Königliches *Schloßbrauerei, Fürstenfeldbrück (Bay)*
Königs Bräu *Altes Brauhaus, Fallersleben (Nie)*
Königs Wusterhausen *Kavalierhäuser, Königs Wusterhausen (Bra)*
Königsbacher *Koblenz (R-P)*
Königsbräu Majer *Oggenhausen (B-W)*
Königbrünner *Charivari-Bräu, Königsbrunn (B-W)*
Königsegger *Walderbräu, Königseggwald (B-W)*
Königstrunk *Tucher, Fürth (Bay)*
Konzeller Weiße *Klett-Bräu, Konzell (Bay)*
Köpf *Aalen (B-W)*
Korbinian *Weihenstephan, Freising (Bay); Zötler, Rettenberg (Bay)*
Kornhus *Bad Münder (Nie)*
Körpricher Landbräu *Körprich (Saar)*
Köss *Weißbräu, Kößlarn (Bay)*
Kössel Bräu *Speiden (Bay)*
Kösslarner *Weißbräu, Kößlarn (Bay)*
Köstritzer *Bad Köstritz (Thü)*
Köthener *Köthener Brauerei, Köthen (S-A, unknown brewer); Köthener Brauhaus, Köthen (S-A)*
Kraft Bräu *Trier (R-P)*
Kraft Protz *Welde-Bräu, Plankstadt (B-W)*
Kraichgau Pilsner *Palmbräu, Eppingen (B-W)*
Krampus *Airbräu, Flughafen-München (Bay)*
Kraus *Hirschaid (Bay)*
Kräusen *Bautzener, Bautzen (Sach); Becher Bräu, Bayreuth (Bay); Haake Beck, Bremen (Bre); Löwenbrauerei Dold, Elzach (B-W); Glückauf, Gersdorf (Sach); Kulturbrauerei, Heidelberg (B-W); Hoepfner, Karlsruhe (B-W); Wolf, Karlsruhe (B-W); Faust, Miltenberg (Bay); Steffens, St. Severinsberg (R-P); Schinkel's, Witzenhausen (Hes)*
Krauter-Bier *Weltenbummler, Berggießhübel (Sach); Altes Brauhaus, Fallersleben (Nie)*
Krautheimer *Düll, Krautheim (Bay)*
Krawendorfer *Heberbräu, Kirchenthumbach (Bay)*
Kreuz *Moosbeuren (B-W)*
Kreuzberger *Klosterbrauerei, Kreuzberg (Bay)*
Krieger *Landau (Bay)*

Kristall *Zeltbräu, Hof (Bay)*
Kroko Spezial Kellerbier *Tucher, Fürth (Bay)*
Krollebock *Bier-Hannes, Frankfurt (Hes)*
Krombacher *Krombach (N-W)*
Kronabier *Drei Kronen, Scheßlitz (Bay)*
Kronator *Kaiserhof, Kronach (Bay)*
Kronberger *Kronberg (Hes)*
Kronburger *Kronburg (Bay)*
Krone *Tettnang (B-W)*
Krone Pils *Kronenbrauerei, Remmingsheim (B-W);*
    Püls Bräu, Weismain (Bay)
Kronen *Kronenbrauerei Halter, Biberach (B-W); DAB,*
    Dortmund (N-W); Kronenbrauerei, Laupheim (B-W);
    Kronen-Brauerei, Lüneberg (Nie, unknown brewer);
    Krone, Tettnang (B-W)
Kronen Bier *Kronenbrauerei Söflingen, Ulm (B-W)*
Kronen Bräu *Kronenbrauerei Halter, Biberach (B-W)*
Kronenbrauerei *Altenmünster (Bay); Biberach (B-W);*
    Gundelfingen (Bay, unknown brewer); Hochdorf (B-W);
    Lüneberg (Nie, unknown brewer); Laupheim (B-W);
    Offenburg (B-W); Remmingsheim (B-W); Ulm (B-W)
Kronenhof *Graf Zeppelin, Bad Homburg (Hes)*
Krones Eifel Böckchen *Gemünder, Gemünd (N-W)*
Krones Eifeler Landbier *Gemünder, Gemünd (N-W)*
Krönle *Kronenbrauerei, Offenburg (B-W);*
Kronprinzen Pils *Zum Alten Brauhaus, Rheinsberg (Bra)*
Krostitzer *Krostitz (Sach)*
Krug *Breitenlesau (Bay); Geisfeld (Bay)*
Kuchems *Pirmasens (R-P)*
Kuchlbauer *Abensberg (Bay)*
Kuckucksbier *Wittenberg, Lutherstadt Wittenberg (S-A)*
Kühbach *Kühbach (Bay)*
Kühler Krug *Karlsruhe (B-W)*
Kühlungsbräu *Ostsee Brauhaus, Kühlungsborn (M-V)*
KuKaKö-stlich *Köthener Brauerei, Köthen (S-A,*
    unknown brewer)
Kulinator *Hutthurmer Bayerwald, Hutthurm (Bay)*
Kulmbacher *Kulmbach (Bay)*
Kulmbacher Kommunbräu *Kumbach (Bay)*
Kult *Kaiser, Geislingen (B-W); Hochdorfer, Hochdorf (B-W)*
Kulturbrauerei *Heidelberg (B-W)*
Kulturbrauhaus *Lörrach (B-W)*
Kummert *Amberg (B-W)*
Kumpel Pils *Ratskeller, Geising (Sach)*
Kumulus *Airbräu, Flughafen-München (Bay)*
Kundmüller *Weiher (Bay)*
Kunobräu *Kunos Braugasthaus, Erlabrunn (Sach)*
Kunos Braugasthaus *Erlabrunn (Sach)*
Kupfer *Bautzener, Bautzen (Sach); Johann Albrecht,*
    Bielefeld (N-W); Erzquell, Bielstein (N-W); Turm,
    Chemnitz (Sach); Johann Albrecht, Düsseldorf (N-W);
    Forstquell, Fürnheim (Bay); Johann Albrecht, Konstanz
    (B-W); Winkler Bräu, Lengenfeld (Bay); Reformator,
    Lutherstadt Eisleben (S-A); Johann Albrecht,
    Meßberg (Ham); Erzquell, Niederschelderhütte (R-P);
    Berghammer, Oberndorf (Bay); Winkler, Schlicht (Bay); Johann
    Albrecht, Soltau (Nie); Alter Fritz, Tegel (Ber);
    Woinemer, Weilheim (B-W)

Kupferbier *Alt Oberurseler, Oberursel (Hes); Lang,*
    Waltershausen (Bay)
Kupferkrönla *Haberstumpf, Trebgast (Bay)*
Küpper's Kölsch *Kölner Verbund Brauereien, Köln (N-W)*
Kuppler *Gosebrauerei Bayerischer Bahnhof, Leipzig (Sach)*
Kur Pils *Häffner Bräu, Bad Rappenau (B-W);*
    Bürgerbräu, Bad Reichenhall (Bay); Bad Wörishofer
    Löwenbräu, Bad Wörishofen (Bay)
Kürassier Hefeweizen *Kaiser Napoleon, Leipzig (Sach)*
Kurfürst Carl Theodor *Frankenthaler, Frankenthal (R-P,*
    unknown brewer)
Kurfürsten Kölsch *Kölner Verbund Brauereien, Köln (N-W)*
Kurpfalz Hefe-Weizen *Kummert, Amberg (Bay)*
Kürzdörfer *Lindenhardt (Bay)*
Küsten-Brauerei *Werdum (Nie)*
Kutscher Alt *Binding, Frankfurt (Hes)*
Kyr *Kirner, Kirn (R-P)*
Kyritzer Mord und Totschlag *Dessow, Dessow (Bra)*

L

Ladenburger *Neuler (B-W)*
Ladykiller Weizenbock *Steinbach Bräu, Erlangen (Bay)*
Lahnsteiner *St. Martin, Oberlahnstein (R-P)*
Lakritzbier *Kneipe Pur, Plaue (Bra)*
Lambertus *Rainer, Welz (N-W)*
Lamm *Zum Goldenen Lamm, Gierstädt (Thü); Lamm-*
    brauerei, Untergröningen (B-W); Wiesensteig (B-W)
Lammbrauerei *Gruibingen (B-W); Untergröningen (B-W);*
    Weilheim (B-W)
Lammsbräu *Neumarkter Lammsbräu, Neumarkt (Bay)*
Lamperl Pils *Lampl-Bräu, Larsbach (Bay)*
Lampl Bräu *Larsbach (Bay)*
Land Weizen *Hald, Dunstelkingen (B-W)*
Landauer *Landau (R-P)*
Landbock *Torgauer, Torgau (Sach)*
Landbräu *Fischer, Wieseth (Bay); Körprich (Saar)*
Landbrauerei *Rickling (S-H)*
Landgasthof zur Linde *Middelhagen (M-V)*
Landgold *Hösl, Mitterteich (Bay)*
Landhaus *Lünne (Nie)*
Landhausbräu Koller *Hergertswiesen (Bay)*
Landherrenbier *Calwer-Eck-Bräu, Stuttgart (B-W)*
Landkrönla *Haberstumpf, Trebgast (Bay)*
Landl Hell *Bender, Mühlhausen (Bay)*
Landlator *Bender, Mühlhausen (Bay)*
Landler *Maierbräu, Altomünster (Bay)*
Landmärzen *Düll, Krautheim (Bay)*
Landpils *Wildbräu-Grandauer, Grafing (Bay); Euler,*
    Wetzlar (Hes, unknown brewer)
Landsbergbräu Export *Meininger, Meiningen (Thü)*
Landsberger *Landsberg, Landsberg (S-A)*
Landshuter Brauhaus *Landshut (Bay)*
Landsknecht Bier *Fürst Wallerstein, Wallerstein (Bay)*
Landskron *Görlitz (Sach)*
Landwehr *Reichelshofen (Bay)*
Lang *Freyung (Bay); Jandelsbrunn (Bay); Reisbach*
    (Bay); Schönbrunn (Bay); Waltershausen (Bay)
Lappmann's Dunkel *Hohenfelder, Langenberg (N-W)*
Larry's Lager *Arcobräu Gräfliches Brauhaus, Moos (Bay)*

Larry's White *Arcobräu Gräfliches Brauhaus, Moos (Bay)*
Larsbacher Weiße *Lampl-Bräu, Larsbach (Bay)*
Lasser *Lörrach (B-W)*
Lätterbacher Weisse *Hennemann, Unterleiterbach (Bay)*
Latzenbier *Schumacher, Düsseldorf (N-W)*
Lauenthaler Zwergenbräu *Brauhaus Goslar, Goslar (Nie)*
Laufer Weißbier *Simon, Lauf (Bay)*
Lauinger *Hirschbrauerei Schwarz, Lauingen (Bay)*
Laupheimer *Kronenbrauerei, Laupheim (B-W)*
Laurentius *Wernecker, Werneck (Bay)*
Laurenzi *Holzkirchner Oberbräu, Holzkirchen (Bay)*
Laurenzi Festbier *Martinsbräu, Marktheidenfeld (Bay)*
Lausitzer Berg-Bock *Bergquell, Löbau (Sach)*
Lausitzer Dunkel *Münch-Bräu, Eibau (Sach)*
Lausitzer Hefeweizen *Bergquell, Löbau (Sach)*
Lausitzer Kindl *Landskron Brauerei, Görlitz (Sach)*
Lausitzer Mühlen-Pils *Bergquell, Löbau (Sach)*
Lausitzer Porter *Bergquell, Löbau (Sach)*
Lausitzer Premium *Stadtbrauerei, Wittichenau (Sach)*
Lauterbacher *Lauterbach (Bay); Burgbrauerei,
    Lauterbach (Hes)*
Lauterecker Brauhaus *Lauterecken (R-P)*
Lautertaler *Gadernheim (Hes)*
Lava Schwarzbier *Metzler, Dingsleben (Thü)*
Lebens Art *Hauf-Bräu, Dentlein (Bay)*
Lebkuchenbier *Bayerisches Brauereimuseum,
    Kulmbach (Bay)*
Lechler *Kirchheim (Bay)*
Lechthaler Leicht *Thorbräu, Augsburg (Bay)*
Lecker Kölsch *Weißbräu, Köln (N-W)*
Lederer *Tucher, Fürth (Bay)*
Legende *Wernesgrüner, Wernesgrün (Sach)*
Lehestener *Jahns-Bräu, Ludwigsstadt (Bay);*
Lehner *Rosenfeld (B-W)*
Leibinger *Ravensburg (B-W)*
Leicht *Pferdsfeld (Bay)*
Leichte Halbe *Ingobräu, Ingolstadt (Bay)*
Leidmann *Unterneukirchen (Bay)*
Leikeim *Altenkunstadt (Bay)*
Leimener *Bergbrauerei, Leimen (B-W)*
Leinburger *Bub, Leinburg (Bay)*
Leipziger Brauhaus zu Reudnitz *Leipzig (Sach)*
Leipziger Gose *Gosebrauerei, Leipzig (Sach)*
Leitner Bräu *Schwabach (Bay)*
Lemke's Spezialitätenbrauerei *Mitte (Ber)*
Lengenfelder Glühbier *Winkler, Lengenfeld (Bay)*
Lenins Hanf *Neustädter, Dresden (Sach)*
Lenzkircher *Rogg, Lenzkirch (B-W)*
Leo Weisse *Schloßbrauerei, Maxlrain (Bay)*
Leonhardi Bock *Schloßbrauerei, Autenried (Bay)*
Leopils *Adler-Bräu, Wiernsheim (B-W)*
Leuchtturm *Gunzenhausen (Bay)*
Leupser *Gradl, Leups (Bay)*
Leusator *Löwenbräu, Bad Wörishofen (Bay)*
Licher *Lich (Hes)*
Lichtenauer Weissbier *Hauff-Bräu, Lichtenau (Bay)*
Lieberator *Liebhart's Brauhaus, Poing (Bay)*
Lieberth *Hallerndorf (Bay)*
Liebhart's Brauhaus *Poing (Bay)*

Liebhardt's Kellerbier *Aying, Aying (Bay)*
Liebus Bräu *Liebhart's Brauhaus, Poing (Bay)*
Life *Lübzer, Lübz (M-V)*
Light & Fit *Schwarzbräu, Zusmarshausen (Bay)*
Light Line *Waldhaus, Waldhaus (B-W)*
Lightlife *Schönbuch-Bräu, Böblingen (B-W)*
Lilienthaler Dunkel *Borgfelder Landhaus, Bremen (Bre)*
Linden *Lindenbrauerei, Unna (N-W)*
Linden-Bräu *Gräfenberg (Bay); Zur Linde, Kolonie (Bra);
    Lindenbrauerei, Mindelheim (Bay); Oberferrieden
    (Bay, unknown brewer); Tiergarten (Ber); Waldbronn
    (B-W)*
Lindenbrauerei *Mindelheim (Bay); Unna (NW,
    unknown brewer); Unna (N-W, new brewery)*
Lindener Spezial *Gilde, Hannover (Nie)*
Lindenhardter *Kürzdörfer, Lindenhardt (Bay)*
Lindenquell *Adler-Bräu, Wiernsheim (B-W)*
Lindner Bräu *Kolbeck, Kötzting (Bay)*
Linsengericht *Altenhaßlau (Hes)*
Lippstädter *Thombansen, Lippstadt (N-W)*
Lipsiator *Thomaskirche, Leipzig (Sach)*
Lisberger Lager *Beck, Trabelsdorf (Bay)*
Löbauer Bergquell *Bergquell, Löbau (Sach)*
Lokalitätenbrauerei *Rinteln (Nie)*
Loffelder Dunkel *Staffelberg-Bräu, Loffeld (Bay)*
Loh *Bräu 'z Loh, Loh (Bay)*
Lohberg *Wismar (M-V)*
Lohmann *Langenfeld (N-W)*
Lohrer Bier *Lohr (Bay)*
Lord Light *Bellheimer, Bellheim (R-P)*
Lord Pils *Bellheimer, Bellheim (R-P); Helbig, Weilburg
    (Hes)*
Lorenzi Bock *Tucher, Fürth & Nürnberg (Bay)*
Lösch Zwerg *Schimpfle, Gessertshausen (Bay)*
Löschauer Dunkel *Döbler, Bad Windsheim (Bay)*
Loscher *Münchsteinach (Bay)*
Lotters *Aue (Sach)*
Löwen *Braunschweig (Nie); Mühlhausen (Thü)*
Löwen Bock *Jahns-Bräu, Ludwigsstadt (Bay);*
Löwen Export *Löwenbrauerei Dold, Elzach (B-W)*
Löwen Krone *Löwenbräu, Bad Wörishofen (Bay)*
Löwen Pils *Löwenbrauerei Dold, Elzach (B-W)*
Löwen Urtrunk *Löwenbräu, Bad Wörishofen (Bay)*
Löwen Weisse *Löwenbräu, München (Bay)*
Löwenbier *Malsfeld (Hes)*
Löwenbräu *Bad Wörishofen (Bay); Löwenbrauerei,
    Bräunlingen (B-W); Buttenheim (Bay); Löwenbrauerei
    Dold, Elzach (B-W); Meckatz (Bay); München (Bay);
    Neuhaus (Bay); Schwäbisch Hall (B-W); Hennemann,
    Stublang (Bay); Neeb, Unterschleichach (Bay);
    Vestenberg (Bay)*
Löwenbrauerei *Aalen (B-W); Baisingen (B-W);
    Bräunlingen (B-W); Elzach (B-W); Passau (Bay); Trier
    (R-P, unknown brewer)*
Löwenpils *Aalener Löwenbrauerei, Aalen (B-W)*
Lübeck *Brauberger, Lübeck (S-H)*
Lübener Tennenbräu *Tennenbräu, Lüben (Nie)*
Lübzer *Mecklenburgische Brauerei, Lübz (M-V)*
Lucas Kranach *Kaiserhof, Kronach (Bay)*

Luckenwalder *Spezialitätenbrauerei, Luckenwalde (Bra)*
Lüdde *Quedlinburg (S-A)*
Ludger's Kleine Brauerei *Littfeld (N-W)*
Ludwig der Kelheimer Dunkel *Krieger, Landau (Bay)*
Ludwig Thoma *Hofbrauhaus, Berchtesgaden (Bay)*
Luisen Bräu *Charlottenburg (Ber)*
Luisenburg Pils *Hönicka-Bräu, Wunsiedel (Bay)*
Lüneburger *Kronen-Brauerei, Lüneberg (Nie, unknown brewer)*
Lupulus Pils *Gladbeck, Gladbeck (N-W)*
Lust *Welde-Bräu, Plankstadt (B-W)*
Lustiger Augustin *Braustelle, Köln (N-W)*
Lütter Krug *Lütte (N-W)*
Lüttje Lage *Gilde, Hannover (Nie); Herrenhäuser, Hannover (Nie); Schaumburger, Stadthagen (Nie)*
Luxus Pils *Baisinger Löwenbrauerei, Baisingen (B-W); Hütt-Brauerei, Knallhütte (Hes)*

M

M. Lager *Michael, Weißenstadt (Bay)*
Machern *Machern (R-P)*
Mäckinger *Selbecke (N-W)*
Mager *Pottenstein (Bay)*
Magisterbräu *Fiedler, Oberscheibe (Sach)*
Mahr's Bräu *Bamberg (Bay)*
Mai Glöckl *Glossner-Bräu, Neumarkt (Bay)*
Maibaumbier *Wernecker, Werneck (Bay)*
Maientags Bier *Kaiser, Geislingen (B-W)*
Maierbräu *Altomünster (Bay)*
Maingold Landbier *Kulmbacher, Kulmbach (Bay)*
Mainkur *Bier Hannes, Frankfurt (Hes)*
Mainlust *Viereth (Bay)*
Maisach *Maisach (Bay)*
Maisel *Bamberg (Bay); Bayreuth (Bay)*
Majer *Königsbräu, Oggenhausen (B-W)*
Mall *Meckesheim (B-W)*
Mallersdorf *Klosterbrauerei, Mallersdorf (Bay)*
Malteser Weisse *Stuttgarter Hofbräu, Stuttgart (B-W)*
Mälzer Brauhaus *Lüneberg (Nie)*
Malzmühle *Köln (N-W)*
Mammut *Sangerhausen (S-A, unknown brewer)*
Manna *Postbrauerei, Frontenhausen (Bay)*
Mannebacher *Mannebach (R-P)*
Mannipulator *Boandl-Bräu, Oberbernbach (Bay)*
Marathon *Klosterbrauerei, Neuzelle (Bra)*
Marcus Bräu *Microbrauerei Barkowsky, Mitte (Ber)*
Markator *Bürgerbräu, Bayreuth (Bay)*
Märkator *Märkl, Freudenberg (Bay)*
Markgrafen Hell *Stadtbrauerei Roth, Roth (Bay)*
Markgrafenbräu *Winkels, Karlsruhe (B-W, unknown brewer)*
Märkischer Bock *Dessow, Dessow (Bra)*
Märkischer Landmann Schwarzbier *Kindl, Neukölln (Ber)*
Märkisches *Dessow, Dessow (Bra)*
Märkl *Freudenberg (Bay)*
Markt *Kaiserslautern (R-P)*
Marktbräu *Nidda (Hes)*
Mariahilfberger *Glossner-Bräu, Neumarkt (Bay)*
Mariahilfer *Kössel-Bräu, Speiden (Bay)*

Mariakirchen *Schlossbräu, Mariakirchen (Bay)*
Marienstatter *Marienstatt (R-P)*
Martin *Unterneuses (Bay)*
Marleusbier *Barbarossa, Schöllkrippen (Bay)*
Maronator *Brauhaus in Spandau, Spandau (Ber)*
Marone *Waldhaus, Erfurt (Thü)*
Marstall Dunkel *Fürstliches Brauhaus, Regensburg (Bay)*
Martin's *Martinsbräu, Marktheidenfeld (Bay)*
Martinator *Martini, Kassel; Anker, Nagold (B-W); St. Martin, Oberlahnstein (R-P)*
Martini *Kassel (Hes)*
Martini Bock *Alpirsbacher Klosterbräu, Alpirsbach (B-W)*
Martini Trunk *Winkler Bräu, Lengenfeld (Bay)*
Martinsbräu *Freiburg (B-W); Marktheidenfeld (Bay)*
Martinus Hell *Stanglbräu, Herrnwahlthann (Bay)*
Mash *Adlerbrauerei, Geislingen (B-W); Stuttgart (B-W)*
Mattler *Mattlerhof, Röttgersbach (N-W)*
Mattlerhof *Röttgersbach (N-W)*
Maueler Hofbräu *Mauel (N-W)*
Mauritius *Zwickau (Sach)*
Max Bräu *Zehendner, Mönchsambach (Bay)*
Max Fünf Komma 2 *Leibinger, Ravensburg (B-W)*
Max & Moritz *Berg (B-W)*
Max Reger Dunkel *Gambrinus-Brauerei, Weiden (Bay)*
Maximator *Max & Moritz, Berg (B-W); Augustiner-Bräu, München (Bay)*
Maximilian Kölsch *Kölner Verbund Brauereien, Köln (N-W)*
Maximillian Ritter Urtyp *Alpirsbacher, Alpirsbach (B-W)*
Maximilians Brauwiesen *Niederlahnstein (R-P)*
Maximilians Kellerbier *Thorbräu, Augsburg (Bay)*
Maximilians Starkbier *Hald, Dunstelkingen (B-W)*
Maximiliansbräu *Traunstein (Bay)*
Maximum *Hohenfelder, Langenberg (N-W)*
Maxlrainer *Schloßbrauerei, Maxlrain (Bay)*
Maxxum *Krefeld (N-W, unknown brewer)*
Maxxximator *Lindenbräu, Waldbronn (B-W)*
Mayday *Airbräu, Flughafen-München (Bay)*
Mayer Bräu *Ludwigshafen (R-P)*
Mayer's *Mayer Bräu, Ludwigshafen (R-P)*
Meckatzer *Löwenbräu, Meckatz (Bay)*
Meckesheimer *Fridolin Mall, Meckesheim (B-W)*
Mecklenburger Landbier *Schweriner, Schwerin (M-V)*
Mecklenburger Pilsener *Darguner, Dargun (M-V)*
Mecklenburgische Brauerei *Lübz (M-V)*
Medardus *Schillerbad, Lüdenscheid (N-W)*
Medium *Hutthurmer Bayerwald, Hutthurm (Bay); Schlossbrauerei, Stein (Bay)*
Mehringer *Weißes Brauhaus Mehringer, Neunburg (Bay)*
Mehrkornbier *Der Hausbrauer Dietz, Bruckberg (B-W)*
Meierator *Meierhof, Ottbergen (N-W)*
Meierei *Potsdam (Bra)*
Meierhof *Ottbergen (N-W)*
Meierhöfer *Vehlen (Nie)*
Meinel Bräu *Hof (Bay)*
Meininger *Meiningen (Thü)*
Meissner Schwerter *Schwerter Wohlers, Meißen (Sach)*
Meister *Unterzaunsbach (Bay)*
Meister Bock *Lammbrauerei, Gruibingen (B-W)*
Meister Bräu *GSM, Freiberg (Sach, unknown brewer)*

Meister Pils *Hald, Dunstelkingen (B-W); Martini, Kassel (Hes); Adlerbrauerei, Mögglingen (B-W); Schmucker, Ober-Mossau (Hes); Dinkelacker-Schwaben-Bräu, Stuttgart (B-W); Weideneder, Tann (Bay); Schloßbrauerei, Unterbaar (Bay)*

Meistergold *Bürgerbräu, Bad Windsheim (Bay); Haller Löwenbräu, Schwäbisch Hall (B-W)*

Meistersud *Wildbräu-Grandauer, Grafing (Bay); Ingobräu, Ingolstadt (Bay)*

Meistertrunk *Peschl, Passau (Bay)*

Melchior *Drei Kronen, Memmelsdorf (Bay)*

Mellert *Steinbach (B-W)*

Memminger *Memmingen (Bay)*

Mensch Maier *Maierbräu, Altomünster (Bay)*

Mephisto Weisse *Lang, Waltershausen (Bay)*

Meranier Schwarzbier *Kaiserdom, Bamberg (Bay)*

Merklein *Mühlenbräu Merklein, Mühlendorf (Bay)*

Merziger Brauhaus *Saarfürst, Merzig (Saar)*

Messhofener *Kolb, Meßhofen (Bay)*

Messing *Johann Albrecht, Bielefeld (N-W); Johann Albrecht, Düsseldorf (N-W); Johann Albrecht, Konstanz (B-W); Johann Albrecht, Meßberg (Ham); Johann Albrecht, Regensburg (Bay); Johann Albrecht, Soltau (Nie); Brauhaus Alter Fritz, Tegel (Ber)*

Mettlacher Abtei-Bräu *Mettlach (Saar)*

Metzgerbräu *Allgäuer Brauhaus, Kempten (Bay); Pürkwang (Bay)*

Metzler *Dingsleben (Thü)*

Metzler *Wulfen (N-W)*

Meusel Bräu *Dreuschendorf (Bay)*

Meyringer *Gutsbrauerei Meyringer, Moosham (Bay)*

Michael *Weißenstadt (Bay)*

Michaeli *Bretten (B-W); Stanglbräu, Herrnwahlthann (Bay); Riedenburger, Riedenburg (Bay); Barbarossa, Schöllkrippen (Bay)*

Michaelsbier *Körpricher Landbräu, Körprich (Saar)*

Michel's *Michelsbräu, Babenhausen (Hes)*

Michelsbräu *Babenhausen (Hes)*

Michelstädter *Dörr, Michelstadt (Hes)*

Michelstädter Rathausbräu *Michelstadt (Hes)*

Mickhausen *Schloßbrauerei, Mickhausen (Bay)*

Microbrauerei Barkowsky *Mitte (Ber)*

Mild *Weber, Röbersdorf (Bay)*

Mild Plus *Heforder, Sundern (N-W)*

Mille Centennium *Ankerbräu, Nördlingen (Bay)*

Millennium Pils *Hofbräu, Abensberg (Bay)*

Mitte *Mitte (Ber)*

Mittenwald *Mittenwald (Bay)*

Mittsommerbier *Meierei, Potsdam (Bra)*

Mittweidaer Löwenbräu *Hartmannsdorfer, Hartmannsdorf (Sach)*

Moerser *Moers (N-W)*

Mögglinger *Adlerbrauerei, Mögglingen (B-W)*

Mohrenköpfle *Haller Löwenbräu, Schwäbisch Hall (B-W)*

Mölmsch *Trinklogistik, Duisburg (N-W, unknown brewer)*

Mönchengladbach *Mönchengladbach (N-W)*

Mönchs Pils *Klosterbrauerei, Neuzelle (Bra)*

Mönchsambacher *Zehendner, Mönchsambach (Bay)*

Mönchshof *Kulmbacher, Kulmbach (Bay)*

Mönchwasen *Simmozheim (B-W)*

Mondscheinbier *Lotters, Aue (Sach); Schloßbrauerei, Fürstliche Drehna (Bra); Brauhaus in Spandau, Spandau (Ber)*

Moninger *Karlsruhe (B-W)*

Mönk *Schmitz-Mönk, Anrath (N-W)*

Moos *Moos (Bay)*

Moosbacher *Scheuerer, Moosbach (Bay)*

Mooswald-Heimbräu *Wolfenweiler (B-W)*

Moravia Pils *Kronen-Brauerei, Lüneberg (Nie, unknown brewer)*

Moritz Fiege *Bochum (N-W)*

Mosbacher *Mosbach (B-W)*

Möwen *Weizenbierglasmuseum, Nürnberg (Bay)*

Mühlbauer *Arnschwang (Bay)*

Mühldorfer Weißbier *Unertl, Mühldorf (Bay)*

Mühlen *Wiesenmühle, Fulda (Hes); Zur Malzmühle, Köln (N-W); Bergquell, Löbau (Sach)*

Mühlenbergbrauerei *Schollene (S-A)*

Mühlenbier *Kalkarer Mühle, Kalkar (N-W)*

Mühlenbräu *Merklein, Mühlendorf (Bay); Stuhrer Mühle, Stuhr (Nie)*

Mühlengrund *Wienhausen (Nie)*

Mühlfelder *Mühlfelder Brauhaus, Mühlfeld (Bay)*

Mühlhäuser Pils *Zum Löwen, Mühlhausen (Thü)*

Mühlheimer Brauhaus *Mühlheim (N-W)*

Müller *Debring (Bay); Pinkus Müller, Münster (N-W); Oberveischeide (N-W); Reundorf (Bay)*

Müller's Demeter Lager *Pinkus Müller, Münster (N-W)*

Müller's Weißbier *Müllerbräu, Pfaffenhofen (Bay)*

Müllerbräu *Neuötting (Bay); Pfaffenhofen (Bay); Reundorf (Bay)*

Mulvany's Dunkel *Schacht 4/8, Duisburg (N-W); Hibernia, Gelsenkirchen (N-W); Mühlheimer Brauhaus, Mühlheim (N-W); Zeche Jacobi, Oberhausen (N-W)*

Mumme *Brauhaus am Lohberg, Wismar (M-V)*

Münch Bräu *Eibau (Sach)*

Münchhausen Brauhaus *Bodenwerder (Nie)*

Münchner Dunkel *Paulaner/Hacker-Pschorr, München (Bay)*

Münchner Gold *Paulaner/Hacker-Pschorr, München (Bay)*

Münchner Hell *Bavaria-Bräu, München (Bay); Paulaner/Hacker-Pschorr, München (Bay); Spaten-Franziskaner-Bräu, München (Bay)*

Münchner Kindl Weissbier *Hofbräu, München (Bay)*

Münchner Sommer *Hofbräu, München (Bay)*

Münchsteinacher *Loscher, Münchsteinach (Bay)*

Münster *Hintereder, Chammünster (Bay)*

Münstereifeler *Eifeler-Brauhaus, Bad Münstereifel (N-W)*

Münsterländische Brauerei Klute *Poppenbeck (N-W)*

Münz *Postbräu, Thannhausen (Bay)*

Murmann *Untersiemau (Bay)*

Murnauer Märzen *Griesbräu, Murnau (Bay)*

Murnauer Weißbier *Karg, Murnau (Bay)*

Museums Löschauer *Freilandmuseum, Bad Windsheim (Bay)*

Museumsbier *Bayerisches Museumsbräu, Kulmbach (Bay)*

Museumsbrauerei *Singen (Thü); Wippra (S-A)*

Musketier Märzen *Kaiser Napoleon, Leipzig (Sach)*

N

Na Klar *Bönnsch, Bonn (N-W)*
Naabecker *Schloßbrauerei, Naabeck (Bay)*
Nachtwächter Schwarzbier *Zwönitz, Zwönitz (Sach)*
Nagolder *Anker, Nagold (B-W)*
Nahetal *Guldenbacher, Windesheim (R-P)*
Nailaer Fichten-Zäpfla *Bürgerbräu, Naila (Bay)*
Nankendorfer *Schroll, Nankendorf (Bay)*
Napoleon *Kaiser Napoleon, Leipzig (Sach)*
Narrenalt *Niddaer Marktbräu, Nidda (Hes)*
Narrenbräu *Garley, Gardelegen (S-A)*
Narrenkrug *Schloßbrauerei, Schwarzbach (Thü)*
Narrentrunk *Lindenbräu, Mindelheim (Bay)*
Narrhallabräu *Rathausbräu, Michelstadt (Hes)*
Nassauer *Nassauische, Hahnstätten (R-P)*
Nassauische *Hahnstätten (R-P)*
Nationalpark Pilsener *Dampfbierbrauerei, Zwiesel (Bay)*
Nattheimer *Ochsen Bräu, Nattheim (B-W)*
Naturblond *Waldgasthaus Steinbach, Kirchheim (N-W)*
Naturdunkel *Waldgasthaus Steinbach, Kirchheim (N-W)*
Natureis Bock *Kronenbrauerei Söflingen, Ulm (B-W)*
Natureis Lager *Kronenbrauerei Söflingen, Ulm (B-W)*
Naturpils *Kössel-Bräu, Speiden (Bay)*
Naturtyp *Mühlengrund, Wienhausen (Nie)*
Neckarmüller *Tübingen (B-W)*
Neckarsulmer *Neckarsulm (B-W)*
Nedensdorfer *Reblitz, Nedensdorf (Bay)*
Neder *Forchheim (Bay)*
Neeb *Unterschleichach (Bay)*
Nette Edel Pils *Königsbacher, Koblenz (R-P)*
Neue Torgauer Brauhaus *Torgau (Sach)*
Neue Weisse *Innstad, Passau (Bay)*
Neues Helles *Innstadt, Passau (Bay); Stöttner, Pfaffenberg (Bay)*
Neuhaus *Löwenbräu, Neuhaus (Bay); Kommunbrauhaus, Neuhaus (Bay); Kommunbrauerei, Neuhaus (Bay)*
Neuhausen *Bärenbräu, Neuhausen (Bay)*
Neuhauser Märzen *Bärenbräu, Neuhausen (Bay)*
Neuhauser Weisse *Weinzierl, Unterneuhausen (Bay)*
Neumann *Haus zur Pfauen, Erfurt (Thü)*
Neumarkter *Glossner-Bräu, Neumarkt (Bay); Lammsbräu, Neumarkt (Bay)*
Neumondbier *Meierei, Potsdam (Bra)*
Neunburg Brauhaus *Weißes Brauhaus, Neunburg (Bay)*
Neunhofer Pils *Wiethaler, Neunhof (Bay)*
Neunspringer *Worbis (Thü)*
Neuöttinger Export *Müllerbräu, Neuötting (Bay)*
Neuschwansteiner *Hirschbräu, Sonthofen (Bay)*
Neustadt *Neustadt (R-P)*
Neustadt Hell *Neustädter, Dresden (Sach)*
Neustadter *Neustadt (R-P)*
Neustädter *Dresden (Sach)*
Neuzeller *Klosterbrauerei, Neuzelle (Bra)*
Nicolator *Christoph-Bräu, Gaggenau (B-W)*
Nickelbier *Johann Albrecht, Düsseldorf (N-W)*
Niddaer Marktbräu *Nidda (Hes)*
Niedermeiers Hof *Reineberg (N-W)*
Niederrhein Alt *Bolten, Korschenbroich (N-W)*

Niedersachsen Pils *Härke, Peine (Nie)*
Nikolator *Zum Schad, Halle (S-A); Lampl-Bräu, Larsbach (Bay); Emsländer, Lünne (Nie); Rathausbräu, Michelstadt (Hes); Braumanufaktur, Potsdam (Bra); Asgaard, Schleswig (S-H)*
Nikolaus Festbier *Vogel Hausbräu, Ettlingen (B-W); Vogelbräu, Karlsruhe (B-W); Vogel Hausbräu, Karlsruhe (B-W)*
Nikolausbier *Webster, Duisburg (N-W); Altes Brauhaus zu Fallersleben, Fallersleben (Nie); Freising, Freising (Bay); Wiesenmühle, Fulda (Hes); Bürgerbräu, Wolnzach (Bay)*
Nikolausbock *Graf Zeppelin, Bad Homburg (Hes); Max & Moritz, Berg (B-W); Landbräu, Körprich (Saar); Domhof, Speyer (R-P); Hagenbräu, Worms (R-P)*
Nittenau *Nittenau (Bay)*
No.1 *Brinkhoff, Dortmund (N-W); Alte Kelter, Lampertheim (Hes); Welde, Plankstadt (B-W); Bruch, Saarbrücken (Saar)*
No.2 *Alte Kelter, Lampertheim (Hes)*
No.3 *Alte Kelter, Lampertheim (Hes)*
No.33 *Hellers, Köln (N-W)*
Nobles Pils *Schlossbräu, Drachselried (Bay)*
Nockherberger *Paulaner, München (Bay)*
Nolte *Lüneberg (Nie)*
Nordbräu *Ingolstadt (Bay)*
Nordeck Trunk *Schübel, Stadtsteinach (Bay)*
Nordgold Pilsener *Darguner, Dargun (M-V)*
Nordisches Weizen *Schleswig, Schleswig (S-H)*
Nördlinger *Ankerbräu, Nördlingen (Bay)*
Nörten-Hardenberger *Martini, Kassel (Hes)*
Nortwald Pils *Jahns-Bräu, Ludwigsstadt (Bay);*
Nothelfer *Trunk, Vierzehnheiligen (Bay)*
Nothhaft *Marktredwitz (Bay)*

O

Oasen Bräu *Graben-Neudorf (B-W)*
Obaladara *Ott, Oberleinleiter (Bay)*
Oberaudorfer *Weißbierbrauerei Bals, Oberaudorf (Bay)*
Oberberg *Gummersbach, Gummersbach (N-W)*
Oberbräu *Holzkirchen (Bay)*
Oberdachstettener *Haag, Oberdachstetten (Bay)*
Obergärig *Gemünder, Gemünd (N-W); St. Martin, Oberlahnstein (R-P); Rehborner Hof-Brauhaus, Rehborn (R-P); Cramer, Wollersheim (N-W)*
Obergäriges Lagerbier *Stiefel-Jürgens, Beckum (N-W)*
Oberhauser Dunkel *Charly Bräu, Augsburg (Bay)*
Obermühle *Braunfels (Hes); Görlitz (Sach)*
Oberpfälzer Landgold *Hösl, Mitterteich (Bay)*
Oberreichenbacher *Geyer, Oberreichenbach (Bay)*
Oberstdorf *Dampfbierbrauerei, Oberstdorf (Bay); Hirschbräu, Sonthofen (Bay)*
Oberthürheimer Bio-Bräu *Oberthürheim (Bay)*
Oberurseler Brauhaus *Oberursel (Hes)*
Ochsen *Ergenzingen (B-W); Nattheim (B-W)*
Ochsenbräu *Ochsen, Ergenzingen (B-W)*
Ochsenfurter Kauzen-Bräu *Ochsenfurt (Bay)*
Odelzhausen *Schloßbrauerei, Taxa (Bay)*
Odin Trunk *Schloßbrauerei, Fürstliche Drehna (Bra)*

Oechsner Ankerbräu *Ochsenfurt (Bay)*
Oeko-Bier *Heller, Herzogenaurach (Bay)*
Oettinger *Dessow, Dessow (Bra); Gotha, Gotha (Thü);
    Mönchengladbach, Mönchengladbach (N-W);
    Oettingen, Oettingen (Bay); Schweriner
    Schloßbrauerei, Schwerin (M-V)*
Oha Bräu *Adlerbrauerei Götz, Geislingen (B-W)*
Ohne Filter *Waldhaus, Waldhaus (B-W)*
Öko Dunkel *Hartinger, Rinteln (Nie)*
Öko Ernteweizen *Hartinger, Rinteln (Nie)*
Öko Hell *Hartinger, Rinteln (Nie)*
Öko Krone Export *Härtsfelder, Dunstelkingen (B-W)*
Öko Lager *Schloßbrauerei, Reuth (Bay);*
Öko Markt *Vachdorf (Thü)*
Öko Pils *Hofmark, Loifling (Bay); Hartinger, Rinteln
    (Nie); Bürgerliches Brauhaus, Wiesen (Bay)*
Öko Räuber Weisse *Bürgerliches Brauhaus, Wiesen (Bay)*
Öko Ur-Pils *Rother-Bräu, Roth (Bay)*
Öko Urtrunk *Rother-Bräu, Roth (Bay)*
Öko Urweizen *Rother-Bräu, Roth (Bay)*
Ökoland *Demmert, Neuendorf (S-A)*
Oktoberrbier *Watzke, Dresden (Sach)*
Olbernhau *Olbernhau (Sach)*
One *Mash, Stuttgart (B-W)*
Operator *Schloßbrauerei Odelzhausen, Taxa (Bay)*
Oraniensteiner *Nassauische, Hahnstätten (R-P)*
Orgelpfeifen Bräu *Fiedler, Oberscheibe (Sach)*
Original Altbayerisch *Gritschenbräu, Schrobenhausen
    (Bay)*
Original Altbayrisch Dunkel *Schönram, Schönram (Bay)*
Original Badebier *Klosterbrauerei, Neuzelle (Bra)*
Original Berliner Weisse *Schultheiss,
    Hohenschönhausen (Ber)*
Original Bitterbier *Hövels, Dortmund (N-W)*
Original Keltisches *Leidmann, Unterneukirchen (Bay)*
Original Leipziger Gose *Gosebrauerei, Leipzig (Sach)*
Original Lübener Tennenbräu *Tennenbräu, Lüben (Nie)*
Original Münchner *Paulaner, München (Bay)*
Original Murnauer Weißbier *Karg, Murnau (Bay)*
Original Neumarkter *Glossner-Bräu, Neumarkt (Bay)*
Original Oettinger *Dessow, Dessow (Bra); Gotha,
    Gotha (Thü); Mönchengladbach, Mönchengladbach
    (N-W); Oettingen, Oettingen (Bay); Schweriner
    Schloßbrauerei, Schwerin (M-V)*
Original Schlüssel Alt *Düsseldorf (N-W)*
Original Urbräu *Tucher, Fürth & Nürnberg (Bay)*
Original Weitnauer *Memminger, Memmingen (Bay)*
Original Wippraer *Museumsbrauerei, Wippra (S-A)*
Original 1649 *Bischofshof, Regensburg (Bay)*
Original 1809 *Kauzen-Bräu, Ochsenfurt (Bay)*
Original 1855 *Peschl, Passau (Bay)*
Orth-Bräu *Sulzbach-Rosenberg (Bay)*
Oscar Maxxum *Maxxum, Krefeld (N-W, unknown brewer)*
Oskar Farny Pils *Edelweissbrauerei, Dürren (B-W)*
Osser *Späth-Bräu, Lohberg (Bay)*
Oster Engel *Engel-Bräu, Crailsheim (B-W)*
Osterhäsle *Anke, Nagold (B-W)*
Ostersud *Landshuter Brauhaus, Landshut (Bay)*
Ostfriesen Bräu *Bagband (Nie)*

Ostfriesische Küsten-Brauerei *Werdum (Nie)*
Ostheim Dunkel *Streck-Bräu, Ostheim (Bay)*
Ostritz *Ostritz (Sach)*
Ostsee Brauhaus *Kühlungsborn (M-V)*
Ott *Oberleinleiter (Bay)*
Ottenbräu *Abensberg (Bay)*
Ottersheimer Bärenbräu *Ottersheim (R-P)*
OXX Lager *Gold Ochsen, Ulm (B-W)*
OXX White *Gold Ochsen, Ulm (B-W)*

P

Paderborner *Paderborn (N-W)*
Päffgen *Köln (N-W)*
Pale Ale *Lemke's Spezialitätenbrauerei, Mitte (Ber)*
Palmator *Prößlbräu, Adlersberg (Bay)*
Palmbräu *Eppingen (B-W)*
Panduren Dunkel *Klingenbrunn, Klingenbrunn (Bay)*
Panduren Weisse *Rhanerbräu, Rhan (Bay)*
Pantaleons Schwarze *Weißbräu, Köln (N-W)*
Papiermühle *Papiermühle, Jena (Thü)*
Papst-Bier *Weideneder, Tann (Bay)*
Pardus *Franken Bräu, Riedbach (B-W)*
Park *Pirmasens (R-P)*
Pater *Klosterbräu, Seemannshausen (Bay)*
Pater Simon *Kapplerbräu, Altomünster (Bay)*
Patrizier *Tucher, Fürth (Bay)*
Paul-Lincke-Treff *Hahnenklee (Nie)*
Paulaner *Paulaner / Hacker-Pschorr, München (Bay)*
Paulaner Bräuhaus *München (Bay)*
Paulaner/Hacker-Pschorr *München (Bay)*
Pauline *Paulaner Bräuhaus München (Bay)*
Peccator *Schloßbrauerei, Au (Bay); Kühbach, Kübach
    (Bay)*
Penning *Hetzelsdorf (Bay)*
Peniger *Spezialitätenbrauerei, Penig (Sach)*
Penzkofer *Eschlkam (Bay, unknown brewer)*
Perle *Maisach, Maisach (Bay)*
Perlweizen *Brauhaus Schweinfurt, Schweinfurt (Bay);
    Gambrinus-Brauerei, Weiden (Bay)*
Peschl *Passau (Bay)*
Peter *Ostheim (Bay)*
Petermännchen Pils *Schweriner, Schwerin (M-V)*
Peters Bauernstube *Haltern (N-W)*
Peters Kölsch *Kölner Brauer Verbuns, Köln (N-W)*
Pfaffen *Kellershohn (N-W)*
Pfaffen Gold *Stöttner, Pfaffenberg (Bay)*
Pfaffenator *Stöttner, Pfaffenberg (Bay)*
Pfaffenberger *Stöttner, Pfaffenberg (Bay)*
Pfaffenhofen *Brauhaus Urban, Pfaffenhofen (Bay)*
Pfälzer Festbier *Bellheimer, Bellheim (R-P)*
Pfauenbräu *Haus zur Pfauen, Erfurt (Thü)*
Pfeffenhausener *Pöllinger, Pfeffenhausen (Bay)*
Pfefferbräu *Erste Dampfbierbrauerei, Zwiesel (Bay)*
Pfiff *Plank, Wiefelsdorf (Bay)*
Pfister *Weigelshofen (Bay)*
Pflug *Pflugbrauerei, Hörvelsingen (B-W)*
Pflugbrauerei *Hörvelsingen (B-W)*
Pforzheim *Pforzheim (B-W)*
Pfungstädter *Pfungstadt (Hes)*

Phantastisches Karpfen *Klosterbrauerei, Kemnath (Bay)*
Piccolo Weizen *Kapplerbräu, Altomünster (Bay)*
Pichelsteiner Festbier *Falter, Regen (Bay)*
Pikantus *Erdinger Weißbräu, Erding (Bay)*
Pils aus Pahres *Hofmann, Pahres (Bay)*
Pils de Luxe *Hochstiftliches Brauhaus, Motten (Bay)*
Pils Juwel *Bucher, Gundelfingen (Bay)*
Pils Krone *Hochdorfer Kronenbrauerei, Hochdorf (B-W)*
Pils Legende *Wernesgrüner, Wernesgrün (Sach)*
Pils Superior *Bürgerbräu, Bad Reichenhall (Bay)*
Pils 03 *Bruckmüller, Amberg (Bay)*
Pilsator *Frankfurter Brauhaus, Frankfurt (Bra)*
Pilsissimus *Forschungsbrauerei, München (Bay)*
Pinkus Müller *Münster (N-W)*
Pirker *Pirk (Bay)*
Pirminator *Park, Pirmasens (R-P)*
Pirna *Copitz (Sach)*
Placidus Cobaldus Dunkel *Bräuhaus, Ummendorf (B-W)*
Plank *Laaber (Bay)*
Plankstettener *Riedenburger, Riedenburg (Bay)*
Plato 13 *Diebels, Issum (N-W)*
Plausch *Kneipe Pur, Plaue (Bra)*
Plinganser Bier *Schloßbrauerei, Arnstorf (Bay)*
Ploss *Selb (Bay)*
Pogorausch *Ziegler, Waldsassen (Bay)*
Polar Weizen *Schönbuch-Bräu, Böblingen (B-W)*
Pöllinger *Pfeffenhausen (Bay)*
Ponter *Besseringen (Saar)*
Poppel Mühle *Poppeltal (B-W)*
Poppelbräu *Poppel-Mühle, Poppeltal (B-W)*
Portator *Thorbräu, Augsburg (Bay)*
Porter *Bosch, Bad Laasphe (N-W); Kirchers, Drebkau (Bra); Watzke, Dresden (Sach); Kulturbrauerei, Heidelberg (B-W); Bergquell, Löbau (Sach); Schwerter Brauerei Wohlers, Meißen (Sach); Lemke's Spezialitätenbrauerei, Mitte (Ber); Kneipe Pur, Plaue (Bra); Ricklinger, Rickling (S-H)*
Pößneck *Rosenbrauerei, Pößneck (Thü)*
Post *Frankenthal (R-P); Weiler (Bay)*
Postbräu *Frontenhausen (Bay); Thannhausen (Bay)*
Postbrauerei *Frontenhausen (Bay); Nesselwang (Bay)*
Postherren Pils *Postbräu, Thannhausen (Bay)*
Posthorn Gold *Postbrauerei, Nesselwang (Bay)*
Posthörnla Rauchbier *Hönig, Tiefenellern (Bay)*
Postillion *Postbrauerei, Nesselwang (Bay)*
Postillon Weiße *Hönig, Tiefenellern (Bay)*
Postmeister *Fürstliches Brauhaus, Regensburg (Bay)*
Postwirt's Dunkel *Postbrauerei, Nesselwang (Bay)*
Potenzbier *Alt Wülfrath, Wülfrath (N-W)*
Potsdamer Landbier *Meierei, Potsdam (Bra)*
Potsdamer Rex Pils *Berliner Kindl, Neukölln (Ber)*
Potsdamer Schwarze *Meierei, Potsdam (Bra)*
Potsdamer Stange *Braumanufaktur, Potsdam (Bra)*
Pott's *Oelde (N-W)*
Pottenstein's Premium Pils *Hufeisen, Pottenstein (Bay)*
Pottensteiner Höhlentrunk *St.Georgen, Buttenheim (Bay)*
Pottensteiner Urdunkel *Hufeisen, Pottenstein (Bay)*
Pöttmes *Schloßbrauerei, Pöttmes (Bay)*
Potz Blitz Bier *Brauhaus in Spandau, Spandau (Ber)*

Prädikator *Landshuter Brauhaus, Landshut (Bay)*
Pralles Pils *Ziegler, Waldsassen (Bay)*
Präsidenten *Präsidenten Pils, Windesheim (R-P)*
Prechtel *Uehlfeld (Bay)*
Prellbock *Gosebrauerei Bayerischer Bahn, Leipzig (Sach)*
Premium Dark *Paderborner, Paderborn (N-W)*
Premium Dry *Paderborner, Paderborn (N-W)*
Premium Gold 1688 *Kesselring, Marktsteft (Bay)*
Premium Ice *Ankerbräu, Nördlingen (Bay)*
Premium Specht *Spessart, Kreuzwertheim (Bay)*
Premium Verum *Warsteiner, Warstein (N-W)*
Preußen Dunkel *Marcus-Bräu, Mitte (Ber)*
Preussen Pils *Brauhaus Preussen Pils, Pritzwalk (Bra)*
Preussen Schwarzbier *Preussen Pils, Pritzwalk (Bra)*
Priesterbock *Brauhaus Zwickau, Zwickau (Sach)*
Priesterdunkel *Brauhaus Zwickau, Zwickau (Sach)*
Priesterhefe *Brauhaus Zwickau, Zwickau (Sach)*
Priesterhell *Brauhaus Zwickau, Zwickau (Sach)*
Priesterrauch *Brauhaus Zwickau, Zwickau (Sach)*
Primus *Charly Bräu, Augsburg (Bay); Kleines Eifeler-Brauhaus, Bad Münstereifel (N-W); Bürgerbräu, Bad Windsheim (Bay); Park, Pirmasens (R-P); Fuchsbeck, Sulzbach-Rosenberg (Bay)*
Prinz Albrecht Trunk *Leitner, Schwabach (Bay)*
Prinz Hendrick Pilsener *Nassauische, Hähnstetten (R-P)*
Prinzenbock *Schloßbrauerei, Grünbach (Bay)*
Prinzensud *Wasserburger, Dingolfing (Bay)*
Prinzregent Luitpold *Schloßbrau, Fürstenfeldbrück (Bay); Schloßbrauerei, Kaltenberg (Bay); Postbräu, Thannhausen (Bay)*
Pritzwalk *Brauhaus Preussen Pils, Pritzwalk (Bra)*
Privat *Augusta, Augsburg (Bay); Hofmühl, Eichstätt (Bay); Einsiedler, Einsiedel (Sach); Kleines Brauhaus, Essing (Bay); Nordbräu, Ingolstadt (Bay); Ludger's Kleine Brauerei, Littfeld (N-W); Mall, Meckesheim (B-W); Schwerter Brauerei Wohlers, Meißen (Sach); Ketterer, Pforzheim (B-W); Falter, Regen (Bay); Schaumburger, Stadthagen (Nie); Weideneder, Tann (Bay); Felsenbräu, Thalmannsfeld (Bay); Ustersbacher, Ustersbach (Bay); Adler-Bräu, Zuzenhausen (B-W)*
Probst Sutor Märzen *Kapplerbräu, Altomünster (Bay)*
Proßlbräu *Adlersberg (Bay)*
Pubarschknall *Lüdde, Quedlinburg (S-A)*
Publiner *Schlossbrauerei, Herrngiersdorf (Bay)*
Püls Bräu *Weismain (Bay)*
Pummpils *Rhönbrauerei Dittmar, Kaltennordheim (Thü)*
Pupen-Schultzes Schwarzes *Landskron, Görlitz (Sach)*
Pur *Kirner, Kirn (R-P)*
Pur Bräu *Kneipe Pur, Plaue (Bra)*
Pürner *Etzelwang (Bay)*
Püt *Püttner, Schlammersdorf (Bay)*
Püttner *Schlammersdorf (Bay)*
Pyraser *Pyras (Bay)*

Q

Qualitätsbier *Lammbrauerei, Untergröningen (B-W)*
Quattro-Bier *Graf Zeppelin, Bad Homburg (Hes)*
Quirinus *Herzoglich Bayerisches Brauhaus, Tegernsee (Bay)*

R

Raab *Hofheim (Bay)*
Rabans Bräu *Häffner Bräu, Bad Rappenau (B-W)*
Racherla *Griess, Geisfeld (Bay)*
Radbier *Radbrauerei Bucher, Günzburg (Bay)*
Radbrauerei Bucher *Günzburg (Bay)*
Radeberger *Radeberg (Sach)*
Radigk's Wirtshausbräu *Finsterwalde (Bra)*
Radigkator *Radigk's Wirtshausbräu, Finsterwalde (Bra)*
Raigeringer *Sterk, Raigering (Bay)*
Rainer *Kleinbrauerei Rain, Rain (Bay); Welz (N-W)*
Raiterla *Rittmayer, Hallerndorf (Bay)*
Rampendahl *Osnabrück (Nie)*
Rapp *Kutzenhausen (Bay)*
Rappen *Rapp, Kutzenhausen (Bay)*
Rappiator *Rapp, Kutzenhausen (Bay)*
Rapunzel *Aktienbrauerei, Simmerberg (Bay)*
Rathaus Pilsner *Alsfeld, Alsfeld (Hes)*
Rathausbräu *Michelstadt (Hes)*
Rathsbräu *König von Preußen, Frauenalb (B-W)*
Ratibor Dunkel *Stadtbrauerei Roth, Roth (Bay)*
Ratinger *Ratingen (N-W)*
Rats Kölsch *Dom, Köln (N-W)*
Ratsbräu *Ratskeller, Darmstadt (Hes); Ratsbrauerei, Weißensee (Thü)*
Ratsbrauerei *Rain (Bay); Weißensee (Thü)*
Ratsbrauhaus *Bad Gandersheim (Nie); Hann. Münden (Nie)*
Ratsherrn *Dörr, Michelstadt (Hes); Bavaria St. Pauli, St. Pauli (Ham, brewed elsewhere)*
Ratskeller *Darmstadt (Hes); Geising (Sach); Gilde, Hannover (Nie); Pforzheim, Pforzheim (B-W)*
Räuber *Hohe Wart Bräu, Hohenwart (Bay)*
Räuber Knießl Dunkel *Maisach, Maisach (Bay)*
Räuber Weisse *Bürgerliches Brauhaus, Wiesen (Bay)*
Räuberbock *Bürgerliches Brauhaus, Wiesen (Bay)*
Raubritter *Bayer Bräu, Rothenfels (Bay)*
Raubritter Dunkel *Sonnenbräu, Lichtenberg (Bay); Schloßbrauerei, Schwarzbach (Thü)*
Rauchbier *Lotters Wirtschaft, Aue (Sach); Heller, Bamberg (Bay); Spezial, Bamberg (Bay); Wallhall, Bruchsal (B-W); Watzke, Dresden (Sach); Waldhaus, Erfurt (Thü); Vogel, Ettlingen (B-W); Altes Brauhaus, Fallersleben (Nie); Wiesenmühle, Fulda (Hes); Christoph-Bräu, Gaggenau (B-W); Greiss, Geisfeld (Bay); Fischer, Greuth (Bay); Sauer, Gunzendorf (Bay); Zum Schad, Halle (S-A); Rittmayer, Hallerndorf (Bay); Barnikel, Herrnsdorf (Bay); Vogelbräu, Karlsruhe (B-W); Vogel Hausbräu, Karlsruhe (B-W); Brauhaus im Wurzgrund, Karlstadt (Bay); Schloßplatzbrauerei, Köpenick (Ber); Andreasbräu, Leopoldshafen (B-W); Rossknecht, Ludwigsburg (B-W); Sudhaus, Ludwigsburg (B-W); Alter Bahnhof, Malsch (B-W); Drei Kronen, Memmelsdorf (Bay); Griesbräu, Murnau (Bay); Geißler, Nürnberg (Bay); Kneipe Pur, Plaue (Bra); Ricklinger, Rickling (S-H); Weber, Röbersdorf (Bay); Extra, Röhrigshof (Hes); Knoblach, Schammelsdorf (Bay); Ploss, Selb (Bay); Hönig, Tiefenellern (Bay); Stierbräu, Vechta (Nie);*

Eschenbräu, Wedding (Ber); Kundmüller, Weiher (Bay); Göller, Zeil (Bay); Brauhaus Zwickau, Zwickau (Sach)
Räucherator *Hummel, Merkendorf (Bay)*
Räucherla *Hummel, Merkendorf (Bay)*
Räuchermännchen *Wurzgrund, Karlstadt (Bay)*
Räuschla *Knoblach, Schammelsdorf (Bay)*
Rawetzer *Nothhaft, Marktredwitz (Bay)*
Rebhuhn-Zoigl *Kommunbrauerei, Eslarn (Bay)*
Reblitz *Nedensdorf (Bay)*
Rechenberger *Rechenberg (Sach)*
Recken *Schloßbrauerei, Reckendorf (Bay)*
Red *Waldhaus, Erfurt (Thü)*
Red Ale *Lemke's Spezialitätenbrauerei, Mitte (Ber)*
Red Lager *Schwerter Brauerei Wohlers, Meißen (Sach)*
Red Lion *Plank, Laaber (Bay)*
Red Weizen Ale *Weißbierbrauerei Hopf, Miesbach (Bay)*
Reformator *Lutherstadt Eisleben (S-A)*
Regenator *Falter, Regen (Bay)*
Regensburger *Bischofshof, Regensburg (Bay); Fürstliches Brauhaus, Regensburg (Bay)*
Reh *Löhndorf (Bay)*
Rehborner Hof Brauhaus *Rehborn (R-P)*
Reichenbrander *Chemnitz (Sach)*
Reichenstein Ur-Weisse *Haberl, Schönsee (Bay)*
Reichold *Hochstahl (Bay)*
Reichsstadtbier *Döbler, Bad Windsheim (Bay)*
Reindler *Jochsberg (Bay)*
Reiners Rosine *Flein (B-W)*
Reischenau Gold *Ustersbacher, Ustersbach (Bay)*
Reissdorf *Köln (N-W)*
Reiter Bräu *Wartenberg (Bay)*
Reitinger *Oberroth (Bay)*
Renator *Weißbräu, Freilassing (Bay)*
Renkl *Postbrauerei, Frontenhausen (Bay)*
Rennsteig Spezial *Eisenacher, Eisenach (Thü)*
Respekt *Schlossbräu, Drachselried (Bay)*
Respektator *Schlossbräu, Drachselried (Bay)*
Rettenberg *Engelbräu, Rettenberg (Bay)*
Reudnitzer *Leipzig (Sach)*
Reusenbräu *Kliesow's Reuse, Alt Reddevitz (M-V)*
Reutberger *Klosterbrauerei, Reutberg (Bay)*
Reuter *Unternbibert (Bay)*
Reuther *Schloßbrauerei, Reuth (Bay)*
Rezent Weizen *Palmbräu, Eppingen (B-W)*
Rhaner Bräu *Rhan (Bay)*
Rheder *Schloßbrauerei, Rheder (N-W)*
Rheinbacher *Rheinbach (N-W)*
Rheinsberg *Rheinsberg (Bra)*
Rhenania Alt *Eichener, Eichen (N-W)*
Rhön *Peter, Ostheim (Bay)*
Rhönator *Rother-Bräu, Roth (Bay)*
Rhönbrauerei Dittmar *Kaltennordheim (Thü)*
Rhöner *Rhönbrauerei Dittmar, Kaltennordheim (Thü)*
Rhöner Dunkel *Karmeliter-Bräu, Bad Neustadt (Bay)*
Richmodis *Gaffel (Porz), Köln (N-W)*
Ricklinger *Rickling (S-H)*
Riebeck *Braugold, Erfurt (Thü)*
Riedenburger *Riedenburg (Bay)*
Riedl *Plößberg (Bay)*

Riegele *Augsburg (Bay)*
Riegeler *Fürstlich Fürstenbergische, Donaueschingen (B-W)*
Riemhofer *Riedenburg (Bay)*
Rieser *Ankerbräu, Nördlingen (Bay)*
Ring *Kirchhellen (N-W)*
Rintelner Lokalitätenbrauerei *Rinteln (Nie)*
Ritter *Brinkhoff, Dortmund (N-W); Zum Ritter, Schwetzingen (B-W)*
Ritter Bier *Ritter St. Georgen, Nennslingen (Bay)*
Ritter Dunkel *Torgau, Torgau (Sach)*
Ritter Kuno Trunk *Gick-Bräu, Burgkunstadt (Bay)*
Ritter Premium *Heidebrauerei, Colbitz (S-A)*
Ritter St. Georgen *Nennslingen (Bay)*
Ritter Trunk *Schloßbrauerei Stelzer, Fattigau (Bay)*
Ritter Weisse *Erharting, Erharting (Bay)*
Ritter Wirnt Trunk *Friedmann, Gräfenberg (Bay)*
Ritter 1645 *Ritter St. Georgen, Nennslingen (Bay)*
Ritterbock *Schloßbrauerei, Fürstenfeldbrück (Bay); Schloßbrauerei, Kaltenberg (Bay)*
Ritterguts Gose *Bauer, Leipzig (Sach)*
Ritterschaft *Dimpfl Bräu Strauß, Furth im Wald (Bay)*
Rittertrunk *Lindenbräu, Mindelheim (Bay)*
Rittmayer *Aisch (Bay); Hallerndorf (Bay); Willersdorf (Bay, unknown brewer)*
Rixdorf *Neukölln (Ber)*
Röbersdorfer *Weber, Röbersdorf (Bay)*
Robesbierre *Bamberg (Bay)*
Röckeleins Kellerbier *Kaiserdom, Bamberg (Bay)*
Rodinger *Greiner, Roding (Bay)*
Rödler Trunk *Aktienbrauerei, Simmerberg (Bay)*
Rogg *Lenzkirch (B-W)*
Roggenbier *Kuchlbauer, Abensberg (Bay); Walhall, Bruchsal (B-W); Kleines Freiburger Brauhaus, Freiburg (B-W); Andreasbräu, Leopoldshafen (B-W); Mannebacher Brauhaus, Mannebach (R-P); Paulaner, München (Bay); Kneipe Pur, Plaue (Bra); Fürstliches Brauhaus, Regensburg (Bay); Spezial, Schierling (Bay); Ploss, Selb (Bay); Kleines Brauhaus, Seligenstadt (Hes)*
Röhr Bräu *Sonneborn (N-W)*
Röhrl *Frontenhausen (Bay); Straubing (Bay)*
Rolhbock *Rossknecht, Ludwigsburg (B-W)*
Rolinck *Steinfurt (N-W)*
Römer *Binding, Frankfurt (Hes)*
Römer Kölsch *Kölner Verbund Brauereien, Köln (N-W)*
Römer Türmle *Bärenbräu, Neuhausen (Bay)*
Römergold *Herrnbräu, Ingolstadt (Bay)*
Römerstein *Hirschbrauerei Schilling, Böhringen (B-W)*
Roppelt *Stiebarlimbach (Bay); Trossenfurt (Bay)*
Rosé Bock *Schmucker, Ober-Mossau (Hes)*
Rosen *Rosenbrauerei, Pößneck (Thü)*
Rosenberger Pils *Sperber-Bräu, Sulzbach-Rosenberg (Bay)*
Rosenbrauerei *Pößneck (Thü)*
Rosenheimer *Auerbräu, Rosenheim (Bay)*
Rossach *Kommunbrauerei, Rossach (Bay)*
Rossdorfer *Sauer, Roßdorf (Bay)*
Rössel Bräu *Dampfbierhaus Rössel Bräu, Willingen (Hes)*

Rossknecht *Ludwigsburg (B-W)*
Rössle *Ehingen (B-W); Ummenhofen (Bay)*
Rostocker *Hanseatische Brauerei, Rostock (M-V)*
Rotbier *Kneipe Pur, Plaue (Bra); Barbarossa, Schöllkrippen (Bay); Spandau, Spandau (Ber)*
Roter Eric *Brauhaus am Lohberg, Wismar (M-V)*
Roter Wedding *Eschenbräu, Wedding (Ber)*
Roter 12er *Kohlenmühle, Neustadt (Bay)*
Roth *Stadtbrauerei, Roth (Bay); Schweinfurt (Bay)*
Rothaus *Badische Staatsbrauerei, Rothaus (B-W)*
Rothebier *Altstadthof, Nürnberg (Bay)*
Rothenbach *Aufseß (Bay)*
Rothenburg Gold *Schaffer-Bräu, Schnaittach (Bay)*
Rothenfelser Raubritter *Bayer Bräu, Rothenfels (Bay)*
Rother Bräu *Roth (Bay)*
Rothmoos *Rothmoos (Bay)*
Rotkehlchen *Bürgerbräu, Friedrichshagen (Ber)*
Rotochsen *Ellwangen (B-W)*
Rötter *Köpf, Aalen (B-W)*
Rötz *Genossenschaftsbrauerei, Rötz (Bay)*
Royal Gründerbier *Zittauer Bürgerbräu, Zittau (Sach)*
Rubin *Charivari-Bräu, Königsbrunn (B-W)*
Rüdenhäuser *Wolf, Rüdenhausen (Bay)*
Ruhr Pott Pils *Schacht 4/8, Duisburg (N-W); Hibernia, Gelsenkirchen (N-W); Mühlheimer Brauhaus, Mühlheim (N-W); Zeche Jacobi, Oberhausen (N-W)*
Rumpelstilz *Krummenhagen (M-V)*
Rundinger Schlossbräu *Schloßbrauerei, Runding (Bay)*
Runner *Roth, Schweinfurt (Bay)*
Ruperti Dunkel *Bürgerbräu, Bad Reichenhall (Bay)*
Ruperti Pils *Wieninger, Teisendorf (Bay)*
Rupertus *Bürgerbräu, Bad Reichenhall (Bay)*
Rupf *Adlerbrauerei, Hailtingen (B-W)*
Rupp Bräu *Lauenau (Nie)*
Ruppaner *Konstanz (B-W)*
Ruprechtus *Weißes Brauhaus, Neunburg (Bay)*
Rüsselsheimer Brauhaus *Alt Haßloch (Hes)*
Rütershoff *Castrop-Rauxel (N-W)*
Rüttenscheider *Essen (N-W)*

S

's Angele Pils *Bräuhaus Ummendorf, Ummendorf (B-W)*
's Blaue *Bräuhaus Ummendorf, Ummendorf (B-W)*
's Kleine Weizen *Hochdorfer, Hochdorf (B-W)*
's Rote *Bräuhaus Ummendorf, Ummendorf (B-W)*
Saalfelder *Bürgerliches Brauhaus, Saalfeld (Thü)*
Saarfürst *Merzig (Saar)*
Sacher *Leonberg (Bay)*
Sachsengold *Werdau (Sach, unknown brewer)*
Sachsenschlösser *Mühlfeld (Sach, unknown brewer)*
Sächsisches Rauchbier *Pirna, Copitz (Sach)*
Salch *Hammelburg (Bay, unknown brewer)*
Saline Bräu *Landsberg, Landsberg (S-A)*
Salonbier *Borbecker Dampfbier-Brauerei, Essen (N-W)*
Salvator *Paulaner, München (Bay)*
Salzscheuer *Marbach (B-W)*
Sandersdorf *Schloßbrauerei (Bay)*
Sanfte Weisse *Flözinger-Bräu, Rosenheim (Bay)*
Sankt Ulrichs Bock *Ulrich Zimmermann, Berg (B-W)*

Sanwald *Dinkelacker-Schwaben-Bräu, Stuttgart (B-W)*
Sapeur Maibock *Kaiser Napoleon, Leipzig (Sach)*
Sauer *Gunzendorf (Bay); Roßdorf (Bay); Röthenbach (Bay)*
Sauerländer Weizenbier *Vormann, Dahl (N-W)*
Säumer *Bucher Bräu, Grafenau (Bay)*
Sauter *Uttenweiler (B-W)*
Sautter's Hofbier *Lauterbach, Lauterbach (Bay)*
Schäazer *Drei Kronen, Scheßlitz (Bay)*
Schacht 4/8 *Duisburg (N-W)*
Schad *Halle (S-A)*
Schadt's *Brauhaus zum Löwen, Braunschweig (Nie), Schadt's Brauerei Gasthaus, Braunschweig (Nie)*
Schäff *Treuchtlingen (Bay)*
Schaffer *Schnaittach (Bay)*
Schäffler *Missen (Bay)*
Schaffner *Gosebrauerei Bayerischer Bahnhof, Leipzig (Sach)*
Schalchner *Weissbräu Schwendl, Schalchen (Bay)*
Schambrinus *Edelweissbrauerei, Dürren (B-W)*
Schammelsdorfer *Knoblach, Schammelsdorf (Bay)*
Schankl *Weideneder, Tann (Bay)*
Schanzer Weiße *Nordbräu, Ingolstadt (Bay)*
Scharpf *Heilgersdorf (Bay)*
Schattenhofer *Beilngries (Bay)*
Schauferts *Schönborn (R-P)*
Schaumburger *Stadthagen (Nie)*
Scheffel's *Kulturbrauerei, Heidelberg (B-W)*
Schefflenzer *Egolf, Schefflenz (B-W)*
Schellenbier *Papiermühle, Jena (Thü)*
Schels *Tirschenreuth (Bay)*
Scherdel *Hof (Bay)*
Schernecker *Schloßbrauerei Scherneck (Bay)*
Scheubel *Possenfelden (Bay); Schlüsselfeld (Bay)*
Scheuerer *Moosbach (Bay)*
Scheyern Kloster *Hasen-Bräu, Augsburg (Bay); Klosterbrauerei, Scheyern (Bay)*
Schierlinger *Spezial-Brauerei, Schierling (Bay)*
Schiessel *Winkler, Amberg (Bay)*
Schiller *Wachau (Sach)*
Schillerbad *Lüdenscheid (N-W)*
Schimmel Weisse *Siegenburger, Siegenburg (Bay)*
Schimmele *Ruppaner, Konstanz (B-W)*
Schimpf *Kronenbrauerei Schimpf, Remmingsheim (B-W)*
Schimpfle *Gessertshausen (Bay)*
Schinkel's *Witzenhausen (Hes)*
Schinner *Bürgerbräu, Bayreuth (Bay)*
Schlachthof *Schlachthof, Nürtingen (B-W)*
Schläfleshimmel *Ulrich Zimmermann, Berg (B-W)*
Schlanke Schwarze *Fuchsbeck, Sulzbach-Rosenb'g (Bay)*
Schlanke Weisse *Lauterbach, Lauterbach (Bay)*
Schlappenbier *Zeltbräu, Hof (Bay)*
Schlappeseppel *Eder & Heylands, Großostheim (Bay)*
Schlaubetaler Landbier *Klosterbrauerei, Neuzelle (Bra)*
Schleicher *Kaltenbrunn (Bay)*
Schlemmer *Kesselring, Marksteft (Bay)*
Schlenkerla *Heller, Bamberg (Bay)*
Schleswig *Schleswig (S-H)*
Schlichter *Winkler-Bräu, Schlicht (Bay)*

Schlierseer *Nordbräu, Ingolstadt (Bay)*
Schlodator *Schloderer, Amberg (Bay);*
Schloderer *Amberg (Bay)*
Schlök *Nassauische, Hähnstetten (R-P)*
Schloß *Schloßbrauerei Stelzer, Fattigau (Bay); Schloßbrauerei, Haimhausen (Bay); Schloßbrauerei, Maxlrain (Bay); Arcobräu, Moos (Bay)*
Schloss Favorit Export *Franz, Rastatt (B-W)*
Schloss Keller *Schloßbrauerei, Fürstenfeldbrück (Bay)*
Schloß Königs Wusterhausen *Königs Wusterhausen (Bra)*
Schloß Leicht *Schloßbrauerei, Hirschau (Bay)*
Schloß Pils *Vereinsbrauerei, Greiz (Thü); Eder & Heylands, Großostheim (Bay); Schloßbrauerei, Mickhausen (Bay); Kalt-Loch-Bräu, Miltenberg (Bay); Stadtbrauerei Roth, Roth (Bay)*
Schloß Privat *Schloßbrauerei, Mickhausen (Bay)*
Schloß Weizen *Kühbach, Kübach (Bay)*
Schloßbräu *Schloßbrauerei, Autenried (Bay); Drachselried (Bay); Schloßbrauerei, Fürstliche Drehna (Bra); Altes Brauhaus, Fallersleben (Nie); Mariakirchen (Bay); Mickhausen (Bay); Schloßbrauerei, Rheder (N-W); Schloßbrauerei, Schwarzbach (Thü); Stamsried (Bay, unknown brewer); Thurnau (Bay); Weesenstein (Sach)*
Schloßbrauerei *Arnstorf (Bay); Au (Bay); Autenried (Bay); Eichhofen (Bay); Fattigau (Bay); Friedenfels (Bay); Fuchsberg (Bay); Fürstenfeldbrück (Bay); Fürstliche Drehna (Bra); Grünbach (Bay); Haimhausen (Bay); Herrngiersdorf (Bay); Hirschau (Bay); Hohenthann (Bay); Holnstein (Bay); Illertissen (Bay); Irlbach (Bay); Kaltenberg (Bay); Maxlrain (Bay); Mickhausen (Bay); Naabeck (Bay); Pöttmes (Bay); Reckendorf (Bay); Reuth (Bay); Rheder (N-W); Runding (Bay); Sandersdorf (Bay); Scherneck (Bay); Schmieheim (B-W); Schwarzbach (Thü); Schwerin (M-V); Stein (Bay); Taxa (Bay); Unterbaar (Bay); Zell (Bay)*
Schlösser *Brinkhoff, Dortmund (N-W)*
Schlossgold *Fürstliches Brauhaus, Ellingen (Bay); Beck, Trabelsdorf (Bay)*
Schloßherrn Export *Sonnenbräu, Lichtenberg (Bay)*
Schlossherrn Pils *Schloßbrauerei, Holnstein (Bay)*
Schloßherrn Weisse *Schloßbrauerei, Irlbach (Bay)*
Schlössle *Neu-Ulm (Bay)*
Schloßplatz *Köpenick (Ber)*
Schloßtaler Weisse *Schloßbrauerei, Grünbach (Bay)*
Schloßturm *Stuttgart (B-W)*
Schloßweiße *Schloßbrauerei, Haimhausen (Bay)*
Schlüchtern *Schlüchtern (Hes)*
Schluck Specht *Sonnenbräu, Ebermannstadt (Bay)*
Schlucke *Schluckebier, Bad Nauheim (Hes)*
Schluckebier *Bad Nauheim (Hes)*
Schlückla *Sauer, Gunzendorf (Bay)*
Schluntz *Neumann, Erfurt (Thü)*
Schlüssel *Düsseldorf (N-W)*
Schlüsselbräu *Giengen (B-W)*
Schlüssele *Schlüsselbräu, Giengen (B-W)*
Schmankerl Weiße *Schweiger, Markt Schwaben (Bay)*
Schmäußbräu *Kaiserhof, Kronach (Bay)*

Schmelzer *Schmelz (Saar)*
Schmetzer *Adlerbrauerei, Michelbach (B-W)*
Schmid *Biberach (Bay)*
Schmidmayer *Siegenburger, Siegenburg (Bay)*
Schmidt Bräu *Schwandorf (Bay)*
Schmidtchen *Schmidtbräu, Schwandorf (Bay)*
Schmidt's Heiner Weisse *Zeltbräu, Hof (Bay)*
Schmieheim *Schloßbrauerei, Schmieheim (B-W)*
Schmiedbräu *Rothmoos, Rothmoos (Bay)*
Schmitt *Singen (Thü); Scheßlitz (Bay, unknown brewer)*
Schmitz Mönk *Anrath (N-W)*
Schmucker *Ober-Mossau (Hes)*
Schnapperla *Prechtel, Uehlfeld (Bay)*
Schnee Bock *St. Martin, Oberlahnstein (R-P)*
Schneewalzer *Herrnbräu, Ingolstadt (Bay)*
Schneeweiße *Erdinger Weißbräu, Erding (Bay)*
Schneider *Kelheim (Bay); Weißenburg (Bay)*
Schneider's *Kleines Brauhaus, Essing (Bay)*
Schnitzei Weisse *Schnitzlbaumer, Traunstein (Bay)*
Schnitzerhalbe *Riedl, Plößberg (Bay)*
Schnitzlbaumer *Traunstein (Bay)*
Schnuckenbräu *Hünzingen (Nie)*
Schnupp *Altdrossenfeld (Bay)*
Schöfferhofer *Binding, Frankfurt (Hes)*
Schollator *Mühlenbergbrauerei, Schollene (S-A)*
Schollener *Mühlenbergbrauerei, Schollene (S-A)*
Schönbrunner *Lang-Bräu, Schönbrunn (Bay)*
Schönbuch *Böblingen (B-W)*
Schongauer Brauhaus *Schongau (Bay)*
Schönitz Pilsener *Hallesches Brauhaus, Halle (S-A)*
Schönram *Schönram (Bay)*
Schopen Pils *Sünner, Köln (N-W)*
Schoppe Bräu *Niederschönhausen (Ber)*
Schöre Bock *Schörebräu, Dietmannsweiler (B-W)*
Schörebräu *Dietmannsweiler (B-W)*
Schorer *Walkertshofen (Bay)*
Schorschbräu *Oberasbach (Bay)*
Schraube Pils *Brauhaus Preussen Pils, Pritzwalk (Bra)*
Schreckenskammer Kölsch *Dom, Köln (N-W)*
Schroll *Nankendorf (Bay); Reckendorf (Bay)*
Schröttinger Bräu *Schrötting (Bay)*
Schrüfer *Priesendorf (Bay)*
Schubeck's *Egelsbach (Hes)*
Schübel *Stadtsteinach (Bay)*
Schuller *Berching (Bay)*
Schultheiss *Berliner-Schultheiss, Hohenschönhausen (Ber)*
Schumacher *Düsseldorf (N-W)*
Schussenrieder *Bad Schussenried (B-W)*
Schuster-Öl *Gick-Bräu, Burgkunstadt (Bay)*
Schutt und Asche Bier *Kommunbräu, Kumbach (Bay)*
Schüttinger *Bremen (Bre)*
Schützen Bock *Ketterer, Hornberg (B-W)*
Schutzenbier *Jahns-Bräu, Ludwigsstadt (Bay);*
Schützenfestbier *Kaiserhof, Kronach (Bay)*
Schwabacher Weisse *Leitner-Bräu, Schwabach (Bay)*
Schwaben Bräu *Dinkelacker-Schwaben, Stuttgart (B-W)*
Schwalm Bräu *Treysa (Hes)*
Schwälmer *Schwalm Bräu, Treysa (Hes)*

Schwanbier *Lemke's Spezialitätenbrauerei, Mitte (Ber)*
Schwanen Weisse *Ebensfelder, Ebensfeld (Bay); Riemhofer, Riedenburg (Bay)*
Schwanenbräu *Bernhausen (B-W); Burgebrach (Bay); Ebensfelder Brauhaus, Ebensfeld (Bay); Ebermannstadt (Bay); Ebing (Bay); Schwanenbrauerei, Ehingen (B-W); Zum Schwanen, Esslingen (B-W); Wertingen (Bay)*
Schwanenbrauerei *Ehingen (B-W)*
Schwanenpower *Riemhofer, Riedenburg (Bay)*
Schwarz *Hirschbrauerei, Lauingen (Bay)*
Schwarzbacher *Schloßbrauerei, Schwarzbach (Thü)*
Schwarzberg Gold *Häffner Bräu, Bad Rappenau (B-W)*
Schwarzbierbrauerei *Bad Köstritz (Thü)*
Schwarzbräu *Zusmarshausen (Bay)*
Schwarze Anna *Neder, Forchheim (Bay)*
Schwarze Jule *Worrich's Pub, Forst (Bra)*
Schwarze Rose *Rosenbrauerei, Pößneck (Thü)*
Schwarze Seele *Erlbacher, Erlbach (Sach)*
Schwarze Tinte *Kommunbräu, Kumbach (Bay)*
Schwarze Wonne *Welde-Bräu, Plankstadt (B-W)*
Schwarzer Abt *Ponter, Besseringen (Saar); Klosterbrauerei, Neuzelle (Bra)*
Schwarzer Baron *Schloßbrauerei, Autenried (Bay)*
Schwarzer Drachen *Eisenacher, Eisenach (Thü)*
Schwarzer Friedrich *Heine Bräu, Halberstadt (S-A)*
Schwarzer Hahn *Hochstiftliches Brauhaus, Fulda (Hes)*
Schwarzer Herzog *Hofbrauhaus Wolters, Braunschweig (Nie)*
Schwarzer Kaiser *Kaiserhof, Kronach (Bay)*
Schwarzer Kapuziner *Paulaner Bräuhaus, München (Bay)*
Schwarzer Kieler *Zwiefalten Klosterbräu, Zwiefalten (B-W)*
Schwarzer Kuni Weizenbock *Simon, Lauf (Bay)*
Schwarzer Löwe *Löwenbräu, Schwäbisch Hall (B-W)*
Schwarzer Molle *Eschenbräu, Wedding (Ber)*
Schwarzer Ochs *Nattheimer, Nattheim (B-W)*
Schwarzer Pandur *Rhanerbräu, Rhan (Bay)*
Schwarzer Peter *Schäffler, Missen (Bay)*
Schwarzer Pfaff *Stöttner, Pfaffenberg (Bay)*
Schwarzer Reiter *Garley, Gardelegen (S-A)*
Schwarzer Ritter *Scheuerer, Moosbach (Bay); Ritter St. Georgen, Nennslingen (Bay)*
Schwarzer Schwan *Herbsthäuser, Herbsthausen (B-W)*
Schwarzer September *Braustelle, Köln (N-W)*
Schwarzer Specht *Specht, Ehrenfriedersdorf (Sach); Spessart, Kreuzwertheim (Bay)*
Schwarzer Steiger *Feldschlößchen, Dresden (Sach)*
Schwarzer Veri *Leibinger, Ravensburg (B-W)*
Schwarzer Wolf *Alte Brauerei, Wolfhagen (Hes)*
Schwarzer Zornickel *Palmbräu, Eppingen (B-W)*
Schwarzer 5er *Wasserburger, Dingolfing (Bay)*
Schwarzes Bergbier *Freiberger, Freiberg (Sach)*
Schwarzes Gold *Hütt-Brauerei, Knallhütte (Hes); Mauritius, Zwickau (Sach)*
Schwarzes Kreuz *Eggolsheim (Bay)*
Schwarzes Röslein *Bayer Bräu, Rothenfels (Bay)*
Schwarzes Schaf *Krug, Geisfeld (Bay)*
Schwarzes Scherdel *Scherdel, Hof (bay)*
Schwarzes Wäldle *Lammbrauerei, Weilheim (B-W)*

Schwarzfischer *Schloßbrauerei, Zell (Bay)*
Schwarzkollm *Schwarzkollm (Sach)*
Schwärzla *Klosterbräu, Bamberg (Bay)*
Schwarzstörchle *Storchenbräu, Pfaffenhausen (Bay)*
Schwarzviertler *Faust, Miltenberg (Bay)*
Schwarzwald Weisse *Waldhaus, Waldhaus (B-W)*
Schwattes *Schillerbad, Lüdenscheid (N-W)*
Schweden *Schwarzbräu, Zusmarshausen (Bay)*
Schwedenquell Pils *Krostitzer, Krostitz (Sach)*
Schwedentrunk *Kaiserhof, Kronach (Bay)*
Schwedter Turmbräu *Turmbräu, Schwedt (Bra)*
Schweiger *Markt Schwaben (Bay)*
Schweighart *Kronburg (Bay)*
Schweinchen Bräu *Kleines Schweinchen, Kassel (Hes)*
Schweinfurt *Schweinfurt (Bay)*
Schweinsbräu *Hermannsdorf (Bay)*
Schwelm *Schwelm (N-W)*
Schwendl *Weissbräu, Schalchen (Bay)*
Schweriner Altstadtbräu *Zum Stadtkrug, Schwerin (M-V)*
Schweriner Schloßbrauerei *Schwerin (M-V)*
Schwert *Ehingen (B-W)*
Schwerter Brauerei Wohlers *Meißen (Sach)*
Schwind *Oberdorf (B-W)*
Schwindbräu *Aschaffenburg (Bay)*
Schwirza vom Landl Dunkel *Hofer, Furth im Wald (Bay)*
Schwoihier Dunkel *Schwindbräu, Aschaffenburg (Bay)*
Scotty *Steinbach Bräu, Erlangen (Bay)*
Sebastian *Ketterer, Pforzheim (B-W)*
Sebastian Riegele's Weisse *Riegele, Augsburg (Bay)*
Seckenator *Reindler, Jochsberg (Bay)*
Sedlmayr Weizen *Maisach, Maisach (Bay)*
See Weisse *Michael, Weißenstadt (Bay)*
See Weizen *Krone, Tettnang (B-W)*
Seelmann *Zettmannsdorf (Bay)*
Seemannshausen *Klosterbräu, Seemannshausen (Bay)*
Sester Kölsch *Kölner Verbund Brauereien, Köln (N-W)*
Seinsheimer Kellerbräu *Seinsheim (Bay)*
Selber Weisse *Brauhaus Ploss, Selb (Bay)*
Senger *Scheßlitz (Bay)*
Seßlacher *Kommunbrauhaus, Seßlach (Bay)*
Severin Kölsch *Sünner, Köln (N-W)*
Sieben Brunnen *Finsterwalde (Bra)*
Siebengebirgsbräu *Alte Bürgerstube, Heisterbacherrott (N-W)*
Siebensternchen Pils *Lang-Bräu, Schönbrunn (Bay)*
Siegburger *Siegburg (N-W)*
Siegel Pils *Brinkhoff, Dortmund (N-W)*
Siegenburger Spezialitätenbrauerei *Siegenburg (Bay)*
Sigi's Lager *Friedmann, Gräfenberg (Bay)*
Sigwart *Weißenburg (Bay)*
Silber *Welde-Bräu, Plankstadt (B-W)*
Silber Krone *Feldschlößchen, Dresden (Nie)*
Silber Pils *Winkler, Amberg (Bay); Bellheimer, Bellheim (R-P)*
Silberbock *Trunk, Vierzehnheiligen (Bay)*
Silberfüchsen Weizen *Füchsen, Düsseldorf (N-W)*
Silvator *Erste Dampfbierbrauerei, Zwiesel (Bay)*
Silver *Adlerbrauerei Götz, Geislingen (B-W)*
Silvesterbier *Wiesenmühle, Fulda (Hes)*

Simmerberger *Aktienbrauerei, Simmerberg (Bay)*
Simon *Lauf (Bay)*
Singer Bier *Museums-Brauerei Schmitt, Singen (Thü)*
Sion Kölsch *Kölner Verbund Brauereien, Köln (N-W)*
Sippel *Baunach (Bay)*
Sitter Bräu *Riedelsbach (Bay)*
Skinny *Webster, Duisburg (N-W)*
Skip Pilsener *Memminger, Memmingen (Bay)*
Soester Zwiebel *Soest (N-W)*
Söhnstetter *Hirsch, Söhnstetten (B-W)*
Sollator *Meierei, Potsdam (Bra)*
Söller *Braumühle, Schmerlecke (N-W)*
Soltmann *Garley, Gardelegen (S-A)*
Sommerlust *Glauchau (Sach)*
Sommerwiese *Braustelle, Köln (N-W)*
Sondersud Vital *Abtei-Bräu, Mettlach (Saar)*
Sonne *Bischberg (Bay); Ebermannstadt (Bay); Herrenzimmern (B-W)*
Sonnen *Sonne, Bischberg (Bay); Sonnenbräu, Ebermannstadt (Bay); Lichtenberg (Bay); Mürsbach (Bay)*
Sonnenbräu *Ebermannstadt (Bay); Lichtenberg (Bay)*
Sonnengold *Sonnenbräu, Ebermannstadt (Bay); Sonnenbräu, Lichtenberg (Bay); Schloßbrauerei, Schwarzbach (Thü)*
Sonnenweisse *Sonnenbräu, Lichtenberg (Bay); Schloßbrauerei, Schwarzbach (Thü)*
Sonnenwendbier *Vogel Hausbräu, Ettlingen (B-W); Vogelbräu, Karlsruhe (B-W); Vogel Hausbräu, Karlsruhe (B-W)*
Sophie's *Stuttgart (B-W)*
Spall *Albert Spall, Ballenberg (B-W)*
Spalter *Stadtbrauerei Spalt, Spalt (Bay)*
Spanberger *Brunner-Bräu, Spanberg (Bay)*
Spandauer Havelbräu *Spandau, Spandau (Ber)*
Sparta *Gambrinus-Brauerei, Weiden (Bay)*
Spaten *Spaten-Franziskaner-Bräu, München (Bay)*
Spaten Franziskaner Bräu *München (Bay)*
Späth Bräu *Mühlbauer, Arnschwang (Bay); Lohberg (Bay)*
Specht *Ehrenfriedersdorf (Sach); Spessart, Kreuzwertheim (Bay)*
Speidel's *Speidel's Brauerei'le, Ödenwaldstetten (B-W)*
Spektakulator *Jodlbauer, Tiefenbach (Bay, unknown brewer)*
Sperber Bräu *Sulzbach-Rosenberg (Bay)*
Spessart *Kreuzwertheim (Bay)*
Spessarträuber *Bayer Bräu, Rothenfels (Bay)*
Spezial *Bamberg (Bay); Schierling (Bay)*
Spezial Domi *Vereinsbrauerei, Apolda (Thü)*
Spezialitätenbrauerei *Gardelegen (S-A); Luckenwalde (Bra); Penig (Sach)*
Speziator *Riegele, Augsburg (Bay)*
Spinola *Lindenbrauerei, Unna (N-W, unknown brewer)*
Spirit Pils *Wolf, Fuchsstadt (Bay)*
Spital *Spitalbrauerei, Regensburg (Bay)*
Spitzkrug Pils *Frankfurter Brauhaus, Frankfurt (Bra)*
Sport Weisse *Schweiger, Markt Schwaben (Bay)*
Spreelator *Spreewalder, Schlepzig (Bra)*
Spreewald *Kirchers, Drebkau (Bra)*

Spreewälder *Spreewalder, Schlepzig (Bra)*
St. Afra Dunkel *Schwerter Brauerei Wohlers, Meißen (Sach)*
St. Ägidi Fastenbock *Gutsbräu, Straßkirchen (Bay)*
St. Annen Dunkel *Schloßbrauerei, Rheder (N-W)*
St. Blasius *Aktienbrauerei, Kaufbeuren (Bay)*
St. Florian Bräu *Friedberger Brauhaus, Friedberg (Hes)*
St. Georg Doppelbock *Fischerbräu, Eitting (Bay)*
St. Georgen *Ritter St. Georgen, Nennslingen (Bay)*
St. Georgen Bock *Brauhaus Pforzheim, Pforzheim (B-W)*
St. Georgen Bräu *Buttenheim (Bay)*
St. Georgs Zoigl *Bräuwirt, Weiden (Bay)*
St. Georgsbock *Holzhausener, Holzhausen (Bay)*
St. Gothardus *Gotha, Gotha (Thü)*
St. Jacobus *Forschungsbrauerei, München (Bay)*
St. Katherinen Spezial *Spitalbrauerei, Regensburg (Bay)*
St. Kunigunden Festbier *Dreykorn, Lauf (Bay)*
St. Laurentius Bock *Schloßbrauerei, Unterbaar (Bay)*
St. Magnus Bock *Allgäuer Brauhaus, Leuterschach (Bay)*
St. Marienstern Klosterbräu *Stadtbrauerei, Wittichenau (Sach)*
St. Marienthal Klosterbier *Münch-Bräu, Eibau (Sach)*
St. Martin *Aktienbrauerei, Kaufbeuren (Bay); Zum Reformator, Lutherstadt Eisleben (S-A); Oberlahnstein (R-P)*
St. Martini *Herrnbräu, Ingolstadt (Bay)*
St. Martins Bier *Braustelle, Köln (N-W)*
St. Martins Bock *Rossknecht, Ludwigsburg (B-W)*
St. Martinus *Klier Bräu, Ettensberg (Bay)*
St. Michaelis Bräu *Eutin, Eutin (S-H)*
St. Michaelsberg *Maisel, Bamberg (Bay)*
St. Nikolaus Bock *Pfungstädter, Pfungstadt (Hes)*
St. Pantaleons Schwarze *Weißbräu, Köln (N-W)*
St. Pauli *Bavaria-St. Pauli, St. Pauli (Ham)*
St. Peter *Einsiedler, Einsiedel (Sach)*
St. Sixtus *Schloßbrauerei, Hohenthann (Bay)*
St. Stephans Bock *Zötler, Rettenberg (Bay)*
St. Urbanus Bock *Brauhaus Urban, Pfaffenhofen (Bay)*
St. Ursula Doppelbock *Alt-Oberurseler, Oberursel (Hes)*
St. Wendeler Brauereihaus *St. Wendel (Saar)*
St. Wolfgang Dunkel *Paulaner, München (Bay)*
Stackmann's Dunkel *Wittinger, Wittingen (Nie)*
Stades Leicht *DAB, Dortmund (N-W)*
Stadl-Bier *Innstadt, Passau (Bay)*
Stadlbräu *Oberhaching (Bay)*
Stadtbrauerei *Arnstadt (Thü); Roth (Bay); Spalt (Bay); Troisdorf (N-W); Wittichenau (Sach)*
Stadter *Sachsendorf (Bay)*
Stadtkrug *Ueckermünde (M-V)*
Stadtpark *Hockenheim (B-W)*
Staffelberg-Bräu *Loffeld (Bay)*
Stammhaus Bier *Mayer Bräu, Ludwigshafen (R-P)*
Standard Hell *Winkler, Amberg (Bay)*
Stanglbräu *Herrnwahlthann (Bay)*
Stark *Lotters, Aue (Sach)*
Starkator *Stärker, Garitz (Bay)*
Stärker *Garitz (Bay)*
Starker Fritz *Hebendanz, Forchheim (Bay)*
Stärker's Hausbräu *Stärker, Garitz (Bay)*

Stärkstes Bier der Welt *Mühlfelder, Mühlfeld (Bay)*
Stationsweizen *Isarbräu, Großhesselohe*
Stauden *Schorer, Walkertshofen (Bay)*
Staudengold *Schorer, Walkertshofen (Bay)*
Staudenweisse *Schorer, Walkertshofen (Bay)*
Staude *Essen (N-W)*
Staufen Bräu *Kaiser, Geislingen (B-W)*
Stecken Kölsch *Hüchelner Urstoff, Hücheln (N-W)*
Stefanus *Menrath (N-W)*
Steffen Leicht *Kesselring, Marksteft (Bay)*
Steffens *St. Severinsberg (R-P)*
Steffi *Steffens, St. Severinsberg (R-P)*
Stegaurach *Hausbräu Stegaurach (Bay)*
Steiger Schwarze *Sperber-Bräu, Sulzbach-Rosenberg (Bay)*
Steigerwald *Waldkasino, Erfurt (Thü); Hike, Marktsteft (Bay, unknown brewer); Löwenbräu Neeb, Unterschleichach (Bay)*
Stein *Schlossbrauerei, Stein (Bay)*
Steinacher *Anker Bräu, Steinach (Thü)*
Steinacher Hausbräu *Bad Waldsee (B-W)*
Steinachtaler *Hösl, Mitterteich (Bay)*
Steinbach *Kirchheim (N-W)*
Steinbach Bräu *Erlangen (Bay)*
Steinbräu *Alzenau (Bay, unknown brewer)*
Steiner *Schlossbrauerei, Stein (Bay)*
Steingadener *Aktienbrauerei, Kaufbeuren (Bay)*
Steinhauer Weisse *Göller, Zeil (Bay)*
Steininger *Frankenthaler, Frankenthal (R-P, unknown brewer)*
Steinpils *Espelkamp, Espelkamp (N-W)*
Steinweizen *Espelkamp, Espelkamp (N-W);*
Stelzer *Schlossbrauerei, Fattigau (Bay)*
Stephansberger Urtyp *Robesbierre, Bamberg (Bay)*
Stephani Weisse Dunkel *Lauterbach, Lauterbach (Bay)*
Stephanus *Coesfeld (N-W)*
Stephanus Bock *Storchenbräu, Pfaffenhausen (Bay)*
Stephanus Bräu Pils *Stiefel-Jürgens, Beckum (N-W)*
Stephanus Doppelbock *Peschl, Passau (Bay)*
Sterk *Raigering (Bay)*
Stern *Staude, Essen (N-W)*
Stern Gold *Sternquell, Plauen (Sach)*
Sternbräu *Elsendorf (Bay); Scheubel, Schlüsselfeld (Bay)*
Sternburg *Leipziger Brauhaus Reudnitz, Leipzig (Sach)*
Sternla *Keesmann, Bamberg (Bay)*
Sternquell *Plauen (Sach)*
Sternweisse *Hacker-Pschorr, München (Bay)*
Stettfelder *Adler Bräu, Stettfeld (Bay)*
Sticke *Uerige, Düsseldorf (N-W)*
Stiefel Bräu *Saarbrücken (Saar)*
Stiefel Jürgens *Beckum (N-W)*
Stiefel Pils *Lammbrauerei Hilsenbeck, Gruibingen (B-W)*
Stierberg *Stierberg (Bay)*
Stierbräu *Vechta (Nie)*
Stifts *DAB, Dortmund (N-W)*
Stifts Weizenbock *Allgäuer, Leuterschach (Bay)*
Stiftsscheuer *Kirchheim (B-W)*
Stiftsherren Pils *Rotochsen, Ellwangen (B-W)*
Stoaner Zwerg *Schlossbrauerei, Stein (Bay)*

Stockdunkel *Waldhaus, Erfurt (Thü)*
Stöckel *Hintergreuth (Bay)*
Stockenfelser Geisterbräu *Nittenau, Nittenau (Bay)*
Stöffla *Drei Kronen, Memmelsdorf (Bay)*
Stolz *Isny (B-W)*
Stöpflder *Adler Bräu, Stettfeld (Bay)*
Storchen *Storchenbräu, Pfaffenhausen (Bay)*
Storchen Leichte *Schnupp, Altdrossenfeld (Bay)*
Storchenbier *Steinbach Bräu, Erlangen (Bay);*
   Schleicher, Kaltenbrunn (Bay)
Storchenbräu *Pfaffenhausen (Bay)*
Störchle *Storchenbräu, Pfaffenhausen (Bay)*
Störtebecker *Stralsunder, Stralsund (M-V)*
Stöttner *Pfaffenberg (Bay)*
Stout *Grafschafter, Nordhorn (Nie); Kneipe Pur, Plaue*
   (Bra); Ricklinger, Rickling (S-H); Stierbräu, Vechta (Nie)
Stralsunder *Stralsund (M-V)*
Strate *Detmold (N-W)*
Straubinger Blauweisse *Röhrl, Straubing (Bay)*
Straubinger Weisse *Röhrl, Straubing (Bay)*
Strauß *Dimpl Bräu, Furth im Wald (Bay); Wettelsheim*
   (Bay)
Streck Bräu *Ostheim (Bay)*
Strong *DAB, Dortmund (N-W)*
Strong Porter *Bergquell, Löbau (Sach)*
Strössner Bräu *Ahornberger, Ahornberg (Bay)*
Stuhrer Mühle *Stuhr (Nie)*
Stülpner Bräu Starkbier *Olbernhau, Olbernhau (Sach)*
Stumm's *Neunkirchen (Saar)*
Stuttgarter Hofbräu *Stuttgart (B-W)*
Sudhang *Sudhang, Amberg (Bay)*
Sudhaus *Detmold (N-W); Ludwigsburg (B-W);*
   Schwäbisch Hall (B-W)
Sudmeister & Fruchtgut *Bochum (N-W, unknown brewer)*
Südstern *Kreuzberg (Ber)*
Suffikator *Bürgerbräu, Bad Reichenhall (Bay)*
Süffikus *Hösl, Mitterteich (Bay)*
Sündenbock *Schlossbrauerei, Herrngiersdorf (Bay)*
Sünner *Köln (N-W)*
Superator *Bruckmüller, Amberg (Bay)*
Superior *Hacker-Pschorr, München (Bay)*
Surtaler Leichter Typ *Schönram, Schönram (Bay)*
Suttroper *Suttrop (N-W)*
Sympator *Würzburger Hofbräu, Würzburg (Bay)*

T

Tafelbier *Eutin, Eutin (S-H)*
Talschänke *Jena (Thü)*
Tannen Bräu *Hessberger, Heßberg (Thü)*
Tannen Leicht *Schloßbrauerei, Hohenthann (Bay)*
Tannen Pils Edelherb *Schloßbrauerei, Hohenthann (Bay)*
Tannenzäpfle *Badische Staatsbrauerei, Rothaus (B-W)*
Tassilator *Wasserburger, Dingolfing (Bay)*
Tauffenbach *Bochum (N-W)*
Taufkirchner *Brauereigenossenschaft, Taufkirchen (Bay)*
Tegernseer *Herzoglich Bayerisches Brauhaus,*
   Tegernsee (Bay)
Teisnacher *Ettl-Bräu, Teisnach (Bay)*
Tennenbräu *Lüben (Nie)*

Tettnager *Kronenbrauerei, Tettnang (B-W)*
Teufel *Baisinger Löwenbrauerei, Baisingen (B-W)*
Teutsch Pils *Allgäuer Brauhaus, Leuterschach (Bay)*
Thannator *Postbräu, Thannhausen (Bay)*
The 4 Elements *Kronenbrauerei Wahl, Gundelfingen*
   (Bay, unknown brewer)
Thein *Lembach (Bay)*
Thier *DAB, Dortmund (N-W)*
Thomann *Wiesen (Bay)*
Thomas Zwickl *Paulaner Bräuhaus, München (Bay)*
Thomaskirche *Leipzig (Sach)*
Thombansen *Lippstadt (N-W)*
Thome *Wolzhausen (Hes)*
Thorbräu *Augsburg (Bay)*
Thundorfer *Gemeindebrauhaus, Thundorf (Bay)*
Thüngener Schloss-Pils *Eder & Heyland, Großostheim*
   (Bay)
Thüringator *Waldhaus, Erfurt (Thü)*
Thüringer Premium Pils *Gotha, Gotha (Thü)*
Thüringia *Meininger, Meiningen (Thü)*
Thurn und Taxis *Paulaner, München (Bay)*
Thurnauer Schloßbräu *Thurnau (Bay)*
Tillator *Woinemer, Weilheim (B-W)*
Tilly Hell *Kleinbrauerei Rain, Rain (Bay)*
Tirschenreuther *Schels, Tirschenreuth (Bay)*
Top Secret Bier *Meierei, Potsdam (Bra)*
Toppler Pils *Landwehr-Bräu, Reichelshofen (Bay)*
Torgauer *Torgau (Sach)*
Torgisch Hell *Torgauer, Torgau (Sach)*
Torschmied's Dunkel *Glossner-Bräu, Neumarkt (Bay)*
Trabelsdorfer Schloßgold *Beck, Trabelsdorf (Bay)*
Tradition *Rotochsen, Ellwangen (B-W); Schloßbrauerei,*
   Fuchsberg (Bay); Nassauische, Hahnstätten (R-P);
   Hutthurmer Bayerwald, Hutthurm (Bay); Herrnbräu,
   Ingolstadt (Bay); Postbrauerei, Nesselwang (Bay);
   Pöllinger, Pfeffenhausen (Bay); Stralsunder,
   Stralsund (M-V); Schloßbrauerei Odelzhausen, Taxa
   (Bay); Weihenstephan, Freising (Bay)
Traditionsbrauerei *Watzdorf (Thü)*
Traditionstrunk *Hösl, Mitterteich (Bay)*
Traugott Simon *Trinklogistik, Duisburg (N-W, unknown*
   brewer)
Trausnitz Pils *Schlossbrauerei, Herrngiersdorf (Bay)*
Trebgaster Zunft Pils *Haberstumpf, Trebgast (Bay)*
Treckeberger *Peters Bauernstube, Haltern (N-W)*
Treib Stoff *Püls Bräu, Weismain (Bay)*
Treiber *Ludwigshafen (R-P, unknown brewer)*
Trend *Kronenbrauerei Schimpf, Remmingsheim (B-W)*
Treuener *Blechschmidt, Treuen (Sach)*
Trinklogistik *Duisburg (N-W, unknown brewer)*
Triumphator *Löwenbräu, München (Bay)*
Troi Pi *Stadtbrauerei, Troisdorf (N-W)*
Troilsch *Stadtbrauerei, Troisdorf (N-W)*
Troisdorfer *Stadtbrauerei, Troisdorf (N-W)*
Trotzenburg *Rostock (M-V)*
Trumpf *Ketterer, Pforzheim (B-W)*
Trunator Vollmond-Bock *Hofbräuhaus, Traunstein (Bay)*
Trunk *Vierzehnheiligen (Bay)*
Tü 8 *Der Bräu im Tü 8, Stuttgart (B-W)*

Tuborg *Mönchengladbach, Mönchengladbach (N-W)*
Tucher *Fürth & Nürnberg (Bay)*
Türkenlouis Bock *Franz, Rastatt (B-W)*
Turm *Arnhausen (Bay); Chemnitz (Sach); Freudenstadt (B-W); Kirchheimbolanden (R-P)*
Turmberg Bräu *Schlossbrauerei, Schmieheim (B-W)*

U

Überraschungsbier *Waldhaus, Erfurt (Thü)*
Übersee Export *Tucher, Fürth & Nürnberg (Bay)*
Uckermärker *Golzow (Bra)*
Ueckermünde *Ueckermünde (M-V)*
Uehlfelder Weisse *Zwanzger, Uehlfeld (Bay)*
Uerige *Düsseldorf (N-W)*
Uhl Pils *Franz, Rastatt (B-W)*
Ulimator *Dachsbräu, Weilheim (Bay)*
Ulmer *Bauhöfer, Ulm (B-W)*
Ulmer Münster *Memminger, Memmingen (Bay)*
Ulrichsbier *Ulrich Zimmermann, Berg (B-W)*
Ultra *Pyraser, Pyras (Bay)*
Ummendorf *Ummendorf (B-W)*
Umstädter *Groß-Umstadt (Hes)*
Unertl *Haag (Bay); Mühldorf (Bay)*
Ungespundet *Mahr's, Bamberg (Bay); Robesbierre, Bamberg (Bay); Spezial, Bamberg (Bay); Löwenbräu, Buttenheim (Bay); Wagner, Kemmern (Bay); Wagner, Merkendorf (Bay); Scheubel, Schlüsselfeld (Bay); Hönig, Tiefenellern (Bay)*
Unimator *Unionsbräu-Haidhausen, München (Bay)*
Unionsbräu *München (Bay)*
Unser Bestes Premium Pils *Palmbräu, Eppingen (B-W)*
Unser Bürgerbräu *Bürgerbräu, Bad Reichenhall (Bay)*
Unser Gebremstes Weizen *Riemhofer, Riedenburg (Bay)*
Unser Hell *Jahns-Bräu, Ludwigsstadt (Bay);*
Unser Helles *Reichenbrander, Chemnitz (Sach)*
Unser Landbier *Hönicka-Bräu, Wunsiedel (Bay)*
Unser Leichtes *Franken Bräu, Riedbach (B-W)*
Unterbaarer *Schloßbrauerei, Unterbaar (Bay)*
Untergärig *Gutmann, Titting (Bay)*
Unternbiberter *Reuter, Unternbibert (Bay)*
Ur Krostitzer *Krostitzer, Krostitz (Sach)*
Ur Saalfelder *Bürgerliches Brauhaus, Saalfeld (Thü)*
Ur Wolfhager *Alte Brauerei, Wolfhagen (Hes)*
Uralb Spezial *Heubacher, Heubach (B-W)*
Urbairisch Dunkel *Allgäuer, Leuterschach (Bay)*
Urbanus *Pfaffenhofen (Bay)*
Urbayrisch Dunkel *Aktienbrauerei, Kaufbeuren (Bay)*
Urbräu *Vormann, Dahl (N-W); Dessow, Dessow (Bra); Tucher, Fürth (Bay); Vereinsbrauerei, Greiz (Thü); Eder & Heylands, Großostheim (Bay); Sauer, Roßdorf (Bay); Weimar-Ehringsdorf, Weimar (Thü)*
Urdeutsch Dunkel *Bucher, Gundelfingen (Bay)*
Ureich Premium Pils *Eichbaum, Mannheim (B-W)*
Urfass *Arcobräu Gräfliches Brauhaus, Moos (Bay)*
Urfels *Walsumer Brauhaus, Alt-Walsum (N-W); Lindenbrauerei, Unna (N-W, unknown brewer)*
Urfränkich Dunkel *Tucher, Fürth & Nürnberg (Bay)*
Urfränkisches Landbier *Kesselring, Marksteft (Bay)*
Urhahn *Lauterbacher Burgbrauerei, Lauterbach (Hes)*

Urig Würzig *Allgäuer Brauhaus, Leuterschach (Bay)*
Urknall *Hütt-Brauerei, Knallhütte (Hes)*
UrMild *Karlsberg, Homburg (Saar)*
Ursberger *Klosterbräuhaus, Ursberg (Bay)*
Ursprung Export *Aldersbach, Aldersbach (Bay); Hald, Dunstelkingen (B-W)*
Ursprung Hell *Winkler-Bräu, Schlicht (Bay)*
Urstoff *Kolberg, Altenau (Nie); Stadtbrauerei, Arnstadt (Thü); Bürgerbräu, Bayreuth (Bay); Hüchelner Urstoff, Frechen (N-W); Wildbräu-Grandauer, Grafing (Bay); Schloßbrauerei, Hohenthann (Bay); Hösl, Mitterteich (Bay); Kloster-Brauerei, Münnerstadt (Bay); Kaiser-Bräu, Neuhaus (Bay); Lammsbräu, Neumarkt (Bay); Hellmuth, Wiesen (Bay)*
Ursud *Unertl Weissbräu, Haag (Bay)*
Urtrüb *Borgfelder, Bremen (Bre); Betz, Celle (Nie); Hövels, Dortmund (N-W); Westerwald, Hachenburg (R-P); Niedermeiers Hof, Reineberg (N-W); Kronenbrauerei Schimpf, Remmingsheim (B-W)*
Urtrunk *Schwanen-Bräu, Ebensfeld (Bay); Bauriedl, Eslarn (Bay); Ganter, Freiburg (B-W); Irseer Klosterbräu, Irsee (Bay); Lasser, Lörrach (B-W); Wochinger, Traunstein (Bay); Albquell Bräuhaus, Trochtelfingen (B-W)*
Urtrunk 1874 *Bauriedl, Eslarn (Bay)*
Urtyp 1878 *Lohrer Bier, Lohr (Bay)*
Usedomer *Heringsdorf (M-V)*
Ustator *Ustersbacher, Ustersbach (Bay)*
Ustersbacher *Ustersbach (Bay)*
Uttenweiler *Sauter, Uttenweiler (B-W)*

V

Valentins *Park, Pirmasens (R-P)*
Valley *Graf Arco, Adldorf (Bay)*
Vampbier *Meierei, Potsdam (Bra)*
Vasold & Schmitt *Neunkirchen (Bay)*
Veischeder Landbier *Müller, Oberveischeide (N-W)*
Velberter *Velbert (N-W)*
Veldensteiner *Kaiser-Bräu, Neuhaus (Bay)*
Veldenz Bräu *Lauterecker Brauhaus, Lauterecken (R-P)*
Veltins *Grevenstein (N-W)*
Verbund Brauereien *Köln (N-W)*
Vereinsbrauerei *Apolda (Thü); Greiz (Thü)*
Verum *Warsteiner, Warstein (N-W)*
Vestenberg *Löwenbräu, Vestenberg (Bay)*
Vetter *Heidelberg (B-W)*
Vetus Millena *Enzensteiner, Enzenreuth (Bay)*
Viagrotor *Weizenbierglasmuseum, Nürnberg (Bay)*
Viechtacher *Gesellschaftsbrauerei, Viechtach (Bay)*
Vielanker *Vielank (M-V)*
Vierkorn *Walhall, Bruchsal (B-W)*
Vilslaus *Postbrauerei, Frontenhausen (Bay)*
Vilstaler Weizen *Kummert, Amberg (Bay)*
Visionator *Schweinsbräu, Hermannsdorf (Bay)*
Vital *Abtei-Bräu, Mettlach (Saar)*
Vogel Hausbräu *Ettlingen (B-W)*
Vogelbräu *Vogel Hausbräu, Ettlingen (B-W); Vogelbräu, Karlsruhe (B-W); Vogel Hausbräu, Karlsruhe (B-W)*
Vogellennium *Vogel Hausbräu, Ettlingen (B-W);*

Vogelbräu, Karlsruhe (B-W); Vogel Hausbräu, Karlsruhe (B-W)

Vogelsberger *Lauterbacher Burgbrauerei, Lauterbach (Hes)*

Volksfestbier *Engel-Bräu, Crailsheim (B-W); Hofmühl, Eichstätt (Bay); Bucher, Grafenau (Bay); Roth, Schweinfurt (Bay); Schweinfurt, Schweinfurt (Bay); Brunner, Spanberg (Bay); Calwer Eck Bräu, Stuttgart (B-W); Dinkelacker-Schwaben, Stuttgart (B-W); Hofbräu, Stuttgart (B-W)*

Vollmond Bier *Schussenrieder, Bad Schussenried (B-W); Alt Oberurseler, Oberursel (Hes); Zötler, Rettenberg (Bay); Beck, Trabelsdorf (Bay); Bauhöfer, Ulm (B-W); Wolfshöher, Wolfshöhe (Bay)*

von Koch'sche *Gottsmannsgrün (Bay)*

Von Raven *Schweriner Schloßbrauerei, Schwerin (M-V)*

Vorder *Vormann, Dahl (N-W)*

Vormann *Dahl (N-W)*

Vredener *Vreden (N-W)*

Vulkan *Mendig (R-P)*

W

Wachauer *Schiller, Wachau (Sach)*

Wacholderbier *Kneipe Pur, Plaue (Bra)*

Wachtersbacher *Würzburger Hofbräu, Würzburg (Bay)*

Wagner *Eschenbach (Bay); Kemmern (Bay); Merkendorf (Bay); Augustiner, München (Bay); Oberhaid (Bay); Kronenbrauerei, Offenburg (B-W)*

Wahl *Gundelfingen (Bay, unknown brewer)*

Waidler Gold *Schlossbräu, Drachselried (Bay)*

Waidler Hell *Adam-Bräu, Bodenmais (Bay)*

Waize *Adler-Bräu, Zuzenhausen (B-W)*

Waldbräu *Röcke (Nie)*

Waldbronner *Lindenbräu, Waldbronn (B-W)*

Wäldches *Frankfurt (Hes)*

Walderbräu *Königseggwald (B-W)*

Waldgasthaus Steinbach *Kirchheim (N-W)*

Waldhaus *Waldhaus (B-W); Erfurt (Thü)*

Waldkasino *Erfurt (Thü)*

Waldquell *Drexler, Pösing (Bay)*

Waldschloss *Frammersbach (Bay); Lindenbrauerei, Unna (N-W, unknown brewer)*

Waldschlösschen *Dresden (Sach)*

Waldschmidt *Penzkofer, Eschlkam (Bay, unknown brewer); Wetzlar (Hes, unknown brewer)*

Walhall *Brauhaus Walhall, Bruchsal (B-W)*

Wallburg *Wagner-Bräu, Eschenbach (Bay)*

Wallerstein *Fürst Wallerstein Brauhaus, Wallerstein (Bay)*

Walsumer *Brauhaus Urfels, Alt-Walsum (N-W)*

Warburger *Kuhlemühle (N-W)*

Warnitzer Burgwall Bräu *Burgwall Bräu, Warnitz (Bra)*

Warsteiner *Warstein (N-W)*

Wartburg *Eisenacher, Eisenach (Thü)*

Wasseralfinger *Löwenbrauerei, Aalen (B-W)*

Wasserburger *Dingolfing (Bay)*

Watt'n Bier *Küsten-Brauer, Werdum (Nie)*

Watzdorfer *Watzdorf (Thü)*

Watzke *Dresden (Sach)*

Weber *Röbersdorf (Bay)*

Webster *Duisburg (N-W)*

Websterator *Webster, Duisburg (N-W);*

Weesensteiner Schlossbräu *Weesenstein (Sach)*

Weib's *Dinkelsbühl (Bay)*

Weideneder *Tann (Bay)*

Weihenstephan *Freising (Bay)*

Weiherer *Kundmüller, Weiher (Bay)*

Weihnachts Engel *Engel-Bräu, Crailsheim (B-W)*

Weihnachts Glöckl *Glossner-Bräu, Neumarkt (Bay)*

Weihnachtsmännchen *Wurzgrund, Karlstadt (Bay)*

Weihnachtstraum *Spezialitäten, Luckenwalde (Bra); Peniger Spezialitätenbrauerei, Penig (Sach)*

Weilburger *Helbig, Weilburg (Hes)*

Weilheimer *Lammbrauerei, Weilheim (B-W); Dachsbräu, Weilheim (Bay)*

Weimarer *Weimar-Ehringsdorf, Weimar (Thü)*

Weinzierl *Unterneuhausen (Bay)*

Weismainer *Püls Bräu, Weismain (Bay)*

Weiß Blaue *Hofbräu, Abensberg (Bay); Schlossbrauerei, Stein (Bay)*

Weiss Gold *Meckatzer Löwenbräu, Meckatz (Bay)*

Weiss Rössl *Kaiser-Bräu, Neuhaus (Bay)*

Weißbierbrauerei *Schneider, Kelheim (Bay); Hopf, Miesbach (Bay); Bals, Oberaudorf (Bay); Bauer, Triftern (Bay); Plank, Wiefelsdorf (Bay); Behringer, Vohenstrauß (Bay)*

Weißbierpils *Fürst Wallerstein, Wallerstein (Bay)*

Weißbräu *Deisenhofen (Bay); Erding (Bay); Freilassing (Bay); Graming (Bay); Haag (Bay); Köln (N-W); Kößlarn (Bay); Rotthalmünster (Bay); Schalchen (Bay)*

Weißenberger *Sigwart, Weißenburg (Bay)*

Weißenhorner *Hasenbrauerei, Weißenhorn (Bay)*

Weißenohe *Klosterbrauerei, Weißenohe (Bay)*

Weißenseer *Ratsbrauerei, Weißensee (Thü)*

Weißenstädter See Weisse *Michael, Weißenstadt (Bay)*

Weißer Franke *Ritter St. Georgen, Nennslingen (Bay)*

Weißer Hase *Hasen-Bräu, Augsburg (Bay)*

Weißer Hirsch *Großrückerswalde (Sach); Hirschbräu, Sonthofen (Bay)*

Weisser Kaiser *Kaiserhof, Kronach (Bay)*

Weisser Leo *Löwenbrauerei, Bräunlingen (B-W)*

Weißer Löwe *Löwenbrauerei Dold, Elzach (B-W)*

Weißes Brauhaus Mehringer *Neunburg (Bay)*

Weißes Gold *Paulaner, München (Bay)*

Weißes Häus'l *Ludwigshafen (R-P)*

Weitnauer Märzen *Memminger, Memmingen (Bay)*

Weizen Lust *Welde-Bräu, Plankstadt (B-W)*

Weizen Wonne *Welde-Bräu, Plankstadt (B-W)*

Weizen Zäpfle *Badische Staatsbrauerei, Rothaus (B-W)*

Weizenbierbrauerei *Andorfer, Ries (Bay)*

Weizenbierglasmuseum *Nürnberg (Bay)*

Weizengold *Weideneder, Tann (Bay)*

Weizenland *Kaiserdom, Bamberg (Bay)*

Weizenstolz *Stolz, Isny (B-W)*

Weizla *Fässla, Bamberg (Bay)*

Welde *Plankstadt (B-W)*

Weltenbummler *Berggießhübel (Sach)*

Weltenburger *Bischofshof, Regensburg (Bay)*

Weltenburger Kloster *Klosterbrauerei, Weltenburg (Bay)*

Wendels *St. Wendeler Brauereihaus, St. Wendel (Saar)*
Wendelsteiner *Weißbierbrauerei Hopf, Miesbach (Bay)*
Wendland Bräu *Satkau (Nie)*
Wenkers *Hövels, Dortmund (N-W)*
Werdenfelser *Mittenwald, Mittenwald (Bay);*
Griesbräu, Murnau (Bay)
Wernecker *Werneck (Bay)*
Werner *Poppenhausen (Bay)*
Wernesgrüner *Wernesgrün (Sach)*
Wernsdörfer *Schönbrunn (Bay)*
Werschemer Woiza *Adler-Bräu, Wiernsheim (B-W)*
Wertinger Original *Schwanen-Bräu, Wertingen (Bay)*
Westerwald *Hachenburg (R-P)*
Westheimer *Gräflich zu Stolberg'sche, Westheim (N-W)*
Westparkbräu *Ingolstadt (Bay)*
Wettelsheimer *Strauß, Wettelsheim (Bay)*
Wetzlarer Dom Pils *Euler, Wetzlar (Hes, unknown brewer)*
Weyberbräu *Weyberhöfe (Bay)*
Whisky Bier *Bärenbräu, Neuhausen (Bay)*
White *Leikeim, Altenkunstadt (Bay)*
White Eisweissbier *Weißbierbrauerei, Miesbach (Bay)*
Wichert *Oberwallenstadt (Bay)*
Wichtel *Ditzingen (B-W); Stuttgart (B-W)*
Wickingerbräu *Asgaard, Schleswig (S-H)*
Wicküler Pilsener *Brinkhoff, Dortmund (N-W)*
Wienhäuser *Mühlengrund, Wienhausen (Nie)*
Wieninger *Teisendorf (Bay)*
Wies'n Bier *Stadtbrauerei, Troisdorf (N-W)*
Wiesen Festbier *Falter, Regen (Bay)*
Wiesener *Bürgerliches Brauhaus, Wiesen (Bay)*
Wiesenmühle *Fulda (Hes)*
Wiesenmühlenbier *Wiesenmühle, Fulda (Hes)*
Wiesensteiger *Zum Lamm, Wiesensteig (B-W)*
Wiesenweizen *Maximilians, Niederlahnstein (R-P)*
Wieser *Wiesmühl (Bay)*
Wiesner Weiße *Hellmuth, Wiesen (Bay)*
Wiess *Hellers, Köln (N-W); Kölner Verbund, Köln (N-W)*
Wiethaler *Neunhof (Bay)*
Wildbräu *Wildbräu-Grandauer, Grafing (Bay)*
Wilder Mann *Neustädter, Dresden (Sach); Bürgerbräu,*
Naila (Bay)
Wilderer Dunkel *Ecker-Bräu, Eck (Bay)*
Wildschütz Klostermann *Wetheimer, Westheim (N-W)*
Will *Schederndorf (Bay)*
Will Bräu *Hochstiftliches Brauhaus, Motten (Bay)*
Willibaldi Sud *Hofmühl, Eichstätt (Bay)*
Willinger *Wilingen (Hes)*
Wilshaus *Braam-Ostwennemaar (N-W)*
Wimmer *Bruckberg (Bay)*
Windsheimer *Gutenstetten (Bay)*
Windsheimer Reichsstadtbier *Döbler, Bad Windsheim*
(Bay)
Winkels *Karlsruhe (B-W), unknown brewer)*
Winkler *Amberg (Bay); Berching (Bay); Lengenfeld*
(Bay); Melkendorf (Bay); Schlicht (Bay)
Winter Böckle *Fürst Wallerstein, Wallerstein (Bay)*
Winter Keiler *Lohrer Bier, Lohr (Bay)*
Wintergold *Kitzmann, Erlangen (Bay); Engelbräu,*
Rettenberg (Bay)

Winterhopfen *Landskron Brauerei, Görlitz (Sach)*
Wintertraum *Leikeim, Altenkunstadt (Bay); Giessener*
Brauhaus, Gießen (Bay); Blauer Löwe, Höchstadt (Bay);
Hohenfelder, Langenberg (N-W); Kronenbrauerei,
Offenburg (B-W); Klosterbrauerei, Weltenburg (Bay)
Wintertrunk *Schloßbrauerei, Friedenfels (Bay)*
Winterwarmerbier *Kneipe Pur, Plaue (Bra)*
Winterzauber *Schäffler, Missen (Bay)*
Winzerbier *Klosterbrauerei, Neuzelle (Bra)*
Wippraer *Museumsbrauerei, Wippra (S-A)*
Wirtsbräu *Homburger, Homburg (Saar)*
Wirtshausbräu *Radigk's, Finsterwalde (Bra)*
Wismarer *Brauhaus am Lohberg, Wismar (M-V)*
Wittelsbacher Turm Bräu *Arnhausen (Bay)*
Wittenberg *Lutherstadt Wittenberg (S-A)*
Wittichenauer *Stadtbrauerei, Wittichenau (Sach)*
Wittinger *Wittingen (Nie)*
Wittmann *Landshut (Bay)*
Witzenhäuser Weizen *Schinkel's, Witzenhausen (Hes)*
Witzenhüsser Kräusen *Schinkel's, Witzenhausen (Hes)*
Witzgall *Schlammersdorf (Bay)*
Wochinger-Bräu *Traunstein (Bay)*
Wodan *Ganter, Freiburg (B-W)*
Wohlers *Meißen (Sach)*
Wohn *Bürgerbräu, Naila (Bay)*
Woinemer *Weinheim (B-W)*
Woiza Light *Schlachthof Bräu, Nürtingen (B-W)*
Wolf *Wolfs-Bier, Durchholz (N-W); Fuchsstadt (Bay);*
Karlsruhe (B-W); Rüdenhausen (Bay)
Wolferstetter *Vilshofen (Bay)*
Wolfhagen *Alte Brauerei, Wolfhagen (Hes)*
Wölfle Pils *Wolf, Karlsruhe (B-W)*
Wolfs Bier *Durchholz (N-W)*
Wolfsblut *Wolf, Karlsruhe (B-W)*
Wolfsbräu *Alte Brauerei, Wolfhagen (Hes)*
Wolfshöher *Wolfshöhe (Bay)*
Wolke *Glossner-Bräu, Neumarkt (Bay)*
Wöllnitzer Weißbier *Talschänke, Jena (Thü)*
Wolnzacher *Bürgerbräu, Wolnzach (Bay)*
Wolters *Hofbrauhaus Wolters, Braunschweig (Nie)*
Wolverother *Alt Wülfrath, Wülfrath (N-W)*
Wonne *Welde-Bräu, Plankstadt (B-W)*
Wonnesud *Hönicka-Bräu, Wunsiedel (Bay)*
Wormser *Hagenbräu, Worms (R-P)*
Worrich's Pub *Forst (Bra)*
Wotans Trunk *Schattenhofer Bräu, Beilngries (Bay)*
Wülfrath *Wülfrath (N-W)*
Wüllner *Gänsefurth (S-A, unknown brewer)*
Wunsiedler *Hönicka-Bräu, Wunsiedel (Bay)*
Wupper *Wuppertaler, Wuppertal (N-W)*
Wuppertaler *Wuppertal (N-W)*
Wurm *Hirschbräu, Bieswang (Bay)*
Würth *Sudhaus, Schwäbisch Hall (B-W);*
Windischeschenbach (Bay)
Würzburger Hofbräu *Würzburg (Bay)*
Wurzgrund *Karlstadt (Bay)*
Würzig *Schimpfle, Gessertshausen (Bay)*
Würzig Herb *Hofmark, Loifling (Bay)*
Würzig Mild *Hofmark, Loifling (Bay)*

Würziges Export *Riegele, Augsburg (Bay)*
Wusterhausener Zwolfender *Kavalierhäuser Schloss, Königs Wusterhausen (Bra)*

X

X Weizen *Kühbach, Kübach (Bay)*
Xamax *Gut Forsting, Forsting (Bay)*
Xan *Weihenstephan, Freising (Bay)*
Xmas *Ratskeller, Geising (Sach)*

Z

'z Loh *Loh (Bay)*
Zäpfle *Badische Staatsbrauerei, Rothaus (B-W)*
Zeche Jacobi *Oberhausen (N-W)*
Zehendner *Mönchsambach (Bay)*
Zeiter Grottenbräu *Landsberg, Landsberg (S-A)*
Zellertal Lager *Schlossbräu, Drachselried (Bay)*
Zeltbräu *Hof (Bay)*
Zenglein *Oberschleichach (Bay)*
Ziegenbock *Zwönitz, Zwönitz (Sach)*
Ziegler Bräu *Mainburg (Bay); Waldsassen (Bay)*
Zipfel *Rogg, Lenzkirch (B-W)*
Zils Bräu *Naurath (R-P)*
Zirndorf *Zirndorf (Bay)*
Zischke *Königsbacher, Koblenz (R-P)*
Zittauer Bürgerbräu *Zittau (Sach)*
Zoigl *Kommunbrauerei, Eslarn (Bay); Kommunbrauerei Markt Falkenberg, Falkenberg (Bay); Schloßbrauerei, Friedenfels (Bay); Hösl, Irschenrieth (Bay); Klosterbrauerei, Mallersdorf (Bay); Nothhaft, Marktredwitz (Bay); Kommunbrauerei, Mittertech (Bay); Scheuerer, Moosbach (Bay); Kommunbrauerei, Neuhaus (Bay); Pirker Brauhaus, Pirk (Bay); Riedl, Plößberg (Bay); Sterk, Raigering (Bay); Schloßbrauerei, Reuth (Bay); Brauhaus Ploss, Selb (Bay); Sperber-Bräu, Sulzbach-Rosenberg (Bay); Bräuwirt, Weiden (Bay); Kommunbrauerei, Windischeschenbach (Bay); Würth, Windischeschenbach (Bay)*
Zoller Hof *Sigmaringen (B-W)*
Zornickel *Palmbräu, Eppingen (B-W)*
Zötler *Rettenberg (Bay)*
Zum Alten Brauhaus *Rheinsberg (Bra)*
Zum Alten Dessauer *Dessau (S-A)*
Zum Bäuml *Rain (Bay)*
Zum Bergschlösschen *Lieske (Sach)*
Zum Goldenen Adler *Höfen (Bay)*
Zum Goldenen Lamm *Gierstädt (Thü)*
Zum Goldenen Löwen *Kallmünz (Bay)*
Zum Goldenen Schwan *Erfurt (Thü)*
Zum Hirsch *Dirlewang (Bay)*
Zum Kuchlbauer *Abensberg (Bay)*
Zum Lamm *Wiesensteig (B-W)*
Zum Löwen *Braunschweig (Nie); Mühlhausen (Thü)*
Zum Pfaffen *Kellershohn (N-W)*
Zum Reformator *Lutherstadt Eisleben (S-A)*
Zum Ritter *Schwetzingen (B-W)*
Zum Rossknecht *Ludwigsburg (B-W)*
Zum Schad *Halle (S-A)*
Zum Schlüssel *Düsseldorf (N-W)*

Zum Schwanen *Esslingen (B-W)*
Zum Stadtkrug *Schwerin (M-V)*
Zum Stadtpark *Hockenheim (B-W)*
Zum Stefanus *Menrath (N-W)*
Zunft Bräu *Kamp-Lintfort (N-W)*
Zunft Kölsch *Erzquell Brauerei Bielstein, Bielstein (N-W)*
Zunft Pils *Haberstumpf, Trebgast (Bay)*
Zunft Trunk *Sonne, Bischberg (Bay)*
Zunftherrn *Rössle-Bräu, Ummenhofen (Bay)*
Zünftige *Schmidt-Bräu, Schwandorf (Bay)*
Zur Goldenen Henne *Jüchsen (Thü)*
Zur Linde *Kolonie (Bra); Middelhagen (M-V)*
Zur Mainkur *Bier-Hannes, Frankfurt (Hes)*
Zur Malzmühle *Köln (N-W)*
Zur Post *Frankenthal (R-P)*
Zur Sonne *Bischberg (Bay)*
Zwanzger *Uehlfeld (Bay)*
Zwergen Bräu *Wüllner, Gänsefurth (S-A, unknown brewer)*
Zwergla *Fässla, Bamberg (Bay)*
Zwergle *Raab, Hofheim (Bay)*
Zwickau *Brauhaus, Zwickau (Sach)*
Zwickauer *Mauritius, Zwickau (Sach)*
Zwickl Max *Schloßbrauerei, Maxlrain (Bay)*
Zwiebel *Soest (N-W)*
Zwiefalter *Klosterbräu, Zwiefaltendorf (B-W)*
Zwölf Apostel *Frankfurt (Hes)*
Zwölfender *Kavalierhäuser, Königs Wusterhausen (Bra)*
Zwönitz *Zwönitz (Sach)*

Numbers

03 *Bruckmüller, Amberg (Bay)*
1. Sächsiches Rauchbier *Pirna, Copitz (Sach)*
2,8er *Holzkirchner Oberbräu, Holzkirchen (Bay)*
2,9 Medium *Wittmann, Landshut (Bay)*
3,8 *Schloßbrauerei, Fürstenfeldbrück (Bay)*
4 Elements *Kronenbrauerei Wahl, Gundelfingen (Bay, unknown brewer)*
5 Korn Ur-Bier *Riedenburger, Riedenburg (Bay)*
6 Korn Bier *Pyraser, Pyras (Bay)*
11er Landbier *Burggraf Bräu, Auerbach (Hes)*
16 Ender *Hirsch-Brauerei Honer, Wurmlingen (B-W)*
18·80 *Brauhaus 18·80, Fritzlar (Hes)*
23.04 *Adler, Zuzenhausen (B-W)*
23.04 Das Jahrgangsbier *Zimmermann, Berg (B-W); Krone, Tettnang (B-W);*
25 Hefe-Weisse *Aktienbrauerei, Kaufbeuren (Bay)*
27er Urtyp *Kummert, Amberg (Bay)*
28 *Kulmbacher, Kulmbach (Bay)*
33 *Vetter, Heidelberg (B-W)*
33 Dry *Hasen-Bräu, Augsburg (Bay)*
93er Hefeweizen *Nordbräu, Ingolstadt (Bay)*
98er Pilsener *Darguner, Dargun (M-V)*
111 *Radigk's Wirtshausbräu, Finsterwalde (Bra)*
111 Hefe Flaschl Weisse *Auerbräu, Rosenheim (Bay)*
111 Zwickl *Auerbräu, Rosenheim (Bay)*
150er *Mayer Bräu, Ludwigshafen (R-P)*
300 Jahr-Bier *Riemhofer, Riedenburg (Bay)*
375 Jahre Jubiläumsbier *Hacklberg, Passau (Bay)*

400 Jubiläumsbier *Ustersbacher, Ustersbach (Bay)*
1050 *Klosterbrauerei, Weltenburg (Bay)*
1308 *Aktienbrauerei, Kaufbeuren (Bay)*
1346 *Hasen-Bräu, Augsburg (Bay)*
1394 *Allgäuer, Leuterschach (Bay)*
1396 *Gaffel (Altstadt), Köln (N-W)*
1402 *Pöllinger, Pfeffenhausen (Bay)*
1417 *Hacker-Pschorr, München (Bay)*
1429 *Wittinger, Wittingen (Nie)*
1516 *Westparkbräu, Ingolstadt (Bay); Aktienbrauerei, Kaufbeuren (Bay)*
1518 *Aktienbrauerei, Kaufbeuren (Bay)*
1543 *Flözinger-Bräu, Rosenheim (Bay)*
1550 *Hartmann, Würgau (Bay)*
1554 *Neder, Forchheim (Bay)*
1580 *Kalt-Loch-Bräu, Miltenberg (Bay)*
1597 *Schloßbrauerei, Reckendorf (Bay)*
1603 *Schloßquellbrauerei, Heidelberg (B-W)*
1605er *Holzkirchner Oberbräu, Holzkirchen (Bay)*
1612er *Hofbräuhaus, Traunstein (Bay)*
1617 *Winkler, Amberg (Bay)*
1643 *Würzburger Hofbräu, Würzburg (Bay)*
1645 *Ritter St. Georgen, Nennslingen (Bay)*
1649 *Bischofshof, Regensburg (Bay)*
1650 *Schloßbrauerei, Autenried (Bay)*
1651 *Lauterbach, Lauterbach (Bay)*
1688 *Kesselring, Marktsteft (Bay)*

1744 *Glaabsbräu, Seligenstadt (Hes)*
1782 *Hirsch-Brauerei Honer, Wurmlingen (B-W)*
1792 *Eder & Heylands, Großostheim (Bay)*
1798 *Trinklogistik, Duisburg (N-W, unknown brewer); Kirner, Kirn (R-P); Püls Bräu, Weismain (Bay)*
1806 *Vereinsbrauerei, Apolda*
1809 *Ochsenfurter Kauzen-Bräu, Ochsenfurt (Bay)*
1813 *Kaiser Napoleon, Leipzig (Sach)*
1831 *Pfungstädter, Pfungstadt (Hes)*
1847 *Darmstädter, Darmstadt (Hes)*
1849 *Hofmark, Loifling (Bay)*
1850 *Lasser, Lörrach (B-W)*
1855 *Peschl, Passau (Bay)*
1861 *Köthener Brauerei, Köthen (S-A, unknown brewer)*
1874 *Bauriedl, Eslarn (Bay)*
1878 *Lohrer Bier, Lohr (Bay)*
1880 *Brauhaus 18·80, Fritzlar (Hes)*
1885 *Aktienbrauerei, Kaufbeuren (Bay)*
1888 *Braugold, Erfurt (Thü)*
1893 *Rapp, Kutzenhausen (Bay)*
1900 *Jura-Bräu, Pegnitz (Bay)*
1901 *Hauf, Dinkelsbühl (Bay)*
1912er *Kneipe Pur, Plaue (Bra)*
2000 *Betz, Celle (Nie); Engel-Bräu, Crailsheim (B-W); Landshuter Brauhaus, Landshut (Bay); Schloßbrauerei, Unterbaar (Bay)*

Books for Beer lovers

*CAMRA Books, the publishing arm of the Campaign for Real Ale,
is the leading publisher of books on beer and pubs. Key titles include:*

Good Beer Guide 2007 *Editor*: **ROGER PROTZ**

The Good Beer Guide is the only guide you will need to find the right pint, in the right place, every time. It's the original and the best independent guide to around 4,500 pubs throughout the UK; the Sun newspaper rated the 2004 edition in the top 20 books of all time! Now in its 34th year, this annual publication is a comprehensive and informative guide to the best real ale pubs in the UK, researched and written exclusively by CAMRA members and fully updated every year.

£13.99   ISBN 1 85249 211 2

Good Beer Guide Belgium *Editor*: **TIM WEBB**

Now in its 5th edition and in full colour, this book has developed a cult following among committed beer lovers and beer tourists. It is the definitive, totally independent guide to understanding and finding the best of Belgian beer and an essential companion for any beer drinker visiting Belgium or seeking out Belgian beer in Britain. Includes details of the 120 breweries and over 800 beers in regular production, as well as 500 of the best hand-picked cafes in Belgium.

£12.99   ISBN 1 85249 210 4

300 Beers to Try Before You Die **ROGER PROTZ**

300 beers from around the world, handpicked by award-winning journalist, author and broadcaster Roger Protz to try before you die! A comprehensive portfolio of top beers from the smallest microbreweries in the United States to family-run British breweries and the world's largest brands. This book is indispensable for both beer novices and aficionados.

£12.99   ISBN 1 85249 213 9

The Big Book of Beer **ADRIAN TIERNEY-JONES**

Everything you could ever want to know about the world's favourite drink; this beautifully illustrated book is an eye-opener to the world of beer articulated by well-known beer experts and those who brew it. A perfect gift for the 'real beer' connoisseur.

£14.99   ISBN 1 85249 212 0

It takes all sorts to
Campaign for Real Ale

CAMRA, the Campaign for Real Ale, is an independent not-for-profit, volunteer-led consumer group. We actively campaign for full pints and more flexible licensing hours, as well as protecting the 'local' pub and lobbying government to champion pub-goers' rights.

CAMRA has 75,000 members from all ages and backgrounds, brought together by a common belief in the issues that CAMRA deals with and their love of good quality British beer. For just £18 a year, that's less than a pint a month, you can join CAMRA and enjoy the following benefits:

A monthly colour newspaper informing you about beer and pub news and detailing events and beer festivals around the country.

Free or reduced entry to over 140 national, regional and local beer festivals.

Money off many of our publications including the *Good Beer Guide* and the *Good Bottled Beer Guide*.

Access to a members-only section of our national website, **www.camra.org.uk** which gives up-to-the-minute news stories and includes a special offer section with regular features saving money on beer and trips away.

The opportunity to campaign to save pubs under threat of closure, for pubs to be open when people want to drink and a reduction in beer duty that will help Britain's brewing industry survive.

Log onto **www.camra.org.uk** for
CAMRA membership information.

CAMPAIGN
FOR
REAL ALE

It takes all sorts to campaign for real a

Join **CAMRA Today...**

Just fill in the form below and send, with a cheque (payable to CAMRA ltd) or for Three Months Free mem
bership (for those renewing or joining by Direct Debit) complete the Direct Debit Form. All forms should be
addressed to membership secretary, CAMRA, 230 Hatfield Road, St Albans, Herts, AL1 4LW. Alternatively
you can join online at www.camra.org.uk. Rates for single membership are £18 and joint £21. Concessio
rates are available on request.

Title   Surname   Forename(s)   Date of Bir

P'tner Surname   Forename(s)   Date of Bir

Address   Postcod

Tel. no.(s)

I wish to join the Campaign for Real Ale, and agree to abide by the Memorandum and Articles of Associat

I enclose a cheque for........... Signed.. Date ....

Applications will be processed within 21 days

Instruction to your Bank or Building Society to pay by Direct Debit ![DIRECT Debit]

Please fill in the form and send to: Campaign for Real Ale Ltd. 230 Hatfield Road, St. Albans, Herts. AL1 4LW

Name and full postal address of your Bank or Building Society

To The Manager   Bank or Building Society

Address

Postcode

Originator's Identification Number

9	2	6	1	2	9

FOR CAMRA OFFICIAL USE ONLY
This is not part of the instruction to your Bank or Building Society

Membership Number

Name

Postcode

Name (s) of Account Holder (s)

Bank or Building Society account number

Branch Sort Code

Reference Number

Instruction to your Bank or Building Society
Please pay CAMRA Direct Debits from the account detailed on this Instruction subject to the safeguards assured by the Direct Debit Guarantee. I understand that this instruction may remain with CAMRA and, if so, will be passed electronically to my Bank/Building Society

Signature(s)

Date

Banks and Building Societies may not accept Direct Debit Instructions for some types of account

---

This Guarantee should be detached
and retained by the payer.

The Direct Debit Guarantee

- This Guarantee is offered by all Banks and Building Societies that take part in the Direct Debit Scheme. The efficiency and security of the Scheme is monitored and protected by your own Bank or Building Society.

- If the amounts to be paid or the payment dates change CAMRA will notify you 10 working days in advance of your account being debited or as otherwise agreed.

- If an error is made by CAMRA or your Bank or Building Society, you guaranteed a full and immediate refund from your branch of the amount paid.

- You can cancel a Direct Debit at any time by writing to your Bank or Building Society. Please also send a copy of your letter to us.